STUDENT CD CONTENT

- Data Sets
- Visual Statistics 2.23
- MegaStat® for Excel 10.1
- MegaStat® Tutorials

Cumulative Areas under the Standard Normal Curve

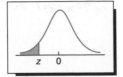

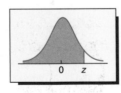

z	.00	.01	.02	.03	.04	.05	.06	.07	.08	.09
−3.4	.0003	.0003	.0003	.0003	.0003	.0003	.0003	.0003	.0003	.0002
−3.3	.0005	.0005	.0005	.0004	.0004	.0004	.0004	.0004	.0004	.0003
−3.2	.0007	.0007	.0006	.0006	.0006	.0006	.0006	.0005	.0005	.0005
−3.1	.0010	.0009	.0009	.0009	.0008	.0008	.0008	.0008	.0007	.0007
−3.0	.0013	.0013	.0013	.0012	.0012	.0011	.0011	.0011	.0010	.0010
−2.9	.0019	.0018	.0018	.0017	.0016	.0016	.0015	.0015	.0014	.0014
−2.8	.0026	.0025	.0024	.0023	.0023	.0022	.0021	.0021	.0020	.0019
−2.7	.0035	.0034	.0033	.0032	.0031	.0030	.0029	.0028	.0027	.0026
−2.6	.0047	.0045	.0044	.0043	.0041	.0040	.0039	.0038	.0037	.0036
−2.5	.0062	.0060	.0059	.0057	.0055	.0054	.0052	.0051	.0049	.0048
−2.4	.0082	.0080	.0078	.0075	.0073	.0071	.0069	.0068	.0066	.0064
−2.3	.0107	.0104	.0102	.0099	.0096	.0094	.0091	.0089	.0087	.0084
−2.2	.0139	.0136	.0132	.0129	.0125	.0122	.0119	.0116	.0113	.0110
−2.1	.0179	.0174	.0170	.0166	.0162	.0158	.0154	.0150	.0146	.0143
−2.0	.0228	.0222	.0217	.0212	.0207	.0202	.0197	.0192	.0188	.0183
−1.9	.0287	.0281	.0274	.0268	.0262	.0256	.0250	.0244	.0239	.0233
−1.8	.0359	.0351	.0344	.0336	.0329	.0322	.0314	.0307	.0301	.0294
−1.7	.0446	.0436	.0427	.0418	.0409	.0401	.0392	.0384	.0375	.0367
−1.6	.0548	.0537	.0526	.0516	.0505	.0495	.0485	.0475	.0465	.0455
−1.5	.0668	.0655	.0643	.0630	.0618	.0606	.0594	.0582	.0571	.0559
−1.4	.0808	.0793	.0778	.0764	.0749	.0735	.0721	.0708	.0694	.0681
−1.3	.0968	.0951	.0934	.0918	.0901	.0885	.0869	.0853	.0838	.0823
−1.2	.1151	.1131	.1112	.1093	.1075	.1056	.1038	.1020	.1003	.0985
−1.1	.1357	.1335	.1314	.1292	.1271	.1251	.1230	.1210	.1190	.1170
−1.0	.1587	.1562	.1539	.1515	.1492	.1469	.1446	.1423	.1401	.1379
−0.9	.1841	.1814	.1788	.1762	.1736	.1711	.1685	.1660	.1635	.1611
−0.8	.2119	.2090	.2061	.2033	.2005	.1977	.1949	.1922	.1894	.1867
−0.7	.2420	.2389	.2358	.2327	.2296	.2266	.2236	.2206	.2177	.2148
−0.6	.2743	.2709	.2676	.2643	.2611	.2578	.2546	.2514	.2483	.2451
−0.5	.3085	.3050	.3015	.2981	.2946	.2912	.2877	.2843	.2810	.2776
−0.4	.3446	.3409	.3372	.3336	.3300	.3264	.3228	.3192	.3156	.3121
−0.3	.3821	.3783	.3745	.3707	.3669	.3632	.3594	.3557	.3520	.3483
−0.2	.4207	.4168	.4129	.4090	.4052	.4013	.3974	.3936	.3897	.3859
−0.1	.4602	.4562	.4522	.4483	.4443	.4404	.4364	.4325	.4286	.4247
−0.0	.5000	.4960	.4920	.4880	.4840	.4801	.4761	.4721	.4681	.4641
0.0	.5000	.5040	.5080	.5120	.5160	.5199	.5239	.5279	.5319	.5359
0.1	.5398	.5438	.5478	.5517	.5557	.5596	.5636	.5675	.5714	.5753
0.2	.5793	.5832	.5871	.5910	.5948	.5987	.6026	.6064	.6103	.6141
0.3	.6179	.6217	.6255	.6293	.6331	.6368	.6406	.6443	.6480	.6517
0.4	.6554	.6591	.6628	.6664	.6700	.6736	.6772	.6808	.6844	.6879
0.5	.6915	.6950	.6985	.7019	.7054	.7088	.7123	.7157	.7190	.7224
0.6	.7257	.7291	.7324	.7357	.7389	.7422	.7454	.7486	.7517	.7549
0.7	.7580	.7611	.7642	.7673	.7704	.7734	.7764	.7794	.7823	.7852
0.8	.7881	.7910	.7939	.7967	.7995	.8023	.8051	.8078	.8106	.8133
0.9	.8159	.8186	.8212	.8238	.8264	.8289	.8315	.8340	.8365	.8389
1.0	.8413	.8438	.8461	.8485	.8508	.8531	.8554	.8577	.8599	.8621
1.1	.8643	.8665	.8686	.8708	.8729	.8749	.8770	.8790	.8810	.8830
1.2	.8849	.8869	.8888	.8907	.8925	.8944	.8962	.8980	.8997	.9015
1.3	.9032	.9049	.9066	.9082	.9099	.9115	.9131	.9147	.9162	.9177
1.4	.9192	.9207	.9222	.9236	.9251	.9265	.9279	.9292	.9306	.9319
1.5	.9332	.9345	.9357	.9370	.9382	.9394	.9406	.9418	.9429	.9441
1.6	.9452	.9463	.9474	.9484	.9495	.9505	.9515	.9525	.9535	.9545
1.7	.9554	.9564	.9573	.9582	.9591	.9599	.9608	.9616	.9625	.9633
1.8	.9641	.9649	.9656	.9664	.9671	.9678	.9686	.9693	.9699	.9706
1.9	.9713	.9719	.9726	.9732	.9738	.9744	.9750	.9756	.9761	.9767
2.0	.9772	.9778	.9783	.9788	.9793	.9798	.9803	.9808	.9812	.9817
2.1	.9821	.9826	.9830	.9834	.9838	.9842	.9846	.9850	.9854	.9857
2.2	.9861	.9864	.9868	.9871	.9875	.9878	.9881	.9884	.9887	.9890
2.3	.9893	.9896	.9898	.9901	.9904	.9906	.9909	.9911	.9913	.9916
2.4	.9918	.9920	.9922	.9925	.9927	.9929	.9931	.9932	.9934	.9936
2.5	.9938	.9940	.9941	.9943	.9945	.9946	.9948	.9949	.9951	.9952
2.6	.9953	.9955	.9956	.9957	.9959	.9960	.9961	.9962	.9963	.9964
2.7	.9965	.9966	.9967	.9968	.9969	.9970	.9971	.9972	.9973	.9974
2.8	.9974	.9975	.9976	.9977	.9977	.9978	.9979	.9979	.9980	.9981
2.9	.9981	.9982	.9982	.9983	.9984	.9984	.9985	.9985	.9986	.9986
3.0	.9987	.9987	.9987	.9988	.9988	.9989	.9989	.9989	.9990	.9990
3.1	.9990	.9991	.9991	.9991	.9992	.9992	.9992	.9992	.9993	.9993
3.2	.9993	.9993	.9994	.9994	.9994	.9994	.9994	.9995	.9995	.9995
3.3	.9995	.9995	.9995	.9996	.9996	.9996	.9996	.9996	.9996	.9997
3.4	.9997	.9997	.9997	.9997	.9997	.9997	.9997	.9997	.9997	.9998

Bruce L. Bowerman

Richard T. O'Connell

Miami University

Julie Aitken Schermer

James Robert Adcock

The University of Western Ontario

BUSINESS STATISTICS IN PRACTICE

CANADIAN EDITION

with additional examples and exercises
by Steven C. Huchendorf

University of Minnesota

with MegaStat software and other contributions by
J. Burdene Orris

Butler University

Toronto Montréal Boston Burr Ridge, IL Dubuque, IA Madison, WI New York
San Francisco St. Louis Bangkok Bogotá Caracas Kuala Lumpur · Lisbon London
Madrid Mexico City Milan New Delhi Santiago Seoul Singapore Sydney Taipei

**McGraw-Hill
Ryerson**

Business Statistics in Practice
Canadian Edition

ISBN-13: 978-0-07-098375-5
ISBN-10: 0-07-098375-5

1 2 3 4 5 6 7 8 9 10 CTPS 0 9 8

Printed and bound in China

Editorial Director: Joanna Cotton
Senior Sponsoring Editor: Rhondda McNabb
Sponsoring Editor: Kimberley Redhead
Marketing Manager: Matthew Busbridge
iLearning Sales Specialist: Joy Armitage Taylor
Managing Editor, Development: Jennifer DiDomenico
Developmental Editor: Sarah Fulton
Editorial Associate: Stephanie Hess
Supervising Editor: Joanne Limebeer
Copy Editor: Julia Cochrane
Technical Checker: Wayne Horn, Carleton University
Senior Production Coordinator: Jennifer Hall
Cover Design: Greg Devitt Design
Cover Image: Copyright © Jeff Sherman/Taxi/Getty Images
Interior Design: Greg Devitt Design
Page Layout: Aptara, Inc.
Printer: China Translation & Printing Services Limited

Library and Archives Canada Cataloguing in Publication Data

Business statistics in practice / Bruce L. Bowerman ... [et al.].—
Canadian ed.

Includes bibliographical references and index.
ISBN 978-0-07-098375-5

1. Commercial statistics.   I. Bowerman, Bruce L.

HF1017.B88 2008   519.502'465   C2007-905153-7

Bruce L. Bowerman
To my wife, children, sister, and other family members:
Drena
Michael, Jinda, Benjamin, and Lex
Asa and Nicole
Susan
Fiona and Radeesa
Daphne, Chloe, and Edgar
Gwyneth and Tony

Richard T. O'Connell
To my wife and children:
Jean
Christopher and Bradley

Julie Aitken Schermer
To my husband Clark, my parents Bob and Audrey,
and my mother-in-law Diane

James Robert Adcock
To my wife Melanie and our families

ABOUT THE AUTHORS

Bruce L. Bowerman   Bruce L. Bowerman is professor of decision sciences at Miami University in Oxford, Ohio. He received his Ph.D. degree in statistics from Iowa State University in 1974, and he has over 37 years of experience teaching basic statistics, regression analysis, time series forecasting, survey sampling, and design of experiments to both undergraduate and graduate students. In 1987, Professor Bowerman received an Outstanding Teaching award from the Miami University senior class, and in 1992 he received an Effective Educator award from the Richard T. Farmer School of Business Administration. Together with Richard T. O'Connell, Professor Bowerman has written 11 textbooks. These include
Forecasting and Time Series: An Applied Approach; Forecasting, Time Series, and Regression: An Applied Approach (also coauthored with Anne B. Koehler); and *Linear Statistical Models: An Applied Approach*. The first edition of *Forecasting and Time Series* earned an Outstanding Academic Book award from *Choice* magazine. Professor Bowerman has also published a number of articles on applied stochastic processes, time series forecasting, and statistical education. In his spare time, Professor Bowerman enjoys watching movies and sports, playing tennis, and designing houses.

Richard T. O'Connell   Richard T. O'Connell is associate professor of decision sciences at Miami University in Oxford, Ohio. He has more than 32 years of experience teaching basic statistics, statistical quality control and process improvement, regression analysis, time series forecasting, and design of experiments to both undergraduate and graduate business students. He also has extensive consulting experience and has taught workshops dealing with statistical process control and process improvement for a variety of companies in the Midwest. In 2000, Professor O'Connell received an Effective Educator award from the Richard T. Farmer School of Business Administration. Together with Bruce L. Bowerman, he has written 11
textbooks. These include *Forecasting and Time Series: An Applied Approach; Forecasting, Time Series, and Regression: An Applied Approach* (also coauthored with Anne B. Koehler); and *Linear Statistical Models: An Applied Approach*. Professor O'Connell has published a number of articles in the area of innovative statistical education. He is one of the first college instructors in the United States to integrate statistical process control and process improvement methodology into his basic business statistics course. He (with Professor Bowerman) has written several articles advocating this approach. He has also given presentations on this subject at meetings such as the Joint Statistical Meetings of the American Statistical Association and the Workshop on Total Quality Management: Developing Curricula and Research Agendas (sponsored by the Production and Operations Management Society). Professor O'Connell received an M.S. degree in decision sciences from Northwestern University in 1973, and he is currently a member of both the Decision Sciences Institute and the American Statistical Association. In his spare time, Professor O'Connell enjoys fishing, collecting 1950s and 1960s rock music, and following the Green Bay Packers and Purdue University sports.

Julie Aitken Schermer   Julie Aitken Schermer (formerly Harris) is an associate professor in the Management and Organizational Studies Program at The University of Western Ontario, London, Canada, where she teaches courses in the areas of business statistics, occupational health and safety, strategic human resources planning, and information management and decision making. She received her Ph.D. degree in personality psychology from The University of Western Ontario in 1999. She has 30 published articles in peer-reviewed journals and has been involved in 47 conference presentations. She has been teaching statistics since 1999. Although she doesn't have a lot of spare time, when not working, she spends time with her husband Clark and walks their dog.

James R. Adcock   James Robert Adcock is a Lecturer in the Department of Statistical and Actuarial Sciences at The University of Western Ontario, London, Canada. He has been teaching at The University of Western Ontario since 1999. He received his M.Sc. degree in Statistics at The University of Western Ontario in 2001. He has a great deal of experience teaching introductory statistics to large-enrolment classes. He also has experience teaching probability and statistical computing. He has been developing courses and course material that he uses to teach statistics courses via WebCT since 2000. At The University of Western Ontario, James spends time mentoring a group of undergraduate students involved in an organization called the Actuarial and Statistical Undergraduate Association (ASUA). He is also an Academic Counsellor in the department, giving undergraduates advice and guidance in order to help them plan their personal and academic careers. In his spare time, James enjoys spending time with his wife and watching football.

BRIEF TABLE OF CONTENTS

TABLE OF CONTENTS

PREFACE

In *Business Statistics in Practice, Canadian Edition*, we provide a modern, practical, and unique framework for teaching the first course in business statistics. This framework features case study and example driven discussions of all basic business statistics topics. In addition, we have endeavoured to make this book the most clearly written, motivating, and easy to use business statistics text available.

Business Statistics in Practice, Canadian Edition, has five attributes that make it an effective learning tool:

- A consistent theme of business improvement through statistical analysis.

- A unique use of "continuing" case studies that integrate different statistical areas.

- A real emphasis on the study of variation that stresses that the analysis of individual observations is as important as the analysis of means.

- A flexible topic flow that facilitates different topic choices and encourages different teaching approaches. In particular, many courses give different emphases to probability, hypothesis testing, regression and statistical modelling, and nonparametric statistics, so this book provides great flexibility with respect to how, when, and whether to cover these topics.

- A modern use of the statistical capabilities of the software packages MINITAB, Excel, and MegaStat (an Excel add-in package included on the text's student CD-ROM) that stresses statistical interpretation and reflects the use of these packages in the real world.

Included in the Canadian edition are

- *Continuing cases with no need to refer back to previously given computer outputs.* Each time a continuing case is revisited, the needed computer output is included with the current case discussion. In addition, whenever possible, the background information needed to understand the current analysis is provided, so the student does not need to refer back to previous material.

- *Confidence intervals for and hypothesis tests about a population mean presented by using the σ known versus σ unknown approach.* This approach simplifies the choice of z- or t-based procedures and is consistent with computerized procedures provided by MINITAB, Excel, and MegaStat. A t distribution table with up to 100 degrees of freedom is given in Table A.4 of Appendix A. Confidence intervals for and hypothesis tests about the difference between two population means are also presented using the σ known versus σ unknown approach.

- *End-of-chapter computer appendices* (available at the Online Learning Centre) that clearly show how to perform statistical analysis using MINITAB (Version 14), Microsoft Excel 2003, and the latest version of MegaStat.

- *Thorough coverage of sampling in Chapter 1.* We discuss using both a random number table and computer-generated random numbers to select a random sample. We also have a section that introduces stratified, cluster, and systematic sampling and discusses the problems of undercoverage, nonresponse, and response bias.

- *A substantial number of real-world data sets in the exercises,* with particular emphasis on Canadian statistics, and many examples drawn from Statistics Canada.

- *An appendix on normal probability plots* (available at the Online Learning Centre) to supplement the normal distribution discussion in Chapter 5.

- *A simple and easy to understand example introducing sampling distributions.* This stock return example motivates the discussion of the sampling distribution of the sample mean in Chapter 6.

- *Emphasis on the concept of the margin of error* to better motivate the discussion of confidence intervals in Chapter 7.

- *A step-by-step hypothesis-testing approach* that is used in almost all hypothesis-testing examples in Chapter 8 (Hypothesis Testing) and Chapter 9 (Statistical Inferences Based on Two Samples). This approach consists of a seven-step procedure that is designed to break hypothesis testing down into small, easy to understand steps and also to clearly show how to use the book's hypothesis-testing summary boxes. Although the seven-step procedure is not formally used after Chapter 9, the students' familiarity with the steps and summary boxes should enable them to successfully carry out hypothesis tests in later chapters.

- *Emphasis in Chapter 9 on the "unequal variances" t-based procedure for comparing two population means.* This procedure is becoming increasingly popular because it is available in most statistical software packages and is a very accurate approximation that does not require assuming equal population variances.

- *A detailed discussion of simple and multiple regression analysis.* In simple regression (Chapter 11), we give concise explanations of the simple linear regression model, least squares, and confidence and prediction intervals. We offer an innovative, modular organization of multiple regression in chapter 12. This will make it easy to selectively cover whatever multiple regression (and model-building) topics are desired. We also offer a simple presentation of dummy variables and a short section on *logistic regression*. In both the simple and multiple regression chapters, we provide clear explanations and use of MINITAB, Excel, and MegaStat regression outputs. Key outputs are clearly annotated to help the beginner find needed regression quantities.

- *An appendix on Holt–Winters' exponential smoothing models*, now available at the book's Online Learning Centre.

In addition, there is a section in Chapter 5 that covers use of the cumulative normal table. Although (because of reviewer input) we use the standard normal table to explain confidence intervals and hypothesis tests based on the normal distribution, we have explicitly designed the figures illustrating normal curve areas so that the intervals and tests can also be explained using the cumulative normal table.

We now discuss in more detail the attributes that make *Business Statistics in Practice, Canadian Edition*, an effective learning tool.

Business improvement through statistical analysis The ultimate goal of statistical analysis in business is business improvement. This theme is the foundation for the case studies and examples in this text, many of which are based on actual, real-world situations. For example, we evaluate the effectiveness of different training methods using experimental designs and analysis of variance, examine feedback from focus group panel members on their views about a new drink bottle design, and track DVD player sales over time.

In each of these cases, statistical analysis leads to an informed action that results in business improvement. These are highlighted by a business improvement icon in the margin. Furthermore, we continue this theme throughout the presentation of all statistical techniques in this book.

A unique continuity of presentation and use of case studies *Business Statistics in Practice, Canadian Edition*, features a unique continuity of presentation that integrates different statistical areas. This integration is achieved by an early emphasis (in Chapters 1 and 2) on the difference between the population and the sample and by a continuing use of practical, realistic case studies that span not only individual chapters but also groups of chapters. Specifically, Chapter 1 shows how to select random (or approximately random) samples from populations and processes by introducing case studies as examples and by presenting additional case studies as exercises. Then, in Chapter 2, we show how to use descriptive statistics to estimate the important aspects of these populations and processes. We continue to employ these case studies through the probability and sampling distribution chapters until we use confidence intervals and hypothesis testing to make statistical inferences. Furthermore, we introduce new case studies in each and every chapter. For example, we introduce several case studies in our presentation of simple linear regression and then extend these case studies when we discuss multiple regression and model building to show how regression is used in the description, prediction, and control of business variables.

A real emphasis on the importance of variation   *Business Statistics in Practice, Canadian Edition*, emphasizes that because businesses must satisfy individual customers, the analysis of individual population observations—which is achieved by analyzing population variation—is as important as analyzing the population mean. Our discussion of variation begins in Chapter 1, where we intuitively examine the variation of sample data. This discussion continues in Chapter 2, where we use the empirical rule to estimate tolerance intervals containing different percentages of population observations.

Our emphasis on variation continues throughout the book. For example, in Chapter 7, we clearly distinguish between a confidence interval for a population mean and a tolerance interval for a given percentage of individual population measurements. In Chapter 8, we discuss the effect of variation on the interpretation of a hypothesis test about the population mean. In Chapters 11 and 12, we show how prediction intervals can be used to evaluate the predictive capabilities of different regression models. In addition, we demonstrate how prediction intervals are used to assess whether any individual population observations are "unusual" enough to suggest the need for process improvement. Furthermore, in all of these chapters we use practical case studies to illustrate the ideas being presented.

A flexible topic flow   Although the table of contents of this book reveals a rather standard topic organization, the book utilizes a flexible topic flow that facilitates different topic choices and encourages different teaching approaches. In particular, because different courses place different amounts of emphasis on probability, hypothesis testing, regression and statistical modelling, and nonparametric statistics, this book provides great flexibility with respect to how, when, and whether to cover these topics. Furthermore, in some sections, appendices, and self-learning exercises, the book gives the student the opportunity to study more advanced topics in a concise and practical way. Thus, as we now discuss, courses with a wide variety of topic coverages and emphases can be taught using this book.

Probability   The most minimal approach to probability would cover Section 3.1 (the concept of probability), Section 4.1 (random variables), Section 5.1 (continuous probability distributions), and Section 5.3 (the normal distribution, including an intuitive example of the addition rule for mutually exclusive events). These sections are the only prerequisites for Chapters 6 through 12 (sampling distributions, confidence intervals, hypothesis testing, statistical inferences, experimental design, and regression).

Instructors who wish to also cover discrete probability distributions (Chapter 4) have the option of doing this either with a fairly minimal probability background or with a complete probability background. The fairly minimal probability background consists of Section 3.1 (the concept of probability) and Section 3.2 (using sample spaces to find probabilities). Note that this background is sufficient because, since Example 4.2 of Chapter 4 intuitively illustrates the multiplication rule for independent events and the addition rule for mutually exclusive events in the context of finding a discrete probability distribution, it is not necessary to cover the complete discussion of probability rules given in Sections 3.3 and 3.4. Of course, this complete discussion is necessary background for covering chi-square tests of independence (Chapter 14) and decision theory (Chapter 15).

Hypothesis testing   In this edition, we have used a seven-step procedure to break hypothesis testing down into small, easy to understand steps and to clearly show how to use the book's hypothesis-testing summary boxes. In addition, we have fully and concisely integrated the discussion of using rejection points and p values. The seven-step procedure shows how to use both approaches, and the hypothesis-testing boxes summarize both rejection points and p values for each test. We have also motivated the link between the approaches by considering how major television networks sometimes use different α values when evaluating advertising claims. We are aware of several courses that introduce hypothesis testing in the context of using p values to test the significance of regression coefficients. This can be done in our book by skipping Chapter 8 and by noting that every section throughout the rest of the book includes self-contained summary boxes (and examples) that fully cover any needed confidence intervals and hypothesis tests. Also, Chapter 6 (sampling distributions) intuitively illustrates the use of p values in the context of evaluating a claim about a population mean and in the context of evaluating a claim about a population proportion. Therefore, Chapter 6 can be used as an extremely short, intuitive introduction to p values.

Regression and statistical modelling This book features an innovative organization of regression analysis that simplifies the flow of the overall discussion and makes it very easy to cover whatever regression topics are desired. We have included a section on residual analysis at the end of the simple linear regression chapter (Chapter 11). In Chapter 12: Multiple Regression and Model Building, we offer a modular organization of the chapter and make it easy to cover whatever portions of multiple regression and model building are desired. As shown in a diagram on its opening page, Chapter 12 consists of four parts. Part 1: Basic Multiple Regression discusses the basic descriptive and inferential techniques of multiple regression analysis and would be a sufficient introduction to this topic for many introductory business statistics courses. After completing Part 1, the reader can study Part 2: Using Squared and Interaction Terms, Part 3: Dummy Variables and Advanced Statistical Inferences, and any section of Part 4: Model Building and Model Diagnostics. These parts can be covered in any order and without loss of continuity (note that Part 4 consists of four self-contained sections: model building and the effects of multicollinearity, residual analysis in multiple regression, diagnostics for detecting outlying and influential observations, and logistic regression). Furthermore, material covering model diagnostics and topics in some of the supplementary exercises tie key portions of the four parts together. This approach allows instructors to easily cover what they consider most important in courses with limited time devoted to regression analysis. Similarly, because many business statistics courses do not have substantial time to devote to experimental design (Chapter 10) and time series forecasting (Chapter 16), we have put great effort into making our presentation of these topics both complete and easy to get through.

Nonparametric statistics We have placed all of the nonparametric techniques covered in the book in Chapter 13. Furthermore, at the end of the discussion of each parametric technique in Chapters 8 through 11, we refer readers to the section in Chapter 13 that discusses the nonparametric technique that would be used if the assumptions for the parametric technique fail to hold. Therefore, the instructor has the option of integrating the discussion of nonparametric statistics into the main flow of Chapters 8 through 11.

Advanced Topics In additional sections, appendices, and self-learning exercises, the book gives the student the opportunity to study more advanced topics in a concise and practical way. Examination of the table of contents reveals that many of the more advanced topics—for example, counting rules (Appendix B, Part 1), the hypergeometric distribution (Appendix B, Part 2), normal probability plots (Appendix C, Part 1), and the Poisson distribution (Section 4.4)— are included in many other business statistics books. However, some of the more advanced topics, while not unique to this book, are less frequently covered in other basic statistics texts. These topics (the most advanced of which are discussed in Online Learning Centre Appendices E through K) are as follows:

- Properties of the Mean and Variance of a Random Variable, and the Covariance (Appendix C, Part 2).

- Derivations of the Mean and the Variance of $\bar{x}$ and $\hat{p}$ (Appendix C, Part 3).

- Confidence Intervals for Parameters of Finite Populations (Section 7.5), including sample size determination (Exercise 7.57).

- An Introduction to Survey Sampling (Section 1.6); estimation formulas, optimal allocation, and sample size determination in stratified random sampling (Appendix E, Part 1); and estimation formulas in one- and two-stage cluster sampling and ratio estimation (Appendix E, Part 2).

- A Comparison of Confidence Intervals and Tolerance Intervals (Section 7.6).

- Using Matrix Algebra to Perform Regression Calculations (Appendix F).

- The regression approach to one-way analysis of variance (Chapter 12), and the regression approach to two-way analysis of variance (Appendix G).

- Advanced Model Diagnostics and Model Building with Squared and Interaction Terms (Chapter 12).

- Logistic Regression and Discriminant Analysis (Chapter 12).

- Factor Analysis, Cluster Analysis, and Multidimensional Scaling (Appendix H).

- The Box–Jenkins methodology, a fairly complete discussion featuring nonseasonal and seasonal modelling, using autocorrelated error term models in regression analysis, intervention analysis, and transfer function models (Appendix I).

- Individual charts and c charts (Appendix K).

Furthermore, we have put great effort into making the discussion of all of the more advanced topics clear, concise, and easy to get through. This gives the instructor considerable flexibility in designing different business statistics courses. For example, a professor teaching a second course in business statistics can opt either to cover a variety of intermediate topics or to present a more in-depth treatment of regression analysis and forecasting.

MINITAB, Excel, and MegaStat *Business Statistics in Practice, Canadian Edition*, features a modern use of the statistical capabilities of the software packages MINITAB, Excel, and the Excel add-in MegaStat. Throughout the book, we provide an abundant number of outputs from all three packages in both examples and exercises that allow students to concentrate on statistical interpretations. This use of outputs is particularly prominent in statistical areas where hand calculations are impractical and where having students run their own programs (while theoretically optimal) would, because of time constraints, not allow them to see a wide variety of applications. These areas include descriptive statistics, analysis of variance, regression, and time series forecasting. In addition, appendices for each chapter (available at the Online Learning Centre) show in detail how to use MINITAB, Excel, and MegaStat to implement the statistical techniques discussed in the chapter. For this edition, the developer of MegaStat, Professor J. B. Orris of Butler University, has worked closely with us. MegaStat is a comprehensive, accurate, and easy to use Excel add-in package. In addition to remedying most of the computational problems associated with Excel Data Analysis Tools, MegaStat is also specifically designed to enhance the use of *Business Statistics in Practice, Canadian Edition*. For example,

- In addition to giving the usual descriptive statistics, frequency distributions, and histograms, MegaStat provides stem-and-leaf displays, box plots, dot plots, runs plots, normal plots, and output for the empirical rule (as well as tolerance intervals estimated to contain any specified percentage of individual observations). MegaStat also gives the option of calculating tolerance intervals and confidence intervals using the same dialogue box. Therefore, students can better understand the crucial difference between these two types of intervals.

- The MegaStat dialogue box for every one- and two-sample hypothesis-testing procedure for means and proportions allows the user to calculate a confidence interval for the population parameter being tested. Therefore, the student is encouraged to evaluate both statistical significance and practical importance. Such evaluation is a consistent theme of *Business Statistics in Practice, Canadian Edition* (in particular, see Chapters 8 and 9).

- MegaStat's one-way analysis of variance, randomized block, and two-factor analysis of variance procedures provide graphical output, helping students to better analyze experimental data. In addition, each procedure provides easy to understand pairwise comparisons of population means using both Tukey procedures and individual t tests. Such graphical analysis and pairwise comparisons are emphasized in Chapter 10.

- In addition to providing confidence intervals and prediction intervals in simple and multiple regression, MegaStat gives a full range of residual plots, normal plots, and outlying and influential observation diagnostics, as well as the variance inflation factors for the independent variables in a regression model. In addition, MegaStat provides an all possible regressions output that summarizes all well-known model selection criteria, as well as the $\hat{p}$ values for the independent variables. MegaStat also gives a stepwise selection procedure that provides more information than given by classical stepwise regression or backward elimination. MegaStat's regression capabilities are designed to enhance the regression coverage in Chapters 11 and 12. Furthermore, all of MegaStat's regression capabilities can be accessed in one very easy to use dialogue box, allowing the student to carry out a wide range of regression procedures in a correct, informative, and simple way.

In addition, MegaStat is fully capable of performing analyses related to discrete and continuous probability distributions, time series forecasting, nonparametric statistics, and chi-square tests—virtually all topics covered by *Business Statistics in Practice, Canadian Edition*. MegaStat is provided on the student CD-ROM.

Further Features   The book's CD-ROM, in addition to containing MegaStat, also features data files, tutorials, and Visual Statistics 2.23 by Doane, Mathieson, and Tracy. Visual Statistics is a Windows software program that helps students learn statistics through interactive experimentation and visualization. Visual statistics icons in the text identify concepts that are further explained by Visual Statistics.

In addition, the book has the following supplements: an instructor's solutions manual and test bank adapted by co-author Julie Aitken Schermer of the University of Western Ontario; a complete set of PowerPoint presentations; an online learning centre with instructor and student resources; and *i*Study, the online study guide (see below).

Available 24/7: Providing instant feedback when you want, how you want, and where you want. This online *i*Study space was developed to help you master the concepts and achieve better grades with all the learning tools you've come to expect.

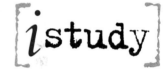

*i*Study can be purchased through the Online Learning Centre or by purchasing a PIN code card through the campus bookstore. Instructors: Please contact your *i*Learning Sales Specialist for more information on how to make *i*Study part of your students' success.

Acknowledgments   The authors are grateful to Bruce Bowerman and Richard O'Connell, authors of the U.S. text, for providing the foundation upon which this Canadian adaptation has been built. We would also like to thank Julia Cochrane and Wayne Horn, as well as the following people at McGraw-Hill Ryerson for their support: Lynn Fisher, Rhondda McNabb, Jennifer Bastarache, Joanne Limebeer, Sarah Fulton, and Matthew Busbridge.

Reviewers for the Canadian Edition

Gordon Anderson, University of Toronto

Peter Au, George Brown College

Henry Bartel, York University

Walid Belassi, Athabasca University

Elisabeth Carter, Douglas College

Marc Jerry, Mount Royal College

Chris Kellman, British Columbia Institute of Technology (BCIT)

Ehsan Latif, Thompson Rivers University

Lisa MacKay, Southern Alberta Institute of Technology (SAIT)

Peter Miller, University of Windsor

John C. Nash, University of Ottawa

Dorit Nevo, Schulich School of Business, York University

Jim Stallard, University of Calgary

George Stroppa, Douglas College

John H. Walker, Brock University

George Wesolowsky, McMaster University

Ann Woodside, Carleton University

Glenn Zabowski, McGill University

Julie Zhou, University of Victoria

GUIDED TOUR

Business Statistics in Practice, Canadian Edition, was written with students' needs in mind. Its clear and understandable explanations and use of real-world case studies and examples present content that business students can relate to. Because today's students learn in a visual and interactive way, the text is supplemented by a student CD-ROM, containing a host of updated resources and helpful study aids. In addition, both students and instructors are provided with additional resources on the text Web site. Thus, students are given a number of statistical tools in a variety of ways and shown how these tools can be used to positively impact business and other organizations.

Chapter Introductions

Each chapter opens with a preview showing how the statistical topics to be discussed apply to real business problems. The continuing case examples that run throughout the book are briefly introduced along with the techniques that will be used to analyze them.

Visual Statistics 2.23

Visual Statistics, described later in the tour, helps students learn statistics through interactive experimentation and visualization. Concepts in the text that are treated in the Visual Statistics software program are identified by this icon, with chapter reference, in the margin of the text next to the concept.

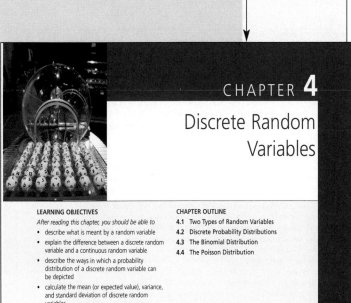

A **random variable** is a variable that assumes numerical values that are determined by the outcome of an experiment, where one and only one numerical value is assigned to each experimental outcome.

Before an experiment is carried out, its outcome is uncertain. It follows that, since a random variable assigns a number to each experimental outcome, a random variable can be thought of as **representing an uncertain numerical outcome**.

To illustrate the idea of a random variable, suppose that Sound City sells and installs car stereo systems. One of Sound City's most popular stereo systems is the top-of-the-line TrueSound-XL. Consider (the experiment of) selling the TrueSound-XL stereo at the Sound City store during a particular week. If we let x denote the number of stereos sold during the week, then x is a random variable. That is, looked at before the week, the number of stereos x that will be sold is uncertain, and, therefore, x is a random variable.

Notice that x, the number of TrueSound-XL stereos sold in a week, might be 0 or 1 or 2 or 3, and so forth. In general, when the possible values of a random variable can be counted or listed, then the random variable is a **discrete random variable**. That is, either a discrete random variable may assume a finite number of possible values or the possible values may take the form of a **countable** sequence or list such as 0, 1, 2, 3, 4, . . . (a **countably infinite** list).

Some other examples of discrete random variables are as follows:

1 The number, x, of the next three customers entering a store who will make a purchase. Here x could be 0, 1, 2, or 3.

2 The number, x, of four patients taking a new antibiotic who experience gastrointestinal distress as a side effect. Here x could be 0, 1, 2, 3, or 4.

3 The number, x, of television sets in a sample of eight five-year-old television sets that have not needed a single repair. Here x could be any of the values 0, 1, 2, 3, 4, 5, 6, 7, and 8.

4 The rating, x, on a 1 through 5 scale given to a song by a listener in a music survey. Here x could be 1, 2, 3, 4, or 5.

5 The number, x, of major fires in a large city during the last two months. Here x could be 0, 1, 2, 3, and so forth (there is no definite maximum number of fires).

The values of the random variables described in (1), (2), (3), and (4) are countable and finite. In contrast, the values of the random variables described in (5) are countable and infinite (or countably infinite lists). For example, in theory there is no limit to the number of major fires that could occur in a city in two months.

Not all random variables have values that are countable. When a random variable may assume any numerical value in one or more intervals on the real number line, then the random variable is a **continuous random variable**.

Example 4.1 The Mass of the Loonie

Consider the Canadian dollar coin (loonie) example that was discussed in Chapters 1 and 2. The mass of a randomly selected coin, x, is a continuous random variable. Even though the masses of the coins have been measured to four decimal places, there is no way of measuring the absolute exact mass of these coins. Theoretically, the mass could be expressed to an infinite number of decimal places, which would be impossible to graph. The masses of the coins vary continuously, but, for the purposes of this example, we have chosen to measure them to four decimal places.

CHAPTER **4**

Discrete Random Variables

LEARNING OBJECTIVES

After reading this chapter, you should be able to

- describe what is meant by a random variable
- explain the difference between a discrete random variable and a continuous random variable
- describe the ways in which a probability distribution of a discrete random variable can be depicted
- calculate the mean (or expected value), variance, and standard deviation of discrete random variables
- distinguish between the binomial distribution and the Poisson distribution

CHAPTER OUTLINE

4.1 Two Types of Random Variables
4.2 Discrete Probability Distributions
4.3 The Binomial Distribution
4.4 The Poisson Distribution

Examples of discrete random variables are the number of heads in *n* tosses of a fair coin, the number of times you hit the snooze button before you wake up, the number of red lights you encounter on the way to school, and the number of courses you take in a school year. Examples of

continuous random variables are the amount of coffee you drink every day (measured in millilitres), the amount of gasoline you put in your car, the amount of time you talk on your cell phone, and the amount of time you wait for the bus.

Case Studies

The text provides a unique use of case studies that span individual chapters and groups of chapters. Cases are used to introduce the concepts, to demonstrate the methods, and to provide students with motivating exercises. These case studies help students see how statistics is used in business and can be used to improve processes.

Student-Friendly Presentation

The authors make learning easier for students. The following examples highlight some of these improvements.

Step-by-Step Hypothesis-Testing Approach

This approach consists of a seven-step procedure designed to break hypothesis testing down into small, easy to understand steps. This procedure is used in almost all the examples in Chapters 8 and 9 and can be applied by students throughout the remainder of the text where hypothesis testing is done.

Greater Accessibility of Continuing Cases

Each time a continuing case is revisited, any needed computer output and, whenever possible, relevant background information is included with the current case discussion. Consequently, students seldom need to refer back to previously covered material in order to grasp the content included in a given case segment.

---

consideration, we know σ. When σ is unknown, we test hypotheses about a population mean by using the *t* **distribution**. In Section 8.5, we study *t* **tests**, and we will revisit the examples of this (and the next) section assuming that σ is unknown.

Testing a "greater than" alternative hypothesis by using a rejection point rule   In Sections 8.1 and 8.2, we explained how to set up appropriate null and alternative hypotheses. We also discussed how to specify a value for α, the probability of a Type I error (also called the **level of significance**) of the hypothesis test, and we introduced the idea of a test statistic. We can use these concepts to begin developing a seven-step hypothesis testing procedure. We will introduce these steps in the context of monthly cable TV subscriptions costs and testing a "greater than" alternative hypothesis.

A marketing company has suggested that the cost of monthly cable TV subscriptions has risen dramatically, which is causing more people to use illegal satellite dishes. Cable TV companies claim that their full cable package subscriptions cost on average $50 a month. The marketing company wants to demonstrate that the cost is significantly greater than $50 and randomly selects 40 cable TV subscribers and determines the price they pay for their monthly cable.

Step 1: State the null hypothesis H_0 and the alternative hypothesis H_a. In this case, we will test H_0: $\mu \leq 50$ versus H_a: $\mu > 50$. Here μ is the mean subscription cost.

Step 2: Specify the level of significance α. The marketing company will be able to support its claim that cable subscription costs have risen if we can reject H_0: $\mu \leq 50$ in favour of H_a: $\mu > 50$ by setting α equal to 0.05.

Step 3: Select the test statistic. In order to test H_0: $\mu \leq 50$ versus H_a: $\mu > 50$, we will test the modified null hypothesis H_0: $\mu = 50$ versus H_a: $\mu > 50$. The idea here is that if there is sufficient evidence to reject the hypothesis that μ equals 50 in favour of $\mu > 50$, then there is certainly also sufficient evidence to reject the hypothesis that μ is less than or equal to 50. In order to test H_0: $\mu = 50$ versus H_a: $\mu > 50$, we randomly select a sample of $n = 40$ subscribers and calculate the mean $\bar{x}$ of the monthly costs. We will then utilize the **test statistic**

$$z = \frac{\bar{x} - 50}{\sigma_{\bar{x}}} = \frac{\bar{x} - 50}{\sigma / \sqrt{n}}.$$

A positive value of this test statistic results from an $\bar{x}$ that is greater than 50 and thus provides evidence against H_0: $\mu = 50$ and in favour of H_a: $\mu > 50$.

Step 4: Determine the rejection point rule for deciding whether to reject H_0. To decide how large the test statistic must be to reject H_0 in favour of H_a by setting the probability of a Type I error equal to α, we do the following:

- Place the probability of a Type I error, α, in the right-hand tail of the standard normal curve and use the normal table (see Table A.3) to find the normal point z_α. Here z_α, which we call a **rejection point** (or **critical point**), is the point on the horizontal axis under the standard normal curve that gives a right-hand tail area equal to α.

- **Reject H_0: $\mu = 50$ in favour of H_a: $\mu > 50$ if and only if the test statistic z is greater than the rejection point z_α.** This is the **rejection point rule**.

Appendix 1.1 ■ Getting Started With MINITAB

We begin with a look at some features of MINITAB that are common to most analyses. When the instructions call for a sequence of selections from a series of menus, the sequence will be presented in the following form:

Stat : Basic Statistics : Descriptive Statistics

This notation indicates that Stat is the first selection from the Minitab menu bar, next Basic Statistics is selected from the Stat pull-down menu, and finally Descriptive Statistics is selected from the Basic Statistics pull-down menu.

Starting MINITAB Procedures for starting MINITAB may vary from one installation to the next. If you are using a public computing laboratory, you may have to consult local documentation. For typical MINITAB installations, you will generally be able to start MINITAB with a sequence of selections from the Microsoft Windows Start menu something like the following:

- Select **Start : Programs : MINITAB 14 for Windows : Minitab 14**

You can also start MINITAB with a previously saved MINITAB worksheet (like Coffee.mtw or one of the many other data files from the CD-ROM included with this text) from the Windows Explorer by double-clicking on the worksheet's icon.

After you start MINITAB, the display is partitioned into two working windows. These windows serve the following functions:

- The "Session" window is the area where MINITAB commands and basic output are displayed.
- The "Data" window is a spreadsheet-style display where data can be entered and edited.

Help resources Like most Windows programs,

Excel/MINITAB/MegaStat Tutorials

The end-of-chapter appendices (available at the Online Learning Centre) contain helpful tutorials that teach students how to carry out statistical analysis using Excel, MINITAB, and MegaStat. These tutorials include step-by-step instructions for performing almost every type of statistical method presented in the book. For additional help, video tutorials for Excel, MINITAB, and MegaStat are provided on the Student CD-ROM.

Excel, MINITAB, and MegaStat Output

Throughout the text, Excel, MINITAB, and MegaStat outputs illustrate how statistical analysis is done electronically.

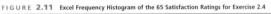

FIGURE **2.11** Excel Frequency Histogram of the 65 Satisfaction Ratings for Exercise 2.4

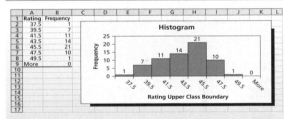

FIGURE **2.14** MINITAB Frequency Histogram of the Waiting Times for Exercise 2.5

FIGURE **2.15** MegaStat Relative Frequency Histogram of the 40 Breaking Strengths for Exercise 2.6

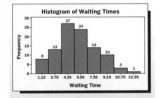

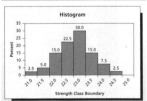

Exercises...

There are over 1,000 exercises in the text. Many use real data from the current business literature. Data sets on the Student CD-ROM are identified by icon in the text. Within each chapter, exercises are broken into two parts— "Concepts" and "Methods and Applications." The methods and applications exercises vary in rigour from routine calculations to fairly sophisticated case study analysis. In addition, there are Internet exercises to help students make use of the Internet for gathering and using real data, and supplementary exercises at the ends of chapters.

...And More Exercises

are found on the student text's Web site.

Exercises for Section 8.4

CONCEPTS

8.35 Suppose we are carrying out a two-sided hypothesis test about a population mean.
  a. Give the rejection point rule for rejecting $H_0: \mu = \mu_0$.
  b. Explain how the p value and α tell us whether $H_0: \mu = \mu_0$ should be rejected.

8.36 Discuss how we assess the practical importance of a statistically significant result.

METHODS AND APPLICATIONS

In Exercises 8.37 through 8.43, we consider using a random sample of $n = 81$ measurements to test $H_0: \mu = 40$ versus $H_a: \mu \neq 40$. Suppose that $\bar{x} = 34$ and $\sigma = 18$.

8.37 Calculate the value of the test statistic z.

8.38 Use rejection points to test H_0 versus H_a by setting α equal to 0.10.

8.39 Use rejection points to test H_0 versus H_a by setting α equal to 0.05.

8.40 Use rejection points to test H_0 versus H_a by setting α equal to 0.01.

8.41 Use rejection points to test H_0 versus H_a by setting α equal to 0.001.
Hint: $z_{0.0005}$ can be shown to equal 3.29.

8.42 Calculate the p value and use it to test H_0 versus H_a at each of $\alpha = 0.10, 0.05, 0.01,$ and 0.001.

8.43 How much evidence is there that $H_0: \mu = 40$ is false and $H_a: \mu \neq 40$ is true?

8.44 Consider the automobile parts supplier in Exercise 8.10. Suppose that a problem-solving team will be assigned to rectify the process producing cylindrical engine parts if the null hypothesis $H_0: \mu = 3$ can be rejected in favour of $H_a: \mu \neq 3$ by setting α equal to 0.05.

3 cm ± 0.05 cm. Use the sample information given in part a to estimate an interval that contains almost all (99.73 percent) of the diameters. Compare this estimated interval with the specification limits. Are the specification limits being met, or are some diameters outside the specification limits? Explain.

8.45 Consider the Classic Bottling Company fill process in Exercise 8.11. Recall that the initial setup of the filler will be adjusted if the null hypothesis $H_0: \mu = 355$ mL is rejected in favour of $H_a: \mu \neq 355$ mL. Suppose that Classic Bottling Company decides to use a level of significance of $\alpha = 0.01$, and suppose a random sample of 36 can fills is obtained from a test run of the filler. For each of the following sample results, determine whether the filler's initial setup should be adjusted. In each case, use a rejection point and a p value, and assume that σ equals 0.1.
  a. $\bar{x} = 355.05$.   **c.** $\bar{x} = 355.02$.
  b. $\bar{x} = 354.96$.

8.46 Use the sample information in part a of Exercise 8.45 and a confidence interval to test $H_0: \mu = 355$ versus $H_a: \mu \neq 355$ by setting α equal to 0.05. What considerations would help you to decide whether the result has practical importance?

8.47 In an article in the *Journal of Marketing*, Bayus studied the mean numbers of auto dealers visited by two types of buyers.
  a. Letting μ be the mean number of dealers visited by the first type of buyer, suppose that we wish to test $H_0: \mu = 4$ versus $H_a: \mu \neq 4$. A random sample of 800 of these buyers yields a mean number of dealers visited of $\bar{x} = 3.3$. Assuming σ equals 0.71, calculate the p value and test H_0 versus H_a. Do we estimate that μ is less than 4 or greater than 4?

Boxed Equations, Formulas, and Definitions

Each chapter contains easy to find boxes that will help students identify and understand the key ideas in the chapter.

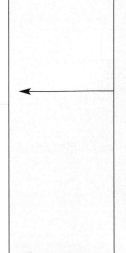

A Hypothesis Test about a Population Mean: Testing $H_0: \mu = \mu_0$ versus a One-Sided Alternative Hypothesis when σ Is Known

Define the test statistic

$$z = \frac{\bar{x} - m_0}{\sigma / \sqrt{n}}$$

and assume that the population sampled is normally distributed, or that the sample size n is large. We can test $H_0: \mu = \mu_0$ versus a particular alternative hypothesis at level of significance α by using the appropriate rejection point rule or, equivalently, the corresponding p value.

Alternative Hypothesis	Rejection Point Rule: Reject H_0 if	p Value (Reject H_0 if p Value $< \alpha$)
$H_a: \mu > \mu_0$	$z > z_\alpha$	The area under the standard normal curve to the right of z
$H_a: \mu < \mu_0$	$z < -z_\alpha$	The area under the standard normal curve to the left of z

---

Chapter-Ending Material

The end of each chapter includes a chapter summary, a comprehensive glossary of terms, and important formula references. The examples shown here are from Chapter 2, Descriptive Statistics.

---

www.mcgrawhill.ca/olc/bowerman

CHAPTER SUMMARY

We began this chapter by studying how to depict the shape of the distribution of a data set. We learned that **stem-and-leaf displays** and **histograms** are useful graphics for portraying a data set's distribution. We also learned about some common population shapes. We saw that data sets often have shapes that are **symmetrical**, **positively skewed (with a tail to the right)**, or **negatively skewed (with a tail to the left)**.

Next we presented and compared several measures of **central tendency**. We defined the **population mean** and we saw how to estimate the population mean by using a **sample mean**. We also defined the **median** and **mode**, and we compared the mean, median, and mode for symmetrical distributions and for distributions that are positively or negatively skewed (to the right or left). We then studied measures of **variation (or spread)**. We defined the **range, variance,** and **standard deviation**, and we saw how to estimate a population variance and standard deviation by using a sample. We learned that a good way to interpret the standard deviation when a population is (approximately) normally distributed is to use the **empirical rule**, and we applied this rule to assess **process capability**. We

next studied **Chebyshev's theorem**, which gives us intervals containing reasonably large fractions of the population units no matter what the population's shape might be. We also saw that, when a data set is highly skewed, it is best to use **percentiles** and **quartiles** to measure variation, and we learned how to construct a **box-and-whiskers display** by using the quartiles.

After learning how to measure and depict central tendency and variability, we presented several methods for portraying qualitative data. In particular, we used **bar charts** and **pie charts** for this purpose. We also discussed using a sample to estimate the proportion of population units that fall into a category of interest.

We studied using **scatter plots** to examine relationships between variables. Next we discussed misleading graphs and statistics, and we explained some of the tactics that are commonly used to try to distort the truth. We also introduced the concept of a **weighted mean** and then explained how to compute descriptive statistics for **grouped data**. Finally, we showed how to calculate the **geometric mean** and demonstrated its interpretation.

GLOSSARY OF TERMS

bar chart: A graphical display of categorical data (data in categories) made up of vertical or horizontal bars. (page 62)
box-and-whiskers display (box plot): A graphical portrayal of a data set that depicts both the central tendency and variability of the data. It is constructed using $Q_1, M_d,$ and Q_3. (page 58)
capable process: A process that is able to consistently produce output that meets (or conforms to) specifications (requirements). (page 51)
central tendency: A term referring to the middle of a population or sample of measurements. (page 38)
Chebyshev's theorem: A theorem that (for any population) allows us to find an interval that contains a specified percentage of the individual measurements in the population. (page 52)
coefficient of variation: A quantity that measures the variation of a population or sample relative to its mean. (page 54)
dependent variable (denoted y): A variable that we wish to describe, predict, or control. (page 68)
empirical rule: For a normally distributed population, this rule tells us that 68.26 percent, 95.44 percent, and 99.73 percent, respectively, of the population measurements are within one, two, and three standard deviations of the population mean. (page 50)
extreme outlier (in a box-and-whiskers display): A measurement located outside the outer fences. (page 59)
extreme value: A measurement in a population or sample that is different from most of the other measurements. (page 42)
first quartile (denoted Q_1): A value below which approximately 25 percent of the measurements lie; the 25th percentile. (page 57)

frequency: The count of the number of measurements in a class or of the number of measurements with a particular value. (page 29)
frequency distribution: A numerical summary that divides values of a variable into classes and gives the number of values in each class. (pages 29 and 30)
geometric mean: The constant return (or rate of change) that yields the same wealth at the end of several time periods as do actual returns. (pages 78 and 79)
grouped data: Data presented in the form of a frequency distribution or a histogram. (page 75)
histogram: A graphical portrayal of a data set that shows the data set's distribution. It divides the data into classes and gives the frequency for each class. Histograms are particularly useful for summarizing large data sets. (page 30)
independent variable (denoted x): A predictor variable that can be used to describe, predict, or control a dependent variable. (page 68)
inner fences (in a box-and-whiskers display): Points located $1.5 \times IQR$ below Q_1 and $1.5 \times IQR$ above Q_3. (page 58)
interquartile range (denoted IQR): The difference between the third quartile and the first quartile (that is, $Q_3 - Q_1$). (page 58)
measure of variation: A descriptive measure of the spread of the values in a population or sample. (page 47)
median (denoted M_d): A measure of central tendency that divides a population or sample into two roughly equal parts. (page 40)
mild outlier (in a box-and-whiskers display): A measurement located between the inner and outer fences. (page 59)

Lyryx Assessment Business Statistics (LABS)

LYRYX LEARNING INC
Online Learning and Assessment
lyryx.com

Based on *Business Statistics in Practice, Canadian Edition* by Bowerman, O'Connell, Schermer, and Adcock, LABS is a leading-edge online assessment system designed to support both students and instructors. The assessment takes the form of a homework assignment called a Lab. The assessments are algorithmically generated and automatically marked so that students get instant marks and feedback. New Labs are randomly generated each time, providing the student with unlimited opportunities to try a type of question. After they submit a Lab for marking, students receive extensive feedback on their work, thus promoting their learning experience.

FOR THE INSTRUCTORS: The goal of the product is for instructors to use these Labs for course marks instead of creating and marking their own labs, giving instructors and teaching assistants valuable time to help students directly. After registering their courses with us, instructors can create Labs of their choice by selecting problems from our test bank, and then set a deadline for each Lab. The content, marking, and feedback of the problems were developed and implemented with the help of experienced instructors in business statistics. Instructors have access to all their students' marks and can view their best Labs. At any time, instructors can download the class marks for their own programs. In addition, because LABS is integrated with *Business Statistics in Practice, Canadian Edition*, it offers a unique, seamless instruction and learning experience.

FOR THE STUDENT: LABS offers algorithmically generated and automatically marked assignments. Students get instant marks and instant feedback—no need to wait until the next class to find out how well they did! Marks are instantly recorded in a mark book that the students can view.

Students are motivated for two reasons: first, because the Lab can be tied to assessment, and second, because they can try the Lab as many times as they wish before the due date with only their best mark being recorded.

Instructors know from experience that if students are doing their business statistics homework, they will be successful in the course. Recent research regarding the use of Lyryx has shown that when Labs are tied to assessment, even if worth only a small percentage of the total mark for the course, students *will* do their homework—and *more than once!*

Please contact your *i*Learning Sales Specialist for additional information on Lyryx Assessment for Business Statistics.

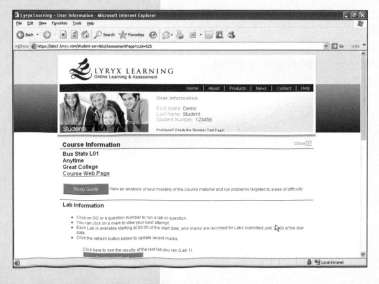

Student CD-ROM

Every new copy of this edition is packaged with a free Student CD-ROM featuring data sets identified by icons in the text; video tutorials in Excel, MINITAB, and MegaStat; MegaStat version 10.1; and Visual Statistics 2.23, which is described later.

Business Statistics in Practice, Canadian Edition, Web site at www.mcgrawhill.ca/olc/bowerman

This text Web site contains a convenient collection of resources for students to help master course content. A password-protected section is also available to instructors with downloadable supplements and links to resources, such as PageOut, for creating a professional, interactive course Web site for students and instructors to access.

Business Statistics in Practice, Canadian Edition, iStudy

Available 24/7: Instant feedback so you can study when you want, how you want, and where you want. The Bowerman online iStudy space was developed to help you master the concepts and achieve better marks with a variety of learning tools. iStudy offers the best, most convenient way to interact, learn, and succeed.

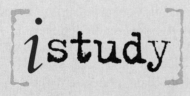

¡Interact ¡Learn ¡Succeed

Visual Statistics 2.23, by Doane, Mathieson, and Tracy

This software program for Windows is designed to teach statistics concepts. It is included on the CD-ROM in both the student and instructor editions. The program is unique in that it is intended to help the instructor teach and students learn the concepts through interactive experimentation and visualization. Active learning is promoted through competency-building exercises and individual and team projects. Visual Statistics contains 21 software modules and coordinating student worktext, all on CD-ROM. An icon appears in the text next to concepts that are further explained and illustrated through Visual Statistics. The samples below show a display of the content and a portion of the tutorial help included in the worktext.

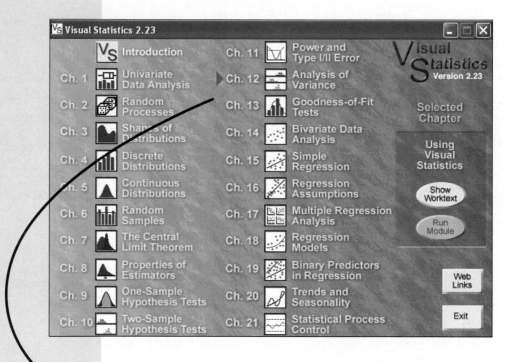

Orientation to Basic Features

This module familiarizes you with a variety of univariate data analysis tools. You can analyze a variety of different data sets by selecting them from the Notebook or create your own using the data editor.

1. Opening screen Start the module by clicking on the module's icon, title, or chapter number in the *Visual Statistics* menu and pressing the **Run Module** button. When the module is loaded, you will be on the introduction page of the Notebook. The **Introduction** and **Concepts** sections describe what will be covered in this module. Click on the

Examples tab, click on **Financial**, select an example, and press **OK**. A Hint appears in the middle of the display. Read it and press **OK**. The upper left of the screen shows a frequency histogram. The Histogram Control Panel appears on the right. On the bottom left is the Dot Plot. On the bottom right is a table of Descriptive Statistics. Other features are controlled from the menu bar at the top of the screen. A flashing **Update Histograms** button will indicate when you have changed one or more control settings.

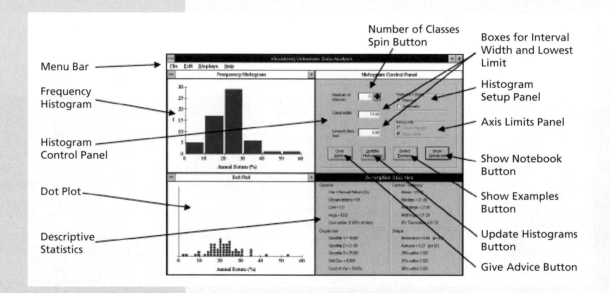

Menu Bar

Frequency Histogram

Histogram Control Panel

Dot Plot

Descriptive Statistics

Number of Classes Spin Button

Boxes for Interval Width and Lowest Limit

Histogram Setup Panel

Axis Limits Panel

Show Notebook Button

Show Examples Button

Update Histograms Button

Give Advice Button

An Introduction to Business Statistics

LEARNING OBJECTIVES

After reading this chapter, you should be able to

- understand how and why research samples are collected
- know the difference between a sample and a population
- explain what is meant by the term *random sample* and explain how a random sample may be generated
- describe the four levels of measurement
- list some of the potential problems associated with surveys

CHAPTER OUTLINE

1.1 Populations and Samples

1.2 Sampling a Population of Existing Units

1.3 Sampling a Process

1.4 Levels of Measurement: Nominal, Ordinal, Interval, and Ratio

1.5 A Brief Introduction to Surveys

1.6 An Introduction to Survey Sampling

The subject of **statistics** involves the study of how to collect, summarize, and interpret data. **Data** are numerical facts and figures from which conclusions can be drawn. Such conclusions are important to the decision-making processes of many professions and organizations. For example, government officials use conclusions drawn from the latest data on unemployment and inflation to make policy decisions. Financial planners use recent trends in stock market prices to make investment decisions. Businesses decide which products to develop and market by using data that reveal consumer preferences. Production supervisors use manufacturing data to evaluate, control, and improve product quality. Politicians rely on data from public opinion polls to formulate legislation and to devise campaign strategies. Physicians and hospitals use data on the effectiveness of drugs and surgical procedures to provide patients with the best possible treatment.

In this chapter, we begin to see how we collect and analyze data. As we proceed through the chapter, we introduce several case studies. These case studies (and others to be introduced later, many from Statistics Canada) are revisited throughout later chapters as we learn the statistical methods needed to analyze the cases. Briefly, we begin to study four cases:

The Cell Phone Case. A bank estimates its cellular phone costs and decides whether to outsource management of its wireless resources by studying the calling patterns of its employees.

The Marketing Research Case. A bottling company investigates consumer reaction to a new bottle design for one of its popular soft drinks.

The Coffee Temperature Case. A fast-food restaurant studies and monitors the temperature of the coffee it serves.

The Mass of the Loonie. A researcher examines the overall distribution of the masses (in grams) of the 1989 Canadian dollar coin (nicknamed the "loonie") to determine the average mass and range of masses.

1.1 Populations and Samples

Statistical methods are very useful for learning about populations. Populations can be defined in various ways, including the following:

A **population** is a set of existing units (usually people, objects, or events).

Examples of populations include (1) all of last year's graduates of Sauder School of Business at UBC, (2) all consumers who bought a cellular phone last year, (3) all accounts receivable invoices accumulated last year by Procter & Gamble, (4) all Toyota Corollas that were produced last year, and (5) all fires reported last month to the Ottawa fire department.

We usually focus on studying one or more characteristics of the population units.

Any characteristic of a population unit is called a **variable**.

For instance, if we study the starting salaries of last year's graduates of an MBA program, the variable of interest is starting salary. If we study the fuel efficiency obtained in city driving by last year's Toyota Corolla, the variable of interest is litres per 100 km in city driving.

We carry out a **measurement** to assign a **value** of a variable to each population unit. For example, we might measure the starting salary of an MBA graduate to the nearest dollar. Or we might measure the fuel efficiency obtained by a car in city driving to the nearest litre per 100 km by conducting a test on a driving course prescribed by the Ministry of Transportation. If the possible measurements are numbers that represent quantities (that is, "how much" or "how many"), then the variable is said to be **quantitative**. For example, starting salary and fuel efficiency are both quantitative. However, if we simply record into which of several categories a population unit falls, then the variable is said to be **qualitative** or **categorical**. Examples of categorical variables include (1) a person's sex, (2) the make of an automobile, and (3) whether a person who purchases a product is satisfied with the product.[1]

If we measure each and every population unit, we have a **population of measurements** (sometimes called **observations**). If the population is small, it is reasonable to do this. For instance, if 150 students graduated last year from an MBA program, it might be feasible to survey the graduates and to record all of their starting salaries. In general:

If we examine all of the population measurements, we say that we are conducting a **census** of the population.

Often the population that we wish to study is very large, and it is too time-consuming or costly to conduct a census. In such a situation, we select and analyze a subset (or portion) of the population.

A **sample** is a subset of the units in a population.

For example, suppose that 8742 students graduated last year from a large university. It would probably be too time-consuming to take a census of the population of all of their starting salaries. Therefore, we would select a sample of graduates, and we would obtain and record their starting salaries. When we measure the units in a sample, we say that we have a **sample of measurements**.

We often wish to describe a population or sample.

Descriptive statistics is the science of describing the important aspects of a set of measurements.

As an example, if we are studying a set of starting salaries, we might wish to describe (1) how large or small they tend to be, (2) what a typical salary might be, and (3) how much the salaries differ from each other.

When the population of interest is small and we can conduct a census of the population, we will be able to directly describe the important aspects of the population measurements. However, if the population is large and we need to select a sample from it, then we use what we call **statistical inference**.

---

[1]In Section 1.4, we discuss two types of quantitative variables (ratio and interval) and two types of qualitative variables (ordinal and nominative). Study Hint: To remember the difference between quantitative and qualitative, remember that quantitative has the letter "n" and "n is for number." Qualitative has an "l" and "l is for letter," so you have to use words to describe the data.

Statistical inference is the science of using a sample of measurements to make generalizations about the important aspects of a population of measurements.

For instance, we might use a sample of starting salaries to **estimate** the important aspects of a population of starting salaries. In the next section, we begin to look at how statistical inference is carried out.

1.2 Sampling a Population of Existing Units

Random samples   If the information contained in a sample is to accurately reflect the population under study, the sample should be **randomly selected** from the population. To intuitively illustrate random sampling, suppose that a small company employs 15 people and wishes to randomly select two of them to attend a convention. To make the random selections, we number the employees from 1 to 15, and we place in a hat 15 identical slips of paper numbered from 1 to 15. We thoroughly mix the slips of paper in the hat and, blindfolded, choose one. The number on the chosen slip of paper identifies the first randomly selected employee. Then, still blindfolded, we choose another slip of paper from the hat. The number on the second slip identifies the second randomly selected employee.

Of course, it is impractical to carry out such a procedure when the population is very large. It is easier to use a **random number table** or a computerized random number generator. To show how to use such a table, we must more formally define a random sample.[2]

A **random sample** is selected so that, on each selection from the population, every unit remaining in the population on that selection has the same chance of being chosen.

To understand this definition, first note that we can randomly select a sample **with or without replacement**. If we **sample with replacement**, we place the unit chosen on any particular selection back into the population. Thus, we give this unit a chance to be chosen on any succeeding selection. In such a case, all of the units in the population remain as candidates to be chosen for each and every selection. Randomly choosing two employees with replacement to attend a convention would make no sense because we wish to send two different employees to the convention. If we **sample without replacement**, we do not place the unit chosen on a particular selection back into the population. Thus, we do not give this unit a chance to be selected on any succeeding selection. In this case, the units remaining as candidates for a particular selection are all of the units in the population except for those that have previously been selected. **It is best to sample without replacement.** Intuitively, because we will use the sample to learn about the population, sampling without replacement will give us the fullest possible look at the population. This is true because choosing the sample without replacement guarantees that all of the units in the sample will be different (and that we are looking at as many different units from the population as possible).

In the following example, we illustrate how to use a random number table, or computer-generated random numbers, to select a random sample.

CHAPTER 1

Example 1.1   The Cell Phone Case: Estimating Cell Phone Costs[3]

Businesses and students have at least two things in common—both find cellular phones to be nearly indispensable because of their convenience and mobility, and both often rack up unpleasantly high cell phone bills. Students' high bills are usually the result of **overage**—a student uses more minutes than their plan allows. Businesses also lose money due to overage and, in addition, lose money due to **underage** when some employees do not use all of the (already-paid-for) minutes allowed by their plans. Because cellular carriers offer a very large number of rate plans,

---

[2]Actually, there are several different kinds of random samples. The type we will define is sometimes called a **simple random sample**. For brevity's sake, however, we will use the term **random sample**.

[3]The authors would like to thank Mr. Doug L. Stevens, Vice President of Sales and Marketing, at MobileSense Inc., Westlake Village, California, for his help in developing this case.

it is nearly impossible for a business to intelligently choose calling plans that will meet its needs at a reasonable cost.

Rising cell phone costs have forced companies with large numbers of cellular users to hire services to manage their cellular and other wireless resources. These cellular management services use sophisticated software and mathematical models to choose cost-efficient cell phone plans for their clients. One such firm, MobileSense Inc. of Westlake Village, California, specializes in automated wireless cost management. According to Doug L. Stevens, Vice President of Sales and Marketing at MobileSense, cell phone carriers count on overage and underage to deliver almost half of their revenues. As a result, a company's typical cost of cell phone use can easily exceed 25 cents per minute. However, Mr. Stevens explains that by using MobileSense automated cost management to select calling plans, this cost can be reduced to 12 cents per minute or less.

In this case, we will demonstrate how a bank can use a random sample of cell phone users to study its cellular phone costs. Based on this cost information, the bank will decide whether to hire a cellular management service to choose calling plans for the bank's employees. While the bank has over 10,000 employees on a variety of calling plans, the cellular management service suggests that by studying the calling patterns of cellular users on 500-minute plans, the bank can accurately assess whether its cell phone costs can be substantially reduced.

The bank has 2,136 employees on a 500-minute-per-month plan with a monthly cost of $50. The overage charge is 40 cents per minute, and there are additional charges for long distance and roaming. The bank will estimate its cellular cost per minute for this plan by examining the number of minutes used last month by each of 100 randomly selected employees on this 500-minute plan. According to the cellular management service, if the cellular cost per minute for the random sample of 100 employees is over 18 cents per minute, the bank should benefit from automated cellular management of its calling plans.

In order to randomly select the sample of 100 cell phone users, the bank will make a numbered list of the 2,136 users on the 500-minute plan. This list is called a **frame**. The bank can then use a **random number table**, such as Table 1.1(a), to select the needed sample. To see how this is done, note that any single-digit number in the table is assumed to have been randomly selected from the digits 0 to 9. Any two-digit number in the table is assumed to have been randomly selected from the numbers 00 to 99. Any three-digit number is assumed to have been randomly selected from the numbers 000 to 999, and so forth. Note that the table entries are segmented into groups of five to make the table easier to read. Because the total number of cell phone users on the 500-minute plan (2,136) is a four-digit number, we arbitrarily select any set of four digits

TABLE **1.1**   Random Numbers

(a) A portion of a random number table

33276	85590	79936	56865	05859	90106	78188
03427	90511	69445	18663	72695	52180	90322
92737	27156	33488	36320	17617	30015	74952
85689	20285	52267	67689	93394	01511	89868
08178	74461	13916	47564	81056	97735	90707
51259	63990	16308	60756	92144	49442	40719
60268	44919	19885	55322	44819	01188	55157
94904	01915	04146	18594	29852	71585	64951
58586	17752	14513	83149	98736	23495	35749
09998	19509	06691	76988	13602	51851	58104
14346	61666	30168	90229	04734	59193	32812
74103	15227	25306	76468	26384	58151	44592
24200	64161	38005	94342	28728	35806	22851
87308	07684	00256	45834	15398	46557	18510
07351	86679	92420	60952	61280	50001	94953

(b) MINITAB output of 100 different four-digit random numbers between 1 and 2136

705	1131	169	1703	1709	609
1990	766	1286	1977	222	43
1007	1902	1209	2091	1742	1152
111	69	2049	1448	659	338
1732	1650	7	388	613	1477
838	272	1227	154	18	320
1053	1466	2087	265	2107	1992
582	1787	2098	1581	397	1099
757	1699	567	1255	1959	407
354	1567	1533	1097	1299	277
663	40	585	1486	1021	532
1629	182	372	1144	1569	1981
1332	1500	743	1262	1759	955
1832	378	728	1102	667	1885
514	1128	1046	116	1160	1333
831	2036	918	1535	660	
928	1257	1468	503	468	

TABLE 1.2 A Sample of Cellular Usages (in minutes) for 100 Randomly Selected Employees
● CellUse

75	485	37	547	753	93	897	694	797	477
654	578	504	670	490	225	509	247	597	173
496	553	0	198	507	157	672	296	774	479
0	822	705	814	20	513	546	801	721	273
879	433	420	521	648	41	528	359	367	948
511	704	535	585	341	530	216	512	491	0
542	562	49	505	461	496	241	624	885	259
571	338	503	529	737	444	372	555	290	830
719	120	468	730	853	18	479	144	24	513
482	683	212	418	399	376	323	173	669	611

in the table (we have circled these digits). This number, which is 0511, identifies the first randomly selected user. Then, moving in any direction from the 0511 (up, down, right, or left—it does not matter which), we select additional sets of four digits. These succeeding sets of digits identify additional randomly selected users. Here we arbitrarily move down from 0511 in the table. The first seven sets of four digits we obtain are

$$0511 \quad 7156 \quad 0285 \quad 4461 \quad 3990 \quad 4919 \quad 1915$$

(See Table 1.1(a)—these numbers are enclosed in a rectangle.) Since there are no users numbered 7156, 4461, 3990, or 4919 (remember only 2,136 users are on the 500-minute plan), we ignore these numbers. This implies that the first three randomly selected users are those numbered 0511, 0285, and 1915. Continuing this procedure, we can obtain the entire random sample of 100 users. Notice that, because we are sampling without replacement, we should ignore any set of four digits previously selected from the random number table.

While using a random number table is one way to select a random sample, this approach has a disadvantage that is illustrated by the current situation. Specifically, since most four-digit random numbers are not between 0001 and 2136, obtaining 100 different four-digit random numbers between 0001 and 2136 will require ignoring a large number of random numbers in the random number table, and we will in fact need to use a random number table that is larger than Table 1.1(a). Although larger random number tables are readily available in books of mathematical and statistical tables, a good alternative is to use a computer software package, which can generate random numbers that are between whatever values we specify. For example, Table 1.1(b) gives the MINITAB output of 100 different four-digit random numbers that are between 0001 and 2136 (note that the "leading 0s" are not included in these four-digit numbers). If used, the random numbers in Table 1.1(b) identify the 100 employees that should form the random sample.

After the random sample of 100 employees is selected, the number of cellular minutes used by each employee during the month (the employee's **cellular usage**) is found and recorded. The 100 cellular-usage figures are given in Table 1.2. Looking at this table, we can see that there is substantial overage and underage—many employees used far more than 500 minutes, while many others failed to use all of the 500 minutes allowed by their plan. In Chapter 2, we will use these 100 usage figures to estimate the cellular cost per minute for the 500-minute plan.

Approximately random samples In general, to take a random sample we must have a list, or **frame**, of all the population units. This is needed because we must be able to number the population units in order to make random selections from them (by, for example, using a random number table). In Example 1.1, where we wished to study a population of 2,136 cell phone users who were on the bank's 500-minute cellular plan, we were able to produce a frame (list) of the population units. Therefore, we were able to select a random sample. Sometimes, however, it is not possible to list and thus number all the units in a population. In such a situation, we often select a **systematic sample**, which approximates a random sample.

Example 1.2   The Marketing Research Case: Rating a New Bottle Design[4]

The design of a package or bottle can have an important effect on a company's bottom line. For example, an article in the September 16, 2004, issue of *USA Today* reported that the introduction of a contoured 1.5-L bottle for Coke drinks played a major role in Coca-Cola's failure to meet third-quarter earnings forecasts in 2004. According to the article, Coke's biggest bottler, Coca-Cola Enterprises, "said it would miss expectations because of the 1.5-liter bottle and the absence of common 2-liter and 12-pack sizes . . . in supermarkets."[5]

In this case, a brand group is studying whether changes should be made in the bottle design for a popular soft drink. To research consumer reaction to a new design, the brand group will use the "mall intercept method," in which shoppers at a large metropolitan shopping mall are intercepted and asked to participate in a consumer survey. Each shopper will be exposed to the new bottle design and asked to rate the bottle image. Bottle image will be measured by combining consumers' responses to five items, with each response measured using a seven-point "Likert scale." The five items and the scale of possible responses are shown in Figure 1.1. Here, since we describe the least favourable response and the most favourable response (and we do not describe the responses between them), we say that the scale is "anchored" at its ends. Responses to the five items will be summed to obtain a composite score for each respondent. It follows that the minimum composite score possible is 5 and the maximum composite score possible is 35. Furthermore, experience has shown that the smallest acceptable composite score for a successful bottle design is 25.

In this situation, it is not possible to list and number each and every shopper at the mall while the study is being conducted. Consequently, we cannot use random numbers (as we did in the cell phone case) to obtain a random sample of shoppers. Instead, we can select a **systematic sample**. To do this, every 100th shopper passing a specified location in the mall will be invited to participate in the survey. Here, selecting every 100th shopper is arbitrary—we could select every 200th, every 300th, and so forth. If we select every 100th shopper, it is probably reasonable to believe that the responses of the survey participants are not related. Therefore, it is reasonable to assume that the sampled shoppers obtained by the systematic sampling process make up an **approximate** random sample.

During a Tuesday afternoon and evening, a sample of 60 shoppers is selected by using the systematic sampling process. Each shopper is asked to rate the bottle design by responding to the five items in Figure 1.1, and a composite score is calculated for each shopper. The 60 composite scores obtained are given in Table 1.3. Since these scores range from 20 to 35, we might infer that **most** of the shoppers at the mall on the Tuesday afternoon and evening of the study would rate the new bottle design between 20 and 35. Furthermore, since 57 of the 60 composite

FIGURE **1.1**   The Bottle Design Survey Instrument

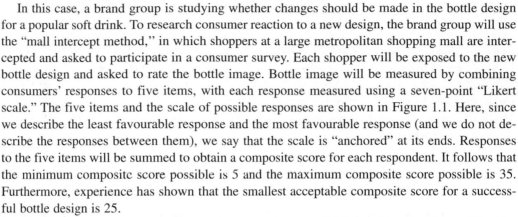

Please circle the response that most accurately describes whether you agree or disagree with each statement about the bottle you have examined.

Statement	Strongly Disagree						Strongly Agree
The size of this bottle is convenient.	1	2	3	4	5	6	7
The contoured shape of this bottle is easy to handle.	1	2	3	4	5	6	7
The label on this bottle is easy to read.	1	2	3	4	5	6	7
This bottle is easy to open.	1	2	3	4	5	6	7
Based on its overall appeal, I like this bottle design.	1	2	3	4	5	6	7

---

[4]This case was motivated by an example in the book *Essentials of Marketing Research,* by W. R. Dillon, T. J. Madden, and N. H. Firtle (Burr Ridge, IL: Richard D. Irwin, 1993). The authors also wish to thank Professor L. Unger of the Department of Marketing at Miami University for helpful discussions concerning how this type of marketing study would be carried out.

[5]Source: "Coke says earnings will come up short," by Theresa Howard, *USA Today,* September 16, 2004, p. 801.

TABLE **1.3**   A Sample of Bottle Design Ratings (Composite Scores for a Systematic Sample
of 60 Shoppers) ● Design

34	33	33	29	26	33	28	25	32	33
32	25	27	33	22	27	32	33	32	29
24	30	20	34	31	32	30	35	33	31
32	28	30	31	31	33	29	27	34	31
31	28	33	31	32	28	26	29	32	34
32	30	34	32	30	30	32	31	29	33

scores are at least 25, we might estimate that the proportion of all shoppers at the mall on the Tuesday afternoon and evening who would give the bottle design a composite score of at least 25 is $57/60 = 0.95$. That is, we estimate that 95 percent of the shoppers would give the bottle design a composite score of at least 25.

In Chapter 2, we will see how to estimate a typical composite score and we will further analyze the composite scores in Table 1.3.

In some situations, we need to decide whether a sample taken from one population can be employed to make statistical inferences about another, related, population. Often logical reasoning is used to do this. For instance, we might reason that the bottle design ratings given by shoppers at the mall on the Tuesday afternoon and evening of the research study would be representative of the ratings given by (1) shoppers at the same mall at other times, (2) shoppers at other malls, and (3) consumers in general. However, if we have no data or other information to back up this reasoning, making such generalizations is dangerous. In practice, marketing research firms choose locations and sampling times that data and experience indicate will produce a representative cross-section of consumers. To simplify our presentation, we will assume that this has been done in the bottle design case. Therefore, we will suppose that it is reasonable to use the 60 bottle design ratings in Table 1.3 to make statistical inferences about **all consumers**.

To conclude this section, we emphasize the importance of taking a random (or approximately random) sample. Statistical theory tells us that, when we select a random (or approximately random) sample, we can use the sample to make valid statistical inferences about the sampled population. However, if the sample is not random, we cannot do this. A classic example occurred prior to the U.S. presidential election of 1936, when the *Literary Digest* predicted that Alf Landon would defeat Franklin D. Roosevelt by a margin of 57 percent to 43 percent. Instead, Roosevelt won the election in a landslide. *Literary Digest*'s error was to sample names from telephone books and club membership rosters. In 1936, the United States had not yet recovered from the Great Depression, and many unemployed and low-income people did not have phones or belong to clubs. The *Literary Digest*'s sampling procedure excluded these people, who overwhelmingly voted for Roosevelt. At this time, George Gallup, founder of the Gallup Poll, was beginning to establish his survey business. He used an approximately random sample to correctly predict Roosevelt's victory.

As another example, today's television and radio stations, as well as newspaper columnists and Web sites, use **voluntary response samples**. In such samples, participants self-select—that is, whoever wishes to participate does so (usually expressing some opinion). These samples overrepresent people with strong (usually negative) opinions. For example, the advice columnist Ann Landers once asked her readers, "If you had it to do over again, would you have children?" Of the nearly 10,000 parents who **voluntarily** responded, 70 percent said that they would not. An approximately random sample taken a few months later found that 91 percent of parents would have children again. We further discuss random sampling in Section 1.5.

Exercises for Sections 1.1 and 1.2

CONCEPTS

1.1 Define a **population**. Give an example of a population that you might study when you start your career after graduating from university.

1.2 Define what we mean by a **variable**, and explain the difference between a quantitative variable and a qualitative (categorical) variable.

1.3 Below we list several variables. Which of these variables are quantitative and which are qualitative? Explain.
   a. The dollar amount on an accounts receivable invoice.
   b. The net profit for a company in 2007.
   c. The stock exchange on which a company's stock is traded.
   d. The national debt of Canada in 2007.
   e. The advertising medium (radio, television, Internet, or print) used to promote a product.

1.4 Explain the difference between a census and a sample.

1.5 Explain each of the following terms:
   a. Descriptive statistics.   **c.** Random sample.
   b. Statistical inference.   **d.** Systematic sample.

1.6 Explain why sampling without replacement is preferred to sampling with replacement.

METHODS AND APPLICATIONS

1.7 *Business News Network (BNN)* has a link on its Web site http://www.bnn.ca to the top 1,000 Canadian companies (ROB Top 1000, 2006 edition). Below we have listed the top 50 best-performing companies in terms of revenue and profit from the *BNN* Web site. ● Top50

The companies listed here are the **50 largest publicly traded Canadian corporations, measured by assets**.

ROB's explanation of the criteria used for these rankings is as follows:

> They are ranked according to their after-tax profits in their most recent fiscal year, excluding extraordinary gains or losses.
>
> When companies state their results in U.S. dollars, we do the same, but rankings are made based on the Canadian dollar equivalent.

Rank 2004	Rank 2003	Company and Year-End	Profit $1000s	Revenue $1000s	Rank
1	1	EnCana Corp. (De04)[1]	3,513,000	12,241,000	21
2	3	Bank of Nova Scotia (Oc04)	2,931,000	16,497,000	19
3	2	Royal Bank of Canada (Oc04)	2,817,000	25,204,000	6
4	11	Manulife Financial (De04)	2,564,000	27,265,000	3
5	7	Bank of Montreal (Oc04)	2,351,000	13,208,000	23
6	19	Toronto-Dominion Bank (Oc04)	2,310,000	16,015,000	20
7	5	Cdn. Imp. Bank of Commerce (Oc04)	2,199,000	16,705,000	17
8	9	Imperial Oil (De04)	2,033,000	21,206,000	11
9	nr	Manufacturers Life Insurance (De04)	2,015,000	19,991,000	13
10	10	Petro-Canada (De04)	1,757,000	14,442,000	22
11	14	Sun Life Financial (De04)	1,681,000	21,769,000	10
12	16	Great-West Lifeco (De04)	1,660,000	21,871,000	9
13	6	Power Financial (De04)	1,558,000	24,077,000	8
14	8	BCE Inc. (De04)	1,524,000	19,285,000	14
15	4	Bell Canada (De04)	1,518,000	16,972,000	16
16	12	Cdn. Natural Resources (De04)	1,405,000	7,179,000	39
17	17	Thomson Corp. (De04)[1]	1,011,000	8,132,000	30
18	28	Canadian National Railway Co. (De04)	1,297,000	6,581,000	44
19	26	Shell Canada (De04)	1,286,000	11,288,000	27
20	25	Great-West Life Assurance (De04)	1,226,000	17,353,000	15
21	18	Suncor Energy (De04)	1,100,000	8,699,000	33
22	22	TransCanada PipeLines (De04)	1,083,000	5,343,000	55
23	23	TransCanada Corp. (De04)	1,032,000	5,343,000	55
24	13	Husky Energy (De04)	1,006,000	8,540,000	35
25	24	Loblaw Companies (Ja05)	968,000	26,209,000	5
26	15	Power Corp. (De04)	949,000	24,470,000	7
27	29	Magna International (De04)[1]	692,000	20,672,000	4
28	33	Brascan Corp. (De04)[1]	688,000	4,372,000	52
29	49	Falconbridge Ltd. (De04)[1]	672,000	3,070,000	67
30	62	Inco Ltd. (De04)[1]	612,000	4,320,000	53
31	31	Nexen Inc. (De04)	793,000	3,884,000	69
32	32	National Bank of Canada (Oc04)	725,000	4,771,000	59

33	180	Noranda Inc. (De04)[1]	551,000	7,002,000	32
34	21	Talisman Energy (De04)	663,000	6,479,000	45
35	30	Enbridge Inc. (De04)	652,200	6,843,700	43
36	36	PetroKazakhstan Inc. (De04)[1]	500,668	1,652,346	102
37	nr	ING Canada (De04)	624,152	3,780,886	71
38	34	IGM Financial (De04)	617,096	2,119,071	104
39	82	Teck Cominco (De04)	617,000	3,452,000	78
40	314	IPSCO Inc. (De04)[1]	438,610	2,458,893	82
41	41	Telus Corp. (De04)	565,800	7,623,400	37
42	43	Canadian Oil Sands Trust (De04)	509,200	1,480,200	130
43	931	Gerdau Ameristeel (De04)[1]	337,669	3,154,390	65
44	27	George Weston (De04)	428,000	29,723,000	2
45	70	Norbord Inc. (De04)[1]	326,000	1,492,000	110
46	79	Canfor Corp. (De04)	420,900	4,120,000	64
47	38	Canadian Pacific Railway Ltd. (De04)	413,000	3,990,900	68
48	994	Potash Corp. of Saskatchewan (De04)[1]	298,600	3,328,200	61
49	46	Placer Dome (De04)[1]	291,000	1,946,000	90
50	100	Dofasco Inc. (De04)	376,900	4,235,400	62

[1]Figures are reported in U.S. dollars.
nr: not ranked
Reprinted with permission from *The Globe and Mail*.

Consider the random numbers given in the random number table of Table 1.1(a) on page 4. Starting in the upper left corner of Table 1.1(a) and moving down the two leftmost columns, we see that the first three two-digit numbers obtained are

$$33 \qquad 03 \qquad 92$$

Starting with these three random numbers, and moving down the two leftmost columns of Table 1.1(a) to find more two-digit random numbers, use Table 1.1 to randomly select five of these companies to be interviewed in detail about their business strategies. Hint: Note that the companies in the *BNN* list are numbered from 1 to 50.

1.8 THE VIDEO GAME SATISFACTION RATING CASE
VideoGame

A company that produces and markets video game systems wishes to assess its customers' level of satisfaction with a relatively new model, the XYZ-Box. In the six months since the introduction of the model, the company has received 73,219 warranty registrations from purchasers. The company will randomly select 65 of these registrations and will conduct telephone interviews with the purchasers. Specifically, each purchaser will be asked to state their level of agreement with each of the seven statements listed on the survey instrument given in Figure 1.2. Here the level of agreement for each statement is measured on a seven-point Likert scale.[7] Purchaser

FIGURE **1.2** **The Video Game Satisfaction Survey Instrument**

Statement	Strongly Disagree						Strongly Agree
The game console of the XYZ-Box is well designed.	1	2	3	4	5	6	7
The game controller of the XYZ-Box is easy to handle.	1	2	3	4	5	6	7
The XYZ-Box has high-quality graphics capabilities.	1	2	3	4	5	6	7
The XYZ-Box has high-quality audio capabilities.	1	2	3	4	5	6	7
The XYZ-Box serves as a complete entertainment centre.	1	2	3	4	5	6	7
There is a large selection of XYZ-Box games to choose from.	1	2	3	4	5	6	7
I am totally satisfied with my XYZ-Box game system.	1	2	3	4	5	6	7

[7] Historical Trivia: The Likert scale is named after Rensis Likert (1903–1981), who originally developed this numerical scale for measuring attitudes in his PhD dissertation in 1932. [Source: *Psychology in America: A Historical Survey*, by E. R. Hilgard (San Diego, CA: Harcourt Brace Jovanovich, 1987).]

TABLE **1.4** Composite Scores for the Video Game
Satisfaction Rating Case
● VideoGame

39	44	46	44	44
45	42	45	44	42
38	46	45	45	47
42	40	46	44	43
42	47	43	46	45
41	44	47	48	
38	43	43	44	
42	45	41	41	
46	45	40	45	
44	40	43	44	
40	46	44	44	
39	41	41	44	
40	43	38	46	
42	39	43	39	
45	43	36	41	

TABLE **1.5** Waiting Times (in Minutes) for the Bank
Customer Waiting Time Case
● WaitTime

1.6	6.2	3.2	5.6	7.9	6.1	7.2
6.6	5.4	6.5	4.4	1.1	3.8	7.3
5.6	4.9	2.3	4.5	7.2	10.7	4.1
5.1	5.4	8.7	6.7	2.9	7.5	6.7
3.9	0.8	4.7	8.1	9.1	7.0	3.5
4.6	2.5	3.6	4.3	7.7	5.3	6.3
6.5	8.3	2.7	2.2	4.0	4.5	4.3
6.4	6.1	3.7	5.8	1.4	4.5	3.8
8.6	6.3	0.4	8.6	7.8	1.8	5.1
4.2	6.8	10.2	2.0	5.2	3.7	5.5
5.8	9.8	2.8	8.0	8.4	4.0	
3.4	2.9	11.6	9.5	6.3	5.7	
9.3	10.9	4.3	1.3	4.4	2.4	
7.4	4.7	3.1	4.8	5.2	9.2	
1.8	3.9	5.8	9.9	7.4	5.0	

satisfaction will be measured by adding the purchaser's responses to the seven statements. It follows that for each consumer the minimum composite score possible is 7 and the maximum is 49. Furthermore, experience has shown that a purchaser of a video game system is "very satisfied" if their composite score is at least 42.

a. Assume that the warranty registrations are numbered from 1 to 73,219 on a computer. Starting in the upper left corner of Table 1.1(a) and moving down the five leftmost columns, we see that the first three five-digit numbers obtained are

33276   03427   92737

Starting with these three random numbers and moving down the five leftmost columns of Table 1.1(a) to find more five-digit random numbers, randomly select the numbers of the first 10 warranty registrations to be included in the sample of 65 registrations.

b. Suppose that when the 65 customers are interviewed, their composite scores are obtained and are as given in Table 1.4. Using the data, estimate limits between which most of the 73,219 composite scores would fall. Also estimate the proportion of the 73,219 composite scores that would be at least 42.

1.9   THE BANK CUSTOMER WAITING TIME CASE
● WaitTime

A bank manager has developed a new system to reduce the time customers spend waiting to be served by tellers during peak business hours. Typical waiting times during peak business hours under the current system are roughly 9 to 10 minutes. The bank manager hopes that the new system will lower typical waiting times to less than six minutes.

A 30-day trial of the new system is conducted. During the trial run, every 150th customer who arrives during peak business hours is selected until a systematic sample of 100 customers is obtained. Each of the sampled customers is observed, and the time spent waiting for teller service is recorded. The 100 waiting times obtained are given in Table 1.5. Moreover, the bank manager feels that this systematic sample is as representative as a random sample of waiting times would be. Using the data, estimate limits between which the waiting times of most of the customers arriving during peak business hours would be. Also estimate the proportion of waiting times of customers arriving during peak business hours that are less than six minutes.

1.10 In an article titled "Turned off" in the June 2–4, 1995, issue of *USA Weekend,* Olmsted and Anders report on the results of a survey conducted by the magazine. Readers were invited to write in and answer several questions about sex and vulgarity on television. Olmsted and Anders summarized the survey results as follows:

Nearly all of the 65,000 readers responding to our write-in survey say TV is too vulgar, too violent, and too racy. TV execs call it reality.

Some of the key survey results were as follows:

SURVEY RESULTS
- 96 percent are very or somewhat concerned about SEX on TV.
- 97 percent are very or somewhat concerned about VULGAR LANGUAGE on TV.
- 97 percent are very or somewhat concerned about VIOLENCE on TV.

Note: Because participants were not chosen at random, the results of the write-in survey may not be scientific.

a. Note the disclaimer at the bottom of the survey results. In a write-in survey, anyone who wishes to participate may respond to the survey questions. Therefore, the sample is not random and we say that the survey is "not scientific." What kind of people would be most likely to respond to a survey about TV sex and violence? Do the survey results agree with your answer?

b. If a random sample of the general population were taken, do you think that its results would be the same? Why or why not? Similarly, for instance, do you think

that 97 percent of the general population is "very or somewhat concerned about violence on TV"?

c. Another result obtained in the write-in survey is as follows:
- Should "V-chips" be installed on TV sets so parents could easily block violent programming?

YES 90%   NO 10%

If you planned to start a business manufacturing and marketing such V-chips (at a reasonable price), would you expect 90 percent of the general population to desire a V-chip? Why or why not?

1.3 Sampling a Process

A population is not always defined to be a set of **existing** units. Often we are interested in studying the population of all of the units that will be or could potentially be produced by a process.

> A **process** is a sequence of operations that takes inputs (labour, materials, methods, machines, and so on) and turns them into outputs (products, services, and the like).

Processes produce output **over time**. For example, this year's Toyota Corolla manufacturing process produces Toyota Corollas over time. Early in the model year, Toyota Canada might wish to study the population of the city fuel efficiency of all Toyota Corollas that will be produced during the model year. Or, even more hypothetically, Toyota Canada might wish to study the population of the city fuel efficiency of all Toyota Corollas that could **potentially** be produced by this model year's manufacturing process. The first population is called a **finite population** because only a finite number of cars will be produced during the year. Any population of existing units is also finite. The second population is called an **infinite population** because the manufacturing process that produces this year's model could in theory always be used to build one more car. That is, theoretically there is no limit to the number of cars that could be produced by this year's process. There are a multitude of other examples of finite or infinite hypothetical populations. For instance, we might study the population of all waiting times that will or could potentially be experienced by patients of a hospital emergency room. Or we might study the population of all the amounts of raspberry jam that will be or could potentially be dispensed into 500-mL jars by an automated filling machine. To study a population of potential process observations, we sample the process—usually at equally spaced time points—over time. This is illustrated in the following case.

Example 1.3 **The Coffee Temperature Case: Monitoring Coffee Temperatures**

According to the Web site of the Association of Trial Lawyers of America,[8] Stella Liebeck of Albuquerque, New Mexico, was severely burned by McDonald's coffee in February 1992. Liebeck, who received third-degree burns over 6 percent of her body, was awarded $160,000 ($US) in compensatory damages and $480,000 ($US) in punitive damages. A postverdict investigation revealed that the coffee temperature at the local Albuquerque McDonald's had dropped from about 85°C before the trial to about 70°C after the trial.

This case concerns coffee temperatures at a fast-food restaurant. Because of the possibility of future litigation and to possibly improve the coffee's taste, the restaurant wishes to study and monitor the temperature of the coffee it serves. To do this, the restaurant personnel measure the temperature of the coffee being dispensed (in degrees Celsius) at half-hour intervals from 10 A.M. to 9:30 P.M. on a given day. Table 1.6 gives the 24 temperature measurements obtained in the time order that they were observed. Here time equals 1 at 10 A.M. and 24 at 9:30 P.M.

---

[8]http://www.atla.org/pressroom/FACTS/frivolous/McdonaldsCoffeecase.aspx, Association of Trial Lawyers of America, January 25, 2005.

TABLE **1.6**   **24 Coffee Temperatures Observed in Time Order (°C)** ● CoffeeTemp

Time		Coffee Temperature	Time		Coffee Temperature	Time		Coffee Temperature
(10:00 A.M.)	1	73°C	(2:00 P.M.)	9	71°C	(6:00 P.M.)	17	70°C
	2	76		10	68		18	77
	3	69		11	75		19	68
	4	67		12	72		20	72
(12:00 noon)	5	74	(4:00 P.M.)	13	67	(8:00 P.M.)	21	69
	6	70		14	74		22	75
	7	69		15	72		23	68
	8	72		16	68		24	73

Examining Table 1.6, we see that the coffee temperatures range from 67°C to 77°C. Based on this, is it reasonable to conclude that the temperature of most of the coffee that will or could potentially be served by the restaurant will be between 67°C and 77°C? The answer is yes if the restaurant's coffee-making process operates consistently over time. That is, this process must be in a state of **statistical control**.

A process is in **statistical control** if it does not exhibit any unusual process variations. Often this means that the process displays a **constant amount of variation** around a **constant**, or horizontal, **level**.

To assess whether a process is in statistical control, we sample the process often enough to detect unusual variations or instabilities. The fast-food restaurant has sampled the coffee-making process every half hour. In other situations, we sample processes with other frequencies—for example, every minute, every hour, or every day. Using the observed process measurements, we can then construct a **runs plot** (sometimes called a **time series plot**).

A **runs plot** is a graph of individual process measurements versus time.

Figure 1.3 shows the Excel outputs of a runs plot of the temperature data. (Some people call such a plot a **line chart** when the plot points are connected by line segments as in the Excel output.) Here we plot each coffee temperature on the vertical scale versus its corresponding

FIGURE **1.3**   **Excel Runs Plots of Coffee Temperatures: The Process Is in Statistical Control**

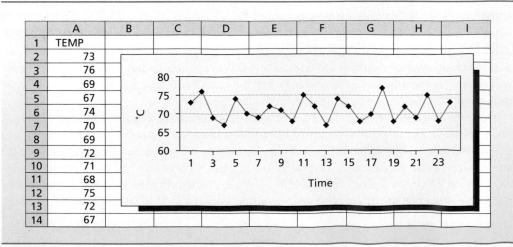

time index on the horizontal scale. For instance, the first temperature (73°C) is plotted versus time equals 1, the second temperature (76°C) is plotted versus time equals 2, and so forth. The runs plot suggests that the temperatures exhibit a relatively constant amount of variation around a relatively constant level. That is, the centre of the temperatures can be pretty much represented by a horizontal line (constant level), and the spread of the points around the line stays about the same (constant variation). Note that the plot points tend to form a horizontal band. Therefore, the temperatures are in statistical control.

In general, assume that we have sampled a process at different (usually equally spaced) time points and made a runs plot of the resulting sample measurements. If the plot indicates that the process is in statistical control, and if it is reasonable to believe that the process will remain in control, then it is probably reasonable to regard the sample measurements as an approximately random sample from the population of all possible process measurements. Furthermore, since the process remains in statistical control, the process performance is **predictable**. This allows us to make statistical inferences about the population of all possible process measurements that will or potentially could result from using the process. For example, assuming that the coffee-making process will remain in statistical control, it is reasonable to conclude that the temperature of most of the coffee that will be or could potentially be served will be between 67°C and 77°C.

To emphasize the importance of statistical control, suppose that another fast-food restaurant observes the 24 coffee temperatures that are plotted versus time in Figure 1.4. These temperatures range between 67°C and 80°C. However, we cannot infer from this that the temperature of most of the coffee that will be or could potentially be served by this other restaurant will be between 67°C and 80°C. This is because the downward trend in the runs plot of Figure 1.4 indicates that the coffee-making process is out of control and will soon produce temperatures below 67°C. Another example of an out-of-control process is illustrated in Figure 1.5. Here the coffee temperatures seem to fluctuate around a constant level but with increasing variation (notice that the plotted temperatures fan out as time advances). In general, the specific pattern of out-of-control behaviour can suggest the reason for this behaviour. For example, the downward trend in the runs plot of Figure 1.4 might suggest that the restaurant's coffeemaker has a defective heating element.

Visually inspecting a runs plot to check for statistical control can be tricky. One reason is that the scale of measurements on the vertical axis can influence whether the data appear to form a horizontal band. For now, we will simply emphasize that a process must be in statistical control in order to make valid statistical inferences about the population of all possible process observations. Also, note that being in statistical control does not necessarily imply that a process is **capable** of producing output that meets our requirements. For example, suppose that marketing research suggests that the fast-food restaurant's customers feel that coffee tastes best if its temperature is between 67°C and 75°C. Since Table 1.6 indicates that the temperature of some of the coffee it serves is not in this range (note that two of the temperatures are 67°C, one is 76°C, and another is 77°C), the restaurant might take action to reduce the variation of the coffee temperatures.

FIGURE **1.4** **A Runs Plot of Coffee Temperatures: The Process Level Is Decreasing**

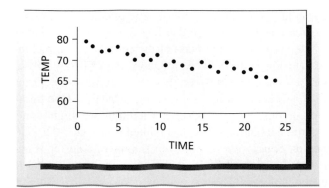

FIGURE **1.5** **A Runs Plot of Coffee Temperatures: The Process Variation Is Increasing**

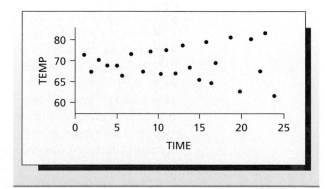

The marketing research and coffee temperature cases are both examples of using the **statistical process** to make a statistical inference. In the next case, we formally describe and illustrate this process.

Example 1.4 The Mass of the Loonie

In 1989, Mr. Steve Kopp, a lecturer in the Department of Statistical and Actuarial Sciences at the University of Western Ontario, decided to weigh 200 one dollar coins (loonies) that were minted in that year. He was curious about the distribution of the mass of the loonie.

From a production standpoint, the loonie would have to be minted within strict specifications. The loonie does in fact have specific minting requirements:

Composition: 91.5% nickel with 8.5% bronze plating
Mass (g): 7
Diameter (mm): 26.5
Thickness (mm): 1.75

A person at the Royal Canadian Mint might be interested in knowing if the minted coins fall within an acceptable tolerance. Remember, these loonies cannot be too light or too heavy, as vending machines are set to accept coins according to mass and size. As a statistician, you may be interested in testing a hypothesis about the mass of the coin. We will use this sample of 200 loonies to ultimately draw conclusions about the entire population of loonies minted in 1989. The steps used in the **statistical process** for making a statistical inference are as follows:

1 **Describe the practical problem of interest and the associated population or process to be studied.** We wish to ultimately determine whether or not the coins are being minted in an acceptable and consistent manner. The coin minter will use statistical processes on a sample to study the population of coins that were minted during that year.

2 **Describe the variable of interest and how it will be measured.** The variable of interest is the mass of the loonie (in grams). The mass was obtained using a highly sensitive scale that gives masses in grams to four decimal places.

3 **Describe the sampling procedure.** A sample of 200 coins was obtained from a local bank in London, Ontario. The coins are packaged in rolls of 25, so eight rolls were obtained at random. These coins may or may not come from the same production run, but we do know that they were minted in the same year (1989). Each coin was carefully weighed, and the masses are given in Table 1.7.

4 **Describe the statistical inference of interest.** The sample of 200 loonies will be used to determine if the distribution of masses follows any specific type of distribution, and we are also interested in knowing if the coins are being minted within the required mass specifications.

5 **Describe how the statistical inference will be made and evaluate the reliability of the inference.** Figure 1.6 gives the MINITAB output of a plot of the 200 masses. Remember, we do not know if the coins were minted in different production runs, but we do know that they could not have all been minted at the same time, so this sample of coins was in fact minted over a period of time. If it's reasonable to believe that loonie masses will remain in control, we can make statistical inferences about the mass of the coin. For example, in Table 1.7 we see that the masses of the coins range between 6.8358 g and 7.2046 g, so we might infer that most loonies would be somewhere between these two masses. In order to determine the "typical" mass of the loonie population, we might try to determine the midpoint of this sample range. When we do this, we get 7.0202 g. Therefore, we might conclude that the typical mass for the entire population of loonies minted is around 7.0202 g. According to specifications outlined on http://www.mint.ca, our sample of coins appears to meet the required standard of a mass of 7 g for each loonie. More analysis would have to be done to arrive at this conclusion, however. This estimate is intuitive, so we do not

TABLE **1.7**   **Loonie Mass Data** ● Loonies

7.0688	7.0196	7.008	7.0252	7.0912	6.9753	6.9720	7.0963
6.9651	6.9911	6.9156	7.0466	7.0948	7.0127	7.0470	7.0215
6.9605	7.0294	7.0050	7.0119	7.0929	7.0706	7.0459	6.9549
6.9797	7.0045	7.0898	7.0354	7.0186	6.9861	7.0339	6.9178
6.9861	6.9605	7.1322	6.9528	7.0648	6.9920	6.9334	7.0584
7.1227	6.9812	6.9873	7.0000	6.8479	7.0100	7.0740	7.0884
6.9861	7.0136	7.0572	6.8959	7.0079	7.0195	6.9888	7.0641
6.9692	7.0185	7.0158	7.0552	7.0478	7.0500	7.0919	7.0107
6.9018	7.1567	7.1135	6.9117	7.0346	7.0627	7.0561	6.8990
7.0574	6.9814	7.0016	7.0026	7.0212	7.0833	7.0343	7.0111
7.0467	7.0413	6.9892	7.0563	7.0374	7.0027	7.0012	7.2046
7.0386	6.9793	6.9074	7.0810	7.0076	7.0797	7.0132	6.9867
6.9799	7.0245	7.0461	6.9430	7.0934	7.0207	6.9364	6.9705
7.0326	7.0295	7.0024	6.9955	7.0184	7.0681	7.0046	7.0092
7.1380	7.0099	6.9936	6.9784	6.9475	7.0708	6.8821	7.0009
7.0908	6.9563	7.0364	6.9575	7.0118	7.0490	7.0426	7.0746
7.0335	6.9785	6.9005	7.1735	6.9034	6.9690	7.0137	6.9876
6.8788	7.0260	7.0216	7.0847	6.9481	6.9891	7.0943	6.9898
7.0654	6.9428	6.9986	6.8801	7.0640	7.0203	6.9521	7.0489
7.0610	7.0784	6.9741	6.9491	6.9541	6.9091	7.0732	6.9874
7.0057	6.9516	6.9477	7.0401	7.0017	7.0222	7.0941	6.8818
7.0277	7.0264	6.9862	7.0396	6.9685	7.0874	7.0024	7.0253
7.0438	7.0291	6.9582	7.0812	7.0780	6.9771	7.0463	7.0304
6.9977	6.9909	6.8358	7.0607	7.0652	7.0148	7.0909	6.9469
6.9531	6.9623	6.9785	6.8395	6.9618	7.0401	6.9994	7.0438

have any information about its **reliability**. In Chapter 2, we will study more precise ways to both define and estimate a "typical" population value. In Chapters 3 through 7, we will study tools for assessing the reliability of estimation procedures and for estimating "with confidence."

FIGURE **1.6**

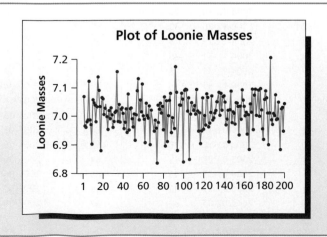

Exercises for Section 1.3

CONCEPTS

1.11 Define a **process**. Then give an example of a process you might study when you start your career after graduating from university.

1.12 Explain what it means to say that a process is in statistical control.

1.13 What is a runs plot? What does a runs plot look like when we sample and plot a process that is in statistical control?

METHODS AND APPLICATIONS

1.14 The data below give 18 measurements of a critical dimension for an automobile part (measurements in centimetres). Here one part has been randomly selected each hour from the previous hour's production, and the measurements are given in time order.
⬤ AutoPart1

Hour	Measurement	Hour	Measurement
1	3.005	10	3.005
2	3.020	11	3.015
3	2.980	12	2.995
4	3.015	13	3.020
5	2.995	14	3.000
6	3.010	15	2.990
7	3.000	16	2.985
8	2.985	17	3.020
9	3.025	18	2.985

Construct a runs plot and determine if the process appears to be in statistical control.

1.15 Table 1.8 presents the time (in days) needed to settle the 67 homeowners' insurance claims handled by an insurance agent over a year. The claims are given in time order by loss date. ⬤ ClaimSet

a. Figure 1.7 shows a MINITAB runs plot of the claims data in Table 1.8. Does the claims-handling process seem to be in statistical control? Why or why not?

b. In March of 2005, the region covered by the insurance company was hit by a widespread ice storm that caused heavy damage to homes in the area. Did this ice storm have a significant impact on the time needed to settle homeowners' claims? Should the agent consider improving procedures for handling claims in emergency situations? Why or why not?

1.16 In the article "Accelerating improvement" published in *Quality Progress* (October 1991), Gaudard, Coates, and Freeman describe a restaurant that caters to business travellers and has a self-service breakfast buffet. Interested in customer satisfaction, the manager conducts a survey over a three-week period and finds that the main customer complaint is having to wait too long to be seated. On each day from September 11, 1989, to October 1, 1989, a problem-solving team records the percentage of patrons who must wait more than one minute to be seated. A runs plot of the daily

TABLE 1.8 Number of Days Required to Settle Homeowners' Insurance Claims (Claims Made from July 2, 2004 to June 25, 2005) ⬤ ClaimSet

Claim	Loss Date	Days to Settle	Claim	Loss Date	Days to Settle	Claim	Loss Date	Days to Settle
1	2004-07-02	111	24	2004-11-05	34	47	2005-03-05	70
2	2004-07-06	35	25	2004-11-13	25	48	2005-03-05	67
3	2004-07-11	23	26	2004-11-21	22	49	2005-03-06	81
4	2004-07-12	42	27	2004-11-23	14	50	2005-03-06	92
5	2004-07-16	54	28	2004-11-25	20	51	2005-03-06	96
6	2004-07-27	50	29	2004-12-01	32	52	2005-03-06	85
7	2004-08-01	41	30	2004-12-08	27	53	2005-03-07	83
8	2004-08-13	12	31	2004-12-10	23	54	2005-03-07	102
9	2004-08-20	8	32	2004-12-20	35	55	2005-03-19	23
10	2004-08-20	11	33	2004-12-23	29	56	2005-03-27	11
11	2004-08-28	11	34	2004-12-31	25	57	2005-04-01	8
12	2004-09-03	31	35	2004-12-31	18	58	2005-04-11	11
13	2004-09-10	35	36	2004-12-31	16	59	2005-04-15	35
14	2004-09-17	14	37	2005-01-05	23	60	2005-04-19	29
15	2004-09-18	14	38	2005-01-08	26	61	2005-05-02	80
16	2004-09-29	27	39	2005-01-16	30	62	2005-05-15	18
17	2004-10-04	14	40	2005-01-18	36	63	2005-05-25	58
18	2004-10-06	23	41	2005-01-22	42	64	2005-06-06	4
19	2004-10-15	47	42	2005-01-25	45	65	2005-06-12	5
20	2004-10-23	17	43	2005-01-27	43	66	2005-06-24	15
21	2004-10-25	21	44	2005-02-05	39	67	2005-06-25	19
22	2004-10-30	18	45	2005-02-09	53			
23	2004-11-02	31	46	2005-02-23	64			

FIGURE **1.7** MINITAB Runs Plot of the Insurance
              Claims Data for Exercise 1.15

FIGURE **1.8** Runs Plot of Daily Percentages of
              Customers Waiting More Than One
              Minute to Be Seated (for Exercise 1.16)

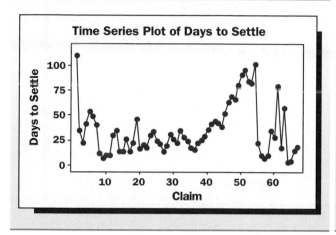

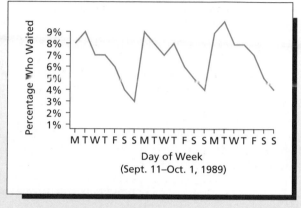

percentages is shown in Figure 1.8.[9] What does the runs plot suggest?

1.17 THE TRASH BAG CASE[10] ● TrashBag

A company that produces and markets trash bags has developed an improved 130-L bag. The new bag is produced using a specially formulated plastic that is both stronger and more biodegradable than previously used plastics, and the company wishes to evaluate the strength of this bag. The **breaking strength** of a trash bag is considered to be the mass (in kilograms) of a representative trash mix that when loaded into a bag suspended in the air will cause the bag to sustain significant damage (such

as ripping or tearing). The company has decided to carry out a 40-hour pilot production run of the new bags. Each hour, at a randomly selected time during the hour, a bag is taken off the production line. The bag is then subjected to a breaking strength test. The 40 breaking strengths obtained during the pilot production run are given in Table 1.9, and an Excel runs plot of these breaking strengths is given in Figure 1.9.

a. Do the 40 breaking strengths appear to be in statistical control? Explain.

b. Estimate limits between which most of the breaking strengths of all trash bags would fall.

TABLE **1.9** Breaking
             Strengths
             ● TrashBag

22.0	23.9	23.0	22.5
23.8	21.6	21.9	23.6
24.3	23.1	23.4	23.6
23.0	22.6	22.3	22.2
22.9	22.7	23.5	21.3
22.5	23.1	24.2	23.3
23.2	24.1	23.2	22.4
22.0	23.1	23.9	24.5
23.0	22.7	23.3	22.4
22.8	22.8	22.5	23.4

FIGURE **1.9** Excel Runs Plot of Breaking Strengths for Exercise 1.17

	A	B	C	D	E	F	G	H	I	J
1	Strength									
2	22.0									
3	23.8									
4	24.3									
5	23.0									
6	22.9									
7	22.5									
8	23.2									
9	22.0									
10	23.0									
11	22.8									
12	23.9									
13	21.6									
14	23.1									
15	22.6									
16	22.7									
17	23.1									
18	24.1									
19	23.1									
20	22.7									
21	22.8									

[9]The source of Figure 1.8 is "Accelerating improvement," by M. Gaudard, R. Coates, and L. Freeman, *Quality Progress,* October 1991, pp. 81–88. Copyright © 1991 American Society for Quality Control. Used with permission.

[10]This case is based on conversations by the authors with several employees working for a leading producer of trash bags. For purposes of confidentiality, we have withheld the company's name.

FIGURE **1.10** MegaStat Runs Plot of Waiting Times for Exercise 1.18

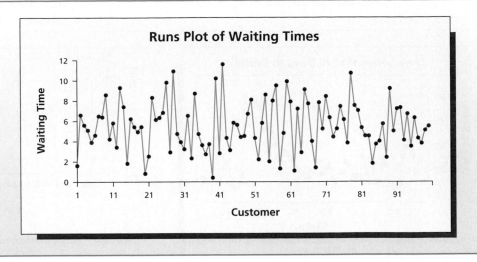

1.18 THE BANK CUSTOMER WAITING TIME CASE ● WaitTime

Recall that every 150th customer arriving during peak business hours was sampled until a systematic sample of 100 customers was obtained. This systematic sampling procedure is equivalent to sampling from a process. Figure 1.10 shows a MegaStat runs plot of the 100 waiting times in Table 1.5. Does the process appear to be in statistical control? Explain.

1.4 Levels of Measurement: Nominal, Ordinal, Interval, and Ratio

In Section 1.1, we said that a variable is **quantitative** if its possible values are **numbers that represent quantities** (that is, "how much" or "how many"). In general, a quantitative variable is measured on a scale with a **fixed unit of measurement** between its possible values. For example, if we measure employees' salaries to the nearest dollar, then one dollar is the fixed unit of measurement between different employees' salaries. There are two types of quantitative variables: **ratio** and **interval**. A **ratio variable** is a quantitative variable measured on a scale such that ratios of its values are meaningful and there is an inherently defined zero value. Variables such as salary, height, weight, time, and distance are ratio variables. For example, a distance of zero kilometres is "no distance at all," and a town that is 30 km away is "twice as far" as a town that is 15 km away.

An **interval variable** is a quantitative variable where ratios of its values are not meaningful and there is no meaningful zero. The 1 to 7 Likert scale example given earlier is an example of an interval scale. The distance from 2 to 3 is the same as that from 5 to 6. The scale could also have been

$$-3 \quad -2 \quad -1 \quad 0 \quad 1 \quad 2 \quad 3$$

Here the zero is the midpoint and represents the same concept as the number 4 in the 1 to 7 scale.

In Section 1.1, we also said that if we simply record into which of several categories a population (or sample) unit falls, then the variable is **qualitative** (or **categorical**). There are two types of qualitative variables: **ordinal** and **nominative** (or **nominal**). An **ordinal variable** is a qualitative variable for which there is a meaningful **ordering**, or **ranking**, of the categories. The measurements of an ordinal variable may be nonnumerical or numerical. For example, a student may be asked to rank their four favourite colours. The person may say that yellow (#1) is their most favourite colour, then green (#2), red (#3), and blue (#4). If asked further, the person may say they really adore yellow and green and that red and blue are "so-so" but that red is slightly better than blue. This ranking does not have equal distances between points in that 1 to 2 is not the same as 2 to 3. Only the order (of preference) is meaningful. In Chapter 13, we will learn how to use **nonparametric statistics** to analyze an ordinal variable without considering the variable to be somewhat quantitative and performing such arithmetic operations. In addition to these four types of variables, data may also take the form of continuous or discrete values. Continuous variables are typically interval or ratio scale numbers and fall along a continuum so that decimals make sense (such as salaries, age, mass, and height). In contrast, discrete variables are nominal or ordinal and represent distinct groups in which decimals do not make sense (such as sex categorization, living in urban or rural communities, and number of children in a household).

To conclude this section, we consider the second type of qualitative variable. A **nominative (or nominal) variable** is a qualitative variable for which there is no meaningful ordering, or ranking, of the categories. A person's sex, the colour of a car, and an employee's city of residence are nominative (or nominal) variables.[11]

Exercises for Section 1.4

CONCEPTS

1.19 Discuss the difference between a ratio variable and an interval variable.

1.20 Discuss the difference between an ordinal variable and a nominative (or nominal) variable.

METHODS AND APPLICATIONS

1.21 Classify each of the following qualitative variables as ordinal or nominative (or nominal). Explain your answers.

Qualitative Variable	Categories					
Statistics course letter mark	A	B	C	D	F	
Door choice on *Let's Make a Deal*	Door #1	Door #2				
Television show classifications	C	C8	G	PG	14+	18+
Personal computer ownership	Yes	No				
Restaurant rating	*****	****	***	**	*	
Income tax filing status	Married	Living common-law	Widowed			
	Divorced	Separated	Single			

1.22 Classify each of the following qualitative variables as ordinal or nominative (or nominal). Explain your answers.

Qualitative Variable	Categories			
Personal computer operating system	Windows XP	Mac 05-X	Windows	
	Unix	Linux	Other	Vista
Motion picture classifications	G PG 14A 18A R A			
Level of education	Elementary	Middle school	High school	University
	Graduate school			
Rankings of top 10 university hockey teams	1 2 3 4 5 6 7 8 9 10			
Exchange on which a stock is traded	S&P/TSX DJIA S&P 500 NASDAQ			
First three characters of postal code	B3J M1J T2K V7E			

1.5 A Brief Introduction to Surveys

The Likert scale was introduced in Section 1.2 and has proven to be a valuable method of measuring topics such as attitudes (such as job satisfaction), values (such as organizational commitment), personality traits, and market research feedback. This section is a brief introduction to survey types and some issues that arise with surveys.

Surveys are also known as questionnaires. The purpose of surveys is typically to elicit responses from the participants. There are typically four steps involved in creating a survey. The first involves deciding upon the content (what is being studied and how the questions will be asked). Question types can vary. For example, the surveyor may want to know factual information (such as demographics of age, sex, and income). The variable of interest might be behavioural (such as what the person does on their holidays). The questions may also be opinion based (such as what fragrance a person prefers in their laundry detergent). Basically, the questions can be about anything of interest to the surveyor.

After the content has been decided upon, the questionnaire creator generates the questions. It is ideal if these questions are as short as possible and are easy to read and understand. Following

---

[11]Study Hint: To remember the levels of measurement, simply remember the French word for "black" (NOIR). This acronym is useful since it also puts the levels into order from simplest level of measurement (nominal or nominative) to most complex (ratio).

the question creation, the response key has to be decided upon. Here there are two options: open and closed. Open-ended questions are ones in which the respondent can answer the question in any manner they wish. These types of responses provide rich information but are difficult to score or code. The closed-ended questions represent those that give the respondent a choice of answers. These responses are typically much easier to code and quantify.

Once the questions and the response system are determined, the questionnaire is compiled. The order of the questions is important, as questions themselves may influence people's responses to following questions. To address the quality of the survey created, the surveyor must complete the fourth step, which is to pilot test the questionnaire and address issues such as stability (reliability) and validity (do the questions actually measure what they were intended to measure?). Following the creation of the survey, the delivery of the questionnaire must be determined.

In general, surveys are delivered using one of three methods: mailed (direct or mass/bulk), telephone, and in-person. Mailed surveys are relatively inexpensive and unobtrusive, but tend to have low response rates (the number of people who complete the survey compared to the number of surveys sent out). Other concerns with mailing surveys is that you are never certain that the person who completed the survey is the person you wanted to complete the survey. As a researcher you also are never certain that the person completing the survey fully understood your questions. In general, if you plan to use mailed surveys, pretest the survey with members of your target audience. A recent trend and variation on the mailed survey is online surveys, but the same concerns with mailed surveys hold true for these as well.

Telephone surveys have increased in popularity with the increase in the number of telephones in people's homes. Using the telephone is less expensive than in-person interviews and tends to be faster. For example, surveys are conducted using telephones by organizations such as Environics Research Group and Ipsos Canada, which has offices across the country. Results from telephone surveys can be conveyed to the public almost immediately. Surveyors can cover a wide geographical region without having to travel. Historically, surveyors used telephone directories to contact people. Most surveyors now use random digit dialling (RDD), which uses the same logic underlying the random number table presented near the start of this chapter. When a surveyor uses RDD, there is an equal probability of any telephone number appearing (including unlisted numbers). The drawbacks are that RDD will also produce telephone numbers that are not in use, fax machine numbers, and nonresidential numbers. The other concerns that telephone surveyors have are the growing public wariness of telemarketers and reluctance to participate in telephone surveys.

A common type of survey is the in-person interview. The face-to-face method is the richest form of communication. The participant in the survey can ask for clarification of the questions. But the in-person method is costly and may be perceived as more intrusive.

In general, there are three types of in-person interviews. The first is the structured interview, in which each respondent is given the same questions in the same order. Many businesses now use this method when interviewing job candidates. The interviewer is trained to act in the same manner for each interviewee. Answers given by respondents are then scored. The second in-person interview type is the intensive interview. Here the style is unstructured and informal. Interviewees are not given the same questions in the same order as in the structured method. This method is typically used in career counselling, performance appraisal feedback, and clinical settings. The third method is the focus group. The logic behind the focus group is that a group of people will provide more information than will individuals. The groups typically range in size from 4 to 15 people, and they will discuss approximately 10 issues. This method is common for market research. In it, responses are coded by a moderator and by observers of the group.

Exercises for Section 1.5

1.23 Describe the steps involved in creating a questionnaire.

1.24 Give an example of how the content of an item might influence responses to subsequent items.

1.25 What are the benefits and drawbacks of using each of the three methods of surveying?
  a. In-person.   **b.** Mailed.   **c.** Telephone.

1.26 Explain what is meant by a "focus group." When would a researcher use a focus group?

1.27 Explain how you would go about requesting that people complete an online survey. How would you contact the people? How would you deal with the question of whether or not the person you contacted was the person who completed the survey?

1.6 An Introduction to Survey Sampling

Random sampling is not the only type of sampling. Methods for obtaining a sample are called **sampling designs**, and the sample we take is sometimes called a **sample survey**. In this section, we explain three sampling designs that are alternatives to random sampling—**stratified random sampling**, **cluster sampling**, and **systematic sampling**.

One common sampling design involves separately sampling important groups within a population. Then the samples are combined to form the entire sample. This approach is the idea behind **stratified random sampling**.

> In order to select a **stratified random sample**, we divide the population into nonoverlapping groups of similar units (people, objects, etc.). These groups are called **strata**. Then a random sample is selected from each stratum, and these samples are combined to form the full sample.

It is wise to stratify when the population consists of two or more groups that differ with respect to the variable of interest. For instance, consumers could be divided into strata based on sex, age, language (e.g., speaks English, French, or other), or income.

As an example, suppose that a department store chain proposes to open a new store in a location that would serve customers who live in a geographical region that consists of (1) an industrial city, (2) a suburban community, and (3) a rural area. In order to assess the potential profitability of the proposed store, the chain wishes to study the incomes of all households in the region. In addition, the chain wishes to estimate the proportion and the total number of households whose members would be likely to shop at the store. The department store chain feels that the industrial city, the suburban community, and the rural area differ with respect to income and the store's potential desirability. Therefore, it uses these subpopulations as strata and takes a stratified random sample.

Taking a stratified sample can be advantageous because such a sample takes advantage of the fact that units in the same stratum are similar to each other. It follows that a stratified sample can provide more accurate information than a random sample of the same size. As a simple example, if all of the units in each stratum were exactly the same, then examining only one unit in each stratum would allow us to describe the entire population. Furthermore, stratification can make a sample easier (or possible) to select. Recall that, in order to take a random sample, we must have a frame, or list, of all of the population units. Although a frame might not exist for the overall population, a frame might exist for each stratum. For example, suppose nearly all the households in the department store's geographical region have telephones. Although there might not be a telephone directory for the overall geographical region, there might be separate telephone directories for the industrial city, the suburb, and the rural area from which samples could be drawn (although recall some of the drawbacks of telephone surveying listed in the previous section).

Sometimes it is advantageous to select a sample in stages. This is a common practice when selecting a sample from a very large geographical region. In such a case, a frame often does not exist. For instance, there is no single list of all households in Canada. In this situation, we can use **multistage cluster sampling**. To illustrate this procedure, suppose we wish to take a sample of households from all households in Canada. We might proceed as follows:

Stage 1: Randomly select a sample of counties from all of the counties in Canada.
Stage 2: Randomly select a sample of townships in each county.
Stage 3: Randomly select a sample of households from each township.

We use the term *cluster sampling* to describe this type of sampling because at each stage we "cluster" the households into subpopulations. For instance, in Stage 1 we cluster the households into counties, and in Stage 2 we cluster the households in each county into townships. Also, notice that the random sampling at each stage can be carried out because there are lists of (1) all counties in Canada, (2) all townships in Canada, and (3) all households in each township.

As another example, consider another way of sampling the households in Canada. We might use Stages 1 and 2 above to select counties and townships within the selected counties. Then, if there is a telephone directory of the households in each township, we can randomly sample households from each selected township by using its telephone directory. Because most households today have telephones, and telephone directories are readily available, most national polls are now conducted by telephone.

It is sometimes a good idea to combine stratification with multistage cluster sampling. For example, suppose a national polling organization wants to estimate the proportion of all registered voters who favour a particular federal party. Because the federal party preferences of voters might tend to vary by geographical region, the polling organization might divide Canada into regions (say, Atlantic Canada, Québec, Ontario, and Western Canada). The polling organization might then use these regions as strata and might take a multistage cluster sample from each stratum (region).[12]

In order to select a random sample, we must number the units in a frame of all the population units. Then we use a random number table (or a random number generator on a computer) to make the selections. However, numbering all the population units can be quite time-consuming. Moreover, random sampling is used in the various stages of many complex sampling designs (requiring the numbering of numerous populations). Therefore, it is useful to have an alternative to random sampling. One such alternative is called **systematic sampling**. In order to systematically select a sample of n units without replacement from a frame of N units, we divide N by n and round the result down to the nearest whole number. Calling the rounded result ℓ, we then randomly select one unit from the first ℓ units in the frame—this is the first unit in the systematic sample. The remaining units in the sample are obtained by selecting every ℓth unit following the first (randomly selected) unit. For example, suppose we wish to sample a population of $N = 14{,}327$ members of an international allergists' association to investigate how often they have prescribed a particular drug during the last year. The association has a directory listing the 14,327 allergists, and we wish to draw a systematic sample of 500 allergists from this frame. Here we compute $14{,}327/500 = 28.654$, which is 28 when rounded down. Therefore, we number the first 28 allergists in the directory from 1 to 28, and we use a random number table to randomly select one of the first 28 allergists. Suppose we select allergist number 19. We interview allergist 19 and every 28th allergist in the frame thereafter, so we choose allergists 19, 47, 75, and so forth until we obtain our sample of 500 allergists. In this scheme, we must number the first 28 allergists, but we do not have to number the rest because we can "count off" every 28th allergist in the directory. Alternatively, we can measure the approximate amount of space in the directory that it takes to list 28 allergists. This measurement can then be used to select every 28th allergist.

In this book, we concentrate on showing how to analyze data produced by random sampling. However, if the order of the population units in a frame is random with respect to the characteristic under study, then a systematic sample should be (approximately) a random sample and we can analyze the data produced by the systematic sample by using the same methods employed to analyze random samples. For instance, it would seem reasonable to assume that the alphabetically ordered allergists in a medical directory would be random (that is, have nothing to do with the number of times the allergists prescribed a particular drug). Similarly, the alphabetically ordered people in a telephone directory would probably be random with respect to many of the people's characteristics that we might wish to study.

When we employ random sampling, we eliminate bias in the choice of the sample from a frame. However, a proper sampling design does not guarantee that the sample will produce accurate information. One potential problem is **undercoverage**.

Undercoverage occurs when some population units are excluded from the process of selecting the sample.

This problem occurs when we do not have a complete, accurate list of all the population units. For example, although telephone polls today are common, some people in Canada do not have telephones. In general, undercoverage usually causes some people to be underrepresented. If underrepresented groups differ from the rest of the population with respect to the characteristic under study, the survey results will be biased. A second potentially serious problem is **nonresponse**.

---

[12]The analysis of data produced by multistage cluster sampling can be quite complicated. We explain how to analyze data produced by one- and two-stage cluster sampling in Appendix E (Part 2). This appendix also includes a discussion of an additional survey sampling technique called **ratio estimation**. For a more detailed discussion of cluster sampling and ratio estimation, see Mendenhall, Schaeffer, and Ott (1986).

Nonresponse occurs when a population unit selected as part of the sample cannot be contacted or refuses to participate.

In some surveys, 35 percent or more of the selected individuals cannot be contacted—even when several callbacks are made. In such a case, other participants are often substituted for the people who cannot be contacted. If the substitute participants differ from the originally selected participants with respect to the characteristic under study, the survey will again be biased. Third, when people are asked potentially embarrassing questions, their responses might not be truthful. We then have what we call **response bias**. Fourth, the wording of the questions asked can influence the answers received. Slanted questions often evoke biased responses. For example, consider the following question:

Which of the following best describes your views on gun control?

1 The government should take away our guns, leaving us defenceless against heavily armed criminals.

2 We have the right to keep guns.

Exercises for Section 1.6

CONCEPTS

1.28 When is it appropriate to use stratified random sampling? What are strata, and how should strata be selected?

1.29 When is cluster sampling used? Why do we describe this type of sampling by using the term *cluster*?

1.30 Explain each of the following terms:
  a. Undercoverage.
  b. Nonresponse.
  c. Response bias.

1.31 Explain how to take a systematic sample of 100 companies from the 1,853 companies that are members of an industry trade association.

1.32 Explain how a stratified random sample is selected. Discuss how you might define the strata to survey student opinion on a proposal to charge all students a $100 fee for a new university-run bus system that will provide transportation between off-campus apartments and campus locations.

1.33 Marketing researchers often use city blocks as clusters in cluster sampling. Using this fact, explain how a market researcher might use multistage cluster sampling to select a sample of consumers from all cities with a population of more than 10,000 in a region having many such cities.

CHAPTER SUMMARY

This chapter has introduced the idea of using **sample data** to make **statistical inferences**—that is, drawing conclusions about populations and processes by using sample data. We began by learning that a **population** is a set of existing units that we wish to study. We saw that, since many populations are too large to examine in their entirety, we often study a population by selecting a **sample**, which is a subset of the population units. Next we learned that, if the information contained in a sample is to accurately represent the population, then the sample should be **randomly selected** from the population, and we saw how **random numbers** (obtained from a **random number table**) can be used to select a **random sample**. We also learned that selecting a random sample requires a **frame** (that is, a list of all of the population units) and that, since a frame does not always exist, we sometimes select a **systematic sample**.

We continued this chapter by studying **processes**. We learned that to make statistical inferences about the population of all possible values of a variable that could be observed when using a process, the process must be in **statistical control**. We learned that a process is in statistical control if it does not exhibit any unusual process variations, and we demonstrated how we might sample a process and how to use a runs plot to try to judge whether a process is in control.

Next, in Section 1.4, we studied different types of quantitative and qualitative variables. We learned that there are two types of **quantitative variables**—**ratio variables**, which are measured on a scale such that ratios of its values are meaningful and there is an inherently defined zero value, and **interval variables**, for which ratios are not meaningful and there is no inherently defined zero value. We also saw that there are two types of **qualitative variables**—**ordinal variables**, for which there is a meaningful ordering of the categories, and **nominative (or nominal) variables**, for which there is no meaningful ordering of the categories.

We concluded this chapter with Sections 1.5 and 1.6, which discuss **survey construction**, **types of survey methods**, and **survey sampling**. We introduced **stratified random sampling**, in which we divide a population into groups (**strata**) and then select a random sample from each group. We also introduced **multistage cluster sampling**, which involves selecting a sample in stages, and we explained how to select a **systematic sample**. Finally, we discussed some potential problems encountered when conducting a sample survey—**undercoverage**, **nonresponse**, **response bias**, and slanted questions.

GLOSSARY OF TERMS

categorical (qualitative) variable: A variable with values that indicate into which of several categories a population unit belongs. (page 2)

census: An examination of all the units in a population. (page 2)

cluster sampling (multistage cluster sampling): A sampling design in which we sequentially cluster population units into subpopulations. (page 21)

descriptive statistics: The science of describing the important aspects of a set of measurements. (page 2)

finite population: A population that contains a finite number of units. (page 11)

frame: A list of all of the units in a population. This is needed in order to select a random sample. (page 4)

infinite population: A population that is defined so that there is no limit to the number of units that could potentially belong to the population. (page 11)

interval variable: A quantitative variable such that ratios of its values are not meaningful and for which there is not an inherently defined zero value. (page 18)

measurement: The process of assigning a value of a variable to each of the units in a population or sample. (page 2)

nominative (or nominal) variable: A qualitative variable for which there is no meaningful ordering, or ranking, of the categories. (page 19)

nonresponse: A situation in which population units selected to participate in a survey do not respond to the survey instrument. (page 23)

ordinal variable: A qualitative variable for which there is a meaningful ordering or ranking of the categories. (page 18)

population: A set of existing or potential units (people, objects, events, or the like) that we wish to study. (page 2)

process: A sequence of operations that takes inputs and turns them into outputs. (page 11)

qualitative (categorical) variable: A variable with values that indicate in which of several categories a population unit belongs. (page 2)

quantitative variable: A variable with values that are numbers representing quantities. (page 2)

random number table: A table containing random digits that is often used to select a random sample. (page 4)

random sample: A sample selected so that, on each selection from the population, every unit remaining in the population on that selection has the same chance of being chosen. (page 3)

ratio variable: A quantitative variable such that ratios of its values are meaningful and for which there is an inherently defined zero value. (page 18)

response bias: A situation in which survey participants do not respond truthfully to the survey questions. (page 23)

runs plot: A graph of individual process measurements versus time. (page 12)

sample: A subset of the units in a population. (page 2)

sampling with replacement: A sampling procedure in which we place any unit that has been chosen back into the population to give the unit a chance to be chosen on succeeding selections. (page 3)

sampling without replacement: A sampling procedure in which we do not place previously selected units back into the population and, therefore, do not give these units a chance to be chosen on succeeding selections. (page 3)

statistical control: A state in which a process does not exhibit any unusual variations. Often this means that the process displays a uniform amount of variation around a constant, or horizontal, level. (page 12)

statistical inference: The science of using a sample of measurements to make generalizations about the important aspects of a population. (page 3)

statistical process control (SPC): A method of analyzing process data in which we monitor and study the process variation. The goal is to stabilize (and reduce) the amount of process variation. (page 12)

strata: The subpopulations in a stratified sampling design. (page 21)

stratified random sampling: A sampling design in which we divide a population into nonoverlapping subpopulations and then select a random sample from each subpopulation (stratum). (page 21)

systematic sample: A sample taken by moving systematically through the population. For instance, we might randomly select one of the first 200 population units and then systematically sample every 200th population unit thereafter. (page 6)

undercoverage: A situation in sampling in which some groups of population units are underrepresented. (page 22)

variable: A characteristic of a population unit. (page 2)

SUPPLEMENTARY EXERCISES

1.34 Some television stations attempt to gauge public opinion by posing a question on the air and asking viewers to call to give their opinions. Suppose that a particular television station asks viewers whether they support or oppose the federal gun registry. Viewers are to call one of two toll-free numbers to register support or opposition. When the results are tabulated, the station reports that 78 percent of those who called are opposed to the registry. What do you think of the sampling method used by the station? Do you think that the percentage of the entire population that opposes the registry is as high as the 78 percent of the sample that was opposed?

1.35 Table 1.10 gives the "35 best companies to work for" as rated on the *Fortune* magazine Web site on March 14, 2005. Use random numbers to select a random sample

of 10 of these companies. Justify that your sample is random by carefully explaining how you obtained it. List the random numbers you used and show how they gave your random sample.

1.36 A bank wishes to study the amount of time it takes to complete a withdrawal transaction from one of its ABMs (automated banking machines). On a particular day, 63 withdrawal transactions are observed between 10 A.M. and noon. The time required to complete each transaction is given in Table 1.11. Figure 1.11 shows an Excel runs plot of the 63 transaction times. Do the transaction times seem to be in statistical control? Why or why not?   ● ABMTime

1.37 Figure 1.12 gives a runs plot of the Edmonton Oilers' point percentages (number of points divided by total number of points available for the regular season) from the 1979/1980 season until the 2006/2007 season. Note that no games were played in the 2004/2005 season due to the lockout. The Oilers were one of the best hockey teams of the 1980s. However, many longtime Oilers fans believe that the 1987 trade of Paul Coffey to the Pittsburgh Penguins was the beginning of the team's decline. That supposedly signalled the beginning of the end of the Stanley Cup Championship "dynasty" in Edmonton. Does the runs plot provide any evidence to support this opinion? Why or why not? What else do you notice about the team's point percentage starting in the 1999/2000 season? Can you give any reasons for the sudden change?

1.38 THE TRASH BAG CASE   ● TrashBag

Recall that the company will carry out a 40-hour pilot production run of the new bags and will randomly select one bag each hour to be subjected to a breaking strength test.

a. Explain how the company can use random numbers to randomly select the times during the 40 hours of the pilot production run at which bags will be tested. Hint: Suppose that a randomly selected time will be determined to the nearest minute.

b. Use the following random numbers (obtained from Table 1.1) to select the times during the first five hours at which the first five bags to be tested will be taken from the production line: 61, 15, 64, 07, 86, 87, 57, 64, 66, 42, 59, 51.

TABLE 1.10 *Fortune's* 35 Best Companies to Work for in March 2005 (for Exercise 1.35)

Rank	Company	Rank	Company
1	Wegmans Food Markets	20	HomeBanc Mortgage
2	W.L. Gore	21	David Weekley Homes
3	Republic Bancorp	22	TD Industries
4	Genentech	23	Valero Energy
5	Xilinx	24	Network Appliance
6	J.M. Smucker	25	JM Family Enterprises
7	S.C. Johnson & Son	26	American Century Investments
8	Griffin Hospital		
9	Alston & Bird	27	Cisco Systems
10	Vision Service Plan	28	American Cast Iron Pipe
11	Starbucks	29	Stew Leonard's
12	Quicken Loans	30	Whole Foods Market
13	Adobe Systems	31	Baptist Health South Florida
14	CDW		
15	Container Store	32	Arnold & Porter
16	SAS Institute	33	Amgen
17	Qualcomm	34	American Fidelity Assurance
18	Robert W. Baird		
19	QuikTrip	35	Goldman Sachs Group

TABLE 1.11 ABM Transaction Times (in Seconds) for 63 Withdrawals ● ABMTime

Transaction	Time	Transaction	Time	Transaction	Time
1	32	22	34	43	37
2	32	23	32	44	32
3	41	24	34	45	33
4	51	25	35	46	33
5	42	26	33	47	40
6	39	27	42	48	35
7	33	28	46	49	33
8	43	29	52	50	39
9	35	30	36	51	34
10	33	31	37	52	34
11	33	32	32	53	33
12	32	33	39	54	38
13	42	34	36	55	41
14	34	35	41	56	34
15	37	36	32	57	35
16	37	37	33	58	35
17	33	38	34	59	37
18	35	39	38	60	39
19	40	40	32	61	44
20	36	41	35	62	40
21	32	42	33	63	39

FIGURE **1.11**   **Excel Runs Plot of ABM Transaction Times for Exercise 1.36**

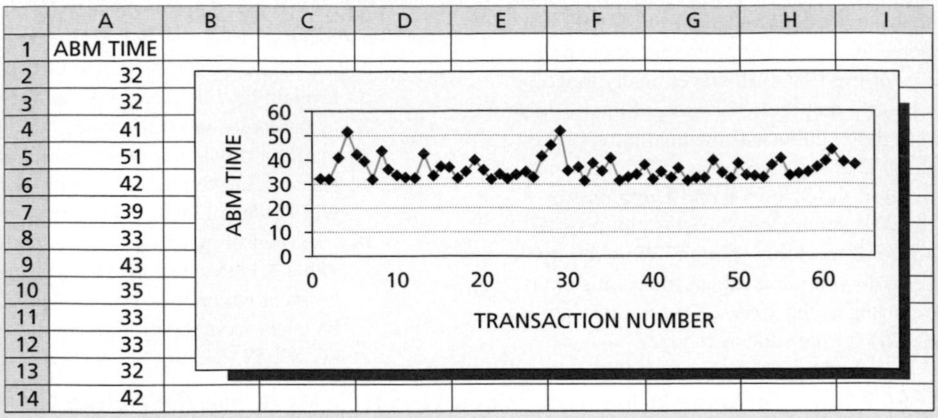

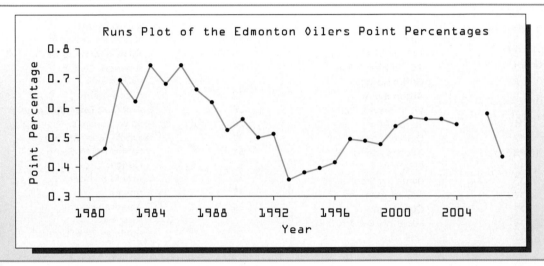

	A	B	C	D	E	F	G	H	I
1	ABM TIME								
2	32								
3	32								
4	41								
5	51								
6	42								
7	39								
8	33								
9	43								
10	35								
11	33								
12	33								
13	32								
14	42								

FIGURE **1.12**   **Runs Plot of the Edmonton Oilers' Point Percentages from 1979/80 to 2006/07 (for Exercise 1.37)**

Descriptive Statistics

In Chapter 1, we saw that although we can sometimes take a census of an entire population, we often must randomly select a sample from a population. When we have taken a census or a sample, we typically wish to describe the observed data set. In particular, we describe a sample in order to make inferences about the sampled population.

In this chapter, we learn about **descriptive statistics**, which is the science of describing the important characteristics of a population or sample. Generally, we look at several important aspects of a set of measurements. One such aspect is the **central tendency**, or middle, of the data set. For instance, we might estimate a typical bottle design rating in a marketing research case. Another important aspect of a data set is the **variability**, or spread, of the data. For example, we

might measure the spread of the bottle design ratings. If the ratings are clustered closely together, consumers' ratings are much the same (or are consistent). If the ratings are spread far apart, then consumers have widely varying opinions of the new bottle design. A third important aspect of a data set is the **shape** of the population or sample. Looking at a data set's shape tells us how the population or sample is distributed over various values (more about this later). Still another important aspect is whether **outliers** exist. For instance, if there are outlying bottle design ratings, then several consumers have opinions about the design that are very different from the opinions of most of the sampled consumers. Descriptive statistics also involves using **graphical methods** to depict data sets and to study relationships between different variables.

In this chapter, we use a variety of methods to describe the cell phone usages, bottle design ratings, coffee temperatures, and coin masses introduced in the cases of Chapter 1. In addition, we introduce two new cases:

The Electronic Articles Surveillance Case. A survey is used to study the unintended effects on consumer attitudes of false electronic article surveillance alarms.

The Marketing Ethics Case. A survey is conducted to study marketing researchers' attitudes toward violating confidentiality in marketing research studies.

2.1 Describing the Shape of a Distribution

CHAPTER 1

We begin looking at the characteristics of a population by describing the population's overall pattern of variation. That is, we describe the shape of the distribution of population measurements. We often employ a sample of measurements taken from a population in order to infer what the population looks like.

Several graphical methods—the **stem-and-leaf display**, the **histogram**, and the **dot plot**—are used to portray shapes of distributions.

Stem-and-leaf displays   We illustrate how to construct stem-and-leaf displays in the following examples.

Example 2.1 The Mass of the Loonie

Recall that a sample of 200 masses of the 1989 loonie was obtained in Example 1.4. To graphically portray the pattern of variation in these masses, we can construct a stem-and-leaf display. In order to do this, we first notice that the sample masses range from a minimum of 6.8358 g to a maximum of 7.2046 g. From these data, we will (somewhat arbitrarily) construct a display using only two decimal places in each measurement. Otherwise, constructing a stem-and-leaf plot for this data set would be quite difficult. The first two digits will constitute the stem and the last digit will constitute the leaf. You will also notice that the leaves are split into two, with the first holding digits 0 to 4 and the second holding digits 5 to 9. These are placed in a column on the left side of the display as in Figure 2.1:

FIGURE 2.1   MINITAB Output of a Stem-and-Leaf Display of 200 Masses

```
Stem-and-leaf of loonie masses   N  = 200
Leaf Unit = 0.010

    3     68   334
    9     68   788899
   26     69   00000111334444444
   76     69   5555555555666666666777777777778888888888888899999999
  (75)    70   000000000000000001111111111111111122222222222222222333333333333344444+
   49     70   5555555566666666666677777778888888899999999999
    7     71   1233
    3     71   57
    1     72   0
```

We summarize how to set up a stem-and-leaf display in the following box:

Constructing a Stem-and-Leaf Display

1 Decide what units will be used for the stems and the leaves. As a general rule, choose units for the stems so that there will be somewhere between 5 and 20 stems.

2 Place the stems in a column with the smallest stem at the top of the column and the largest stem at the bottom.

3 Enter the leaf for each measurement into the row corresponding to the proper stem. The leaves should be single-digit numbers (these can be rounded values that were originally more than one digit).

4 If desired, rearrange the leaves so that they are in increasing order from left to right.

Some stem-and-leaf displays do not appear symmetrical. This is illustrated in the next example.

Example 2.2 The Marketing Research Case

Consider the sample of 60 bottle design ratings in Table 2.1. These bottle design ratings are the composites of responses to the scale in Figure 2.2 and range from 20 to 35, so a stem-and-leaf display of the ratings is as shown in the right page margin under the heading "Ratings." Looking at this display, we see that the distribution of bottle design ratings seems to be skewed toward the smaller ratings. That is, we say the distribution is **skewed with a tail to the left** (or **negatively skewed**). This says that a few of the ratings are somewhat lower than the rest of the ratings.[1]

```
Ratings
20  0
21
22  0
23
24  0
25  0 0
26  0 0
27  0 0 0
28  0 0 0 0
29  0 0 0 0 0
30  0 0 0 0 0 0
31  0 0 0 0 0 0 0 0
32  0 0 0 0 0 0 0 0 0 0 0
33  0 0 0 0 0 0 0 0 0 0
34  0 0 0 0 0
35  0
```

TABLE 2.1 A Sample of Bottle Design Ratings (Composite Scores for a Systematic Sample of 60 Shoppers) ◔ Design

34	33	33	29	26	33	28	25	32	33
32	25	27	33	22	27	32	33	32	29
24	30	20	34	31	32	30	35	33	31
32	28	30	31	31	33	29	27	34	31
31	28	33	31	32	28	26	29	32	34
32	30	34	32	30	30	32	31	29	33

FIGURE 2.2 The Bottle Design Survey Instrument

Please circle the response that most accurately describes whether you agree or disagree with each statement about the bottle you have examined.

Statement	Strongly Disagree						Strongly Agree
The size of this bottle is convenient.	1	2	3	4	5	6	7
The contoured shape of this bottle is easy to handle.	1	2	3	4	5	6	7
The label on this bottle is easy to read.	1	2	3	4	5	6	7
This bottle is easy to open.	1	2	3	4	5	6	7
Based on its overall appeal, I like this bottle design.	1	2	3	4	5	6	7

Frequency distributions and histograms The **count of the number of measurements in a class** defined by a stem is called the **frequency** of the class. One advantage of a stem-and-leaf display is that it gives the frequencies of the different classes and also lists the specific measurements in each class. However, such listings for the different classes can be unwieldy if we are

---

[1]If the reverse were true and most of the cases were at the low end and only a few of the cases were at the high end, then the shape would be described as **skewed with a tail to the right** (or **positively skewed**). The direction of the skew deals with the number line in which positive numbers are to the right and negative numbers are to the left, i.e.,

$$-2 \quad -1 \quad 0 \quad +1 \quad +2$$

portraying a large number of measurements. For example, while it is convenient to display the ratings by 60 shoppers using the stem-and-leaf display, summarizing 500 ratings with the same type of format would be difficult.

When we have many measurements, it is best to group them into the classes of a **frequency distribution** and to display the data by using what is called a **histogram**. These are also useful for summarizing more moderately sized data sets. We illustrate this in the following example.

Example 2.3   Age Groupings by Statistics Canada

Statistics Canada (http://www.statcan.ca) provides demographic information for communities based on the most recent population census. When we report on the frequency of age, we group individual age values together into classes. When classes are defined, the situation must be that one and only one case will fall into a class. The group labelled "85+" is considered to be an **open class** in which no upper limit is given. Figure 2.3 provides the age groupings and frequency values for London, Ontario. Also in Figure 2.3 is the corresponding **histogram**. A histogram provides a method of graphically portraying the distribution of ages. To set up a **frequency histogram**, we draw rectangles representing the classes. Here the base of a rectangle represents the age group and the height of the rectangle represents the class or group **frequency**. To construct histograms, we employ what we call **class boundaries**, which represent the upper and lower class limits. An alternative to using class boundaries is to use **class midpoints**, which represent the halfway mark between the upper and lower class limits.

FIGURE **2.3**

Age	Frequency
0 to 4	19,235
5 to 15	44,925
15 to 19	22,720
20 to 24	25,880
25 to 44	102,765
45 to 54	47,310
55 to 64	29,670
65 to 74	23,175
75 to 84	16,145
85+	4,715

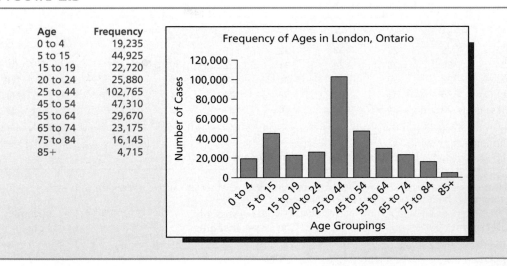

The data reported above were grouped by Statistics Canada. If raw data are available and these are to be grouped into the classes of a frequency distribution, we must first decide how many classes to use. A general rule says that the number of classes should be the smallest whole number K that makes the quantity 2^K greater than the total number of measurements n. We then find the length of each class by computing

$$\text{Class length} = \frac{\text{Largest measurement} - \text{Smallest measurement}}{K}.$$

The smallest and largest data values that can belong to a given class are called the **lower and upper class limits**, and the largest **observed** value is contained in the last class. In cases where the largest measurement is not contained in the last class, we simply add another class.

TABLE 2.2 DVD Price Points

(a) A sample of 49 DVD price points

30.8	30.9	32.0	32.3	32.6
31.7	30.4	31.4	32.7	31.4
30.1	32.5	30.8	31.2	31.8
31.6	30.3	32.8	30.6	31.9
32.1	31.3	32.0	31.7	32.8
33.3	32.1	31.5	31.4	31.5
31.3	32.5	32.4	32.2	31.6
31.0	31.8	31.0	31.5	30.6
32.0	30.4	29.8	31.7	32.2
32.4	30.5	31.1	30.6	

(b) A frequency distribution and a relative frequency distribution of 49 DVD price points

Class	Frequency	Relative Frequency	Boundaries	Midpoint
29.8–30.3	3	3/49 = 0.0612	29.75, 30.35	30.05
30.4–30.9	9	9/49 = 0.1837	30.35, 30.95	30.65
31.0–31.5	12	12/49 = 0.2449	30.95, 31.55	31.25
31.6–32.1	13	13/49 = 0.2653	31.55, 32.15	31.85
32.2–32.7	9	9/49 = 0.1837	32.15, 32.75	32.45
32.8–33.3	3	3/49 = 0.0612	32.75, 33.35	33.05

Once we have formed the classes, we record the number of measurements that fall into each class. We can also compute the relative frequency for each class. The **relative frequency** of a class is the proportion (fraction) of the total number of measurements that are in the class. For example, there are 44,925 individuals in London who are between 5 and 14 years old. The population of London at the time of the census was 336,540, so the relative frequency is 44,925/336,540 = 0.1335, or 13.35% of the population of London at the time of the census was between 5 and 14 years old.

In general, we can have MINITAB, Excel, or MegaStat form a histogram by using classes that we specify or by having these computer packages automatically select classes for us. When specifying classes, we usually express the lower and upper class limits to the same decimal place accuracy as the observed data values. As another example, consider grouping $n = 49$ randomly selected DVD prices from a store (see Table 2.2(a)) into the classes of a frequency distribution. Because $2^5 = 32$ is less than 49 and $2^6 = 64$ is greater than 49, we should use $K = 6$ classes. The largest and smallest DVD prices found in this sample are 33.3 and 29.8, and so we find the class length by computing $(33.3 - 29.8)/6 = 0.5833$. To obtain a more convenient class length, we round this value up to 0.6, which is expressed to the same decimal place accuracy as the prices. To form the first class, we start with the lowest price—29.8—and add 0.5 (one-tenth less than the class length 0.6) to obtain the class 29.8–30.3. To form the second class, we start with the price 30.4 and add 0.5 to obtain the class 30.4–30.9. Continuing this process, we obtain the six classes shown in Table 2.2(b). Here the highest price—33.3—is just barely included in the last class. If we group the 49 price points into the classes, we obtain the frequencies and relative frequencies given in Table 2.2(b). A MegaStat output of a relative frequency histogram of the price points is shown in Figure 2.4. This histogram uses the class boundaries as the labels on its horizontal axis.

FIGURE 2.4 MegaStat Output of a Relative Frequency Histogram of 49 DVD Price Points

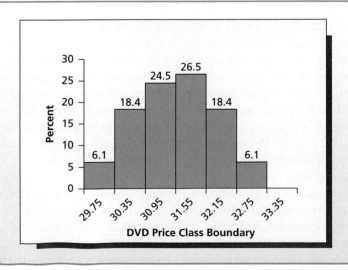

Similar to a stem-and-leaf display, a histogram describes the overall pattern of variation displayed by the data. Examining the histogram in Figure 2.4, we see that the distribution of the 49 price points appears quite symmetrical.

In the following box, we summarize the steps needed to set up a frequency distribution and histogram:

Constructing Frequency Distributions and Histograms

1. Decide how many classes will be employed. Generally, the number of classes K should equal the smallest whole number that makes the quantity 2^K greater than the total number of measurements n.

2. Compute the **class length**:

$$\frac{\text{Largest measurement} - \text{Smallest measurement}}{K}.$$

If desired, round this value to obtain a more convenient class length.

3. For each class, determine the **lower and upper class limits**—the smallest and largest measurements that can belong to the class.

4. Calculate **class boundaries**. These will be values halfway between the upper class limit of one class and the lower class limit of the next class.

5. Calculate the **frequency** for each class. **The frequency for a class is a count of the number of measurements that fall into the class.**

6. For a frequency histogram, plot each frequency as the height of a rectangle positioned over its corresponding class. Use the class boundaries to separate adjacent rectangles.

7. For a **relative frequency histogram**, plot each relative frequency as the height of a rectangle positioned over its corresponding class. **The relative frequency of a class is its frequency divided by the total number of measurements n.**

CHAPTER 1

In general, when constructing a histogram, the **area** of the rectangle positioned over a particular class should represent the **relative proportion of measurements in the class. When we use equal class lengths, this can be accomplished by making the height of the rectangle over a particular class represent the relative proportion of measurements in the class** (as described in the previous summary box for constructing histograms). This is because the area of a rectangle is its base multiplied by its height and because, if we are using equal class lengths, the bases of all the rectangles over the various classes are the same.

However, it is sometimes necessary to draw histograms with unequal class lengths, particularly when analyzing data published in the form of a frequency distribution with unequal class lengths. Often economic and social data are published in this form. In such a case, one must vary the rectangle heights to make the areas of the rectangles represent the relative proportions of measurements in the classes. How to do this is discussed in Exercise 2.8.

Some common population shapes   Often we construct a stem-and-leaf display or histogram for a sample to make inferences about the shape of the sampled population. Sometimes it is useful to describe the shape of a population by using a smooth **curve**. For instance, the stem-and-leaf display for the loonie coin masses looks quite symmetrical and **bell-shaped**. Therefore, it is reasonable to infer that the population of all loonie coin masses can be described by a symmetrical, bell-shaped curve. Such a curve is shown in Figure 2.5. Several different kinds of symmetrical, bell-shaped curves are used to describe populations. One such curve that is particularly useful is called the **normal curve**.

To intuitively understand the normal curve, recall from our discussion of histograms that if we use classes of equal lengths, then the height of the rectangle over a given class represents the relative proportion of measurements in the class. Similarly, **the height of the normal curve over a given point represents the relative proportion of population measurements that are near the given point**.

Many real populations are distributed according to the symmetrical, bell-shaped normal curve. We say that such populations are **normally distributed**. However, instead of being symmetrical and bell-shaped, the overall shape of a population may be **positively skewed** (with a tail to the right), as is the curve in Figure 2.6, or **negatively skewed** (with a tail to the left), as

FIGURE **2.5**

A Symmetrical,
Bell-Shaped Curve

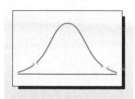

FIGURE **2.6**

A Curve That Is Positively
Skewed (with a Tail to the Right)

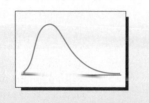

FIGURE **2.7**

A Curve That Is Negatively
Skewed (with a Tail to the Left)

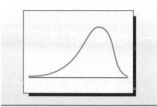

is the curve in Figure 2.7. Many other population shapes are also possible. If the stem-and-leaf display and/or histogram of a random sample of measurements looks like one of these curves, this suggests that the curve describes the overall shape of the entire population of measurements. In this case, the curve is called the **relative frequency curve** that describes the population. Said another way, **the population is distributed according to the relative frequency curve**. In a relative frequency curve, **the height of the curve over a given point represents the relative proportion of population measurements that are near the given point**.

Further graphical techniques, and detecting outliers One of the authors of this book recently taught a course in business statistics to a class of 40 students. A comparison of the scores received by these students on the first two 100-point exams is given by the **back-to-back stem-and-leaf display** in Figure 2.8 and by the two **dot plots** in Figure 2.9. Note that to make each dot plot, we draw a number line on which we measure the exam scores. We then place dots above the number line to represent the exam scores. The number of dots located above a particular exam score indicates how many students received that exam score. After noticing the two-peaked appearance of the stem-and-leaf display and dot plot for Exam 1, the author investigated and found that most of the students who scored less than 70 on the exam had not been attending class regularly. Because of this, the author implemented a mandatory attendance policy. The stem-and-leaf display and dot plot for Exam 2 are single-peaked and indicate a considerable improvement in student performance. Of course, this does not prove that the attendance policy was solely responsible for the improved performance. However, many students told the author that attending class improved their test scores.

Stem-and-leaf displays and dot plots are useful for detecting **outliers**, which are unusually large or small observations that are well separated from the remaining observations. For example, the stem-and-leaf display and dot plot for Exam 1 indicate that the score 32 seems unusually low. How we handle an outlier depends on its cause. If the outlier results from a measurement error or an error in recording or processing the data, it should be corrected. If the error cannot be corrected, it should

FIGURE **2.8** A Back-to-Back Stem-and-Leaf
Display

Exam 1		Exam 2
2	3*	
	3	
	4*	
5	4	
0	5*	
8 6	5	5
4 4 3 1 1 0	6*	2 3
9 9 8 7 7 6 5	6	6 7 7
2	7*	1 3 4 4 4
8 6	7	5 6 7 7 8
3 3 1	8*	0 2 3 4
9 8 7 7 6 5	8	5 6 6 7 7 8 9
4 3 3 2 2 1 0 0	9*	0 1 1 2 3 3 4 4
8 6	9	5 7 9

FIGURE **2.9** Dot Plots of the Scores on Exams 1 and 2

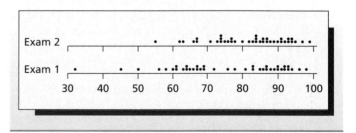

be discarded. If an outlier is not the result of an error in measuring or recording the data, its cause may reveal important information. For example, the outlying exam score of 32 convinced the author that the student needed a tutor. After working with a tutor, the student showed considerable improvement on Exam 2. A more precise way to detect outliers is presented in Section 2.4.

Exercises for Section 2.1

CONCEPTS

2.1 What does each of the following population shapes look like? Explain each in words and then draw a picture to illustrate each shape.
  a. Symmetrical and bell-shaped.
  b. Double-peaked.
  c. Negatively skewed (with a tail to the left).
  d. Positively skewed (with a tail to the right).

2.2 Explain
  a. How to construct a stem-and-leaf display; a histogram; a dot plot.
  b. How class limits, class boundaries, and class midpoints differ.
  c. What outliers are and how they are handled.

METHODS AND APPLICATIONS

2.3 *The Globe and Mail's Report on Business Magazine* publishes the "Top 1000" company lists by certain categories (such as profit and size). Table 2.3 gives the 50 Biggest Companies by Revenue in Canada in 2006. ● Top 50
Construct a stem-and-leaf display of the revenue values given in Table 2.3. Use the billion dollar numbers from 4 to 35 as the stems. Then describe the distribution of the revenue values.

2.4 **THE VIDEO GAME SATISFACTION RATING CASE** ● VideoGame

Table 2.4 presents the satisfaction ratings for the XYZ-Box video game system that have been given by 65 randomly selected purchasers. Figure 2.10 gives the MegaStat output of a stem-and-leaf display, and Figure 2.11 gives the Excel output of a frequency histogram of the 65 satisfaction ratings.
  a. Verify that the classes and class frequencies given in Figure 2.11 are those obtained by using the histogram construction method discussed in this section.
  b. Using Figures 2.10 and 2.11, infer the shape of the relative frequency distribution describing the population of all possible customer satisfaction ratings for the XYZ-Box video game system.
  c. Construct a relative frequency histogram of the 65 satisfaction ratings.

2.5 **THE BANK CUSTOMER WAITING TIME CASE** ● WaitTime

Table 2.5 presents the waiting times for teller service during peak business hours of 100 randomly selected bank customers. Figure 2.13 gives the MINITAB output of a stem-and-leaf display, and Figures 2.12 and 2.14 give the Excel and MINITAB outputs of a frequency histogram of the 100 waiting times.

  a. Verify that the class boundaries (in Figure 2.12), the class midpoints (in Figure 2.14), and the class frequencies are those obtained by using the histogram construction method discussed in this section.
  b. Using Figures 2.12, 2.13, and 2.14, infer the shape of the relative frequency distribution describing the population of all possible customer waiting times during peak business hours.

2.6 **THE TRASH BAG CASE** ● TrashBag

Table 2.6 presents the breaking strengths of 40 trash bags selected during a 40-hour pilot production run. Figure 2.15 gives the MegaStat output of a relative frequency histogram and Figure 2.16 gives the MegaStat output of a stem-and-leaf display of the 40 breaking strengths.
  a. Verify that the classes and class relative frequencies given in Figure 2.15 are those obtained by using the histogram construction method discussed in this section.
  b. Using Figures 2.15 and 2.16, infer the shape of the relative frequency distribution describing the population of all possible trash bag breaking strengths.

2.7 Babe Ruth's record of 60 home runs in a single year was broken by Roger Maris, who hit 61 home runs in 1961. The yearly home run totals for Ruth in his career as a New York Yankee are (arranged in increasing order) 22, 25, 34, 35, 41, 41, 46, 46, 46, 47, 49, 54, 54, 59, and 60. The yearly home run totals for Maris over his career in the American League are (arranged in increasing order) 8, 13, 14, 16, 23, 26, 28, 33, 39, and 61. Compare Ruth's and Maris's home run totals by constructing a back-to-back stem-and-leaf display. What would you conclude about Maris's record-breaking year? ● HomeRuns

2.8 In this exercise, we consider how to deal with class lengths that are unequal (and with open-ended classes) when setting up histograms. Often data are published in this form and we wish to construct a histogram. An example is provided by data concerning the benefits of ISO 9000 registration published by CEEM Information Services. According to CEEM:[2]

> ISO 9000 is a series of international standards for quality assurance management systems. It establishes the organizational structure and processes for assuring that the production of goods or services meet a consistent and agreed-upon level of quality for a company's customers.

CEEM presents the results of a Quality Systems Update/Deloitte & Touche survey of ISO 9000–registered companies conducted in July 1993. Included in the results is a summary of the total annual savings associated with ISO 9000 implementation for surveyed companies. The findings (in the form of a frequency distribution of

---

[2]Source: *Is ISO 9000 for You?* (Fairfax, VA: CEEM Information Services).

TABLE 2.3 50 Biggest Companies by Revenue in Canada ● Top 50

Rank	Company (Year-End)	Revenue ($ 000s)	Revenue %CHG	Rank	Company (Year-End)	Revenue ($ 000s)	Revenue %CHG
1	General Motors of Canada (De05)	34,991,000	−5.90	26	Jean Coutu Group (My05)*	9,617,363	196.14
2	Manulife Financial (De05)	32,187,000	18.85	27	Hydro-Quebec (De05)	10,914,000	2.65
3	Royal Bank of Canada (Oc05)	29,403,000	16.36	28	Desjardins Group (De05)	10,900,000	7.16
4	Loblaw Companies (De05)	27,812,000	6.12	29	Thomson Corp. (De05)*	8,719,000	7.76
5	Magna International (De05)*	22,873,000	10.49	30	Suncor Energy (De05)	10,561,000	20.74
6	Imperial Oil (De05)	26,936,000	27.08	31	Husky Energy (De05)	10,528,000	20.64
7	Power Corp. (De05)	26,738,000	9.18	32	Cdn. Natural Resources (De05)	10,239,000	34.05
8	Alcan Inc. (De05)*	20,408,000	−18.20	33	Quebecor Inc. (De05)	10,216,200	−3.83
9	Sun Life Financial (De05)	21,871,000	0.55	34	Alimentation Couche-Tard (Ap05)	10,215,800	73.96
10	DaimlerChrysler Canada (De05)	20,819,000	8.71	35	Novelis Inc. (De04)*	7,798,000	24.95
11	BCE Inc. (De05)	19,150,000	3.73	36	ACE Aviation Holdings (De05)	10,132,000	17.76
12	Cdn. Imp. Bank of Commerce (Oc05)	18,677,000	11.81	37	Falconbridge Ltd. (De05)*	8,194,000	12.35
13	Toronto-Dominion Bank (Oc05)	18,665,000	16.55	38	Talisman Energy (De05)	9,649,000	48.93
14	Bank of Nova Scotia (Oc05)	18,332,000	11.12	39	Ultramar Ltd. (De05)*	7,591,000	43.47
15	Bombardier Inc. (Ja06)*	14,882,000	−11.40	40	Enbridge Inc. (De05)	8,697,100	7.23
16	Petro-Canada (De05)	17,673,000	22.37	41	Costco Wholesale Canada (Fe05)*	6,728,156	7.69
17	Onex Corp. (De05)	17,626,000	27.36	42	Telus Corp. (De05)	8,201,400	7.58
18	EnCana Corp. (De05)*	14,322,000	24.58	43	Canadian Tire (De05)	7,774,600	8.68
19	Bank of Montreal (Oc05)	15,138,000	14.61	44	Rogers Communications (De05)	7,520,582	34.01
20	Caisse de depot et placement (De05)	14,967,000	50.09	45	Canada Mortgage & Housing (De05)	7,334,000	11.80
21	Shell Canada (De05)	14,394,000	27.52	46	Canadian National Railway (De05)	7,252,000	10.20
22	Ford Motor Co. of Canada (De05)	13,800,000	−23.76	47	Shoppers Drug Mart (De05)	7,151,115	8.91
23	Nortel Networks (De05)*	10,664,000	10.59	48	McKesson Canada (De05)	7,133,274	6.85
24	Honda Canada (Ma06)	12,900,000	−0.77	49	Fairfax Financial Holdings (De05)*	5,878,200	−5.55
25	Sobeys Inc. (My05)	12,189,400	8.26	50	Canada Post (De05)	6,974,000	4.64

*Figures for fiscal periods other than 12 months are annualized for rankings and calculating returns. Foreign currencies are converted into Canadian dollars at the end of the relevant period for balance sheet items and at the average exchange rate for the relevant period for earnings items.

TABLE 2.4 Composite Scores for the Video Game Satisfaction Rating Case ● VideoGame

39	44	46	44	44
45	42	45	44	42
38	46	45	45	47
42	40	46	44	43
42	47	43	46	45
41	44	47	48	
38	43	43	44	
42	45	41	41	
46	45	40	45	
44	40	43	44	
40	46	44	44	
39	41	41	44	
40	43	38	46	
42	39	43	39	
45	43	36	41	

FIGURE 2.10 MegaStat Stem-and-Leaf Display of the 65 Satisfaction Ratings for Exercise 2.4

Stem and Leaf plot for Rating

stem unit = 1   leaf unit = 0.1

Frequency	Stem	Leaf
1	36	0
0	37	
3	38	000
4	39	0000
5	40	00000
6	41	000000
6	42	000000
8	43	00000000
12	44	000000000000
9	45	000000000
7	46	0000000
3	47	000
1	48	0
65		

FIGURE **2.11**   Excel Frequency Histogram of the 65 Satisfaction Ratings for Exercise 2.4

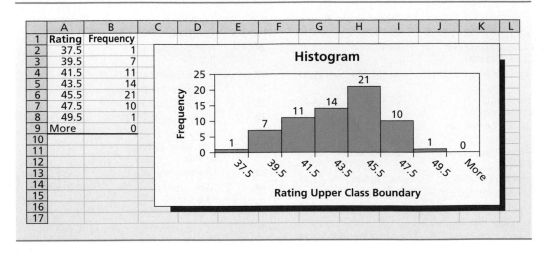

TABLE **2.5**   Waiting Times (in Minutes) for the Bank Customer Waiting Time Case   ⊙ WaitTime

1.6	6.2	3.2	5.6	7.9	6.1	7.2
6.6	5.4	6.5	4.4	1.1	3.8	7.3
5.6	4.9	2.3	4.5	7.2	10.7	4.1
5.1	5.4	8.7	6.7	2.9	7.5	6.7
3.9	0.8	4.7	8.1	9.1	7.0	3.5
4.6	2.5	3.6	4.3	7.7	5.3	6.3
6.5	8.3	2.7	2.2	4.0	4.5	4.3
6.4	6.1	3.7	5.8	1.4	4.5	3.8
8.6	6.3	0.4	8.6	7.8	1.8	5.1
4.2	6.8	10.2	2.0	5.2	3.7	5.5
5.8	9.8	2.8	8.0	8.4	4.0	
3.4	2.9	11.6	9.5	6.3	5.7	
9.3	10.9	4.3	1.3	4.4	2.4	
7.4	4.7	3.1	4.8	5.2	9.2	
1.8	3.9	5.8	9.9	7.4	5.0	

FIGURE **2.12**   Excel Frequency Histogram of the 100 Waiting Times for Exercise 2.5

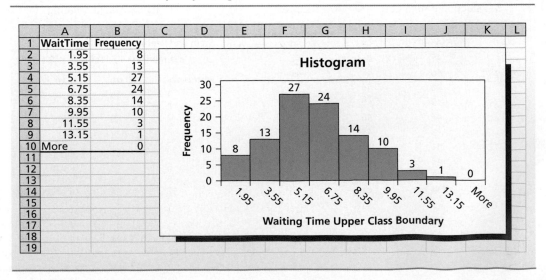

FIGURE **2.13** MINITAB Stem-and-Leaf Display of the Waiting Times for Exercise 2.5

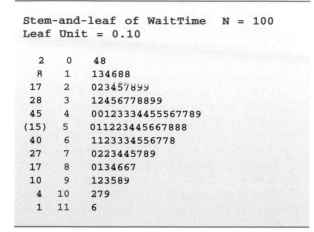

```
Stem-and-leaf of WaitTime   N = 100
Leaf Unit = 0.10

   2     0   48
   8     1   134688
  17     2   023457899
  28     3   12456778899
  45     4   00123334455567789
 (15)    5   011223445667888
  40     6   1123334556778
  27     7   0223445789
  17     8   0134667
  10     9   123589
   4    10   279
   1    11   6
```

FIGURE **2.14** MINITAB Frequency Histogram of the Waiting Times for Exercise 2.5

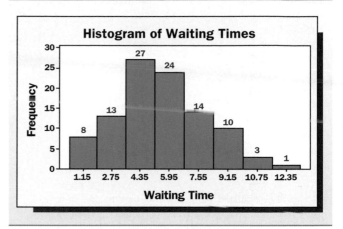

TABLE **2.6** Trash Bag Breaking Strengths ⬥ TrashBag

22.0	23.9	23.0	22.5
23.8	21.6	21.9	23.6
24.3	23.1	23.4	23.6
23.0	22.6	22.3	22.2
22.9	22.7	23.5	21.3
22.5	23.1	24.2	23.3
23.2	24.1	23.2	22.4
22.0	23.1	23.9	24.5
23.0	22.7	23.3	22.4
22.8	22.8	22.5	23.4

FIGURE **2.15** MegaStat Relative Frequency Histogram of the 40 Breaking Strengths for Exercise 2.6

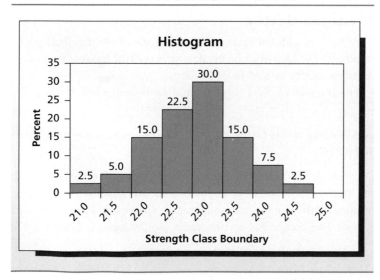

FIGURE **2.16** MegaStat Stem-and-Leaf Display of the Breaking Strengths for Exercise 2.6

```
Stem and Leaf plot for Strength
        stem unit = 1   leaf unit = 0.1

Frequency      Stem      Leaf
    1           21        3
    2           21        6 9
    6           22        0 0 2 3 4 4
    9           22        5 5 5 6 7 7 8 8 9
   12           23        0 0 0 1 1 1 2 2 3 3 4 4
    6           23        5 6 6 8 9 9
    3           24        1 2 3
    1           24        5
   ──
   40
```

ISO 9000 savings) are given on page 38. Notice that the classes in this distribution have unequal lengths and that there is an open-ended class (>$500K).

To construct a histogram for these data, we select one of the classes as a base. It is often convenient to choose the shortest class as the base (although it is not necessary to do so). Using this choice, the 0 to $10K class is the base. This means that we will draw a rectangle over the 0 to $10K class with a height equal to 162 (the frequency given for this class in the published data). Because the other classes are longer than the base, the heights of the rectangles above these classes

● ISO 9000

Annual Savings	Number of Companies
0 to $10K	162
$10K to $25K	62
$25K to $50K	53
$50K to $100K	60
$100K to $150K	24
$150K to $200K	19
$200K to $250K	22
$250K to $500K	21
(>$500K)	37

Note: K = 1000.

will be adjusted. Remembering that the area of a rectangle positioned over a particular class should represent the relative proportion of measurements in the class, we proceed as follows. The length of the $10K to $25K class differs from the base class by a factor of $(25 - 10)/(10 - 0) = 3/2$, and, therefore, we make the height of the rectangle over the $10K to 25K class equal to $(2/3)(62) = 41.333$. Similarly, the length of the $25K to $50K class differs from the length of the base class by a factor of $(50 - 25)/(10 - 0) = 5/2$, and, therefore, we make the height of the rectangle over the $25K to $50K class equal to $(2/5)(53) = 21.2$.

a. Use the procedure just outlined to find the heights of the rectangles drawn over all the other classes (with the exception of the open-ended class, >$500K).

b. Draw the appropriate rectangles over the classes (except for >$500K). Note that the $250K to $500K class is a lot longer than the others. There is nothing

wrong with this as long as we adjust its rectangle's height.

c. We complete the histogram by placing a star (∗) to the right of $500K on the scale of measurements and by noting "37" next to the ∗ to indicate 37 companies saved more than $500K. Complete the histogram by doing this.

2.9 A basketball player practises free throws by taking 25 shots each day and records the number of shots missed each day in order to track his progress. The numbers of shots missed on days 1 through 30 are 17, 15, 16, 18, 14, 15, 13, 12, 10, 11, 11, 10, 9, 10, 9, 9, 9, 10, 8, 10, 6, 8, 9, 8, 7, 9, 8, 7, 5, 8. Construct a stem-and-leaf display and runs plot of the numbers of missed shots. Do you think that the stem-and-leaf display is representative of the numbers of shots that the player will miss on future days? Why or why not?
● FreeThrw

2.2 Describing Central Tendency

The mean, median, and mode In addition to describing the shape of the distribution of a sample or population of measurements, we also describe the data set's **central tendency**. A measure of central tendency represents the **centre** or **middle** of the data.

One important measure of central tendency for a population of measurements is the **population mean**.

CHAPTER 3

The **population mean**, which is denoted by the Greek letter μ (*mu*, pronounced *mew*) is the average of the population measurements.

More precisely, the population mean is calculated by adding all the population measurements and then dividing the resulting sum by the number of population measurements. For instance, consider the population of revenues for the five biggest companies in Canada in 2006 as reported by *Report on Business Magazine*. The companies and revenues (to the nearest billion dollar value) are as follows:

● Revenue

Company	Revenue ($billions)
General Motors of Canada	$35
Manulife Financial	32
Royal Bank of Canada	29
Loblaw Companies	28
Magna International	23

The mean μ of this population of revenues is

$$\mu = \frac{35 + 32 + 29 + 28 + 23}{5} = \frac{147}{5} = \$29.4 \text{ billion (\$Cdn)}.$$

Since this population of five revenues is small, it is possible to compute the population mean. Often, however, a population is very large and we cannot obtain a measurement for each population unit. Therefore, we cannot compute the population mean. In such a case, we must estimate the population mean by using a sample of measurements.

In order to understand how to estimate a population mean, we must realize that the population mean is a **population parameter**.

A **population parameter** is a number calculated using the population measurements that describes some aspect of the population. That is, a population parameter is a descriptive measure of the population.

There are many population parameters, and we discuss several of them in this chapter. The simplest way to estimate a population parameter is to make what is called a **point estimate**.

A **point estimate** is a one-number estimate of the value of a population parameter.

Although a point estimate is a guess of a population parameter's value, it is not a blind guess. Rather, it is an educated guess based on sample data. One way to find a point estimate of a population parameter is to use a **sample statistic**.

A **sample statistic** is a number calculated using the sample measurements that describes some aspect of the sample. That is, a sample statistic is a descriptive measure of the sample.

The sample statistic that we use to estimate the population mean is the **sample mean**, which is denoted as $\bar{x}$ (*x bar*) or M (M = mean) and is the average of the sample measurements.

In order to write a formula for the sample mean, we employ the letter n to represent the number of sample measurements, and we refer to n as the **sample size**. Furthermore, we denote the sample measurements as $x_1, x_2, \ldots, x_n$. Here x_1 is the first sample measurement, x_2 is the second sample measurement, and so forth. We denote the last sample measurement as x_n. Moreover, when we write formulas we often use **summation notation** for convenience. For instance, we write the sum of the sample measurements

$$x_1 + x_2 + \cdots + x_n$$

as $\sum_{i=1}^{n} x_i$. Here the Greek letter Σ (*sigma*) says that we are writing out a sum of **like terms**. The general term x_i says that all the terms we are adding up look like x_i. The index $i = 1$ to n says that we let the subscript i in the general term x_i range from 1 to n, and we add up all these terms. Thus,

$$\sum_{i=1}^{n} x_i = x_1 + x_2 + \cdots + x_n.$$

The **sample mean** $\bar{x}$ is defined to be

$$\bar{x} = \frac{\sum_{i=1}^{n} x_i}{n} = \frac{x_1 + x_2 + \cdots + x_n}{n}$$

and is the **point estimate of the population mean** μ.

Example 2.4 Hourly Wages for Some Job Types in Ontario

Statistics Canada (http://www.statcan.ca) provides lists of average hourly wages for types of jobs in different provinces in Canada. The February 2006 statistics for Ontario suggest that the average hourly wage for certain vocational areas varies. For example, for management positions, the average hourly wage is \$32.06, for business and finance it is \$19.46, for natural and applied sciences it is \$29.64, for health occupations it is \$23.23, and for sales it is \$13.13. To calculate the average of these values, calculate the sum of the five hourly rates and divide the total by 5:

$$\sum_{i=1}^{5} x_i = x_1 + x_2 + x_3 + x_4 + x_5$$

$$= 32.06 + 19.46 + 29.64 + 23.23 + 13.13$$
$$= 117.52,$$

$$\bar{x} = \frac{117.52}{5} = 23.50.$$

The results here suggest that the average hourly rate of the five vocational types in Ontario is $23.50 and represents a point estimate of the average hourly wages. Due to concerns such as rounding, underreporting, and failing to include all possible vocational types, the point estimate may be somewhat unreliable.

In later chapters, we discuss how to assess the **reliability** of the sample mean and how to use a measure of reliability to decide whether sample information provides definitive evidence.

Another descriptive measure of the central tendency of a population or a sample of measurements is the **median** (M_d). Intuitively, the median divides a population or sample into two roughly equal parts.[3]

Consider a population or a sample of measurements, and arrange the measurements in increasing order. The **median**, M_d, is found as follows:

1   If the number of measurements is odd, the median is the middle measurement in the ordering.

2   If the number of measurements is even, the median is the average of the two middle measurements in the ordering.

Example 2.5

Statistics Canada (http://www.statcan.ca) compiles data on personal expenditures. Listed below are the average annual amounts people in Canada spent on rent for the years 1997 to 2005 (covering 9 years):

● AvgRent

6,606   6,806   7,043   7,265   (7,523)   7,873   8,207   8,533   8,856

Computing the median   Because the number of annual rent payment values is odd, the median of this sample is the middle value in the list (note that average annual rent has increased from 1997 to 2005, so the data are already in ascending order). The median is therefore $7,523 (it is circled).

Example 2.6

The manufacturer of a DVD recorder randomly selects a sample of 20 purchasers who have owned the recorder for one year. Each purchaser in the sample is asked to rank their satisfaction with the recorder on the following 10-point scale:

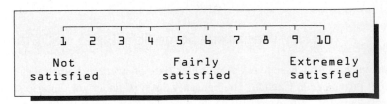

---

[3] Study Hint: To remember the median, remember that it is the same name given to the boundary separating highway lanes and there is typically an equal number of lanes on either side of the median.

Suppose that the following rankings, arranged in increasing order, are obtained:

1 3 5 5 7 8 8 8 8 ⑧ ⑧ 9 9 9 9 9 10 10 10 10

🔘 DVDSat

Because the number of satisfaction ratings is even, the median of this sample is the average of the two middle ratings. Both of these ratings are 8—they are circled. Therefore, the median of this sample is 8, and we estimate that the median satisfaction rating of all the DVD recorder owners is 8. This estimated median satisfaction rating seems relatively high. Note, however, that there are four rather low individual satisfaction ratings: 1, 3, 5, and 5. This suggests that some DVD recorders may be of low quality. If the manufacturer wishes to satisfy all of its customers, the company must investigate the situation.

BI

A third measure of the central tendency of a population or sample is the **mode**, which is denoted M_o.

> The **mode**, M_o, of a population or sample of measurements is the measurement that occurs most frequently.

For example, the mode of the satisfaction ratings given in Example 2.6 is 8. This is because more purchasers (six) gave the DVD recorder a rating of 8 than any other rating. Sometimes the highest frequency occurs at two or more different measurements. When this happens, two or more modes exist. When exactly two modes exist, we say the data are **bimodal**. When more than two modes exist, we say the data are **multimodal**. Finally, when data are presented in classes (such as in a frequency histogram), the class with the highest frequency is called the **modal class**.

Comparing the mean, median, and mode   In order to compare the mean, median, and mode, look at Figure 2.17. Part (a) of this figure depicts a population described by a symmetrical relative frequency curve. For such a population, the mean (μ), median (M_d), and mode (M_o) are all equal. Note that in this case all three of these quantities are located under the highest point of the curve. It follows that when the frequency distribution of a sample of measurements is approximately symmetrical, then the sample mean, median, and mode will be nearly the same. For instance, consider the sample of 49 DVD price points, and note that the stem-and-leaf display of these prices is given in the page margin. Because the number of prices is odd, the median is the middle price, the 25th price. Counting 25 prices from the top of the stem-and-leaf display, we find that the median is 31.6. Furthermore, since the stem-and-leaf display is fairly symmetrical, this sample median is approximately equal to the sample mean, which was calculated to be 31.55.

DVD Prices
29 8
30 1344
30 5666889
31 001233444
㉛ 555⑥6777889
32 0001122344
32 556788
33 3

Figure 2.17(b) depicts a population that is positively skewed (to the right). Here the population mean is larger than the population median, and the population median is larger than the population mode (the mode is located under the highest point of the relative frequency curve).

FIGURE 2.17   Relationships among the Mean μ, the Median M_d, and the Mode M_o

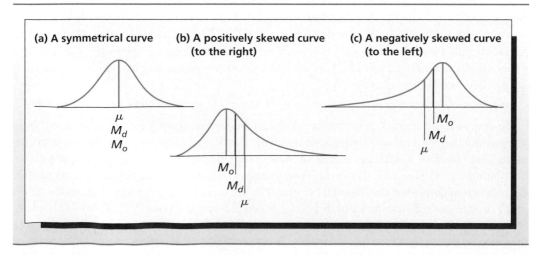

Salaries

```
12  | 7
13  | 2 8
14  | 1 4 6
⑮   | ②4
16  | 2
17  | 1 7
18  |
19  | 2
20  |
21  |
22  |
23  |
24  | 1
```

Ratings

```
 1  | 0
 2  |
 3  | 0
 4  |
 5  | 0 0
 6  |
 7  | 0
 ⑧  | 0 0 0 0 ⓪⓪
 9  | 0 0 0 0 0
10  | 0 0 0 0
```

In this case, the population mean **averages in** the large values in the upper tail of the distribution. Thus, the population mean is more affected by these large values than is the population median. To understand this, note that the stem-and-leaf display of a sample of 13 internists' salaries is given in the page margin and is skewed to the right. Here the mean of the 13 salaries, which is 159.769 (or \$159,769), is affected by averaging in the large salaries (192 and 241) in the right-hand tail of the distribution. Thus, this mean is larger than the sample median, \$152,000. The median is said to be **resistant** to the large salaries 192 and 241 because the value of the median is affected only by the fact that these salaries are the two largest salaries in the sample. The value of the median is not affected by the **exact sizes** of the salaries 192 and 241. For example, if the largest salary were smaller—say 200—the median would remain the same but the mean would decrease. If the largest salary were larger—say 300—the median would also remain the same but the mean would increase. Therefore, **the median is resistant to extreme values but the mean is not**.

Figure 2.17(c) depicts a population that is negatively skewed (to the left). Here the population mean is smaller than the population median, and the population median is smaller than the population mode. In this case, the population mean averages in the small values in the lower tail of the distribution, and the mean is more affected by these small values than is the median. For instance, the stem-and-leaf display of a sample of purchaser satisfaction ratings is given in the page margin and is skewed to the left. In this case, the mean of these ratings, which equals 7.7, is affected by averaging in the smaller ratings (1, 3, 5, and 5) in the left-hand tail of the distribution. Thus, the mean is smaller than the sample median, 8.

When a population is positively or negatively skewed (to the right or left) with a very long tail, the population mean can be substantially affected by the extreme values in the tail of the distribution. In such a case, the median might be better than the mean as a measure of central tendency. The following case illustrates that the choice of the mean or the median as a measure of central tendency can depend on the purpose of the study being conducted.

When a population is symmetrical or not highly skewed, then the population mean and the population median are either equal or roughly equal, and both provide a good measure of the population central tendency. In this situation, we usually make inferences about the population mean because much of statistical theory is based on the mean rather than the median. We illustrate these ideas in the following case, which also shows that we can obtain the mean and the median by using MINITAB, Excel, and MegaStat outputs.

Example 2.7 The Marketing Research Case

The Excel output in Figure 2.18(a) tells us that the mean and the median of the sample of 60 bottle design ratings are 30.35 and 31, respectively. Because the stem-and-leaf display of the bottle design ratings is not highly negatively skewed (to the left), the sample mean is not much less than the sample median. Therefore, using the mean as our measure of central tendency, we estimate that the mean rating of the new bottle design that would be given by all consumers is 30.35. This is considerably higher than the minimum standard of 25 for a successful bottle design.

To conclude this example, note that Figures 2.18(b), 2.18(c), and 2.19 give the Excel and MegaStat outputs of the previously discussed means and medians for internists' salaries, customer satisfaction ratings, and DVD prices. Other quantities on the outputs will be discussed as we proceed through this chapter.

To conclude this section, note that the mean and the median convey useful information about a population having a relative frequency curve with a sufficiently regular shape. For instance, the mean and median would be useful in describing the mound-shaped, or single-peaked, distributions in Figure 2.17. However, these measures of central tendency do not adequately describe a double-peaked distribution. For example, the mean and the median of the exam scores in the double-peaked stem-and-leaf display of Figure 2.8 (page 33) are 75.225 and 77. Looking at the display, neither the mean nor the median represents a typical exam score. This is because the exam scores really have no central value. In this case, the most important message conveyed by the double-peaked stem-and-leaf display is that the exam scores fall into two distinct groups.

FIGURE **2.18** **Excel Outputs of Statistics Describing Three Data Sets**

(a) Statistics describing the 60 bottle design ratings		(b) Statistics describing 13 internists' salaries		(c) Statistics describing 20 customer satisfaction ratings	
STATISTICS		**STATISTICS**		**STATISTICS**	
Mean	30.35	Mean	159.7692	Mean	7.7
Standard Error	0.401146	Standard Error	8.498985	Standard Error	0.543381
Median	31	Median	152	Median	8
Mode	32	Mode	#N/A	Mode	8
Standard Deviation	3.107263	Standard Deviation	30.64353	Standard Deviation	2.430075
Sample Variance	9.655085	Sample Variance	939.0256	Sample Variance	5.905263
Kurtosis	1.423397	Kurtosis	3.409669	Kurtosis	2.128288
Skewness	−1.17688	Skewness	1.695197	Skewness	−1.56682
Range	15	Range	114	Range	9
Minimum	20	Minimum	127	Minimum	1
Maximum	35	Maximum	241	Maximum	10
Sum	1821	Sum	2077	Sum	154
Count	60	Count	13	Count	20

FIGURE **2.19** **MegaStat Output of Statistics Describing the 49 DVD Price Points**

Descriptive statistics

	Prices	empirical rule	
count	49	mean − 1s	30.754
mean	31.553	mean + 1s	32.352
sample variance	0.639	percent in interval (68.26%)	63.3%
sample standard deviation	0.799	mean − 2s	29.955
minimum	29.8	mean + 2s	33.152
maximum	33.3	percent in interval (95.44%)	95.9%
range	3.5	mean − 3s	29.155
sum	1,546.100	mean + 3s	33.951
sum of squares	48,814.850	percent in interval (99.73%)	100.0%
deviation sum of squares (SS)	30.662		
1st quartile	31.000	low extremes	0
median	31.600	low outliers	0
3rd quartile	32.100	high outliers	0
interquartile range	1.100	high extremes	0
mode	31.700		

Exercises for Section 2.2

CONCEPTS

2.10 Explain the difference between each of the following:
  a. A population parameter and its point estimate.
  b. A population mean and a corresponding sample mean.

2.11 Explain how the population mean, median, and mode compare when the population's relative frequency curve is
  a. Symmetrical.
  b. Negatively skewed (with a tail to the left).
  c. Positively skewed (with a tail to the right).
  d. Normally distributed.

METHODS AND APPLICATIONS

2.12 Calculate the mean, median, and mode of each of the following populations of numbers:
  a. 9, 8, 10, 10, 12, 6, 11, 10, 12, 8
  b. 110, 120, 70, 90, 90, 100, 80, 130, 140

2.13 Calculate the mean, median, and mode of each of the following populations of numbers:
  a. 17, 23, 19, 20, 25, 18, 22, 15, 21, 20
  b. 505, 497, 501, 500, 507, 510, 501

2.14 **THE VIDEO GAME SATISFACTION RATING CASE**
  ● VideoGame

  Recall that Table 2.4 (page 35) presents the satisfaction ratings for the XYZ-Box game system that have been given by 65 randomly selected purchasers. Figures 2.20 and 2.23(a) give the MINITAB and MegaStat outputs of statistics describing the 65 satisfaction ratings.
  a. Does the sample mean $\bar{x} = 42.954$ provide evidence that the mean of the population of all possible customer satisfaction ratings for the XYZ-Box is at least 42? (Recall that a "very satisfied" customer gives a rating that is at least 42.) Explain your answer.
  b. Use the stem-and-leaf display in Figure 2.10 (page 35) to verify that the median of the satisfaction ratings is 43. How do the mean and median

FIGURE **2.20**   MINITAB Output of Statistics Describing the 65 Satisfaction Ratings

Variable	Count	Mean	StDev	Variance
Ratings	65	42.954	2.642	6.982

Variable	Minimum	Q1	Median	Q3	Maximum	Range
Ratings	36.000	41.000	43.000	45.000	48.000	12.000

FIGURE **2.21**   MINITAB Output of Statistics Describing the 100 Waiting Times

Variable	Count	Mean	StDev	Variance
WaitTime	100	5.460	2.475	6.128

Variable	Minimum	Q1	Median	Q3	Maximum	Range
WaitTime	0.400	3.800	5.250	7.200	11.600	11.200

FIGURE **2.22**   MINITAB Output of Statistics Describing the 40 Breaking Strengths

Variable	Mean	StDev	Variance	Minimum	Q1	Median	Q3	Maximum
Strength	22.990	0.743	0.552	21.300	22.500	23.000	23.425	24.500

Variable	Range
Strength	3.200

FIGURE **2.23**   MegaStat Outputs of Statistics Describing Three Data Sets

(a) Satisfaction rating statistics

Descriptive statistics

	Rating
count	65
mean	42.95
median	43.00
sample variance	6.98
sample standard deviation	2.64
minimum	36
maximum	48
range	12
empirical rule	
mean − 1s	40.31
mean + 1s	45.60
percent in interval (68.26%)	63.1%
mean − 2s	37.67
mean + 2s	48.24
percent in interval (95.44%)	98.5%
mean − 3s	35.03
mean + 3s	50.88
percent in interval (99.73%)	100.0%

(b) Waiting time statistics

Descriptive statistics

	WaitTime
count	100
mean	5.460
median	5.250
sample variance	6.128
sample standard deviation	2.475
minimum	0.4
maximum	11.6
range	11.2
empirical rule	
mean − 1s	2.985
mean + 1s	7.935
percent in interval (68.26%)	66.0%
mean − 2s	0.509
mean + 2s	10.411
percent in interval (95.44%)	96.0%
mean − 3s	−1.966
mean + 3s	12.886
percent in interval (99.73%)	100.0%

(c) Breaking strength statistics

Descriptive statistics

	Strength
count	40
mean	22.990
sample variance	0.552
sample standard deviation	0.743
minimum	21.3
maximum	24.5
range	3.2
empirical rule	
mean − 1s	22.247
mean + 1s	23.733
percent in interval (68.26%)	67.5%
mean − 2s	21.504
mean + 2s	24.476
percent in interval (95.44%)	95.0%
mean − 3s	20.762
mean + 3s	25.218
percent in interval (99.73%)	100.0%

compare? What does the stem-and-leaf display tell you about why they compare in this way?

2.15   THE BANK CUSTOMER WAITING TIME CASE
  ◉ WaitTime

Recall that Table 2.5 (page 36) presents the waiting times for teller service during peak business hours of 100 randomly selected bank customers. Figures 2.21 and 2.23(b) give the MINITAB and MegaStat outputs of statistics describing the 100 waiting times.

a. Does the sample mean $\bar{x} = 5.46$ provide evidence that the mean of the population of all possible customer waiting times during peak business hours is less than six minutes (as is desired by the bank manager)? Explain your answer.

b. Use the stem-and-leaf display in Figure 2.13 (page 37) to verify that the median of the waiting times is 5.25. How do the mean and median compare? What does the stem-and-leaf display tell you about why they compare in this way?

TABLE 2.7 Data Comparing Transportation Fatalities by Mode for North America ● Transport

	Canada 2003	USA 2003	Mexico 2003
Air	68	700	49
Air carriers	15	69	0
General aviation	53	631	49
Road	2,766	42,643	10,052
Passenger cars and light trucks	1,990	31,904	3,706
Passenger cars	U	19,460	3,586
Motorcycles	177	3,661	6
Buses	3	40	43
Large trucks	93	723	150
Pedestrians	376	4,749	1,478
Other	127	1,566	19
Pipeline	0	12	U
Rail	79	856	U
Grade crossing	27	329	59
Railroad	52	531	U
Transit, total	N	188	U
Transit rail	N	97	U
Water transport	U	816	28
Passenger vessels	U	U	N
Recreational boats	U	703	N
Commercial passenger vessels	4	U	N
Commercial freight vessels	2	N	U

Source: North American Transportation Statistics Database, available at http://nats.sct.gob.mx/nats/sys/tables.jsp?i=3&id=12
as of April 12, 2004.
U = unavailable
N = data are nonexistent

2.16 THE TRASH BAG CASE ● TrashBag

Consider the trash bag problem. Suppose that an independent laboratory has tested 130-L trash bags and has found that none of the bags currently on the market have a mean breaking strength of 23 kg or more. On the basis of these results, the producer of the new, improved trash bag feels sure that its bag will be the strongest such bag on the market if the new trash bag's mean breaking strength can be shown to be at least 23 kg. Recall that Table 2.6 (page 37) presents the breaking strengths of 40 trash bags of the new type that were selected during a 40-hour pilot production run. Figures 2.22 and 2.23(c) give the MINITAB and MegaStat outputs of statistics describing the 40 breaking strengths.

a. Does the sample mean $\bar{x} = 22.990$ provide evidence that the mean of the population of all possible trash bag breaking strengths is at least 23 kg? Explain your answer.

b. Use the stem-and-leaf display in Figure 2.16 (page 37) to verify that the median of the breaking strengths is 23.00. How do the mean and median compare? What does the stem-and-leaf display tell you about why they compare in this way?

Exercises 2.17 through 2.21 refer to the information in Table 2.7, which gives data concerning the number of fatalities by different modes of transportation for the year 2003 for Canada, the United States, and Mexico. In each exercise:

a. Compute the mean and median.

b. Compare the mean and median and explain if there is a case to be made for skewness.

c. Plot the values for the separate countries.

2.17 Analyze the data concerning air fatalities in Table 2.7 as described above. ● Transport

2.18 Analyze the data concerning passenger cars and light trucks in Table 2.7 as described above.
● Transport

2.19 Analyze the data concerning pedestrians in Table 2.7 as described above. ● Transport

2.20 Analyze the data concerning motorcycles in Table 2.7 as described above. ● Transport

2.21 Analyze the data concerning total rail fatalities in Table 2.7 as described above. ● Transport

2.22 In 2004, the NHL's collective bargaining agreement was set to expire. At that time, the owners wanted to adopt a salary cap to help combat escalating players' salaries and to create parity in the league. The players, of course, were against a cap of any kind. The payrolls for each NHL team in the 2003/2004 season are given in Table 2.8. A bar chart and a frequency histogram of the data are given in Figure 2.24. Using these data, answer the following questions: ● SalaryCap

a. Calculate the mean and median payrolls and comment on the shape of the distribution.

b. What percentage of Canadian team payrolls exceed the mean salary? exceed the median salary?

c. In 2005, a salary cap of $42.9 million ($Cdn) was imposed for each team, with each team's payroll to be no lower than $23.15 million. Approximately what percentage of the teams in the NHL were affected immediately by this salary cap?

d. A salary cap is supposed to create parity in the league, to give everyone an equal chance, since all teams are able to spend the same amount of money. Which measure do you feel will be more affected by a salary cap? Would it be the mean salary, median salary, modal salary, or perhaps some other measure not involving central tendency? Think about how much the salaries varied before the cap. Would this be the case after the cap?

TABLE 2.8 ● SalaryCap

Team	Payroll ($Cdn)	Team	Payroll ($Cdn)
Detroit Red Wings	$85,641,720	Phoenix Coyotes	$43,174,725
New York Rangers	84,137,588	Montréal Canadiens	42,742,700
Dallas Stars	75,436,774	Calgary Flames	40,042,833
Philadelphia Flyers	74,992,772	Carolina Hurricanes	39,499,612
Colorado Avalanche	69,720,704	San Jose Sharks	37,900,500
Toronto Maple Leafs	68,703,954	Tampa Bay Lightning	37,471,917
St. Louis Blues	67,842,500	Columbus Blue Jackets	37,400,000
Los Angeles Kings	59,217,180	Edmonton Oilers	36,712,500
Anaheim Mighty Ducks	58,626,425	Buffalo Sabres	36,249,675
Washington Capitals	55,985,325	Chicago Blackhawks	33,954,252
New Jersey Devils	53,824,824	Atlanta Thrashers	31,402,250
Boston Bruins	51,225,900	Minnesota Wild	29,920,550
Vancouver Canucks	46,281,950	Florida Panthers	28,740,250
New York Islanders	44,952,050	Pittsburgh Penguins	25,740,000
Ottawa Senators	43,549,000	Nashville Predators	24,125,750

Source: National Hockey League Players' Association.

FIGURE 2.24   **NHL Team Payrolls**

(a) Bar chart of NHL team payrolls

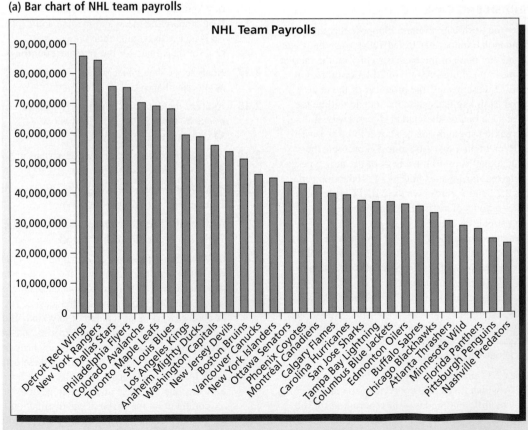

(b) Frequency histogram of NHL team payrolls

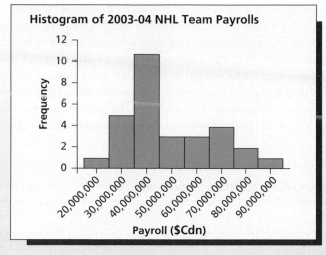

2.3 Measures of Variation

Range, variance, and standard deviation   In addition to estimating a population's central tendency, it is important to estimate the **variation** of the population's individual values. For example, Figure 2.25 shows two histograms. Each portrays the distribution of 20 repair times (in days) for personal computers at a major service centre. Because the mean (and median and mode) of each distribution equals four days, the measures of central tendency do not indicate any difference between the Local and National Service Centres. However, the repair times for the Local Service Centre are clustered quite closely together, whereas the repair times for the National Service Centre are spread farther apart (the repair time might be as little as one day, but could also be as long as seven days). Therefore, we need measures of variation to express how the two distributions differ.

One way to measure the variation of a set of measurements is to calculate the **range**.

The **range** of the measurements is the largest measurement minus the smallest measurement.

In Figure 2.25, the smallest and largest repair times for the Local Service Centre are three days and five days; therefore, the range is $5 - 3 = 2$ days. On the other hand, the range for the National Service Centre is $7 - 1 = 6$ days. The National Service Centre's larger range indicates that this service centre's repair times exhibit more variation.

CHAPTER 3

FIGURE **2.25**   **Repair Times for Personal Computers at Two Service Centres**

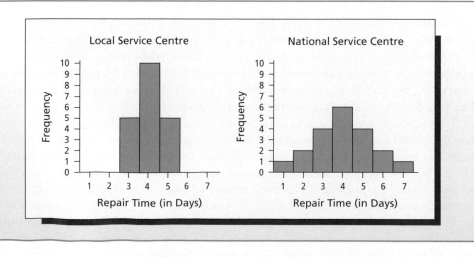

In general, the range is not the best measure of a data set's variation. One reason is that it is based on only the smallest and largest measurements in the data set and therefore may reflect an extreme measurement that is not entirely representative of the data set's variation. For example, in the marketing research case, the smallest and largest ratings in the sample of 60 bottle design ratings are 20 and 35. However, to simply estimate that most bottle design ratings are between 20 and 35 misses the fact that 57, or 95 percent, of the 60 ratings are at least as large as the minimum rating of 25 for a successful bottle design. In general, to fully describe a population's variation, it is useful to estimate intervals that contain **different percentages** (for example, 70 percent, 95 percent, or almost 100 percent) of the individual population values. To estimate such intervals, we use the **population variance** and the **population standard deviation**.

The Population Variance and Standard Deviation

The **population variance** σ^2 (*sigma squared*) is the average of the squared deviations of the individual population measurements from the population mean μ.

The **population standard deviation** σ (*sigma*) is the square root of the population variance.

For example, consider again the population of revenues for five of the biggest companies in Canada as reported by *The Globe and Mail* for 2006. These revenues (in billions of dollars) are 35, 32, 29, 28, and 23. To calculate the variance and standard deviation of these revenues, we first calculate the population mean, which is 29.4. Next we calculate the deviations of the individual population measurements from the population mean $\mu = 29.4$ as follows:

$$(35 - 29.4) = 5.6, \quad (32 - 29.4) = 2.6, \quad (29 - 29.4) = -0.4, \quad (28 - 29.4) = -1.4,$$
$$(23 - 29.4) = -6.4.$$

Then we compute the sum of the squares of these deviations:

$$(5.6)^2 + (2.6)^2 + (-0.4)^2 + (-1.4)^2 + (-6.4)^2 = 31.36 + 6.76 + 0.16 + 1.96 + 40.96 = 81.2.$$

Finally, we calculate the population variance σ^2, the average of the squared deviations, by dividing the sum of the squared deviations, 81.2, by the number of squared deviations, 5. That is, σ^2 equals $81.2/5 = 16.24$. Furthermore, this implies that the population standard deviation σ—the square root of σ^2—is $\sqrt{16.24} = 4.03$.

To see that the variance and standard deviation measure the variation, or spread, of the individual population measurements, suppose that the measurements are spread far apart. Then, many measurements will be far from the mean μ, many of the squared deviations from the mean will be large, and the sum of squared deviations will be large. It follows that the average of the squared deviations—the population variance—will be relatively large. On the other hand, if the population measurements are clustered close together, many measurements will be close to μ, many of the squared deviations from the mean will be small, and the average of the squared deviations— the population variance—will be small. Therefore, the more spread out the population measurements, the larger is the population variance, and the larger is the population standard deviation.

To further understand the population variance and standard deviation, note that one reason we square the deviations of the individual population measurements from the population mean is that the sum of the raw deviations themselves is zero. This is because the negative deviations cancel the positive deviations. For example, in the revenue situation, the raw deviations are 5.6, 2.6, -0.4, -1.4, and -6.4, which sum to zero. Of course, we could make the deviations positive by finding their absolute values. We square the deviations instead because the resulting population variance and standard deviation have many important interpretations that we study throughout this book. Because the population variance is an average of squared deviations of the original population values, the variance is expressed in squared units of the original population values. On the other hand, the population standard deviation—the square root of the population variance—is expressed in the same units as the original population values. Because the population standard deviation is expressed in the same units as the population values, it is more often used to make practical interpretations about the variation of these values.

When a population is too large to measure all the population units, we estimate the population variance and the population standard deviation by the **sample variance** and the **sample standard deviation**. We calculate the sample variance by dividing the sum of the squared deviations of the sample measurements from the sample mean by $n - 1$, the sample size minus one.[4] Although we might intuitively think that we should divide by n rather than by $n - 1$, it can be shown that dividing by n tends to produce an estimate of the population variance that is too small. On the other hand, dividing by $n - 1$ tends to produce a larger estimate that is more appropriate. Therefore, we obtain the following:

The Sample Variance and the Sample Standard Deviation

The **sample variance s^2** (s squared) is defined to be

$$s^2 = \frac{\sum_{i=1}^{n}(x_i - \bar{x})^2}{n - 1} = \frac{(x_1 - \bar{x})^2 + (x_2 - \bar{x})^2 + \cdots + (x_n - \bar{x})^2}{n - 1}$$

and is the **point estimate of the population variance σ^2**.

The **sample standard deviation $s = \sqrt{s^2}$** is the square root of the sample variance and is the **point estimate of the population standard deviation σ**.

Example 2.8

To illustrate the calculation of the sample variance and standard deviation, we begin by considering the loonie masses: $x_1 = 7.0688$, $x_2 = 6.9651$, $x_3 = 6.9605$, . . . , $x_{200} = 7.0438$. We have already determined that $\bar{x} = 7.0120$ g. It then follows that

$$\sum_{i=1}^{200}(x_1 - \bar{x})^2 + (x_2 - \bar{x})^2 + (x_3 - \bar{x})^2 + \cdots + (x_{200} - \bar{x})^2$$

$$= (7.0688 - 7.0120)^2 + (6.9651 - 7.0120)^2 + (6.9605 - 7.0120)^2 + \cdots$$
$$+ (7.0438 - 7.0120)^2 = 0.72358191.$$

Therefore, the variance and the standard deviation of the sample of 200 weights are

$$s^2 = \frac{0.72358191}{199} = 0.00363609 \text{ and } s = \sqrt{0.00363609} = 0.0603.$$

Here $s^2 = 0.00363609$ and $s = 0.0603$ are the point estimates of the variance and standard deviation, σ^2 and σ, respectively, of the entire population. Recall that the population represents the masses of all of the loonies produced in 1989. Furthermore, the sample standard deviation, s, is expressed in the same units as the sample values. Therefore, we say that $s = 0.0603$ g.

Before explaining how we can use s^2 and s in a practical way, we present a formula that makes it easier to compute s^2. This formula is useful when we are using a handheld calculator that is not equipped with a statistics mode to compute s^2.

The **sample variance** can be calculated using the computational formula

$$s^2 = \frac{1}{n - 1}\left[\sum_{i=1}^{n}x_i^2 - \frac{\left(\sum_{i=1}^{n}x_i\right)^2}{n}\right].$$

---

[4] Note that this value of one represents a "lost degree of freedom." When dealing with a sample, one data point must remain fixed so that there is a reference point to examine the other data points. As an exercise, find a few friends and try to put yourselves in a line in terms of height from tallest to shortest. To do this, you will need one person to stand still to be a reference point to compare yourself and others to (you will not be able to form a line if everyone keeps moving around). This fixed point (person) is then no longer free to move and is said to be a lost degree (point) of freedom.

A practical interpretation: The empirical rule   In the next box, we give a practical interpretation of the population standard deviation. This interpretation is often referred to as the **empirical rule for a normally distributed population**.

The Empirical Rule for a Normally Distributed Population

If a population has **mean μ** and **standard deviation σ** and is **described by a normal curve**, then, as illustrated in Figure 2.26,

1. 68.26 percent of the population measurements are within (plus or minus) one standard deviation of the mean and thus lie in the interval $[\mu - \sigma, \mu + \sigma] = [\mu \pm \sigma]$.

2. 95.44 percent of the population measurements are within (plus or minus) two standard deviations of the mean and thus lie in the interval $[\mu - 2\sigma, \mu + 2\sigma] = [\mu \pm 2\sigma]$.

3. 99.73 percent of the population measurements are within (plus or minus) three standard deviations of the mean and thus lie in the interval $[\mu - 3\sigma, \mu + 3\sigma] = [\mu \pm 3\sigma]$.

FIGURE 2.26   **The Empirical Rule**

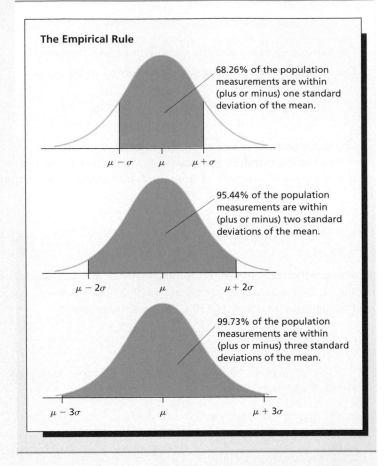

The Empirical Rule

68.26% of the population measurements are within (plus or minus) one standard deviation of the mean.

95.44% of the population measurements are within (plus or minus) two standard deviations of the mean.

99.73% of the population measurements are within (plus or minus) three standard deviations of the mean.

In general, an interval that contains a specified percentage of the individual measurements in a population is called a **tolerance interval**. It follows that the one, two, and three standard deviation intervals around μ are tolerance intervals containing, respectively, 68.26 percent, 95.44 percent, and 99.73 percent of the measurements in a normally distributed population. Often we interpret the **three-sigma interval** $[\mu \pm 3\sigma]$ to be a tolerance interval that contains **almost all** of the measurements in a normally distributed population. Of course, we usually do not know the true values of μ and σ. Therefore, we must estimate the tolerance intervals by replacing μ and σ in these intervals with the mean $\bar{x}$ and standard deviation s of a sample that has been randomly selected from the normally distributed population.

Example 2.9   DVD Price Points

Again consider the sample of 49 DVD prices. We have seen that $\bar{x} = 31.5531$ and $s = 0.7992$ for this sample are the point estimates of the mean μ and the standard deviation σ of the population of all DVD prices. Furthermore, the stem-and-leaf display and histogram of the 49 DVD prices suggest that the population of all DVD prices is normally distributed. To more simply illustrate the empirical rule, we will round $\bar{x}$ to 31.6 and s to 0.8. It follows that, using the interval

1   $[\bar{x} \pm s] = [31.6 \pm 0.8] = [31.6 - 0.8, 31.6 + 0.8] = [30.8, 32.4]$, we estimate that 68.26 percent of all individual DVDs will cost between \$30.80 and \$32.40.

2   $[\bar{x} \pm 2s] = [31.6 \pm 2(0.8)] = [31.6 \pm 1.6] = [30.0, 33.2]$, we estimate that 95.44 percent of all individual DVDs will cost between \$30.00 and \$33.20.

3   $[\bar{x} \pm 3s] = [31.6 \pm 3(0.8)] = [31.6 \pm 2.4] = [29.2, 34.0]$, we estimate that 99.73 percent of all individual DVDs will cost between \$29.20 and \$34.00.

Because the difference between the upper and lower limits of each tolerance interval is fairly small, we might conclude that the variability of the individual DVD prices around the estimated mean of \$31.60 is fairly small. Furthermore, the interval $[\bar{x} \pm 3s] = [29.2, 34.0]$ implies that almost any individual DVD that a customer might purchase this year will cost between \$29.20 and \$34.00.

Before continuing, recall that we have rounded $\bar{x}$ and s to one decimal point accuracy in order to simplify our initial example of the empirical rule. If, instead, we calculate the empirical rule intervals by using $\bar{x} = 31.5531$ and $s = 0.7992$ and then round the interval endpoints to one decimal place accuracy at the end of the calculations, we obtain the same intervals as obtained above. In general, however, rounding intermediate calculated results can lead to inaccurate final results. Because of this, throughout this book we will avoid greatly rounding intermediate results.

We next note that if we actually count the number of the 49 DVD prices in Table 2.2(a) that are contained in each of the intervals $[\bar{x} \pm s] = [30.8, 32.4]$, $[\bar{x} \pm 2s] = [30.0, 33.2]$, and $[\bar{x} \pm 3s]$ $= [29.2, 34.0]$, we find that these intervals contain, respectively, 33, 47, and 49 of the 49 DVD prices. The corresponding sample percentages—67.35 percent, 95.92 percent, and 100 percent—are close to the theoretical percentages—68.26 percent, 95.44 percent, and 99.73 percent—that apply to a normally distributed population. This is further evidence that the population of all DVD prices is (approximately) normally distributed and thus that the empirical rule holds for this population.

A quality improvement application: Meeting customer requirements   Tolerance intervals are often used to determine whether customer requirements are being met. Customer requirements often specify that a quality characteristic must be inside an acceptable range of values called **specifications**. Specifications are written for **individual measurements**. For example, suppose that marketing research done by the fast-food restaurant of Example 1.3 (pages 11 and 12) suggests that coffee tastes best if its temperature is between 67°C and 75°C. Therefore, the customer requirements (specifications) would say that the temperature of each individual cup of coffee must be between 67°C and 75°C (this specification would typically be written as 71°C ± 4°C).

If a process is able to consistently produce output that meets customer requirements (specifications), we say that the process is **capable** (of meeting the requirements). From a practical standpoint, this means that almost all of the individual measurements must be within the specification limits. Furthermore, if the population of all process measurements is approximately normally distributed, it is common practice to conclude that a process that is in statistical control is capable of meeting customer requirements if the three-sigma tolerance interval estimate $[\bar{x} \pm 3s]$ is within the specification limits. We say this because, if this interval is within the specification limits, then we estimate that almost all (99.73 percent) of the process measurements are within the specification limits.

For example, recall that the runs plot of the 24 coffee temperatures in Figure 1.3 (page 12) indicates that the fast-food restaurant's coffee-making process is in statistical control. The mean and the standard deviation of these temperatures are $\bar{x} = 71.2083$ and $s = 2.9779$, and a stem-and-leaf display indicates that the temperatures are approximately normally distributed. It follows that we estimate that the interval

$$[\bar{x} \pm 3s] = [71.2083 \pm 3(2.9779)]$$

$$= [62.27, 80.14]$$

contains 99.73 percent of all coffee temperatures. Because this interval tells us that some coffee temperatures are outside the customer specifications of 67°C to 75°C, the coffee-making process is not capable of meeting customer requirements. Here, although the process is exhibiting a constant amount of variation around a constant level (or mean), the constant amount of variation—as indicated by the standard deviation of $s = 2.9779$—is too large. Suppose that to reduce the standard deviation of the coffee temperatures, the restaurant tests a new coffeemaker. A sample of 24 coffee temperatures is in control and approximately normally distributed with a mean of $\bar{x} = 71.1208$ and a reduced standard deviation of $s = 0.9597$. It follows that we estimate that the interval

$$[\bar{x} \pm 3s] = [71.1208 \pm 3(0.9597)]$$
$$= [68.24, 74.00]$$

contains 99.73 percent of all coffee temperatures. We infer that almost all coffee temperatures produced by the new coffee-making process are within the customer specifications of 65°C to 75°C. Therefore, the improved process is capable of meeting customer requirements.

Skewness and the empirical rule   The empirical rule holds for normally distributed populations. In addition, this rule also approximately holds for populations having **mound-shaped** (single-peaked) distributions that are not very positively or negatively skewed (to the right or left).

In some situations, the skewness of a mound-shaped distribution of population measurements can make it tricky to know whether and how to use the empirical rule. For example, we previously concluded that the distribution of 60 bottle design ratings is somewhat but not highly negatively skewed (to the left). The mean and the standard deviation of the 60 bottle design ratings are $\bar{x} = 30.35$ and $s = 3.1073$. If we actually count the number of ratings contained in each of the intervals $[\bar{x} \pm s] = [27.2, 33.5]$, $[\bar{x} \pm 2s] = [24.1, 36.6]$, and $[\bar{x} \pm 3s] = [21, 39.7]$, we find that these intervals contain, respectively, 44, 57, and 59 of the 60 ratings. The corresponding sample percentages—73.33 percent, 95 percent, and 98.33 percent—are, respectively, greater than, approximately equal to, and less than the theoretical percentages—68.26 percent, 95.44 percent, and 99.73 percent—given by the empirical rule. Therefore, if we consider the population of all consumer ratings of the bottle design, we might estimate that (1) at least 68.26 percent of all ratings will be between 27 and 34, (2) approximately 95.44 percent of the ratings will be between 24 and 35 (a rating cannot exceed 35), and (3) less than 99.73 percent of the ratings will be between 21 and 35. Result (3), and the low ratings of 20 and 22 found, suggests that the bottle design ratings distribution is too negatively skewed (to the left) to use the empirical rule to make conclusions about almost all ratings. However, we are not necessarily concerned about almost all ratings, because the bottle design will be successful if it appeals to a large percentage of consumers. Results (1) and (2), which describe 68.26 percent and 95.44 percent of all consumer ratings, imply that large percentages of consumer ratings will exhibit reasonably small variability around the estimated mean rating of 30.35. This, and the fact that 57, or 95 percent, of the 60 ratings are at least as large as the minimum rating of 25 for a successful bottle design, suggest that the bottle design will be successful.

Chebyshev's theorem   If we fear that the empirical rule does not hold for a particular population, we can consider using **Chebyshev's theorem** to find an interval that contains a specified percentage of the individual measurements in the population.

Chebyshev's Theorem

Consider any population that has mean μ and standard deviation σ. Then, for any value of k greater than 1, at least $100(1 - 1/k^2)$ percent of the population measurements lie in the interval $[\mu \pm k\sigma]$.

For example, if we choose k equal to 2, then at least $100(1 - 1/2^2)\% = 100(3/4)\% = 75\%$ of the population measurements lie in the interval $[\mu \pm 2\sigma]$. As another example, if we choose k equal to 3, then at least $100(1 - 1/3^2)\% = 100(8/9)\% = 88.89\%$ of the population measurements lie in the interval $[\mu \pm 3\sigma]$. As yet a third example, suppose that we wish to find an interval containing at least 99.73 percent of all population measurements. Here we would set $100(1 - 1/k^2)$ percent equal to 99.73 percent, which implies that $(1 - 1/k^2) = 0.9973$. If we solve for k, we find that $k = 19.25$. This says that at least 99.73 percent of all population measurements lie in the interval $[\mu \pm 19.25\sigma]$.

Unless σ is extremely small, this interval will be so long that it will tell us very little about where the population measurements lie. We conclude that Chebyshev's theorem can help us find an interval that contains a reasonably high percentage (such as 75 percent or 88.89 percent) of all population measurements. However, unless σ is extremely small, Chebyshev's theorem will not provide a useful interval that contains almost all (say, 99.73 percent) of the population measurements.

Although Chebyshev's theorem technically applies to any population, it is only of practical use when analyzing a **non-mound-shaped** (for example, a double-peaked) **population that is not extremely positively or negatively skewed (to the right or left)**. Why is this? First, **we would not use Chebyshev's theorem to describe a mound-shaped population that is not very skewed because we can use the empirical rule** to do this. In fact, the empirical rule is better for such a population because it gives us a shorter interval that will contain a given percentage of measurements. For example, if the empirical rule can be used to describe a population, the interval [$\mu \pm 3\sigma$] will contain 99.73 percent of all measurements. On the other hand, if we use Chebyshev's theorem, the interval [$\mu \pm 19.25\sigma$] is needed. As another example, the empirical rule tells us that 95.44 percent of all measurements lie in the interval [$\mu \pm 2\sigma$], whereas Chebyshev's theorem tells us only that at least 75 percent of all measurements lie in this interval.

It is also not appropriate to use Chebyshev's theorem—or any other result making use of the population standard deviation σ—to describe a population that is extremely skewed. This is because, if a population is extremely skewed, the measurements in the long tail to the left or right will greatly inflate σ. This implies that tolerance intervals calculated using σ will be so long that they are of little use. In this case, it is best to measure variation by using **percentiles**, which are discussed in the next section.

z scores We can determine the relative location of any value in a population or sample by using the mean and standard deviation to compute the value's z score. For any value x in a population or sample, the **z score** corresponding to x is defined as follows:

z score:

$$z = \frac{x - \text{mean}}{\text{standard deviation}}.$$

The z score, which is also called the **standardized value**, is the number of standard deviations that x is from the mean. A positive z score says that x is above (greater than) the mean, while a negative z score says that x is below (less than) the mean. For instance, a z score equal to 2.3 says that x is 2.3 standard deviations above the mean. Similarly, a z score equal to -1.68 says that x is 1.68 standard deviations below the mean. A z score equal to zero says that x equals the mean.

A z score indicates the relative location of a value within a population or sample. For example, below we calculate the z scores for each of the revenues for the five biggest companies in Canada in 2006 as reported by *The Globe and Mail*. Recall that for these companies, the mean revenue is \$29.4 billion and the standard deviation is \$4.03 billion.

Company	Revenue	x − Mean	z score
General Motors of Canada	35	$(35 - 29.4) = 5.6$	$5.6/4.03 = 1.39$
Manulife Financial	32	$(32 - 29.4) = 2.6$	$2.6/4.03 = 0.64$
Royal Bank of Canada	29	$(29 - 29.4) = -0.4$	$-0.4/4.03 = -0.10$
Loblaw Companies	28	$(28 - 29.4) = -1.4$	$-1.4/4.03 = -0.35$
Magna International	23	$(23 - 29.4) = -6.4$	$-6.4/4.03 = -1.59$

These z scores tell us that General Motors of Canada is the farthest above the mean, with revenues 1.39 standard deviations above the mean. Magna International is the farthest below the mean. If a company had a z score of zero, then the company's revenues would be the same as the mean for the five companies.

Values in two different populations or samples with the same z score are the same number of standard deviations from their respective means and, therefore, have the same relative locations. For example, suppose that the mean score on the midterm exam for students in Section A of a statistics course is 65 and the standard deviation of the scores is 10. Meanwhile, the mean score on the same exam for students in Section B is 80 and the standard deviation is 5. A student in Section A who scores an 85 and a student in Section B who scores a 90 have the same relative locations within their respective sections because their z scores, $(85 - 65)/10 = 2$ and $(90 - 80)/5 = 2$, are equal.

The coefficient of variation   Sometimes we need to measure the size of the standard deviation of a population or sample relative to the size of the population or sample mean. The **coefficient of variation**, which makes this comparison, is defined for a population or sample as follows:

$$\text{Coefficient of variation} = \frac{\text{standard deviation}}{\text{mean}} \times 100.$$

The coefficient of variation compares populations or samples with different means and different standard deviations. For example, Morningstar.com[5] gives the mean and standard deviation[6] of the returns for each of the Morningstar Top 25 Large Growth Funds. As given on the Morningstar Web site, the mean return for the Strong Advisor Select A fund is 10.39 percent with a standard deviation of 16.18 percent, while the mean return for the Nations Marisco 21st Century fund is 17.7 percent with a standard deviation of 15.81 percent. It follows that the coefficient of variation for the Strong Advisor fund is $(16.18/10.39) \times 100 = 155.73$, and the coefficient of variation for the Nations Marisco fund is $(15.81/17.7) \times 100 = 89.32$. This tells us that, for the Strong Advisor fund, the standard deviation is 155.73 percent of the value of its mean return. For the Nations Marisco fund, the standard deviation is 89.32 percent of the value of its mean return.

In the context of situations like the stock fund comparison, the coefficient of variation is often used as a measure of **risk** because it measures the variation of the returns (the standard deviation) relative to the size of the mean return. For instance, although the Strong Advisor fund and the Nations Marisco fund have comparable standard deviations (16.18 percent versus 15.81 percent), the Strong Advisor fund has a higher coefficient of variation than does the Nations Marisco fund (155.73 versus 89.32). This says that, **relative to the mean return**, the variation in returns for the Strong Advisor fund is higher. That is, we would conclude that investing in the Strong Advisor fund is riskier than investing in the Nations Marisco fund.

[5]Source: http://poweredby.morningstar.com/Selectors/AolTop25/AolTop25List.html, March 17, 2005.
[6]Annualized return based on the last 36 monthly returns.

Exercises for Section 2.3

CONCEPTS

2.23 Define the range, variance, and standard deviation for a population.

2.24 Discuss how the variance and the standard deviation measure variation.

2.25 Why are the variance and standard deviation usually considered more effective measures of variation than the range?

2.26 The empirical rule for a normally distributed population and Chebyshev's theorem have the same basic purpose. In your own words, explain what this purpose is.

2.27 When is a process capable, and what are process specification limits? Give an example of a situation in which process capability is important.

METHODS AND APPLICATIONS

2.28 Consider the following population of five numbers: 5, 8, 10, 12, 15. Calculate the range, variance, and standard deviation of this population.

2.29 Table 2.9 lists the number of university degrees, diplomas, and certificates granted in each province in Canada in 2003. These data are available from Statistics Canada (http://www.statcan.ca). Calculate the range, variance, and standard deviation of this population of educational attainment numbers.   ⬤ UniDegree

2.30 Table 2.10 lists the aircraft movement statistics from Transport Canada for January 2006 compared to January 2005 at tower-controlled airports (see http://www.tc.gc.ca).   ⬤ AirMove
  a. Calculate the population range, variance, and standard deviation of the five percentage change values (note that negative values indicate that there was greater movement in 2005 than in 2006).
  b. Using the population of change values, compute and interpret the z score for each type of air transportation movement.

2.31 In order to control costs, a company wishes to study the amount of money its sales force spends entertaining

TABLE **2.9** University Degrees, Diplomas, and Certificates Granted by Provinces in 2003 ● UniDegree

Province	
Newfoundland and Labrador	2,975
Prince Edward Island	625
Nova Scotia	8,785
New Brunswick	4,555
Quebec	57,705
Ontario	79,000
Manitoba	5,870
Saskatchewan	5,865
Alberta	17,200
British Columbia	19,015

Source: Adapted form the Statistics Canada CANSIM database http://cansim2.statcan.ca, table number 477-0014, February 2006.

TABLE **2.10** Percentage Change of Movement of Aircraft in Tower-Controlled Airports in Canada ● AirMove

Air Carriers	1.2
Other Commercial	3.2
Private	11.0
Government	
• Civil	5.9
• Military	−1.5

Source: Adapted from Statistics Canada, *Aircraft Movement Statistics: NAV CANADA Towers and Flights Service Stations*, Catalogue 51-007, Volume 1, no. 1, January 2006.

clients. The following is a random sample of six entertainment expenses (lunch costs for four people) from expense reports submitted by members of the sales force. ● LunchCost

$157 $132 $109 $145 $125 $139

a. Calculate $\bar{x}$, s^2, and s for the expense data. In addition, show that the two different formulas for calculating s^2 give the same result.

b. Assuming that the distribution of entertainment expenses is approximately normally distributed, calculate estimates of tolerance intervals containing 68.26 percent, 95.44 percent, and 99.73 percent of all entertainment expenses by the sales force.

c. If a member of the sales force submits an entertainment expense (lunch cost for four) of $190, should this expense be considered unusually high (and possibly worthy of investigation by the company)? Explain your answer.

d. Compute and interpret the z score for each of the six entertainment expenses.

2.32 THE TRASH BAG CASE ● TrashBag

The mean and the standard deviation of the sample of 40 trash bag breaking strengths are $\bar{x} = 22.990$ and $s = 0.7428$.

a. What do the stem-and-leaf display and histogram in Figures 2.15 and 2.16 (page 37) say about whether the empirical rule should be used to describe the trash bag breaking strengths?

b. Use the empirical rule to calculate estimates of tolerance intervals containing 68.26 percent, 95.44 percent, and 99.73 percent of all possible trash bag breaking strengths.

c. Does the estimate of a tolerance interval containing 99.73 percent of all breaking strengths provide evidence that almost any bag a customer might purchase will have a breaking strength that exceeds 20 kg? Explain your answer.

d. How do the percentages of the 40 breaking strengths in Table 2.6 (page 37) that actually fall into the intervals $[\bar{x} \pm s]$, $[\bar{x} \pm 2s]$, and $[\bar{x} \pm 3s]$ compare to those given by the empirical rule? Do these compar-

isons indicate that the statistical inferences you made in parts b and c are reasonably valid?

2.33 THE BANK CUSTOMER WAITING TIME CASE ● WaitTime

The mean and the standard deviation of the sample of 100 bank customer waiting times are $\bar{x} = 5.46$ and $s = 2.475$.

a. What do the stem-and-leaf display and histogram in Figures 2.13 and 2.14 (page 37) say about whether the empirical rule should be used to describe the bank customer waiting times?

b. Use the empirical rule to calculate estimates of tolerance intervals containing 68.26 percent, 95.44 percent, and 99.73 percent of all possible bank customer waiting times.

c. Does the estimate of a tolerance interval containing 68.26 percent of all waiting times provide evidence that at least two thirds of all customers will have to wait less than eight minutes for service? Explain your answer.

d. How do the percentages of the 100 waiting times in Table 2.5 (page 36) that actually fall into the intervals $[\bar{x} \pm s]$, $[\bar{x} \pm 2s]$, and $[\bar{x} \pm 3s]$ compare to those given by the empirical rule? Do these comparisons indicate that the statistical inferences you made in parts b and c are reasonably valid?

2.34 THE VIDEO GAME SATISFACTION RATING CASE ● VideoGame

The mean and the standard deviation of the sample of 65 customer satisfaction ratings are $\bar{x} = 42.95$ and $s = 2.6424$.

a. What do the stem-and-leaf display and histogram in Figures 2.10 and 2.11 (pages 35 and 36) say about whether the empirical rule should be used to describe the satisfaction ratings?

b. Use the empirical rule to calculate estimates of tolerance intervals containing 68.26 percent, 95.44 percent, and 99.73 percent of all possible satisfaction ratings.

c. Does the estimate of a tolerance interval containing 99.73 percent of all satisfaction ratings provide evidence that 99.73 percent of all customers will give a satisfaction rating for the XYZ-Box game system that is at least 35 (the minimal rating of a "satisfied" customer)? Explain your answer.

d. How do the percentages of the 65 customer satisfaction ratings in Table 2.4 (page 35) that actually fall into the intervals $[\bar{x} \pm s]$, $[\bar{x} \pm 2s]$, and $[\bar{x} \pm 3s]$ compare to those given by the empirical rule? Do these comparisons indicate that the statistical inferences you made in parts b and c are reasonably valid?

2.35 Consider the 63 automated banking machine (ABM) transaction times given in Table 1.11 (page 25).
   a. Construct a stem-and-leaf display for the 63 ABM transaction times. Describe the shape of the distribution of transaction times. ● ABMTime
   b. When we compute the sample mean and sample standard deviation for the transaction times, we find that $\bar{x} = 36.56$ and $s = 4.475$. Compute each of the intervals $[\bar{x} \pm s]$, $[\bar{x} \pm 2s]$, and $[\bar{x} \pm 3s]$. Then count the number of transaction times that actually fall into each interval and find the percentage of transaction times that actually fall into each interval.
   c. How do the percentages of transaction times that fall into the intervals $[\bar{x} \pm s]$, $[\bar{x} \pm 2s]$, and $[\bar{x} \pm 3s]$ compare to those given by the empirical rule? How do the percentages of transaction times that fall into the intervals $[\bar{x} \pm 2s]$ and $[\bar{x} \pm 3s]$ compare to those given by Chebyshev's theorem?
   d. Explain why the empirical rule does not describe the transaction times extremely well.

2.36 The Morningstar Top Fund lists at the Morningstar.com Web site give the mean yearly return and the standard deviation of the returns for each of the listed funds. As given by Morningstar.com on March 17, 2005, the RS Internet Age Fund has a mean yearly return of 10.93 percent with a standard deviation of 41.96 percent, the Franklin Income A fund has a mean yearly return of 13 percent with a standard deviation of 9.36 percent, and the Jacob Internet fund has a mean yearly return of 34.45 percent with a standard deviation of 41.16 percent.
   a. For each mutual fund, find an interval in which you would expect 95.44 percent of all yearly returns to fall. Assume returns are normally distributed.
   b. Using the intervals you computed in part a, compare the three mutual funds with respect to average yearly returns and with respect to variability of returns.
   c. Calculate the coefficient of variation for each mutual fund, and use your results to compare the funds with respect to risk. Which fund is riskier?

2.37 Consider the data concerning a critical dimension of an auto part given in Exercise 1.14 (page 16), and assume that the process producing this part is in statistical control.
   a. When we compute the sample mean and sample standard deviation of the 18 dimensions, we obtain $\bar{x} = 3.0028$ and $s = 0.01437$. Assuming the dimensions are mound-shaped, use these values to compute an estimated tolerance interval that you would expect to contain almost all (99.73 percent) of the auto part's dimensions. Based on this interval, can we conclude that the process is capable of meeting specifications of 3.00 ± 0.03—that is, 2.97 to 3.03? Explain your answer.
   b. After a research and development program is carried out to improve the manufacturing process that produces the auto part, the following 18 measurements of the dimension are obtained (they are given in time order). Does the process appear to be in statistical control? Justify your answer. ● AutoPart2

Hour	Measurement (cm)	Hour	Measurement (cm)
1	3.010	10	3.005
2	3.005	11	2.995
3	2.990	12	2.995
4	3.010	13	3.010
5	2.995	14	3.000
6	2.990	15	2.990
7	3.000	16	2.995
8	2.990	17	3.010
9	3.010	18	3.000

   c. When we compute the sample mean and sample standard deviation of the 18 observed dimensions from the improved process, we obtain $\bar{x} = 3$ and $s = 0.00786$. Assuming the measurements are normally distributed, use these results to compute an estimated tolerance interval that you would expect to contain almost all (99.73 percent) of the dimensions produced by the improved process. Based on this interval, can we conclude that the improved process is capable of meeting specifications of 3.00 ± 0.03—that is, 2.97 to 3.03? Explain your answer.

2.4 Percentiles, Quartiles, and Box-and-Whiskers Displays

Percentiles, quartiles, and five-number displays In this section, we consider **percentiles** and their applications. We begin by defining the **pth percentile**.

> For a set of measurements arranged in increasing order, the **pth percentile** is a value such that p percent of the measurements fall at or below the value, and $(100 - p)$ percent of the measurements fall at or above the value.

There are various procedures for calculating percentiles. One procedure is as follows: To calculate the pth percentile for a set of n measurements, we first arrange the measurements in increasing order (by, for example, constructing a stem-and-leaf display). Then we calculate the index $i = (p/100)n$. If i is not an integer, the next integer greater than i denotes the position of the pth

FIGURE 2.27   Using Stem-and-Leaf Displays to Find Percentiles and Five-Number Summaries

(a) The 75th percentile of 65 test scores, and a five-number summary

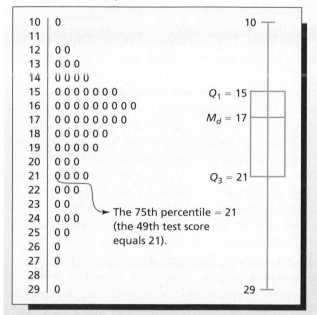

(b) The 5th percentile of the 60 bottle design ratings, and a five-number summary

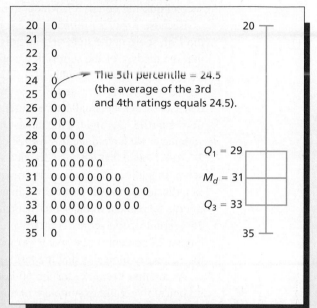

percentile in the ordered arrangement. If i is an integer, then the pth percentile is the average of the measurements in positions i and $i + 1$ in the ordered arrangement. For example, Figure 2.27(a) presents the stem-and-leaf display of 65 test scores. In order to calculate the 75th percentile of these 65 scores, we calculate the index $i = (75/100)65 = 48.75$. Because $i = 48.75$ is not an integer, the 75th percentile is the 49th score in the stem-and-leaf display. Counting up to the 49th score in this display, we find that the 75th percentile is 21 (see Figure 2.27(a)). This implies that we estimate that approximately 75 percent of all scores are less than or equal to 21. As another example, Figure 2.27(b) presents the stem-and-leaf display of the 60 bottle design ratings. In order to calculate the fifth percentile of these 60 ratings, we calculate the index $i = (5/100)60 = 3$. Because $i = 3$ is an integer, the fifth percentile is the average of the third and fourth ratings in the stem-and-leaf display. Counting up to these ratings in this display, we find that the fifth percentile is $(24 + 25)/2 = 24.5$ (see Figure 2.27(b)). Since any rating is a whole number, we estimate that approximately 5 percent of all ratings are 24 or less and that approximately 95 percent of all ratings are 25 or more.

In general, unless percentiles correspond to very high or very low percentages, they are resistant (like the median) to extreme values. For example, the 75th percentile of the test scores would remain 21 even if the three largest scores—26, 27, and 29—were, instead, 35, 56, and 84. On the other hand, the standard deviation in this situation would increase from 3.9612 to 10.2119. In general, if a population is highly positively or negatively skewed (to the right or left), it can be best to describe the variation of the population by using various percentiles. For example, we might describe the variation of the yearly incomes of all people in Canada by using the 10th, 25th, 50th, 75th, and 90th percentiles of these incomes.

One appealing way to describe the variation of a set of measurements is to divide the data into four parts, each containing approximately 25 percent of the measurements. This can be done by defining the **first, second,** and **third quartiles** as follows:

The **first quartile**, denoted Q_1, is the **25th percentile**.
The **second quartile** (or **median**), denoted M_d, is the **50th percentile**.
The **third quartile**, denoted Q_3, is the **75th percentile**.

Note that the second quartile is simply another name for the median. Furthermore, the procedure we have described here that would be used to find the 50th percentile (second quartile) will always give the same result as the previously described procedure for finding the median. For example, to find the second quartile of the 65 test scores, we find the 50th percentile by calculating $i = (50/100)65 = 32.5$, which says that the second quartile is the 33rd score in the stem-and-leaf display of Figure 2.27(a). Counting up to the 33rd score in the display, we find that the second quartile equals 17, which is the median of the scores.

Because $i = (25/100)65 = 16.25$, the first quartile (25th percentile) of the 65 test scores is the 17th score in the stem-and-leaf display of Figure 2.27(a). Therefore, $Q_1 = 15$. Remembering that the median of the scores is 17, and that the 75th percentile of the scores is 21, the quartiles are $Q_1 = 15$, $M_d = 17$, and $Q_3 = 21$.

We often describe a set of measurements by using a **five-number summary**. The summary consists of (1) the smallest measurement, (2) the first quartile, Q_1, (3) the median, M_d, (4) the third quartile, Q_3, and (5) the largest measurement. It is easy to graphically depict a five-number summary; we have done this for the 65 test scores alongside the stem-and-leaf display of Figure 2.27(a). Notice that we have drawn a vertical line extending from the smallest score to the largest score. In addition, a rectangle is drawn that extends from Q_1 to Q_3, and a horizontal line is drawn to indicate the location of the median. The summary divides the scores into four parts, with the middle 50 percent of the scores depicted by the rectangle. The summary indicates that the largest 25 percent of the scores is more spread out than the smallest 25 percent, and that the second-largest 25 percent of the scores is more spread out than the second-smallest 25 percent. Overall, the summary indicates that the test scores are somewhat positively skewed (to the right).

As another example, for the 60 bottle design ratings, $Q_1 = 29$, $M_d = 31$, and $Q_3 = 33$. The graphical five-number summary of the ratings is shown alongside the stem-and-leaf display of the ratings in Figure 2.27(b). The summary shows that the smallest 25 percent of the ratings is more spread out than any of the other quarters of the ratings, and that the other three quarters are equally spread out. Overall, the summary shows that the bottle design ratings are negatively skewed (to the left).

Using the first and third quartiles, we define the **interquartile range** to be $IQR = Q_3 - Q_1$. This quantity can be interpreted as the length of the interval that contains the **middle 50 percent** of the measurements. For instance, Figure 2.27(a) tells us that the interquartile range of the sample of 65 test scores is $Q_3 - Q_1 = 21 - 15 = 6$. This says that we estimate that the middle 50 percent of all scores fall within a range of six points.

The procedure we have presented for calculating the first and third quartiles is not the only procedure for computing these quantities. In fact, several procedures exist, and, for example, different statistical computer packages use several somewhat different methods for computing the quartiles. One procedure calculates what are called **lower** and **upper hinges** and then defines the first quartile to be the lower hinge and the third quartile to be the upper hinge. In general, the different methods for computing the first and third quartiles sometimes produce somewhat different results. However, no matter what procedure is used to compute the quartiles, the objective is to divide the data into four parts, each containing approximately 25 percent of the measurements.

Box-and-whiskers displays (box plots)   A more sophisticated modification of the graphical five-number summary is called a **box-and-whiskers display** (sometimes called a **box plot**). Such a display is constructed by using Q_1, M_d, Q_3, and the interquartile range. As an example, again consider the 20 customer satisfaction ratings:

1   3   5   5   7   8   8   8   8   8   9   9   9   9   9   9   10   10   10   10

CHAPTER 1 It can be shown that $Q_1 = 7.5$, $M_d = 8$, $Q_3 = 9$, and $IQR = Q_3 - Q_1 = 9 - 7.5 = 1.5$ for these ratings. To construct a box-and-whiskers display, we first draw a box that extends from Q_1 to Q_3. As shown in Figure 2.28(a), for the satisfaction ratings data this box extends from $Q_1 = 7.5$ to $Q_3 = 9$. The box contains the middle 50 percent of the data set. Next, a vertical line is drawn through the box at the value of the median M_d (sometimes a plus sign $(+)$ is plotted at the median instead of a vertical line). This line divides the data set into two roughly equal parts. We next define what we call **inner** and **outer fences**. The **inner fences** are located $1.5 \times IQR$ below Q_1 and $1.5 \times IQR$ above Q_3. For the satisfaction ratings data, the inner fences are

$$Q_1 - 1.5(IQR) = 7.5 - 1.5(1.5) = 5.25 \quad \text{and} \quad Q_3 + 1.5(IQR) = 9 + 1.5(1.5) = 11.25$$

FIGURE 2.28 **A Box-and-Whiskers Display of the Satisfaction Ratings**

(a) Constructing the display

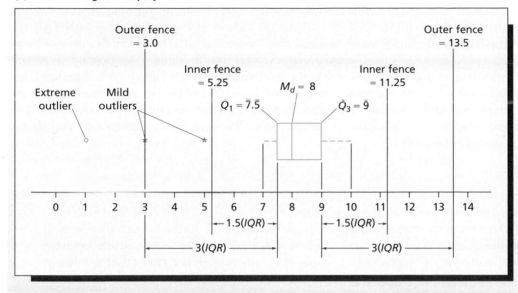

(b) MINITAB output

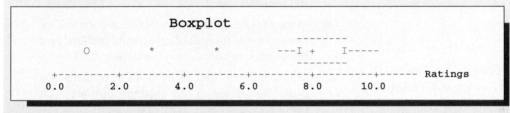

(c) MegaStat output

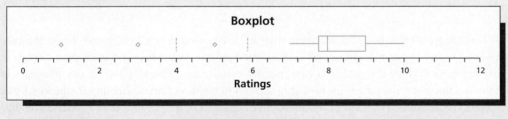

(again see Figure 2.28(a)). The **outer fences** are located $3 \times IQR$ below Q_1 and $3 \times IQR$ above Q_3. For the satisfaction ratings data, the outer fences are

$$Q_1 - 3(IQR) = 7.5 - 3(1.5) = 3.0 \qquad \text{and} \qquad Q_3 + 3(IQR) = 9 + 3(1.5) = 13.5$$

(these are also shown in Figure 2.28(a)). The inner and outer fences help us to draw the plot's **whiskers**: dashed lines extending below Q_1 and above Q_3 (as in Figure 2.28(a)). One whisker is drawn from Q_1 to the smallest measurement between the inner fences. For the satisfaction ratings data, this whisker extends from $Q_1 = 7.5$ down to 7, because 7 is the smallest rating between the inner fences 5.25 and 11.25. The other whisker is drawn from Q_3 to the largest measurement between the inner fences. For the satisfaction ratings data, this whisker extends from $Q_3 = 9$ up to 10, because 10 is the largest rating between the inner fences 5.25 and 11.25. The inner and outer fences are also used to identify **outliers**. An **outlier** is a measurement that is separated from (that is, different from) most of the other measurements in the data set. Measurements that are located between the inner and outer fences are considered to be **mild outliers**, whereas measurements that are located outside the outer fences are considered to be **extreme outliers**. We indicate the locations of mild outliers by plotting these measurements with the symbol ∗, and we indicate the locations of extreme outliers by plotting these measurements with the symbol o. For the satisfaction ratings data, the ratings 3 and 5 are mild outliers (∗) because these ratings are between the inner fence of 5.25 and the outer fence of 3.0. The rating 1 is an extreme outlier (o) because this rating is outside the outer fence 3.0. These outliers are plotted in Figure 2.28(a). Parts (b) and (c) of Figure 2.28 give MINITAB and MegaStat outputs of the box-and-whiskers plot. Notice that MINITAB identifies the median by using a plus sign (+), while MegaStat uses a vertical line. In addition, MegaStat plots all outliers using the same symbol and marks the inner and outer fences using vertical dashed lines. Note here that MegaStat computes the quartiles Q_1 and Q_3 and the inner and outer fences using methods that differ slightly from the methods we have described. The MegaStat Help menus describe how the calculations are done. We now summarize how to construct a box-and-whiskers display.

Constructing a Box-and-Whiskers Display (Box Plot)

1 Draw a **box** that extends from the first quartile Q_1 to the third quartile Q_3. Also draw a vertical line through the box located at the median M_d.

2 Determine the values of the **inner fences** and **outer fences**. The inner fences are located $1.5 \times IQR$ below Q_1 and $1.5 \times IQR$ above Q_3. That is, the **inner fences** are

$$Q_1 - 1.5(IQR) \quad \text{and} \quad Q_3 + 1.5(IQR).$$

The outer fences are located $3 \times IQR$ below Q_1 and $3 \times IQR$ above Q_3. That is, the **outer fences** are

$$Q_1 - 3(IQR) \quad \text{and} \quad Q_3 + 3(IQR).$$

3 Draw **whiskers** as dashed lines that extend below Q_1 and above Q_3. Draw one whisker from Q_1 to the **smallest** measurement that is between the inner fences. Draw the other whisker from Q_3 to the **largest** measurement that is between the inner fences.

4 Measurements that are located between the inner and outer fences are called **mild outliers**. Plot these measurements using the symbol ∗.

5 Measurements that are located outside the outer fences are called **extreme outliers**. Plot these measurements using the symbol o.

When interpreting a box-and-whiskers display, keep several points in mind. First, the box (between Q_1 and Q_3) contains the middle 50 percent of the data. Second, the median (which is inside the box) divides the data into two roughly equal parts. Third, if one of the whiskers is longer than the other, the data set is probably skewed in the direction of the longer whisker. Last, observations designated as outliers should be investigated. Understanding the root causes behind the outlying observations will often provide useful information. For instance, understanding why several of the satisfaction ratings in the box plot of Figure 2.28 are substantially lower than the great majority of the ratings may suggest actions that can improve the DVD recorder manufacturer's product and/or service. Outliers can also be caused by inaccurate measuring, reporting, or plotting of the data. Such possibilities should be investigated, and incorrect data should be adjusted or eliminated.

Generally, a box plot clearly depicts the central tendency, variability, and overall range of a set of measurements. A box plot also portrays whether the measurements are symmetrically distributed. However, the exact shape of the distribution is better portrayed by a stem-and-leaf display and/or a histogram. For instance, Figure 2.29 shows the MegaStat output of the stem-and-leaf display and box plot of scores on a 100-point statistics exam that was given before an attendance policy was begun. We see that, although the box plot in Figure 2.29 tells us that the exam scores are somewhat negatively skewed with a tail to the left, it does not reveal the double-peaked nature of the exam score distribution. On the other hand, the stem-and-leaf display clearly shows that this distribution is double-peaked. In summary, graphical five-number summaries and box-and-whiskers displays are perhaps best used to compare different sets of measurements, for example, 3-month returns for investment funds of all types versus 12-month returns.

FIGURE 2.29   MegaStat Output of a Stem-and-Leaf Display and Box Plot of Exam Scores

Stem and Leaf plot for ExamScore

stem unit = 10   leaf unit = 1

Frequency	Stem	Leaf
1	3	2
0	3	
0	4	
1	4	5
1	5	0
2	5	68
6	6	011344
7	6	5677899
1	7	2
2	7	68
3	8	133
6	8	567789
8	9	00122334
2	9	68
40		

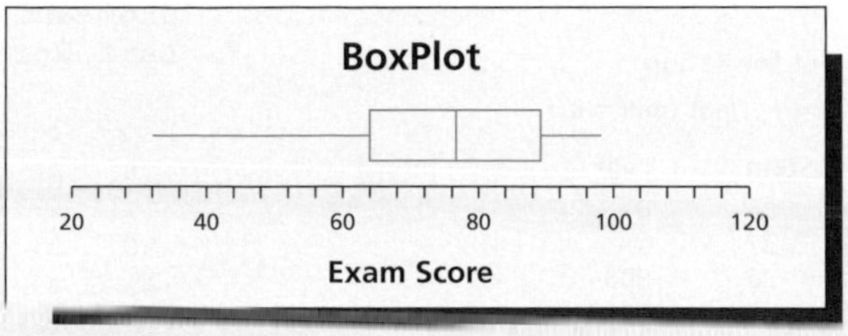

BoxPlot

Exam Score

Exercises for Section 2.4

CONCEPTS

2.38 Explain each of the following in your own words: a percentile; the first quartile, Q_1; the third quartile, Q_3; and the interquartile range, IQR.

2.39 Suppose that we are using a box-and-whiskers display to depict a population or sample of measurements. How would you interpret each of the following?
   a. The whisker to the right is much longer than the whisker to the left.
   b. The interquartile range is much longer than either of the whiskers and there are no outliers.
   c. The distance between Q_1 and the median is far less than the distance between the median and Q_3.
   d. The interquartile range is very short.

METHODS AND APPLICATIONS

2.40 Consider the 65 game system satisfaction ratings, the 100 bank customer waiting times, and the 40 trash bag breaking strengths.
   a. Using the stem-and-leaf displays of these data sets on the next page, find for each data set
   (1) The 90th percentile.   **(4)** The third quartile.
   (2) The median.   **(5)** The 10th percentile.
   (3) The first quartile.   **(6)** The interquartile range.
   b. Construct a five-number summary and a box-and-whiskers display for each data set.   ● VideoGame   ● WaitTime   ● TrashBag

2.41 Statistics Canada (http://www.statcan.ca) provides data about the average number of days lost per worker by cause for each province. Listed on the next page are the values of days lost for each province because of "Personal or Family Responsibility" (PorF) and "Illness or Disability" (IorD) for 2004.   ● LostDays

   a. For the Personal or Family Responsibility values, compute the mean, median, mode, standard deviation, variance, and range.
   b. Based on the values computed in part a, describe the shape of the distribution (this exercise might be easier to complete if you create stem-and-leaf and box-and-whisker displays).
   c. For the Illness or Disability values, compute the mean, median, mode, standard deviation, variance, and range.
   d. Based on the values computed in part c, describe the shape of the distribution (this exercise might be easier to complete if you create stem-and-leaf and bax-and-whisker displays).

2.42 In Section 2.4, we presented a commonly accepted way to compute the first, second, and third quartiles. Some statisticians, however, advocate an alternative method for computing Q_1 and Q_3. This method defines the first quartile, Q_1, as the **lower hinge** and defines the third quartile, Q_3, as the **upper hinge**. In order to calculate these quantities for a set of n measurements, we first arrange the measurements in increasing order. Then, if n is even, the lower hinge is the median of the smallest $n/2$ measurements, and the upper hinge is the median of the largest $n/2$ measurements. If n is odd, we insert M_d into the data set to obtain a set of $n + 1$ measurements. Then, the lower hinge is the median of the smallest $(n + 1)/2$ measurements, and the upper hinge is the median of the largest $(n + 1)/2$ measurements.

   a. Consider a sample of $n = 20$ customer satisfaction ratings:

   1 3 5 5 7 8 8 8 8   8 9 9 9 9 9 10 10 10 10

   The smallest 10 ratings   The largest 10 ratings

MegaStat Stem-and-Leaf Display of the 65 Satisfaction Ratings

Stem and Leaf plot for Rating

stem unit = 1   leaf unit = 0.1

Frequency	Stem	Leaf
1	36	0
0	37	
3	38	000
4	39	0000
5	40	00000
6	41	000000
6	42	000000
8	43	00000000
12	44	000000000000
9	45	000000000
7	46	0000000
3	47	000
1	48	0
65		

MINITAB Stem-and-Leaf Display of the Waiting Times

```
Stem-and-leaf of WaitTime   N = 100
Leaf Unit = 0.10

    2    0    48
    8    1    134688
   17    2    023457899
   28    3    12456778899
   45    4    00123334455567789
  (15)   5    011223445667888
   40    6    1123334556778
   27    7    0223445789
   17    8    0134667
   10    9    123589
    4   10    279
    1   11    6
```

MegaStat Stem-and-Leaf Display of the Breaking Strengths

Stem and Leaf plot for Strength

stem unit = 1   leaf unit = 0.1

Frequency	Stem	Leaf
1	21	3
2	21	6 9
6	22	0 0 2 3 4 4
9	22	5 5 5 6 7 7 8 8 9
12	23	0 0 0 1 1 1 2 2 3 3 4 4
6	23	5 6 6 8 9 9
3	24	1 2 3
1	24	5
40		

Average Number of Days Lost Per Worker by Cause

● LostDays

Province	PorF	IorD
Newfoundland and Labrador	1.5	8.8
Prince Edward Island	1.6	6.0
Nova Scotia	1.9	9.1
New Brunswick	1.7	8.0
Québec	1.4	9.4
Ontario	1.9	6.7
Manitoba	1.8	8.0
Saskatchewan	2.2	8.0
Alberta	1.9	5.6
British Columbia	1.5	7.3

Source: Adapted from the Statistics Canada CANSIM database
http://cansim2.statcan.ca, table number 279-0029, February 2006.

Using the method presented in Section 2.4, find Q_1 and Q_3. Then find the lower hinge and the upper hinge for the satisfaction ratings. How do your results compare?   ● DVDSat

b. Consider the following sample of $n = 11$ doctors' salaries (in thousands of dollars):

127 132 138 141 146 152 154 171 177 192 241

Using the method presented in Section 2.4, find Q_1 and Q_3. The median of the 11 salaries is $M_d = 152$. If we insert this median into the data set, we obtain the following set of $n + 1 = 12$ salaries:

127 132 138 141 146 152 | 152 154 171 177 192 241

The smallest 6 salaries   The largest 6 salaries

Find the lower hinge and the upper hinge for the salaries. Compare your values of Q_1 and Q_3 with the lower and upper hinges.   ● DrSalary

c. For the 11 doctors' salaries, which quantities —Q_1, M_d, and Q_3 as defined in Section 2.4 or the lower hinge, M_d, and the upper hinge—in your opinion best divide the salaries into four parts?

2.5 Describing Qualitative Data

Bar charts and pie charts   Recall that when we employ a **qualitative** or **categorical variable** we simply record into which of several categories a population element falls. For example, for each automobile produced in Canada we might record the manufacturer—Daimler Chrysler, Ford, General Motors, or some other manufacturer. We often display such data graphically. For instance, Figure 2.30 gives the Excel output of a **bar chart** of the number of military personnel

FIGURE 2.30   **Number of Military Personnel by Province**

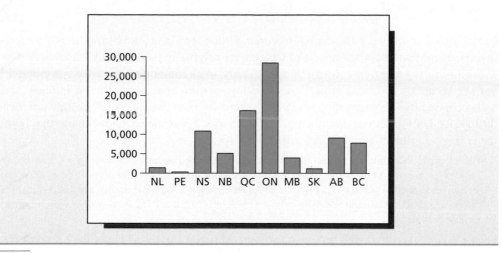

Source: Adapted from the Statistics Canada CANSIM database http://cansim2.statcan.ca, table number 183-0004 and from the publication *Public Sector Statistics,* Catalogue 68-213-XIE, February 2006.

FIGURE 2.31   **Number of Military Personnel by Province**

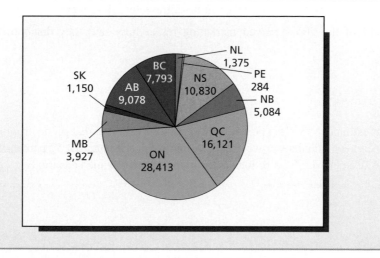

Source: Adapted from the Statistics Canada CANSIM database http://cansim2.statcan.ca, table number 183-0004 and from the publication *Public Sector Statistics,* Catalogue 68-213-XIE, February 2006.

for each province in Canada in 2005 according to Statistics Canada (http://www.statcan.ca). Figure 2.31 provides the same information in a **pie chart** format.

In general, bar charts and pie charts are convenient ways to summarize the percentages of population units that are contained in several different categories.

Estimating proportions   Suppose that a population unit can fall into one of several categories. Often we are interested in a specific category, and, in such cases, we often wish to estimate

p = the proportion of all population elements that are contained in the category of interest.

In order to estimate this proportion, we can randomly select a sample from the population. Then, the **sample proportion**

$\hat{p}$ = the proportion of the sample elements that are contained in the category of interest

is a reasonable point estimate of the **population proportion p**.

In the following examples, we introduce two new cases that illustrate estimating a population proportion p.

Example 2.10 The Marketing Ethics Case: Estimating Marketing Researchers' Disapproval Rates

In the book *Essentials of Marketing Research*, Dillon, Madden, and Firtle discuss a survey of marketing professionals, the results of which were originally published by Akoah and Riordan in the *Journal of Marketing Research*. In the study, marketing researchers were presented with various scenarios involving ethical issues such as confidentiality, conflict of interest, and social acceptability. The marketing researchers were asked to indicate whether they approved or disapproved of the actions described in each scenario. For instance, one scenario that involved the issue of confidentiality was described as follows:

> **Use of ultraviolet ink**   A project director went to the marketing research director's office and requested permission to use an ultraviolet ink to precode a questionnaire for a mail survey. The project director pointed out that although the cover letter promised confidentiality, respondent identification was needed to permit adequate cross-tabulations of the data. The marketing research director gave approval.

Of the 205 marketing researchers who participated in the survey, 117 said they disapproved of the actions taken in the scenario.

In this situation, we would like to make an inference about the population of all marketing researchers. Specifically, we wish to estimate the population proportion

p = the proportion of all marketing researchers who disapprove
of the actions taken in the ultraviolet ink scenario.

Because 117 of the 205 surveyed marketing researchers said they disapproved, the sample proportion

$$\hat{p} = \frac{117}{205} = 0.57$$

is the point estimate of p. This point estimate says we estimate that p, the proportion of all marketing researchers who disapprove, is 0.57. That is, we estimate that 57 percent of all marketing researchers disapprove of the actions taken in the ultraviolet ink scenario.

Example 2.11 The Electronic Article Surveillance Case: Estimating Consumer Reaction to False Alarms

In an article titled "Consumer responses to electronic article surveillance alarms" in the *Journal of Retailing*, Dawson studies the unintended effects of false electronic article surveillance (EAS) alarms. EAS, an important weapon used by retailers to combat shoplifting, places a small sensor on an item of merchandise. If a shoplifter attempts to exit the store with the item, an electronic alarm is set off by the sensor. When an item is legitimately purchased, the sales clerk removes the sensor to prevent the alarm from sounding when the customer exits the store. Sometimes, however, the clerk forgets to remove the sensor during the purchase. This results in a false alarm when the customer exits—an embarrassing situation for everyone involved (especially the customer). Such false alarms occur quite frequently. In fact, according to Dawson's article, "nearly half of all consumers have experienced an accidental EAS alarm."

Dawson conducted a survey to study consumer reaction to such false alarms. Based on a systematic random sample of 250 consumers, 40 of these consumers said that, if they were to set off an EAS alarm because store personnel did not deactivate the merchandise, "they would never shop at the store again."

Suppose we wish to estimate p, the population proportion of all consumers who would say they would never shop at the store again if subjected to an EAS false alarm. Since 40 of the 250 sampled consumers said they would never shop at the store again, the sample proportion $\hat{p} = 40/250 = 0.16$ is the point estimate of p. This point estimate says we estimate that 16 percent of all consumers would say they would never shop at the store again if subjected to an EAS false alarm.

Finally, suppose a retailer is considering the installation of an EAS system. In an attempt to convince the retailer to purchase the system, a company that markets EAS systems claims that no more than 5 percent of consumers would say that they would never shop at a store again if they were subjected to an EAS false alarm. Based on Dawson's survey results, the retailer would have a hard time believing this claim. That is, the sample proportion $\hat{p} = 0.16$ suggests that more than 5 percent of all consumers would say that they would never shop at the store again. But is the evidence here conclusive? We will address this question in later chapters.

The Pareto chart **Pareto charts** are used to help identify important quality problems and opportunities for process improvement. By using these charts we can prioritize problem-solving activities. The Pareto chart is named for Vilfredo Pareto (1848–1923), an Italian economist. Pareto suggested that, in many economies, most of the wealth is held by a small minority of the population. It has been found that the **Pareto principle** often applies to defects. That is, only a few defect types account for most of a product's quality problems.

Here defects can be divided into two categories—the **vital few** and the **trivial many**. The vital few are the small number of defects that account for a large percentage of the total, while the trivial many are the large number of defects that account for the small remaining percentage of the total. If the vital few defects are very costly to an organization, it may wish to work on eliminating their causes before working to solve other problems.

To illustrate the use of Pareto charts, suppose that a jam producer wishes to evaluate the labels being placed on 500-mL jars of raspberry jam. Every day for two weeks, all defective labels found on inspection are classified by type of defect. If a label has more than one defect, we will record the type of defect that is most noticeable. The Excel output in Figure 2.32 presents the frequencies and percentages of the types of defects observed over the two-week period.

In general, the first step in setting up a Pareto chart summarizing data concerning types of defects (or categories) is to construct a frequency table like the one in Figure 2.32. Defects or categories should be listed at the left of the table in **decreasing order by frequencies**—the defect with the highest frequency will be at the top of the table, the defect with the second-highest

FIGURE **2.32** **Excel Frequency Table and Pareto Chart of Labelling Defects** ● Labels

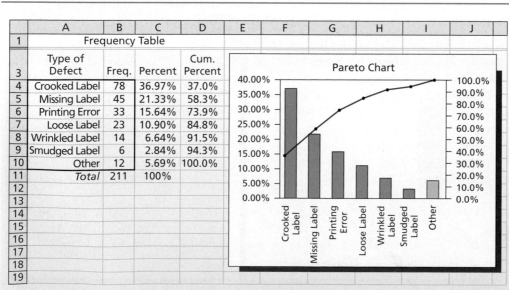

	Type of Defect	Freq.	Percent	Cum. Percent
	Frequency Table			
Crooked Label		78	36.97%	37.0%
Missing Label		45	21.33%	58.3%
Printing Error		33	15.64%	73.9%
Loose Label		23	10.90%	84.8%
Wrinkled Label		14	6.64%	91.5%
Smudged Label		6	2.84%	94.3%
Other		12	5.69%	100.0%
Total		211	100%	

frequency below the first, and so forth. If an "other" category is employed, it should be placed at the bottom of the table. The "other" category should not make up 50 percent or more of the total of the frequencies, and the frequency for the "other" category should not exceed the frequency for the defect at the top of the table. If the frequency for the "other" category is too high, data should be collected so that the "other" category can be broken down into new categories. Once the frequency and the percentage for each category are determined, a cumulative percentage for each category is computed. As illustrated in Figure 2.32, the cumulative percentage for a particular category is the sum of the percentages corresponding to the particular category and the categories that are above that category in the table.

The Pareto chart is a **bar chart**. Different kinds of defects or problems are listed on the horizontal scale. The heights of the bars on the vertical scale typically represent the frequency of occurrence (or the percentage of occurrence) for each defect or problem. The bars are arranged in decreasing height from left to right. Thus, the most frequent defect will be at the far left, the next most frequent defect to its right, and so forth. If an "other" category is employed, its bar is placed at the far right. The Pareto chart for the labelling defects data is given in Figure 2.32. Here the heights of the bars represent the percentages of occurrences for the different labelling defects, and the vertical scale on the far left corresponds to these percentages. The chart graphically illustrates that crooked labels, missing labels, and printing errors are the most frequent labelling defects.

As is also illustrated in Figure 2.32, a Pareto chart is sometimes augmented by plotting a **cumulative percentage point** for each bar in the Pareto chart. The vertical coordinate of this cumulative percentage point equals the cumulative percentage in the frequency table corresponding to the bar. The cumulative percentage points corresponding to the different bars are connected by line segments, and a vertical scale corresponding to the cumulative percentages is placed on the far right. Examining the cumulative percentage points in Figure 2.32, we see that crooked and missing labels make up 58.3 percent of the labelling defects and that crooked labels, missing labels, and printing errors make up 73.9 percent of the labelling defects.

Exercises for Section 2.5

CONCEPTS

2.43 Find an example of a pie chart or bar chart in a newspaper or magazine. Copy it, and hand it in with a written analysis of the information conveyed by the chart.

2.44 What is a population proportion? Give an example of a population proportion that might interest you in the profession you intend to enter.

METHODS AND APPLICATIONS

2.45 Statistics Canada reports on exports to other countries on a monthly basis. Below are the export values to our principal trading partners for September 2006. Also presented are an Excel bar chart and pie chart. Using these graphics, write an analysis of which visual presentation is the most informative and why.
  🌐 ExportVal

Country	Export ($ millions)
U.S.	29,208
Japan	882
United Kingdom	1,043
Other European Countries	1,885
All Others	4,865

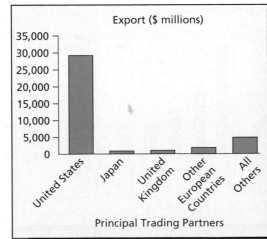

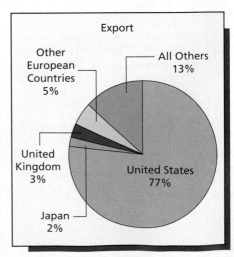

Source: Adapted from Statistics Canada CANSIM database http://cansim2.statcan.ca, table no. 228-0001, March 2006.

Country	Import ($ millions)
U.S.	21,906
Japan	1,039
United Kingdom	942
Other European Countries	2,763
All Others	7,263

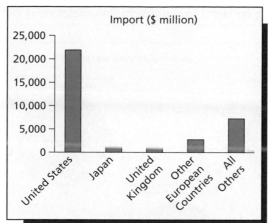

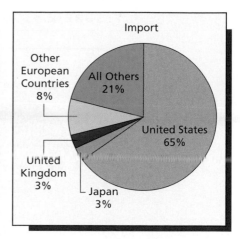

Source: Adapted from Statistics Canada CANSIM database http://cansim2.statcan.ca, table no. 228-0001 March 2006.

2.46 At the top of this page are the import values for Canada's principal trading partners for September 2006 as well as Excel bar and pie charts. Using these graphics, write an analysis of which visual presentation is the most informative and why. ● ImportVal

2.47 Comparing the graphics for Exercises 2.45 and 2.46 (exports versus imports), which chart (bar or pie chart) would you use to make comparisons?

2.48 THE MARKETING ETHICS CASE: CONFLICT OF INTEREST

Consider the marketing ethics case described in Example 2.10. One of the scenarios presented to the 205 marketing researchers is as follows:

> A marketing testing firm to which X company gives most of its business recently went public. The marketing research director of X company had been looking for a good investment and proceeded to buy $20 000 of their stock. The firm continues as X company's leading supplier for testing.

Of the 205 marketing researchers who participated in the ethics survey, 111 said that they disapproved of the actions taken in the scenario. Use this sample result to compute a point estimate of the proportion of all marketing researchers who disapprove of the actions taken in this conflict of interest scenario.

2.49 In the Fall 1993 issue of *VALIC Investment Digest,* the Variable Annuity Life Insurance Company used pie charts to illustrate an investment strategy called **rebalancing**. This strategy involves reviewing an investment portfolio annually to return the asset mix (stocks, bonds, Treasury bills, and so on) to a preselected allocation mix. VALIC describes rebalancing as follows (refer to the pie charts in Figure 2.33):

> *Rebalancing—A Strategy to Keep Your Allocation on Track*
> Once you've established your ideal asset allocation mix, many experts recommend that you review your portfolio at least once a year to make sure your portfolio remains consistent with your preselected asset allocation mix. This practice is referred to as *rebalancing.*

For example, let's assume a moderate asset allocation mix of 50 percent equities funds, 40 percent bond funds, and 10 percent cash equivalent funds. The chart [see Figure 2.33], based on data provided by Ibbotson, a major investment and consulting firm, illustrates how rebalancing works. Using the Standard & Poor's 500 Index, the Salomon Brothers Long-Term High-Grade Corporate Bond Index, and the U.S. 30-day Treasury bill average as a cash-equivalent rate, our hypothetical portfolio balance on 12/31/90 is $10,000. One year later the account had grown to $12,380. By the end of 1991, the allocation had changed to 52.7%/38.7%/8.5%. The third pie chart illustrates how the account was once again rebalanced to return to a 50%/40%/10% asset allocation mix.

Rebalancing has the potential for more than merely helping diversify your portfolio. By continually returning to your original asset allocation, it is possible to avoid exposure to more risk than you previously decided you were willing to assume.

a. Suppose you control a $100,000 portfolio and have decided to maintain an asset allocation mix of 60 percent stock funds, 30 percent bond funds, and 10 percent government securities. Draw a pie chart illustrating your portfolio (like the ones in Figure 2.33).

b. Over the next year, your stock funds earn a return of 30 percent, your bond funds earn a return of 15 percent, and your government securities earn a return of 6 percent. Calculate the end-of-year values of your stock funds, bond funds, and government securities. After calculating the end-of-year value of your entire portfolio, determine the asset allocation mix (percent stock funds, percent bond funds, and percent government securities) of your portfolio before rebalancing. Finally, draw an end-of-year pie chart of your portfolio before rebalancing.

c. Rebalance your portfolio. That is, determine how much of the portfolio's end-of-year value must be

FIGURE **2.33**   Using Pie Charts to Illustrate Portfolio Rebalancing (for Exercise 2.49)

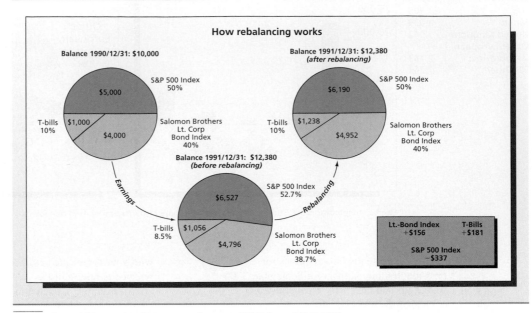

Source: The Variable Annuity Life Insurance Company, *VALIC* 6, no. 4 (Fall 1993).

invested in stock funds, bond funds, and government securities in order to restore your original asset allocation mix of 60 percent stock funds, 30 percent bond funds, and 10 percent government securities. Draw a pie chart of your portfolio after rebalancing.

CHAPTER 14

2.6 Using Scatter Plots to Study Relationships between Variables

Statistical methods are often used to study and quantify relationships between variables. The purpose of studying such relationships is often to **describe**, **predict**, or **control** a variable of interest called the **dependent variable** (which is denoted y). We accomplish this by relating y to one or more other variables that are called **independent variables**. One way to relate variables is to perform **regression analysis**. This technique allows us to find an equation that relates y to the independent variable(s). Then, for instance, we might use the regression equation to predict y on the basis of the independent variable(s). We explain regression analysis in detail in Chapters 12 and 16. A simpler way to relate variables is to graphically study relationships between the variables. We discuss the graphical approach in this section.

One way to explore the relationship between a dependent variable y and an independent variable (denoted x) is to make a **scatter diagram**, or **scatter plot**, of y versus x. First, data concerning the two variables are observed in pairs. To construct the scatter plot, each value of y is plotted against its corresponding value of x. If y and x are related, the plot shows us the direction of the relationship. That is, y could be positively related to x (y increases as x increases) or y could be negatively related to x (y decreases as x increases).

Example 2.12

A manufacturer produces a bulk chemical product. Customer requirements state that this product must have a specified viscosity when melted at a temperature of 150°C (viscosity measures how thick and gooey the product is when melted). Chemical XB-135 is used in the production of this chemical product, and the company's chemists feel that the amount of chemical XB-135 may be related to viscosity. In order to verify and quantify this relationship, 24 batches of the product are

TABLE **2.11**   **Viscosity Data for 24 Batches of a Chemical Product Produced on August 1, 2005**
🌑 Viscosity

Batch	Kilograms of Chemical XB-135 (x)	Viscosity (y)	Batch	Kilograms of Chemical XB-135 (x)	Viscosity (y)
1	10.0	31.76	13	11.2	32.93
2	10.0	31.91	14	11.2	33.19
3	10.2	32.02	15	11.4	33.35
4	10.2	31.85	16	11.4	32.76
5	10.4	32.17	17	11.6	33.33
6	10.4	32.30	18	11.6	33.19
7	10.6	32.60	19	11.8	33.28
8	10.6	32.15	20	11.8	33.57
9	10.8	32.52	21	12.0	33.60
10	10.8	32.46	22	12.0	33.43
11	11.0	32.41	23	12.2	33.91
12	11.0	32.77	24	12.2	33.76

FIGURE **2.34**   **MINITAB Output of a Scatter Plot of Viscosity versus Amount of Chemical XB-135**

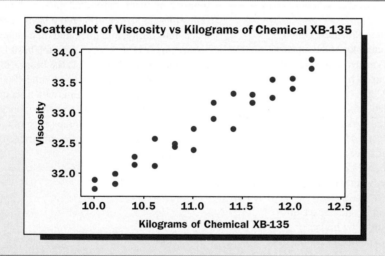

produced. The amount (x) of chemical XB-135 (in kilograms) is varied from batch to batch and the viscosity (y) obtained for each batch is measured. Table 2.11 gives (in time order) the values of x and the corresponding values of y obtained for the 24 batches. The MINITAB output of a scatter plot of y versus x is given in Figure 2.34. The scatter plot indicates a strong positive relationship between y and x—that is, as the amount of chemical XB-135 used is increased, the viscosity of the product increases. We must now be careful. It would be tempting to conclude that increases in the amount of chemical XB-135 **cause** increases in viscosity. However, this is not necessarily the case. Perhaps some other factor could be causing the apparent relationship. For instance, the 24 batches were produced in time order. If some other variable that affects viscosity (such as temperature or pressure in the reaction chamber, or the composition of a raw material) is changing over time, this change could be responsible for the observed increases in viscosity. Assuming that we have held other variables that may affect viscosity constant, the evidence supporting a cause-and-effect relationship may be quite strong. This is because the manufacturer has purposely varied the amount of chemical XB-135 used. However, it is really up to the scientific community to establish and understand any cause-and-effect relationship that may exist.

   If we are convinced that we can control viscosity by changing the amount of chemical XB-135, we may wish to quantify the relationship between y and x. One way to do this is to calculate the **covariance** and the **correlation coefficient** between y and x. How this is done is discussed in Chapter 12. We would also like to develop an equation relating y to x. This can be done by using regression analysis (see Chapter 12). With such an equation, we can predict y on the basis of x, and we can determine the amount of chemical XB-135 to use in order to achieve a specified viscosity.

Because the plot points in Figure 2.34 seem to fluctuate around a straight line, we say that there is a **straight line** (or **linear**) **relationship between y and x**. However, not all relationships are linear. For example, demand for a product, y, might increase at an increasing or decreasing rate as advertising expenditure to promote the product, x, increases. In this case, we say that there is a **curved relationship** between y and x. We discuss curved relationships in Chapter 16.

Exercises for Section 2.6

CONCEPTS

2.50 Draw a scatter plot of y versus x in which y increases in a linear (straight-line) fashion as x increases.

2.51 Draw a scatter plot of y versus x in which y decreases linearly as x increases.

2.52 What is the difference between a scatter plot and a runs plot?

METHODS AND APPLICATIONS

2.53 In the book *Essentials of Marketing Research*, Dillon, Madden, and Firtle present a scatter plot of the number of units sold of 20 varieties of a canned soup versus the amount of shelf space allocated to each variety. The scatter plot is shown in Figure 2.35.

a. Does there appear to be a relationship between y (units sold) and x (shelf space)? Does the relationship appear to be straight-line (linear) or curved? How does y (units sold) change as x (shelf space) increases?

b. If you were told that a variety of soup is allotted a small amount of shelf space, what would you guess about sales?

c. Do you think that the amount of shelf space allocated to a variety causes sales to be higher or lower? Give an alternative explanation for the appearance of the scatter plot.

2.54 **THE FAST-FOOD RESTAURANT RATING CASE** 🖱 FastFood

Recently, researchers at The Ohio State University studied consumer ratings of fast-food restaurants. Each of 406 randomly selected individuals rated the six fast-food restaurants shown in the Excel output of Figure 2.36. Each individual gave each restaurant a rating of 1, 2, 3, 4, 5, or 6 on the basis of taste, convenience, familiarity, and price and then ranked the restaurants from 1 through 6 on the basis of overall preference. In each case, 1 is the best rating and 6 the worst. The mean ratings given by the 406 individuals are given in Figure 2.36 along with a scatter plot of mean preference versus mean taste. Construct scatter plots of mean preference versus each of mean convenience, mean familiarity, and mean price. Then interpret all the scatter plots.

FIGURE **2.35** **A Scatter Plot of Units Sold versus Shelf Space**

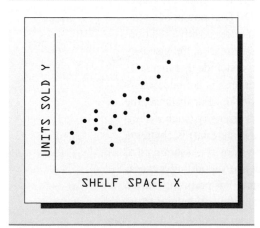

Source: *Essentials of Marketing Research*, by W. R. Dillon, T. J. Madden, and N. H. Firtle (Burr Ridge, IL: Richard D. Irwin, 1993), p. 452. Copyright © 1993. Reprinted by permission of McGraw-Hill Companies, Inc.

FIGURE **2.36** Excel Output of the Mean Restaurant Ratings and a Scatter Plot of Mean Preference versus Mean Taste 🖱 FastFood

	A	B	C	D	E	F
1	Restaurant	Meantaste	Meanconv	Meanfam	Meanprice	Meanpref
2	Borden Burger	3.5659	2.7005	2.5282	2.9372	4.2552
3	Hardee's	3.329	3.3483	2.7345	2.7513	4.0911
4	Burger King	2.4231	2.7377	2.3368	3.0761	3.0052
5	McDonald's	2.0895	1.938	1.4619	2.4884	2.2429
6	Wendy's	1.9661	2.892	2.3376	4.0814	2.5351
7	White Castle	3.8061	3.7242	2.6515	1.708	4.7812

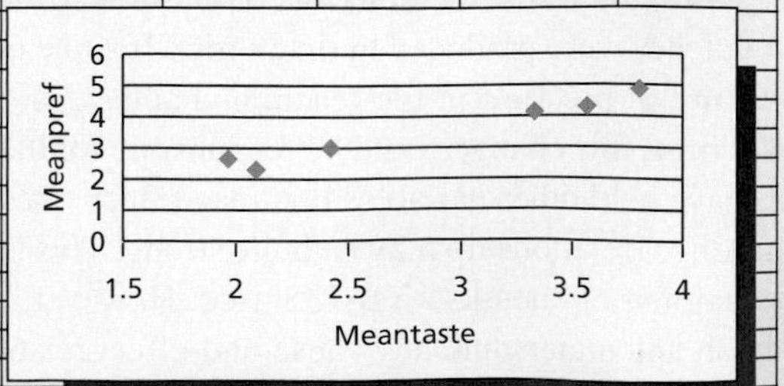

Source: The Ohio State University.

2.7 Misleading Graphs and Charts

The statistical analyst's goal should be to present the most accurate and truthful portrayal of a data set that is possible. Such a presentation allows managers using the analysis to make informed decisions. However, it is possible to construct statistical summaries that are misleading. Although we do not advocate using misleading statistics, you should be aware of some of the ways statistical graphs and charts can be manipulated in order to distort the truth. By knowing what to look for, you can avoid being misled by a small number of unscrupulous practitioners.

As an example, suppose that the faculty at a major university will soon vote on a proposal to join a union. Both the union organizers and the university administration plan to distribute recent salary statistics to the entire faculty. Suppose that the mean faculty salary at the university and the mean salary increase at the university (expressed as a percentage) for each of the years 2002 through 2005 are as follows:

Year	Mean Salary (All Ranks)	Mean Salary Increase (Percent)
2002	$60,000	3.0%
2003	61,600	4.0
2004	63,500	4.5
2005	66,100	6.0

The university administration does not want the faculty to unionize and, therefore, hopes to convince the faculty that substantial progress has been made to increase salaries without a union. On the other hand, the union organizers wish to portray the salary increases as minimal so that the faculty will feel the need to unionize.

Figure 2.37 gives two bar charts of the mean salaries at the university for each year from 2002 to 2005. Notice that in Figure 2.37(a) the administration has started the vertical scale of the bar chart at a salary of $58,000 by using a **scale break** (⌇). Alternatively, the chart could be set up without the scale break by simply starting the vertical scale at $58,000. Starting the vertical scale at a value far above zero makes the salary increases look more dramatic. Notice that when the union organizers present the bar chart in Figure 2.37(b), which has a vertical scale starting at zero, the salary increases look far less impressive.

Figure 2.38 presents two bar charts of the mean salary increases (in percentages) at the university for each year from 2002 to 2005. In Figure 2.38(a), the administration has made the

FIGURE 2.37 **Two Bar Charts of the Mean Salaries at a Major University from 2002 to 2005**

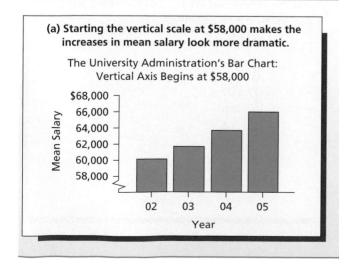

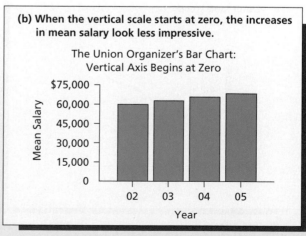

widths of the bars representing the percentage increases proportional to their heights. This makes the upward movement in the mean salary increases look more dramatic because the observer's eye tends to compare the areas of the bars, while the improvements in the mean salary increases are really only proportional to the heights of the bars. When the union organizers present the bar chart of Figure 2.38(b), the improvements in the mean salary increases look less impressive because each bar has the same width.

Figure 2.39 gives two runs plots (also called **time series plots**) of the mean salary increases at the university from 2002 to 2005. In Figure 2.39(a), the administration has stretched the vertical axis of the graph. That is, the vertical axis is set up so that the distances between the percentages are large. This makes the upward trend of the mean salary increases appear to be steep. In Figure 2.39(b), the union organizers have compressed the vertical axis (that is, the distances between the percentages are small). This makes the upward trend of the mean salary increases appear to be gradual. As we will see in the exercises, stretching and compressing the horizontal axis in a runs plot can also greatly affect the impression given by the plot.

FIGURE 2.38   Two Bar Charts of the Mean Salary Increases at a Major University from 2002 to 2005

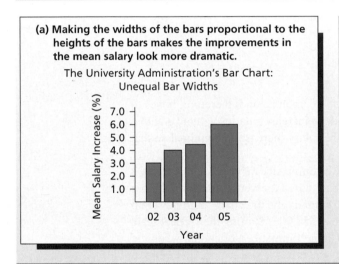

(a) Making the widths of the bars proportional to the heights of the bars makes the improvements in the mean salary look more dramatic.

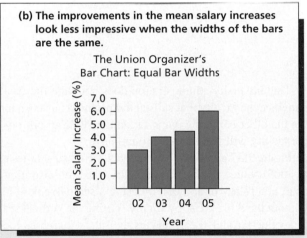

(b) The improvements in the mean salary increases look less impressive when the widths of the bars are the same.

FIGURE 2.39   Two Runs Plots of the Mean Salary Increases at a Major University from 2002 to 2005

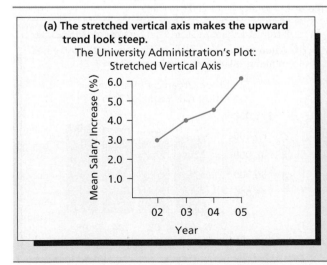

(a) The stretched vertical axis makes the upward trend look steep.

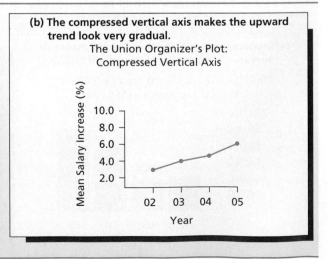

(b) The compressed vertical axis makes the upward trend look very gradual.

It is also possible to create totally different interpretations of the same statistical summary by simply using different labelling or captions. For example, consider the bar chart of mean salary increases in Figure 2.38(b). To create a favourable interpretation, the university administration might use the caption "Salary Increase Is Higher for the Fourth Year in a Row." On the other hand, the union organizers might create a negative impression by using the caption "Salary Increase Fails to Reach 10% for Fourth Straight Year."

In summary, we do not approve of using statistics to mislead and distort reality. Statistics should be used to present the most truthful and informative summary of the data that is possible. However, it is important to carefully study any statistical summary so that you will not be misled. Look for manipulations such as stretched or compressed axes on graphs, axes that do not begin at zero, and bar charts with bars of varying widths. Also carefully think about assumptions, and make your own conclusions about the meaning of any statistical summary rather than relying on captions written by others. Doing these things will help you to see the truth and to make well-informed decisions.

Exercises for Section 2.7

CONCEPTS

2.55 When we construct a bar chart or graph, what is the effect of starting the vertical axis at a value that is far above zero? Explain.

2.56 Find an example of a misleading use of statistics in a newspaper, magazine, corporate annual report, or other source. Then explain why your example is misleading.

METHODS AND APPLICATIONS

2.57 Figure 2.40 gives two more time series plots of the previously discussed salary increases. In Figure 2.40(a), the administration has compressed the horizontal axis. In Figure 2.40(b), the union organizers have stretched the horizontal axis. Discuss the different impressions given by the two time series plots.

2.58 In the article "How to display data badly" in the May 1984 issue of *The American Statistician,*

Wainer presents a **stacked bar chart** of the number of public and private elementary schools (1929–1970). This bar chart is given in Figure 2.41. Wainer also gives a line graph of the number of private elementary schools (1930–1970). This graph is shown in Figure 2.42.

a. Looking at the bar chart of Figure 2.41, does there appear to be an increasing trend in the number of private elementary schools from 1930 to 1970?

b. Looking at the line graph of Figure 2.42, does there appear to be an increasing trend in the number of private elementary schools from 1930 to 1970?

c. Which portrayal of the data do you think is more appropriate? Explain.

d. Is either portrayal of the data entirely appropriate? Explain.

FIGURE **2.40** Two Runs Plots of the Mean Salary Increases at a Major University from 2002 to 2005

(a) The administration's plot: Compressed horizontal axis

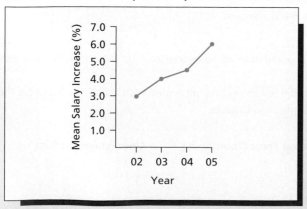

(b) The union organizers' plot: Stretched horizontal axis

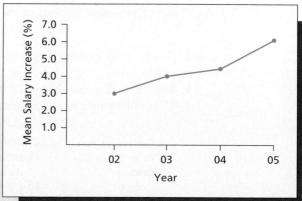

FIGURE **2.41** **Wainer's Stacked Bar Chart**

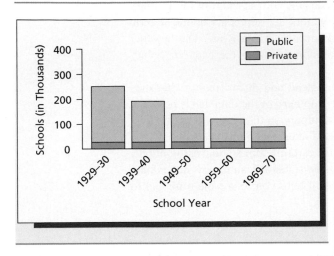

FIGURE **2.42** **Wainer's Line Graph**

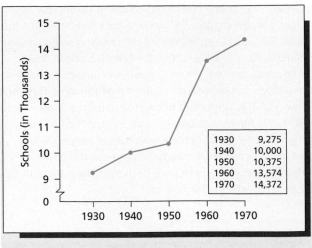

Source: "How to display data badly," by H. Wainer, *The American Statistician,* May 1984, pp. 137–147. Copyright © 1984 American Statistical Association.
Used with permission.

2.8 Weighted Means and Grouped Data

Weighted means   In Section 2.2, we studied the mean, which is an important measure of central tendency. In order to calculate a mean, we sum the population (or sample) measurements and then divide this sum by the number of measurements in the population (or sample). When we do this, each measurement counts equally. That is, each measurement is given the same importance or weight.

Sometimes it makes sense to give different measurements unequal weights. In such a case, a measurement's weight reflects its importance, and the mean calculated using the unequal weights is called a **weighted mean**.

We calculate a weighted mean by multiplying each measurement by its weight, summing the resulting products, and dividing the resulting sum by the sum of the weights:

Weighted Mean

The weighted mean equals

$$\frac{\sum w_i x_i}{\sum w_i},$$

where
x_i = the value of the ith measurement,
w_i = the weight applied to the ith measurement.

Such a quantity can be computed for a population of measurements or for a sample of measurements.

In order to illustrate the need for a weighted mean and the required calculations, consider the 2005 unemployment rates for various regions in Canada:[7]

Census Region	Civilian Labour Force (Thousands)	Unemployment Rate
Atlantic	1,912.4	11.0%
Québec	6,182.2	8.3%
Ontario	10,070.4	6.6%
West	7,640.5	4.9%

[7]Source: Adapted from the Statistics Canada CANSIM database http://cansim2.statcan.ca, table number 282-0002, February, 2006.

If we wish to compute a mean unemployment rate for Canada, we should use a weighted mean. This is because each of the four regional unemployment rates applies to a different number of workers in the labour force. For example, the 11.0 percent unemployed for Atlantic Canada applies to a labour force of 1,912,400 workers and thus should count less heavily than the 6.6 percent unemployed for Ontario, which applies to a larger labour force of 10 070 400 workers.

The unemployment rate measurements are $x_1 = 11.0$ percent, $x_2 = 8.3$ percent, $x_3 = 6.6$ percent, and $x_4 = 4.9$ percent, and the weights applied to these measurements are $w_1 = 1,912.4$, $w_2 = 6,182.2$, $w_3 = 10,070.4$, and $w_4 = 7,640.5$. That is, we are weighting the unemployment rates by the regional labour force sizes. The weighted mean is computed as follows:

$$\mu = \frac{1,912.4(11.0) + 6,182.2(8.3) + 10,070.4(6.6) + 7,640.5(4.9)}{1,912.4 + 6,182.2 + 10,070.4 + 7,640.5}$$
$$= \frac{176,251.75}{25,805.5}$$
$$= 6.83\%.$$

In this case, the unweighted mean of the four regional unemployment rates is 7.7 percent. Therefore, the unweighted mean overestimates the Canadian unemployment rate by 0.87 percentage points (or overestimates Canadian unemployment by 0.0087(25,805.5 thousand) = 224,508 workers.

The weights chosen for calculating a weighted mean will vary depending on the situation. For example, in order to compute the mean percentage return for a portfolio of investments, the percentage returns for various investments might be weighted by the dollar amounts invested in each. Or, in order to compute a mean profit margin for a company consisting of several divisions, the profit margins for the different divisions might be weighted by the sales volumes of the divisions. Again, the idea is to choose weights that represent the relative importance of the measurements in the population or sample.

Descriptive statistics for grouped data   We usually calculate measures of central tendency and variability using the individual measurements in a population or sample. However, sometimes the only data available are in the form of a frequency distribution or a histogram. For example, newspapers and magazines often summarize data using frequency distributions and histograms without giving the individual measurements in a data set. Data summarized in frequency distribution or histogram form are often called **grouped data**. In this section, we show how to compute descriptive statistics for such data.

Suppose we are given a frequency distribution summarizing a sample of 65 customer satisfaction ratings for a consumer product.   ● SatRatings

Satisfaction Rating	Frequency
36–38	4
39–41	15
42–44	25
45–47	19
48–50	2

Because we do not know each of the 65 individual satisfaction ratings, we cannot compute an exact value for the mean satisfaction rating. However, we can calculate an approximation of this mean. In order to do this, we use the midpoint of each class to represent the measurements in the class. When we do this, we are really assuming that the average of the measurements in each class equals the class midpoint. Letting M_i denote the midpoint of class i, and letting f_i denote the frequency of class i, we compute the mean by calculating a weighted mean of the class midpoints using the class frequencies as the weights. The logic here is that if f_i measurements are included in class i, then the midpoint of class i should count f_i times in the weighted mean. In this case, the sum of the weights equals the sum of the class frequencies, which equals the sample size. Therefore, we obtain the following equation for the sample mean of grouped data:

Sample Mean for Grouped Data

$$\bar{x} = \frac{\sum f_i M_i}{\sum f_i} = \frac{\sum f_i M_i}{n},$$

where
   $f_i =$ the frequency for class i,
   $M_i =$ the midpoint for class i,
   $n = \sum f_i =$ the sample size.

Table 2.12 summarizes the calculation of the mean satisfaction rating for the previously given frequency distribution of satisfaction ratings. Note that in this table each midpoint is halfway between its corresponding class limits. For example, for the first class $M_1 = (36 + 38)/2 = 37$. We find that the sample mean satisfaction rating is 43.

   We can also compute an approximation of the sample variance for grouped data. Recall that when we compute the sample variance using individual measurements, we compute the squared deviation from the sample mean $(x_i - \bar{x})^2$ for each individual measurement x_i and then sum the squared deviations. For grouped data, we do not know each of the x_i values. Because of this, we again let the class midpoint M_i represent each measurement in class i. It follows that we compute the squared deviation $(M_i - \bar{x})^2$ for each class and then sum these squares, weighting each squared deviation by its corresponding class frequency f_i. That is, we approximate $\sum (x_i - \bar{x})^2$ by using $\sum f_i(M_i - \bar{x})^2$. Finally, we obtain the sample variance for the grouped data by dividing this quantity by the sample size minus 1. We summarize this calculation in the following box:

Sample Variance for Grouped Data

$$s^2 = \frac{\sum f_i(M_i - \bar{x})^2}{n - 1},$$

where $\bar{x}$ is the sample mean for the grouped data.

   Table 2.13 illustrates calculating the sample variance of the previously given frequency distribution of satisfaction ratings. We find that the sample variance is $s^2 = 8.15625$ and, therefore, that the sample standard deviation is $s = \sqrt{8.15625} = 2.8559$.

TABLE **2.12**   Calculating the Sample Mean Satisfaction Rating

Satisfaction Rating	Frequency (f_i)	Class Midpoint (M_i)	$f_i M_i$
36–38	4	37	4(37) = 148
39–41	15	40	15(40) = 600
42–44	25	43	25(43) = 1,075
45–47	19	46	19(46) = 874
48–50	2	49	2(49) = 98
	$n = 65$		2,795

$$\bar{x} = \frac{\sum f_i M_i}{n} = \frac{2,795}{65} = 43$$

TABLE 2.13   Calculating the Sample Variance of the Satisfaction Ratings

Satisfaction Rating	Frequency f_i	Class Midpoint M_i	Deviation $(M_i - \bar{x})$	Squared Deviation $(M_i - \bar{x})^2$	$f_i(M_i - \bar{x})^2$
36–38	4	37	$37 - 43 = -6$	36	$4(36) = 144$
39–41	15	40	$40 - 43 = -3$	9	$15(9) = 135$
42–44	25	43	$43 - 43 = 0$	0	$25(0) = 0$
45–47	19	46	$46 - 43 = 3$	9	$19(9) = 171$
48–50	2	49	$49 - 43 = 6$	36	$2(36) = 72$
	65				$\sum f_i(M_i - \bar{x})^2 = 522$

$$s^2 = \text{sample variance} = \frac{\sum f_i(M_i - \bar{x})^2}{n - 1} = \frac{522}{65 - 1} = 8.15625$$

Finally, although we have illustrated calculating the mean and variance for grouped data in the context of a sample, similar calculations can be done for a population of measurements. If we let N be the size of the population, the grouped data formulas for the population mean and variance are given in the following box:

Population Mean for Grouped Data

$$\mu = \frac{\sum f_i M_i}{N}$$

Population Variance for Grouped Data

$$\sigma^2 = \frac{\sum f_i(M_i - \mu)^2}{N}$$

Exercises for Section 2.8

CONCEPTS

2.59 Consider calculating a student's grade point average using a scale where 4.0 represents an A and 0.0 represents an F. Explain why the grade point average is a weighted mean. What are the x_i values? What are the weights?

2.60 When we perform grouped data calculations, we represent the measurements in a class by using the midpoint of the class. Explain the assumption that is being made when we do this.

2.61 When we compute the mean, variance, and standard deviation using grouped data, the results obtained are approximations of the population (or sample) mean, variance, and standard deviation. Explain why this is true.

METHODS AND APPLICATIONS

2.62 According to the Morningstar.com Web site, the 2004 total return percentages for several popular funds were as follows: ● FundReturns

Fund	2004 Total Return %
Vanguard 500 Index	10.7
Wasatch Core Growth	21.7
Fidelity Stock Selector	9.9
Fidelity Dividend Growth	5.8
Janus Worldwide	5.5

Source: http://quicktake.morningstar.com/Fund/TotalReturns.asp, March 17, 2005.

Suppose that an investor had $100,000 invested in the Vanguard 500 Index fund, $500,000 invested in the Wasatch Core Growth fund, $500,000 invested in the Fidelity Stock Selector fund, $200,000 invested in the Fidelity Dividend Growth fund, and $50,000 invested in the Janus Worldwide fund.

a. Compute a weighted mean that measures the 2004 average total return for the investor's portfolio.

b. Compare your weighted mean with the unweighted mean of the five total return percentages. Explain why they differ.

2.63 The following are the 2006 unemployment rates and civilian labour force sizes for five provinces in Canada.   ● UnEmpCan

Province	Size of Civilian Labour Force (Thousands)	Unemployment Rate (%)
NL	429.7	15.2
PE	111.6	10.8
NS	760.7	8.4
NB	610.4	9.7
QC	6,182.2	8.3

Source: Adapted from the Statistics Canada CANSIM database http://cansim2.statcan.ca, table number 282-0002, February 2006.

Using a weighted mean, compute an average unemployment rate for the five provinces.

2.64 The following frequency distribution summarizes the masses of 195 fish caught by anglers participating in a professional fishing tournament.   ● BassMass

Weight (kg)	Frequency
1–3	53
4–6	118
7–9	21
10–12	3

a. Calculate the (approximate) sample mean for these data.

b. Calculate the (approximate) sample variance for these data.

2.65 The following is a frequency distribution summarizing earnings per share (EPS) growth data for the 30 fastest-growing firms as given on *Fortune* magazine's Web site on March 16, 2005.   ● EPSGrowth

EPS Growth (Percent)	Frequency
0–49	1
50–99	17
100–149	5
150–199	4
200–249	1
250–299	2

Source: http://www.fortune.com, March 16, 2005.

Calculate the (approximate) population mean, variance, and standard deviation for these data.

2.66 The Data and Story Library Web site (a Web site devoted to applications of statistics) gives a histogram of the ages of a sample of 60 CEOs taken in 1993. We present the data in the form of a frequency distribution below.   ● CEOAges

Age (Years)	Frequency
28–32	1
33–37	3
38–42	3
43–47	13
48–52	14
53–57	12
58–62	9
63–67	1
68–72	3
73–77	1

Source: http://lib.stat.cmu.edu/DASL/Stories/ceo.html, April 15, 2005.

Calculate the (approximate) sample mean, variance, and standard deviation of these data.

2.9 The Geometric Mean

In Section 2.2, we defined the mean to be the average of a set of population or sample measurements. This mean is sometimes referred to as the arithmetic mean. While very useful, the arithmetic mean is not a good measure of the rate of change exhibited by a variable over time. To see this, consider the rate at which the value of an investment changes—its rate of return. Suppose that an initial investment of $10,000 increases in value to $20,000 at the end of one year and then decreases in value to its original $10,000 after two years. The rate of return for the first year, R_1, is

$$R_1 = \left(\frac{20,000 - 10,000}{10,000}\right) \times 100\% = 100\%,$$

and the rate of return for the second year, R_2, is

$$R_2 = \left(\frac{10,000 - 20,000}{20,000}\right) \times 100\% = -50\%.$$

Although the value of the investment at the beginning and end of the two-year period is the same, the arithmetic mean of the yearly rates of return is $(R_1 + R_2)/2 = (100\% + (-50\%))/2 = 25\%$. This arithmetic mean does not communicate the fact that the value of the investment is unchanged at the end of the two years.

To remedy this situation, we define the **geometric mean** of the returns to be **the constant return, R_g, that yields the same wealth at the end of the investment period as do the actual**

returns. In our example, this says that if we express R_g, R_1, and R_2 as decimal fractions (here $R_1 = 1$ and $R_2 = -0.5$),

$$(1 + R_g)^2 \times 10{,}000 = (1 + R_1)(1 + R_2) \times 10{,}000$$

or

$$R_g = \sqrt{(1 + R_1)(1 + R_2)} - 1$$
$$= \sqrt{(1 + 1)(1 + (-0.5))} - 1$$
$$= \sqrt{1} - 1 = 0.$$

Therefore, the geometric mean R_g expresses the fact that the value of the investment is unchanged after two years.

In general, if $R_1, R_2, \ldots, R_n$ are returns (expressed in decimal form) over n time periods:

The **geometric mean** of the returns $R_1, R_2, \ldots, R_n$ is

$$R_g = \sqrt[n]{(1 + R_1)(1 + R_2) \cdots (1 + R_n)} - 1,$$

and the ending value of an initial investment I experiencing returns $R_1, R_2, \ldots, R_n$ is $I(1 + R_g)^n$.

As another example, suppose that in year 3 our investment's value increases to $25,000, which says that the rate of return for year 3 (expressed as a percentage) is

$$R_3 = \left(\frac{25{,}000 - 10{,}000}{10{,}000}\right) \times 100\%$$

$$= 150\%.$$

Since (expressed as decimals) $R_1 = 1$, $R_2 = -0.5$, and $R_3 = 1.5$, the geometric mean return at the end of year 3 is

$$R_g = \sqrt[3]{(1 + 1)(1 + (-0.5))(1 + 1.5)} - 1$$

$$= 1.3572 - 1$$

$$= 0.3572,$$

and the value of the investment after three years is

$$\$10{,}000 \, (1 + 0.3572)^3 = \$25{,}000.$$

Exercises for Section 2.9

CONCEPTS

2.67 In words, explain the interpretation of the geometric mean return for an investment.

2.68 If we know the initial value of an investment and its geometric mean return over a period of years, can we compute the ending value of the investment? If so, how?

METHODS AND APPLICATIONS

2.69 Suppose that a company's sales were $5,000,000 three years ago. Since that time sales have grown at annual rates of 10 percent, -10 percent, and 25 percent.
   a. Find the geometric mean growth rate of sales over this three-year period.
   b. Find the ending value of sales after this three-year period.

2.70 Suppose that a company's sales were $1,000,000 four years ago and are $4,000,000 at the end of the four years. Find the geometric mean growth rate of sales.

2.71 The Standard & Poor's 500 stock index is a commonly used measure of stock market performance in the United States. In the table below, we give the value of the S&P 500 index on the first day of market trading for each year from 2000 to 2005.   ● S&P500

Year	S&P 500 Index
2000	1,455.22
2001	1,283.27
2002	1,154.67
2003	909.03
2004	1,108.48
2005	1,211.92

Source: http://table.finance.yahoo.com.

   a. Show that the percentage changes (rates of return) for the S&P 500 index for the years from 2000 to

2001 and from 2001 to 2002 are, respectively,
−11.8 percent and −10.0 percent (that is, −0.118
and −0.100 expressed as decimal fractions).

b. Find the rates of return for the S&P 500 index for
each of the years from 2002 to 2003; from 2003 to
2004; from 2004 to 2005.

c. Calculate the geometric mean return for the S&P
500 index over the period from 2000 to 2005.

d. Suppose that an investment of $1,000,000 is made
in 2000 and that the portfolio performs with returns
equal to those of the S&P 500 index. What is the
investment portfolio worth in 2005?

CHAPTER SUMMARY

We began this chapter by studying how to depict the shape of the distribution of a data set. We learned that **stem-and-leaf displays** and **histograms** are useful graphics for portraying a data set's distribution. We also learned about some common population shapes. We saw that data sets often have shapes that are **symmetrical**, **positively skewed (with a tail to the right)**, or **negatively skewed (with a tail to the left)**.

Next we presented and compared several measures of **central tendency**. We defined the **population mean** and we saw how to estimate the population mean by using a **sample mean**. We also defined the **median** and **mode**, and we compared the mean, median, and mode for symmetrical distributions and for distributions that are positively or negatively skewed (to the right or left). We then studied measures of **variation** (or **spread**). We defined the **range**, **variance**, and **standard deviation**, and we saw how to estimate a population variance and standard deviation by using a sample. We learned that a good way to interpret the standard deviation when a population is (approximately) normally distributed is to use the **empirical rule**, and we applied this rule to assess **process capability**. We

next studied **Chebyshev's theorem**, which gives us intervals containing reasonably large fractions of the population units no matter what the population's shape might be. We also saw that, when a data set is highly skewed, it is best to use **percentiles** and **quartiles** to measure variation, and we learned how to construct a **box-and-whiskers display** by using the quartiles.

After learning how to measure and depict central tendency and variability, we presented several methods for portraying qualitative data. In particular, we used **bar charts** and **pie charts** for this purpose. We also discussed using a sample to estimate the proportion of population units that fall into a category of interest.

We studied using **scatter plots** to examine relationships between variables. Next we discussed misleading graphs and statistics, and we explained some of the tactics that are commonly used to try to distort the truth. We also introduced the concept of a **weighted mean** and then explained how to compute descriptive statistics for **grouped data**. Finally, we showed how to calculate the **geometric mean** and demonstrated its interpretation.

GLOSSARY OF TERMS

bar chart: A graphical display of categorical data (data in categories) made up of vertical or horizontal bars. (page 62)

box-and-whiskers display (box plot): A graphical portrayal of a data set that depicts both the central tendency and variability of the data. It is constructed using Q_1, M_d, and Q_3. (page 58)

capable process: A process that is able to consistently produce output that meets (or conforms to) specifications (requirements). (page 51)

central tendency: A term referring to the middle of a population or sample of measurements. (page 38)

Chebyshev's theorem: A theorem that (for any population) allows us to find an interval that contains a specified percentage of the individual measurements in the population. (page 52)

coefficient of variation: A quantity that measures the variation of a population or sample relative to its mean. (page 54)

dependent variable (denoted y): A variable that we wish to describe, predict, or control. (page 68)

empirical rule: For a normally distributed population, this rule tells us that 68.26 percent, 95.44 percent, and 99.73 percent, respectively, of the population measurements are within one, two, and three standard deviations of the population mean. (page 50)

extreme outlier (in a box-and-whiskers display): A measurement located outside the outer fences. (page 59)

extreme value: A measurement in a population or sample that is different from most of the other measurements. (page 42)

first quartile (denoted Q_1): A value below which approximately 25 percent of the measurements lie; the 25th percentile. (page 57)

frequency: The count of the number of measurements in a class or of the number of measurements with a particular value. (page 29)

frequency distribution: A numerical summary that divides the values of a variable into classes and gives the number of values in each class. (pages 29 and 30)

geometric mean: The constant return (or rate of change) that yields the same wealth at the end of several time periods as do actual returns. (pages 78 and 79)

grouped data: Data presented in the form of a frequency distribution or a histogram. (page 75)

histogram: A graphical portrayal of a data set that shows the data set's distribution. It divides the data into classes and gives the frequency for each class. Histograms are particularly useful for summarizing large data sets. (page 30)

independent variable (denoted x): A predictor variable that can be used to describe, predict, or control a dependent variable. (page 68)

inner fences (in a box-and-whiskers display): Points located $1.5 \times IQR$ below Q_1 and $1.5 \times IQR$ above Q_3. (page 58)

interquartile range (denoted IQR): The difference between the third quartile and the first quartile (that is, $Q_3 − Q_1$). (page 58)

measure of variation: A descriptive measure of the spread of the values in a population or sample. (page 47)

median (denoted M_d): A measure of central tendency that divides a population or sample into two roughly equal parts. (page 40)

mild outlier (in a box-and-whiskers display): A measurement located between the inner and outer fences. (page 59)

mode (denoted M_o): The measurement in a sample or a population that occurs most frequently. (page 41)

mound-shaped: Description of a relative frequency curve that is "piled up in the middle." (page 52)

negatively skewed (to the left): Description of a relative frequency curve with a long tail to the left. (page 32)

normal curve: A bell-shaped, symmetrical relative frequency curve. We will present the exact equation that gives this curve in Chapter 5. (page 32)

outer fences: Points located $3 \times IQR$ below Q_1 and $3 \times IQR$ above Q_3. (page 59)

outlier: An unusually large or small observation that is well separated from the remaining observations. (page 59)

Pareto chart: A bar chart of the frequencies or percentages for various types of defects. These are used to identify opportunities for improvement. (page 65)

percentile: The value such that a specified percentage of the measurements in a population or sample fall at or below it. (page 56)

pie chart: A graphical display of categorical data (data in categories) made up of "pie slices." (page 63)

point estimate: A one-number estimate for the value of a population parameter. (page 39)

population mean (denoted μ): The average of a population of measurements. (page 38)

population parameter: A descriptive measure of a population. It is calculated using the population measurements. (page 39)

population proportion (denoted p): The proportion of population units that are contained in a category of interest. (page 63)

population standard deviation (denoted σ): The square root of the population variance. It is a measure of the variation of the population measurements. (page 48)

population variance (denoted σ^2): The average of the squared deviations of the individual population measurements from the population mean. It is a measure of the variation of the population measurements. (page 48)

positively skewed (to the right): Description of a relative frequency curve with a long tail to the right. (page 32)

range: The difference between the largest and smallest measurements in a population or sample. It is a simple measure of variation. (page 47)

relative frequency: The frequency of a class divided by the total number of measurements. (page 31)

relative frequency curve: A curve that describes the shape of a population of measurements. (page 31)

relative frequency histogram: A graphical portrayal of a data set that shows the data set's distribution. It divides the data into classes, gives the relative frequency for each class, and is particularly useful for summarizing large data sets. (page 31)

sample mean (denoted $\bar{x}$): The average of the measurements in a sample. It is the point estimate of the population mean. (page 39)

sample proportion (denoted $\hat{p}$): The proportion of sample elements that are contained in a category of interest. (page 63)

sample size (denoted n): The number of measurements in a sample. (page 39)

sample standard deviation (denoted s): The square root of the sample variance. It is the point estimate of the population standard deviation. (page 49)

sample statistic: A descriptive measure of a sample. It is calculated from the measurements in the sample. (page 39)

sample variance (denoted s^2): A measure of the variation of the sample measurements. It is the point estimate of the population variance. (page 49)

scatter plot: A plot of the values of a dependent variable y versus the values of an independent variable x. (page 68)

stem-and-leaf display: A graphical portrayal of a data set that shows the data set's distribution. It displays the data in the form of stems and leaves. (page 29)

third quartile (denoted Q_3): A value below which approximately 75 percent of the measurements lie; the 75th percentile. (page 57)

tolerance interval: An interval of numbers that contains a specified percentage of the individual measurements in a population. (page 50)

weighted mean: A mean where different measurements are given different weights based on their importance. (page 74)

z score (of a measurement): The number of standard deviations that a measurement is from the mean. This quantity indicates the relative location of a measurement within its distribution. (page 53)

IMPORTANT FORMULAS

The population mean, μ: page 38

The sample mean, $\bar{x}$: page 39

The median: page 40

The mode: page 41

The population range: page 47

The population variance, σ^2: page 49

The population standard deviation, σ: page 49

The sample variance, s^2: page 49

The sample standard deviation, s: page 49

Computational formula for s^2: page 49

The empirical rule: page 50

Chebyshev's theorem: page 52

z score: page 53

The coefficient of variation: page 54

The pth percentile: page 56

The quartiles: page 57

The weighted mean: page 74

Sample mean for grouped data: page 76

Sample variance for grouped data: page 76

Population mean for grouped data: page 77

Population variance for grouped data: page 77

The geometric mean: page 79

SUPPLEMENTARY EXERCISES

2.72 In the book *Modern Statistical Quality Control and Improvement*, Farnum presents data concerning the elapsed times from the completion of medical lab tests until the results are recorded on patients' charts.

Table 2.14 gives the times it took (in hours) to deliver and chart the results of 84 lab tests over one week.
 LabTest

TABLE **2.14**   Elapsed Time (in Hours) for Completing and Delivering Medical Lab Tests

🌑 LabTest

6.1	8.7	1.1	4.0
2.1	3.9	2.2	5.0
2.1	7.1	4.3	8.8
3.5	1.2	3.2	1.3
1.3	9.3	4.2	7.3
5.7	6.5	4.4	16.2
1.3	1.3	3.0	2.7
15.7	4.9	2.0	5.2
3.9	13.9	1.8	2.2
8.4	5.2	11.9	3.0
24.0	24.5	24.8	24.0
1.7	4.4	2.5	16.2
17.8	2.9	4.0	6.7
5.3	8.3	2.8	5.2
17.5	1.1	3.0	8.3
1.2	1.1	4.5	4.4
5.0	2.6	12.7	5.7
4.7	5.1	2.6	1.6
3.4	8.1	2.4	16.7
4.8	1.7	1.9	12.1
9.1	5.6	13.0	6.4

Source: *Modern Statistical Quality Control and Improvement,* by N. R. Farnum (Belmont, CA: Duxbury Press, 1994), p. 55. Reprinted by permission of Brooks/ Cole, an imprint of the Wadsworth Group, a division of Thompson Learning. Fax 1-800-730-2215.

FIGURE **2.43**   Software Performance at NASA's Goddard Space Center, 1976–1990

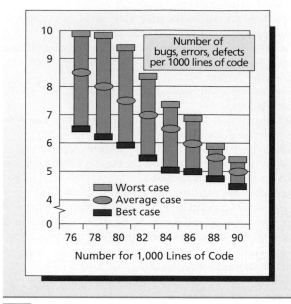

Source: Reprinted from the January 15, 1992, issue of *Business Week* by special permission. Copyright © 1992 by The McGraw-Hill Companies.

a. Construct a frequency histogram and a relative frequency histogram for the lab test waiting time data.

b. Looking at the histogram, are most of the test results delivered and charted within several hours?

c. Are there some deliveries with excessively long waiting times? Which deliveries might be investigated in order to discover reasons behind unusually long delays?

2.73   Figure 2.43 depicts data for a study of 80 software projects at NASA's Goddard Space Center. The figure shows the number of bugs per 1,000 lines of code from 1976 to 1990. Write a short paragraph describing how the reliability of the software has improved. Explain how the data indicate improvement.

2.74   It is well known to long-term investors that portfolio diversification is important. The phrase "Don't put all your eggs in one basket" rings very true in this case. That is, investors should invest in a variety of investments with differing levels of historical return and risk. This risk is often measured in terms of the volatility of an investment over time. When volatility, sometimes referred to as **standard deviation**, increases, so too does the level of return. The opposite is also true.

The answer seems to lie in asset allocation. Investment experts know the importance of asset allocation. In a nutshell, asset allocation is a method of creating a diversified portfolio of investments that minimize historical risk and maximize potential returns to help you meet your retirement goals and needs.

The mean return and standard deviation combinations for the various investment classes are shown in Table 2.15.

Suppose that future returns of each investment class will continue to behave in the future as they have over the past 10 years. That is, for each investment class, regard the mean return and standard deviation in Table 2.15 as the population mean and the population standard deviation of all possible future returns. Then do the following:

🌑 InvestClass

a. Assuming that future returns for the various investment classes are mound-shaped, for each investment class compute intervals that will contain approximately 68.26 percent and 99.73 percent of all future returns.

b. Making no assumption about the population shapes of future returns, for each investment class, compute the intervals that will contain at least 75 percent and 88.89 percent of all future returns.

c. Assuming that future returns are mound-shaped, find
   (1)   An estimate of the maximum return that might be realized for each investment class.
   (2)   An estimate of the minimum return (or maximum loss) that might be realized for each investment class.

2.75   Table 2.16 presents data on the average annual amount Canadians spent on food and nonalcoholic beverages, alcoholic beverages (bought in stores), and tobacco products for the years 1997 to 2005. Depict the data graphically and summarize what the data suggest in terms of changes in expenditures over time.

🌑 CanSpend

TABLE **2.15** Mean Return and Standard Deviation for Seven Investment Classes over a 10-Year Period ● InvestClass

Investment Class	Mean Return	Std. Deviation
Money Market	2.75%	0.08%
Fixed Income	−0.8	1.0
Balanced	6.4	1.48
Canadian Equity	19.6	2.75
U.S. Equity	12.4	3.1
Global Equity	22.3	5.1
Sector Funds	33.1	5.9

TABLE **2.16** Personal Expenditure on Food, Beverages, and Tobacco in Canada (figures are given in millions of dollars) ● CanSpend

Year	1997	1998	1999	2000	2001	2002	2003	2004	2005
Food and nonalcoholic beverages	12,580	13,039	13,493	14,137	14,946	15,581	16,173	16,851	17,732
Alcoholic beverages bought in stores	2,476	2,620	2,781	2,915	3,105	3,329	3,509	3,645	3,831
Tobacco products	2,185	2,326	2,311	2,338	2,543	3,041	3,388	3,621	3,547

Source: Adapted from Statistics Canada, http://www.statcan.ca, *National Income and Expenditure Accounts, Quarterly Estimates*, Catalogue 13-001-XIB, reference period 1997–2005.

2.76 THE INTERNATIONAL BUSINESS TRAVEL EXPENSE CASE

Suppose that a large international corporation wishes to obtain its own benchmark for one-day travel expenses in Moscow. To do this, it records the one-day travel expenses for a random sample of 35 executives visiting Moscow. The mean and the standard deviation of these expenses are calculated to be $\bar{x} = \$538$ and $s = \$41$. Furthermore, a histogram shows that the expenses are approximately normally distributed.

a. Find an interval that we estimate contains 99.73 percent of all one-day travel expenses in Moscow.

b. If an executive submits an expense of $720 for a one-day stay in Moscow, should this expense be considered unusually high? Why or why not?

2.77 THE U.K. INSURANCE CASE

Figure 2.44 summarizes information concerning insurance expenditures of households in the United Kingdom in 1993.

a. Approximately what percentage of households spent on life insurance?

b. What is the approximate average expenditure (in UKL) per household on life insurance? Note: The averages given in Figure 2.44 are for households that spend in the class.

2.78 Figure 2.45 was used in various Chevrolet magazine advertisements in 1997 to compare the overall resale values of Chevrolet, Dodge, and Ford trucks in the years from 1990 to 1997. What is somewhat misleading about this graph?

FIGURE **2.44** Insurance Expenditures of Households in the United Kingdom (1993)

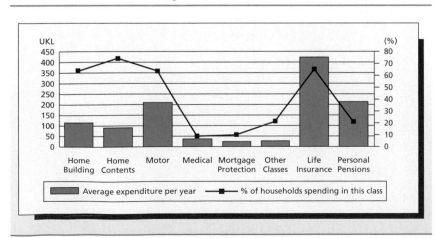

Source: CSO family expenditure survey.

FIGURE **2.45** A Graph Comparing the Resale Values of Chevy, Dodge, and Ford Trucks

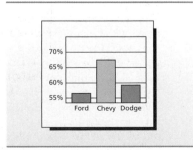

Source: Reprinted courtesy of General Motors Corporation.

2.79   INTERNET EXERCISE

Overview: The Data and Story Library (DASL) houses a rich collection of data sets useful for teaching and learning statistics, from a variety of sources, contributed primarily by university faculty members. DASL can be reached through the BSC by clicking on the Data Bases button in the BSC home screen and then by clicking on the Data and Story Library link. The screen image to the right shows the BSC Data Base page. The DASL can also be reached directly using the URL http://lib.stat.cmu.edu/DASL/. Using the link http://lib.stat.cmu.edu/DASL/Datafiles/ceodat.html, retrieve the data set of chief executive officer salaries and their ages and construct a histogram or stem-and-leaf plot of the salaries and ages. Calculate the mean, median, and standard deviation of the salaries and ages. Compare the plots of the distributions to check for similarities or differences (e.g., look for symmetry, skewness, or outliers).

Probability

The word *probability* has many interpretations. An easy way to understand probability is to think of it as a measure of the degree of certainty or uncertainty of an event occurring in the long run. Probability is a measuring stick. It can by no means predict the outcome of an individual event unless you know that the probability is 0 or 1.

Have you ever played poker and wondered what the probability of getting three of a kind or a full house is? Have you ever been to a casino and wondered what the probability of winning at the dice game craps is? Have you ever wondered about the probability of passing a multiple choice exam when you have not studied at all? Maybe you have played roulette and seen the colour red come up 10 times in a row and wondered what the probability of red occurring again was. To help you answer these and other questions, basic rules for probability will be introduced in this chapter, as well as a new case.

The BBM Canada Radio Ratings Case. If you were conducting research to assess how many people listened to a certain radio station, how would you get started? Radio rating companies survey a selection of people (a sample) from the target area (or population of interest). Data obtained from a survey conducted in London, Ontario, by BBM Canada (http://www.bbm.ca) will be used to demonstrate probability rules.

3.1 The Concept of Probability

The concept of **probability** deals with uncertainty. Intuitively, the probability of an event is a number that measures the chance, or likelihood, that the event will occur. For instance, the probability that your favourite hockey team will win its next game measures the likelihood of a victory. The probability of an event is always a number between 0 and 1. The closer an event's probability is to 1, the greater is the likelihood that the event will occur; the closer the event's probability is to 0, the smaller is the likelihood that the event will occur. For example, if you believe that the probability that your favourite hockey team will win its next game is 0.95, then you are almost sure that your team will win. However, if you believe that the probability of victory is only 0.10, then you have very little confidence that your team will win.

When performing statistical studies, we sometimes collect data by **performing a controlled experiment**. For instance, we might purposely vary the operating conditions of a manufacturing process in order to study the effects of these changes on the process output. Alternatively, we sometimes obtain data by **observing uncontrolled events**. For example, we might observe the closing price of a share of General Motors of Canada's stock every day for 30 trading days.

CHAPTER 2

An **experiment** is any process of observation that has an uncertain outcome. The possible outcomes for an experiment are called **experimental outcomes**.

For example, if the experiment consists of tossing a coin, the experimental outcomes are "head" and "tail." If the experiment consists of rolling a die, the experimental outcomes are 1, 2, 3, 4, 5, and 6. If the experiment consists of subjecting an automobile to a tailpipe emissions test, the experimental outcomes are pass and fail.

We often wish to assign probabilities to experimental outcomes. This can be done by several methods. Regardless of the method used, **probabilities must be assigned to the experimental outcomes so that two conditions are met**:

1   The probability assigned to each experimental outcome must be between 0 and 1. That is, if E represents an experimental outcome and if $P(E)$ represents the probability of this outcome, then $0 \leq P(E) \leq 1$.

2   The probabilities of all of the experimental outcomes must sum to 1 for a single experiment.

Sometimes, when all of the experimental outcomes are equally likely, we can use logic to assign probabilities. This method is called the **classical method**. As a simple example, consider the experiment of tossing a fair coin. Here there are **two** equally likely experimental outcomes—head (H) and tail (T). Therefore, logic suggests that the probability of observing a head, denoted $P(H)$, is $1/2 = 0.5$, and the probability of observing a tail, denoted $P(T)$, is also $1/2 = 0.5$. Notice that each probability is between 0 and 1. Furthermore, because H and T are all of the experimental outcomes, $P(H) + P(T) = 1$.

Probability is often interpreted to be a **long-run relative frequency**. As an example, consider repeatedly tossing a coin. If we get 6 heads in the first 10 tosses, then the relative frequency, or fraction, of heads is $6/10 = 0.6$. If we get 47 heads in the first 100 tosses, the relative frequency of heads is $47/100 = 0.47$. If we get 5,067 heads in the first 10,000 tosses, the relative frequency of heads is $5,067/10,000 = 0.5067$.[1] Since the relative frequency of heads is approaching (that is, getting closer to) 0.5, we might estimate that the probability of obtaining a head when tossing the coin is 0.5. When we say this, we mean that, if we tossed the coin an indefinitely large number of times (that is, a number of times **approaching infinity**), the relative frequency of heads obtained would approach 0.5. Of course, in actuality it is impossible to toss a coin (or perform any experiment) an indefinitely large number of times. Therefore, a relative frequency interpretation of probability is a mathematical idealization. To summarize, suppose that E is an experimental outcome that might occur when a particular experiment is performed. Then, the probability that E will occur, $P(E)$, can be interpreted to be the number that would be approached by the relative frequency of E if we performed the experiment an indefinitely large number of times. It follows that we often think of a probability in terms of the

---

[1] The English mathematician John Kerrich actually obtained this result when he tossed a coin 10,000 times while imprisoned by the Germans during World War II.

percentage of the time the experimental outcome would occur in many repetitions of the experiment. For instance, when we say that the probability of obtaining a head when we toss a coin is 0.5, we are saying that, when we repeatedly toss the coin an indefinitely large number of times, we will obtain a head on 50 percent of the repetitions.

Sometimes it is either difficult or impossible to use the classical method to assign probabilities. Since we can often make a relative frequency interpretation of probability, we can estimate a probability by performing the experiment in which an outcome might occur many times. Then we estimate the probability of the experimental outcome to be the proportion of the time that the outcome occurs during the many repetitions of the experiment. For example, to estimate the probability that a randomly selected consumer prefers Coca-Cola to all other soft drinks, we perform an experiment in which we ask a randomly selected consumer for their preference. There are two possible experimental outcomes: "prefers Coca-Cola" and "does not prefer Coca-Cola." However, we have no reason to believe that these experimental outcomes are equally likely, so we cannot use the classical method. We might perform the experiment, say, 1,000 times by surveying 1,000 randomly selected consumers. Then, if 140 of those surveyed said that they prefer Coca-Cola, we would estimate the probability that a randomly selected consumer prefers Coca-Cola to all other soft drinks to be $140/1,000 = 0.14$. This is called the **relative frequency method** for assigning probability.

If we cannot perform the experiment many times, we might estimate the probability by using our previous experience with similar situations, intuition, or special expertise that we may possess. For example, a company president might estimate the probability of success for a one-time business venture to be 0.7. Here, on the basis of knowledge of the success of previous similar ventures, the opinions of company personnel, and other pertinent information, the president believes that there is a 70 percent chance the venture will be successful.

When we use experience, intuitive judgment, or expertise to assess a probability, we call it a **subjective probability**. Such a probability may or may not have a relative frequency interpretation. For instance, when the company president estimates that the probability of a successful business venture is 0.7, this may mean that, if business conditions similar to those that are about to be encountered could be repeated many times, then the business venture would be successful in 70 percent of the repetitions. Or, the president may not be thinking in relative frequency terms but rather may consider the venture a "one-shot" proposition. We will discuss some other subjective probabilities later. However, the interpretations of statistical inferences we will explain in later chapters are based on the relative frequency interpretation of probability. For this reason, we will concentrate on this interpretation.

3.2 Sample Spaces and Events

In order to calculate probabilities by using the classical method, it is important to understand and use the idea of a **sample space**.

The **sample space** of an experiment is the set of all possible experimental outcomes. The experimental outcomes in the sample space are often called **sample space outcomes**.

CHAPTER 2

Example 3.1

A company is choosing a new chief executive officer (CEO). It has narrowed the list of candidates to four finalists (identified by last name only)—Adams, Chung, Hill, and Rankin. If we consider our experiment to be making a final choice of the company's CEO, then the experiment's sample space consists of the four possible experimental outcomes:

$A \equiv$ Adams is chosen as CEO.

$C \equiv$ Chung is chosen as CEO.

$H \equiv$ Hill is chosen as CEO.

$R \equiv$ Rankin is chosen as CEO.

Each of these outcomes is a sample space outcome, and the set of these sample space outcomes is the sample space.

Next, suppose that industry analysts feel (subjectively) that the probabilities that Adams, Chung, Hill, and Rankin will be chosen as CEO are 0.1, 0.2, 0.5, and 0.2, respectively. That is, in probability notation,

$$P(A) = 0.1, \quad P(C) = 0.2, \quad P(H) = 0.5, \quad \text{and} \quad P(R) = 0.2.$$

Notice that each probability assigned to a sample space outcome is between 0 and 1 and that the sum of the probabilities equals 1.

Example 3.2

A student takes a pop quiz that consists of three true–false questions. If we consider our experiment to be answering the three questions, each question can be answered correctly or incorrectly. We will let C denote answering a question correctly and I denote answering a question incorrectly. Then, Figure 3.1 depicts a tree diagram of the sample space outcomes for the experiment. The diagram portrays the experiment as a three-step process—answering the first question (correctly or incorrectly, that is, C or I), answering the second question, and answering the third question. The tree diagram has eight different branches, and the eight sample space outcomes are listed at the ends of the branches. We see that the sample space is

$$\begin{array}{cccc} CCC & CCI & CIC & CII \\ ICC & ICI & IIC & III \end{array}$$

Next suppose that the student was totally unprepared for the quiz and had to blindly guess the answer to each question. That is, the student had a 50–50 chance (or 0.5 probability) of correctly

FIGURE **3.1**   **A Tree Diagram of Answering Three True–False Questions**

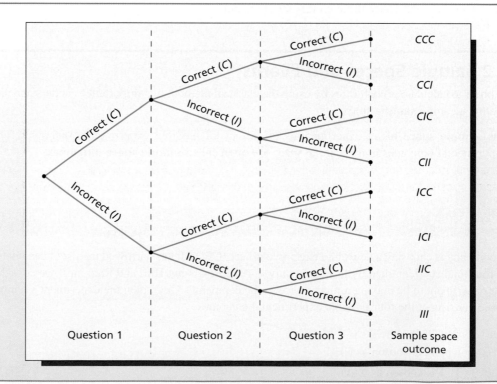

answering each question. Intuitively, this would say that each of the eight sample space outcomes is equally likely to occur. That is,

$$P(CCC) = P(CCI) = \cdots = P(III) = \frac{1}{8}.$$

Here, as in Example 3.1, the sum of the probabilities of the sample space outcomes is equal to 1.

Events and finding probabilities by using sample spaces   At the beginning of this chapter, we informally talked about events. We now give the formal definition of an event.

An **event** is a set (or collection) of sample space outcomes.

For instance, if we consider the pop quiz situation, the event "the student will answer at least two out of three questions correctly" consists of the sample space outcomes *CCC*, *CCI*, *CIC*, and *ICC*, while the event "the student will answer all three questions correctly" consists of the sample space outcome *CCC*. In general, we see that the word description of an event determines the sample space outcomes that correspond to the event.

Suppose that we wish to find the probability that an event will occur. We can find such a probability as follows:

The **probability of an event** is the **sum of the probabilities of the sample space outcomes** that correspond to the event.

As an example, in the CEO situation, suppose only Adams and Hill are internal candidates (they already work for the company). Letting *INT* denote the event that "an internal candidate is selected for the CEO position," then *INT* consists of the sample space outcomes *A* and *H* (that is, *INT* will occur if and only if either of the sample space outcomes *A* or *H* occurs). It follows that $P(INT) = P(A) + P(H) = 0.1 + 0.5 = 0.6$. This says that the probability that an internal candidate will be chosen to be CEO is 0.6.

In general, we have seen that the probability of any sample space outcome (experimental outcome) is a number between 0 and 1, and we have also seen that the probabilities of all the sample space outcomes sum to 1. It follows that **the probability of an event** (that is, the probability of a set of sample space outcomes) **is a number between 0 and 1**.

If *A* is an event, then $0 \leq P(A) \leq 1$.
   Moreover:

   1   If an event never occurs, then the probability of this event equals 0.
   2   If an event is certain to occur, then the probability of this event equals 1.

Example 3.3

Again consider the pop quiz consisting of three true–false questions, and suppose that the student blindly guesses the answers. Remembering that in this case each sample space outcome has a probability equal to 1/8, then:

   1   The probability that the student will get all three questions correct is

$$P(CCC) = \frac{1}{8}.$$

   2   The probability that the student will get exactly two questions correct is

$$P(CCI) + P(CIC) + P(ICC) = \frac{1}{8} + \frac{1}{8} + \frac{1}{8} = \frac{3}{8},$$

   since two questions will be answered correctly if and only if one of the sample space outcomes *CCI*, *CIC*, or *ICC* occurs.

3 The probability that the student will get exactly one question correct is

$$P(CII) + P(ICI) + P(IIC) = \frac{1}{8} + \frac{1}{8} + \frac{1}{8} = \frac{3}{8},$$

since one question will be answered correctly if and only if one of the sample space outcomes *CII, ICI*, and *IIC* occurs.

4 The probability that the student will get at most one question correct is

$$P(III) + P(CII) + P(ICI) + P(IIC) = \frac{1}{8} + \frac{1}{8} + \frac{1}{8} + \frac{1}{8} = \frac{1}{2},$$

since at most one question will be answered correctly if and only if one of the sample space outcomes *III, CII, ICI*, and *IIC* occurs.

5 The probability that the student will get at least two questions correct is

$$P(CCC) + P(CCI) + P(CIC) + P(ICC) = \frac{1}{8} + \frac{1}{8} + \frac{1}{8} + \frac{1}{8} = \frac{1}{2},$$

since the student will get at least two questions correct if and only if one of the sample space outcomes *CCC, CCI, CIC*, and *ICC* occurs.

Notice that in the true–false question situation we find that, for instance, the probability that the student will get exactly two questions correct equals the ratio

$$\frac{\text{the number of sample space outcomes resulting in two correct answers}}{\text{the total number of sample space outcomes}} = \frac{3}{8}.$$

In general, when a sample space is finite, we can use the following method for computing the probability of an event.

If all of the sample space outcomes are equally likely, then the probability that an event will occur is equal to the ratio

$$\frac{\text{the number of sample space outcomes that correspond to the event}}{\text{the total number of sample space outcomes}}.$$

When we use this rule, we are using the classical method for computing probabilities. Furthermore, it is important to emphasize that we can use this rule only when all of the sample space outcomes are equally likely (as they are in the true–false question situation). For example, if we were to use this rule in the CEO situation, we would find that the probability of choosing an internal candidate as CEO is

$$P(INT) = \frac{\text{the number of internal candidates}}{\text{the total number of candidates}} = \frac{2}{4} = 0.5.$$

This result is not equal to the correct value of $P(INT)$, which we previously found to be equal to 0.6. Here, this rule does not give us the correct answer because the sample space outcomes A, C, H, and R are not equally likely—recall that $P(A) = 0.1, P(C) = 0.2, P(H) = 0.5$, and $P(R) = 0.2$.

Example 3.4

Suppose that 650,000 of 1,000,000 households in a Canadian city subscribe to a newspaper called the *Canadian Chronicle*, and consider randomly selecting one of the households in this city. That is, consider selecting one household by giving each and every household in the city the same chance of being selected. Let A be the event that the randomly selected household subscribes to the *Canadian Chronicle*. Then, because the sample space of this experiment consists of 1,000,000 equally likely sample space outcomes (households), it follows that

$$P(A) = \frac{\text{the number of households that subscribe to the } Canadian\ Chronicle}{\text{the total number of households in the city}}$$

$$= \frac{650,000}{1,000,000}$$

$$= 0.65.$$

This says that the probability that the randomly selected household subscribes to the *Canadian Chronicle* is 0.65.

Example 3.5 The BBM Canada Radio Ratings Case

As discussed in the introduction to this chapter, BBM Canada is a radio ratings service. Figure 3.2 gives portions of a BBM ratings report for the London, Ontario, market for two surveys. Each survey was conducted from September to October, for the years 2005 and 2006. This report is based on sampling people 12 years of age or older and gives the "share," or estimated total hours, as a percentage, of people who tuned into that radio station compared to all hours listening to the radio. As stated by BBM, "Share does not indicate the size of a station's audience—only its relative performance compared to other stations." As shown in Figure 3.2, the station with the largest share for 2006 is CIQM-FM, at 15.7 percent (this station also had the largest share in the 2005 survey, at 14.4 percent). BBM's computation of share is as follows:

$$\text{Share} = \frac{\text{number of people listening to that station}}{\text{total number of people listening to the radio}}.$$

If you add the share percentages, the total is 72.2 percent. What this means is 27.8 percent of those people surveyed were either listening to a radio station not on the list or not listening at all. To compute the percentage of people who listen to a station for at least 15 minutes in a week, the equation is

$$\text{Percentage listening} = \frac{\text{central (Ctrl) number}}{\text{Ctrl reach total}}.$$

So, if you look at the station CFHK-FM, the percentage of people in the London market who listen to this station for at least 15 minutes in a week is $80.5/571.7 = 14.08\%$.

FIGURE 3.2 Top-Line Radio Statistics: London Ctrl S4-2006

Source: BBM Canada
Demographics: A12+
Area: 5369 (London Ctrl)
Timeblock: Monday–Sunday 5 A.M.–1 A.M.

| Station | Market | Sep.–Oct. 2006 405 295 | | Sep.–Oct. 2005 402 314 | |
	Universe	Share	Ctrl Reach	Share	Ctrl Reach
		%	(000)	%	(000)
CFHKFM	London Ctrl	7.5	80.5	7.6	89.6
CFPL	London Ctrl	3.7	37.9	3.9	49.0
CFPLFM	London Ctrl	11.0	85.3	11.6	93.5
CHSTFM	London Ctrl	11.0	78.1	10.9	83.2
CIQMFM	London Ctrl	15.7	100.5	14.4	97.6
CJBK	London Ctrl	3.5	38.8	4.9	41.0
CJBXFM	London Ctrl	13.7	83.3	11.1	66.4
CKDKFM	Woodstock/London Ctrl	4.1	52.7	5.6	57.0
CKSL	London Ctrl	2.0	14.6	2.7	22.1

TERMS
Central (Ctrl) Market Area: A BBM-defined geographical area, usually centred around one urban centre. The definition of a Central Market Area generally corresponds to Statistics Canada Census Metropolitan Areas, Census Agglomeration, Cities, Counties, Census Divisions, or Regional Districts.

Universe: Estimated Population of the Central Market Area.

Share: Within the central market area, the estimated total hours tuned to that station expressed as a percentage of total hours tuned to all radio.

Central (Ctrl) Reach: The estimated number of different people, within the central market area, who tuned to that station for at least one quarter hour during the week.

To conclude this section, we note that in Appendix B (Part 1) we discuss several **counting rules** that can be used to count the number of sample space outcomes in an experiment. These rules are particularly useful when there are many sample space outcomes and thus these outcomes are difficult to list.

Exercises for Sections 3.1 and 3.2

CONCEPTS

3.1 Define the following terms: *experiment*, *event*, *probability*, *sample space*.

3.2 Explain the properties that must be satisfied by a probability.

METHODS AND APPLICATIONS

3.3 Two randomly selected grocery store patrons are each asked to take a blind taste test and then to state which of three diet colas (marked as *A*, *B*, or *C*) they prefer.
  a. Draw a tree diagram depicting the sample space outcomes for the test results.
  b. List the sample space outcomes that correspond to each of the following events:
      (1) Both patrons prefer diet cola *A*.
      (2) The two patrons prefer the same diet cola.
      (3) The two patrons prefer different diet colas.
      (4) Diet cola *A* is preferred by at least one of the two patrons.
      (5) Neither of the patrons prefers diet cola *C*.
  c. Assuming that all sample space outcomes are equally likely, find the probability of each of the events given in part b.

3.4 Suppose that a couple will have three children. Let *B* denote a boy and *G* denote a girl.
  a. Draw a tree diagram depicting the sample space outcomes for this experiment.
  b. List the sample space outcomes that correspond to each of the following events:
      (1) All three children will have the same sex.
      (2) Exactly two of the three children will be girls.
      (3) Exactly one of the three children will be a girl.
      (4) The oldest child is a girl.
  c. Assuming that all sample space outcomes are equally likely, find the probability of each of the events given in part b.

3.5 Four people will enter an automobile showroom, and each will either purchase a car (*P*) or not purchase a car (*N*).
  a. Draw a tree diagram depicting the sample space of all possible purchase decisions that could potentially be made by the four people.
  b. List the sample space outcomes that correspond to each of the following events:
      (1) Exactly three people will purchase a car.
      (2) Two or fewer people will purchase a car.
      (3) One or more people will purchase a car.
      (4) All four people will make the same purchase decision.
  c. Assuming that all sample space outcomes are equally likely, find the probability of each of the events given in part b.

3.6 **THE BBM CANADA RADIO RATING CASE**
  a. Using the information given in the BBM Canada report in Figure 3.2, find estimates for each of the following:
      (1) The probability that a randomly selected resident of London would report listening to CFPL at least 15 minutes in one week in 2005.
      (2) The probability that a randomly selected resident of London would report listening to CFPL at least 15 minutes in one week in 2006.
  b. How do the values differ (if at all) between 2005 and 2006 for CFPL listeners?
  c. What is the likelihood that someone reports **not** listening to CJBX-FM in 2006?
  d. Which station showed the greatest change in share percentage between 2005 and 2006?

3.7 Let *A*, *B*, *C*, *D*, and *E* be sample space outcomes forming a sample space. Suppose that $P(A) = 0.2$, $P(B) = 0.15$, $P(C) = 0.3$, and $P(D) = 0.2$. What is $P(E)$? Explain how you got your answer.

3.3 Some Elementary Probability Rules

We can often calculate probabilities by using formulas called **probability rules**. We will begin by presenting the simplest probability rule: the **rule of complements**. To start, we define the **complement** of an event:

> Given an event *A*, the **complement of** *A* is the event consisting of all sample space outcomes that do not correspond to the occurrence of *A*. The complement of *A* is denoted $\overline{A}$. Furthermore, $P(\overline{A})$ denotes **the probability that *A* will not occur**.

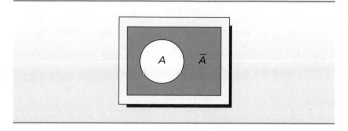

FIGURE **3.3** **The Complement of an Event (the Shaded Region Is $\overline{A}$, the Complement of A)**

Figure 3.3 is a **Venn diagram** depicting the complement $\overline{A}$ of an event A. $\overline{A}$ is the set of all sample space outcomes that are not in A. In any probability situation, either an event A or its complement $\overline{A}$ must occur. Therefore, we have

$$P(A) + P(\overline{A}) = 1.$$

The Rule of Complements

Consider an event A. Then, **the probability that A *will not occur*** is

$$P(\overline{A}) = 1 - P(A).$$

Example 3.6

Recall from Example 3.4 that the probability that a randomly selected household in a Canadian city subscribes to the *Canadian Chronicle* is 0.65. It follows that the probability of the complement of this event (that is, the probability that a randomly selected household in the Canadian city does not subscribe to the *Canadian Chronicle*) is $1 - 0.65 = 0.35$.

Example 3.7

Consider Example 3.4, and recall that 650,000 of the 1,000,000 households in a Canadian city subscribe to the *Canadian Chronicle*. Also, suppose that 500,000 households in the city subscribe to a competing newspaper, *News Matters*, and further suppose that 250,000 households subscribe to both the *Canadian Chronicle* and *News Matters*. As in Example 3.4, we consider randomly selecting one household in the city, and we define the following events.

- $A \equiv$ the randomly selected household subscribes to the *Canadian Chronicle*.
- $\overline{A} \equiv$ the randomly selected household does not subscribe to the *Canadian Chronicle*.
- $B \equiv$ the randomly selected household subscribes to *News Matters*.
- $\overline{B} \equiv$ the randomly selected household does not subscribe to *News Matters*.

Using the notation $A \cap B$ to denote **both A and B**, we also define

$A \cap B \equiv$ the randomly selected household subscribes to both the *Canadian Chronicle* and *News Matters*.

Since 650,000 of the 1,000,000 households subscribe to the *Canadian Chronicle* (that is, correspond to the event A occurring), then 350,000 households do not subscribe to the *Canadian Chronicle* (that is, correspond to the event $\overline{A}$ occurring). Similarly, 500,000 households subscribe to *News Matters* (B), so 500,000 households do not subscribe to *News Matters* ($\overline{B}$). We summarize this information, as well as the 250,000 households that correspond to the event $A \cap B$ occurring, in Table 3.1.

TABLE **3.1**   A Summary of the Number of Households Corresponding to the
Events A, $\bar{A}$, B, $\bar{B}$, and $A \cap B$

Events	Subscribes to News Matters, B	Does Not Subscribe to News Matters, $\bar{B}$	Total
Subscribes to Canadian Chronicle, A	250,000		650,000
Does Not Subscribe to Canadian Chronicle, $\bar{A}$			350,000
Total	500,000	500,000	1,000,000

Next, consider the events

$A \cap \bar{B} \equiv$ the randomly selected household subscribes to the *Canadian Chronicle* and does not subscribe to *News Matters*.

$\bar{A} \cap B \equiv$ the randomly selected household does not subscribe to the *Canadian Chronicle* and does subscribe to *News Matters*.

$\bar{A} \cap \bar{B} \equiv$ the randomly selected household does not subscribe to the *Canadian Chronicle* and does not subscribe to *News Matters*.

Since 650,000 households subscribe to the *Canadian Chronicle* (A) and 250,000 households subscribe to both the *Canadian Chronicle* and *News Matters* ($A \cap B$), it follows that 650,000 − 250,000 = 400,000 households subscribe to the *Canadian Chronicle* but do not subscribe to *News Matters* ($A \cap \bar{B}$). This subtraction is illustrated in Table 3.2(a). By similar logic:

1   As illustrated in Table 3.2(b), 500,000 − 250,000 = 250,000 households do not subscribe to the *Canadian Chronicle* but do subscribe to *News Matters* ($\bar{A} \cap B$).

2   As illustrated in Table 3.2(c), 350,000 − 250,000 = 100,000 households do not subscribe to the *Canadian Chronicle* and do not subscribe to *News Matters* ($\bar{A} \cap \bar{B}$).

We summarize all of these results in Table 3.3, which is called a **contingency table**. Because we will randomly select one household (making all of the households equally likely to be chosen), the probability of any of the previously defined events is the ratio of the number of households corresponding to the event's occurrence to the total number of households in the city. Therefore, for example,

$$P(A) = \frac{650,000}{1,000,000} = 0.65, \qquad P(B) = \frac{500,000}{1,000,000} = 0.5,$$

$$P(A \cap B) = \frac{250,000}{1,000,000} = 0.25.$$

This last probability says that the probability that the randomly selected household subscribes to both the *Canadian Chronicle* and *News Matters* is 0.25.

Next, letting $A \cup B$ denote A or B (or both), we consider finding the probability of the event

$A \cup B \equiv$ the randomly selected household subscribes to the *Canadian Chronicle* or *News Matters* (or both)—that is, subscribes to at least one of the two newspapers.

Looking at Table 3.3, we see that the households subscribing to the *Canadian Chronicle* or *News Matters* are (1) the 400,000 households that subscribe to only the *Canadian Chronicle*, $A \cap \bar{B}$, (2) the 250,000 households that subscribe to only *News Matters*, $\bar{A} \cap B$, and (3) the 250,000 households that subscribe to both the *Canadian Chronicle* and *News Matters*, $A \cap B$.

TABLE 3.2 Subtracting to Find the Number of Households Corresponding to the Events $A \cap \bar{B}$, $\bar{A} \cap B$, and $\bar{A} \cap \bar{B}$

(a) The number of households corresponding to (A and $\bar{B}$)

Events	Subscribes to News Matters, B	Does Not Subscribe to News Matters, $\bar{B}$	Total
Subscribes to Canadian Chronicle, A	250,000	650,000 − 250,000 = 400,000	650,000
Does Not Subscribe to Canadian Chronicle, $\bar{A}$			350,000
Total	500,000	500,000	1,000,000

(b) The number of households corresponding to ($\bar{A}$ and B)

Events	Subscribes to News Matters, B	Does Not Subscribe to News Matters, $\bar{B}$	Total
Subscribes to Canadian Chronicle, A	250,000	650,000 − 250,000 = 400,000	650,000
Does Not Subscribe to Canadian Chronicle, $\bar{A}$	500,000 − 250,000 = 250,000		350,000
Total	500,000	500,000	1,000,000

(c) The number of households corresponding to ($\bar{A}$ and $\bar{B}$)

Events	Subscribes to News Matters, B	Does Not Subscribe to News Matters, $\bar{B}$	Total
Subscribes to Canadian Chronicle, A	250,000	650,000 − 250,000 = 400,000	650,000
Does Not Subscribe to Canadian Chronicle, $\bar{A}$	500,000 − 250,000 = 250,000	350,000 − 250,000 = 100,000	350,000
Total	500,000	500,000	1,000,000

TABLE 3.3 A Contingency Table Summarizing Subscription Data for the Canadian Chronicle and News Matters

Events	Subscribes to News Matters, B	Does Not Subscribe to News Matters, $\bar{B}$	Total
Subscribes to Canadian Chronicle, A	250,000	400,000	650,000
Does Not Subscribe to Canadian Chronicle, $\bar{A}$	250,000	100,000	350,000
Total	500,000	500,000	1,000,000

Therefore, since a total of 900,000 households subscribe to the Canadian Chronicle or News Matters or both, it follows that

$$P(A \cup B) = \frac{900,000}{1,000,000} = 0.9.$$

This says that the probability that the randomly selected household subscribes to the Canadian Chronicle or News Matters or both is 0.90. That is, 90 percent of the households in the city subscribe to the *Canadian Chronicle* or *News Matters* or both. Notice that $P(A \cup B) = 0.90$ does not equal

$$P(A) + P(B) = 0.65 + 0.5 = 1.15.$$

Logically, the reason for this is that both $P(A) = 0.65$ and $P(B) = 0.5$ count the 25 percent of the households that subscribe to both newspapers. Therefore, the sum of $P(A)$ and $P(B)$ counts this 25 percent of the households once too often. It follows that if we subtract $P(A \cap B) = 0.25$ from the sum of $P(A)$ and $P(B)$, then we will obtain $P(A \cup B)$. That is,

$$P(A \cup B) = P(A) + P(B) - P(A \cap B)$$
$$= 0.65 + 0.5 - 0.25 = 0.90.$$

In order to generalize the ideas in the previous example, we make the following definitions:

The Intersection and Union of Two Events

Given two events A and B,

1   The **intersection of A and B** is the event consisting of the sample space outcomes belonging to both A and B. The intersection is denoted by $(A \cap B)$. Furthermore, $P(A \cap B)$ denotes **the probability that both A and B will simultaneously occur.**

2   The **union of A and B** is the event consisting of the sample space outcomes belonging to A or B (or both). The union is denoted $(A \cup B)$. Furthermore, $P(A \cup B)$ denotes **the probability that A or B (or both) will occur.** This probability is also equivalent to at least one of A or B occurring.

Noting that Figure 3.4 shows **Venn diagrams** depicting the events A, B, $A \cap B$, and $A \cup B$, we have the following general result:

The Addition Rule

Let A and B be events. Then, **the probability that A or B (or both) will occur** is
$$P(A \cup B) = P(A) + P(B) - P(A \cap B).$$

The reasoning behind this result was illustrated at the end of Example 3.7. Similarly, the Venn diagrams in Figure 3.4 show that when we compute $P(A) + P(B)$, we are counting each of the sample space outcomes in $A \cap B$ twice. We correct for this by subtracting $P(A \cap B)$.

We next define the idea of **mutually exclusive events**:

Mutually Exclusive Events

Two events A and B are **mutually exclusive** if they have no sample space outcomes in common. In this case, the events A and B cannot occur simultaneously, and thus
$$P(A \cap B) = 0.$$

Noting that Figure 3.5 is a Venn diagram depicting two mutually exclusive events, we consider the following example.

FIGURE **3.4**   Venn Diagrams Depicting the Events *A*, *B*, *A* ∩ *B*, and *A* ∪ *B*

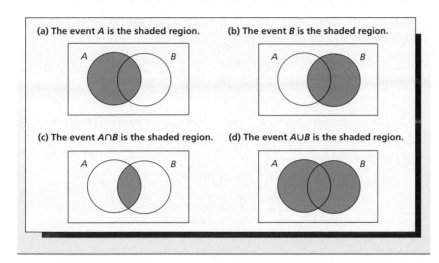

FIGURE **3.5**   Two Mutually Exclusive Events

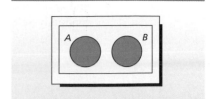

Example 3.8

Consider randomly selecting a card from a standard deck of 52 playing cards. We define the following events:

    $J \equiv$ the randomly selected card is a jack.

    $Q \equiv$ the randomly selected card is a queen.

    $R \equiv$ the randomly selected card is a red card (that is, a diamond or a heart).

Because there is no card that is both a jack and a queen, the events *J* and *Q* are mutually exclusive. On the other hand, there are two cards that are both jacks and red cards—the jack of diamonds and the jack of hearts—so the events *J* and *R* are not mutually exclusive.

We have seen that for any two events *A* and *B*, the probability that *A* or *B* (or both) will occur is

$$P(A \cup B) = P(A) + P(B) - P(A \cap B).$$

Therefore, when calculating $P(A \cup B)$, we should always subtract $P(A \cap B)$ from the sum of $P(A)$ and $P(B)$. However, when *A* and *B* are mutually exclusive, $P(A \cap B)$ equals 0. Therefore, in this case—and only in this case—we have the following:

The Addition Rule for Two Mutually Exclusive Events

Let *A* and *B* be **mutually exclusive** events. Then, **the probability that *A* or *B* will occur** is

$$P(A \cup B) = P(A) + P(B).$$

Example 3.9

Again consider randomly selecting a card from a standard deck of 52 playing cards, and define the following events:

    $J \equiv$ the randomly selected card is a jack.

    $Q \equiv$ the randomly selected card is a queen.

    $R \equiv$ the randomly selected card is a red card (a diamond or a heart).

Since there are 4 jacks, 4 queens, and 26 red cards, we have $P(J) = \frac{4}{52}$, $P(Q) = \frac{4}{52}$, and $P(R) = \frac{26}{52}$. Furthermore, since there is no card that is both a jack and a queen, the events J and Q are mutually exclusive and thus $P(J \cap Q) = 0$. It follows that the probability that the randomly selected card is a jack or a queen is

$$P(J \cup Q) = P(J) + P(Q)$$
$$= \frac{4}{52} + \frac{4}{52} = \frac{8}{52} = \frac{2}{13}.$$

Since there are two cards that are both jacks and red cards—the jack of diamonds and the jack of hearts—the events J and R are not mutually exclusive. Therefore, the probability that the randomly selected card is a jack or a red card is

$$P(J \cup R) = P(J) + P(R) - P(J \cap R)$$
$$= \frac{4}{52} + \frac{26}{52} - \frac{2}{52} = \frac{28}{52} = \frac{7}{13}.$$

We now consider an arbitrary group of events—$A_1, A_2, \ldots, A_N$. We will denote the probability that A_1 or A_2 or $\ldots$ or A_N occurs (that is, the probability that at least one of the events occurs) as $P(A_1 \cup A_2 \cup \cdots \cup A_N)$. We can use sample spaces to reason out such a probability. For instance, in the playing card situation of Example 3.9, there are 4 jacks, 4 queens, and 22 red cards that are not jacks or queens (the 26 red cards minus the 2 red jacks and the 2 red queens). Therefore, because there are a total of 30 cards corresponding to the event $J \cup Q \cup R$, it follows that

$$P(J \cup Q \cup R) = \frac{30}{52} = \frac{15}{26}.$$

Because some cards are both jacks and red cards, and because some cards are both queens and red cards, we say that the events J, Q, and R are not mutually exclusive. When, however, a group of events is mutually exclusive, there is a simple formula for the probability that at least one of the events will occur:

The Addition Rule for N Mutually Exclusive Events

The events $A_1, A_2, \ldots, A_N$ are mutually exclusive if no two of the events have any sample space outcomes in common. In this case, no two of the events can occur simultaneously, and

$$P(A_1 \cup A_2 \cup \cdots \cup A_N) = P(A_1) + P(A_2) + \cdots + P(A_N).$$

As an example of using this formula, again consider the playing card situation and the events J and Q. If we define the event

$$K \equiv \text{the randomly selected card is a king},$$

then the events J, Q, and K are mutually exclusive. Therefore,

$$P(J \cup Q \cup K) = P(J) + P(Q) + P(K)$$
$$= \frac{4}{52} + \frac{4}{52} + \frac{4}{52} = \frac{12}{52} = \frac{3}{13}.$$

Example 3.10   The BBM Canada Radio Ratings Case

Recall that Figure 3.2 gives the BBM Canada estimates of the share of each radio station in the London, Ontario, market. Because the share percentages provide the relative performance of certain stations, the nine percentages are mutually exclusive. Therefore, the probability that a randomly selected resident of London listens to at least one of the nine stations listed is the sum of the individual station probabilities

$$P(\text{CFHK-FM}) + P(\text{CFPL}) + \cdots + P(\text{CKSL})$$

or

$$0.075 + 0.037 + \cdots + 0.020 = 0.722.$$

As stated earlier, this total is less than one because some people do not listen to the radio and other people may be listening to a station not in the area.

Exercises for Section 3.3

CONCEPTS

3.8 Explain what it means for two events to be mutually exclusive; for N events.

3.9 If A and B are events, define $\overline{A}$, $A \cup B$, $A \cap B$, and $\overline{A} \cap \overline{B}$.

METHODS AND APPLICATIONS

3.10 Consider a standard deck of 52 playing cards, a randomly selected card from the deck, and the following events:

R = red, B = black, A = ace, N = nine, D = diamond, C = club.

a. Describe the sample space outcomes that correspond to each of these events.

b. For each of the following pairs of events, indicate whether the events are mutually exclusive. In each case, if you think the events are mutually exclusive, explain why the events have no common sample space outcomes. If you think the events are not mutually exclusive, list the sample space outcomes that are common to both events.

(1) R and A.   (3) A and N.   (5) D and C.
(2) R and C.   (4) N and C.

3.11 Of 10,000 students at a university, 2,500 have a MasterCard card (M), 4,000 have a Visa card (V), and 1,000 have both.

a. Find the probability that a randomly selected student
(1) Has a MasterCard card.
(2) Has a Visa card.
(3) Has both credit cards.

b. Construct and fill in a contingency table summarizing the credit card data. Employ the following pairs of events: M and $\overline{M}$, V and $\overline{V}$.

c. Use the contingency table to find the probability that a randomly selected student
(1) Has a MasterCard card or a Visa card.
(2) Has neither credit card.
(3) Has exactly one of the two credit cards.

3.12 The card game of Euchre employs a deck that consists of all four of each of the aces, kings, queens, jacks, tens, and nines (one of each suit—clubs, diamonds, spades, and hearts).

a. Find the probability that a randomly selected card from a Euchre deck is
(1) A jack (J).   (3) A jack or an ace (A).
(2) A spade (S).   (4) A jack or a spade.

b. Are the events J and A mutually exclusive? J and S? Why or why not?

3.13 Each month, a brokerage house studies various companies and rates each company's stock as being either "low risk" or "moderate to high risk." In a recent report, the brokerage house summarized its findings about 15 Internet services companies and 25 financial sector companies in the following table:

Company Type	Low Risk	Moderate to High Risk
Internet Services	6	9
Financial Sector	20	5

If we randomly select one of the total of 40 companies, find

a. The probability that the company is in the financial sector.

b. The probability that the company's stock is "low risk."

c. The probability that the company's stock is "moderate to high risk."

d. The probability that the company is in the financial sector and has a stock that is "low risk."

e. The probability that the company is in Internet services or has a stock that is "low risk."

3.14 In the book *Essentials of Marketing Research*, Dillon, Madden, and Firtle present the results of a concept study for a new wine cooler. Three hundred consumers between 21 and 49 years old were randomly selected. After sampling the new beverage, each was asked to rate the appeal of the phrase

Not sweet like wine coolers, not filling like beer, and more refreshing than wine or mixed drinks

as it relates to the new wine cooler. The rating was made on a scale from 1 to 5, with 5 representing "extremely appealing" and 1 representing "not at all appealing." The results obtained are given in Table 3.4.
◆ WineCooler

Based on these results, estimate the probability that a randomly selected 21- to 49-year-old consumer

a. Would give the phrase a rating of 5.

b. Would give the phrase a rating of 3 or higher.

c. Is in the 21–24 age group; the 25–34 age group; the 35–49 age group.

TABLE **3.4**   Results of a Concept Study for a New Wine Cooler   ● WineCooler

Rating	Total	Gender		Age Group		
		Male	Female	21–24	25–34	35–49
Extremely appealing (5)	151	68	83	48	66	37
(4)	91	51	40	36	36	19
(3)	36	21	15	9	12	15
(2)	13	7	6	4	6	3
Not at all appealing (1)	9	3	6	4	3	2

Source: *Essentials of Marketing Research,* by W. R. Dillon, T. J. Madden, and N. H. Firtle (Burr Ridge, IL: Richard D. Irwin, 1993), p. 390.

d. Is a male who gives the phrase a rating of 4.

e. Is a 35- to 49-year-old who gives the phrase a rating of 1.

3.15 THE BBM CANADA RADIO RATING CASE

Using the information from 2006 in Figure 3.2, find an estimate of the probability that a randomly selected London, Ontario, resident (12 years of age or older) would

a. Listen to at least one of the top two radio stations in terms of share percentage (CIQM-FM and CJBX-FM).

b. Not listen to one of the top five radio stations.

c. Not listen to one of the nine stations listed.

d. Listen to at least one of the bottom three stations (CKSL, CJBX, or CFPL).

3.4 Conditional Probability and Independence

Conditional probability   In Table 3.5, we repeat the contingency table summarizing the subscription data for the *Canadian Chronicle* and *News Matters*. Suppose that we randomly select a household, and that the chosen household reports that it subscribes to *News Matters*. Given this new information, we wish to find the probability that the household subscribes to the *Canadian Chronicle*. This new probability is called a **conditional probability**.

> The **probability of the event A, given the condition that the event B has occurred**, is written as $P(A|B)$—"the probability of A given B." We often refer to such a probability as the **conditional probability of A given B**.

In order to find the conditional probability that a household subscribes to the *Canadian Chronicle*, given that it subscribes to *News Matters*, notice that if we know that the randomly selected household subscribes to *News Matters*, we know that we are considering one of 500 000 households (see Table 3.5). That is, we are now considering what we might call a reduced sample space of 500,000 households. Since 250,000 of these 500,000 *News Matters* subscribers also subscribe to the *Canadian Chronicle*, we have

$$P(A|B) = \frac{250,000}{500,000} = 0.5.$$

TABLE **3.5**   A Contingency Table Summarizing Subscription Data for the *Canadian Chronicle* and *News Matters*

Events	Subscribes to *News Matters,* B	Does Not Subscribe to *News Matters,* $\bar{B}$	Total
Subscribes to *Canadian Chronicle*, A	250,000	400,000	650,000
Does Not Subscribe to *Canadian Chronicle*, $\bar{A}$	250,000	100,000	350,000
Total	500,000	500,000	1,000,000

This says that the probability that the randomly selected household subscribes to the *Canadian Chronicle,* given that the household subscribes to *News Matters,* is 0.5. That is, 50 percent of the *News Matters* subscribers also subscribe to the *Canadian Chronicle.*

Next suppose that we randomly select another household from the community of 1,000,000 households, and suppose that this newly chosen household reports that it subscribes to the *Canadian Chronicle.* We now wish to find the probability that this household subscribes to *News Matters.* We write this new probability as $P(B|A)$. If we know that the randomly selected household subscribes to the *Canadian Chronicle,* we know that we are considering a reduced sample space of 650,000 households (see Table 3.5). Since 250,000 of these 650,000 *Canadian Chronicle* subscribers also subscribe to *News Matters,* we have

$$P(B|A) = \frac{250,000}{650,000} = 0.3846.$$

This says that the probability that the randomly selected household subscribes to *News Matters,* given that the household subscribes to the *Canadian Chronicle,* is 0.3846. That is, 38.46 percent of the *Canadian Chronicle* subscribers also subscribe to *News Matters.*

If we divide both the numerator and denominator of each of the conditional probabilities $P(A \mid B)$ and $P(B \mid A)$ by 1,000,000, we obtain

$$P(A|B) = \frac{250,000}{500,000} = \frac{250,000/1,000,000}{500,000/1,000,000} = \frac{P(A \cap B)}{P(B)},$$

$$P(B|A) = \frac{250,000}{650,000} = \frac{250,000/1,000,000}{650,000/1,000,000} = \frac{P(A \cap B)}{P(A)}.$$

We express these conditional probabilities in terms of $P(A)$, $P(B)$, and $P(A \cap B)$ in order to obtain a more general formula for a conditional probability. We need a more general formula because, although we can use the reduced sample space approach we have demonstrated to find conditional probabilities when all of the sample space outcomes are equally likely, this approach may not give correct results when the sample space outcomes are **not** equally likely. We now give expressions for conditional probability that are valid for any sample space.

Conditional Probability

1   The **conditional probability that *A* will occur given that *B* will occur** is written $P(A \mid B)$ and is defined to be

$$P(A|B) = \frac{P(A \cap B)}{P(B)}.$$

Here we assume that $P(B)$ is greater than 0.

2   The **conditional probability that *B* will occur given that *A* will occur** is written $P(B \mid A)$ and is defined to be

$$P(B|A) = \frac{P(A \cap B)}{P(A)}.$$

Here we assume that $P(A)$ is greater than 0.

If we multiply both sides of the equation

$$P(A \mid B) = \frac{P(A \cap B)}{P(B)}$$

by $P(B)$, we obtain the equation

$$P(A \cap B) = P(B)P(A \mid B).$$

Similarly, if we multiply both sides of the equation

$$P(B|A) = \frac{P(A \cap B)}{P(A)}$$

by $P(A)$, we obtain the equation

$$P(A \cap B) = P(A)P(B|A).$$

In summary, we now have two equations that can be used to calculate $P(A \cap B)$. These equations are often referred to as the **general multiplication rule** for probabilities. These equations are very useful for solving Bayes' theorem questions. We will explore Bayes' theorem in the next section.

The General Multiplication Rule—Two Ways to Calculate $P(A \cap B)$

Given any two events A and B,

$$P(A \cap B) = P(A)P(B|A)$$
$$= P(B)P(A|B).$$

Example 3.11

In a soft drink taste test, each of 1,000 consumers chose between two colas—Cola 1 and Cola 2—and stated whether they preferred their cola drinks sweet or very sweet. Unfortunately, some of the survey information was lost. The following information remains:

1   68.3 percent of the consumers (that is, 683 consumers) preferred Cola 1 to Cola 2.

2   62 percent of the consumers (that is, 620 consumers) preferred their cola sweet (rather than very sweet).

3   85 percent of the consumers who said that they liked their cola sweet preferred Cola 1 to Cola 2.

To recover all of the lost survey information, consider randomly selecting one of the 1000 survey participants, and define the following events:

$C1 \equiv$ the randomly selected consumer prefers Cola 1.

$C2 \equiv$ the randomly selected consumer prefers Cola 2.

$S \equiv$ the randomly selected consumer prefers sweet cola drinks.

$V \equiv$ the randomly selected consumer prefers very sweet cola drinks.

From the survey information that remains, (1) says that $P(C1) = 0.683$, (2) says that $P(S) = 0.62$, and (3) says that $P(C1 \mid S) = 0.85$.

We will see that we can recover all of the lost survey information if we can find $P(C1 \cap S)$. The general multiplication rule says that

$$P(C1 \cap S) = P(C1)P(S \mid C1) = P(S)P(C1 \mid S).$$

Although we know that $P(C1) = 0.683$, we do not know $P(S \mid C1)$. Therefore, we cannot calculate $P(C1 \cap S)$ as $P(C1)P(S \mid C1)$. However, because we know that $P(S) = 0.62$ and that $P(C1 \mid S) = 0.85$, we can calculate

$$P(C1 \cap S) = P(S)P(C1 \mid S) = (0.62)(0.85) = 0.527.$$

This implies that 527 consumers preferred Cola 1 and preferred their cola sweet. Since 683 consumers preferred Cola 1, and 620 consumers preferred sweet cola drinks, we can summarize the numbers of consumers corresponding to the events $C1$, $C2$, S, V, and $C1 \cap S$ as shown in Table 3.6. Furthermore, by performing subtractions as shown in Table 3.7, the numbers of consumers corresponding to the events $C1 \cap V$, $C2 \cap S$, and $C2 \cap V$ can be obtained. We summarize all of our results in Table 3.8. We will use these results in the next subsection to investigate the relationship between cola preference and sweetness preference.

TABLE **3.6** A Summary of the Number of Consumers Corresponding to the Events $C1, C2, S, V,$ and $C1 \cap S$

Events	S (Sweet)	V (Very Sweet)	Total
C1 (Cola 1)	527		683
C2 (Cola 2)			317
Total	620	380	1,000

TABLE **3.7** Subtractions to Obtain the Number of Consumers Corresponding to the Events $C1 \cap V, C2 \cap S,$ and $C2 \cap V$

Events	S (Sweet)	V (Very Sweet)	Total
C1 (Cola 1)	527	683 − 527 = 156	683
C2 (Cola 2)	620 − 527 = 93	380 − 156 = 224	317
Total	620	380	1,000

TABLE **3.8** A Contingency Table Summarizing the Cola Brand and Sweetness Preferences

Events	S (Sweet)	V (Very Sweet)	Total
C1 (Cola 1)	527	156	683
C2 (Cola 2)	93	224	317
Total	620	380	1,000

Independence We have seen in Example 3.11 that $P(C1) = 0.683$, while $P(C1 \mid S) = 0.85$. Because $P(C1 \mid S)$ is greater than $P(C1)$, the probability that a randomly selected consumer will prefer Cola 1 is higher if we know that the person prefers sweet cola than it is if we have no knowledge of the person's sweetness preference. Another way to see this is to use Table 3.8 to calculate

$$P(C1 \mid V) = \frac{P(C1 \cap V)}{P(V)} = \frac{156/1{,}000}{380/1{,}000} = 0.4105.$$

Since $P(C1 \mid S) = 0.85$ is greater than $P(C1 \mid V) = 0.4105$, the probability that a randomly selected consumer will prefer Cola 1 is higher if the consumer prefers sweet colas than it is if the consumer prefers very sweet colas. Since the probability of the event $C1$ is influenced by whether the event S occurs, we say that the events $C1$ and S are **dependent**. If $P(C1 \mid S)$ were equal to $P(C1)$, then the probability of the event $C1$ would not be influenced by whether S occurs. In this case, we would say that the events $C1$ and S are **independent**. This leads to the following definition of **independence**:

Independent Events

Two events A and B are **independent** if and only if

1 $P(A \mid B) = P(A)$ or, equivalently,

2 $P(B \mid A) = P(B)$.

Here we assume that $P(A)$ and $P(B)$ are greater than 0.

When we say that conditions (1) and (2) are equivalent, we mean that condition (1) holds if and only if condition (2) holds. Although we will not prove this, we will demonstrate it in the next example.

Example 3.12

In the soft drink taste test of Example 3.11, we saw that $P(C1 \mid S) = 0.85$ does not equal $P(C1) = 0.683$. This implies that $P(S \mid C1)$ does not equal $P(S)$. To demonstrate this, note from Table 3.8 that

$$P(S \mid C1) = \frac{P(C1 \cap S)}{P(C1)} = \frac{527/1{,}000}{683/1{,}000} = 0.7716.$$

This probability is larger than $P(S) = 620/1,000 = 0.62$. In summary:

1 A comparison of $P(C1 \mid S) = 0.85$ and $P(C1) = 0.683$ says that a consumer is more likely to prefer Cola 1 if the consumer prefers sweet colas.

2 A comparison of $P(S \mid C1) = 0.7716$ and $P(S) = 0.62$ says that a consumer is more likely to prefer sweet colas if the consumer prefers Cola 1.

This suggests, but does not prove, that one reason Cola 1 is preferred to Cola 2 is that Cola 1 is sweet (as opposed to very sweet).

If the occurrences of the events A and B have nothing to do with each other, then we know that A and B are independent events. This implies that $P(A \mid B)$ equals $P(A)$ and that $P(B \mid A)$ equals $P(B)$. Recall that the general multiplication rule tells us that, for any two events A and B, we can say that

$$P(A \cap B) = P(A)P(B \mid A).$$

Therefore, if $P(B \mid A)$ equals $P(B)$, it follows that

$$P(A \cap B) = P(A)P(B),$$

which is called the **multiplication rule for independent events**. To summarize:

The Multiplication Rule for Two Independent Events

If A and B are **independent events**, then

$$P(A \cap B) = P(A)P(B).$$

As a simple example, define the events U and P as follows:

$U \equiv$ your favourite university football team wins its first game next season.

$P \equiv$ your favourite professional football team wins its first game next season.

Suppose you believe that for next season $P(U) = 0.6$ and $P(P) = 0.6$. Then, because the outcomes of a university football game and a professional football game would probably have nothing to do with each other, it is reasonable to assume that U and P are independent events. It follows that

$$P(U \cap P) = P(U)P(P) = (0.6)(0.6) = 0.36.$$

This probability might be surprisingly low. That is, since you believe that each of your teams has a 60 percent chance of winning, you might feel reasonably confident that both your university and professional teams will win their first game. Yet the chance of this happening is really only 0.36!

Next consider a group of events $A_1, A_2, \ldots, A_N$. Intuitively, the events $A_1, A_2, \ldots, A_N$ are independent if the occurrences of these events have nothing to do with each other. Denoting the probability that A_1 and A_2 and . . . and A_N will simultaneously occur as $P(A_1 \cap A_2 \cap \cdots \cap A_N)$, we have the following:

The Multiplication Rule for N Independent Events

If $A_1, A_2, \ldots, A_N$ are independent events, then

$$P(A_1 \cap A_2 \cap \cdots \cap A_N) = P(A_1)P(A_2) \cdots P(A_N).$$

This says that the multiplication rule for two independent events can be extended to any number of independent events.

Example 3.13

This example is based on a real situation encountered by a major producer and marketer of consumer products. The company assessed the service it provides by surveying the attitudes of its customers regarding 10 different aspects of customer service—order filled correctly, billing amount on invoice correct, delivery made on time, and so forth. When the survey results were analyzed, the company was dismayed to learn that only 59 percent of the survey participants indicated that they were satisfied with all 10 aspects of the company's service. Upon investigation, each of the 10 departments responsible for the aspects of service considered in the study insisted that it satisfied its customers 95 percent of the time. That is, each department claimed that its error rate was only 5 percent. Company executives were confused and felt that there was a substantial discrepancy between the survey results and the claims of the departments providing the services. However, a company statistician pointed out that there was no discrepancy. To understand this, consider randomly selecting a customer from among the survey participants, and define 10 events (corresponding to the 10 aspects of service studied):

$A_1 \equiv$ the customer is satisfied that the order is filled correctly (aspect 1).

$A_2 \equiv$ the customer is satisfied that the billing amount on the invoice is correct (aspect 2).

$\vdots$

$A_{10} \equiv$ the customer is satisfied that the delivery is made on time (aspect 10).

Also, define the event

$S \equiv$ the customer is satisfied with all 10 aspects of customer service.

Since 10 different departments are responsible for the 10 aspects of service being studied, it is reasonable to assume that all 10 aspects of service are independent of each other. For instance, billing amounts would be independent of delivery times. Therefore, $A_1, A_2, \ldots, A_{10}$ are independent events, and

$$P(S) = P(A_1 \cap A_2 \cap \cdots \cap A_{10})$$
$$= P(A_1)P(A_2) \cdots P(A_{10}).$$

If, as the departments claim, each department satisfies its customers 95 percent of the time, then the probability that the customer is satisfied with all 10 aspects is

$$P(S) = (0.95)(0.95) \cdots (0.95) = (0.95)^{10} = 0.5987.$$

This result is almost identical to the 59 percent satisfaction rate reported by the survey participants.

If the company wants to increase the percentage of its customers who are satisfied with all 10 aspects of service, it must improve the quality of service provided by the 10 departments. For example, to satisfy 95 percent of its customers with all 10 aspects of service, the company must require each department to raise the fraction of the time it satisfies its customers to x, where

$$(x)^{10} = 0.95.$$

It follows that

$$x = (0.95)^{\frac{1}{10}} = 0.9949$$

and that each department must satisfy its customers 99.49 percent of the time (rather than the current 95 percent of the time).

Exercises for Section 3.4

CONCEPTS

3.16 Explain the concept of a conditional probability. Give an example of a conditional probability that would be of interest to a university student; to a business.

3.17 Explain what it means for two events to be independent.

METHODS AND APPLICATIONS

3.18 Recall from Exercise 3.11 (page 99) that of 10,000 students at university, 2,500 have a MasterCard card (M), 4,000 have a Visa card (V), and 1,000 have both.

a. Find the proportion of MasterCard holders who have Visa cards. Interpret and write this proportion as a conditional probability.

b. Find the proportion of Visa cardholders who have MasterCard cards. Interpret and write this proportion as a conditional probability.

c. Are the events *having a MasterCard card* and *having a Visa card* independent? Justify your answer.

3.19 Recall from Exercise 3.13 (page 99) that each month a brokerage house studies various companies and rates each company's stock as being either "low risk" or "moderate to high risk." In a recent report, the brokerage house summarized its findings about 15 Internet services companies and 25 financial sector companies in the following table:

Company Type	Low Risk	Moderate to High Risk
Internet Services	6	9
Financial Sector	20	5

Suppose we randomly select one of the total of 40 companies.
  a. Find the probability that the company's stock is moderate to high risk given that the firm is in the financial sector.
  b. Find the probability that the company's stock is moderate to high risk given that the firm is an Internet services company.
  c. Determine if the company type is independent of the level of risk of the firm's stock.

3.20 John and Jane are housemates. The probability that John watches a certain television show is 0.4. The probability that Jane watches the show is 0.5. The probability that John watches the show, given that Jane does, is 0.7.
  a. Find the probability that both John and Jane watch the show.
  b. Find the probability that Jane watches the show, given that John does.
  c. Do John and Jane watch the show independently of each other? Justify your answer.

3.21 In Exercise 3.20, find the probability that either John or Jane watches the show.

3.22 In the July 29, 2001, issue of *The Journal News* (Hamilton, Ohio), Lynn Elber of the Associated Press reported that "while 40 percent of American families own a television set with a V-chip installed to block designated programs with sex and violence, only 17 percent of those parents use the device."[2]
  a. Use the report's results to find an estimate of the probability that a randomly selected American family has used a V-chip to block programs containing sex and violence.
  b. According to the report, more than 50 percent of parents have used the TV rating system (TV-14, etc.) to control their children's TV viewing. How does this compare to the percentage using the V-chip?

3.23 According to the Associated Press report (in Exercise 3.22), 47 percent of parents who purchased TV sets after V-chips became standard equipment in January 2000 are aware that their sets have V-chips, and of those who are aware of the option, 36 percent have programmed their V-chips. Using these results, find an estimate of the probability that a randomly selected parent who has bought a TV set since January 2000 has programmed the V-chip.

3.24 Fifteen percent of the employees in a company have managerial positions, and 25 percent of the employees in the company have MBA degrees. Also, 60 percent of the managers have MBA degrees.

  a. Using the probability formulas,
    (1) Find the proportion of employees who are managers and have MBA degrees.
    (2) Find the proportion of MBAs who are managers.
  b. Are the events *being a manager* and *having an MBA* independent? Justify your answer.

3.25 In Exercise 3.24, find the proportion of employees who either have MBAs or are managers.

3.26 Consider Exercise 3.14 (pages 99 and 100). Using the results in Table 3.4 (page 100), estimate the probability that a randomly selected 21- to 49-year-old consumer would
  a. Give the phrase a rating of 4 or 5 given that the consumer is male; give the phrase a rating of 4 or 5 given that the consumer is female. Based on these results, is the appeal of the phrase among males much different from the appeal of the phrase among females? Explain.
  b. Give the phrase a rating of 4 or 5, given that the consumer is in the 21–24 age group; given that the consumer is in the 25–34 age group; given that the consumer is in the 35–49 age group. Based on these results, which age group finds the phrase most appealing? least appealing?

3.27 In a survey of 100 insurance claims, 40 are fire claims (*FIRE*), 16 of which are fraudulent (*FRAUD*). Also there are 40 fraudulent claims in total.
  a. Construct a contingency table summarizing the claims data. Use the pairs of events *FIRE* and $\overline{FIRE}$, *FRAUD* and $\overline{FRAUD}$.
  b. What proportion of the fire claims are fraudulent?
  c. Are the events *a claim is fraudulent* and *a claim is a fire claim* independent? Use your probability of part b to prove your answer.

3.28 Recall from Exercise 3.3 (page 92) that two randomly selected customers are each asked to take a blind taste test and then to state which of three diet colas (marked as *A*, *B*, or *C*) they prefer. Suppose that cola *A*'s distributor claims that 80 percent of all people prefer cola *A* and that only 10 percent prefer each of colas *B* and *C*.

  a. Assuming that the distributor's claim is true and that the two taste test participants make independent cola preference decisions, find the probability of each sample space outcome.

  b. Find the probability that neither taste test participant will prefer cola *A*.

  c. If, when the taste test is carried out, neither participant prefers cola *A*, use the probability you computed in part b to decide whether the distributor's claim seems valid. Explain.

3.29 A sprinkler system inside an office building has two types of activation devices, *D*1 and *D*2, which operate independently. When there is a fire, if either device operates correctly, the sprinkler system is turned on. In case of fire, the probability that *D*1 operates correctly is 0.95, and the probability that *D*2 operates correctly is 0.92. Find the probability that

  a. Both *D*1 and *D*2 will operate correctly.

  b. The sprinkler system will come on.

  c. The sprinkler system will fail.

3.30 A product is assembled using 10 different components, each of which must meet specifications for five different quality characteristics. Suppose that there is a 0.9973 probability that each individual specification will be met.

  a. Assuming that all 50 specifications are met independently, find the probability that the product meets all 50 specifications.

  b. Suppose that we wish to have a 99.73 percent chance that all 50 specifications will be met. If each specification will have the same chance of being met, how large must we make the probability of meeting each individual specification?

3.31 In a murder trial in Vancouver, the prosecution claims that the defendant was cut on the left middle finger at the murder scene, but the defendant claims the cut occurred in Winnipeg, the day after the murders had been committed. Because the defendant is a sports celebrity, many people noticed him before he reached Winnipeg. Twenty-two people saw him casually, one person on the plane to Winnipeg carefully studied his hands looking for a championship ring, and another person stood with him as he signed autographs and drove him from the airport to the hotel. None of these 24 people saw a cut on the defendant's finger. If in fact he was not cut at all, it would be extremely unlikely that he left blood at the murder scene.

  a. Since a person casually meeting the defendant would not be looking for a cut, assume that the probability is 0.9 that such a person would not have seen the cut, even if it was there. Furthermore, assume that the person who carefully looked at the defendant's hands had a 0.5 probability of not seeing the cut even if it was there and that the person who drove the defendant from the airport to the hotel had a 0.6 probability of not seeing the cut even if it was there. Given these assumptions, and also assuming that all 24 people looked at the defendant independently of each other, what is the probability that all 24 people would not have seen the cut, even if it was there?

  b. What is the probability that at least one of the 24 people would have seen the cut if it was there?

  c. Given the result of part b and given the fact that none of the 24 people saw a cut, do you think the defendant had a cut on his hand before he reached Winnipeg?

  d. How might we estimate what the assumed probabilities in part a would actually be? (Note: This would not be easy.)

3.5 Bayes' Theorem

Sometimes we have an initial or **prior** probability that an event will occur. Then, based on new information, we revise the prior probability to what is called a **posterior** probability. This revision can be done by using a theorem called **Bayes' theorem**.

Example 3.14

Two sections of a statistics course are being taught. From what she has heard about the two instructors, Melanie estimates that the chances of passing the course are 0.90 if she gets Professor Chapin and 0.75 if she gets Professor Fulford. The section that she is put in is determined by the Registrar's Office. Suppose that her chances of being put in Professor Chapin's section are 40 percent. Melanie does indeed pass the course. What are the chances that she was enrolled in Professor Chapin's section?

  P(being enrolled in Chapin's class) $= 0.40$ and P(not being in Chapin's class) $= 0.60$.

  P(pass | enrolled in Chapin's class) $= 0.90$ and P(fail | enrolled in Chapin's class) $= 0.10$.

Also,

  P(pass | enrolled in Fulford's class) $= 0.75$ and P(fail | enrolled in Fulford's class) $= 0.25$.

We want to know $P(\text{enrolled in Chapin's class} \mid \text{passed})$.

$P(\text{enrolled in Chapin's class} \mid \text{passed})$

$$= \frac{P(\text{Chapin} \cap \text{passed})}{P(\text{passed})} = \frac{P(\text{Chapin})P(\text{passed} \mid \text{Chapin})}{P(\text{Chapin})P(\text{passed} \mid \text{Chapin}) + P(\text{Fulford})P(\text{passed} \mid \text{Fulford})}.$$

This implies that

$$P(\text{enrolled in Chapin's class} \mid \text{passed}) = \frac{(0.4)(0.9)}{(0.4)(0.9) + (0.6)(0.75)} = \frac{0.36}{0.81} = \frac{4}{9}.$$

In the preceding example, there were two **states of nature**—C (in Chapin's class) and $\overline{C}$ (not in Chapin's class)—and two outcomes of the course—P (pass) and $\overline{P}$ (fail). In general, there might be any number of states of nature and any number of experimental outcomes. This leads to a general statement of Bayes' theorem.

Bayes' Theorem

Let $S_1, S_2, \ldots, S_k$ be k mutually exclusive states of nature, one of which must be true, and suppose that $P(S_1), P(S_2), \ldots, P(S_k)$ are the prior probabilities of these states of nature. Also let E be a particular outcome of an experiment designed to help determine which state of nature is really true. Then, the **posterior probability** of a particular state of nature, say S_i, given the experimental outcome E, is

$$P(S_i \mid E) = \frac{P(S_i \cap E)}{P(E)} = \frac{P(S_i)P(E \mid S_i)}{P(E)},$$

where

$$P(E) = P(S_1 \cap E) + P(S_2 \cap E) + \cdots + P(S_k \cap E)$$
$$= P(S_1)P(E \mid S_1) + P(S_2)P(E \mid S_2) + \cdots + P(S_k)P(E \mid S_k).$$

We illustrate Bayes' theorem in the following case.

Example 3.15   The Oil-Drilling Case

An oil company is attempting to decide whether to drill for oil on a particular site. There are three possible states of nature:

1   No oil (state of nature S_1, which we will denote as *none*).

2   Some oil (state of nature S_2, which we will denote as *some*).

3   Much oil (state of nature S_3, which we will denote as *much*).

Based on experience and knowledge concerning the site's geological characteristics, the oil company feels that the prior probabilities of these states of nature are as follows:

$$P(S_1 \equiv \text{none}) = 0.7, \qquad P(S_2 \equiv \text{some}) = 0.2, \qquad P(S_3 \equiv \text{much}) = 0.1.$$

In order to obtain more information about the potential drilling site, the oil company can perform a seismic experiment, which has three readings—low, medium, and high. Moreover, information exists concerning the accuracy of the seismic experiment. The company's historical records tell us that

1   Of 100 past sites that were drilled and produced no oil, 4 sites gave a high reading. Therefore,

$$P(\text{high} \mid \text{none}) = \frac{4}{100} = 0.04.$$

2   Of 400 past sites that were drilled and produced some oil, 8 sites gave a high reading. Therefore,

$$P(\text{high} \mid \text{some}) = \frac{8}{400} = 0.02.$$

3 Of 300 past sites that were drilled and produced much oil, 288 sites gave a high reading. Therefore,

$$P(\text{high} \mid \text{much}) = \frac{288}{300} = 0.96.$$

Intuitively, these conditional probabilities tell us that sites that produce no oil or some oil seldom give a high reading, while sites that produce much oil often give a high reading. Figure 3.6(a) shows a tree diagram that illustrates the prior probabilities of no, some, and much oil and the above

---

FIGURE 3.6 **A Tree Diagram and Probability Revision Tables for Bayes' Theorem in the Oil-Drilling Example**

(a) A tree diagram illustrating the prior and conditional probabilities

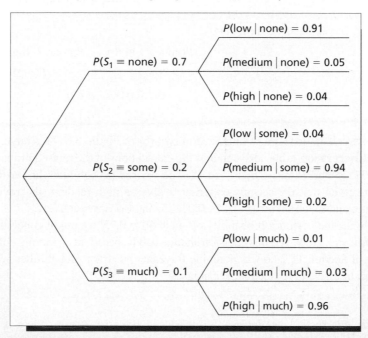

(b) A probability revision table for calculating the probability of a high reading and the posterior probabilities of no oil (S_1), some oil (S_2), and much oil (S_3), given a high reading

S_j	$P(S_j)$	$P(\text{high} \mid S_j)$	$P(S_j \cap \text{high}) = P(S_j)P(\text{high} \mid S_j)$	$P(S_j \mid \text{high}) = P(S_j \cap \text{high})/P(\text{high})$
$S_1 \equiv$ none	$P(\text{none}) = 0.7$	$P(\text{high} \mid \text{none}) = 0.04$	$P(\text{none} \cap \text{high}) = 0.7(0.04) = 0.028$	$P(\text{none} \mid \text{high}) = 0.028/0.128 = 0.21875$
$S_2 \equiv$ some	$P(\text{some}) = 0.2$	$P(\text{high} \mid \text{some}) = 0.02$	$P(\text{some} \cap \text{high}) = 0.2(0.02) = 0.004$	$P(\text{some} \mid \text{high}) = 0.004/0.128 = 0.03125$
$S_3 \equiv$ much	$P(\text{much}) = 0.1$	$P(\text{high} \mid \text{much}) = 0.96$	$P(\text{much} \cap \text{high}) = 0.1(0.96) = 0.096$	$P(\text{much} \mid \text{high}) = 0.096/0.128 = 0.75$
Total	1		$P(\text{high}) = 0.028 + 0.004 + 0.096 = 0.128$	1

(c) A probability revision table for calculating the probability of a medium reading and the posterior probabilities of no oil (S_1), some oil (S_2), and much oil (S_3), given a medium reading

S_j	$P(S_j)$	$P(\text{medium} \mid S_j)$	$P(S_j \cap \text{medium}) = P(S_j)P(\text{medium} \mid S_j)$	$P(S_j \mid \text{medium}) = P(S_j \cap \text{medium})/P(\text{medium})$
$S_1 \equiv$ none	$P(\text{none}) = 0.7$	$P(\text{medium} \mid \text{none}) = 0.05$	$P(\text{none} \cap \text{medium}) = 0.7(0.05) = 0.035$	$P(\text{none} \mid \text{medium}) = 0.035/0.226 = 0.15487$
$S_2 \equiv$ some	$P(\text{some}) = 0.2$	$P(\text{medium} \mid \text{some}) = 0.94$	$P(\text{some} \cap \text{medium}) = 0.2(0.94) = 0.188$	$P(\text{some} \mid \text{medium}) = 0.188/0.226 = 0.83186$
$S_3 \equiv$ much	$P(\text{much}) = 0.1$	$P(\text{medium} \mid \text{much}) = 0.03$	$P(\text{much} \cap \text{medium}) = 0.1(0.03) = 0.003$	$P(\text{much} \mid \text{medium}) = 0.003/0.226 = 0.01327$
Total	1		$P(\text{medium}) = 0.035 + 0.188 + 0.003 = 0.226$	1

(d) A probability revision table for calculating the probability of a low reading and the posterior probabilities of no oil (S_1), some oil (S_2), and much oil (S_3), given a low reading

S_j	$P(S_j)$	$P(\text{low} \mid S_j)$	$P(S_j \cap \text{low}) = P(S_j)P(\text{low} \mid S_j)$	$P(S_j \mid \text{low}) = P(S_j \cap \text{low})/P(\text{low})$
$S_1 \equiv$ none	$P(\text{none}) = 0.7$	$P(\text{low} \mid \text{none}) = 0.91$	$P(\text{none} \cap \text{low}) = 0.7(0.91) = 0.637$	$P(\text{none} \mid \text{low}) = 0.637/0.646 = 0.98607$
$S_2 \equiv$ some	$P(\text{some}) = 0.2$	$P(\text{low} \mid \text{some}) = 0.04$	$P(\text{some} \cap \text{low}) = 0.2(0.04) = 0.008$	$P(\text{some} \mid \text{low}) = 0.008/0.646 = 0.01238$
$S_3 \equiv$ much	$P(\text{much}) = 0.1$	$P(\text{low} \mid \text{much}) = 0.01$	$P(\text{much} \cap \text{low}) = 0.1(0.01) = 0.001$	$P(\text{much} \mid \text{low}) = 0.001/0.646 = 0.00155$
Total	1		$P(\text{low}) = 0.637 + 0.008 + 0.001 = 0.646$	1

conditional probabilities. This figure also gives the conditional probabilities for medium and low readings of the seismic experiment given each of the states of nature (none, some, or much).

Now suppose that when the company performs the seismic experiment on the site in question, it obtains a high reading. The previously given conditional probabilities suggest that, given this new information, the company might feel that the likelihood of much oil is higher than its prior probability $P(\text{much}) = 0.1$, and that the likelihoods of some oil and no oil are lower than the prior probabilities $P(\text{some}) = 0.2$ and $P(\text{none}) = 0.7$. To be more specific, we wish to **revise the prior probabilities** of no, some, and much oil to what we call **posterior probabilities**. We can do this by using Bayes' theorem as follows.

If we wish to compute $P(\text{none} \mid \text{high})$, we first calculate

$$P(\text{high}) = P(\text{none} \cap \text{high}) + P(\text{some} \cap \text{high}) + P(\text{much} \cap \text{high})$$
$$= P(\text{none})P(\text{high} \mid \text{none}) + P(\text{some})P(\text{high} \mid \text{some}) + P(\text{much})P(\text{high} \mid \text{much})$$
$$= (0.7)(0.04) + (0.2)(0.02) + (0.1)(0.96) = 0.128.$$

Then, Bayes' theorem says that

$$P(\text{none} \mid \text{high}) = \frac{P(\text{none} \cap \text{high})}{P(\text{high})} = \frac{P(\text{none})P(\text{high} \mid \text{none})}{P(\text{high})}$$

$$= \frac{0.7(0.04)}{0.128} = \frac{0.028}{0.128} = 0.21875.$$

These calculations are summarized in part (b) of Figure 3.6. This table, which is called a **probability revision table**, also contains the calculations of the revised probabilities $P(\text{some} \mid \text{high}) = 0.031\,25$ and $P(\text{much} \mid \text{high}) = 0.75$. The revised probabilities in part (b) of Figure 3.6 tell us that, given that the seismic experiment gives a high reading, the revised probabilities of no, some, and much oil are 0.21875, 0.03125, and 0.75, respectively.

Since the posterior probability of much oil is 0.75, we might conclude that we should drill on the oil site. However, this decision should also be based on economic considerations, and we will see in Section 15.2 how to combine Bayesian posterior probabilities with economic considerations to arrive at reasonable decisions.

In this section, we have only introduced Bayes' theorem. There is an entire subject called **Bayesian statistics**, which uses Bayes' theorem to update prior belief about a probability or population parameter to posterior belief. The use of Bayesian statistics is controversial in the case where the prior belief is largely based on subjective considerations, because many statisticians do not believe that we should base decisions on subjective considerations. Realistically, however, we all do this in our daily lives. For example, how each of us viewed the evidence in the O. J. Simpson trial had a great deal to do with our prior beliefs about both O. J. Simpson and the police.

Exercises for Section 3.5

CONCEPTS

3.32 What is a prior probability? What is a posterior probability?

3.33 Explain the purpose behind using Bayes' theorem.

METHODS AND APPLICATIONS

3.34 Suppose that A_1, A_2, and B are events where A_1 and A_2 are mutually exclusive and

$$P(A_1) = 0.8, \qquad P(B \mid A_1) = 0.1,$$
$$P(A_2) = 0.2, \qquad P(B \mid A_2) = 0.3.$$

Use this information to find $P(A_1 \mid B)$ and $P(A_2 \mid B)$.

3.35 Suppose that A_1, A_2, A_3, and B are events where A_1, A_2, and A_3 are mutually exclusive and

$$P(A_1) = 0.2, \qquad P(A_2) = 0.5, \qquad P(A_3) = 0.3,$$
$$P(B \mid A_1) = 0.02, \quad P(B \mid A_2) = 0.05, \quad P(B \mid A_3) = 0.04.$$

Use this information to find $P(A_1 \mid B)$, $P(A_2 \mid B)$, and $P(A_3 \mid B)$.

3.36 Consider a screening test for a certain type of cancer. Suppose that it is known that 0.5 percent of the population actually have this type of cancer. The test cannot perfectly screen for the disease, but suppose that it properly detects cancer 95% of the time and it improperly detects cancer 2 percent of the time. If the result of the test is positive, what is the chance that the person will actually have cancer?

3.37 A department store is considering a new credit policy to try to reduce the number of customers defaulting on payments. A suggestion is made to discontinue credit to any customer who has been one week or more late with their payment at least twice. Past records show 95 percent of defaults were late at least twice. Also, 3 percent of all customers default, and 30 percent of those who have not defaulted have had at least two late payments.
a. Find the probability that a customer with at least two late payments will default.
b. Based on part a, should the policy be adopted? Explain.

3.38 A company administers an "aptitude test for managers" to aid in selecting new management trainees. Prior experience suggests that 60 percent of all applicants for management trainee positions would be successful if they were hired. Furthermore, past experience with the aptitude test indicates that 85 percent of applicants who turn out to be successful managers pass the test and 90 percent of applicants who turn out not to be successful managers fail the test.
a. If an applicant passes the aptitude test for managers, what is the probability that the applicant will succeed in a management position?
b. Based on your answer to part a, do you think that the aptitude test for managers is a valuable way to screen applicants for management trainee positions? Explain.

3.39 Three data entry specialists enter requisitions into a computer. Specialist 1 processes 30 percent of the requisitions, specialist 2 processes 45 percent, and specialist 3 processes 25 percent. The proportions of incorrectly entered requisitions by data entry specialists 1, 2, and 3 are 0.03, 0.05, and 0.02, respectively. Suppose that a random requisition is found to have been incorrectly entered. What is the probability that it was processed by data entry specialist 1? by data entry specialist 2? by data entry specialist 3?

3.40 A truth serum given to a suspect is known to be 90 percent reliable when the person is guilty and 99 percent reliable when the person is innocent. In other words, 10 percent of the guilty are judged innocent by the serum and 1 percent of the innocent are judged guilty. If the suspect was selected from a group of suspects of which only 5 percent are guilty of having committed a crime, and the serum indicates that the suspect is guilty of having committed a crime, what is the probability that the suspect is innocent?

3.41 A firm designs and builds automatic electronic control devices and installs them in customers' plants. In shipment, a device has a prior probability of 0.10 of getting out of alignment. Before a control device is installed, test equipment is used to check the device's alignment. The test equipment has two readings, "in" or "out" of alignment. If the control device is in alignment, there is a 0.8 probability that the test equipment will read "in." If the control device is not in alignment, there is a 0.9 probability that the test equipment will read "out."
a. Draw a tree diagram illustrating the prior and conditional probabilities for this situation.
b. Construct a probability revision table for calculating the probability that the test equipment reads "in" and for calculating the posterior probabilities of the control device being in alignment and out of alignment given that the test equipment reads "in." What is $P(\text{in} \mid \text{reads "in"})$? What is $P(\text{out} \mid \text{reads "in"})$?
c. Construct a probability revision table for calculating the probability that the test equipment reads "out" and for calculating the posterior probabilities of the control device being in alignment and out of alignment given that the test equipment reads "out." What is $P(\text{in} \mid \text{reads "out"})$? What is $P(\text{out} \mid \text{reads "out"})$?

3.42 Suppose that a box contains one fair coin and one coin with heads on both sides. One coin is selected from the box at random and tossed once and the result is a head.
a. What is the chance that the coin is the fair coin?
b. Now suppose that the same coin is tossed again, and the result is a head again. What is the chance that this coin is the fair coin?

CHAPTER SUMMARY

In this chapter, we studied **probability**. We began by defining an **event** to be an experimental outcome that may or may not occur and by defining the **probability of an event** to be a number that measures the likelihood that the event will occur. We learned that a probability is often interpreted as a **long-run relative frequency**, and we saw that probabilities can be found by examining **sample spaces** and by using **probability rules**. We learned several important probability rules—**addition rules**, **multiplication rules**, and **the rule of complements**. We also studied a special kind of probability called a **conditional probability**, which is the probability that one event will occur given that another event occurs, and we used probabilities to define **independent events**.

We concluded this chapter by discussing **Bayes' theorem**. We learned that this theorem is used to revise **prior probabilities** to **posterior probilities**, which are revised probabilities based on new information. We saw that the **general multiplication rule** for probabilities is very useful when solving **Bayes' theorem** problems.

GLOSSARY OF TERMS

Bayes' theorem: A theorem (formula) that is used to compute posterior probabilities by revising prior probabilities. (page 108)

Bayesian statistics: An area of statistics that uses Bayes' theorem to update prior belief about a probability or population parameter to posterior belief. (page 110)

complement (of an event): If *A* is an event, the complement of *A* is the event that *A* will not occur. (page 92)

conditional probability: The probability that one event will occur given that we know that another event occurs. (page 100)

dependent events: When the probability of one event is influenced by whether another event occurs, the events are said to be dependent. (page 103)

event: A set of sample space outcomes. (page 89)

experiment: A process of observation that has an uncertain outcome. (page 86)

independent events: When the probability of one event is not influenced by whether another event occurs, the events are said to be independent. (page 103)

mutually exclusive events: Events that have no sample space outcomes in common and, therefore, cannot occur simultaneously. (page 96)

posterior probability: A revised probability obtained by updating a prior probability after receiving new information. (page 107)

prior probability: The initial probability that an event will occur. (page 107)

probability (of an event): A number that measures the chance, or likelihood, that an event will occur when an experiment is carried out. (page 89)

sample space: The set of all possible experimental outcomes (sample space outcomes). (page 87)

sample space outcome: A distinct outcome of an experiment (that is, an element in the sample space). (page 87)

subjective probability: A probability assessment that is based on experience, intuitive judgment, or expertise. (page 87)

IMPORTANT FORMULAS

Probabilities when all sample space outcomes are equally likely: page 90

The rule of complements: page 93

The addition rule for two events: page 96

The addition rule for two mutually exclusive events: page 97

The addition rule for *N* mutually exclusive events: page 98

Conditional probability: page 101

The general multiplication rule: page 102

Independence: page 103

The multiplication rule for two independent events: page 104

The multiplication rule for *N* independent events: page 104

Bayes' theorem: page 108

Probability revision table: page 110

SUPPLEMENTARY EXERCISES

Exercises 3.43 through 3.46 are based on the following situation: An investor holds two stocks, each of which can rise (*R*), remain unchanged (*U*), or decline (*D*) on any particular day.

3.43 Construct a tree diagram showing all possible combined movements for both stocks on a particular day (for instance, *RR*, *RD*, and so on, where the first letter denotes the movement of the first stock and the second letter denotes the movement of the second stock).

3.44 If all outcomes are equally likely, find the probability that both stocks rise; that both stocks decline; that exactly one stock declines.

3.45 Find the probabilities you found in Exercise 3.44 by assuming that for each stock $P(R) = 0.6$, $P(U) = 0.1$, and

$P(D) = 0.3$, and assuming that the two stocks move independently.

3.46 Assume that for the first stock (on a particular day)

$$P(R) = 0.4, \ P(U) = 0.2, \ P(D) = 0.4,$$

and that for the second stock (on a particular day)

$$P(R) = 0.8, \ P(U) = 0.1, \ P(D) = 0.1.$$

Assuming that these stocks move independently, find the probability that both stocks decline; the probability that exactly one stock rises; the probability that exactly one stock is unchanged; the probability that both stocks rise.

Statistics Canada (http://www.statcan.ca) reports various employment statistics. The recent values of employment (employed or not employed) by sex and age for 2005 are provided below.

(Note: Some rounding has been done to ease the calculations; numbers are in thousands.) Using the information contained in the tables, answer Exercises 3.47 through 3.51. 🐾 CanEmp

Employment: Age	Women		Men		Both Sexes	
	Yes	No	Yes	No	Yes	No
15–24 years	1,234	146	1,239	204	2,473	350
25–44 years	6,342	378	7,356	444	13,680	822
45–64 years	2,672	148	3,120	176	5,792	324
65 and older	104	4	204	7	308	11

Source: Adapted from the Statistics Canada Web site, http://www.40statcan.ca101cst01/labor20a.htm.

3.47 Find the probability that a randomly selected woman aged 15–24 is employed. ● CanEmp

3.48 Find the probability that a randomly selected woman aged 45–64 is unemployed. ● CanEmp

3.49 Find the probability that a randomly selected woman is employed if she is older than 25 years. ● CanEmp

3.50 Repeat Exercises 3.47 to 3.49 for a randomly selected male.

3.51 Find the probability that a randomly selected individual (regardless of sex) is employed and is older than 45 years.

Suppose that in a survey of 1,000 Ontario residents, 721 residents believed that the amount of violent television programming had increased over the past 10 years, 454 residents believed that the overall quality of television programming had decreased over the past 10 years, and 362 residents believed both. Use this information to do Exercises 3.52 through 3.58.

3.52 What proportion of the 1,000 Ontario residents believed that the amount of violent programming had increased over the past 10 years?

3.53 What proportion of the 1,000 Ontario residents believed that the overall quality of programming had decreased over the past 10 years?

3.54 What proportion of the 1,000 Ontario residents believed that both the amount of violent programming had increased and the overall quality of programming had decreased over the past 10 years?

3.55 What proportion of the 1,000 Ontario residents believed that either the amount of violent programming had increased or the overall quality of programming had decreased over the past 10 years?

3.56 What proportion of the Ontario residents who believed that the amount of violent programming had increased believed that the overall quality of programming had decreased?

3.57 What proportion of the Ontario residents who believed that the overall quality of programming had decreased believed that the amount of violent programming had increased?

3.58 What sort of dependence seems to exist between whether Ontario residents believed that the amount of violent programming had increased and whether Ontario residents believed that the overall quality of programming had decreased? Explain your answer.

3.59 Enterprise Industries has been running a television advertisement for Fresh liquid laundry detergent. When a survey was conducted, 21 percent of the individuals surveyed had purchased Fresh, 41 percent of the individuals surveyed had recalled seeing the advertisement, and 13 percent of the individuals surveyed had purchased Fresh and recalled seeing the advertisement.

   a. What proportion of the individuals surveyed who recalled seeing the advertisement had purchased Fresh?

   b. Based on your answer to part a, does the advertisement seem to have been effective? Explain.

3.60 A company employs 400 salespeople. Of these, 83 received a bonus last year, 100 attended a special sales training program at the beginning of last year, and 42 both attended the special sales training program and received a bonus. (Note: The bonus was based totally on sales performance.)

   a. What proportion of the 400 salespeople received a bonus last year?

   b. What proportion of the 400 salespeople attended the special sales training program at the beginning of last year?

   c. What proportion of the 400 salespeople both attended the special sales training program and received a bonus?

   d. What proportion of the salespeople who attended the special sales training program received a bonus?

   e. Based on your answers to parts a and d, does the special sales training program seem to have been effective? Explain your answer.

3.61 Suppose that A and B are events and that $P(A)$ and $P(B)$ are both positive.

   a. If A and B are mutually exclusive, what is $P(A \cap B)$?

   b. If A and B are independent events, explain why $P(A \cap B)$ is positive.

   c. Can two mutually exclusive events, each having a positive probability of occurrence, also be independent? Prove your answer using your answers to parts a and b.

3.62 On any given day, the probability that the Ohio River at Cincinnati is polluted by a carbon tetrachloride spill is 0.10. Each day, a test is conducted to determine whether the river is polluted by carbon tetrachloride. This test has proved correct 80 percent of the time. Suppose that on a particular day the test indicates carbon tetrachloride pollution. What is the probability that such pollution actually exists?

3.63 A marketing major will interview for an internship with a major consumer products manufacturer/distributor. Before the interview, the marketing major feels that the chances of being offered an internship are 40 percent. Suppose that of the students who have been offered internships with this company, 90 percent had good interviews, and that of the students who have not been offered internships, 50 percent had good interviews. If the marketing major has a good interview, what is the probability that they will be offered an internship?

3.64 Suppose you are at a house party and 35 people are present. You have recently taken a statistics course and you wonder how many people in this group of 35 have the same birthday. You get everyone to write their birthday down (just the month and day) on a cocktail napkin.

   a. What is the chance that you will share a birthday with someone else at the party?

   b. What is the chance that there will be atleast one matched birthday at this party?

   c. How many need to attend the party in order for there to be about a 50 percent chance that there is at least one matched birthday?

3.65   In the book *Making Hard Decisions: An Introduction to Decision Analysis*, Clemen presents an example in which he discusses the 1982 John Hinckley trial. In describing the case, Clemen says:

> In 1982 John Hinckley was on trial, accused of having attempted to kill President Reagan. During Hinckley's trial, Dr. Daniel R. Weinberger told the court that when individuals diagnosed as schizophrenics were given computerized axial tomography (CAT) scans, the scans showed brain atrophy in 30% of the cases compared with only 2% of the scans done on normal people. Hinckley's defense attorney wanted to introduce as evidence Hinckley's CAT scan, which showed brain atrophy. The defense argued that the presence of atrophy strengthened the case that Hinckley suffered from mental illness.

a. Approximately 1.5 percent of the people in the United States suffer from schizophrenia. If we consider the prior probability of schizophrenia to be 0.015, use the information given to find the probability that a person has schizophrenia given that a person's CAT scan shows brain atrophy.

b. John Hinckley's CAT scan showed brain atrophy. Discuss whether your answer to part a helps or hurts the case that Hinckley suffered from mental illness.

c. It can be argued that 0.015 is not a reasonable prior probability of schizophrenia. This is because 0.015 is the probability that a randomly selected U.S. citizen has schizophrenia. However, John Hinckley is not a randomly selected U.S. citizen. Rather, he was accused of attempting to assassinate the president. Therefore, it might be reasonable to assess a higher prior probability of schizophrenia. Suppose you are a juror who believes there is only a 10 percent chance that Hinckley suffers from schizophrenia. Using 0.10 as the prior probability of schizophrenia, find the probability that a person has schizophrenia given that a person's CAT scan shows brain atrophy.

d. If you are a juror with a prior probability of 0.10 that John Hinckley suffers from schizophrenia and given your answer to part c, does the fact that Hinckley's CAT scan showed brain atrophy help the case that Hinckley suffered from mental illness?

e. If you are a juror with a prior probability of 0.25 that Hinckley suffers from schizophrenia, find the probability of schizophrenia given that Hinckley's CAT scan showed brain atrophy. In this situation, how strong is the case that Hinckley suffered from mental illness?

3.66   INTERNET EXERCISE

BBM Canada reports on radio statistics for a variety of cities across the country. Go to the 2006 data at http://www.bbm.ca/en/radio_top_line.html and compare the share aggregates found for the city of your choice to those reported in this chapter for London, Ontario. How do the aggregates compare? What factor do you feel would make the aggregates differ?

CHAPTER **4**

Discrete Random Variables

LEARNING OBJECTIVES

After reading this chapter, you should be able to

- describe what is meant by a random variable
- explain the difference between a discrete random variable and a continuous random variable
- describe the ways in which a probability distribution of a discrete random variable can be depicted
- calculate the mean (or expected value), variance, and standard deviation of discrete random variables
- distinguish between the binomial distribution and the Poisson distribution

CHAPTER OUTLINE

Examples of discrete random variables are the number of heads in *n* tosses of a fair coin, the number of times you hit the snooze button before you wake up, the number of red lights you encounter on the way to school, and the number of courses you take in a school year. Examples of continuous random variables are the amount of coffee you drink every day (measured in millilitres), the amount of gasoline you put in your car, the amount of time you talk on your cell phone, and the amount of time you wait for the bus.

4.1 Two Types of Random Variables

A **random variable** is a variable that assumes numerical values that are determined by the outcome of an experiment, where one and only one numerical value is assigned to each experimental outcome.

Before an experiment is carried out, its outcome is uncertain. It follows that, since a random variable assigns a number to each experimental outcome, a random variable can be thought of as **representing an uncertain numerical outcome**.

To illustrate the idea of a random variable, suppose that Sound City sells and installs car stereo systems. One of Sound City's most popular stereo systems is the top-of-the-line TrueSound-XL. Consider (the experiment of) selling the TrueSound-XL stereo at the Sound City store during a particular week. If we let x denote the number of stereos sold during the week, then x is a random variable. That is, looked at before the week, the number of stereos x that will be sold is uncertain, and, therefore, x is a random variable.

Notice that x, the number of TrueSound-XL stereos sold in a week, might be 0 or 1 or 2 or 3, and so forth. In general, when the possible values of a random variable can be counted or listed, then the random variable is a **discrete random variable**. That is, either a discrete random variable may assume a finite number of possible values or the possible values may take the form of a **countable** sequence or list such as 0, 1, 2, 3, 4, . . . (a **countably infinite** list).

CHAPTER 3

Some other examples of discrete random variables are as follows:

1   The number, x, of the next three customers entering a store who will make a purchase. Here x could be 0, 1, 2, or 3.

2   The number, x, of four patients taking a new antibiotic who experience gastrointestinal distress as a side effect. Here x could be 0, 1, 2, 3, or 4.

3   The number, x, of television sets in a sample of eight five-year-old television sets that have not needed a single repair. Here x could be any of the values 0, 1, 2, 3, 4, 5, 6, 7, and 8.

4   The rating, x, on a 1 through 5 scale given to a song by a listener in a music survey. Here x could be 1, 2, 3, 4, or 5.

5   The number, x, of major fires in a large city during the last two months. Here x could be 0, 1, 2, 3, and so forth (there is no definite maximum number of fires).

The values of the random variables described in (1), (2), (3), and (4) are countable and finite. In contrast, the values of the random variables described in (5) are countable and infinite (or countably infinite lists). For example, in theory there is no limit to the number of major fires that could occur in a city in two months.

Not all random variables have values that are countable. When a random variable may assume any numerical value in one or more intervals on the real number line, then the random variable is a **continuous random variable**.

Example 4.1 The Mass of the Loonie

Consider the Canadian dollar coin (loonie) example that was discussed in Chapters 1 and 2. The mass of a randomly selected coin, x, is a continuous random variable. Even though the masses of the coins have been measured to four decimal places, there is no way of measuring the absolute exact mass of these coins. Theoretically, the mass could be expressed to an infinite number of decimal places, which would be impossible to graph. The masses of the coins vary continuously, but, for the purposes of this example, we have chosen to measure them to four decimal places.

Some other examples of continuous random variables are as follows:

1 The temperature (in degrees Celsius) of a cup of coffee served at a McDonald's restaurant.
2 The volume (in millilitres) of strawberry jam dispensed by an automatic filling machine into a 500-mL jar.
3 The time (in minutes) that a customer in a store must wait to receive a credit card authorization.
4 The interest rate (in percent) charged for mortgage loans at a bank.

Exercises for Section 4.1

CONCEPTS

4.1 Explain the concept of a random variable.

4.2 Explain how the values of a discrete random variable differ from the values of a continuous random variable.

4.3 Classify each of the following random variables as discrete or continuous:
  a. x = the number of girls born to a couple who will have three children.
  b. x = the number of defects found on an automobile at final inspection.

  c. x = the mass (in grams) of the sandwich meat in a submarine sandwich.
  d. x = the number of incorrect lab procedures conducted at a hospital during a particular week.
  e. x = the number of customers served during a given day at a drive-through window.
  f. x = the time needed by a clerk to complete a task.
  g. x = the temperature of a pizza oven at a particular time.

4.2 Discrete Probability Distributions

The value assumed by a discrete random variable depends on the outcome of an experiment. Because the outcome of the experiment will be uncertain, the value assumed by the random variable will also be uncertain. However, it is often useful to know the probabilities that are associated with the different values that the random variable can take on. That is, we often wish to know the random variable's **probability distribution**.

The **probability distribution** of a discrete random variable is a table, graph, or formula that gives the probability associated with each possible value that the random variable can assume.

We denote the probability distribution of the discrete random variable x as $p(x)$. As will be demonstrated in the following example, we can sometimes use the sample space of an experiment and probability rules to find the probability distribution of a random variable.

Example 4.2

Consider the pop quiz consisting of three true–false questions in Chapter 3. Remember that the sample space when a student takes such a quiz consists of the outcomes

$$CCC \quad CCI \quad CIC \quad ICC$$
$$CII \quad ICI \quad IIC \quad III$$

We now define the random variable x to be the number of questions that the student answers correctly. Here x can assume the value 0, 1, 2, or 3. That is, the student could answer anywhere between 0 and 3 questions correctly. In Examples 3.2 and 3.3, we assumed that the student is totally unprepared for the quiz and thus has only a 0.5 probability of answering each question correctly. We now assume that the student studies and has a 0.9 probability of answering each question correctly. Table 4.1 summarizes finding the probabilities associated with each of the values of x (0, 1, 2, and 3). As an example of the calculations, consider finding the probability that x equals 2. Two questions will be answered correctly if and only if we obtain one of the sample space outcomes

$$CCI \quad CIC \quad ICC$$

TABLE **4.1**   Finding the Probability Distribution of $x =$ the Number of Questions Answered Correctly When the Student Studies and Has a 90 Percent Chance of Answering Each Question Correctly

Value of x = the Number of Correct Answers	Sample Space Outcomes Corresponding to Value of x	Probability of Sample Space Outcome	p(x) = Probability of the Value of x
$x = 0$ (no correct answers)	III	$(0.1)(0.1)(0.1) = 0.001$	$p(0) = 0.001$
$x = 1$ (one correct answer)	CII	$(0.9)(0.1)(0.1) = 0.009$	$p(1) = 0.009 + 0.009 + 0.009 = 0.027$
	ICI	$(0.1)(0.9)(0.1) = 0.009$	
	IIC	$(0.1)(0.1)(0.9) = 0.009$	
$x = 2$ (two correct answers)	CCI	$(0.9)(0.9)(0.1) = 0.081$	$p(2) = 0.081 + 0.081 + 0.081 = 0.243$
	CIC	$(0.9)(0.1)(0.9) = 0.081$	
	ICC	$(0.1)(0.9)(0.9) = 0.081$	
$x = 3$ (three correct answers)	CCC	$(0.9)(0.9)(0.9) = 0.729$	$p(3) = 0.729$

Assuming that the three questions will be answered independently, these sample space outcomes have probabilities

$$P(CCI) = (0.9)(0.9)(0.1) = 0.081,$$
$$P(CIC) = (0.9)(0.1)(0.9) = 0.081,$$
$$P(ICC) = (0.1)(0.9)(0.9) = 0.081.$$

Therefore,

$$P(x = 2) = P(CCI) + P(CIC) + P(ICC)$$
$$= 0.081 + 0.081 + 0.081$$
$$= 0.243.$$

Similarly, we can obtain probabilities associated with $x = 0$, $x = 1$, and $x = 3$. The probability distribution of x is summarized as follows:

x, Number of Questions Answered Correctly	p(x), Probability of x
0	$p(0) = P(x = 0) = 0.001$
1	$p(1) = P(x = 1) = 0.027$
2	$p(2) = P(x = 2) = 0.243$
3	$p(3) = P(x = 3) = 0.729$

Notice that the probabilities in this probability distribution sum to $0.001 + 0.027 + 0.243 + 0.729 = 1$.

To show the advantage of studying, note that the above probability distribution says that if the student has a 0.9 probability of answering each question correctly, then the probability that the student will answer all three questions correctly is 0.729. Furthermore, the probability that the student will answer **at least** two out of three questions correctly is (since the events $x = 2$ and $x = 3$ are mutually exclusive)

$$P(x \geq 2) = P(x = 2 \text{ or } x = 3)$$
$$= P(x = 2) + P(x = 3)$$
$$= 0.243 + 0.729$$
$$= 0.972.$$

By contrast, we saw in Example 3.3 that if the student is totally unprepared and has only a 0.5 probability of answering each question correctly, then the probabilities that the student will answer zero, one, two, and three questions correctly are, respectively, 1/8, 3/8, 3/8, and 1/8. Therefore, the probability that the unprepared student will answer all three questions correctly is only $1/8 = 0.125$, and the probability that this student will answer at least two out of three questions correctly is only $(3/8 + 1/8) = 0.5$.

In general, a discrete probability distribution $p(x)$ must satisfy two conditions:

A **discrete probability distribution $p(x)$** must be such that

1 $p(x) \geq 0$ for each value of x,

2 $\displaystyle\sum_{\text{All } x} p(x) = 1$.

The first of these conditions says that each probability in a probability distribution must be zero or positive. The second condition says that the probabilities in a probability distribution must sum to 1. Looking at the probability distribution illustrated in Example 4.2, we can see that these properties are satisfied.

Often it is not possible to examine the entire sample space of an experiment. In such a case, we sometimes collect data that will allow us to estimate the probabilities in a probability distribution.

Example 4.3

Recall that Sound City sells the TrueSound-XL car stereo system, and define the random variable x to be the number of such stereos sold in a particular week. In order to know the true probabilities of the various values of x, we would have to observe sales during all of the (potentially infinite number of) weeks in which the TrueSound-XL stereo could be sold. That is, if we consider an experiment in which we randomly select a week and observe sales of the TrueSound-XL, the sample space would consist of a potentially infinite number of equally likely weeks. Obviously, it is not possible to examine this entire sample space.

Suppose, however, that Sound City has kept historical records of TrueSound-XL sales during the last 100 weeks. These records tell us that

1 No stereos have been sold in 3 (that is, $3/100 = 0.03$) of the weeks.

2 One stereo has been sold in 20 (that is, 0.20) of the weeks.

3 Two stereos have been sold in 50 (that is, 0.50) of the weeks.

4 Three stereos have been sold in 20 (that is, 0.20) of the weeks.

5 Four stereos have been sold in 5 (that is, 0.05) of the weeks.

6 Five stereos have been sold in 2 (that is, 0.02) of the weeks.

7 No more than five stereos were sold in any of the past 100 weeks.

It follows that we might **estimate** that the probability distribution of x, the number of TrueSound-XL stereos sold during a particular week at Sound City, is as shown in Table 4.2. A graph of this distribution is shown in Figure 4.1.

TABLE **4.2** An Estimate (Based on 100 Weeks of Historical Data) of the Probability Distribution of x, the Number of TrueSound-XL Stereos Sold at Sound City in a Week

x, Number of Stereos Sold	$p(x)$, the Probability of x
0	$p(0) = P(x = 0) = 3/100 = 0.03$
1	$p(1) = P(x = 1) = 20/100 = 0.20$
2	$p(2) = P(x = 2) = 50/100 = 0.50$
3	$p(3) = P(x = 3) = 20/100 = 0.20$
4	$p(4) = P(x = 4) = 5/100 = 0.05$
5	$p(5) = P(x = 5) = 2/100 = 0.02$

FIGURE 4.1   **A Graph of the Probability Distribution of x, the Number of TrueSound-XL Stereos Sold at Sound City in a Week**

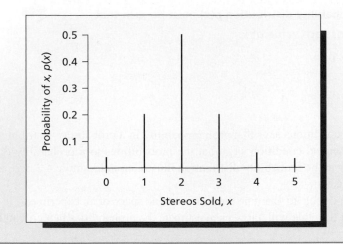

Finally, it is reasonable to use the historical sales data from the past 100 weeks to estimate the true probabilities associated with the various numbers of stereos sold if the sales process remains stable over time and is not seasonal (that is, if stereo sales are not higher at one time of the year than at others).

Suppose that the experiment described by a random variable x is repeated an indefinitely large number of times. If the values of the random variable x observed on the repetitions are recorded, we will obtain the population of all possible observed values of the random variable x. This population has a mean, which we denote as μ_x and which we sometimes call the **expected value of x**. In order to calculate μ_x, we multiply each value of x by its probability $p(x)$ and then sum the resulting products over all possible values of x.

The **mean**, or **expected value**, of a discrete random variable x is

$$\mu_x = \sum_{\text{All } x} x p(x).$$

In the next example, we illustrate how to calculate μ_x, and we reason that the calculation really does give the mean of all possible observed values of the random variable x.

Example 4.4

Remember that Table 4.2 gives the probability distribution of x, the number of TrueSound-XL stereo systems sold in a week at Sound City. Using this distribution, it follows that

$$\mu_x = \sum_{\text{All } x} x p(x)$$

$$= 0p(0) + 1p(1) + 2p(2) + 3p(3) + 4p(4) + 5p(5)$$

$$= 0(0.03) + 1(0.20) + 2(0.50) + 3(0.20) + 4(0.05) + 5(0.02)$$

$$= 2.1.$$

To see that such a calculation gives the mean of all possible observed values of x, recall from Example 4.3 that the probability distribution in Table 4.2 was estimated from historical records of TrueSound-XL sales during the last 100 weeks. Also recall that these historical records tell us that during the last 100 weeks Sound City sold

1 Zero stereos in 3 of the 100 weeks, for a total of 0(3) = 0 stereos.

2 One stereo in 20 of the 100 weeks, for a total of 1(20) = 20 stereos.

3 Two stereos in 50 of the 100 weeks, for a total of 2(50) = 100 stereos.

4 Three stereos in 20 of the 100 weeks, for a total of 3(20) = 60 stereos.

5 Four stereos in 5 of the 100 weeks, for a total of 4(5) = 20 stereos.

6 Five stereos in 2 of the 100 weeks, for a total of 5(2) = 10 stereos.

In other words, Sound City sold a total of

$$0 + 20 + 100 + 60 + 20 + 10 = 210 \text{ stereos}$$

in 100 weeks, or an average of $210/100 = 2.1$ stereos per week. Now the average

$$\frac{210}{100} = \frac{0 + 20 + 100 + 60 + 20 + 10}{100}$$

can be written as

$$\frac{0(3) + 1(20) + 2(50) + 3(20) + 4(5) + 5(2)}{100},$$

which can be rewritten as

$$0\left(\frac{3}{100}\right) + 1\left(\frac{20}{100}\right) + 2\left(\frac{50}{100}\right) + 3\left(\frac{20}{100}\right) + 4\left(\frac{5}{100}\right) + 5\left(\frac{2}{100}\right)$$
$$= 0(0.03) + 1(0.20) + 2(0.50) + 3(0.20) + 4(0.05) + 5(0.02),$$

which equals $\mu_x = 2.1$. That is, if observed sales values occur with relative frequencies equal to those specified by the probability distribution in Table 4.2, then the average number of stereos sold per week is equal to the expected value of x.

Of course, if we observe stereo sales for another 100 weeks, the relative frequencies of the observed sales values would probably not be exactly as specified by the estimated probabilities in Table 4.2. Rather, the observed relative frequencies would differ somewhat, and the average number of stereos sold per week would not exactly equal $\mu_x = 2.1$ (although the average would likely be close). However, the point is this: If the probability distribution in Table 4.2 were the true probability distribution of weekly stereo sales, and if we were to observe stereo sales for an indefinitely large number of weeks, then we would observe sales values with relative frequencies that are exactly equal to those specified by the probabilities in Table 4.2. In this case, when we calculate the expected value of x to be $\mu_x = 2.1$, we are saying that **in the long run** (that is, over an indefinitely large number of weeks), Sound City would average selling 2.1 TrueSound-XL stereo systems per week.

As another example, again consider Example 4.2, and let the random variable x denote the number of the three true–false questions that the student who studies answers correctly. Using the probability distribution shown in Table 4.1, the expected value of x is

$$\mu_x = 0(0.001) + 1(0.027) + 2(0.243) + 3(0.729)$$
$$= 2.7.$$

This expected value says that if a student takes a large number of three-question true–false quizzes and has a 0.9 probability of answering any single question correctly, then the student will average approximately 2.7 correct answers per quiz.

Example 4.5

An insurance company sells a $20 000 whole life insurance policy for an annual premium of $300. Actuarial tables show that a person who would be sold such a policy with this premium has a 0.001 probability of death during a year. Let x be a random variable representing the insurance company's profit made on one of these policies during a year. The probability distribution of x is as follows:

x, Profit	p(x), Probability of x
$300 (if the policyholder lives)	0.999
$300 − $20,000 = −$19,700 (a $19,700 loss if the policyholder dies)	0.001

The expected value of x (expected profit per year) is

$$\mu_x = \$300(0.999) + (-\$19{,}700)(0.001)$$
$$= \$280.$$

This says that if the insurance company sells a very large number of these policies, it will average a profit of $280 per policy per year. Since insurance companies actually do sell large numbers of policies, it is reasonable for these companies to make profitability decisions based on expected values.

Next suppose that we wish to find the premium that the insurance company must charge for a $20,000 policy if the company wishes the average profit per policy per year to be greater than $0. If we let *prem* denote the premium the company will charge, then the probability distribution of the company's yearly profit x is as follows:

x, Profit	p(x), Probability of x
prem (if policyholder lives)	0.999
prem − $20,000 (if policyholder dies)	0.001

The expected value of x (expected profit per year) is

$$\mu_x = prem(0.999) + (prem - 20{,}000)(0.001)$$
$$= prem - 20.$$

In order for this expected profit to be greater than zero, the premium must be greater than $20. If, as previously stated, the company charges $300 for such a policy, the $280 charged in excess of the needed $20 compensates the company for commissions paid to salespeople, administrative costs, dividends paid to investors, and other expenses.

In general, it is reasonable to base decisions on an expected value if we perform the experiment related to the decision (for example, if we sell the life insurance policy) many times. If we do not (for instance, if we perform the experiment only once), then it may not be a good idea to base decisions on the expected value. For example, it might not be wise for you—as an individual—to sell one person a $20,000 life insurance policy for a premium of $300. To see this, again consider the probability distribution of yearly profit:

x, Profit	p(x), Probability of x
$300 (if policyholder lives)	0.999
$300 − $20,000 = −$19,700 (if policyholder dies)	0.001

Then recall that the expected profit per year is $280. However, since you are selling only one policy, you will not receive the $280. You will either gain $300 (with probability 0.999) or you will lose $19,700 (with probability 0.001). Although the decision is personal, and although the chance of losing $19,700 is very small, many people would not risk such a loss when the potential gain is only $300.

Just as the population of all possible observed values of a discrete random variable x has a mean μ_x, this population also has a variance σ_x^2 and a standard deviation σ_x. Recall that the variance of a population is the average of the squared deviations of the different population values from the population mean. To find σ_x^2, we calculate $(x - \mu_x)^2$ for each value of x, multiply $(x - \mu_x)^2$ by the probability $p(x)$, and sum the resulting products over all possible values of x.

The Variance and Standard Deviation of a Discrete Random Variable

The **variance** of a discrete random variable x is

$$\sigma_x^2 = \sum_{\text{All } x} (x - \mu_x)^2 p(x).$$

The **standard deviation** of x is the square root of the variance of x. That is,

$$\sigma_x = \sqrt{\sigma_x^2}.$$

Example 4.6

Table 4.2 gives the probability distribution of x, the number of TrueSound-XL stereo systems sold in a week at Sound City. Remembering that we have calculated μ_x (in Example 4.4) to be 2.1, it follows that

$$
\begin{aligned}
\sigma_x^2 &= \sum_{\text{All } x} (x - \mu_x)^2 p(x) \\
&= (0 - 2.1)^2 p(0) + (1 - 2.1)^2 p(1) + (2 - 2.1)^2 p(2) + (3 - 2.1)^2 p(3) \\
&\quad + (4 - 2.1)^2 p(4) + (5 - 2.1)^2 p(5) \\
&= (4.41)(0.03) + (1.21)(0.20) + (0.01)(0.50) + (0.81)(0.20) + (3.61)(0.05) \\
&\quad + (8.41)(0.02) \\
&= 0.89
\end{aligned}
$$

and that the standard deviation of x is $\sigma_x = \sqrt{0.89} = 0.9434$.

The variance σ_x^2 and the standard deviation σ_x measure the spread of the population of all possible observed values of the random variable. To see how to use σ_x, remember that Chebyshev's theorem (see Chapter 2, page 52) tells us that, for any value of k that is greater than 1, at least $100(1 - 1/k^2)$ percent of all possible observed values of the random variable x lie in the interval $[\mu_x \pm k\sigma_x]$. Stated in terms of a probability, we have

$$P(x \text{ falls in the interval } [\mu_x \pm k\sigma_x]) \geq 1 - 1/k^2.$$

For example, consider the probability distribution (in Table 4.2) of x, the number of TrueSound-XL stereo systems sold in a week at Sound City. If we set k equal to 2, and if we use $\mu_x = 2.1$ and $\sigma_x = 0.9434$ to calculate the interval

$$
\begin{aligned}
[\mu_x \pm 2\sigma_x] &= [2.1 \pm 2(0.9434)] \\
&= [0.2132, \ 3.9868],
\end{aligned}
$$

then Chebyshev's theorem tells us that

$$P(x \text{ falls in the interval } [0.2132, \ 3.9868]) \geq 1 - 1/2^2 = 3/4.$$

This says that in at least 75 percent of all weeks, Sound City will sell between 0.2132 and 3.9868 TrueSound-XL stereo systems. As illustrated in Figure 4.2, there are three values of x between

FIGURE **4.2**   The Interval $[\mu_x \pm 2\sigma_x]$ for the Probability Distribution Describing TrueSound-XL Stereo Sales (see Table 4.2)

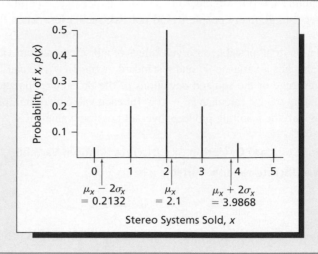

0.2132 and 3.9868—namely, $x = 1$, $x = 2$, and $x = 3$. Therefore, the exact probability that x will be in the interval $[\mu_x \pm 2\sigma_x]$ is

$$p(1) + p(2) + p(3) = 0.20 + 0.50 + 0.20 = 0.90.$$

This illustrates that, although Chebyshev's theorem guarantees us that at least $100(1 - 1/k^2)$ percent of all possible observed values of a random variable x fall in the interval $[\mu_x \pm k\sigma_x]$, often the percentage is considerably higher.

In some cases, the graph of the probability distribution of a discrete random variable has the symmetrical, bell-shaped appearance of a normal curve. For example, the graph in Figure 4.2 is roughly bell-shaped and symmetrical. In such a situation—and **under certain additional assumptions**—the probability distribution can sometimes be **approximated** by a normal curve. We will discuss the needed assumptions in Chapter 5. As an example of such assumptions, note that although the graph in Figure 4.2 is roughly bell-shaped and symmetrical, it can be shown that there are not enough values of x, and thus not enough probabilities $p(x)$, for us to approximate the probability distribution by using a normal curve. If, however, the probability distribution of a discrete random variable x can be approximated by a normal curve, then the **empirical rule** for normally distributed populations describes the population of all possible values of x. Specifically, we can say that approximately 68.26 percent, 95.44 percent, and 99.73 percent of all possible observed values of x fall in the intervals $[\mu_x \pm \sigma_x]$, $[\mu_x \pm 2\sigma_x]$, and $[\mu_x \pm 3\sigma_x]$, respectively.

To summarize, the standard deviation σ_x of a discrete random variable measures the spread of the population of all possible observed values of x. When the probability distribution of x can be approximated by a normal curve, this spread can be characterized by the empirical rule. When this is not possible, we can use Chebyshev's theorem to characterize the spread of x.

Exercises for Section 4.2

CONCEPTS

4.4   What is a discrete probability distribution? Explain in your own words.

4.5   What conditions must be satisfied by the probabilities in a discrete probability distribution? Explain what these conditions mean.

4.6   Describe how to compute the mean (or expected value) of a discrete random variable, and interpret what this quantity tells us about the observed values of the random variable.

4.7   Describe how to compute the standard deviation of a discrete random variable, and interpret what this quantity tells us about the observed values of the random variable.

METHODS AND APPLICATIONS

4.8   Explain whether each of the following is a valid probability distribution. If the probability distribution is valid, show why. Otherwise, show which condition(s) of a probability distribution are not satisfied.

a.

x	p(x)
−1	0.2
0	0.6
1	0.2

c.

x	p(x)
1/2	−1
3/4	0
1	2

b.

x	p(x)
2	0.25
4	0.35
6	0.3

d.

x	p(x)
0.1	2/7
0.7	4/7
0.9	1/7

4.9 Consider each of the following probability distributions.

a.

x	p(x)
0	0.2
1	0.8

c.

x	p(x)
−2	0.1
0	0.3
2	0.4
5	0.2

b.

x	p(x)
0	0.25
1	0.45
2	0.2
3	0.1

Calculate μ_x and σ_x for each distribution. Then explain, using the probabilities, why μ_x is the mean of all possible observed values of x.

4.10 For each of the following, write out and graph the probability distribution of x. That is, list all the possible values of x and also list the corresponding probabilities. Then graph the distribution.
  a. Refer to Exercise 3.3 (page 92), and let x equal the number of patrons who prefer diet cola A.
  b. Refer to Exercise 3.4 (page 92), and let x equal the number of girls born to the couple.
  c. Refer to Exercise 3.5 (page 92), and let x equal the number of people who will purchase a car.

4.11 For each of the following, find μ_x, σ_x^2, and σ_x. Then interpret in words the meaning of μ_x, and employ Chebyshev's theorem to find intervals that contain at least 3/4 and 8/9 of the observed values of x.
  a. x = the number of patrons who prefer diet cola A as defined in Exercise 4.10a.
  b. x = the number of girls born to the couple as defined in Exercise 4.10b.
  c. x = the number of people who will purchase a car as defined in Exercise 4.10c.

4.12 Suppose that the probability distribution of a random variable x can be described by the formula

$$p(x) = \frac{x}{15}$$

for each of the values x = 1, 2, 3, 4, and 5. For example, $P(x = 2) = p(2) = 2/15$.

a. Write out the probability distribution of x.
b. Show that the probability distribution of x satisfies the properties of a discrete probability distribution.
c. Calculate the mean of x.
d. Calculate the variance, σ_x^2, and the standard deviation, σ_x.

4.13 The following table summarizes investment outcomes and corresponding probabilities for a particular oil well:

x = the outcome in $	p(x)
−$40,000 (no oil)	0.25
10,000 (some oil)	0.7
70,000 (much oil)	0.05

Find the expected monetary outcome and interpret this value.

4.14 In the book *Foundations of Financial Management* (7th Cdn. ed.), Block, Hirt, and Short discuss risk measurement for investments. Block, Hirt, and Short present an investment with the possible outcomes and associated probabilities given in Table 4.3. The authors state that the probabilities

> are generally based on some combination of past experience, industry ratios and trends, interviews with company executives, and sophisticated simulation techniques. The probability values may be easy to estimate for the introduction of a mechanical stamping process for which the manufacturer has 10 years of past data, but they are difficult to assess for a new product in a foreign market. (p. 451)

a. Use the probability distribution in Table 4.3 to calculate the expected value (mean) and the standard deviation of the investment outcomes. Interpret the expected value.
b. Block, Hirt, and Short interpret the standard deviation of the investment outcomes as follows: "Generally, the larger the standard deviation (or spread of possible outcomes), the greater is the risk" (p. 452). Explain why this makes sense. Use Chebyshev's theorem to illustrate your point.
c. Block, Hirt, and Short compare three investments with the following means and standard deviations of the investment outcomes:

Investment 1	Investment 2	Investment 3
$\mu = \$600$	$\mu = \$600$	$\mu = \$600$
$\sigma = \$20$	$\sigma = \$190$	$\sigma = \$300$

TABLE 4.3 Probability Distribution of Outcomes for an Investment

Outcome	Probability of Outcome	Assumptions
$300	0.2	Pessimistic
600	0.6	Moderately successful
900	0.2	Optimistic

Source: *Foundations of Financial Management*, by S. B. Block, G. A. Hirt, and D. Short, 7th Cdn. ed., p. 451. Copyright © 2005. Reprinted by permission of McGraw-Hill Companies, Inc.

Which of these investments involves the most risk? The least risk? Explain why by using Chebyshev's theorem to compute an interval for each investment that will contain at least 8/9 of the investment outcomes.

d. Block, Hirt, and Short continue by comparing two more investments:

Investment A	Investment B
$\mu = \$6000$	$\mu = \$600$
$\sigma = \$600$	$\sigma = \$190$

The authors explain that Investment A

appears to have a high standard deviation, but not when related to the expected value of the distribution. A standard deviation of $600 on an investment with an expected value of $6,000 may indicate less risk than a standard deviation of $190 on an investment with an expected value of only $600.

We can eliminate the size difficulty by developing a third measure, the **coefficient of variation** (V), which allows for a comparable scale across different investments. This rather imposing term calls for nothing more difficult than dividing the standard deviation of an investment by the expected value. Generally, the larger the coefficient of variation, the greater is the risk. (p. 453)

Calculate the coefficient of variation for investments A and B:

$$\text{Coefficient of variation } (V) = \frac{\sigma}{\mu}.$$

Which investment carries the greater risk?

e. Calculate the coefficient of variation for investments 1, 2, and 3 in part c. Based on the coefficient of variation, which investment involves the most risk? The least risk? Do we obtain the same results as we did by comparing standard deviations (in part c)? Why?

4.15 An insurance company will insure a $50,000 diamond for its full value against theft at a premium of $400 per year. Suppose that the probability that the diamond will be stolen is 0.005, and let x denote the insurance company's profit.

a. Set up the probability distribution of the random variable x.

b. Calculate the insurance company's expected profit.

c. Find the premium that the insurance company should charge if it wants its expected profit to be $1,000.

4.16 In the book *Foundations of Financial Management* (7th Cdn. ed.), Block, Hirt, and Short discuss a semiconductor firm that is considering two choices: (1) expanding the production of semiconductors for sale to end users and (2) entering the highly competitive home computer market. The cost of both projects is $60 million, but the net present value of the cash flows from sales and the risks are different.

Figure 4.3 gives a tree diagram of the project choices. The tree diagram gives a probability distribution of expected sales for each project. It also gives the present value of cash flows from sales and the net present value (NPV = present value of cash flow from sales minus initial cost) corresponding to each sales alternative.

a. For each project choice, calculate the expected net present value.

b. For each project choice, calculate the variance and standard deviation of the net present value.

c. Calculate the coefficient of variation for each project choice. See Exercise 4.14d for a discussion of the coefficient of variation.

FIGURE 4.3   A Tree Diagram of Two Project Choices

		(1) Expected Sales	(2) Probability	(3) Present Value of Cash Flow from Sales ($ millions)	(4) Initial Cost ($ millions)	(5) Net Present Value, NPV = (3) − (4) ($ millions)
Expand semiconductor capacity		High	0.50	$100	$60	$40
		Moderate	0.25	75	60	15
		Low	0.25	40	60	−20
A						
Start						
B						
Enter home computer market		High	0.20	$200	$60	$140
		Moderate	0.50	75	60	15
		Low	0.30	25	60	−35

Source: *Foundations of Financial Management*, by S. B. Block, G. A. Hirt, and D. Short, 7th Cdn. ed., p. 462. Copyright © 2005. Reprinted by permission of McGraw-Hill Companies, Inc.

TABLE 4.4 Return Distributions for Companies A, B, and C and for Two Possible Acquisitions

Economic Condition	Probability	Company A Returns	Company B Returns	Company C Returns	Company A + B Returns	Company A + C Returns
1	0.2	17%	19%	13%	18%	15%
2	0.2	15	17	11	16	13
3	0.2	13	15	15	14	14
4	0.2	11	13	17	12	14
5	0.2	9	11	19	10	14

d. Which project has the higher expected net present value?

e. Which project carries the lesser risk? Explain.

f. In your opinion, which project should be undertaken? Justify your answer.

4.17 Five thousand raffle tickets are to be sold at $10 each to benefit a local community group. The prizes, the number of each prize to be given away, and the dollar value of winnings for each prize are as follows:

Prize	Number to Be Given Away	Dollar Value
Automobile	1	$13,000
Entertainment centre	2	3,000 each
VCR	5	400 each
Gift certificate	50	20 each

If you buy one ticket, calculate your expected winnings. (Form the probability distribution of x = your dollar winnings, and remember to subtract the cost of your ticket.)

4.18 Company A is considering the acquisition of two separate but large companies, Company B and Company C, having sales and assets equal to its own. Table 4.4 gives the probabilities of returns for each of the three companies under various economic conditions. The table also gives the probabilities of returns for each possible combination: Company A plus Company B, and Company A plus Company C.

a. For each of Companies A, B, and C, find the mean return and the standard deviation of returns.

b. Find the mean return and the standard deviation of returns for the combination of Company A plus Company B.

c. Find the mean return and the standard deviation of returns for the combination of Company A plus Company C.

d. Compare the mean returns for each of the two possible combinations—Company A plus Company B and Company A plus Company C. Is either mean higher? How do they compare to Company A's mean return?

e. Compare the standard deviations of the returns for each of the two possible combinations—Company A plus Company B and Company A plus Company C. Which standard deviation is smaller? Which possible combination involves less risk? How does the risk carried by this combination compare to the risk carried by Company A alone?

f. Which acquisition would you recommend—Company A plus Company B or Company A plus Company C?

4.3 The Binomial Distribution

In this section, we discuss what is perhaps the most important discrete probability distribution—the binomial distribution.[1] We begin with an example.

CHAPTER 4

Example 4.7

Suppose that historical sales records indicate that 40 percent of all customers who enter a discount department store make a purchase. What is the probability that two of the next three customers will make a purchase?

In order to find this probability, we first note that the experiment of observing three customers making a purchase decision has several distinguishing characteristics:

1 The experiment consists of three identical **trials**; each trial consists of a customer making a purchase decision.

---
[1]Study Hint: Remember that "bi" means two, so that the "binomial" term will mean "two numbers" or, generally, two possible options/outcomes.

2   Two outcomes are possible on each trial: the customer makes a purchase (which we call a **success** and denote as S), or the customer does not make a purchase (which we call a **failure** and denote as F).

3   Since 40 percent of all customers make a purchase, it is reasonable to assume that $P(S)$, the probability that a customer makes a purchase, is 0.4 and is constant for all customers. This implies that $P(F)$, the probability that a customer does not make a purchase, is 0.6 and is constant for all customers.

4   We assume that customers make independent purchase decisions. That is, we assume that the outcomes of the three trials are independent of each other.

   It follows that the sample space of the experiment consists of the following eight sample space outcomes:

SSS	*FFS*
SSF	*FSF*
SFS	*SFF*
FSS	*FFF*

Here the sample space outcome *SSS* represents all three customers making purchases. The sample space outcome *SFS* represents the first customer making a purchase, the second customer not making a purchase, and the third customer making a purchase.

   Two out of three customers make a purchase if one of the sample space outcomes *SSF*, *SFS*, and *FSS* occurs. Furthermore, since the trials (purchase decisions) are independent, we can simply multiply the probabilities associated with the different trial outcomes (each of which is S or F) to find the probability of a sequence of outcomes:

$$P(SSF) = P(S)P(S)P(F) = (0.4)(0.4)(0.6) = (0.4)^2(0.6),$$

$$P(SFS) = P(S)P(F)P(S) = (0.4)(0.6)(0.4) = (0.4)^2(0.6),$$

$$P(FSS) = P(F)P(S)P(S) = (0.6)(0.4)(0.4) = (0.4)^2(0.6).$$

It follows that the probability that two out of the next three customers make a purchase is

$$P(SSF) + P(SFS) + P(FSS)$$
$$= (0.4)^2(0.6) + (0.4)^2(0.6) + (0.4)^2(0.6)$$
$$= 3(0.4)^2(0.6) = 0.288.$$

   We can now generalize the previous result and find the probability that x of the next n customers will make a purchase. Here we will assume that p is the probability that a customer makes a purchase, $q = 1 - p$ is the probability that a customer does not make a purchase, and purchase decisions (trials) are independent. To generalize the probability that two out of the next three customers make a purchase, which equals

$$3(0.4)^2(0.6),$$

we note the following:

1   The 3 in this expression is the number of sample space outcomes (*SSF*, *SFS*, and *FSS*) that correspond to the event *two out of the next three customers make a purchase*. Note that this number equals the number of ways we can arrange two successes among the three trials.

2   The 0.4 is p, the probability that a customer makes a purchase.

3   The 0.6 is $q = 1 - p$, the probability that a customer does not make a purchase.

Therefore, the probability that two of the next three customers make a purchase is

$$\left(\begin{array}{c} \text{The number of ways} \\ \text{to arrange 2 successes} \\ \text{among 3 trials} \end{array} \right) p^2 q^1.$$

Now notice that, although each of the sample space outcomes *SSF*, *SFS*, and *FSS* represents a different arrangement of the two successes among the three trials, each of these sample space outcomes consists of two successes and one failure. For this reason, the probability of each of these sample space outcomes equals $(0.4)^2(0.6)^1 = p^2q^1$. It follows that p is raised to a power that equals the number of successes (2) in the three trials, and q is raised to a power that equals the number of failures (1) in the three trials.

In general, each sample space outcome describing the occurrence of x successes (purchases) in n trials represents a different arrangement of x successes in n trials. However, each outcome consists of x successes and $n - x$ failures. Therefore, the probability of each sample space outcome is p^xq^{n-x}. It follows by analogy that the probability that x of the next n trials are successes (purchases) is

$$\begin{pmatrix} \text{The number of ways} \\ \text{to arrange } x \text{ successes} \\ \text{among } n \text{ trials} \end{pmatrix} p^xq^{n-x}.$$

We can use the expression we have just arrived at to compute the probability of x successes in the next n trials if we can find a way to calculate the number of ways to arrange x successes among n trials. It can be shown that

The number of ways to arrange x successes among n trials equals

$$\frac{n!}{x!\,(n-x)!},$$

where $n!$ is pronounced "n factorial" and is calculated as $n! = n(n-1)(n-2) \cdots (1)$ and where (by definition) $0! = 1$.

For instance, using this formula, we can see that the number of ways to arrange $x = 2$ successes among $n = 3$ trials equals

$$\frac{n!}{x!\,(n-x)!} = \frac{3!}{2!\,(3-2)!} = \frac{3!}{2!\,1!} = \frac{3 \cdot 2 \cdot 1}{2 \cdot 1 \cdot 1} = 3.$$

Of course we have previously seen that the three ways to arrange $x = 2$ successes among $n = 3$ trials are *SSF*, *SFS*, and *FSS*.

Using the preceding formula, we obtain the following general result:

The Binomial Distribution

A **binomial experiment** has the following characteristics:

1   The experiment consists of n **identical trials**.

2   Each trial results in a **success** or a **failure**.

3   The probability of a success on any trial is p and remains constant from trial to trial. This implies that the probability of failure, q, on any trial is $1 - p$ and remains constant from trial to trial.

4   The trials are **independent** (that is, the results of the trials have nothing to do with each other).

Furthermore, if we define the random variable

   x = the total number of successes in n trials of a binomial experiment,

then we call x a **binomial random variable**, and the probability of obtaining x successes in n trials is

$$p(x) = \frac{n!}{x!\,(n-x)!}\, p^xq^{n-x}.$$

Noting that we sometimes refer to the formula for $p(x)$ as the **binomial formula**, we illustrate the use of this formula in the following example.

Example 4.8

Consider the discount department store situation discussed in Example 4.7. In order to find the probability that three of the next five customers make purchases, we calculate

$$p(3) = \frac{5!}{3! \, (5-3)!} (0.4)^3 (0.6)^{5-3} = \frac{5!}{3! \, 2!} (0.4)^3 (0.6)^2$$

$$= \frac{5 \cdot 4 \cdot 3 \cdot 2 \cdot 1}{(3 \cdot 2 \cdot 1)(2 \cdot 1)} (0.4)^3 (0.6)^2$$

$$= 10(0.064)(0.36)$$

$$= 0.2304.$$

Here we see that

1 $\frac{5!}{3! \, (5-3)!} = 10$ is the number of ways to arrange three successes among five trials. For instance, two ways to do this are described by the sample space outcomes *SSSFF* and *SFSSF*. There are eight other ways.

2 $(0.4)^3 (0.6)^2$ is the probability of any sample space outcome consisting of three successes and two failures.

Thus far we have shown how to calculate binomial probabilities. We next give several examples that illustrate some practical applications of the binomial distribution. As we demonstrate in the first example, the term *success* does not necessarily refer to a **desirable** experimental outcome. Rather, it refers to an outcome that we wish to investigate.

Example 4.9

Antibiotics occasionally cause nausea as a side effect. A major drug company has developed a new antibiotic called Phe-Mycin. The company claims that, at most, 10 percent of all patients treated with Phe-Mycin would experience nausea as a side effect of taking the drug. Suppose that we randomly select $n = 4$ patients and treat them with Phe-Mycin. Each patient will either experience nausea (which we arbitrarily call a success) or will not experience nausea (a failure). We will assume that p, the true probability that a patient will experience nausea as a side effect, is 0.10, the maximum value of p claimed by the drug company. Furthermore, it is reasonable to assume that patients' reactions to the drug would be independent of each other. Let x denote the number of patients among the four who will experience nausea as a side effect. It follows that x is a binomial random variable, which can take on any of the potential values 0, 1, 2, 3, and 4. That is, anywhere between none of the patients and all four of the patients could potentially experience nausea as a side effect. Furthermore, we can calculate the probability associated with each possible value of x as shown in Table 4.5. For instance, the probability that none of the four randomly selected patients experience nausea is

$$p(0) = P(x = 0) = \frac{4!}{0! \, (4-0)!} (0.1)^0 (0.9)^{4-0}$$

$$= \frac{4!}{0! \, 4!} (0.1)^0 (0.9)^4$$

$$= \frac{4!}{(1)(4!)} (1)(0.9)^4$$

$$= (0.9)^4 = 0.6561.$$

TABLE 4.5 The Binomial Probability Distribution of x, the Number of Four Randomly Selected Patients Who Will Experience Nausea as a Side Effect of Being Treated with Phe-Mycin

x (Number Who Experience Nausea)	$p(x) = \dfrac{n!}{x!\,(n-x)!}\,p^x(1-p)^{n-x}$
0	$p(0) = P(x = 0) = \dfrac{4!}{0!\,(4-0)!}\,(0.1)^0(0.9)^{4-0} = 0.6561$
1	$p(1) = P(x = 1) = \dfrac{4!}{1!\,(4-1)!}\,(0.1)^1(0.9)^{4-1} = 0.2916$
2	$p(2) = P(x = 2) = \dfrac{4!}{2!\,(4-2)!}\,(0.1)^2(0.9)^{4-2} = 0.0486$
3	$p(3) = P(x = 3) = \dfrac{4!}{3!\,(4-3)!}\,(0.1)^3(0.9)^{4-3} = 0.0036$
4	$p(4) = P(x = 4) = \dfrac{4!}{4!\,(4-4)!}\,(0.1)^4(0.9)^{4-4} = 0.0001$

FIGURE 4.4 The Binomial Probability Distribution with $p = 0.10$ and $n = 4$

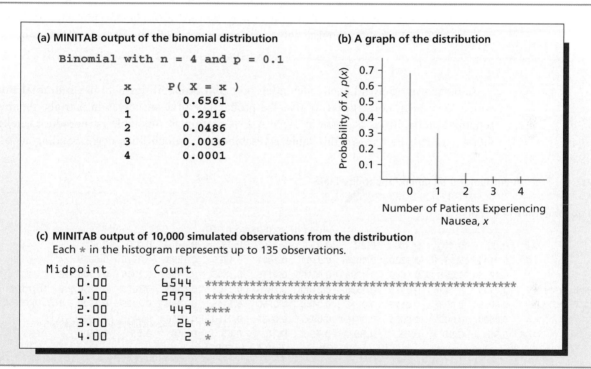

(a) MINITAB output of the binomial distribution

Binomial with n = 4 and p = 0.1

x	P(X = x)
0	0.6561
1	0.2916
2	0.0486
3	0.0036
4	0.0001

(b) A graph of the distribution

(c) MINITAB output of 10,000 simulated observations from the distribution
Each * in the histogram represents up to 135 observations.

Midpoint	Count	
0.00	6544	**
1.00	2979	**********************
2.00	449	****
3.00	26	*
4.00	2	*

Because Table 4.5 lists each possible value of x and also gives the probability of each value, we say that this table gives the **binomial probability distribution of x**.

The binomial probabilities given in Table 4.5 need not be hand calculated. MINITAB, Excel, and MegaStat can be used to calculate binomial probabilities. For instance, Figure 4.4(a) gives the MINITAB output of the binomial probability distribution listed in Table 4.5.[2] Figure 4.4(b) shows a graph of this distribution.

In order to interpret these binomial probabilities, consider administering the antibiotic Phe-Mycin to all possible samples of four randomly selected patients. Then, for example,

$$P(x = 0) = 0.6561$$

---

[2]As we will see in this chapter's appendices, we can use Excel or MegaStat to obtain output of the binomial distribution that is essentially identical to the output given by MINITAB.

says that none of the four sampled patients would experience nausea in 65.61 percent of all possible samples. Furthermore, as another example,

$$P(x = 3) = 0.0036$$

says that three out of the four sampled patients would experience nausea in only 0.36 percent of all possible samples.

To better understand these interpretations, we can use MINITAB to **simulate** giving the antibiotic to a large number of samples of four randomly selected patients. That is, we can use MINITAB to randomly select a large number of observations from the binomial distribution of Table 4.5. The MINITAB output of a simulation of 10,000 samples of four randomly selected patients is given in Figure 4.4(c). In other words, this figure gives the results obtained when MINITAB has randomly selected 10,000 observations from the binomial distribution with $p = 0.10$ and $n = 4$. Each observation (or simulated sample of four patients) results in 0, 1, 2, 3, or 4 patients experiencing nausea. The MINITAB output presents the results in the form of a histogram that shows the number of simulated samples in which 0, 1, 2, 3, or 4 patients experienced nausea. For instance, none of the four patients experienced nausea in 6,544 (that is, in 65.44 percent) of the 10,000 samples, while 3 out of 4 patients experienced nausea in 26 (or in 0.26 percent) of the 10,000 samples. These simulated results are quite close to the percentages given by the probabilities in Table 4.5. If we could use MINITAB to simulate an indefinitely large number of samples of four patients, then the simulated percentages would be exactly equal to the percentages given by the binomial probabilities. Note that we cannot do this—we can simulate only some large number of samples (say, 10,000 samples).

Another way to avoid hand calculating binomial probabilities is to use **binomial tables**, which have been constructed to give the probability of x successes in n trials. A table of binomial probabilities is given in Table A.1. A portion of this table is reproduced in Table 4.6(a) and (b). Part (a) of this table gives binomial probabilities corresponding to $n = 4$

TABLE **4.6**   A Portion of a Binomial Probability Table

(a) A table for $n = 4$ trials

Values of p (0.05 to 0.50)

↓	0.05	0.10	0.15	0.20	0.25	0.30	0.35	0.40	0.45	0.50	
0	0.8145	0.6561	0.5220	0.4096	0.3164	0.2401	0.1785	0.1296	0.0915	0.0625	4
1	0.1715	0.2916	0.3685	0.4096	0.4219	0.4116	0.3845	0.3456	0.2995	0.2500	3
2	0.0135	0.0486	0.0975	0.1536	0.2109	0.2646	0.3105	0.3456	0.3675	0.3750	2
3	0.0005	0.0036	0.0115	0.0256	0.0469	0.0756	0.1115	0.1536	0.2005	0.2500	1
4	0.0000	0.0001	0.0005	0.0016	0.0039	0.0081	0.0150	0.0256	0.0410	0.0625	0
	0.95	0.90	0.85	0.80	0.75	0.70	0.65	0.60	0.55	0.50	↑

Number of Successes (left); Number of Successes (right)

Values of p (0.50 to 0.95)

(b) A table for $n = 8$ trials

Values of p (0.05 to 0.50)

↓	0.05	0.10	0.15	0.20	0.25	0.30	0.35	0.40	0.45	0.50	
0	0.6634	0.4305	0.2725	0.1678	0.1001	0.0576	0.0319	0.0168	0.0084	0.0039	8
1	0.2793	0.3826	0.3847	0.3355	0.2670	0.1977	0.1373	0.0896	0.0548	0.0313	7
2	0.0515	0.1488	0.2376	0.2936	0.3115	0.2965	0.2587	0.2090	0.1569	0.1094	6
3	0.0054	0.0331	0.0839	0.1468	0.2076	0.2541	0.2786	0.2787	0.2568	0.2188	5
4	0.0004	0.0046	0.0185	0.0459	0.0865	0.1361	0.1875	0.2322	0.2627	0.2734	4
5	0.0000	0.0004	0.0026	0.0092	0.0231	0.0467	0.0808	0.1239	0.1719	0.2188	3
6	0.0000	0.0000	0.0002	0.0011	0.0038	0.0100	0.0217	0.0413	0.0703	0.1094	2
7	0.0000	0.0000	0.0000	0.0001	0.0004	0.0012	0.0033	0.0079	0.0164	0.0313	1
8	0.0000	0.0000	0.0000	0.0000	0.0000	0.0001	0.0002	0.0007	0.0017	0.0039	0
	0.95	0.90	0.85	0.80	0.75	0.70	0.65	0.60	0.55	0.50	↑

Number of Successes (left); Number of Successes (right)

Values of p (0.50 to 0.95)

trials. Values of p, the probability of success, are listed across the top of the table (ranging from $p = 0.05$ to $p = 0.50$ in steps of 0.05), and more values of p (ranging from $p = 0.50$ to $p = 0.95$ in steps of 0.05) are listed across the bottom of the table. When the value of p being considered is one of those across the top of the table, values of x (the number of successes in four trials) are listed down the left side of the table. For instance, to find the probabilities that we have computed in Table 4.5, we look in part (a) of Table 4.6 ($n = 4$) and read down the column labelled 0.10. Remembering that the values of x are on the left side of the table because $p = 0.10$ is on top of the table, we find the probabilities in Table 4.5 (they are shaded). For example, the probability that none of the four patients experience nausea is $p(0) = 0.6561$, the probability that one of the the four patients experiences nausea is $p(1) = 0.2916$, and so forth. If the value of p is across the bottom of the table, then we read the values of x from the right side of the table. As an example, if p equals 0.60, then the probability of two successes in four trials is $p(2) = 0.3456$ (we have shaded this probability).

Example 4.10

Suppose that we wish to investigate whether p, the probability that a patient will experience nausea as a side effect of taking Phe-Mycin, is greater than 0.10, the maximum value of p claimed by the drug company. This assessment will be made by assuming that p equals 0.10 and by using sample information to weigh the evidence against this assumption and in favour of the conclusion that p is greater than 0.10. Suppose that when a sample of $n = 4$ randomly selected patients is treated with Phe-Mycin, three of the four patients experience nausea. Since the fraction of patients in the sample that experience nausea is $3/4 = 0.75$, which is far greater than 0.10, we have some evidence contradicting the assumption that p equals 0.10. To evaluate the strength of this evidence, we calculate the probability that at least 3 out of 4 randomly selected patients would experience nausea as a side effect if, in fact, p equals 0.10. Using the binomial probabilities in Table 4.6(a), and realizing that the events $x = 3$ and $x = 4$ are mutually exclusive, we have

$$
\begin{aligned}
P(x \geq 3) &= P(x = 3 \text{ or } x = 4) \\
&= P(x = 3) + P(x = 4) \\
&= 0.0036 + 0.0001 \\
&= 0.0037.
\end{aligned}
$$

This probability says that, if p equals 0.10, then in only 0.37 percent of all possible samples of four randomly selected patients would at least three of the four patients experience nausea as a side effect. This implies that, if we are to believe that p equals 0.10, then we must believe that we have observed a sample result that is so rare that it can be described as a 37 in 10 000 chance. Because observing such a result is very unlikely, we have very strong evidence that p does not equal 0.10 and is, in fact, greater than 0.10.

Next suppose that we consider what our conclusion would have been if only one of the four randomly selected patients had experienced nausea. Since the sample fraction of patients who experienced nausea is $1/4 = 0.25$, which is greater than 0.10, we would have some evidence to contradict the assumption that p equals 0.10. To evaluate the strength of this evidence, we calculate the probability that at least one out of four randomly selected patients would experience nausea as a side effect of being treated with Phe-Mycin if, in fact, p equals 0.10. Using the binomial probabilities in Table 4.6(a), we have

$$
\begin{aligned}
P(x \geq 1) &= P(x = 1 \text{ or } x = 2 \text{ or } x = 3 \text{ or } x = 4) \\
&= P(x = 1) + P(x = 2) + P(x = 3) + P(x = 4) \\
&= 0.2916 + 0.0486 + 0.0036 + 0.0001 \\
&= 0.3439.
\end{aligned}
$$

This probability says that, if p equals 0.10, then in 34.39 percent of all possible samples of four randomly selected patients, at least one of the four patients would experience nausea. Since it is not particularly difficult to believe that a 34.39 percent chance has occurred, we would not have much evidence against the claim that p equals 0.10.

Example 4.10 illustrates what is sometimes called the **rare event approach to making a statistical inference**. The idea of this approach is that if the probability of an observed sample result under a given assumption is **small**, then we have **strong evidence** that the assumption is false. Although there are no strict rules, many statisticians judge the probability of an observed sample result to be small if it is less than 0.05. The logic behind this will be explained more fully in Chapter 8.

Example 4.11

The manufacturer of the ColourSmart-5000 television set claims that 95 percent of its sets last at least five years without requiring a single repair. Suppose that we contact $n = 8$ randomly selected ColourSmart-5000 purchasers five years after they purchased their sets. Each purchaser's set will have needed no repairs (a success) or will have been repaired at least once (a failure). We will assume that p, the true probability that a purchaser's television set will require no repairs within five years, is 0.95, as claimed by the manufacturer. Furthermore, it is reasonable to believe that the repair records of the purchasers' sets are independent of each other. Let x denote the number of the $n = 8$ randomly selected sets that have lasted at least five years without a single repair. Then, x is a binomial random variable that can take on any of the potential values 0, 1, 2, 3, 4, 5, 6, 7, and 8. The binomial distribution of x is listed in Table 4.7. Here we have obtained these probabilities from Table 4.6(b). To use the table, we look at the column corresponding to $p = 0.95$. Because $p = 0.95$ is listed at the bottom of the table, we read the values of x and their corresponding probabilities from bottom to top (we have shaded the probabilities). Notice that the values of x are listed on the right side of the table.

Figure 4.5(a) gives the MINITAB output of the binomial distribution with $p = 0.95$ and $n = 8$ (that is, the binomial distribution of Table 4.7). This binomial distribution is graphed in Figure 4.5(b), and Figure 4.5(c) gives the MINITAB output of 10,000 simulated observations from this distribution. Looking at Figure 4.5(c), we see that, for example, seven out of eight sets have lasted at least five years without a single repair in 2,785 (27.85 percent) of the 10,000 simulated samples. This result is very close to the percentage (27.93 percent) given by the binomial distribution (see Figure 4.5(a)).

TABLE **4.7**   **The Binomial Distribution of x, the Number of Eight ColourSmart-5000 Television Sets That Have Lasted at Least Five Years Without Needing a Single Repair, When $p = 0.95$**

x, Number of Sets That Require No Repairs	$p(x) = \dfrac{8!}{x!\,(8-x)!}(0.95)^x(0.05)^{8-x}$
0	$p(0) = 0.0000$
1	$p(1) = 0.0000$
2	$p(2) = 0.0000$
3	$p(3) = 0.0000$
4	$p(4) = 0.0004$
5	$p(5) = 0.0054$
6	$p(6) = 0.0515$
7	$p(7) = 0.2793$
8	$p(8) = 0.6634$

FIGURE **4.5** The Binomial Probability Distribution with $p = 0.95$ and $n = 8$

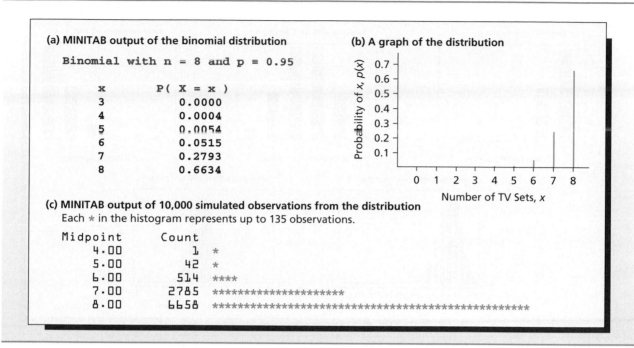

(a) MINITAB output of the binomial distribution

Binomial with n = 8 and p = 0.95

x	P(X = x)
3	0.0000
4	0.0004
5	0.0054
6	0.0515
7	0.2793
8	0.6634

(b) A graph of the distribution

(c) MINITAB output of 10,000 simulated observations from the distribution
Each * in the histogram represents up to 135 observations.

Midpoint	Count	
4.00	1	*
5.00	42	*
6.00	514	****
7.00	2785	********************
8.00	6658	***

Next suppose that when we actually contact eight randomly selected purchasers, we find that five out of the eight television sets owned by these purchasers have lasted at least five years without a single repair. Since the sample fraction, $5/8 = 0.625$, of television sets needing no repairs is less than 0.95, we have some evidence contradicting the manufacturer's claim that p equals 0.95. To evaluate the strength of this evidence, we will calculate the probability that five or fewer of the eight randomly selected televisions would last five years without a single repair if, in fact, p equals 0.95. Using the binomial probabilities in Table 4.7, we have

$$P(x \leq 5) = P(x = 5 \text{ or } x = 4 \text{ or } x = 3 \text{ or } x = 2 \text{ or } x = 1 \text{ or } x = 0)$$
$$= P(x = 5) + P(x = 4) + P(x = 3) + P(x = 2) + P(x = 1) + P(x = 0)$$
$$= 0.0054 + 0.0004 + 0.0000 + 0.0000 + 0.0000 + 0.0000$$
$$= 0.0058.$$

This probability says that, if p equals 0.95, then in only 0.58 percent of all possible samples of eight randomly selected ColourSmart-5000 televisions would five or fewer of the eight televisions last five years without a single repair. Therefore, if we are to believe that p equals 0.95, we must believe that a 58 in 10,000 chance has occurred. Since it is difficult to believe that such a small chance has occurred, we have strong evidence that p does not equal 0.95, and is, in fact, less than 0.95.

In Examples 4.9 and 4.11, we have illustrated binomial distributions with different values of n and p. The values of n and p are often called the **parameters** of the binomial distribution. Figure 4.6 shows several different binomial distributions. We see that, depending on the parameters, a binomial distribution can be positively skewed (to the right), negatively skewed (to the left), or symmetrical.

We next consider calculating the mean, variance, and standard deviation of a binomial random variable. If we place the binomial probability formula into the expressions (given in Section 4.2) for the mean and variance of a discrete random variable, we can derive formulas that allow us to easily compute μ_x, σ_x^2, and σ_x for a binomial random variable.

FIGURE **4.6**   **Several Binomial Distributions**

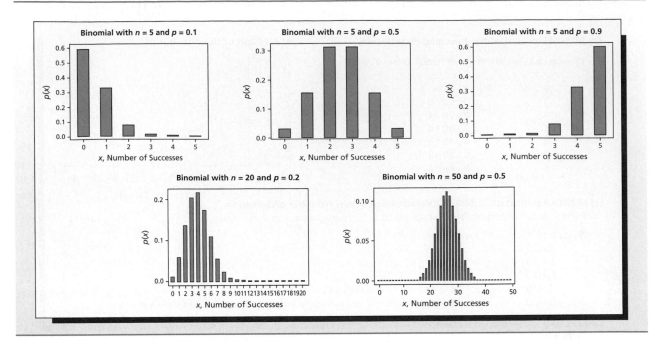

The Mean, Variance, and Standard Deviation of a Binomial Random Variable

If x is a binomial random variable, then

$$\mu_x = np, \qquad \sigma_x^2 = npq, \quad \text{and} \quad \sigma_x = \sqrt{npq},$$

where n is the number of trials, p is the probability of success on each trial, and $q = 1 - p$ is the probability of failure on each trial.

As a simple example, again consider the television manufacturer, and recall that x is the number of eight randomly selected ColourSmart-5000 televisions that last five years without a single repair. If the manufacturer's claim that p equals 0.95 is true (which implies that q equals $1 - p = 1 - 0.95 = 0.05$), it follows that

$$\mu_x = np = 8(0.95) = 7.6,$$

$$\sigma_x^2 = npq = 8(0.95)(0.05) = 0.38,$$

$$\sigma_x = \sqrt{npq} = \sqrt{0.38} = 0.6164.$$

In order to interpret $\mu_x = 7.6$, suppose that we were to randomly select all possible samples of eight ColourSmart-5000 televisions and record the number of sets in each sample that last five years without a repair. If we averaged all of our results, we would find that the average number of sets per sample that last five years without a repair is equal to 7.6.

To conclude this section, note that in Appendix B (Part 2) we discuss the **hypergeometric distribution**. This distribution is related to the binomial distribution. The main difference between the two distributions is that in the case of the hypergeometric distribution, the trials are not independent and the probabilities of success and failure change from trial to trial. This occurs when we sample without replacement from a finite population. However, when the finite population is large compared to the sample, the binomial distribution can be used to approximate the hypergeometric distribution. The details are explained in Appendix B (Part 2).

Exercises for Section 4.3

CONCEPTS

4.19 List the four characteristics of a binomial experiment.

4.20 Suppose that x is a binomial random variable. Explain what the values of x represent. That is, how are the values of x defined?

4.21 Explain the logic behind the rare event approach to making statistical inferences.

METHODS AND APPLICATIONS

4.22 Suppose that x is a binomial random variable with $n = 5$, $p = 0.3$, and $q = 0.7$.
   a. Write the binomial formula for this situation and list the possible values of x.
   b. For each value of x, calculate $p(x)$, and graph the binomial distribution.
   c. Find $P(x = 3)$.
   d. Find $P(x \leq 3)$.
   e. Find $P(x < 3)$.
   f. Find $P(x \geq 4)$.
   g. Find $P(x > 2)$.
   h. Use the probabilities you computed in part b to calculate the mean, μ_x, the variance, σ_x^2, and the standard deviation, σ_x, of this binomial distribution. Show that the formulas for μ_x, σ_x^2, and σ_x given in this section give the same results.
   i. Calculate the interval $[\mu_x \pm 2\sigma_x]$. Use the probabilities of part b to find the probability that x will be in this interval.

4.23 Thirty percent of all customers who enter a store will make a purchase. Suppose that six customers enter the store and that these customers make independent purchase decisions.
   a. Let $x =$ the number of the six customers who will make a purchase. Write the binomial formula for this situation.
   b. Use the binomial formula to calculate
      (1) The probability that exactly five customers make a purchase.
      (2) The probability that at least three customers make a purchase.
      (3) The probability that two or fewer customers make a purchase.
      (4) The probability that at least one customer makes a purchase.

4.24 The customer service department for a wholesale electronics outlet claims that 90 percent of all customer complaints are resolved to the satisfaction of the customer. In order to test this claim, a random sample of 15 customers who have filed complaints is selected.
   a. Let $x =$ the number of sampled customers whose complaints were resolved to the customer's satisfaction. Assuming the claim is true, write the binomial formula for this situation.
   b. Use the binomial tables (see Table A.1) to find each of the following if we assume that the claim is true:
      (1) $P(x \leq 13)$.
      (2) $P(x > 10)$.

      (3) $P(x \geq 14)$.
      (4) $P(9 \leq x \leq 12)$.
      (5) $P(x \leq 9)$.
   c. Suppose that of the 15 customers selected, 9 have had their complaints resolved satisfactorily. Using part b, do you believe the claim of 90 percent satisfaction? Explain.

4.25 An industry representative claims that 50 percent of all satellite dish owners subscribe to at least one premium movie channel. In an attempt to justify this claim, the representative will poll a randomly selected sample of dish owners.
   a. Suppose that the representative's claim is true, and suppose that a sample of four dish owners is randomly selected. Assuming independence, use an appropriate formula to compute
      (1) The probability that none of the dish owners in the sample subscribes to at least one premium movie channel.
      (2) The probability that more than two dish owners in the sample subscribe to at least one premium movie channel.
   b. Suppose that the representative's claim is true, and suppose that a sample of 20 dish owners is randomly selected. Assuming independence, what is the probability that
      (1) Nine or fewer dish owners in the sample subscribe to at least one premium movie channel?
      (2) More than 11 dish owners in the sample subscribe to at least one premium movie channel?
      (3) Fewer than five dish owners in the sample subscribe to at least one premium movie channel?
   c. Suppose that, when we survey 20 randomly selected dish owners, we find that 4 of the dish owners actually subscribe to at least one premium movie channel. Using a probability you found in this exercise as the basis for your answer, do you believe the industry representative's claim? Explain.

4.26 For each of the following, calculate μ_x, σ_x^2, and σ_x by using the formulas given in this section. Then (1) interpret the meaning of μ_x and (2) find the probability that x falls in the interval $[\mu_x \pm 2\sigma_x]$.
   a. The situation of Exercise 4.23, where $x =$ the number of the six customers who will make a purchase.
   b. The situation of Exercise 4.24, where $x =$ the number of 15 sampled customers whose complaints were resolved to the customer's satisfaction.

4.27 The January 1986 mission of the Space Shuttle Challenger was the 25th shuttle mission. It was unsuccessful due to an explosion caused by an O-ring seal failure.
   a. According to NASA, the probability of such a failure in a single mission was 1/60,000. Using this value of p and assuming all missions are independent, calculate the probability of no mission failures in 25 attempts. Then calculate the probability of at least one mission failure in 25 attempts.

b. According to a study conducted for the U.S. Air Force, the probability of such a failure in a single mission was 1/35. Recalculate the probability of no mission failures in 25 attempts and the probability of at least one mission failure in 25 attempts.

c. Based on your answers to parts a and b, which value of p seems more likely to be true? Explain.

d. How small must p be made in order to ensure that the probability of no mission failures in 25 attempts is 0.999?

CHAPTER 4

4.4 The Poisson Distribution

We now discuss a discrete random variable that describes the number of occurrences of an event over a specified interval of time or space. For instance, we might wish to describe (1) the number of customers who arrive at the checkout counters of a grocery store in one hour or (2) the number of major fires in a city during the last two months.

Such a random variable can often be described by a **Poisson distribution**. We describe this distribution and give two assumptions needed for its use in the following box:

The Poisson Distribution

Consider the number of times an event occurs over an interval of time or space, and assume that

1   The probability of the event's occurrence is the same for any two intervals of equal length.

2   Whether the event occurs in any interval is independent of whether the event occurs in any other nonoverlapping interval.

Then, the probability that the event will occur x times in a specified interval is

$$p(x) = \frac{e^{-\mu}\mu^x}{x!}.$$

Here μ is the mean (or expected) number of occurrences of the event in the specified interval, and $e = 2.718281 \ldots$ is the base of the natural logarithm.

In theory, there is no limit to how large x might be. That is, theoretically speaking, the event under consideration could occur an indefinitely large number of times during any specified interval. This says that a **Poisson random variable** might take on any of the values 0, 1, 2, 3, . . . and so forth. We will now look at an example.

Example 4.12

In an article[3] in the August 15, 1998, edition of *The Journal News* (Hamilton, Ohio), the Associated Press reported that the Cleveland Air Route Traffic Control Center, the busiest in the nation for guiding planes on cross-country routes, had experienced an unusually high number of errors since the end of July. An error occurs when controllers direct flights either within five miles (8 km) of each other horizontally, or within 2,000 feet (610 m) vertically at a height of 18,000 feet (5.5 km) or more (the standard is 1,000 feet (305 m) vertically at heights less than 18,000 feet (5.5 km)). The controllers' union blamed the errors on a staff shortage, whereas the U.S. Federal Aviation Administration claimed that the cause was improved error reporting and an unusual number of thunderstorms.

Suppose that an air traffic control centre has been averaging 20.8 errors per year and that the centre experiences 3 errors in a week. The Canadian Air Transport Security Authority (CATSA) must decide whether this occurrence is unusual enough to warrant an investigation of the

---

[3]"Errors on the rise at traffic control center in Ohio," by F. J. Frommer, *The Journal News*, August 15, 1998.

TABLE **4.8** A Portion of a Poisson Probability Table

x, Number of Occurrences	μ, Mean Number of Occurrences									
	0.1	0.2	0.3	0.4	0.5	0.6	0.7	0.8	0.9	1.0
0	0.9048	0.8187	0.7408	0.6703	0.6065	0.5488	0.4966	0.4493	0.4066	0.3679
1	0.0905	0.1637	0.2222	0.2681	0.3033	0.3293	0.3476	0.3595	0.3659	0.3679
2	0.0045	0.0164	0.0333	0.0536	0.0758	0.0988	0.1217	0.1438	0.1647	0.1839
3	0.0002	0.0011	0.0033	0.0072	0.0126	0.0198	0.0284	0.0383	0.0494	0.0613
4	0.0000	0.0001	0.0003	0.0007	0.0016	0.0030	0.0050	0.0077	0.0111	0.0153
5	0.0000	0.0000	0.0000	0.0001	0.0002	0.0004	0.0007	0.0012	0.0020	0.0031
6	0.0000	0.0000	0.0000	0.0000	0.0000	0.0000	0.0001	0.0002	0.0003	0.0005

x, Number of Occurrences	μ, Mean Number of Occurrences									
	1.1	1.2	1.3	1.4	1.5	1.6	1.7	1.8	1.9	2.0
0	0.3329	0.3012	0.2725	0.2466	0.2231	0.2019	0.1827	0.1653	0.1496	0.1353
1	0.3662	0.3614	0.3543	0.3452	0.3347	0.3230	0.3106	0.2975	0.2842	0.2707
2	0.2014	0.2169	0.2303	0.2417	0.2510	0.2584	0.2640	0.2678	0.2700	0.2707
3	0.0738	0.0867	0.0998	0.1128	0.1255	0.1378	0.1496	0.1607	0.1710	0.1804
4	0.0203	0.0260	0.0324	0.0395	0.0471	0.0551	0.0636	0.0723	0.0812	0.0902
5	0.0045	0.0062	0.0084	0.0111	0.0141	0.0176	0.0216	0.0260	0.0309	0.0361
6	0.0008	0.0012	0.0018	0.0026	0.0035	0.0047	0.0061	0.0078	0.0098	0.0120
7	0.0001	0.0002	0.0003	0.0005	0.0008	0.0011	0.0015	0.0020	0.0027	0.0034
8	0.0000	0.0000	0.0001	0.0001	0.0001	0.0002	0.0003	0.0005	0.0006	0.0009

Source: From Brooks/Cole, Copyright © 1991.

causes of the (possible) increase in errors. To investigate this possibility, we will find the probability distribution of x, the number of errors in a week, when we assume that the centre is still averaging 20.8 errors per year.

Arbitrarily choosing a time unit of one week, the average (or expected) number of errors per week is $20.8/52 = 0.4$. Therefore, we can use the Poisson formula (note that the Poisson assumptions are probably satisfied) to calculate the probability of no errors in a week to be

$$p(0) = P(x = 0) = \frac{e^{-\mu}\mu^0}{0!} = \frac{e^{-0.4}(0.4)^0}{1} = 0.6703.$$

Similarly, the probability of three errors in a week is

$$p(3) = P(x = 3) = \frac{e^{-0.4}(0.4)^3}{3!} = \frac{e^{-0.4}(0.4)^3}{3\cdot 2\cdot 1} = 0.0072.$$

As with the binomial distribution, tables have been constructed that give Poisson probabilities. A table of these probabilities is given in Table A.2. A portion of this table is reproduced in Table 4.8. In this table, values of the mean number of occurrences, μ, are listed across the top of the table, and values of x (the number of occurrences) are listed down the left side of the table. In order to use the table in the traffic control situation, we look at the column in Table 4.8 corresponding to 0.4, and we find the probabilities of 0, 1, 2, 3, 4, 5, and 6 errors (we have shaded these probabilities). For instance, the probability of one error in a week is 0.2681. Also note that the probability of any number of errors greater than six is so small that it is not listed in the table. Table 4.9 summarizes the Poisson distribution of x, the number of errors in a week. This table also shows how the probabilities associated with the different values of x are calculated.

Poisson probabilities can also be calculated by using MINITAB, Excel, and MegaStat. For instance, Figure 4.7(a) gives the MINITAB output of the Poisson distribution presented in Table 4.9.[4] This Poisson distribution is graphed in Figure 4.7(b), and Figure 4.7(c) gives the

[4] As we will show in the appendices to this chapter, we can use Excel and MegaStat to obtain output of the Poisson distribution that is essentially identical to the output given by MINITAB.

TABLE 4.9   The Poisson Distribution of x, the Number of Errors at an Air Traffic Control Centre in a Week, When $\mu = 0.4$

x, the Number of Errors in a Week	$p(x) = \dfrac{e^{-\mu}\mu^x}{x!}$
0	$p(0) = \dfrac{e^{-0.4}(0.4)^0}{0!} = 0.6703$
1	$p(1) = \dfrac{e^{-0.4}(0.4)^1}{1!} = 0.2681$
2	$p(2) = \dfrac{e^{-0.4}(0.4)^2}{2!} = 0.0536$
3	$p(3) = \dfrac{e^{-0.4}(0.4)^3}{3!} = 0.0072$
4	$p(4) = \dfrac{e^{-0.4}(0.4)^4}{4!} = 0.0007$
5	$p(5) = \dfrac{e^{-0.4}(0.4)^5}{5!} = 0.0001$
6	$p(6) = \dfrac{e^{-0.4}(0.4)^6}{6!} = 0.0000$

FIGURE 4.7   The Poisson Probability Distribution with $\mu = 0.4$

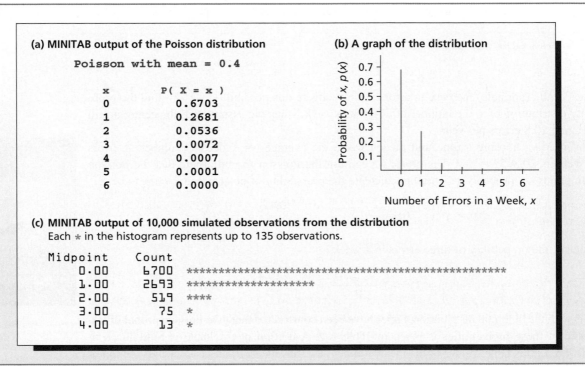

(a) MINITAB output of the Poisson distribution

```
Poisson with mean = 0.4

  x          P( X = x )
  0           0.6703
  1           0.2681
  2           0.0536
  3           0.0072
  4           0.0007
  5           0.0001
  6           0.0000
```

(b) A graph of the distribution

(c) MINITAB output of 10,000 simulated observations from the distribution
Each * in the histogram represents up to 135 observations.

```
Midpoint    Count
  0.00       6700    **************************************************
  1.00       2693    ********************
  2.00        519    ****
  3.00         75    *
  4.00         13    *
```

MINITAB output of a histogram of 10,000 simulated observations from this distribution. Looking at Figure 4.7(c), we see that, for example, three errors have occurred in 75 (0.75 percent) of the 10,000 simulated weeks. This result is very close to the percentage (0.72 percent) given by the Poisson distribution (see Figure 4.7(a)).

Next recall that there have been three errors at the air traffic control centre in the last week. This is considerably more errors than 0.4, the expected number of errors assuming the centre is still averaging 20.8 errors per year. Therefore, we have some evidence to contradict this assumption. To evaluate the strength of this evidence, we calculate the probability that at least three errors will occur in a week if, in fact, μ equals 0.4. Using the Poisson probabilities in Table 4.9 (for $\mu = 0.4$), we obtain

$$P(x \geq 3) = p(3) + p(4) + p(5) + p(6) = 0.0072 + 0.0007 + 0.0001 + 0.0000 = 0.008.$$

This probability says that, if the centre is averaging 20.8 errors per year, then there would be three errors in a week in only 0.8 percent of all weeks. That is, if we are to believe that the control centre is averaging 20.8 errors per year, then we must believe that an 8 in 1,000 chance has occurred. Since it is very difficult to believe that such a rare event has occurred, we have strong evidence that the average number of errors per week has increased. Therefore, an investigation by CATSA into the reasons for such an increase is probably justified.

Example 4.13

In the book *Modern Statistical Quality Control and Improvement,* Farnum presents an example dealing with the quality of computer software. In the example, Farnum measures software quality by monitoring the number of errors per 1,000 lines of computer code.

Suppose that the number of errors per 1,000 lines of computer code is described by a Poisson distribution with a mean of four errors per 1,000 lines of code. If we wish to find the probability of obtaining eight errors in 2,500 lines of computer code, we must adjust the mean of the Poisson distribution. To do this, we arbitrarily choose a **space unit** of one line of code, and we note that a mean of four errors per 1,000 lines of code is equivalent to $4/1,000$ of an error per line of code. Therefore, the mean number of errors per 2,500 lines of code is $(4/1,000)(2,500) = 10$. It follows that

$$p(8) = \frac{e^{-\mu}\mu^8}{8!} = \frac{e^{-10}10^8}{8!} = 0.1126.$$

The mean, μ, is often called the **parameter** of the Poisson distribution. Figure 4.8 shows several Poisson distributions. We see that, depending on its parameter (mean), a Poisson distribution can be very positively skewed (to the right) or can be quite symmetrical.

Finally, if we place the Poisson probability formula into the general expressions (of Section 4.2) for μ_x, σ_x^2, and σ_x, we can derive formulas for calculating the mean, variance, and standard deviation of a Poisson distribution:

The Mean, Variance, and Standard Deviation of a Poisson Random Variable

Suppose that x is a **Poisson random variable**. If μ is the average number of occurrences of an event over the specified interval of time or space of interest, then

$$\mu_x = \mu, \qquad \sigma_x^2 = \mu, \qquad \sigma_x = \sqrt{\mu}.$$

Here we see that both the mean and the variance of a Poisson random variable equal the average number of occurrences μ of the event of interest over the specified interval of time or space. For example, in the air traffic control situation, the Poisson distribution of x, the number of errors at the air traffic control centre in a week, has a mean of $\mu_x = 0.4$ and a standard deviation of $\sigma_x = \sqrt{0.4} = 0.6325$.

FIGURE **4.8** **Several Poisson Distributions**

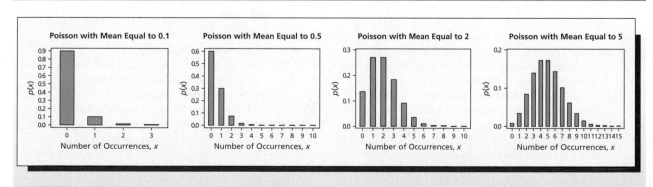

Exercises for Section 4.4

CONCEPTS

4.28 The values of a Poisson random variable are $x = 0, 1, 2, 3, \ldots$. Explain what these values represent.

4.29 Explain the assumptions that must be satisfied when a Poisson distribution adequately describes a random variable x.

METHODS AND APPLICATIONS

4.30 Suppose that x has a Poisson distribution with $\mu = 2$.
   a. Write the Poisson formula and describe the possible values of x.
   b. Starting with the smallest possible value of x, calculate $p(x)$ for each value of x until $p(x)$ becomes smaller than 0.001.
   c. Graph the Poisson distribution using your results of part b.
   d. Find $P(x = 2)$.
   e. Find $P(x \leq 4)$.
   f. Find $P(x < 4)$.
   g. Find $P(x \geq 1)$ and $P(x > 2)$.
   h. Find $P(1 \leq x \leq 4)$.
   i. Find $P(2 < x < 5)$.
   j. Find $P(2 \leq x < 6)$.

4.31 Suppose that x has a Poisson distribution with $\mu = 2$.
   a. Use the formulas given in this section to compute the mean, μ_x, variance, σ_x^2, and standard deviation, σ_x.
   b. Calculate the intervals $[\mu_x \pm 2\sigma_x]$ and $[\mu_x \pm 3\sigma_x]$. Then use the probabilities you calculated in Exercise 4.30 to find the probability that x will be inside each of these intervals.

4.32 A coffee-shop manager wishes to provide prompt service for customers at the drive-up window. The coffee shop currently can serve up to 10 customers per 15-minute period without significant delay. The average arrival rate is seven customers per 15-minute period. Let x denote the number of customers arriving per 15-minute period. Assume x has a Poisson distribution.
   a. Find the probability that 10 customers will arrive in a particular 15-minute period.
   b. Find the probability that 10 or fewer customers will arrive in a particular 15-minute period.
   c. Find the probability that there will be a significant delay at the drive-up window. That is, find the probability that more than 10 customers will arrive during a particular 15-minute period.

4.33 A telephone company's goal is to have no more than five monthly line failures on any 100 km of line. The company currently experiences an average of two monthly line failures per 50 km of line. Let x denote the number of monthly line failures per 100 km of line. Assume x has a Poisson distribution.
   a. Find the probability that the company will meet its goal on a particular 100 km of line.
   b. Find the probability that the company will not meet its goal on a particular 100 km of line.
   c. Find the probability that the company will have no more than five monthly failures on a particular 200 km of line.

   d. Find the probability that the company will have more than 12 monthly failures on a particular 150 km of line.

4.34 A local law enforcement agency claims that the number of times that a patrol car passes through a particular neighbourhood follows a Poisson process with a mean of three times per nightly shift. Let x denote the number of times that a patrol car passes through the neighbourhood during a nightly shift.
   a. Calculate the probability that no patrol cars pass through the neighbourhood during a nightly shift.
   b. Suppose that during a randomly selected night shift no patrol cars pass through the neighbourhood. Based on your answer in part a, do you believe the agency's claim? Explain.
   c. Assuming that nightly shifts are independent and assuming that the agency's claim is correct, find the probability that exactly one patrol car will pass through the neighbourhood on each of four consecutive nights.

4.35 When the number of trials, n, is large, binomial probability tables may not be available. Furthermore, if a computer is not available, hand calculations will be tedious. As an alternative, the Poisson distribution can be used to approximate the binomial distribution when n is large and p is small. Here the mean of the Poisson distribution is taken to be $\mu = np$. That is, when n is large and p is small, we can use the Poisson formula with $\mu = np$ to calculate binomial probabilities; we will obtain results close to those we would obtain by using the binomial formula. A common rule is to use this approximation when $n/p \geq 500$.

   For example, in the movie *Coma*, a young female intern at a Boston hospital was very upset when her friend, a young nurse, went into a coma during routine anaesthesia at the hospital. Upon investigation, she found that 10 of the last 30,000 healthy patients at the hospital had gone into comas during routine anaesthesias. When she confronted the hospital administrator with this fact and the fact that the national average was 6 out of 100,000 healthy patients going into comas during routine anaesthesias, the administrator replied that 10 out of 30,000 was still quite small and thus not that unusual.
   a. Use the Poisson distribution to approximate the probability that 10 or more of 30,000 healthy patients would slip into comas during routine anaesthesias, if in fact the true average at the hospital was 6 in 100,000. Hint: $\mu = np = 30,000(6/100,000) = 1.8$.
   b. Given the hospital's record and part a, what conclusion would you draw about the hospital's medical practices regarding anaesthesia?
   (Note: It turned out that the hospital administrator was part of a conspiracy to sell body parts and was purposely putting healthy adults into comas during routine anaesthesias. If the intern had taken a statistics course, she could have avoided a great deal of danger.)

4.36 Suppose that an automobile parts wholesaler claims that 0.5 percent of the car batteries in a shipment are defective. A random sample of 200 batteries is taken, and four are found to be defective.

 a. Use the Poisson approximation discussed in Exercise 4.35 to find the probability that four or

more car batteries in a random sample of 200 such batteries would be found to be defective, if we assume that the wholesaler's claim is true.

 b. Based on your answer to part a, do you believe the claim? Explain.

CHAPTER SUMMARY

In this chapter, we began our study of **random variables**. We learned that **a random variable represents an uncertain numerical outcome**. We also learned that a random variable whose values can be listed is called a **discrete random variable**, while the values of a **continuous random variable** correspond to one or more intervals on the real number line. We saw that a **probability distribution** of a discrete random variable is a table, graph, or formula that gives the probability associated with each of the random variable's possible values. We also discussed several descriptive measures of a discrete random variable—its **mean** (or **expected value**), its **variance**, and its **standard deviation**. We concluded this chapter by studying two important, commonly used discrete probability distributions—the **binomial distribution** and the **Poisson distribution**—and we demonstrated how these distributions can be used to make statistical inferences.

GLOSSARY OF TERMS

binomial distribution: The probability distribution that describes a binomial random variable. (page 129)

binomial experiment: An experiment that consists of n independent, identical trials, each of which results in either a success or a failure and is such that the probability of success on any trial is the same. (page 129)

binomial random variable: A random variable that is defined to be the total number of successes in n trials of a binomial experiment. (page 129)

binomial tables: Tables in which we can look up binomial probabilities. (page 132)

continuous random variable: A random variable whose values correspond to one or more intervals of numbers on the real number line. (page 116)

discrete random variable: A random variable whose values can be counted or listed. (page 116)

expected value (of a random variable): The mean of the population of all possible observed values of a random variable. That is, the long-run average value obtained if values of a random variable are observed a (theoretically) infinite number of times. (page 120)

Poisson distribution: The probability distribution that describes a Poisson random variable. (page 138)

Poisson random variable: A discrete random variable that can often be used to describe the number of occurrences of an event over a specified interval of time or space. (page 138)

probability distribution (of a discrete random variable): A table, graph, or formula that gives the probability associated with each of the random variable's values. (page 117)

random variable: A variable that assumes numerical values that are determined by the outcome of an experiment. That is, a variable that represents an uncertain numerical outcome. (page 116)

standard deviation (of a random variable): The standard deviation of the population of all possible observed values of a random variable. It measures the spread of the population of all possible observed values of the random variable. (page 123)

variance (of a random variable): The variance of the population of all possible observed values of a random variable. It measures the spread of the population of all possible observed values of the random variable. (page 123)

IMPORTANT FORMULAS

Properties of a discrete probability distribution: page 119

The mean (expected value) of a discrete random variable: page 120

Variance and standard deviation of a discrete random variable: page 123

Binomial probability formula: page 129

Mean, variance, and standard deviation of a binomial random variable: page 136

Poisson probability formula: page 138

Mean, variance, and standard deviation of a Poisson random variable: page 141

SUPPLEMENTARY EXERCISES

4.37 An investor holds two stocks, each of which can rise (R), remain unchanged (U), or decline (D) on any particular day. Let x equal the number of stocks that rise on a particular day.

    a. Write the probability distribution of x assuming that all outcomes are equally likely.

    b. Write the probability distribution of x assuming that for each stock $P(R) = 0.6$, $P(U) = 0.1$, and $P(D) = 0.3$ and assuming that movements of the two stocks are independent.

    c. Write the probability distribution of x assuming that for the first stock

$$P(R) = 0.4, \quad P(U) = 0.2, \quad P(D) = 0.4$$

and that for the second stock

$$P(R) = 0.8, \quad P(U) = 0.1, \quad P(D) = 0.1$$

and assuming that movements of the two stocks are independent.

4.38 Repeat Exercise 4.37, letting x equal the number of stocks that decline on that particular day.

4.39 **a.** Consider Exercise 4.37, and let x equal the number of stocks that rise on that particular day. Find μ_x and σ_x for

      (1) The probability distribution of x in Exercise 4.37a.

      (2) The probability distribution of x in Exercise 4.37b.

      (3) The probability distribution of x in Exercise 4.37c.

    b. In which case is μ_x the largest? Interpret what this means in words.

    c. In which case is σ_x the largest? Interpret what this means in words.

4.40 Suppose that the probability distribution of a random variable x can be described by the formula

$$p(x) = \frac{(x - 3)^2}{55}$$

for each of the values $x = -2, -1, 0, 1,$ and 2.

    a. Write the probability distribution of x.

    b. Show that the probability distribution of x satisfies the properties of a discrete probability distribution.

    c. Calculate the mean of x.

    d. Calculate the variance and standard deviation of x.

4.41 A rock concert promoter has scheduled an outdoor concert on Canada Day. If it does not rain, the promoter will make $30,000. If it does rain, the promoter will lose $15,000 in guarantees made to the band and other expenses. The probability of rain on Canada Day is 0.4.

    a. What is the promoter's expected profit? Is the expected profit a reasonable decision criterion? Explain.

    b. How much should an insurance company charge to insure the promoter's full losses? Explain your answer.

4.42 The demand (in number of copies per day) for a city newspaper is listed below with corresponding probabilities:

x = Demand	p(x)
50,000	0.1
70,000	0.25
90,000	0.4
110,000	0.2
130,000	0.05

    a. Find the expected demand and interpret this value.

    b. Using Chebyshev's theorem, find the minimum percentage of all possible daily demand values that will fall in the interval $[\mu_x \pm 2\sigma_x]$.

    c. Calculate the interval $[\mu_x \pm 2\sigma_x]$. According to the probability distribution of demand x previously given, what percentage of all possible daily demand values fall in the interval $[\mu_x \pm 2\sigma_x]$?

4.43 United Medicine, Inc., claims that a drug, Viro, significantly relieves the symptoms of a certain viral infection for 80 percent of all patients. Suppose that this drug is given to eight randomly selected patients who have been diagnosed with the viral infection.

    a. Let x equal the number of the eight randomly selected patients whose symptoms are significantly relieved. What distribution describes the random variable x? Explain.

    b. Assuming that the company's claim is correct, find $P(x \leq 3)$.

    c. Suppose that of the eight randomly selected patients, three have had their symptoms significantly relieved by Viro. Based on the probability in part b, would you believe the claim of United Medicine, Inc.? Explain.

4.44 A consumer advocate claims that 80 percent of cable television subscribers are not satisfied with their cable service. In an attempt to justify this claim, a randomly selected sample of cable subscribers will be polled on this issue.

    a. Suppose that the advocate's claim is true, and suppose that a random sample of five cable subscribers is selected. Assuming independence, use an appropriate formula to compute the probability that four or more subscribers in the sample are not satisfied with their service.

    b. Suppose that the advocate's claim is true, and suppose that a random sample of 25 cable subscribers is selected. Assuming independence, find

      (1) The probability that 15 or fewer subscribers in the sample are not satisfied with their service.

      (2) The probability that more than 20 subscribers in the sample are not satisfied with their service.

(3) The probability that between 20 and 24 (inclusive) subscribers in the sample are not satisfied with their service.

(4) The probability that exactly 24 subscribers in the sample are not satisfied with their service.

c. Suppose that when we survey 25 randomly selected cable television subscribers, we find that 15 are actually not satisfied with their service. Using a probability you found in this exercise as the basis for your answer, do you believe the consumer advocate's claim? Explain.

4.45 A retail store has implemented procedures aimed at reducing the number of bad cheques cashed by its cashiers. The store's goal is to cash no more than eight bad cheques per week. The average number of bad cheques cashed is three per week. Let x denote the number of bad cheques cashed per week. Assuming that x has a Poisson distribution:

a. Find the probability that the store's cashiers will not cash any bad cheques in a particular week.

b. Find the probability that the store will meet its goal during a particular week.

c. Find the probability that the store will not meet its goal during a particular week.

d. Find the probability that the store's cashiers will cash no more than 10 bad cheques per two-week period.

e. Find the probability that the store's cashiers will cash no more than five bad cheques per three-week period.

4.46 Suppose that the number of accidents occurring in an industrial plant is described by a Poisson process with an average of 1.5 accidents every three months. During the last three months, four accidents occurred.

a. Find the probability that no accidents will occur during the current three-month period.

b. Find the probability that fewer accidents will occur during the current three-month period than occurred during the last three-month period.

c. Find the probability that no more than 12 accidents will occur during a particular year.

d. Find the probability that no accidents will occur during a particular year.

4.47 A high-security government installation has installed four security systems to detect attempted break-ins. The four security systems operate independently of each other, and each has a 0.85 probability of detecting an attempted break-in. Assume an attempted break-in occurs. Use the binomial distribution to find the probability that at least one of the four security systems will detect it.

4.48 A new stain removal product claims to completely remove the stains on 90 percent of all stained garments. Assume that the product will be tested on 20 randomly selected stained garments, and let x denote the number of these garments from which the stains will be completely removed. Use the binomial distribution to find $P(x \leq 13)$ if the stain removal product's claim is correct. If x actually turns out to be 13, what do you think of the claim?

4.49 Consider Exercise 4.48, and find $P(x \leq 17)$ if the stain removal product's claim is correct. If x actually turns out to be 17, what do you think of the claim?

4.50 A province has averaged one small business failure per week over the past several years. Let x denote the number of small business failures in the next eight weeks. Use the Poisson distribution to find $P(x \geq 17)$ if the mean number of small business failures remains what it has been. If x actually turns out to be 17, what does this imply?

4.51 A candy company claims that its new chocolate almond bar averages 10 almonds per bar. Let x denote the number of almonds in the next bar that you buy. Use the Poisson distribution to find $P(x \leq 4)$ if the candy company's claim is correct. If x actually turns out to be 4, what do you think of the claim?

4.52 Consider Exercise 4.51, and find $P(x \leq 8)$ if the candy company's claim is true. If x actually turns out to be 8, what do you think of the claim?

CHAPTER 5

Continuous Random Variables

In Chapter 4, we defined discrete and continuous random variables. We also discussed discrete probability distributions, which are used to compute the probabilities of values of discrete random variables. In this chapter, we discuss **continuous probability distributions**. These are used to find probabilities concerning continuous random variables. We begin by explaining the general idea behind a continuous probability distribution. Then we present three important continuous distributions—the **uniform, normal**, and **exponential distributions**. We also study when and how the normal distribution can be used to approximate the binomial distribution (which was discussed in Chapter 4).

In order to illustrate the concepts in this chapter, we continue with a previously discussed case, and we also introduce a new case:

The Coffee Temperature Case: The fast-food restaurant uses the normal distribution to estimate the proportion of coffee it serves that has a temperature outside the range 67°C to 75°C, the customer requirement for best-tasting coffee.

The Cheese Spread Case: A food-processing company markets a soft cheese spread that is sold in a plastic container. The company has developed a new spout for the container. However, the new spout will be used only if less than 10 percent of all current purchasers would no longer buy the cheese spread if the new spout were used. The company uses sample information and a probability based on approximating the binomial distribution by the normal distribution to provide very strong evidence that less than 10 percent of all current purchasers would stop buying the spread if the new spout were used. This implies that the company can use the new spout without alienating its current customers.

5.1 Continuous Probability Distributions

Remember (from Section 4.1) that the values of a continuous random variable correspond to one or more intervals on the real number line. We often wish to compute probabilities about the range of values that a continuous random variable x might attain. We do this by assigning probabilities to **intervals of values** by using what we call a **continuous probability distribution**. To understand this idea, suppose that $f(x)$ is a continuous function of the numbers on the real line, and consider the continuous curve that results when $f(x)$ is graphed. Such a curve is illustrated in Figure 5.1.

CHAPTER 3

Continuous Probability Distributions

The curve $f(x)$ is the **continuous probability distribution** of the random variable x if the probability that x will be in a specified interval of numbers is the area under the curve $f(x)$ corresponding to the interval. Sometimes we refer to a continuous probability distribution as a **probability curve** or as a **probability density function**.

An **area** under a continuous probability distribution (or probability curve) is a **probability**. For instance, consider the range of values on the number line from the number a to the number b—that is, the interval of numbers from a to b. If the continuous random variable x is described by the probability curve $f(x)$, then the area under $f(x)$ corresponding to the interval from a to b is the probability that x will attain a value between a and b. Such a probability is illustrated as the shaded area in Figure 5.1. We write this probability as $P(a \leq x \leq b)$. Since there is no area under a continuous curve at a single point, the probability that a continuous random variable x attains a single value is always equal to 0. It follows that in Figure 5.1 we have $P(x = a) = 0$ and $P(x = b) = 0$. Therefore, $P(a \leq x \leq b)$ equals $P(a < x < b)$ because each of the interval endpoints a and b has a probability that is equal to 0.

We know that any probability is 0 or positive, and we also know that the probability assigned to all possible values of x must be 1. It follows that, similar to the conditions required for a discrete probability distribution, a probability curve must satisfy the following properties:

Properties of a Continuous Probability Distribution

The **continuous probability distribution** (or **probability curve**) $f(x)$ of a random variable x must satisfy the following two conditions:

1 $f(x) \geq 0$ for any value of x.
2 The total area under the curve of $f(x)$ is equal to 1.

FIGURE 5.1 **An Example of a Continuous Probability Distribution $f(x)$**

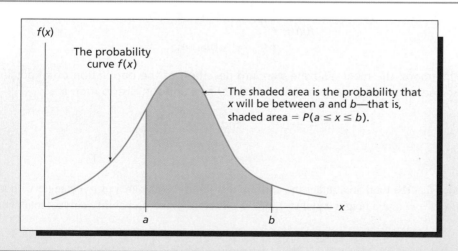

$f(x)$

The probability curve $f(x)$

The shaded area is the probability that x will be between a and b—that is, shaded area = $P(a \leq x \leq b)$.

a b x

Any continuous curve $f(x)$ that satisfies these conditions is a valid continuous probability distribution. Such probability curves can have a variety of shapes—bell-shaped and symmetrical, positively skewed (to the right), negatively skewed (to the left), or any other shape. In a practical problem, the shape of a probability curve would be estimated by looking at a frequency (or relative frequency) histogram of observed data (as we have done in Chapter 2). Later in this chapter, we study probability curves with several different shapes. For example, in the next section we introduce the **uniform distribution**, which has a rectangular shape.

It is important to point out that **the height of a probability curve $f(x)$ at a particular point is not a probability. In order to calculate a probability concerning a continuous random variable, we must compute an appropriate area under the curve $f(x)$.** In theory, such areas are calculated by calculus methods and/or numerical techniques, and needed areas under commonly used probability curves have been compiled in statistical tables.

Finally, we wish to emphasize that a continuous (or discrete) probability distribution is used to represent a population. That is, if $f(x)$ is a continuous probability distribution for a random variable x, then the area under the curve $f(x)$ between a and b—that is, $P(a \leq x \leq b)$—is **the proportion of values in the population of all possible values of x that are between a and b.** For instance, suppose that the probability curve $f(x)$ describes the random variable $x =$ the fuel efficiency obtained by a midsize car model. Then the area under the curve $f(x)$ between 3.3 L/100 km and 3.9 L/100 km is the proportion of fuel efficiency values in the population of all possible midsize car fuel efficiency values that are between 3.3 L/100 km and 3.9 L/100 km.

5.2 The Uniform Distribution

Suppose that over a period of several days the manager of a large hotel has recorded the waiting times of 1,000 people waiting for an elevator in the lobby at dinnertime (5:00 P.M. to 7:00 P.M.). The observed waiting times range from zero to four minutes. Furthermore, when the waiting times are arranged into a histogram, the bars making up the histogram have approximately equal heights, giving the histogram a rectangular appearance. This implies that the relative frequencies of all waiting times from zero to four minutes are about the same. Therefore, it is reasonable to use the **uniform distribution** to describe the random variable x, the amount of time a randomly selected hotel patron spends waiting for the elevator. In general, the equation that describes the uniform distribution is given in the following box, and this equation is graphed in Figure 5.2(a).

The Uniform Distribution

If c and d are numbers on the real line, the probability curve describing the **uniform distribution** is

$$f(x) = \begin{cases} \dfrac{1}{d - c} & \text{for } c \leq x \leq d, \\ 0 & \text{otherwise.} \end{cases}$$

Furthermore, the mean and the standard deviation of the population of all possible observed values of a random variable x that has a uniform distribution are

$$\mu_x = \frac{c + d}{2} \quad \text{and} \quad \sigma_x = \frac{d - c}{\sqrt{12}}.$$

Notice that the total area under the uniform distribution is the area of a rectangle with a base equal to $(d - c)$ and a height equal to $1/(d - c)$. Therefore, the probability curve's total area is

$$\text{base} \times \text{height} = (d - c)\left(\frac{1}{d - c}\right) = 1$$

FIGURE **5.2** **The Uniform Distribution**

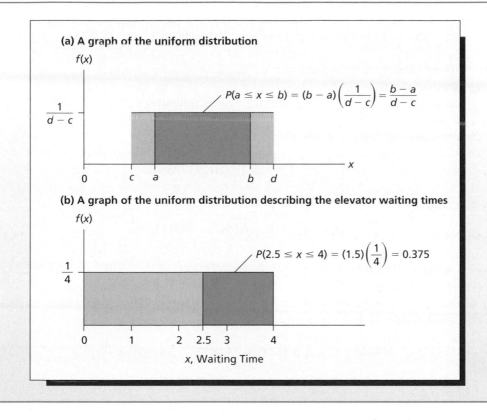

(a) A graph of the uniform distribution

(b) A graph of the uniform distribution describing the elevator waiting times

(remember that the total area under any continuous probability curve must equal 1). Furthermore, if a and b are numbers that are as illustrated in Figure 5.2(a), then the probability that x will be between a and b is the area of a rectangle with base $(b - a)$ and height $1/(d - c)$. That is,

$$P(a \leq x \leq b) = \text{base} \times \text{height}$$
$$= (b - a)\left(\frac{1}{d - c}\right)$$
$$= \frac{b - a}{d - c}.$$

Example 5.1

In the introduction to this section, we said that the amount of time, x, that a randomly selected hotel patron spends waiting for the elevator at dinnertime is uniformly distributed between zero and four minutes. In this case, $c = 0$ and $d = 4$. Therefore,

$$f(x) = \begin{cases} \dfrac{1}{d - c} = \dfrac{1}{4 - 0} = \dfrac{1}{4} & \text{for } 0 \leq x \leq 4, \\ 0 & \text{otherwise.} \end{cases}$$

Noting that this equation is graphed in Figure 5.2(b), suppose that the hotel manager wishes to find the probability that a randomly selected patron will spend at least 2.5 minutes waiting for the elevator. This probability is the area under the curve $f(x)$ that corresponds to the interval [2.5, 4]. As shown in Figure 5.2(b), this probability is the area of a rectangle with a base equal to $4 - 2.5 = 1.5$ and a height equal to $1/4$. That is,

$$P(x \geq 2.5) = P(2.5 \leq x \leq 4) = \text{base} \times \text{height} = 1.5 \times \frac{1}{4} = 0.375.$$

Similarly, the probability that a randomly selected patron will spend less than one minute waiting for the elevator is

$$P(x < 1) = P(0 \le x \le 1) = \text{base} \times \text{height} = 1 \times \frac{1}{4} = 0.25.$$

We next note that the mean waiting time for the elevator at dinnertime is

$$\mu_x = \frac{c + d}{2} = \frac{0 + 4}{2} = 2 \text{ (minutes)}$$

and that the standard deviation of this waiting time is

$$\sigma_x = \frac{d - c}{\sqrt{12}} = \frac{4 - 0}{\sqrt{12}} = 1.1547 \text{ (minutes).}$$

Therefore, because

$$\mu_x - \sigma_x = 2 - 1.1547 = 0.8453$$

and

$$\mu_x + \sigma_x = 2 + 1.1547 = 3.1547,$$

the probability that the waiting time of a randomly selected patron will be within (plus or minus) one standard deviation of the mean waiting time is

$$P(0.8453 \le x \le 3.1547) = (3.1547 - 0.8453) \times \frac{1}{4}$$

$$= 0.57735.$$

Exercises for Sections 5.1 and 5.2

CONCEPTS

5.1 A discrete probability distribution assigns probabilities to individual values. To what are probabilities assigned by a continuous probability distribution?

5.2 How do we use the continuous probability distribution (or probability curve) of a random variable x to find probabilities? Explain.

5.3 What two properties must be satisfied by a continuous probability distribution (or probability curve)?

5.4 Explain the meaning of the height of a probability curve over a given point.

5.5 When is it appropriate to use the uniform distribution to describe a random variable x?

METHODS AND APPLICATIONS

5.6 Suppose that the random variable x has a uniform distribution with $c = 2$ and $d = 8$.
  a. Write the formula for the probability curve of x, and write an interval that gives the possible values of x.
  b. Graph the probability curve of x.
  c. Find $P(3 \le x \le 5)$.
  d. Find $P(1.5 \le x \le 6.5)$.
  e. Calculate the mean μ_x, variance σ_x^2, and standard deviation σ_x.

  f. Calculate the interval $[\mu_x \pm 2\sigma_x]$. What is the probability that x will be in this interval?

5.7 Consider the figure given below. Find the value h that makes the function $f(x)$ a valid continuous probability distribution.

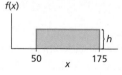

5.8 Assume that the waiting time x for an elevator is uniformly distributed between zero and six minutes.
  a. Write the formula for the probability curve of x.
  b. Graph the probability curve of x.
  c. Find $P(2 \le x \le 4)$.
  d. Find $P(3 \le x \le 6)$.
  e. Find $P(\{0 \le x \le 2\}$ or $\{5 \le x \le 6\})$.

5.9 Refer to Exercise 5.8.
  a. Calculate the mean, μ_x, the variance, σ_x^2, and the standard deviation, σ_x.
  b. Find the probability that the waiting time of a randomly selected patron will be within one standard deviation of the mean.

5.10 Consider the figure given below. Find the value K that makes the function $f(x)$ a valid continuous probability distribution.

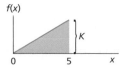

5.11 Suppose that an airline quotes a flight time of 2 hours, 10 minutes between two cities. Furthermore, suppose that historical flight records indicate that the actual flight time between the two cities, x, is uniformly distributed between 2 hours and 2 hours, 20 minutes. Let the time unit be one minute.
   a. Write the formula for the probability curve of x.
   b. Graph the probability curve of x.
   c. Find $P(125 \leq x \leq 135)$.
   d. Find the probability that a randomly selected flight between the two cities will be at least five minutes late.

5.12 Refer to Exercise 5.11.
   a. Calculate the mean flight time and the standard deviation of the flight time.

   b. Find the probability that the flight time will be within one standard deviation of the mean.

5.13 Consider the figure given below. Find the value c that makes the function $f(x)$ a valid continuous probability distribution.

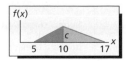

5.14 A weather forecaster predicts that the May rainfall in a local area will be between 3 cm and 6 cm but has no idea where within the interval the amount will be. Let x be the amount of May rainfall in the local area, and assume that x is uniformly distributed in the interval 3 cm to 6 cm.
   a. Write the formula for the probability curve of x.
   b. Graph the probability curve of x.
   c. What is the probability that May rainfall will be at least 4 cm? at least 5 cm? at most 4.5 cm?

5.15 Refer to Exercise 5.14.
   a. Calculate the expected May rainfall.
   b. What is the probability that the observed May rainfall will fall within two standard deviations of the mean? within one standard deviation of the mean?

5.3 The Normal Probability Distribution

The normal curve   The bell-shaped appearance of the normal probability distribution is illustrated in Figure 5.3. The equation that defines this normal curve is given in the following box: CHAPTER 5

The Normal Probability Distribution

The **normal probability distribution** is defined by the equation

$$f(x) = \frac{1}{\sigma\sqrt{2\pi}}\, e^{-\frac{1}{2}\left(\frac{x-\mu}{\sigma}\right)^2} \quad \text{for all values of } x \text{ on the real line.}$$

Here μ and σ are the mean and standard deviation of the population of all possible observed values of the random variable x under consideration. Furthermore, $\pi = 3.141592\ldots$, and $e = 2.718281\ldots$ is the base of the natural logarithm.

The normal probability distribution has several important properties:

1   There is an entire family of normal probability distributions; the specific shape of each normal distribution is determined by its mean μ and its standard deviation σ.

2   The highest point on the normal curve is located at the mean, which is also the median and the mode of the distribution.

3   The normal distribution is symmetrical: The curve's shape to the left of the mean is the mirror image of its shape to the right of the mean.

4   The tails of the normal curve extend to infinity in both directions and never touch the horizontal axis. However, the tails get close enough to the horizontal axis quickly enough to ensure that the total area under the normal curve equals 1.

5   Since the normal curve is symmetrical, the area under the normal curve to the right of the mean (μ) equals the area under the normal curve to the left of the mean, and each of these areas equals 0.5 (see Figure 5.3).

   Intuitively, the mean μ positions the normal curve on the real line. This is illustrated in Figure 5.4(a). This figure shows two normal curves with different means μ_1 and μ_2 (where μ_1

FIGURE **5.3**   The Normal Probability Curve

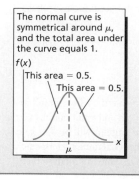

The normal curve is symmetrical around μ, and the total area under the curve equals 1.

$f(x)$

This area = 0.5.

This area = 0.5.

μ

x

FIGURE **5.4**   How the Mean μ and Standard Deviation σ Affect the Position and Shape of a Normal Probability Curve

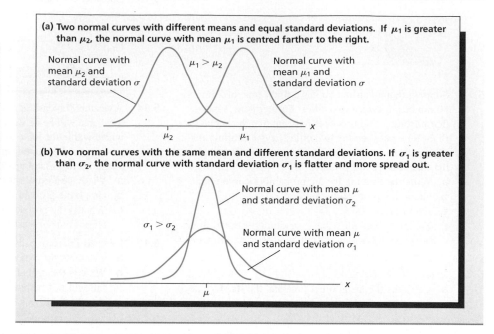

(a) Two normal curves with different means and equal standard deviations. If μ_1 is greater than μ_2, the normal curve with mean μ_1 is centred farther to the right.

Normal curve with mean μ_2 and standard deviation σ

$\mu_1 > \mu_2$

Normal curve with mean μ_1 and standard deviation σ

μ_2 μ_1 x

(b) Two normal curves with the same mean and different standard deviations. If σ_1 is greater than σ_2, the normal curve with standard deviation σ_1 is flatter and more spread out.

Normal curve with mean μ and standard deviation σ_2

$\sigma_1 > \sigma_2$

Normal curve with mean μ and standard deviation σ_1

μ x

FIGURE **5.5**   An Area under a Normal Curve Corresponding to the Interval [a, b]

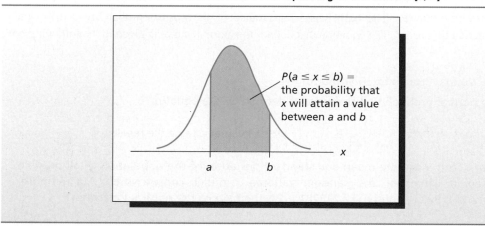

$P(a \leq x \leq b) =$ the probability that x will attain a value between a and b

a b x

is greater than μ_2) and with equal standard deviations. We see that the normal curve with mean μ_1 is centred farther to the right.

The variance σ^2 (and the standard deviation σ) measure the spread of the normal curve. This is illustrated in Figure 5.4(b), which shows two normal curves with the same mean and two different standard deviations σ_1 and σ_2. Because σ_1 is greater than σ_2, the normal curve with standard deviation σ_1 is more spread out (flatter) than the normal curve with standard deviation σ_2. In general, larger standard deviations result in normal curves that are flatter and more spread out, while smaller standard deviations result in normal curves that have higher peaks and are less spread out.

Suppose that a random variable x is normally distributed with mean μ and standard deviation σ. If a and b are numbers on the real line, we consider the probability that x will attain a value between a and b. That is, we consider

$$P(a \leq x \leq b),$$

which equals the area under the normal curve with mean μ and standard deviation σ corresponding to the interval [a, b]. Such an area is depicted in Figure 5.5 and can be found using a statistical table called a **normal table**. There are three important areas under a normal curve. These areas form the basis for the **empirical rule** for a normally distributed population (discussed on page 50 in

FIGURE **5.6**   **Three Important Percentages Concerning a Normally Distributed Random Variable
x with Mean μ and Standard Deviation σ**

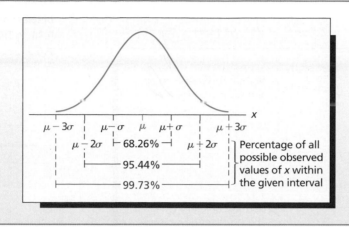

Chapter 2). Specifically, if x is normally distributed with mean μ and standard deviation σ, the following can be shown (using a normal table), as illustrated in Figure 5.6:

Three Important Areas under the Normal Curve

1   $P(\mu - \sigma \le x \le \mu + \sigma) = 0.6826$.

This means that 68.26 percent of all possible observed values of x are within (plus or minus) one standard deviation of μ.

2   $P(\mu - 2\sigma \le x \le \mu + 2\sigma) = 0.9544$.

This means that 95.44 percent of all possible observed values of x are within (plus or minus) two standard deviations of μ.

3   $P(\mu - 3\sigma \le x \le \mu + 3\sigma) = 0.9973$.

This means that 99.73 percent of all possible observed values of x are within (plus or minus) three standard deviations of μ.

Finding normal curve areas   There is a unique normal curve for every combination of μ and σ. Since there are many (theoretically, an unlimited number of) such combinations, we would like to have one table of normal curve areas that applies to all normal curves. There is such a table, and we can use it by thinking in terms of how many standard deviations a value of interest is from the mean. Specifically, consider a random variable x that is normally distributed with mean μ and standard deviation σ. Then, the random variable

$$z = \frac{x - \mu}{\sigma}$$

expresses the number of standard deviations that x is from the mean μ. To understand this idea, notice that if x equals μ (that is, x is zero standard deviations from μ), then $z = (\mu - \mu)/\sigma = 0$. However, if x is one standard deviation above the mean (that is, if x equals $\mu + \sigma$), then $x - \mu = \sigma$ and $z = \sigma/\sigma = 1$. Similarly, if x is two standard deviations below the mean (that is, if x equals $\mu - 2\sigma$), then $x - \mu = -2\sigma$ and $z = -2\sigma/\sigma = -2$. Figure 5.7 illustrates that for values of x of, respectively, $\mu - 3\sigma$, $\mu - 2\sigma$, $\mu - \sigma$, μ, $\mu + \sigma$, $\mu + 2\sigma$, and $\mu + 3\sigma$, the corresponding values of z are $-3, -2, -1, 0, 1, 2$, and 3. This figure also illustrates the following general result:

The Standard Normal Distribution

If a random variable x (or, equivalently, the population of all possible observed values of x) is normally distributed with mean μ and standard deviation σ, then the random variable

$$z = \frac{x - \mu}{\sigma}$$

(or, equivalently, the population of all possible observed values of z) is normally distributed with mean 0 and standard deviation 1. A normal distribution (or curve) with mean 0 and standard deviation 1 is called a **standard normal distribution** (or **curve**).

FIGURE **5.7**   If *x* Is Normally Distributed with Mean μ and Standard Deviation σ, Then $z = \dfrac{x - \mu}{\sigma}$ Is Normally Distributed with Mean 0 and Standard Deviation 1

FIGURE **5.8**

The Area under the Standard Normal Curve between 0 and 1 Equals 0.3413; That Is, $P(0 \le z \le 1) = 0.3413$

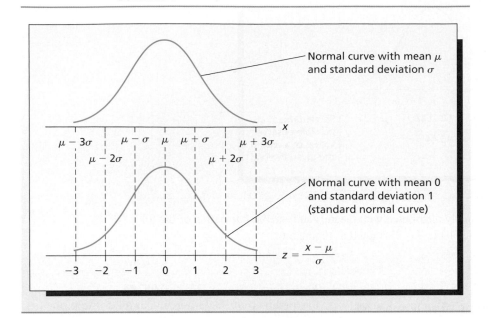

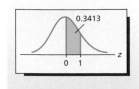

Table A.3 is a table of areas under the standard normal curve. This table is called a **normal table**, and it is reproduced in Table 5.1. Specifically,

The normal table gives, for many different values of *z*, the area under the standard normal curve between 0 and *z*.

The values of *z* in the table range from 0.00 to 3.09 in increments of 0.01. As can be seen from Table 5.1, values of *z* accurate to the nearest tenth (0.0, 0.1, 0.2, . . . , 2.9, 3.0) are given in the far left column (headed *z*) of the table. Further graduations to the nearest hundredth (0.00, 0.01, 0.02, . . . , 0.09) are given across the top of the table. The areas under the normal curve are given in the body of the table, accurate to four decimal places.

As a first example, suppose that we wish to find the area under the standard normal curve between 0 and 1. In order to find this area, we must find the area in the normal table corresponding to a *z* value of 1.00. Looking at Table 5.1, we first scan down the far left column of the table (starting at the top) until we find the value 1.0. Having found this value, we now scan across the row in the table corresponding to the *z* value 1.0 until we find the column in the table corresponding to 0.00. The desired area is in the row corresponding to the *z* value 1.0 and in the column headed 0.00. We see that this area equals 0.3413 (we have shaded it), and we illustrate this area in Figure 5.8. The area under the standard normal curve between 0 and 1 is the probability that the random variable *z* will be between 0 and 1. That is, we have found that

$$P(0 \le z \le 1) = 0.3413.$$

Next suppose that a random variable *x* is normally distributed with mean μ and standard deviation σ, and remember that *z* is the number of standard deviations σ that *x* is from μ. It follows that, when we say that $P(0 \le z \le 1)$ equals 0.3413, we are saying that 34.13 percent of all possible observed values of *x* are between the mean μ (where *z* equals 0) and a point that is one standard deviation above μ (where *z* equals 1). That is, 34.13 percent of all possible observed values of *x* are between μ and $\mu + \sigma$. The normal curve in Figure 5.9(a) illustrates that, by the symmetry of the normal curve, the area under the standard normal curve between -1 and 0 is equal to the area under this curve between 0 and 1. That is,

$$P(-1 \le z \le 0) = P(0 \le z \le 1) = 0.3413.$$

TABLE 5.1 A Table of Areas under the Standard Normal Curve

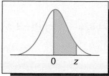

z	0.00	0.01	0.02	0.03	0.04	0.05	0.06	0.07	0.08	0.09
0.0	0.0000	0.0040	0.0080	0.0120	0.0160	0.0199	0.0239	0.0279	0.0319	0.0359
0.1	0.0398	0.0438	0.0478	0.0517	0.0557	0.0596	0.0636	0.0675	0.0714	0.0753
0.2	0.0793	0.0832	0.0871	0.0910	0.0948	0.0987	0.1026	0.1064	0.1103	0.1141
0.3	0.1179	0.1217	0.1255	0.1293	0.1331	0.1368	0.1406	0.1443	0.1480	0.1517
0.4	0.1554	0.1591	0.1628	0.1664	0.1700	0.1736	0.1772	0.1808	0.1844	0.1879
0.5	0.1915	0.1950	0.1985	0.2019	0.2054	0.2088	0.2123	0.2157	0.2190	0.2224
0.6	0.2257	0.2291	0.2324	0.2357	0.2389	0.2422	0.2454	0.2486	0.2517	0.2549
0.7	0.2580	0.2611	0.2642	0.2673	0.2704	0.2734	0.2764	0.2794	0.2823	0.2852
0.8	0.2881	0.2910	0.2939	0.2967	0.2995	0.3023	0.3051	0.3078	0.3106	0.3133
0.9	0.3159	0.3186	0.3212	0.3238	0.3264	0.3289	0.3315	0.3340	0.3365	0.3389
1.0	0.3413	0.3438	0.3461	0.3485	0.3508	0.3531	0.3554	0.3577	0.3599	0.3621
1.1	0.3643	0.3665	0.3686	0.3708	0.3729	0.3749	0.3770	0.3790	0.3810	0.3830
1.2	0.3849	0.3869	0.3888	0.3907	0.3925	0.3944	0.3962	0.3980	0.3997	0.4015
1.3	0.4032	0.4049	0.4066	0.4082	0.4099	0.4115	0.4131	0.4147	0.4162	0.4177
1.4	0.4192	0.4207	0.4222	0.4236	0.4251	0.4265	0.4279	0.4292	0.4306	0.4319
1.5	0.4332	0.4345	0.4357	0.4370	0.4382	0.4394	0.4406	0.4418	0.4429	0.4441
1.6	0.4452	0.4463	0.4474	0.4484	0.4495	0.4505	0.4515	0.4525	0.4535	0.4545
1.7	0.4554	0.4564	0.4573	0.4582	0.4591	0.4599	0.4608	0.4616	0.4625	0.4633
1.8	0.4641	0.4649	0.4656	0.4664	0.4671	0.4678	0.4686	0.4693	0.4699	0.4706
1.9	0.4713	0.4719	0.4726	0.4732	0.4738	0.4744	0.4750	0.4756	0.4761	0.4767
2.0	0.4772	0.4778	0.4783	0.4788	0.4793	0.4798	0.4803	0.4808	0.4812	0.4817
2.1	0.4821	0.4826	0.4830	0.4834	0.4838	0.4842	0.4846	0.4850	0.4854	0.4857
2.2	0.4861	0.4864	0.4868	0.4871	0.4875	0.4878	0.4881	0.4884	0.4887	0.4890
2.3	0.4893	0.4896	0.4898	0.4901	0.4904	0.4906	0.4909	0.4911	0.4913	0.4916
2.4	0.4918	0.4920	0.4922	0.4925	0.4927	0.4929	0.4931	0.4932	0.4934	0.4936
2.5	0.4938	0.4940	0.4941	0.4943	0.4945	0.4946	0.4948	0.4949	0.4951	0.4952
2.6	0.4953	0.4955	0.4956	0.4957	0.4959	0.4960	0.4961	0.4962	0.4963	0.4964
2.7	0.4965	0.4966	0.4967	0.4968	0.4969	0.4970	0.4971	0.4972	0.4973	0.4974
2.8	0.4974	0.4975	0.4976	0.4977	0.4977	0.4978	0.4979	0.4979	0.4980	0.4981
2.9	0.4981	0.4982	0.4982	0.4983	0.4984	0.4984	0.4985	0.4985	0.4986	0.4986
3.0	0.4987	0.4987	0.4987	0.4988	0.4988	0.4989	0.4989	0.4989	0.4990	0.4990

This says that 34.13 percent of all possible observed values of x are between $\mu - \sigma$ and μ. If we add the two areas in Figure 5.9(a), we have

$$P(-1 \leq z \leq 1) = 0.3413 + 0.3413 = 0.6826.$$

That is, 68.26 percent of all possible observed values of x are within (plus or minus) one standard deviation of the mean μ. Similarly, if we look up the z value 2.00 in the normal table, we find that $P(0 \leq z \leq 2) = 0.4772$. This implies, as illustrated in Figure 5.9(b), that $P(-2 \leq z \leq 2) = 0.4772 + 0.4772 = 0.9544$. In other words, 95.44 percent of all possible observed values of x are within (plus or minus) two standard deviations of μ. Furthermore, if we look up the z value 3.00 in the normal table, we find that $P(0 \leq z \leq 3) = 0.4987$. This implies, as illustrated in Figure 5.9(c), that $P(-3 \leq z \leq 3) = 0.4987 + 0.4987 = 0.9974$. Actually, the probability 0.4987 in Table 5.1 is rounded slightly, and a more precise calculation shows that $P(-3 \leq z \leq 3)$ is actually closer to 0.9973. This says that 99.73 percent of all possible observed values of x are within (plus or minus) three standard deviations of the mean μ.

As a final example of this kind of area, consider finding the area under the standard normal curve between 0 and 2.53. There is nothing special about this area, but we want to demonstrate using the normal table when the needed z value does not end in .00. To look up this area, we locate the area in the normal table in the row corresponding to 2.5 and in the column headed by 0.03. This area is 0.4943 (we have shaded it in Table 5.1), which implies that $P(0 \leq z \leq 2.53) = 0.4943$. This implies, as illustrated in Figure 5.9(d), that $P(-2.53 \leq z \leq 2.53) = 0.4943 + 0.4943 = 0.9886$. In other

FIGURE 5.9 Some Areas under the Standard Normal Curve

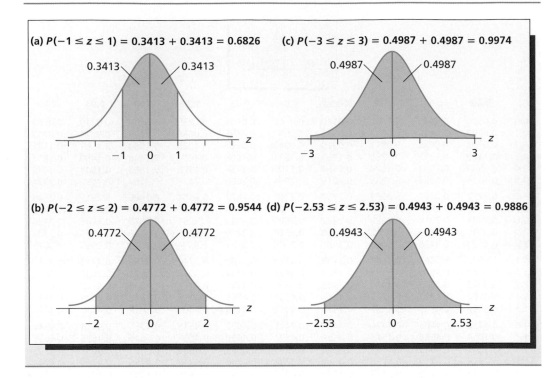

(a) $P(-1 \leq z \leq 1) = 0.3413 + 0.3413 = 0.6826$

0.3413   0.3413

$-1 \quad 0 \quad 1$

(c) $P(-3 \leq z \leq 3) = 0.4987 + 0.4987 = 0.9974$

0.4987   0.4987

$-3 \quad 0 \quad 3$

(b) $P(-2 \leq z \leq 2) = 0.4772 + 0.4772 = 0.9544$

0.4772   0.4772

$-2 \quad 0 \quad 2$

(d) $P(-2.53 \leq z \leq 2.53) = 0.4943 + 0.4943 = 0.9886$

0.4943   0.4943

$-2.53 \quad 0 \quad 2.53$

words, 98.86 percent of all possible observed values of x are within (plus or minus) 2.53 standard deviations of the mean μ.

Before continuing, recall that there is no area under a continuous probability curve at a single value of a random variable. Because the standard normal curve is a continuous probability curve, it follows, for example, that $P(-2.53 \leq z \leq 2.53)$ equals $P(-2.53 < z < 2.53)$. Keep this idea in mind as we continue through this section.

Thus far we have shown how to find **the area under the standard normal curve between 0 and a positive z value**, which, by the symmetry of the curve, **equals the area under the curve between 0 and the corresponding negative z value**. We now show how to find some other areas that will be important in later sections.

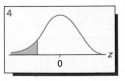

1. **The area under the standard normal curve to the left of a positive z value:** Suppose that we want to find the area under the standard normal curve to the left of the z value 1. As illustrated in Figure 5.10, this is the area under the curve between 0 and 1, which the normal table tells us is 0.3413, plus the area under the curve to the left of 0 (the mean), which is 0.5. Therefore, $P(z \leq 1) = 0.5 + 0.3413 = 0.8413$.

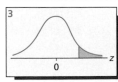

2. **The area under the standard normal curve to the right of a negative z value:** As illustrated in Figure 5.11, the area under the standard normal curve to the right of the z value -1 is $P(z \geq -1) = 0.3413 + 0.5 = 0.8413$.

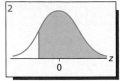

3. **The area under the standard normal curve to the right of a positive z value—a right-hand tail area:** Consider finding the area under the standard normal curve to the right of the z value 1. As illustrated in Figure 5.12, this is the area under the curve to the right of 0, which is 0.5, minus the area under the curve between 0 and 1, which the normal table tells us is 0.3413. Therefore, $P(z \geq 1) = 0.5 - 0.3413 = 0.1587$.

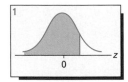

4. **The area under the standard normal curve to the left of a negative z value—a left-hand tail area:** As illustrated in Figure 5.13, the symmetry of the standard normal curve implies that the area under the standard normal curve to the left of the z value -1 equals the area under this curve to the right of the z value 1. That is, $P(z \leq -1)$ equals $P(z \geq 1)$. Therefore, $P(z \leq -1) = 0.5 - 0.3413 = 0.1587$.

FIGURE **5.10**   Calculating $P(z \leq 1)$

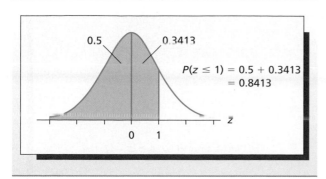

FIGURE **5.11**   Calculating $P(z \geq -1)$

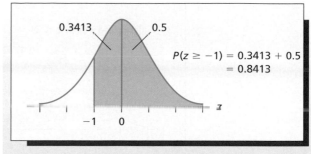

FIGURE **5.12**   Calculating $P(z \geq 1)$

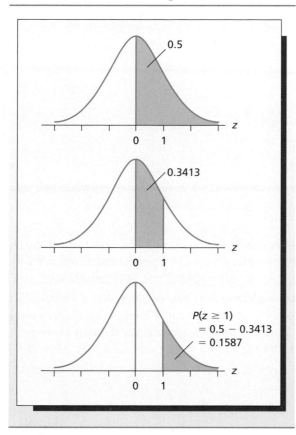

FIGURE **5.13**   Calculating $P(z \leq -1)$

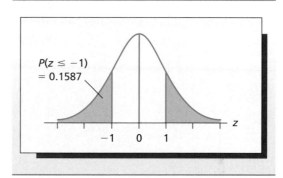

FIGURE **5.14**   Calculating $P(z \geq 3.09)$

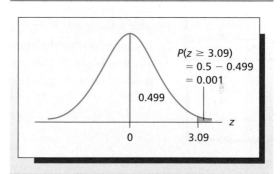

5   **Right-hand tail areas corresponding to z values greater than 3.09, and left-hand tail areas corresponding to z values less than -3.09:** The largest z value in the normal table is 3.09. Because the area under the standard normal curve between 0 and 3.09 is 0.499, the area under this curve to the right of 3.09 is $0.5 - 0.499 = 0.001$ (see Figure 5.14). Therefore, if we wish to find the area under the standard normal curve to the right of any z value greater than 3.09, the most we can say (without using a computer) is that this area is less than 0.001. Similarly, the area under the standard normal curve to the left of any z value less than -3.09 is also less than 0.001.

6   **The area under the standard normal curve between two positive z values:** Consider finding the area under the standard normal curve between 1 and 2. As illustrated in

FIGURE 5.15   Calculating $P(1 \leq z \leq 2)$ and $P(-2 \leq z \leq -1)$

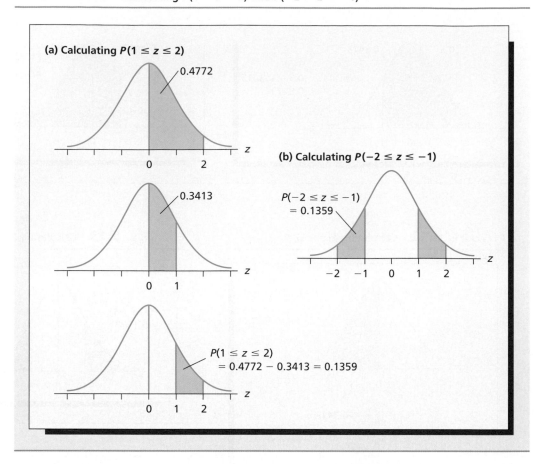

Figure 5.15(a), this area equals the area under the curve between 0 and 2, which the normal table tells us is 0.4772, minus the area under the curve between 0 and 1, which the normal table tells us is 0.3413. Therefore, $P(1 \leq z \leq 2) = 0.4772 - 0.3413 = 0.1359$.

7   **The area under the standard normal curve between two negative z values:** As illustrated in Figure 5.15(b), the symmetry of the normal curve implies that the area under the standard normal curve between -2 and -1 equals the area under this curve between 1 and 2. That is, $P(-2 \leq z \leq -1)$ equals $P(1 \leq z \leq 2)$. Therefore, $P(-2 \leq z \leq -1) = 0.4772 - 0.3413 = 0.1359$.

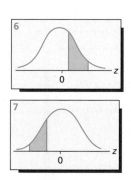

Finding Normal Probabilities

1   Formulate the problem in terms of the random variable x.

2   Calculate relevant z values and restate the problem in terms of the standard normal random variable

$$z = \frac{x - \mu}{\sigma}.$$

3   Find the required area under the standard normal curve by using the normal table.

4   Note that it is always useful to draw a picture illustrating the needed area before using the normal table.

Some practical applications   We have seen how to use z values and the normal table to find areas under the standard normal curve. However, most practical problems are not stated in such terms. We now consider an example in which we must restate the problem in terms of the standard normal random variable z before using the normal table.

Example 5.2   The Coffee Temperature Case

Recall that the runs plot and histogram of the sample of 24 coffee temperatures indicate that the coffee-making process is in statistical control and that the population of all coffee temperatures is normally distributed. Also recall that customer requirements state that each cup of coffee should have a temperature between 67°C and 75°C. The mean and standard deviation of the sample of 24 coffee temperatures are $\bar{x} = 71.2083$ and $s = 2.9779$. Using $\bar{x}$ and s as point estimates of the population mean μ and population standard deviation σ, we want to calculate the probability that x, the temperature of a randomly selected cup of coffee, is outside the requirements (that is, less than 67°C or greater than 75°C). In order to compute the probability $P(x < 67$ or $x > 75)$, we compute the z values

$$z = \frac{67 - 71.2083}{2.9779} = -1.41 \quad \text{and} \quad z = \frac{75 - 71.2083}{2.9779} = 1.27.$$

Because the events $\{x < 67\}$ and $\{x > 75\}$ are mutually exclusive, we have

$$
\begin{aligned}
P(x < 67 \text{ or } x > 75) &= P(x < 67) + P(x > 75) \\
&= P(z < -1.41) + P(z > 1.27) \\
&= (0.5 - 0.4207) + (0.5 - 0.3980) \\
&= 0.0793 + 0.102 = 0.1813.
\end{aligned}
$$

This calculation is illustrated in Figure 5.16. The probability of 0.1813 says that 18.13 percent of the coffee temperatures do not meet customer requirements. Therefore, if management believes that meeting this requirement is important, the coffee-making process must be improved.

FIGURE **5.16**   Finding $P(x < 67$ or $x > 75)$ in the Coffee Temperature Case

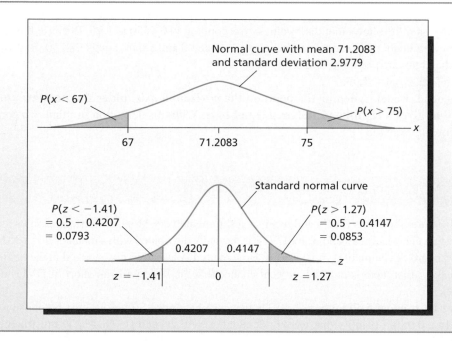

Finding a point on the horizontal axis under a normal curve   In order to use many of the formulas given in later chapters, we must be able to find the z value so that the tail area to the right of z under the standard normal curve is a particular value. For instance, we might need to find the z value so that the tail area to the right of z under the standard normal curve is 0.025.

FIGURE **5.17**   The Point $z_{0.025} = 1.96$

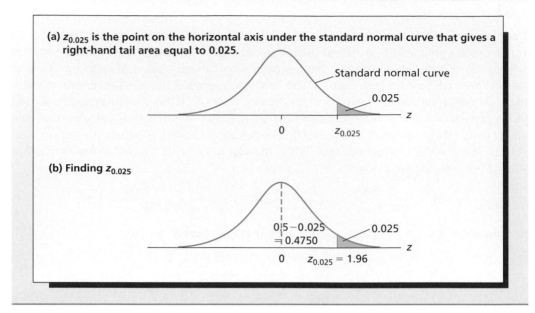

(a) $z_{0.025}$ is the point on the horizontal axis under the standard normal curve that gives a right-hand tail area equal to 0.025.

Standard normal curve

0.025

z

0    $z_{0.025}$

(b) Finding $z_{0.025}$

0.5 − 0.025
= 0.4750

0.025

z

0    $z_{0.025} = 1.96$

This z value is denoted $z_{0.025}$, and we illustrate $z_{0.025}$ in Figure 5.17(a). We refer to $z_{0.025}$ as **the point on the horizontal axis under the standard normal curve that gives a right-hand tail area equal to 0.025**. It is easy to use a normal table to find such a z point. For instance, in order to find $z_{0.025}$, we note from Figure 5.17(b) that the area under the standard normal curve between 0 and $z_{0.025}$ equals $0.5 - 0.025 = 0.4750$. Remembering that areas under the standard normal curve between 0 and z are the four-digit numbers given in the body of a normal table, we scan the body of the table and find the area 0.4750. We have shaded this area in Table 5.1 (page 155), and we note that the area 0.4750 is in the row corresponding to a z value of 1.9 and the column headed by 0.06. It follows that the z value corresponding to 0.4750 is 1.96. Because this z value gives an area under the standard normal curve between 0 and z that equals 0.4750, it also gives a right-hand tail area equal to 0.025.

Therefore, $z_{0.025} = 1.96$.

In general, **we let z_α denote the point on the horizontal axis under the standard normal curve that gives a right-hand tail area equal to α**. With this definition in mind, we consider the following example.

A local Future Shop sells DVDs and receives a shipment every Monday. Historical sales records indicate that the weekly demand, x, for DVDs is normally distributed with a mean of $\mu = 100$ DVDs and a standard deviation of $\sigma = 10$ DVDs. How many DVDs should be stocked at the beginning of a week so that there is only a 5 percent chance that the store will run short of DVDs during the week?

If we let st equal the number of DVDs that will be stocked, then st must be chosen to allow only a 0.05 probability that weekly demand, x, will exceed st. That is, st must be chosen so that

$$P(x > st) = 0.05.$$

Figure 5.18(a) shows that the number of DVDs stocked, st, is located under the right-hand tail of the normal curve with mean $\mu = 100$ and standard deviation $\sigma = 10$. In order to find st, we need to determine how many standard deviations st must be above the mean in order to give a right-hand tail area that is equal to 0.05.

FIGURE 5.18 Finding the Number of DVDs Stocked, st, so That $P(x > st) = 0.05$ When $\mu = 100$ and $\sigma = 10$

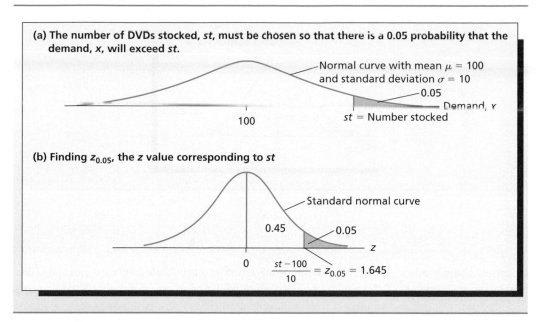

(a) The number of DVDs stocked, st, must be chosen so that there is a 0.05 probability that the demand, x, will exceed st.

Normal curve with mean $\mu = 100$ and standard deviation $\sigma = 10$

0.05

Demand, x

100   st = Number stocked

(b) Finding $z_{0.05}$, the z value corresponding to st

Standard normal curve

0.45   0.05

z

0    $\dfrac{st - 100}{10} = z_{0.05} = 1.645$

The z value corresponding to st is

$$z = \frac{st - \mu}{\sigma} = \frac{st - 100}{10},$$

and this z value is the number of standard deviations that st is from μ. This z value is illustrated in Figure 5.18(b), and it is the point on the horizontal axis under the standard normal curve that gives a right-hand tail area equal to 0.05. That is, the z value corresponding to st is $z_{0.05}$. Since the area under the standard normal curve between 0 and $z_{0.05}$ is $0.5 - 0.05 = 0.45$—see Figure 5.18(b)—we look for 0.45 in the body of the normal table. In Table 5.1, we see that the areas closest to 0.45 are 0.4495, which has a corresponding z value of 1.64, and 0.4505, which has a corresponding z value of 1.65. Although it would probably be sufficient to use either of these z values, we interpolate halfway between them and assume that $z_{0.05}$ equals 1.645. To find st, we solve the equation

$$\frac{st - 100}{10} = 1.645$$

for st. Doing this yields

$$st - 100 = 1.645(10)$$

or

$$st = 100 + 1.645(10) = 116.45.$$

This last equation says that st is 1.645 standard deviations ($\sigma = 10$) above the mean ($\mu = 100$). Rounding $st = 116.45$ up so that the store's chances of running short of DVDs will be **no more than 5 percent**, the store should plan to stock 117 DVDs at the beginning of each week.

Sometimes we need to find the point on the horizontal axis under the standard normal curve that gives a particular **left-hand tail area** (say, for instance, an area of 0.025). Looking at Figure 5.19, it is easy to see that, if, for instance, we want a left-hand tail area of 0.025, the needed z value is $-z_{0.025}$, where $z_{0.025}$ gives a right-hand tail area equal to 0.025. Therefore, since $z_{0.025} = 1.96$, it follows that $-z_{0.025} = -1.96$ gives a left-hand tail area equal to 0.025. In general, $-z_\alpha$ **is the point on the horizontal axis under the standard normal curve that gives a left-hand tail area equal to α.**

FIGURE 5.19 The z Value $-z_{0.025} = -1.96$ Gives a Left-Hand Tail Area of 0.025 under the Standard Normal Curve

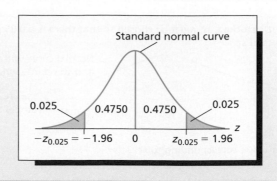

Example 5.4

Extensive testing indicates that the lifetime of the Everlast automobile battery is normally distributed with a mean of $\mu = 60$ months and a standard deviation of $\sigma = 6$ months. The Everlast's manufacturer has decided to offer a free replacement battery to any purchaser whose Everlast battery does not last at least as long as the minimum lifetime specified in its guarantee. How can the manufacturer establish the guarantee period so that only 1 percent of the batteries will need to be replaced free of charge?

If the battery will be guaranteed to last l months, l must be chosen to allow only a 0.01 probability that the lifetime, x, of an Everlast battery will be less than l. That is, we must choose l so that

$$P(x < l) = 0.01.$$

Figure 5.20(a) shows that the guarantee period, l, is located under the left-hand tail of the normal curve with mean $\mu = 60$ and standard deviation $\sigma = 6$. In order to find l, we need to determine how many standard deviations l must be below the mean in order to give a left-hand tail area that equals 0.01. The z value corresponding to l is

$$z = \frac{l - \mu}{\sigma} = \frac{l - 60}{6},$$

and this z value is the number of standard deviations that l is from μ. This z value is illustrated in Figure 5.20(b), and it is the point on the horizontal axis under the standard normal curve that gives a left-hand tail area equal to 0.01. That is, the z value corresponding to l is $-z_{0.01}$. Since

FIGURE 5.20   Finding the Guarantee Period, l, so That $P(x < l) = 0.01$ When $\mu = 60$ and $\sigma = 6$

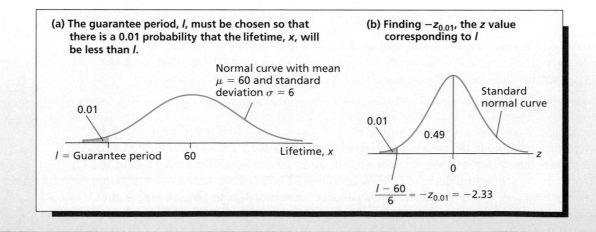

the area under the standard normal curve between 0 and $-z_{0.01}$ is $5 - 0.01 = 0.49$—see Figure 5.20(b)—we look for 0.49 in the body of the normal table. In Table 5.1 (page 155), we see that the area closest to 0.49 is 0.4901, which has a corresponding z value of 2.33. Therefore, $-z_{0.01}$ is (roughly) -2.33. To find l, we solve the equation

$$\frac{l - 60}{6} = -2.33$$

for l. Doing this yields

$$l - 60 = -2.33(6)$$

or

$$l = 60 - 2.33(6) = 46.02.$$

Note that this last equation says that l is 2.33 standard deviations ($\sigma = 6$) below the mean ($\mu = 60$). Rounding $l = 46.02$ down so that **no more** than 1 percent of the batteries will need to be replaced free of charge, it seems reasonable to guarantee the Everlast battery to last 46 months.

In Section 2.3, we saw that the intervals $[\mu \pm \sigma]$, $[\mu \pm 2\sigma]$, and $[\mu \pm 3\sigma]$ are **tolerance intervals** containing, respectively, 68.26 percent, 95.44 percent, and 99.73 percent of the measurements in a normally distributed population having mean μ and standard deviation σ. In the following example, we demonstrate how to use the normal table to find the value k so that the interval $[\mu \pm k\sigma]$ contains any desired percentage of the measurements in a normally distributed population.

Example 5.5

Consider computing a tolerance interval $[\mu \pm k\sigma]$ that contains 99 percent of the measurements in a normally distributed population with mean μ and standard deviation σ. As illustrated in Figure 5.21, we must find the value k so that the area under the normal curve with mean μ and standard deviation σ between $(\mu - k\sigma)$ and $(\mu + k\sigma)$ is 0.99. As also shown in this figure, the area under this normal curve between μ and $(\mu + k\sigma)$ is equal to 0.495. Because the z value corresponding to a value of x tells us how many standard deviations x is from μ, the z value corresponding to $(\mu + k\sigma)$ is obviously k. It follows that k is the point on the horizontal axis under the standard normal curve so that the area under this curve between 0 and k is 0.495. Looking up 0.495 in the body of the normal table (Table 5.1 on page 155), we find that the values closest to 0.495 are 0.4949, which has a corresponding z value of 2.57, and 0.4951, which has a corresponding z value of 2.58. Although it would be sufficient to use either of these z values, we interpolate halfway between them and assume that k equals 2.575. It follows that the interval $[\mu \pm 2.575\sigma]$ contains 99 percent of the measurements in a normally distributed population with mean μ and standard deviation σ.

FIGURE 5.21 Finding a Tolerance Interval $[\mu \pm k\sigma]$ That Contains 99 Percent of the Measurements in a Normally Distributed Population

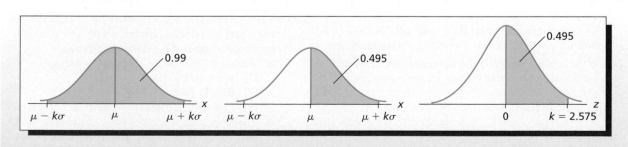

Whenever we use a normal table to find a z value corresponding to a particular normal curve area, we will use the **halfway interpolation** procedure illustrated in Examples 5.3 and 5.5 if the area we are looking for is exactly halfway between two areas in the table. Otherwise, as illustrated in Example 5.4, we will use the z value corresponding to the area in the table that is closest to the desired area.

Exercises for Section 5.3

CONCEPTS

5.16 List five important properties of the normal probability curve.

5.17 Explain
    a. What the mean, μ, tells us about a normal curve.
    b. What the standard deviation, σ, tells us about a normal curve.

5.18 If the random variable x is normally distributed, what percentage of all possible observed values of x will be
    a. Within one standard deviation of the mean?
    b. Within two standard deviations of the mean?
    c. Within three standard deviations of the mean?

5.19 Explain how to compute the z value corresponding to a value of a normally distributed random variable. What does the z value tell us about the value of the random variable?

5.20 Explain how x relates to the mean μ if the z value corresponding to x
    a. Equals zero.
    b. Is positive.
    c. Is negative.

5.21 Why do we compute z values when using the normal table? Explain.

METHODS AND APPLICATIONS

5.22 In each case, sketch the two specified normal curves on the same set of axes:
    a. A normal curve with $\mu = 20$ and $\sigma = 3$, and a normal curve with $\mu = 20$ and $\sigma = 6$.
    b. A normal curve with $\mu = 20$ and $\sigma = 3$, and a normal curve with $\mu = 30$ and $\sigma = 3$.
    c. A normal curve with $\mu = 100$ and $\sigma = 10$, and a normal curve with $\mu = 200$ and $\sigma = 20$.

5.23 Let x be a normally distributed random variable with mean $\mu = 30$ and standard deviation $\sigma = 5$. Find the z value for each of the following observed values of x:
    a. $x = 25$.   **d.** $x = 40$.
    b. $x = 15$.   **e.** $x = 50$.
    c. $x = 30$.
    In each case, explain what the z value tells us about how the observed value of x compares to the mean, μ.

5.24 If the random variable z has a standard normal distribution, sketch and find each of the following probabilities:
    a. $P(0 \leq z \leq 1.5)$.   **f.** $P(-1 \leq z \leq 1)$.
    b. $P(z \geq 2)$.   **g.** $P(-2.5 \leq z \leq 0.5)$.
    c. $P(z \leq 1.5)$.   **h.** $P(1.5 \leq z \leq 2)$.
    d. $P(z \geq -1)$.   **i.** $P(-2 \leq z \leq -0.5)$.
    e. $P(z \leq -3)$.

5.25 Suppose that the random variable z has a standard normal distribution. Sketch each of the following z_α points, and use the normal table to find each z_α point.
    a. $z_{0.01}$.   **d.** $-z_{0.01}$.
    b. $z_{0.05}$.   **e.** $-z_{0.05}$.
    c. $z_{0.02}$.   **f.** $-z_{0.10}$.

5.26 Suppose that the random variable x is normally distributed with mean $\mu = 1,000$ and standard deviation $\sigma = 100$. Sketch and find each of the following probabilities:
    a. $P(1,000 \leq x \leq 1,200)$.   **e.** $P(x \leq 700)$.
    b. $P(x > 1,257)$.   **f.** $P(812 \leq x \leq 913)$.
    c. $P(x < 1,035)$.   **g.** $P(x > 891)$.
    d. $P(857 \leq x \leq 1,183)$.   **h.** $P(1,050 \leq x \leq 1,250)$.

5.27 Suppose that the random variable x is normally distributed with mean $\mu = 500$ and standard deviation $\sigma = 100$. For each of the following, use the normal table to find the needed value k. In each case, draw a sketch.
    a. $P(x \geq k) = 0.025$.   **f.** $P(x > k) = 0.95$.
    b. $P(x \geq k) = 0.05$.   **g.** $P(x \leq k) = 0.975$.
    c. $P(x < k) = 0.025$.   **h.** $P(x \geq k) = 0.0228$.
    d. $P(x \leq k) = 0.015$.   **i.** $P(x > k) = 0.9772$.
    e. $P(x < k) = 0.985$.

5.28 Stanford–Binet IQ Test scores are normally distributed with a mean score of 100 and a standard deviation of 16.
    a. Sketch the distribution of Stanford–Binet IQ test scores.
    b. Write the equation that gives the z value corresponding to a Stanford–Binet IQ test score. Sketch the distribution of such z values.
    c. Find the probability that a randomly selected person has an IQ test score
        (1) Over 140.
        (2) Under 88.
        (3) Between 72 and 128.
        (4) Within 1.5 standard deviations of the mean.
    d. Suppose you take the Stanford–Binet IQ Test and receive a score of 136. What percentage of people would receive a score higher than yours?

5.29 Weekly demand at a grocery store for a brand of breakfast cereal is normally distributed with a mean of 800 boxes and a standard deviation of 75 boxes.
    a. What is the probability that weekly demand is
        (1) 959 boxes or less?
        (2) Greater than 1,004 boxes?
        (3) Less than 650 boxes or greater than 950 boxes?
    b. The store orders cereal from a distributor weekly. How many boxes should the store order for a week to have only a 2.5 percent chance of running short of this brand of cereal during the week?

5.30 The lifetimes of a particular brand of DVD player are normally distributed with a mean of eight years and a standard deviation of six months. Find each of the following probabilities, where x denotes the lifetime in years. In each case, sketch the probability.

a. $P(7 \leq x \leq 9)$.
b. $P(8.5 \leq x \leq 9.5)$.
c. $P(6.5 \leq x \leq 7.5)$.
d. $P(x \geq 8)$.
e. $P(x \leq 7)$.
f. $P(x \geq 7)$.
g. $P(x \leq 10)$.
h. $P(x > 10)$.

5.31 An investment broker reports that the yearly returns on common stocks are approximately normally distributed with a mean return of 12.4 percent and a standard deviation of 20.6 percent. The firm also reports that the yearly returns on tax-free municipal bonds are approximately normally distributed with a mean return of 5.2 percent and a standard deviation of 8.6 percent. Find the probability that a randomly selected

a. Common stock will give a positive yearly return.
b. Tax-free municipal bond will give a positive yearly return.
c. Common stock will give more than a 10 percent return.
d. Tax-free municipal bond will give more than a 10 percent return.
e. Common stock will give a loss of at least 10 percent.
f. Tax-free municipal bond will give a loss of at least 10 percent.

5.32 A tire company has developed a new type of steel-belted radial tire. Extensive testing indicates the population of lifetimes obtained by all tires of this new type is normally distributed with a mean of 65,000 km and a standard deviation of 6,500 km. The company wishes to offer a guarantee providing a discount on a new set of tires if the original tires purchased do not exceed the lifetime stated in the guarantee. What should the guaranteed lifetime be if the tire company desires that no more than 2 percent of the tires will fail to meet the guaranteed lifetime?

5.33 Recall from Exercise 5.31 that yearly returns on common stocks are normally distributed with a mean of 12.4 percent and a standard deviation of 20.6 percent.

a. What percentage of yearly returns are at or below the 10th percentile of the distribution of yearly returns? What percentage are at or above the 10th percentile? Find the 10th percentile of the distribution of yearly returns.
b. Find the first quartile, Q_1, and the third quartile, Q_3, of the distribution of yearly returns.

5.34 Two students take a personality questionnaire known to have a normal distribution of scores. The students receive raw scores of 63 and 93, which correspond to z values (often called the standardized scores) of -1 and 1.5, respectively. Find the mean and standard deviation of the distribution of raw scores.

5.35 **THE TRASH BAG CASE** ◆ TrashBag

Suppose that a population of measurements is normally distributed with mean μ and standard deviation σ.

a. Write an expression (involving μ and σ) for a tolerance interval containing 98 percent of all the population measurements.

b. Estimate a tolerance interval containing 98 percent of all the trash bag breaking strengths by using the fact that a random sample of 40 breaking strengths has a mean of $\bar{x} = 22.990$ and a standard deviation of $s = 0.7428$.

5.36 Consider the situation of Exercise 5.31.

a. Use the investment broker's report to estimate the maximum yearly return that might be obtained by investing in tax-free municipal bonds.
b. Find the probability that the yearly return obtained by investing in common stocks will be higher than the maximum yearly return that might be obtained by investing in tax-free municipal bonds.

5.37 Suppose that yearly dental care expenses for a family of four are normally distributed with a mean expense equal to $3,000 and a standard deviation of $500. An insurance company has decided to offer a dental insurance premium reduction if a policyholder's dental care expenses do not exceed a specified dollar amount. What dollar amount should be established if the insurance company wants families with the lowest 33 percent of yearly dental care expenses to be eligible for the premium reduction?

5.38 Suppose that the 33rd percentile of a normal distribution is equal to 656 and that the 97.5th percentile of this normal distribution is 896. Find the mean μ and the standard deviation σ of the normal distribution. Hint: Sketch these percentiles.

5.39 In the book *Advanced Managerial Accounting*, Magee discusses monitoring cost variances. A **cost variance** is the difference between a budgeted cost and an actual cost. Magee describes the following situation:

Michael Bitner has responsibility for control of two manufacturing processes. Every week he receives a cost variance report for each of the two processes, broken down by labor costs, materials costs, and so on. One of the two processes, which we'll call process A, involves a stable, easily controlled production process with little fluctuation in variances. Process B involves more random events: the equipment is more sensitive and prone to breakdown, the raw material prices fluctuate more, and so on.

"It seems like I'm spending more of my time with process B than with process A," says Michael Bitner. "Yet I know that the probability of an inefficiency developing and the expected costs of inefficiencies are the same for the two processes. It's just the magnitude of random fluctuations that differs between the two, as you can see in the information below.

"At present, I investigate variances if they exceed $2,500, regardless of whether it was process A or B. I suspect that such a policy is not the most efficient. I should probably set a higher limit for process B."

The means and standard deviations of the cost variances of processes A and B, when these processes are in control, are as follows:

	Process A	Process B
Mean Cost Variance (in Control)	$ 0	$ 0
Standard Deviation of Cost Variance (in Control)	$5,000	$10,000

Furthermore, the means and standard deviations of the cost variances of processes A and B, when these processes are out of control, are as follows:

	Process A	Process B
Mean Cost Variance (out of Control)	$7,500	$ 7,500
Standard Deviation of Cost Variance (out of Control)	$5,000	$10,000

a. Recall that the current policy is to investigate a cost variance if it exceeds $2,500 for either process. Assume that cost variances are normally distributed and that both Process A and Process B cost variances are in control. Find the probability that a cost variance for Process A will be investigated. Find the probability that a cost variance for Process B will be investigated. Which in-control process will be investigated more often?

b. Assume that cost variances are normally distributed and that both Process A and Process B cost variances are out of control. Find the probability that a cost variance for Process A will be investigated. Find the probability that a cost variance for Process B will be investigated. Which out-of-control process will be investigated more often?

c. If both Processes A and B are almost always in control, which process will be investigated more often?

d. Suppose that we wish to reduce the probability that Process B will be investigated (when it is in control) to 0.3085. What cost variance investigation policy should be used? That is, how large a cost variance should trigger an investigation? Using this new policy, what is the probability that an out-of-control cost variance for Process B will be investigated?

5.4 Approximating the Binomial Distribution by Using the Normal Distribution

Figure 5.22 illustrates several binomial distributions. In general, we can see that as n gets larger and as p gets closer to 0.5, the graph of a binomial distribution tends to have the symmetrical, bell-shaped appearance of a normal curve. It follows that, under the conditions given in the following box, we can approximate the binomial distribution by using a normal distribution.

The Normal Approximation of the Binomial Distribution

Consider a binomial random variable x, where n is the number of trials performed and p is the probability of success on each trial. If n and p have values so that $np \geq 5$ and $n(1 - p) \geq 5$, then x is approximately normally distributed with mean $\mu = np$ and standard deviation $\sigma = \sqrt{npq}$, where $q = 1 - p$.

FIGURE 5.22　Several Binomial Distributions

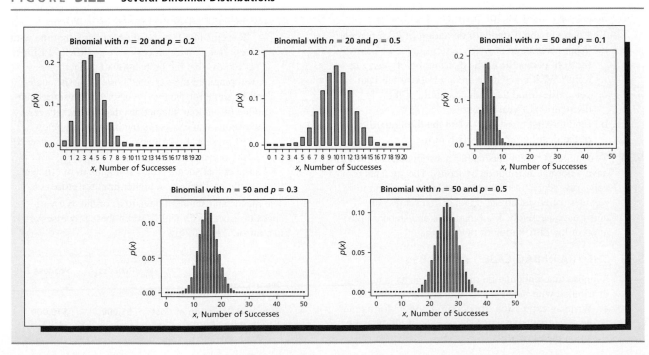

This approximation is often useful because binomial tables for large values of n are often unavailable. The conditions $np \geq 5$ and $n(1 - p) \geq 5$ must be met in order for the approximation to be appropriate. Note that if p is near 0 or near 1, then n must be larger for a good approximation, while if p is near 0.5, then n need not be as large.[1]

When we say that we can approximate the binomial distribution by using a normal distribution, we are saying that we can compute binomial probabilities by finding corresponding areas under a normal curve (rather than by using the binomial formula). We illustrate how to do this in the following example.

Example 5.6

Consider the binomial random variable x with $n = 50$ trials and probability of success $p = 0.5$. This binomial distribution is one of those illustrated in Figure 5.22. Suppose we want to use the normal approximation to this binomial distribution to compute the probability of 23 successes in the 50 trials. That is, we wish to compute $P(x = 23)$. Because $np = (50)(0.5) = 25$ is at least 5, and $n(1 - p) = 50(1 - 0.5) = 25$ is also at least 5, we can appropriately use the approximation. Moreover, we can approximate the binomial distribution of x by using a normal distribution with mean $\mu = np = 50(0.5) = 25$ and standard deviation $\sigma = \sqrt{npq} = \sqrt{50(0.5)(1 - 0.5)} = 3.5355$.

In order to compute the needed probability, we must make a **continuity correction**. This is because a discrete distribution (the binomial) is being approximated by a continuous distribution (the normal). Because there is no area under a normal curve at the single point $x = 23$, we must assign an area under the normal curve to the binomial outcome $x = 23$. It is logical to assign the area corresponding to the interval from 22.5 to 23.5 to the integer outcome $x = 23$. That is, the area under the normal curve corresponding to all values within 0.5 units of the integer outcome $x = 23$ is assigned to the value $x = 23$. So we approximate the binomial probability $P(x = 23)$ by calculating the normal curve area $P(22.5 \leq x \leq 23.5)$. This area is illustrated in Figure 5.23. Calculating the z values

$$z = \frac{22.5 - 25}{3.5355} = -0.71 \quad \text{and} \quad z = \frac{23.5 - 25}{3.5355} = -0.42,$$

we find that $P(22.5 \leq x \leq 23.5) = P(-0.71 \leq z \leq -0.42) = 0.2611 - 0.1628 = 0.0983$. Therefore, we estimate that the binomial probability $P(x = 23)$ is 0.0983.

FIGURE 5.23 **Approximating the Binomial Probability $P(x = 23)$ by Using the Normal Curve When $\mu = np = 25$ and $\sigma = \sqrt{npq} = 3.5355$**

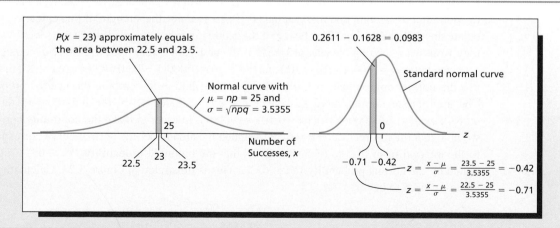

---

[1]As an alternative to the rule that both np and $n(1 - p)$ must be at least 5, some statisticians suggest using the more conservative rule that both np and $n(1 - p)$ must be at least 10.

TABLE **5.2**   Several Examples of the Continuity Correction ($n = 50$)

Binomial Probability	Numbers of Successes Included in Event	Normal Curve Area (with Continuity Correction)
$P(25 < x \leq 30)$	26, 27, 28, 29, 30	$P(25.5 \leq x \leq 30.5)$
$P(x \leq 27)$	0, 1, 2, . . . , 26, 27	$P(x \leq 27.5)$
$P(x > 30)$	31, 32, 33, . . . , 50	$P(x \geq 30.5)$
$P(27 < x < 31)$	28, 29, 30	$P(27.5 \leq x \leq 30.5)$

Making the proper continuity correction can sometimes be tricky. A good way to approach this is to list the numbers of successes that are included in the event for which the binomial probability is being calculated. Then assign the appropriate area under the normal curve to each number of successes in the list. Putting these areas together gives the normal curve area that must be calculated. For example, again consider the binomial random variable x with $n = 50$ and $p = 0.5$. If we wish to find $P(27 \leq x \leq 29)$, then the event $27 \leq x \leq 29$ includes 27, 28, and 29 successes. Because we assign the areas under the normal curve corresponding to the intervals [26.5, 27.5], [27.5, 28.5], and [28.5, 29.5] to the values 27, 28, and 29, respectively, then the area to be found under the normal curve is $P(26.5 \leq x \leq 29.5)$. Table 5.2 gives several other examples.

Example 5.7   The Cheese Spread Case

A food-processing company markets a soft cheese spread that is sold in a plastic container with an "easy pour" spout. Although this spout works extremely well and is popular with consumers, it is expensive to produce. Because of the spout's high cost, the company has developed a new, less expensive spout. While the new, cheaper spout may alienate some purchasers, a company study shows that its introduction will increase profits if less than 10 percent of the cheese spread's current purchasers are lost. That is, if we let p be the true proportion of all current purchasers who would stop buying the cheese spread if the new spout were used, profits will increase as long as p is less than 0.10.

Suppose that (after trying the new spout) 63 of 1,000 randomly selected purchasers say that they would stop buying the cheese spread if the new spout were used. To assess whether p is less than 0.10, we will assume for the sake of argument that p equals 0.10, and we will use the sample information to weigh the evidence against this assumption and in favour of the conclusion that p is less than 0.10. Let the random variable x represent the number of the 1,000 purchasers who say they would stop buying the cheese spread. Assuming that p equals 0.10, then x is a binomial random variable with $n = 1,000$ and $p = 0.10$. Since the sample result of 63 is less than $\mu = np = 1,000(0.1) = 100$, the expected value of x when p equals 0.10, we have some evidence to contradict the assumption that p equals 0.10. To evaluate the strength of this evidence, we calculate the probability that **63 or fewer** of the 1,000 randomly selected purchasers would say that they would stop buying the cheese spread if the new spout were used if, in fact, p equals 0.10.

Since both $np = 1,000(0.10) = 100$ and $n(1 - p) = 1,000(1 - 0.10) = 900$ are at least 5, we can use the normal approximation to the binomial distribution to compute the needed probability. The appropriate normal curve has mean $\mu = np = 1,000(0.10) = 100$ and standard deviation $\sigma = \sqrt{npq} = \sqrt{1,000(0.10)(1 - 0.10)} = 9.4868$. In order to make the continuity correction, we note that the discrete value $x = 63$ is assigned the area under the normal curve corresponding to the interval from 62.5 to 63.5. It follows that the binomial probability $P(x \leq 63)$ is approximated by the normal probability $P(x \leq 63.5)$. This is illustrated in Figure 5.24. Calculating the z value for 63.5 to be

$$z = \frac{63.5 - 100}{9.4868} = -3.85,$$

we find that

$$P(x \leq 63.5) = P(z \leq -3.85).$$

Because 3.85 is larger than 3.09, which is the largest z value in the normal table, the area under the standard normal curve to the left of -3.85 is less than $0.5 - 0.499 = 0.001$. This says that,

FIGURE **5.24** **Approximating the Binomial Probability $P(x \leq 63)$ by Using the Normal Curve When $\mu = np = 100$ and $\sigma = \sqrt{npq} = 9.4868$**

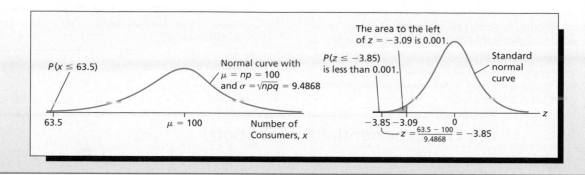

if p equals 0.10, then in fewer than 1 in 1,000 of all possible random samples of 1,000 purchasers would 63 or fewer say they would stop buying the cheese spread if the new spout were used. Since it is very difficult to believe that such a small chance (a smaller than 1 in 1,000 chance) has occurred, we have very strong evidence that p does not equal 0.10 and is, in fact, less than 0.10. Therefore, it seems that using the new spout will be profitable.

Exercises for Section 5.4

CONCEPTS

5.40 Explain why it might be convenient to approximate binomial probabilities by using areas under an appropriate normal curve.

5.41 Under what condition may we use the normal approximation to the binomial distribution?

5.42 Explain how we make a continuity correction. Why is a continuity correction needed when we approximate a binomial distribution by a normal distribution?

METHODS AND APPLICATIONS

5.43 Suppose that x has a binomial distribution with $n = 200$ and $p = 0.4$.
   a. Show that the normal approximation to the binomial can appropriately be used to calculate probabilities about x.
   b. Make continuity corrections for each of the following, and then use the normal approximation to the binomial to find each probability:
   (1) $P(x = 80)$.
   (2) $P(x \leq 95)$.
   (3) $P(x < 65)$.
   (4) $P(x \geq 100)$.
   (5) $P(x > 100)$.

5.44 Repeat Exercise 5.43 with $n = 200$ and $p = 0.5$.

5.45 An advertising agency conducted an ad campaign aimed at making consumers in a Western province aware of a new product. Upon completion of the campaign, the agency claimed that 20 percent of consumers in the province had become aware of the product. The product's distributor surveyed 1,000 consumers in the province and found that 150 were aware of the product.
   a. Assuming that the ad agency's claim is true:
   (1) Verify that we may use the normal approximation to the binomial.

(2) Calculate the mean, μ, and the standard deviation, σ, we should use in the normal approximation.

(3) Find the probability that 150 or fewer consumers in a random sample of 1,000 consumers would be aware of the product.
   b. Should the distributor believe the ad agency's claim? Explain.

5.46 **THE MARKETING ETHICS CASE**
Recall that in Example 2.10 (page 64) we found that of the 205 randomly selected marketing researchers who participated in the survey, 117 said they disapprove of the actions taken in the ultraviolet ink scenario. Suppose that, before the survey was taken, a marketing manager claimed that at least 65 percent of all marketing researchers would disapprove of that scenario.
   a. Assuming that the manager's claim is correct, calculate the probability that 117 or fewer of 205 randomly selected marketing researchers would disapprove of the scenario. Use the normal approximation to the binomial.
   b. Based on your result of part a, do you believe the marketing manager's claim? Explain.

5.47 A department store will place a sale item in a special display for a one-day sale. Previous experience suggests that 20 percent of all customers who pass such a special display will purchase the item. If 2,000 customers will pass the display on the day of the sale, and if a one-item-per-customer limit is placed on the sale item, how many units of the sale item should the store stock in order to have at most a 1 percent chance of running short of the item on the day of the sale? Assume here that customers make independent purchase decisions.

5.48   THE ELECTRONIC ARTICLE SURVEILLANCE CASE

Recall that in Example 2.11 (page 64) we found that based on a survey of 250 consumers, 40 said that if they were to set off an EAS alarm because store personnel failed to deactivate merchandise leaving the store, then they would never shop at that store again. A company marketing the alarm system claimed that no more than 5 percent of all consumers would say that they would never shop at that store again if they were subjected to a false alarm.

a. Assuming that the company's claim is valid, use the normal approximation to the binomial to calculate the probability that at least 40 of the 250 randomly selected consumers would say that they would never shop at that store again if they were subjected to a false alarm.

b. Do you believe the company's claim based on your answer to part a? Explain.

5.5 The Exponential Distribution

Suppose that the number of times that a particular event occurs over an interval of time or space has a Poisson distribution. Furthermore, consider an arbitrary time or space unit (for example, minute, week, centimetre, hectare), and let x denote the number of time or space units between successive occurrences of the event. Then, it can be shown that x is described by an **exponential distribution** with parameter λ. Here λ is the mean number of events that occur per time or space unit. Furthermore, the mean value of x can be proven to be $1/\lambda$. In words, $1/\lambda$ is **the mean number of time or space units between successive occurrences of the event**. In general, we can describe the exponential distribution as follows:

The Exponential Distribution

If λ is a positive number, then the equation describing the exponential distribution is

$$f(x) = \begin{cases} \lambda e^{-\lambda x} & \text{for } x \geq 0, \\ 0 & \text{otherwise.} \end{cases}$$

Using this probability curve, it can be shown that

$$P(a \leq x \leq b) = e^{-\lambda a} - e^{-\lambda b}.$$

In particular, since $e^0 = 1$ and $e^{-\infty} = 0$, this implies that

$$P(x \leq c) = 1 - e^{-\lambda c} \quad \text{and} \quad P(x \geq c) = e^{-\lambda c}.$$

Furthermore, the mean and the standard deviation of the population of all possible observed values of a random variable x that has an exponential distribution are

$$\mu_x = \frac{1}{\lambda} \quad \text{and} \quad \sigma_x = \frac{1}{\lambda}.$$

The graph of the equation describing the exponential distribution and the probability $P(a \leq x \leq b)$, where x is described by this exponential distribution, is illustrated in Figure 5.25.

We illustrate the use of the exponential distribution in the following examples.

FIGURE 5.25   A Graph of the Exponential Distribution $f(x) = \lambda e^{-\lambda x}$

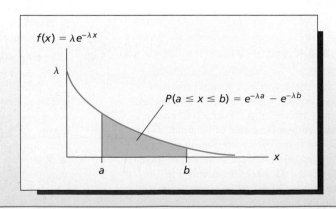

Example 5.8

Recall from Example 4.12 (pages 138–141) that an air traffic control centre is experiencing an average of 20.8 errors per year and that it is reasonable to believe that the number of errors in a given time period is described by a Poisson distribution. If we consider x to be the number of weeks between successive errors, then x is described by an exponential distribution. Furthermore, since the air traffic control centre is averaging 20.8 errors per year, it follows that λ, the average number of errors per week, is $20.8/52 = 0.4$. Therefore, the equation of the exponential distribution describing x is $f(x) = \lambda e^{-\lambda x} = 0.4e^{-0.4x}$, and the mean number of weeks between successive errors is $1/\lambda = 1/0.4 = 2.5$. For example, the probability that the time between successive errors will be between 1 and 2 weeks is

$$P(1 \leq x \leq 2) = e^{-\lambda a} - e^{-\lambda b} = e^{-\lambda(1)} - e^{-\lambda(2)}$$
$$= e^{-0.4(1)} - e^{-0.4(2)} = e^{-0.4} - e^{-0.8}$$
$$= 0.6703 - 0.4493 = 0.221.$$

Example 5.9

Suppose that the number of people who arrive at a hospital emergency room during a given time period has a Poisson distribution. It follows that the time, x, between successive arrivals of people to the emergency room has an exponential distribution. Furthermore, historical records indicate that the mean time between successive arrivals of people to the emergency room is seven minutes. Therefore, $\mu_x = 1/\lambda = 7$, which implies that $\lambda = 1/7 = 0.14286$. Noting that $\sigma_x = 1/\lambda = 7$, it follows that

$$\mu_x - \sigma_x = 7 - 7 = 0 \qquad \text{and} \qquad \mu_x + \sigma_x = 7 + 7 = 14.$$

Therefore, the probability that the time between successive arrivals of people to the emergency room will be within (plus or minus) one standard deviation of the mean interarrival time is

$$P(0 \leq x \leq 14) = e^{-\lambda a} - e^{-\lambda b}$$
$$= e^{-(0.14286)(0)} - e^{-(0.14286)(14)}$$
$$= 1 - 0.1353$$
$$= 0.8647.$$

To conclude this section, we note that the exponential and related Poisson distributions are useful in analyzing waiting lines, or **queues**. In general, **queueing theory** attempts to determine the number of servers (for example, doctors in an emergency room) that strikes an optimal balance between the time customers wait for service and the cost of providing service. The reader is referred to any textbook on management science or operations research for a discussion of queueing theory.

Exercises for Section 5.5

CONCEPTS

5.49 Give two examples of situations in which the exponential distribution might appropriately be used. In each case, define the random variable that has the exponential distribution.

5.50 State the formula for the exponential probability curve. Define each symbol in the formula.

5.51 Explain the relationship between the Poisson and exponential distributions.

METHODS AND APPLICATIONS

5.52 Suppose that the random variable x has an exponential distribution with $\lambda = 2$.
   a. Write the formula for the exponential probability curve of x. What are the possible values of x?
   b. Sketch the probability curve.
   c. Find $P(x \leq 1)$.
   d. Find $P(0.25 \leq x \leq 1)$.
   e. Find $P(x \geq 2)$.

f. Calculate the mean, μ_x, the variance, σ_x^2, and the standard deviation, σ_x, of the exponential distribution of x.

g. Find the probability that x will be in the interval $[\mu_x \pm 2\sigma_x]$.

5.53 Repeat Exercise 5.52 with $\lambda = 3$.

5.54 Recall in Exercise 4.32 (page 142) that the number of customer arrivals at a coffee shop's drive-up window in a 15-minute period is Poisson distributed with a mean of seven customer arrivals per 15-minute period. Define the random variable x to be the time (in minutes) between successive customer arrivals at the drive-up window.

a. Write the formula for the exponential probability curve of x.

b. Sketch the probability curve of x.

c. Find the probability that the time between arrivals is
  (1) Between one and two minutes.
  (2) Less than one minute.
  (3) More than three minutes.
  (4) Between 0.5 and 3.5 minutes.

d. Calculate μ_x, σ_x^2, and σ_x.

e. Find the probability that the time between arrivals falls within one standard deviation of the mean; within two standard deviations of the mean.

5.55 The length of a particular telemarketing phone call, x, has an exponential distribution with mean equal to 1.5 minutes.

a. Write the formula for the exponential probability curve of x.

b. Sketch the probability curve of x.

c. Find the probability that the length of a randomly selected call will be
  (1) No more than three minutes.
  (2) Between one and two minutes.

(3) More than four minutes.
(4) Less than 30 seconds.

5.56 The maintenance department in a factory claims that the number of breakdowns of a particular machine follows a Poisson distribution with a mean of two breakdowns every 500 hours. Let x denote the time (in hours) between successive breakdowns.

a. Find λ and μ_x.

b. Write the formula for the exponential probability curve of x.

c. Sketch the probability curve.

d. Assuming that the maintenance department's claim is true, find the probability that the time between successive breakdowns is at most five hours.

e. Assuming that the maintenance department's claim is true, find the probability that the time between successive breakdowns is between 100 and 300 hours.

f. Suppose that the machine breaks down five hours after its most recent breakdown. Based on your answer to part d, do you believe the maintenance department's claim? Explain.

5.57 Suppose that the number of accidents occurring in an industrial plant is described by a Poisson distribution with an average of one accident per month. Let x denote the time (in months) between successive accidents.

a. Find the probability that the time between successive accidents is
  (1) More than two months.
  (2) Between one and two months.
  (3) Less than one week (1/4 of a month).

b. Suppose that an accident occurs less than one week after the plant's most recent accident. Would you consider this event unusual enough to warrant special investigation? Explain.

5.6 The Cumulative Normal Table

The cumulative normal table is a table of cumulative areas under the standard normal curve, and it is reproduced in Table 5.3. Specifically,

The **cumulative normal table** gives, for many different values of z, the area under the standard normal curve at or below z.

Two such areas are shown in the figures to the right of Table 5.3—one with a negative z value and one with a positive z value. The values of z in the cumulative normal table range from -3.49 to 3.49 in increments of 0.01. As can be seen from Table 5.3, values of z accurate to the nearest tenth are given in the far left column (headed z) of the table. Further graduations to the nearest hundredth (0.00, 0.01, 0.02, . . . , 0.09) are given across the top of the table. The areas under the normal curve are given in the body of the table, accurate to four decimal places.

As an example, suppose that we wish to find the area under the standard normal curve at or below a z value of 1.00. This area is illustrated in Figure 5.26. To find this area, we scan down the far left column of the table (starting at the top) until we find the value 1.0. We now scan across the row in the table corresponding to the z value 1.0 until we find the column corresponding to the heading 0.00. The desired area (which we have shaded red) is in the row corresponding to the z value 1.0 and in the column headed 0.00. This area, which equals 0.8413, is the probability that the random variable z is less than or equal to 1.00. That is, we have found that $P(z \leq 1.00) = 0.8413$. As another example, the area under the standard normal curve at or below

TABLE 5.3 Cumulative Areas under the Standard Normal Curve

z	0.00	0.01	0.02	0.03	0.04	0.05	0.06	0.07	0.08	0.09
−3.4	0.0003	0.0003	0.0003	0.0003	0.0003	0.0003	0.0003	0.0003	0.0003	0.0002
−3.3	0.0005	0.0005	0.0005	0.0004	0.0004	0.0004	0.0004	0.0004	0.0004	0.0003
−3.2	0.0007	0.0007	0.0006	0.0006	0.0006	0.0006	0.0006	0.0005	0.0005	0.0005
−3.1	0.0010	0.0009	0.0009	0.0009	0.0008	0.0008	0.0008	0.0008	0.0007	0.0007
−3.0	0.0013	0.0013	0.0013	0.0012	0.0012	0.0011	0.0011	0.0011	0.0010	0.0010
−2.9	0.0019	0.0018	0.0018	0.0017	0.0016	0.0016	0.0015	0.0015	0.0014	0.0014
−2.8	0.0026	0.0025	0.0024	0.0023	0.0023	0.0022	0.0021	0.0021	0.0020	0.0019
−2.7	0.0035	0.0034	0.0033	0.0032	0.0031	0.0030	0.0029	0.0028	0.0027	0.0026
−2.6	0.0047	0.0045	0.0044	0.0043	0.0041	0.0040	0.0039	0.0038	0.0037	0.0036
−2.5	0.0062	0.0060	0.0059	0.0057	0.0055	0.0054	0.0052	0.0051	0.0049	0.0048
−2.4	0.0082	0.0080	0.0078	0.0075	0.0073	0.0071	0.0069	0.0068	0.0066	0.0064
−2.3	0.0107	0.0104	0.0102	0.0099	0.0096	0.0094	0.0091	0.0089	0.0087	0.0084
−2.2	0.0139	0.0136	0.0132	0.0129	0.0125	0.0122	0.0119	0.0116	0.0113	0.0110
−2.1	0.0179	0.0174	0.0170	0.0166	0.0162	0.0158	0.0154	0.0150	0.0146	0.0143
−2.0	0.0228	0.0222	0.0217	0.0212	0.0207	0.0202	0.0197	0.0192	0.0188	0.0183
−1.9	0.0287	0.0281	0.0274	0.0268	0.0262	0.0256	0.0250	0.0244	0.0239	0.0233
−1.8	0.0359	0.0351	0.0344	0.0336	0.0329	0.0322	0.0314	0.0307	0.0301	0.0294
−1.7	0.0446	0.0436	0.0427	0.0418	0.0409	0.0401	0.0392	0.0384	0.0375	0.0367
−1.6	0.0548	0.0537	0.0526	0.0516	0.0505	0.0495	0.0485	0.0475	0.0465	0.0455
−1.5	0.0668	0.0655	0.0643	0.0630	0.0618	0.0606	0.0594	0.0582	0.0571	0.0559
−1.4	0.0808	0.0793	0.0778	0.0764	0.0749	0.0735	0.0721	0.0708	0.0694	0.0681
−1.3	0.0968	0.0951	0.0934	0.0918	0.0901	0.0885	0.0869	0.0853	0.0838	0.0823
−1.2	0.1151	0.1131	0.1112	0.1093	0.1075	0.1056	0.1038	0.1020	0.1003	0.0985
−1.1	0.1357	0.1335	0.1314	0.1292	0.1271	0.1251	0.1230	0.1210	0.1190	0.1170
−1.0	0.1587	0.1562	0.1539	0.1515	0.1492	0.1469	0.1446	0.1423	0.1401	0.1379
−0.9	0.1841	0.1814	0.1788	0.1762	0.1736	0.1711	0.1685	0.1660	0.1635	0.1611
−0.8	0.2119	0.2090	0.2061	0.2033	0.2005	0.1977	0.1949	0.1922	0.1894	0.1867
−0.7	0.2420	0.2389	0.2358	0.2327	0.2296	0.2266	0.2236	0.2206	0.2177	0.2148
−0.6	0.2743	0.2709	0.2676	0.2643	0.2611	0.2578	0.2546	0.2514	0.2483	0.2451
−0.5	0.3085	0.3050	0.3015	0.2981	0.2946	0.2912	0.2877	0.2843	0.2810	0.2776
−0.4	0.3446	0.3409	0.3372	0.3336	0.3300	0.3264	0.3228	0.3192	0.3156	0.3121
−0.3	0.3821	0.3783	0.3745	0.3707	0.3669	0.3632	0.3594	0.3557	0.3520	0.3483
−0.2	0.4207	0.4168	0.4129	0.4090	0.4052	0.4013	0.3974	0.3936	0.3897	0.3859
−0.1	0.4602	0.4562	0.4522	0.4483	0.4443	0.4404	0.4364	0.4325	0.4286	0.4247
−0.0	0.5000	0.4960	0.4920	0.4880	0.4840	0.4801	0.4761	0.4721	0.4681	0.4641
0.0	0.5000	0.5040	0.5080	0.5120	0.5160	0.5199	0.5239	0.5279	0.5319	0.5359
0.1	0.5398	0.5438	0.5478	0.5517	0.5557	0.5596	0.5636	0.5675	0.5714	0.5753
0.2	0.5793	0.5832	0.5871	0.5910	0.5948	0.5987	0.6026	0.6064	0.6103	0.6141
0.3	0.6179	0.6217	0.6255	0.6293	0.6331	0.6368	0.6406	0.6443	0.6480	0.6517
0.4	0.6554	0.6591	0.6628	0.6664	0.6700	0.6736	0.6772	0.6808	0.6844	0.6879
0.5	0.6915	0.6950	0.6985	0.7019	0.7054	0.7088	0.7123	0.7157	0.7190	0.7224
0.6	0.7257	0.7291	0.7324	0.7357	0.7389	0.7422	0.7454	0.7486	0.7517	0.7549
0.7	0.7580	0.7611	0.7642	0.7673	0.7704	0.7734	0.7764	0.7794	0.7823	0.7852
0.8	0.7881	0.7910	0.7939	0.7967	0.7995	0.8023	0.8051	0.8078	0.8106	0.8133
0.9	0.8159	0.8186	0.8212	0.8238	0.8264	0.8289	0.8315	0.8340	0.8365	0.8389
1.0	0.8413	0.8438	0.8461	0.8485	0.8508	0.8531	0.8554	0.8577	0.8599	0.8621
1.1	0.8643	0.8665	0.8686	0.8708	0.8729	0.8749	0.8770	0.8790	0.8810	0.8830
1.2	0.8849	0.8869	0.8888	0.8907	0.8925	0.8944	0.8962	0.8980	0.8997	0.9015
1.3	0.9032	0.9049	0.9066	0.9082	0.9099	0.9115	0.9131	0.9147	0.9162	0.9177
1.4	0.9192	0.9207	0.9222	0.9236	0.9251	0.9265	0.9279	0.9292	0.9306	0.9319
1.5	0.9332	0.9345	0.9357	0.9370	0.9382	0.9394	0.9406	0.9418	0.9429	0.9441
1.6	0.9452	0.9463	0.9474	0.9484	0.9495	0.9505	0.9515	0.9525	0.9535	0.9545
1.7	0.9554	0.9564	0.9573	0.9582	0.9591	0.9599	0.9608	0.9616	0.9625	0.9633
1.8	0.9641	0.9649	0.9656	0.9664	0.9671	0.9678	0.9686	0.9693	0.9699	0.9706
1.9	0.9713	0.9719	0.9726	0.9732	0.9738	0.9744	0.9750	0.9756	0.9761	0.9767
2.0	0.9772	0.9778	0.9783	0.9788	0.9793	0.9798	0.9803	0.9808	0.9812	0.9817
2.1	0.9821	0.9826	0.9830	0.9834	0.9838	0.9842	0.9846	0.9850	0.9854	0.9857
2.2	0.9861	0.9864	0.9868	0.9871	0.9875	0.9878	0.9881	0.9884	0.9887	0.9890
2.3	0.9893	0.9896	0.9898	0.9901	0.9904	0.9906	0.9909	0.9911	0.9913	0.9916
2.4	0.9918	0.9920	0.9922	0.9925	0.9927	0.9929	0.9931	0.9932	0.9934	0.9936

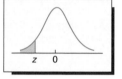

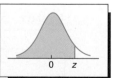

TABLE **5.3**   (*Continued*)

z	0.00	0.01	0.02	0.03	0.04	0.05	0.06	0.07	0.08	0.09
2.5	0.9938	0.9940	0.9941	0.9943	0.9945	0.9946	0.9948	0.9949	0.9951	0.9952
2.6	0.9953	0.9955	0.9956	0.9957	0.9959	0.9960	0.9961	0.9962	0.9963	0.9964
2.7	0.9965	0.9966	0.9967	0.9968	0.9969	0.9970	0.9971	0.9972	0.9973	0.9974
2.8	0.9974	0.9975	0.9976	0.9977	0.9977	0.9978	0.9979	0.9979	0.9980	0.9981
2.9	0.9981	0.9982	0.9982	0.9983	0.9984	0.9984	0.9985	0.9985	0.9986	0.9986
3.0	0.9987	0.9987	0.9987	0.9988	0.9988	0.9989	0.9989	0.9989	0.9990	0.9990
3.1	0.9990	0.9991	0.9991	0.9991	0.9992	0.9992	0.9992	0.9992	0.9993	0.9993
3.2	0.9993	0.9993	0.9994	0.9994	0.9994	0.9994	0.9994	0.9995	0.9995	0.9995
3.3	0.9995	0.9995	0.9995	0.9996	0.9996	0.9996	0.9996	0.9996	0.9996	0.9997
3.4	0.9997	0.9997	0.9997	0.9997	0.9997	0.9997	0.9997	0.9997	0.9997	0.9998

the z value 2.53 is found in the row corresponding to 2.5 and in the column corresponding to 0.03. We find that this area is 0.9943—that is, $P(z \le 2.53) = 0.9943$.

We now show how to use the cumulative normal table to find several other kinds of normal curve areas. First, suppose that we wish to find the area under the standard normal curve at or above a z value of 2—that is, we wish to find $P(z \ge 2)$. This area is illustrated in Figure 5.27 and is called a **right-hand tail area**. Since the total area under the normal curve equals 1, the area under the curve at or above 2 equals 1 minus the area under the curve at or below 2. That is, we find that $P(z \ge 2) = 1 - P(z \le 2) = 1 - 0.9772 = 0.0228$.

Next suppose that we wish to find the area under the standard normal curve at or below a z value of -1. That is, we wish to find $P(z \le -1)$. This area is illustrated in Figure 5.28 and is called a **left-hand tail area**. The needed area is found in the row of the cumulative normal table corresponding to -1 and in the column headed by 0.00. We find that $P(z \le -1) = 0.1587$. Notice that the area under the standard normal curve at or below -1 is equal to the area under this curve at or above 1. This is true because of the symmetry of the normal curve. Therefore, $P(z \ge 1) = 0.1587$.

Finally, suppose that we wish to find the area under the standard normal curve between the z values of -1 and 1. This area is illustrated in Figure 5.29, and we can see that this area

FIGURE **5.26**   Finding $P(z \le 1)$

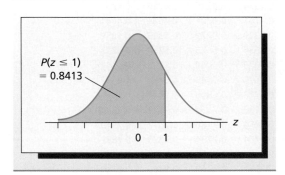

FIGURE **5.27**   Finding $P(z \ge 2)$

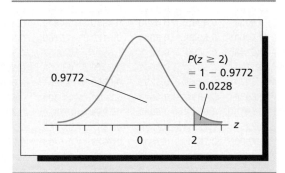

FIGURE **5.28**   Finding $P(z \le -1)$ or $P(z \ge 1)$

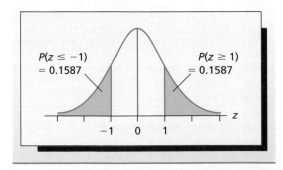

FIGURE **5.29**   Finding $P(-1 \le z \le 1)$

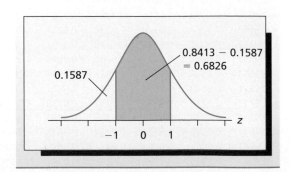

equals the area under the curve at or below 1 minus the area under the curve at or below -1. Referring to Table 5.3, we see that $P(-1 \leq z \leq 1) = P(z \leq 1) - P(z \leq -1) = 0.8413 - 0.1587 = 0.6826$.

Example 5.10   The Coffee Temperature Case

Recall that the runs plot and histogram of the sample of 24 coffee temperatures indicate that the coffee-making process is in statistical control and that the population of all coffee temperatures is normally distributed. Also recall that customer requirements state that each cup of coffee should have a temperature between 67°C and 75°C. The mean and standard deviation of the sample of 24 coffee temperatures are $\bar{x} = 71.2083$ and $s = 2.9779$. Using $\bar{x}$ and s as point estimates of the population mean μ and population standard deviation σ, we want to calculate the probability that x, the temperature of a randomly selected cup of coffee, is outside the requirements (that is, less than 67°C or greater than 75°C). In order to compute the probability $P(x < 67$ or $x > 75)$, we compute the z values

$$z = \frac{67 - 71.2083}{2.9779} = -1.41 \quad \text{and} \quad z = \frac{75 - 71.2083}{2.9779} = 1.27.$$

These z values tell us that 67°C is 1.41 standard deviations below the mean and that 75°C is 1.27 standard deviations above the mean. Because the events $\{x < 67\}$ and $\{x > 75\}$ are mutually exclusive, $P(x < 67$ or $x > 75)$ is the sum of $P(x < 67)$ and $P(x > 75)$. As shown in Figure 5.30, $P(x < 67)$ equals $P(z < -1.41)$. We obtain this probability by finding the entry in Table 5.3 corresponding to the z value -1.41, which is 0.0793. As also shown in Figure 5.30, $P(x > 75)$ equals $P(z > 1.27)$. Finding the entry in Table 5.3 corresponding to the z value 1.27, we find that $P(z \leq 1.27) = 0.8980$. It follows that $P(z > 1.27)$ equals $1 - 0.8980 = 0.1020$. Finally, $P(x < 67$ or $x > 75) = 0.0793 + 0.1020 = 0.1813$. This probability says that 18.13 percent of the coffee temperatures do not meet customer requirements. Therefore, if management believes that meeting this requirement is important, the coffee-making process must be improved.

FIGURE **5.30**   Finding $P(x < 67$ or $x > 75)$ in the Coffee Temperature Case

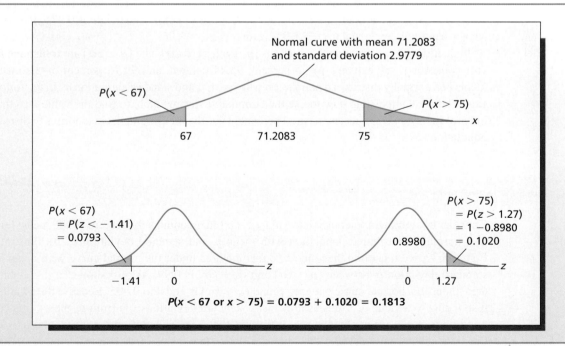

FIGURE **5.31**   The Point $z_{0.025} = 1.96$

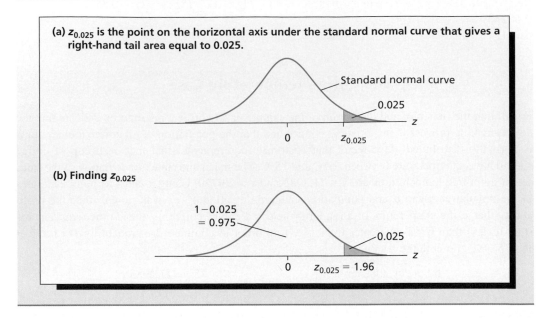

In order to use many of the formulas given in later chapters, we must be able to find the z value so that the tail area to the right of z under the standard normal curve is a particular value. For instance, we might need to find the z value so that the tail area to the right of z under the standard normal curve is 0.025. This z value is denoted $z_{0.025}$, and we illustrate $z_{0.025}$ in Figure 5.31. We refer to $z_{0.025}$ as **the point on the horizontal axis under the standard normal curve that gives a right-hand tail area equal to 0.025**. It is easy to use the cumulative normal table to find such a point. For instance, in order to find $z_{0.025}$, we note from Figure 5.31 that the area under the standard normal curve at or below $z_{0.025}$ equals 0.975. Remembering that areas under the standard normal curve at or below z are the four-digit numbers given in the body of Table 5.3, we scan the body of the table and find the area 0.9750. We have shaded this area in Table 5.3, and we note that the area 0.9750 is in the row corresponding to a z of 1.9 and in the column headed by 0.06. It follows that the z value corresponding to 0.9750 is 1.96. Because the z value 1.96 gives an area under the standard normal curve at or below z that equals 0.975, it also gives a right-hand tail area equal to 0.025. Therefore, $z_{0.025} = 1.96$.

In Section 2.3, we saw that the intervals $[\mu \pm \sigma]$, $[\mu \pm 2\sigma]$, and $[\mu \pm 3\sigma]$ are **tolerance intervals** containing, respectively, 68.26 percent, 95.44 percent, and 99.73 percent of the measurements in a normally distributed population with mean μ and standard deviation σ. In the following example, we demonstrate how to use the cumulative normal table to find the value k so that the interval $[\mu \pm k\sigma]$ contains any desired percentage of the measurements in a normally distributed population.

Example 5.11

Consider computing a tolerance interval $[\mu \pm k\sigma]$ that contains 99 percent of the measurements in a normally distributed population with mean μ and standard deviation σ. As illustrated in Figure 5.32, we must find the value k so that the area under the normal curve with mean μ and standard deviation σ between $(\mu - k\sigma)$ and $(\mu + k\sigma)$ is 0.99. As also shown in this figure, the area under this normal curve between μ and $(\mu + k\sigma)$ is equal to 0.495. Because the z value corresponding to a value of x tells us how many standard deviations x is from μ, the z value corresponding to $(\mu + k\sigma)$ is obviously k. It follows that k is the point on the horizontal axis under the standard normal curve so that the area under this curve at or below k equals 0.995 (see Figure 5.32). Looking for 0.995 in the body of the cumulative normal table (Table 5.3), we find

FIGURE 5.32 Finding a Tolerance Interval [$\mu \pm k\sigma$] That Contains 99 Percent of the Measurements in a Normally Distributed Population

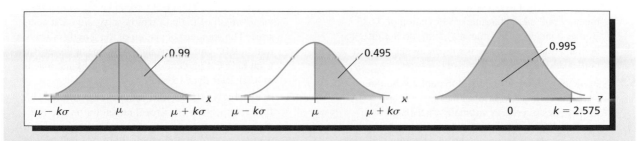

that the values closest to 0.995 are 0.9949, which has a corresponding z value of 2.57, and 0.9951, which has a corresponding z value of 2.58. Although it would be sufficient to use either of these z values, we interpolate halfway between them and assume that k equals 2.575. It follows that the interval [$\mu \pm 2.575\sigma$] contains 99 percent of the measurements in a normally distributed population with mean μ and standard deviation σ.

CHAPTER SUMMARY

In this chapter, we discussed **continuous probability distributions**. We began by learning that **a continuous probability distribution is described by a continuous probability curve** and that in this context **probabilities are areas under the probability curve**. We next studied several important continuous probability distributions—**the uniform distribution, the normal distribution**, and **the exponential distribution**. In particular, we concentrated on the normal distribution, which is the most important continuous probability distribution. We learned about the properties of the normal curve, and we saw how to use a **normal table** to find various areas under a normal curve. We also saw that the normal curve can be employed to approximate binomial probabilities, and we demonstrated how we can use a normal curve probability to make a statistical inference. We concluded this chapter with a section that covers the **cumulative normal table**.

GLOSSARY OF TERMS

continuous probability distribution (or probability curve): A curve that is defined so that the probability that a random variable will be in a specified interval of numbers is the area under the curve corresponding to the interval. (page 147)

exponential probability distribution: A probability distribution that describes the time or space between successive occurrences of an event when the number of times the event occurs over an interval of time or space is described by a Poisson distribution. (page 170)

normal probability distribution: The most important continuous probability distribution. Its probability curve is the bell-shaped normal curve. (page 151)

normal table: A table in which we can look up areas under the standard normal curve. (pages 152–155, 172–174)

queueing theory: A methodology that attempts to determine the number of servers that strikes an optimal balance between

the time customers wait for service and the cost of providing service. (page 171)

standard normal distribution (or curve): A normal distribution (or curve) with mean 0 and standard deviation 1. (page 153)

uniform distribution: A continuous probability distribution with a rectangular shape that says the probability is distributed evenly (or uniformly) over an interval of numbers. (page 148)

z_α point: The point on the horizontal axis under the standard normal curve that gives a right-hand tail area equal to α. (page 160)

$-z_\alpha$ point: The point on the horizontal axis under the standard normal curve that gives a left-hand tail area equal to α. (page 161)

z value: A value that tells us the number of standard deviations that a value x is from the mean of a normal curve. If the z value is positive, then x is above the mean. If the z value is negative, then x is below the mean. (page 153)

IMPORTANT FORMULAS

The uniform probability curve: page 148

Mean and standard deviation of a uniform distribution: page 148

The normal probability curve: page 151

z values: page 153

Finding normal probabilities: page 158

Normal approximation to the binomial distribution: page 166

The exponential probability curve: page 170

Mean and standard deviation of an exponential distribution: page 170

SUPPLEMENTARY EXERCISES

5.58   In a bottle-filling process, the amount of drink injected into 500-mL bottles is normally distributed with a mean of 500 mL and a standard deviation of 0.625 mL. Bottles containing less than 498.5 mL do not meet the bottler's quality standard. What percentage of filled bottles do not meet the standard?

5.59   In the movie *Forrest Gump*, the public school required an IQ of at least 80 for admittance.
   a. If IQ test scores are normally distributed with mean 100 and standard deviation 16, what percentage of people would qualify for admittance to the school?
   b. If the public school wishes 95 percent of all children to qualify for admittance, what minimum IQ test score should be required for admittance?

5.60   The amount of sales tax paid on a purchase is rounded to the nearest cent. Assume that the round-off error is uniformly distributed in the interval −0.5 to 0.5 cents.
   a. Write the formula for the probability curve describing the round-off error.
   b. Graph the probability curve describing the round-off error.
   c. What is the probability that the round-off error exceeds 0.3 cents or is less than −0.3 cents?
   d. What is the probability that the round-off error exceeds 0.1 cents or is less than −0.1 cents?
   e. Find the mean and the standard deviation of the round-off error.
   f. Find the probability that the round-off error will be within one standard deviation of the mean.

5.61   A **consensus forecast** is the average of a large number of individual analysts' forecasts. Suppose the individual forecasts for a particular interest rate are normally distributed with a mean of 5.0 percent and a standard deviation of 1.2 percent. A single analyst is randomly selected. Find the probability that their forecast is
   a. At least 3.5 percent.
   b. At most 6 percent.
   c. Between 3.5 percent and 6 percent.

5.62   Recall from Exercise 5.61 that individual forecasts of a particular interest rate are normally distributed with a mean of 5 percent and a standard deviation of 1.2 percent.
   a. What percentage of individual forecasts are at or below the 10th percentile of the distribution of forecasts? What percentage are at or above the 10th percentile? Find the 10th percentile of the distribution of individual forecasts.
   b. Find the first quartile, Q_1, and the third quartile, Q_3, of the distribution of individual forecasts.

5.63   The scores on the entrance exam at a well-known, exclusive private school are normally distributed with a mean score of 200 and a standard deviation equal to 50. At what value should the lowest passing score be set if the school wishes only 2.5 percent of those taking the test to pass?

5.64   A machine is used to cut a metal automobile part to its desired length. The machine can be set so that the mean length of the part will be any value that is desired. The standard deviation of the lengths always runs at 0.02 cm. Where should the mean be set if we want only 0.4 percent of the parts cut by the machine to be shorter than 15 cm long?

5.65   A motel accepts 325 reservations for 300 rooms on July 1, expecting 10 percent no-shows on average from past records. Use the normal approximation to the binomial to find the probability that all guests who arrive on July 1 will receive a room.

5.66   Suppose a software company finds that the number of errors in its software per 1,000 lines of code is described by a Poisson distribution. Furthermore, it is found that there is an average of four errors per 1,000 lines of code. Let x denote the number of lines of code between successive errors.
   a. Find the probability that there will be at least 400 lines of code between successive errors in the company's software.
   b. Find the probability that there will be no more than 100 lines of code between successive errors in the company's software.

5.67   **THE INVESTMENT CASE**   ⬤ InvestRet

For each investment class in Table 2.15 (page 83), assume that future returns are normally distributed with the population mean and standard deviation given in Table 2.15.
   a. For each investment class, find the probability of a return that is less than zero (that is, find the probability of a loss). Is your answer reasonable for all investment classes? Explain.
   b. For each investment class, find the probability of a return that is
      (1) Greater than 5 percent.
      (2) Greater than 10 percent.
      (3) Greater than 20 percent.
      (4) Greater than 50 percent.
   c. For which investment classes is the probability of a return greater than 50 percent essentially zero? For which investment classes is the probability of such a return greater than 1 percent? greater than 5 percent?
   d. For which investment classes is the probability of a loss essentially zero? For which investment classes is the probability of a loss greater than 1 percent? greater than 10 percent? greater than 20 percent?

5.68   The daily water consumption for an Ontario community is normally distributed with a mean consumption of 800,000 L and a standard deviation of 80,000 L. The community water system will experience a noticeable drop in water pressure when the daily water consumption exceeds 984,000 L. What is the probability of experiencing such a drop in water pressure?

5.69 Suppose the times required for a cable company to fix cable problems in its customers' homes are uniformly distributed between 10 minutes and 25 minutes. What is the probability that a randomly selected cable repair visit will take at least 15 minutes?

5.70 Suppose the waiting time to get food after placing an order at a fast-food restaurant is exponentially distributed with a mean of 60 seconds. If a randomly selected customer orders food at the restaurant, what is the probability that the customer will wait at least

 a. One minute, 30 seconds?

 b. Two minutes?

5.71 Net interest margin—often referred to as **spread**—is the difference between the rate banks pay on deposits and the rate they charge for loans. Suppose that the net interest margins for all Canadian banks are normally distributed with a mean of 4.15 percent and a standard deviation of 0.5 percent.

 a. Find the probability that a randomly selected bank will have a net interest margin that exceeds 5.40 percent.

 b. Find the probability that a randomly selected bank will have a net interest margin less than 4.40 percent.

 c. A bank wants its net interest margin to be less than the net interest margins of 95 percent of all Canadian banks. Where should the bank's net interest margin be set?

5.72 In an article in the November 11, 1991, issue of *Advertising* Age, Giges studies global spending patterns. Giges presents data concerning the percentage of adults in various countries who have purchased various consumer items (such as soft drinks, athletic footware, blue jeans, beer) in the past three months.

 a. Suppose we wish to justify the claim that less than 50 percent of adults in Germany have purchased blue jeans in the past three months. The survey reported by Giges found that 45 percent of the respondents in Germany had purchased blue jeans in the past three months.[2]

 Assume that a random sample of 400 German adults was employed, and let p be the proportion of all German adults who have purchased blue jeans in the past three months. If we assume that $p = 0.5$, use the normal approximation to the binomial distribution to calculate the probability that 45 percent or fewer of 400 randomly selected German adults would have purchased blue jeans in the past three months. Note: Because 45 percent of 400 is 180, you should calculate the probability that 180 or fewer of 400 randomly selected German adults would have purchased blue jeans in the past three months.

 b. Based on the probability you computed in part a, would you conclude that p is really less than 0.5? That is, would you conclude that less than 50 percent of adults in Germany have purchased blue jeans in the past three months? Explain.

5.73 Assume that the ages for first marriages are normally distributed with a mean of 26 years and a standard deviation of 4 years. What is the probability that a person getting married for the first time is in their twenties?

[2]Source: "Global spending patterns emerge," by N. Giges, *Advertising Age,* November 11, 1991, p. 64.

CHAPTER 6

Sampling Distributions

LEARNING OBJECTIVES

After reading this chapter, you should be able to

- understand that the sample mean and sample proportion are statistics and are functions of a random variable
- understand that the probability distribution of a statistic is referred to as a sampling distribution
- recognize that the mean (expected value) of the sampling distribution of $\bar{x}$ is equal to the population mean
- recognize that the mean (expected value) of the sampling distribution of $\hat{p}$ is equal to the population proportion
- understand why the variance of a statistic is smaller than the variance of the underlying population
- recognize the shape of the sampling distributions of $\hat{p}$ and $\bar{x}$
- define and understand the central limit theorem
- explain the difference between a biased estimate and an unbiased estimate

CHAPTER OUTLINE

6.1 The Sampling Distribution of the Sample Mean

6.2 The Sampling Distribution of the Sample Proportion

You may wonder why sampling is necessary or even practical. A statistician might be hired to find answers to questions concerning populations, such as the spending habits of people aged 18 to 25, the average income level of women aged 25 to 34, the average age of marriage in Canada, and even the potential voting habits of Canadians. Intuitively, if you wanted this information, you would just speak to the entire population. Most times this is not possible due to lack of time or money. Instead, a statistician will often sample from that population and use the information from that sample to make an inference about the population.

Suppose you have a job as a beer taster during the summer and the company that you work for wants to know if a new beer they are brewing is appealing or

not. A vat of 1,000 L is produced. Suppose you are on a panel of 10 independent beer tasters. The panel of tasters can do one of two things. They can each taste a sample of the beer, or they can drink all of it. Some of you may not see a problem with the second option, but it is not necessary. There is no reason not to believe that all 1,000 L of beer from the same vat is the same. There might be slight variations due to material settling on the bottom or floating to the top, but we will assume that the beer is relatively uniform throughout. A sample from this population (the vat of beer) is all that is needed to get an idea of how the entire batch tastes.

Generally speaking, this is the basis for inferential statistics. Statisticians take random samples of populations in order to make inferences about the populations of interest. Estimates are obtained from the samples. Confidence intervals are constructed and hypotheses are tested based on the sample information.

The Mass of a Loonie. We can use the properties of the sampling distribution of the sampling mean and its sample of $n = 200$ Canadian loonie coin masses from 1989 to provide statistical evidence that the population of loonies weighs more than the required 7 g.
The Cheese Spread Case. The food-processing company uses the properties of the sampling distribution

Confidence intervals and hypothesis tests will be discussed a little later on in the text. In order to help explain these sampling distributions, we consider two previously introduced cases:

of the sample proportion and its survey results to provide extremely strong evidence that less than 10 percent of all current purchasers would stop buying the cheese spread if the new spout were used.

We also introduce two new cases, the **Stock Return Case** and the **Payment Time Case**.

6.1 The Sampling Distribution of the Sample Mean

Suppose that we are about to randomly select a sample of n measurements from a population of measurements with mean μ and standard deviation σ. **Before** we actually select the sample, there are many different samples of n measurements that we might potentially obtain. Because different samples generally have different sample means, there are many different sample means that we might potentially obtain. It follows that, **before we draw the sample, the sample mean $\bar{x}$ is a random variable**.

The **sampling distribution of the sample mean** $\bar{x}$ is the probability distribution of the population of all possible sample means obtained from samples of size n.

Example 6.1 The Stock Return Case

To illustrate the sampling distribution of the sample mean, we consider the population of last year's percentage returns for six stocks (see Table 6.1). This population consists of the percentage returns 10 percent, 20 percent, 30 percent, 40 percent, 50 percent, and 60 percent (which we have arranged in increasing order). Table 6.1 and Figure 6.1(a) (on the next page) show the relative frequency distribution and the relative frequency histogram describing the population of six returns. The mean and the standard deviation of this population can be calculated to be 35 percent and 17.078 percent, respectively. Now consider randomly selecting without replacement a sample of $n = 2$ returns from the population of six returns. Table 6.2(a) lists the 15 distinct samples of $n = 2$ returns that could be obtained and also shows the mean of each sample (note that each sample is specified only with respect to which two returns are contained in the sample, and not with respect to the different orders in which the returns could be randomly selected). To describe what the distribution of the population of 15 sample means looks like, we form the

TABLE **6.1**   A Relative Frequency Distribution Describing the Population of Six Individual Stock Returns

Stock	Percentage Return	Frequency	Relative Frequency
Stock A	10	1	1/6
Stock B	20	1	1/6
Stock C	30	1	1/6
Stock D	40	1	1/6
Stock E	50	1	1/6
Stock F	60	1	1/6

FIGURE **6.1**   A Comparison of Individual Stock Returns and Sample Mean Returns

TABLE **6.2**   The Population of Sample Means

(a) A relative frequency histogram describing the population of six individual stock returns

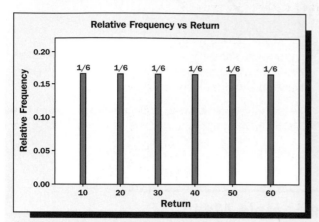

(b) A relative frequency histogram describing the population of 15 sample mean returns

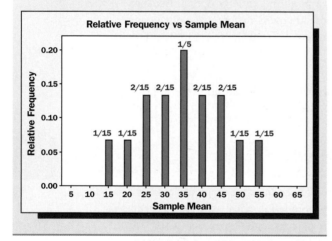

(a) The population of the 15 samples of $n = 2$ returns and corresponding sample means

Sample	$n = 2$ Returns in Sample		Sample Mean
1	10	20	15
2	10	30	20
3	10	40	25
4	10	50	30
5	10	60	35
6	20	30	25
7	20	40	30
8	20	50	35
9	20	60	40
10	30	40	35
11	30	50	40
12	30	60	45
13	40	50	45
14	40	60	50
15	50	60	55

(b) A relative frequency distribution describing the population of 15 sample mean returns

Sample Mean	Frequency	Relative Frequency
15	1	1/15
20	1	1/15
25	2	2/15
30	2	2/15
35	3	3/15
40	2	2/15
45	2	2/15
50	1	1/15
55	1	1/15

relative frequency distribution shown in Table 6.2(b) and the relative frequency histogram shown in Figure 6.1(b). Comparing Figure 6.1(a) and (b), we see that, although the histogram of six individual returns and the histogram of 15 sample mean returns seem to be centred over the same mean of 35 percent, the histogram of sample mean returns in Figure 6.1(b) looks **more bell-shaped** and **less spread out** than the histogram of individual returns in Figure 6.1(a).

In general, there are several relationships between (1) a population of individual measurements and (2) the population of all possible sample means based on all samples of size n that can be randomly selected from the population of individual measurements. To illustrate, we will consider the monthly returns of the TSX for the past 50 years. Over this time, as you can imagine, there has been some volatility. There were some very good months, a lot of average months, and a few very bad months. Figure 6.2(a) shows the relative frequency histogram of the monthly percentage returns for the 50-year period ended December 2006. The mean and standard deviation of the monthly returns are 0.624 percent and 4.42 percent, respectively.

Thus far we have considered two stock return examples. Together, these examples illustrate several important facts about randomly selecting a sample of n individual measurements from a population of individual measurements with mean μ and standard deviation σ. Specifically, the following can be shown:

1   **If the population of individual measurements is normally distributed, then the population of all possible sample means is also normally distributed.** This is illustrated in

FIGURE **6.2**   Monthly Returns of the TSX from 1956 to 2006: A Comparison of Monthly Stock Returns and Sample Mean Returns

(a) **The relative frequency histogram describing the population of monthly stock returns from Jan. 1956 to Dec. 2006**

(b) **A relative frequency histogram of 1 000 000 samples of size $n = 20$ from the population of monthly stock returns**

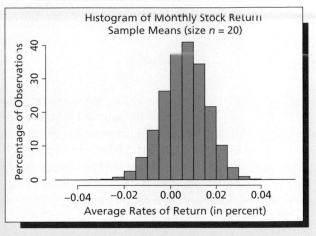

Figure 6.2 is adapted with permission from TSX Datalinx.

Figure 6.2(a) and (b): Because the population of individual stock returns is (approximately) normally distributed, the population of all possible sample mean returns is also (approximately) normally distributed.

2   **Even if the population of individual measurements is not normally distributed, there are circumstances when the population of all possible sample means is approximately normally distributed.** This result is based on a theorem called the **central limit theorem** (see the next section). The result is intuitively illustrated in Figure 6.1(a) and (b). Although the population of six stock returns does not have a normal distribution (it has a uniform distribution), the population of 15 sample mean returns has a distribution that looks somewhat like a normal distribution.

3   **The mean, $\mu_{\bar{x}}$, of the population of all possible sample means equals μ, the mean of the population of individual measurements.** This is illustrated in both Figures 6.1 and 6.2. That is, in each stock return example, the histogram of monthly stock returns and the histogram of sample mean returns are centred over the same mean μ (note that μ equals 35 percent in Figure 6.1 and 0.624 percent in Figure 6.2). Furthermore, this implies that, although the sample mean return for a particular sample of n randomly selected stocks probably will not equal the population mean return μ, the mean of the population of all possible sample mean returns (based on all possible samples of n stocks) is equal to μ.

4   **The standard deviation, $\sigma_{\bar{x}}$, of the population of all possible sample means is less than σ, the standard deviation of the population of individual measurements.**[1] This is also illustrated in both Figures 6.1 and 6.2. That is, in each stock return example, the histogram of all possible sample mean returns is less spread out than the histogram of individual stock returns. Intuitively, $\sigma_{\bar{x}}$ is smaller than σ because each possible sample mean is an average of n measurements (stock returns). Thus, **each sample mean *averages out* high and low sample measurements (stock returns) and can be expected to be closer to the population mean μ than many of the individual population measurements (stock returns) would be.** It follows that the different possible sample means are more closely clustered around μ than are the individual population measurements. In terms of investing in the stock market, a sample of n stocks is a portfolio of n stocks, and the sample mean return is the percentage return that an investor would realize if they invested equal amounts in the stocks in the portfolio. Therefore, Figures 6.1 and 6.2 illustrate that the variation among portfolio returns is

---

[1]This is true if the sample size is greater than 1.

considerably less than the variation among individual stock returns. Of course one would probably not invest in the stock market by randomly selecting stocks. However, we have nevertheless illustrated an important investment principle—diversification reduces risk.

There is a formula that tells us the exact relationship between $\sigma_{\bar{x}}$ and σ. This formula says that, if certain conditions are satisfied, $\sigma_{\bar{x}}$ equals σ divided by the square root of the sample size n. That is,

$$\sigma_{\bar{x}} = \frac{\sigma}{\sqrt{n}}.$$

It follows that $\sigma_{\bar{x}}$ is less than σ if the sample size n is greater than 1. Furthermore, this formula is valid if the sampled population is infinite and is approximately valid if the sampled population is finite and much larger than (say, at least 20 times) the size of the sample. For example, consider randomly selecting $n = 20$ monthly stock returns from the TSX data. The population size of 600 monthly returns is more than 20 times the sample size of 20 ($20 \times 20 = 400$). The population standard deviation of the monthly stock returns is 4.42 percent over the 50-year period, so it follows that

$$\sigma_{\bar{x}} = \frac{\sigma}{\sqrt{n}} = \frac{4.42}{\sqrt{20}} = 0.988\%.$$

Figure 6.2(a) and (b) illustrates the fact that the spread of the distribution of average monthly returns (0.988 percent) is indeed smaller than the spread of the distribution of monthly returns (4.42 percent).

We now summarize what we have learned about the sampling distribution of $\bar{x}$.

The Sampling Distribution of $\bar{x}$

Assume that the population from which we will randomly select a sample of n measurements has mean μ and standard deviation σ. Then, the population of all possible sample means

1   Has a normal distribution if the sampled population has a normal distribution.

2   Has mean $\mu_{\bar{x}} = \mu$.

3   Has variance $\sigma_{\bar{x}}^2 = \dfrac{\sigma^2}{n}$ and standard deviation
$$\sigma_{\bar{x}} = \frac{\sigma}{\sqrt{n}}.$$

The formulas for $\sigma_{\bar{x}}^2$ and $\sigma_{\bar{x}}$ in (3) hold exactly if the sampled population is infinite and hold approximately if the sampled population is finite and much larger than (say, at least 20 times) the size of the sample.

Stated equivalently, the sampling distribution of $\bar{x}$ has mean $\mu_{\bar{x}} = \mu$, has standard deviation $\sigma_{\bar{x}} = \sigma/\sqrt{n}$ (under the conditions described above), and is a normal distribution (if the sampled population has a normal distribution).

In the stock return case, we know the values of the mean μ and the standard deviation σ of the sampled population of monthly stock returns. In most situations, however, we randomly select a sample from a population in order to estimate the unknown mean μ and the unknown standard deviation σ of the population. We have seen that the sample mean $\bar{x}$ is the point estimate of μ and the sample standard deviation s is the point estimate of σ. Furthermore, a larger sample is more likely to give a more accurate point estimate $\bar{x}$ of μ and a more accurate point estimate s of σ. Furthermore, we can use the formula $\sigma_{\bar{x}} = \sigma/\sqrt{n}$ to demonstrate why a larger sample is more likely to give a more accurate point estimate $\bar{x}$ of μ. Notice that the sample size n is in the denominator of the formula $\sigma_{\bar{x}} = \sigma/\sqrt{n}$. This implies that the larger the sample size n is, the smaller is $\sigma_{\bar{x}}$. This is logical because, the larger the sample size is, the better is the chance that the high and low measurements in the sample will cancel each other out to give a sample mean near μ (because more measurements are being averaged). Therefore, when the sample size is large, the possible sample means will be more closely clustered around μ than when the sample size is smaller. This implies that the sample mean calculated from the actual sample that we select is more likely to be near μ. In the following example, we illustrate this idea and also show how the sampling distribution of $\bar{x}$ can help us to make a statistically based conclusion about a population mean μ.

Example 6.2 The Mass of a Loonie

The Royal Canadian Mint would probably want to ensure that the loonies produced in 1989 (and any other year for that matter) met the required specifications. The loonie has to weigh 7 g, according to specifications listed on the Web site of the Royal Canadian Mint (http://www.mint.ca). Of course we know that not every loonie in the production run for any given year would weigh **exactly** 7 g, but if we took the average of the masses of the entire production run, the target, or average, mass would be $\mu = 7$ g. Suppose that the population standard deviation is known to be $\sigma = 0.06$ g. Recall that, in our example, we had a **sample** of 200 loonie masses. The sample mean was 7.012 g and the sample standard deviation was 0.0603 g. The distribution of the loonie masses also appeared to be approximately normal in shape. It then follows that if we take a sample of n loonies from the population, the distribution of the sample mean would follow an approximately normal distribution with mean μ and standard deviation $\sigma_{\bar{x}} = \sigma/\sqrt{n}$. If we increase the sample size n, we see that $\sigma_{\bar{x}} = \sigma/\sqrt{n}$ becomes smaller for larger n (see Figure 6.3). Thus, a larger sample would be much

FIGURE 6.3 A Comparison of (1) the Population of All Loonie Masses, (2) the Sampling Distribution of the Sample Mean $\bar{x}$ When $n = 5$, and (3) the Sampling Distribution of the Sample Mean $\bar{x}$ When $n = 50$

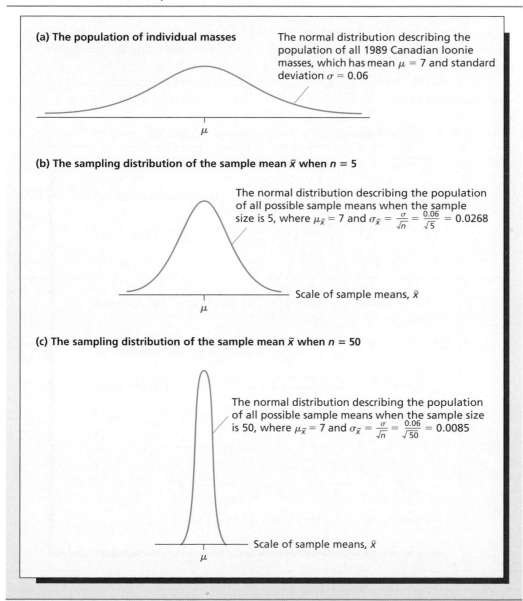

(a) The population of individual masses

The normal distribution describing the population of all 1989 Canadian loonie masses, which has mean $\mu = 7$ and standard deviation $\sigma = 0.06$

(b) The sampling distribution of the sample mean $\bar{x}$ when $n = 5$

The normal distribution describing the population of all possible sample means when the sample size is 5, where $\mu_{\bar{x}} = 7$ and $\sigma_{\bar{x}} = \frac{\sigma}{\sqrt{n}} = \frac{0.06}{\sqrt{5}} = 0.0268$

Scale of sample means, $\bar{x}$

(c) The sampling distribution of the sample mean $\bar{x}$ when $n = 50$

The normal distribution describing the population of all possible sample means when the sample size is 50, where $\mu_{\bar{x}} = 7$ and $\sigma_{\bar{x}} = \frac{\sigma}{\sqrt{n}} = \frac{0.06}{\sqrt{50}} = 0.0085$

Scale of sample means, $\bar{x}$

more likely to produce a more accurate estimate of μ. So, a sample of size $n = 200$ is more likely to give a sample mean $\bar{x}$ that is closer to μ than a sample of size $n = 100$.

Recall that our sample of $n = 200$ loonies had a mean of $\bar{x} = 7.012$ g. Now we wish to determine whether or not this sample information provides strong statistical evidence that the population mean mass μ (of all loonies in production in 1989) might actually be greater than 7 g. If this were the case, then adjustments would have to be made to the production process.

In order to determine whether or not the mean population mass is indeed greater than 7 g, we will assume, for now, that $\mu = 7$ g and we will use the sample information to determine whether or not we can reject this assumption ($\mu = 7$ g) in favour of the alternative claim that the population mean μ might actually be greater than 7 g.

We know that the distribution of loonie masses is approximately normal. Our sample of $n = 200$ produced a sample mean of $\bar{x} = 7.012$ g, and the population standard deviation is known, as mentioned above, to be $\sigma = 0.06$ g. Therefore, the sampling distribution of the sample mean $\bar{x}$ is approximately normal with mean $\mu_{\bar{x}} = \mu$ and standard deviation $\sigma_{\bar{x}} = \sigma/\sqrt{n} = 0.06/\sqrt{200} = 0.00424$. Therefore, we need to determine

$$P(\bar{x} \geq 7.012 \text{ if } \mu = 7) = P\left(\frac{\bar{x} - \mu_{\bar{x}}}{\sigma_{\bar{x}}} \geq \frac{7.012 - 7}{0.00424}\right) = P(z \geq 2.83).$$

Looking this up in the normal probability table, we see that $P(z \geq 2.83) = 1 - 0.9977 = 0.0023$. This says that if $\mu = 7$ g, then about 23 in 10,000 of all possible sample means are at least as large as the sample mean $\bar{x} = 7.012$ g (see Figure 6.4). This suggests that it is very unlikely that $\mu = 7$ g. There is very little support for that claim (0.0023) based on the sample information. This evidence would probably convince the Royal Canadian Mint that the mean mass of the Canadian loonie in 1989 exceeded the specified mass of 7 g. What might the consequences of this be? Perhaps 1989 loonies get rejected in video games or vending machines more often than loonies from other years.

FIGURE 6.4 **The Probability That $\bar{x} \geq 7.012$ g When $\mu = 7$ g in the Loonie Case**

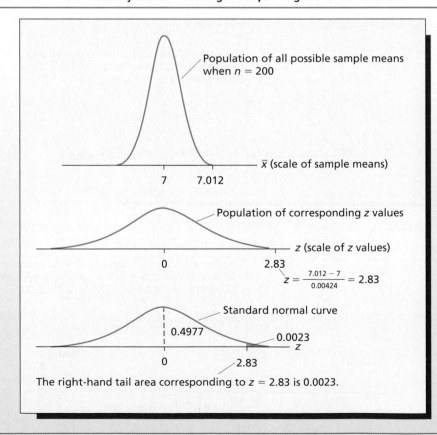

In the preceding example, the population standard deviation σ was known to be 0.06 g. Of course, in almost all real-world situations, the value of σ is unknown. If we do not know μ, why would we know σ? For now, though, we will assume, through extensive experience with the population or production process under consideration, that we know the true value of σ.

Sampling a nonnormally distributed population: The central limit theorem   We now consider what can be said about the sampling distribution of x when the sampled population is not normally distributed. First, as previously stated, the fact that $\mu_{\bar{x}} = \mu$ is still true. Second, as also previously stated, the formula $\sigma_{\bar{x}} = \sigma/\sqrt{n}$ is exactly correct if the sampled population is infinite and is approximately correct if the sampled population is finite and much larger than (say, at least 20 times as large as) the sample size. Third, an extremely important result called the **central limit theorem** tells us that, **if the sample size n is large, the sampling distribution of $\bar{x}$ is approximately normal, even if the sampled population is not normally distributed.**

The Central Limit Theorem

If the sample size n is sufficiently large, then the population of all possible sample means is approximately normally distributed (with mean $\mu_{\bar{x}} = \mu$ and standard deviation $\sigma_{\bar{x}} = \sigma/\sqrt{n}$), no matter what probability distribution describes the sampled population. Furthermore, the larger the sample size n is, the more nearly normally distributed is the population of all possible sample means.

The central limit theorem is illustrated in Figure 6.5 for several population shapes. Notice that as the sample size increases (from 2 to 6 to 30), the populations of all possible sample means become more nearly normally distributed. This figure also illustrates that, as the sample size

CHAPTERS
7 AND 8

FIGURE 6.5   **The Central Limit Theorem Says That the Larger the Sample Size Is, the More Nearly Normally Distributed Is the Population of All Possible Sample Means**

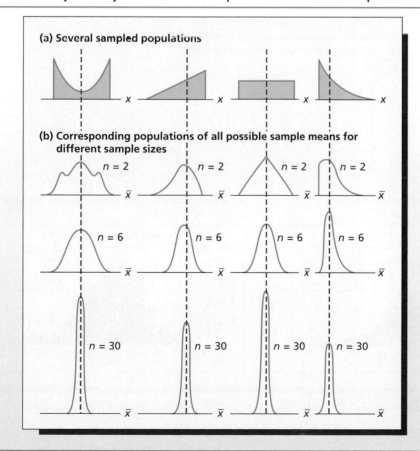

increases, the spread of the distribution of all possible sample means decreases (remember that this spread is measured by $\sigma_{\bar{x}}$, which decreases as the sample size increases).

How large must the sample size be for the sampling distribution of $\bar{x}$ to be approximately normal? In general, the more skewed the probability distribution of the sampled population, the larger the sample size must be for the population of all possible sample means to be approximately normally distributed. For some sampled populations, particularly those described by symmetric distributions, the population of all possible sample means is approximately normally distributed for a fairly small sample size. In addition, studies indicate that, **if the sample size is at least 30, for most sampled populations, the population of all possible sample means is approximately normally distributed**. For the subsequent cases, whenever the sample size n is at least 30, we will assume that the sampling distribution of $\bar{x}$ is approximately a normal distribution.

We can see the shapes of sampling distributions such as those illustrated in Figure 6.5 by using computer simulation. Specifically, for a population with a particular probability distribution, we can have the computer draw a given number of samples of n observations, compute the mean of each sample, and arrange the sample means into a histogram.[2] To illustrate this, consider Figure 6.6(a), which shows the exponential distribution describing the hospital emergency room interarrival times discussed in Chapter 5 (page 171). Figure 6.6(b) gives the results of a simulation in which MINITAB randomly selected 1,000 samples of five interarrival times from this exponential distribution, calculated the mean of each sample, and arranged the 1,000 sample means into a histogram. Figure 6.6(c) gives the results of a simulation in which MINITAB randomly selected 1,000 samples of 30 interarrival times from the exponential distribution, calculated the mean of each sample, and arranged the 1,000 sample means into a histogram. Note that, whereas the histogram in Figure 6.6(b) is somewhat positively skewed (to the right), the histogram in Figure 6.6(c) appears approximately bell-shaped. Therefore, we might conclude that when we randomly select a sample of n observations from an exponential distribution, the sampling distribution of the sample mean is somewhat positively skewed (to the right) when $n = 5$ and is approximately normal when $n = 30$.

FIGURE 6.6   Simulating the Sampling Distribution of the Sample Mean When Sampling from an Exponential Distribution

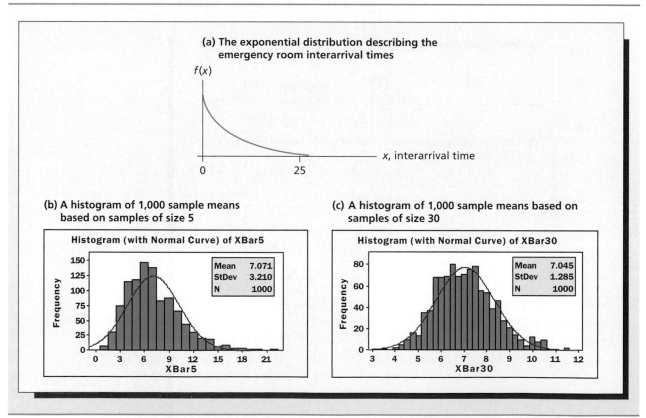

---

[2]The use of a computer to simulate sampling from a population is called a Monte Carlo study or simulation. These simulations are very useful in verifying that $\bar{x}$ is a reliable estimate of μ.

Example 6.3 The Payment Time Case

A management consulting firm has installed a new computer-based billing system in a trucking company. Because of the advantages of the new billing system, and because the trucking company's clients are receptive to using this system, the management consulting firm believes that the new system will reduce the mean bill payment time by more than 50 percent. The mean payment time using the old billing system was approximately equal to, but no less than, 39 days. Therefore, if μ denotes the new mean payment time, the consulting firm believes that μ will be less than 19.5 days. To assess whether μ is less than 19.5, we will assume that μ equals 19.5 and use a sample of $n = 65$ payment times to weigh the evidence against this assumption and in favour of the conclusion that μ is less than 19.5. The consulting firm finds that the mean of the 65 payment times is $\bar{x} = 18.1077$, and because this sample mean is less than 19.5, we have some evidence contradicting the assumption that μ equals 19.5. To evaluate the strength of this evidence, we calculate the probability of observing a sample mean that is less than or equal to 18.1077 if, in fact, μ equals 19.5. The management consulting firm plotted the 65 payment times in a stem-and-leaf display, which indicated that the population of all payment times is positively skewed (with a tail to the right). However, the central limit theorem tells us that, because the sample size $n = 65$ is large, the sampling distribution of $\bar{x}$ is approximately a normal distribution with mean $\mu_{\bar{x}} = \mu$ and standard deviation $\sigma_{\bar{x}} = \sigma/\sqrt{n}$. Assuming that the population standard deviation σ is known to be 4.2 days, $\sigma_{\bar{x}}$ equals $4.2/\sqrt{65} = 0.5209$. It follows that

$$P(\bar{x} \leq 18.1077 \text{ if } \mu = 19.5) = P\left(z \leq \frac{18.1077 - 19.5}{0.5209}\right)$$
$$= P(z \leq -2.67).$$

The normal table tells us that the area under the standard normal curve from -2.67 to 0 is 0.4962. It follows that the tail area under this curve to the left of -2.67 is $0.5 - 0.4962 = 0.0038$. Therefore,

$$P(\bar{x} \leq 18.1077 \text{ if } \mu = 19.5) = 0.0038.$$

This probability says that, if μ equals 19.5, then only 0.0038 of all possible sample means are at least as small as the sample mean $\bar{x} = 18.1077$ that we have actually observed. If we are to believe that μ equals 19.5, then we must believe that we have observed a sample mean that can be described as a 38 in 10,000 chance. It is very difficult to believe that such a small chance would occur, so we have very strong evidence that μ does not equal 19.5 and is, in fact, less than 19.5. We conclude that the new billing system has reduced the mean bill payment time by more than 50 percent.

Unbiasedness and minimum-variance estimates Recall that a sample statistic is any descriptive measure of the sample measurements. For instance, the sample mean $\bar{x}$ is a statistic, and so are the sample median, the sample variance s^2, and the sample standard deviation s. Not only do different samples give different values of $\bar{x}$, different samples also give different values of the median, s^2, s, or any other statistic. It follows that, **before we draw the sample, any sample statistic is a random variable**, and

VS
CHAPTERS
7 AND 8

The **sampling distribution** of a sample statistic is the probability distribution of the population of all possible values of the sample statistic.

For example, Figure 6.7(a) gives the population of the 20 samples of $n = 3$ stock returns that can be randomly selected from the population of the six stock returns -36, -15, 3, 15, 33, and 54. This figure also gives the mean, median, and standard deviation of each sample, and Figure 6.7(b) and (c) shows the relative frequency histograms describing the populations of the 20 sample means, 20 sample medians, and 20 sample standard deviations. In general, we wish to estimate a population parameter by using a sample statistic that we call an **unbiased point estimate** of the parameter.

A sample statistic is an **unbiased point estimate** of a population parameter if the mean of the population of all possible values of the sample statistic equals the population parameter.

We use the sample mean $\bar{x}$ as the point estimate of the population mean μ because $\bar{x}$ **is an unbiased point estimate of μ.** That is, $\mu_{\bar{x}} = \mu$, or the average of all the different possible sample means (that we could obtain from all the different possible samples) equals μ. For example, consider the summary of sample means and medians given at the bottom of Figure 6.7(a). We see that (1) the mean of the population of 20 sample means and (2) the mean of the population of 20 sample medians are both equal to 9, which is the mean of the sampled population of six stock returns ($-36, -15, 3, 15, 33,$ and 54). Thus, in this situation both the sample mean and the sample median are unbiased estimates of the population mean. In general, the sample mean is always an unbiased estimate of the population mean. However, the sample median is **not** always an unbiased estimate of the population mean.

Although we want a sample statistic to be an unbiased point estimate of the population parameter of interest, we also want the possible values of the sample statistic to be closely clustered around the population parameter. If this is the case, when we actually randomly select one sample and compute the sample statistic, its value is likely to be close to the value of the population parameter. For example, note from the bottom of Figure 6.7(a) that, although both the sample mean and the sample median are unbiased estimates of the population mean in this situation, the standard deviation of the population of 20 sample means, which is 13.26, is less than the standard deviation of the population of 20 sample medians, which is 15.88. This says, as is illustrated in Figure 6.7(b), that the 20 sample means are more closely clustered around the population mean

FIGURE 6.7 Populations of Sample Means, Medians, and Standard Deviations

(a) The population of the 20 samples of $n = 3$ returns and corresponding populations of sample means, medians, and standard deviations

Sample	$n = 3$ Returns in Sample			Sample Statistics Mean	Median	Std. Dev.
1	−36	−15	3	−16.00	−15.00	19.52
2	−36	−15	15	−12.00	−15.00	25.63
3	−36	−15	33	−6.00	−15.00	35.37
4	−36	−15	54	1.00	−15.00	47.09
5	−36	3	15	−6.00	3.00	26.66
6	−36	3	33	0.00	3.00	34.60
7	−36	3	54	7.00	3.00	45.13
8	−36	15	33	4.00	15.00	35.79
9	−36	15	54	11.00	15.00	45.13
10	−36	33	54	17.00	33.00	47.09
11	−15	3	15	1.00	3.00	15.10
12	−15	3	33	7.00	3.00	24.25
13	−15	3	54	14.00	3.00	35.79
14	−15	15	33	11.00	15.00	24.25
15	−15	15	54	18.00	15.00	34.60
16	−15	33	54	24.00	33.00	35.37
17	3	15	33	17.00	15.00	15.10
18	3	15	54	24.00	15.00	26.66
19	3	33	54	30.00	33.00	25.63
20	15	33	54	34.00	33.00	19.52

Summary of sample means and medians

Mean of the 20 sample means = 9
Mean of the 20 sample medians = 9
Standard deviation of the 20 sample means = 13.26
Standard deviation of the 20 sample medians = 15.88

(b) The relative frequency histograms describing the populations of sample means and medians

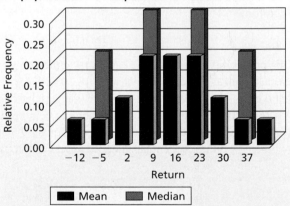

(c) The relative frequency histogram describing the population of sample standard deviations

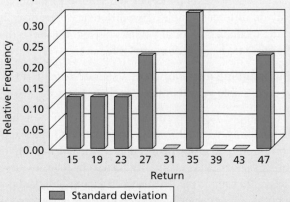

than are the 20 sample medians. Therefore, the sample mean is the preferred point estimate of the population mean. Furthermore, although the sampled population of six stock returns is not normally distributed, some general results apply to estimating the mean μ of a normally distributed population. In this situation, it can be shown that both the sample mean and the sample median are unbiased point estimates of μ. In fact, there are many unbiased point estimates of μ. However, it can be shown that the variance of the population of all possible sample means is smaller than the variance of the population of all possible values of any other unbiased point estimate of μ. For this reason, **we call the sample mean a minimum-variance unbiased point estimate of μ.** When we use the sample mean as the point estimate of μ, we are more likely to obtain a point estimate close to μ than if we used any other unbiased sample statistic as the point estimate of μ. This is one reason why we use the sample mean as the point estimate of the population mean.

Technical Note: If we randomly select a sample of size n without replacement from a finite population of size N, then it can be shown that $\sigma_{\bar{x}} = (\sigma/\sqrt{n})\sqrt{(N - n)/(N - 1)}$, where the quantity $\sqrt{(N - n)/(N - 1)}$ is called the **finite population multiplier**. If the size of the sampled population is at least 20 times the size of the sample (that is, if $N \geq 20n$), then the finite population multiplier is approximately equal to one, and $\sigma_{\bar{x}}$ approximately equals $\sigma/\sqrt{n}$. However, if the population size N is smaller than 20 times the size of the sample, then the finite population multiplier is substantially less than one, and we must include this multiplier in the calculation of $\sigma_{\bar{x}}$. For instance, in our initial stock return example on page 181 (where $N = 6$ is only three times $n = 2$), we have

$$\sigma_{\bar{x}} = \frac{\sigma}{\sqrt{n}}\sqrt{\frac{N - n}{N - 1}} = \left(\frac{17.078}{\sqrt{2}}\right)\sqrt{\frac{6 - 2}{6 - 1}} = 12.076(0.8944) = 10.8.$$

We will see how this formula can be used to make statistical inferences in Section 7.5.

Exercises for Section 6.1

CONCEPTS

6.1 Suppose that we will randomly select a sample of four measurements from a larger population of measurements. The sampling distribution of the sample mean $\bar{x}$ is the probability distribution of a population. In your own words, describe the units in this population.

6.2 Suppose that we will randomly select a sample of n measurements from a normally distributed population of measurements with mean μ and standard deviation σ. Consider the sampling distribution of $\bar{x}$ (that is, consider the population of all possible sample means).
  a. Describe the shape of the population of all possible sample means.
  b. Write formulas that express the central tendency and the variability of the population of all possible sample means. Explain what these formulas say in your own words.

6.3 Explain how the central tendency of the population of all possible sample means compares to the central tendency of the individual measurements in the population from which the sample will be taken.

6.4 Explain how the variability of the population of all possible sample means compares to the variability of the individual measurements in the population from which the sample will be taken. Assume here that the sample size is greater than 1. Intuitively explain why this is true.

6.5 What does the central limit theorem tell us about the sampling distribution of the sample mean?

6.6 In your own words, explain what is meant by an unbiased point estimate.

METHODS AND APPLICATIONS

6.7 Suppose that we will take a random sample of size n from a population with mean μ and standard deviation σ. For each of the following situations, find the mean, variance, and standard deviation of the sampling distribution of the sample mean $\bar{x}$:
  a. $\mu = 10$, $\sigma = 2$, $n = 25$.
  b. $\mu = 500$, $\sigma = 0.5$, $n = 100$.
  c. $\mu = 3$, $\sigma = 0.1$, $n = 4$.
  d. $\mu = 100$, $\sigma = 1$, $n = 1,600$.

6.8 For each situation in Exercise 6.7, find an interval that contains (approximately or exactly) 99.73 percent of all the possible sample means. In which cases must we assume that the population is normally distributed? Why?

6.9 Suppose that we will randomly select a sample of 64 measurements from a population with a mean equal to 20 and a standard deviation equal to 4.
  a. Describe the shape of the sampling distribution of the sample mean $\bar{x}$. Do we need to make any assumptions about the shape of the population? Why or why not?
  b. Find the mean and the standard deviation of the sampling distribution of the sample mean $\bar{x}$.
  c. Calculate the probability that we will obtain a sample mean greater than 21; that is, calculate $P(\bar{x} > 21)$. Hint: Find the z value corresponding to 21 by using $\mu_{\bar{x}}$ and $\sigma_{\bar{x}}$ because we wish to calculate a

probability about $\bar{x}$. Then sketch the sampling distribution and the probability.

   d. Calculate the probability that we will obtain a sample mean less than 19.385; that is, calculate $P(\bar{x} < 19.385)$.

6.10 Suppose that the percentage returns for a given year for all stocks listed on the Toronto Stock Exchange are approximately normally distributed with a mean of 12.4 percent and a standard deviation of 20.6 percent. Consider drawing a random sample of $n = 5$ stocks from the population of all stocks and calculating the mean return, $\bar{x}$, of the sampled stocks. Find the mean and the standard deviation of the sampling distribution of $\bar{x}$, and find an interval containing 95.44 percent of all possible sample mean returns.

6.11 **THE BANK CUSTOMER WAITING TIME CASE**
   ⬤ WaitTime

Recall from Exercise 1.9 on page 10 that the bank manager wants to show that the new system reduces typical customer waiting times to less than six minutes. One way to do this is to demonstrate that the mean of the population of all customer waiting times is less than 6. Letting this mean be μ, in this exercise we wish to investigate whether the sample of 100 waiting times provides evidence to support the claim that μ is less than 6.

We will begin by assuming that μ equals 6, and we will then attempt to use the sample to contradict this assumption in favour of the conclusion that μ is less than 6. Recall that the mean of the sample of 100 waiting times is $\bar{x} = 5.46$ and assume that σ, the standard deviation of the population of all customer waiting times, is known to be 2.47.

   a. Consider the population of all possible sample means obtained from random samples of 100 waiting times. What is the shape of this population of sample means? That is, what is the shape of the sampling distribution of $\bar{x}$? Why is this true?

   b. Find the mean and standard deviation of the population of all possible sample means when we assume that μ equals 6.

   c. The sample mean that we have actually observed is $\bar{x} = 5.46$. Assuming that μ equals 6, find the probability of observing a sample mean that is less than or equal to $\bar{x} = 5.46$.

   d. If μ equals 6, what percentage of all possible sample means are less than or equal to 5.46? Since we have actually observed a sample mean of $\bar{x} = 5.46$, is it more reasonable to believe that (1) μ equals 6 and we have observed one of the sample means that is less than or equal to 5.46 when μ equals 6 or (2) that we have observed a sample mean less than or equal to 5.46 because μ is less than 6? Explain. What do you conclude about whether the new system has reduced the typical customer waiting time to less than six minutes?

6.12 **THE VIDEO GAME SATISFACTION RATING CASE**
   ⬤ VideoGame

Recall (see Chapter 1, Exercise 1.8) that a customer is considered to be very satisfied with their XYZ-Box video game system if the customer's composite score on the survey is at least 42. One way to show that customers are typically very satisfied is to show that the mean of the population of all satisfaction ratings is at least 42. Letting this mean be μ, in this exercise we wish to investigate whether the sample of 65 satisfaction ratings provides evidence to support the claim that μ exceeds 42 (and, therefore, is at least 42).

We begin by assuming that μ equals 42, and we then attempt to use the sample to contradict this assumption in favour of the conclusion that μ exceeds 42. Recall that the mean of the sample of 65 satisfaction ratings is $\bar{x} = 42.95$, and assume that σ, the standard deviation of the population of all satisfaction ratings, is known to be 2.64.

   a. Consider the sampling distribution of $\bar{x}$ for random samples of 65 customer satisfaction ratings. Use the properties of this sampling distribution to find the probability of observing a sample mean greater than or equal to 42.95 when we assume that μ equals 42.

   b. If μ equals 42, what percentage of all possible sample means are greater than or equal to 42.95? Since we have actually observed a sample mean of $\bar{x} = 42.95$, is it more reasonable to believe that (1) μ equals 42 and we have observed a sample mean that is greater than or equal to 42.95 when μ equals 42 or (2) that we have observed a sample mean that is greater than or equal to 42.95 because μ is greater than 42? Explain. What do you conclude about whether customers are typically very satisfied with the XYZ-Box video game system?

6.13 In an article in the *Journal of Management*, Martocchio studied and estimated the costs of employee absences. Based on a sample of 176 blue-collar workers, Martocchio estimated that the mean amount of paid time lost during a three-month period was 1.4 days per employee with a standard deviation of 1.3 days. Martocchio also estimated that the mean amount of unpaid time lost during a three-month period was 1.0 day per employee with a standard deviation of 1.8 days.

   a. Suppose we randomly select a sample of 100 blue-collar workers. Based on Martocchio's estimates,

     (1) What is the probability that the average amount of paid time lost during a three-month period for the 100 blue-collar workers will exceed 1.5 days?

     (2) What is the probability that the average amount of unpaid time lost during a three-month period for the 100 blue-collar workers will exceed 1.5 days?

   b. Suppose we randomly select a sample of 100 blue-collar workers, and suppose the sample mean amount of unpaid time lost during a three-month period actually exceeds 1.5 days. Would it be reasonable to conclude that the mean amount of unpaid time lost has increased above the previously estimated 1.0 days? Explain.

6.14 When a pizza restaurant's delivery process is operating effectively, pizzas are delivered in an average of 45 minutes with a standard deviation of 6 minutes. To monitor its delivery process, the restaurant randomly selects five pizzas each night and records their delivery times.

   a. Assume that the population of all delivery times on a given evening is normally distributed with a mean of $\mu = 45$ minutes and a standard deviation of $\sigma = 6$ minutes. (That is, we assume that the delivery process is operating effectively.)

(1) Describe the shape of the population of all possible sample means. How do you know what the shape is?

(2) Find the mean of the population of all possible sample means.

(3) Find the standard deviation of the population of all possible sample means.

(4) Calculate an interval containing 99.73 percent of all possible sample means.

b. Suppose that the mean of the five sampled delivery times on a particular evening is $\bar{x} = 55$ minutes. Using the interval that you calculated in a(4), what would you conclude about whether the restaurant's delivery process is operating effectively? Why?

6.2 The Sampling Distribution of the Sample Proportion

A food-processing company markets a soft cheese spread that is sold in a plastic container with an "easy pour" spout. Although this spout works extremely well and is popular with consumers, it is expensive to produce. Because of the spout's high cost, the company has developed a new, less expensive spout. While the new, cheaper spout may alienate some purchasers, a company study shows that its introduction will increase profits if less than 10 percent of the cheese spread's current purchasers are lost. That is, if we let p be the true proportion of all current purchasers who would stop buying the cheese spread if the new spout were used, profits will increase as long as p is less than 0.10.

Suppose that (after trying the new spout) 63 of 1,000 randomly selected purchasers say that they would stop buying the cheese spread if the new spout were used. The point estimate of the population proportion p is the sample proportion $\hat{p} = 63/1,000 = 0.063$. This sample proportion says that we estimate that 6.3 percent of all current purchasers would stop buying the cheese spread if the new spout were used. Since $\hat{p}$ equals 0.063, we have some evidence that the population proportion p is less than 0.10. In order to determine the strength of this evidence, we need to consider the sampling distribution of $\hat{p}$. In general, assume that we will randomly select a sample of n units from a population, and assume that a proportion p of all the units in the population fall into a particular category (for instance, the category of consumers who would stop buying the cheese spread). Before we actually select the sample, there are many different samples of n units that we might potentially obtain. The number of units that fall into the category in question will vary from sample to sample, so the sample proportion of units falling into the category will also vary from sample to sample. Therefore, we might potentially obtain many different sample proportions. It follows that, before we draw the sample, the sample proportion $\hat{p}$ is a random variable. In the following box, we give the properties of the probability distribution of this random variable, which is called **the sampling distribution of the sample proportion $\hat{p}$**:

The Sampling Distribution of the Sample Proportion $\hat{p}$

The population of all possible sample proportions

1 Has an approximately normal distribution if the sample size n is large.

2 Has mean $\mu_{\hat{p}} = p$.

3 Has variance $\sigma_{\hat{p}}^2 = \dfrac{p(1 - p)}{n}$ and standard deviation $\sigma_{\hat{p}} = \sqrt{\dfrac{p(1 - p)}{n}}$.

Property 1 in the box says that, if n is large, the population of all possible sample proportions has an approximately normal distribution. Here it can be shown that **n should be considered large if both np and $n(1 - p)$ are at least 5.**[3] Property 2, which says that $\mu_{\hat{p}} = p$, is valid for any sample size and tells us that $\hat{p}$ is an unbiased estimate of p. That is, although the sample proportion $\hat{p}$ that we calculate probably does not equal p, the average of all the different sample proportions that we could have calculated (from all the different possible samples) is equal to p. Property 3, which says that

$$\sigma_{\hat{p}}^2 = \frac{p(1 - p)}{n} \quad \text{and} \quad \sigma_{\hat{p}} = \sqrt{\frac{p(1 - p)}{n}},$$

[3]Some statisticians suggest using the more conservative rule that both np and $n(1 - p)$ must be at least 10.

is exactly correct if the sampled population is infinite and is approximately correct if the sampled population is finite and much larger than (say, at least 20 times as large as) the sample size. Property 3 tells us that the variance and the standard deviation of the population of all possible sample proportions decrease as the sample size increases. That is, the larger n is, the more closely clustered are all the different sample proportions around the true population proportion.

Example 6.4 The Cheese Spread Case

In the cheese spread situation, the food-processing company must decide whether p, the proportion of all current purchasers who would stop buying the cheese spread if the new spout were used, is less than 0.10. In order to do this, we assume that p equals 0.10. Then we use the sample information to weigh the evidence against this assumption and in favour of the conclusion that p is less than 0.10. Remember that when 1,000 purchasers of the cheese spread are randomly selected, 63 of these purchasers say they would stop buying the cheese spread if the new spout were used. Because the sample proportion $\hat{p} = 0.063$ is less than 0.10, we have some evidence contradicting the assumption that p equals 0.10. To evaluate the strength of this evidence, we calculate the probability of observing a sample proportion that is less than or equal to 0.063 if, in fact, p equals 0.10.

If p equals 0.10, we can assume that the sampling distribution of $\hat{p}$ is approximately a normal distribution because both $np = 1,000(0.10) = 100$ and $n(1 - p) = 1,000(1 - 0.10) = 900$ are at least 5. Furthermore, the mean and standard deviation of the sampling distribution of $\hat{p}$ are $\mu_{\hat{p}} = p = 0.10$ and

$$\sigma_{\hat{p}} = \sqrt{\frac{p(1 - p)}{n}} = \sqrt{\frac{(0.10)(0.90)}{1,000}} = 0.0094868.$$

Therefore,

$$P(\hat{p} \leq 0.063 \text{ if } p = 0.10) = P\left(z \leq \frac{0.063 - \mu_{\hat{p}}}{\sigma_{\hat{p}}}\right) = P\left(z \leq \frac{0.063 - 0.10}{0.0094868}\right)$$

$$= P(z \leq -3.90).$$

Because the tail area under the normal curve to the left of -3.90 is smaller than the tail area to the left of -3.09, this probability is less than 0.001. It says that, if p equals 0.10, fewer than 1 in 1000 of all possible sample proportions are at least as small as the sample proportion $\hat{p} = 0.063$ that we have actually observed. If we are to believe that p equals 0.10, then we must believe that we have observed a sample proportion that can be described as less than a 1 in 1000 chance. Therefore, we have extremely strong evidence that p does not equal 0.10 and is, in fact, less than 0.10. That is, we conclude that we have extremely strong evidence that less than 10 percent of current purchasers would stop buying the cheese spread if the new spout were used. Therefore, we have extremely strong evidence that introducing the new spout will be profitable.

Exercises for Section 6.2

CONCEPTS

6.15 What population is described by the sampling distribution of $\hat{p}$?

6.16 Suppose that we will randomly select a sample of n units from a population and that we will compute the sample proportion $\hat{p}$ of these units that fall into a category of interest. Consider the sampling distribution of $\hat{p}$.

    a. If the sample size n is large, the sampling distribution of $\hat{p}$ is approximately a normal distribution.

    What condition must be satisfied to guarantee that n is large enough to say that $\hat{p}$ is normally distributed?

    b. Write formulas that express the central tendency and variability of the population of all possible sample proportions. Explain what each of these formulas means in your own words.

6.17 Describe the effect of increasing the sample size on the population of all possible sample proportions.

METHODS AND APPLICATIONS

6.18 In each of the following cases, determine whether the sample size n is large enough to say that the sampling distribution of $\hat{p}$ is a normal distribution.

    a. $p = 0.4$, $n = 100$.   **d.** $p = 0.8$, $n = 400$.

    b. $p = 0.1$, $n = 10$.   **e.** $p = 0.98$, $n = 1{,}000$.

    c. $p = 0.1$, $n = 50$.   **f.** $p = 0.99$, $n = 400$.

6.19 In each of the following cases, find the mean, variance, and standard deviation of the sampling distribution of the sample proportion $\hat{p}$.

    a. $p = 0.5$, $n = 250$.   **c.** $p = 0.8$, $n = 400$.

    b. $p = 0.1$, $n = 100$.   **d.** $p = 0.98$, $n = 1{,}000$.

6.20 For each situation in Exercise 6.19, find an interval that contains approximately 95.44 percent of all the possible sample proportions.

6.21 Suppose that we will randomly select a sample of $n = 100$ units from a population and that we will compute the sample proportion $\hat{p}$ of these units that fall into a category of interest. Suppose the true population proportion p equals 0.9.

    a. Describe the shape of the sampling distribution of $\hat{p}$. Why can we validly describe the shape?

    b. Find the mean and the standard deviation of the sampling distribution of $\hat{p}$.

    c. Calculate the following probabilities about the sample proportion $\hat{p}$. In each case, sketch the sampling distribution and the probability.

        (1) $P(\hat{p} \geq 0.96)$.

        (2) $P(0.855 \leq \hat{p} \leq 0.945)$.

        (3) $P(\hat{p} \leq 0.915)$.

6.22 In the July 29, 2001, issue of *The Journal News* (Hamilton, Ohio), Lynn Elber of the Associated Press reported on a study conducted by the Kaiser Family Foundation regarding parents' use of television set V-chips for controlling their children's TV viewing. The study asked parents who own TVs equipped with V-chips whether they use the devices to block programs with objectionable content.

    a. Suppose that we wish to use the study results to justify the claim that less than 20 percent of parents who own TV sets with V-chips use the devices. The study actually found that 17 percent of the parents polled used their V-chips.[4] If the poll surveyed 1,000 parents, and if we assume that 20 percent of parents who own V-chips actually use the devices (that is, $p = 0.2$), calculate the probability of observing a sample proportion of 0.17 or less. That is, calculate $P(\hat{p} \leq 0.17)$.

    b. Based on the probability you computed in part a, would you conclude that less than 20 percent of parents who own TV sets equipped with V-chips actually use the devices? Explain.

6.23 On May 16, 2007, Ipsos Reid released the results of a poll concerning Canadian attitudes toward spring cleaning. The poll results were based on online interviews of a randomly selected sample of 1,317 adult Canadians from May 1 to 4, 2007.

    a. The poll's results state that 39 percent of Canadians would rather clean out their basements or their garages than look at their taxes or finances.[5] Suppose we want to use these results to test a claim. Assume that we believe that one third of Canadian adults would rather clean out their basements or garages than look at their taxes or finances (that is, $p = 1/3$). Calculate the probability of observing a sample proportion of 0.39 or higher. That is, calculate $P(\hat{P} \geq 0.39)$.

    b. Based on the probability you calculated in part a, does it seem very likely that more than one third of Canadians would rather clean out their basements or garages than look at their taxes or finances?

6.24 A bank published a report on improvements in customer satisfaction and loyalty. A key measure of customer satisfaction is the response (on a scale from 1 to 10) to the question, "Considering all the business you do with the bank, what is your overall satisfaction?" Here a response of 9 or 10 represents "customer delight."

    a. Historically, the percentage of bank customers expressing customer delight has been 48 percent. Suppose that we wish to use the results of a survey of 350 bank customers to justify the claim that more than 48 percent of all current bank customers would express customer delight. The survey finds that 189 of 350 randomly selected bank customers express customer delight. If we assume that the proportion of customer delight is $p = 0.48$, calculate the probability of observing a sample proportion greater than or equal to $189/350 = 0.54$. That is, calculate $P(\hat{p} \geq 0.54)$.

    b. Based on the probability you computed in part a, would you conclude that more than 48 percent of current bank customers express customer delight? Explain.

6.25 Again consider the survey of 350 bank customers discussed in Exercise 6.24.

    a. Assume that 48 percent of bank customers would currently express customer delight. That is, assume $p = 0.48$.

        (1) Find the probability that the sample proportion obtained from the sample of 350 customers would be within three percentage points of the population proportion. That is, find $P(0.45 \leq \hat{p} \leq 0.51)$.

        (2) Find the probability that the sample proportion obtained from the sample of 350 customers would be within six percentage points of the population proportion. That is, find $P(0.42 \leq \hat{p} \leq 0.54)$.

    b. Based on your results of part a, would it be reasonable to state that the survey's "margin of error" is ± 3 percentage points? ± 6 percentage points? Explain.

6.26 THE MARKETING ETHICS CASE: CONFLICT OF INTEREST

    a. Consider the Marketing Ethics Case from Chapter 2 and remember that 111 of 205 randomly selected marketing researchers disapproved of the actions taken in the conflict of interest scenario. Suppose that we wish to justify the claim that a majority (more than 50 percent) of all marketing researchers

---

[4]Source: "Study: Parents make scant use of TV V-chip," by L. Elber, *The Journal News* (Hamilton, Ohio), July 29, 2001, p. c5.

[5]Source: World Wide Web, http://www.ipsos-na.com/news/ pressrelease.cfm?id=3492, "Canadians would rather clean the garage than do spring cleaning!" May 16, 2007.

disapprove of these actions. If we assume that p, the proportion of all marketing researchers who disapprove of the actions taken, equals 0.5, calculate a probability that expresses the amount of doubt cast by the sample result on the assumption that p equals 0.5.

b. Based on the probability you computed in part a, would you conclude that p is really greater than 0.5? That is, would you conclude that a majority of marketing researchers disapprove of the actions taken in the conflict of interest scenario? Explain.

6.27 A special advertising section in the July 20, 1998, issue of *Fortune* magazine discusses "outsourcing." According to the article, outsourcing is "the assignment of critical, but noncore, business functions to outside specialists." This allows a company to immediately bring operations up to best-in-world standards while avoiding huge capital investments. The article includes the results of a poll of business executives addressing the benefits of outsourcing.

a. Suppose we wish to use the poll's results to justify the claim that less than 26 percent of business executives feel that the benefits of outsourcing are either "less or much less than expected." The poll actually found that 15 percent of the respondents felt that the benefits of outsourcing were either "less or much less than expected."[6] If 1,000 randomly selected business executives were polled, and if we assume

that 20 percent of all business executives feel that the benefits of outsourcing are either less or much less than expected (that is, $p = 0.20$), calculate the probability of observing a sample proportion of 0.15 or less. That is, calculate $P(\hat{p} \leq 0.15)$.

b. Based on the probability you computed in part a, would you conclude that less than 20 percent of business executives feel that the benefits of outsourcing are either "less or much less than expected"? Explain.

6.28 On April 16, 2007, Ipsos Reid released the results of a poll concerning Canadian teens' attitudes toward the environment. The poll results were based on an online poll between March 22 and April 22 via an online sample of 1,996 Canadian teens aged 13 to 19.

a. The poll's results state that 19 percent of Canadian teens consider themselves to be "green fiends"— people who recycle everything, conserve energy, and encourage others to do the same.[7] Assume that we believe that one sixth of Canadian teens fall into this category (that is, $p = 1/6$). Calculate the probability of observing a sample proportion of 0.19 or higher. That is, calculate $P(\hat{P} \geq 0.19)$.

b. Based on the probability you calculated in part a, does it seem very likely that more than one sixth of Canadian teens recycle everything, conserve energy, and encourage others to do so? Explain.

---

[6]Source: "Outsourcing 98," by M. R. Ozanne and M. F. Corbette, *Fortune* (July 20, 1998), p. 510.
[7]Source: World Wide Web, http://www.ipsos-na.com/news/pressrelease.cfm?id=3441, "Teens talk the talk but don't walk the walk," April 16, 2007.

CHAPTER SUMMARY

A **sampling distribution** is the probability distribution that describes the population of all possible values of a sample statistic. In this chapter, we studied the properties of two important sampling distributions—the sampling distribution of the sample mean, $\bar{x}$, and the sampling distribution of the sample proportion, $\hat{p}$.

Because different samples that can be randomly selected from a population give different sample means, there is a population of sample means corresponding to a particular sample size. The probability distribution describing the population of all possible sample means is called the **sampling distribution of the sample mean, $\bar{x}$.** We studied the properties of this sampling distribution when the sampled population is and is not normally distributed. We found that, when the sampled population has a normal distribution, then the sampling distribution of the sample mean is a normal distribution. Furthermore, the **central limit theorem** tells us that, if the sampled population is not normally distributed, then the sampling distribution of the sample mean is approximately a normal distribution when the sample size is large

(at least 30). We also saw that the mean of the sampling distribution of $\bar{x}$ always equals the mean of the sampled population, and we presented formulas for the variance and the standard deviation of this sampling distribution. Finally, we explained that the sample mean is a **minimum-variance unbiased point estimate** of the mean of a normally distributed population.

We also studied the properties of the **sampling distribution of the sample proportion $\hat{p}$**. We found that, if the sample size is large, then this sampling distribution is approximately a normal distribution, and we gave a rule for determining whether the sample size is large. We found that the mean of the sampling distribution of $\hat{p}$ is the population proportion p, and we gave formulas for the variance and the standard deviation of this sampling distribution.

Finally, we demonstrated that knowing the properties of sampling distributions can help us make statistical inferences about population parameters. In fact, we will see that the properties of various sampling distributions provide the foundation for most of the techniques to be discussed in future chapters.

GLOSSARY OF TERMS

central limit theorem: A theorem telling us that when the sample size n is sufficiently large, then the population of all possible sample means is approximately normally distributed no matter what probability distribution describes the sampled population. (page 187)
minimum-variance unbiased point estimate: An unbiased point estimate of a population parameter with a variance that is smaller than the variance of any other unbiased point estimate of the parameter. (page 191)

sampling distribution of a sample statistic: The probability distribution of the population of all possible values of the sample statistic. (page 189)
sampling distribution of the sample mean $\bar{x}$: The probability distribution of the population of all possible sample means obtained from samples of a particular size n. (page 181)
    when a population is normally distributed (page 184)
    central limit theorem (page 187)

sampling distribution of the sample proportion $\hat{p}$: The probability distribution of the population of all possible sample proportions obtained from samples of a particular size n. (page 193)

unbiased point estimate: A sample statistic is an unbiased point estimate of a population parameter if the mean of the population of all possible values of the sample statistic equals the population parameter. (page 190)

IMPORTANT FORMULAS

The sampling distribution of the sample mean: pages 184 and 187

The sampling distribution of the sample proportion: page 193

SUPPLEMENTARY EXERCISES

6.29 A chain of audio/video equipment discount stores employs 36 salespeople. Daily dollar sales for individual sellers employed by the chain have a mound-shaped distribution with a mean of $2,000 and a standard deviation of $300.

  a. Suppose that the chain's management decides to implement an incentive program that awards a daily bonus to any salesperson who achieves daily sales over $2,150. Calculate the probability that an individual salesperson will earn the bonus on any particular day.

  b. Suppose that (as an alternative) the chain's management decides to award a daily bonus to the entire sales force if all 36 achieve an **average** daily sales figure that exceeds $2,150. Calculate the probability that average daily sales for the entire sales force will exceed $2,150 on any particular day.

  c. Intuitively, do you think it would be more difficult for an individual salesperson to achieve a daily sales figure that exceeds $2,150 or for the entire sales force of 36 to achieve an **average** sales figure that exceeds $2,150? Are the probabilities you computed in parts a and b consistent with your intuition? Explain.

  d. Sketch the distribution of individual daily sales figures and the probability you computed in part a. Place values that are three standard deviations above and below the mean in the tails of the distribution. Also sketch the distribution of all possible sample means (the sampling distribution of $\bar{x}$) and the probability you computed in part b. Place values that are three standard deviations of $\bar{x}$ above and below the mean in the tails of the sampling distribution. Compare the sketches. Do you see why the results in parts a and b turned out the way they did? Explain why.

6.30 In the book *Essentials of Marketing Research*, Dillon, Madden, and Firtle discuss an advertising study for a new suntan lotion. In this study, each respondent is assigned to a group whose members will evaluate an ad for the new lotion. Each respondent is asked to rate the ad on six items:

  high quality/low quality   persuasive/nonpersuasive

  informative/uninformative   artful/artless

  good/bad   refined/vulgar

The rating for each item is made using a seven-point scale, where, for example, a rating of 1 on the informative/uninformative dimension indicates that the ad is extremely uninformative, and a rating of 7 says that the ad is extremely informative.

Rating	Probability
1	0
2	0.05
3	0.05
4	0.10
5	0.20
6	0.40
7	0.20

Suppose experience shows that a "very informative" ad is typically rated by a large group of respondents according to the probability distribution given in the table above.

  a. Calculate the mean, variance, and standard deviation of the ratings for a typical "very informative" ad.

  b. Suppose that a group of 36 randomly selected respondents rates a typical "very informative" ad, and consider the sample mean $\bar{x}$ of the 36 ratings. Find the mean and standard deviation of the population of all possible sample means. What is the shape of the population of all possible sample means? How do you know?

  c. Draw a sketch of the sampling distribution of the sample mean $\bar{x}$ and compare it to a sketch of the distribution of individual ratings.

  d. Suppose that a randomly selected group of 36 respondents rates a typical "very informative" ad. Find the probability that the respondents give the ad a sample mean rating less than 5.

  e. Suppose that 36 randomly selected respondents are exposed to a new ad in order to determine whether the ad is "very informative," and suppose that the sample mean rating is less than 5. In light of the probability you computed in part d, what would you conclude about whether the new ad is "very informative"? Explain.

6.31 On December 18, 2006, Ipsos Reid released the results of a poll concerning the top priorities for Canadians when it comes to planning for retirement, financially speaking. The poll results were based on a representative randomly selected sample of 1,201 adult Canadians interviewed by telephone from October 12 to 26, 2006.

  a. The poll's results state that 61 percent of Canadians feel that home ownership is the top priority when it comes to planning for retirement, financially speaking.[8] Suppose we want to use these results to

---

[8] Source: World Wide Web, http://www.ipsos-na.com/news/ pressrelease.cfm?id=3309, "RBC RRSP poll shows retirement planning can pay off," December 18, 2006.

test a claim. Assume that we believe that two thirds of Canadian adults believe this to be true (that is, $p = 2/3$). Calculate the probability of observing a sample proportion of 0.61 or lower. That is, calculate $P(\hat{p} \leq 0.61)$.

b. Based on the probability you calculated in part a, does it seem very likely that less than two thirds of Canadian adults feel that home ownership is the top priority when it comes to planning for retirement, financially speaking? Explain.

6.32 Suppose that we randomly select a sample of size 100.

a. What is the probability of obtaining a sample mean greater than 50.2 when the sampled population has mean 50 and standard deviation 1? Must we assume that the population is normally distributed in order to answer this question? Why or why not?

b. Rework part a of this exercise with a sample size of 225. Compare your answer here with that of part a. Why are they different?

6.33 Each day, a manufacturing plant receives a large shipment of drums of Chemical ZX-900. These drums are supposed to have a mean fill of 200 L, while the fills have a standard deviation known to be 100 L.

a. Suppose that the mean fill for the shipment is actually 200 L. If we draw a random sample of 100 drums from the shipment, what is the probability that the average fill for the 100 drums is between 188 L and 189 L?

b. The plant manager is worried that the drums of Chemical ZX-900 are underfilled. Because of this, the manager decides to draw a sample of 100 drums from each daily shipment and will reject the shipment (send it back to the supplier) if the average fill for the 100 drums is less than 189 L. Suppose that a shipment that actually has a mean fill of 200 L is received. What is the probability that this shipment will be rejected and sent back to the supplier?

6.34 In its October 12, 1992, issue, *The Milwaukee Journal* published the results of an Ogilvy, Adams, and Rinehart poll of 1,250 American investors that was conducted in early October 1992. The poll investigated the stock market's appeal to investors five years after the market suffered its biggest one-day decline to that point (in 1987).

Assume that 50 percent of all American investors in 1992 found the stock market less attractive than it was in 1987 (that is, $p = 0.5$).

a. Find the probability that the sample proportion obtained from the sample of 1,250 investors would be

(1) Within 4 percentage points of the population proportion—that is, find $P(0.46 \leq \hat{p} \leq 0.54)$.

(2) Within 2 percentage points of the population proportion.

(3) Within 1 percentage point of the population proportion.

b. Based on these probabilities, would it be reasonable to claim a ± 2 percentage point margin of error? a ± 1 percentage point margin of error? Explain.

6.35 Again consider the stock market poll discussed in Exercise 6.34.

a. Suppose we wish to use the poll's results to justify the claim that less than 50 percent of American in-

vestors in 1992 found the stock market less attractive than in 1987. The poll actually found that 41 percent of the respondents said the stock market was less attractive than in 1987. If we assume that $p = 0.5$, calculate the probability of observing a sample proportion of 0.41 or less. That is, calculate $P(\hat{p} \leq 0.41)$.

b. Based on the probability you computed in part a, would you conclude that less than 50 percent of American investors in 1992 found the stock market to be less attractive than in 1987? Explain.

6.36 Canco Heating and Cooling, Inc., advertises that any customer buying an air conditioner during the first 16 days of July will receive a 25 percent discount if the average high temperature for this 16-day period is more than five degrees above normal.

a. If daily high temperatures in July are normally distributed with a mean of 29°C and a standard deviation of 13°C, what is the probability that Canco Heating and Cooling will have to give its customers the 25 percent discount?

b. Based on the probability you computed in part a, do you think that Canco's promotion is ethical? Write a paragraph justifying your opinion.

6.37 **THE TRASH BAG CASE**

Recall that the trash bag manufacturer has concluded that its new 130-L bag will be the strongest such bag on the market if its mean breaking strength is at least 23 kg. In order to provide statistical evidence that the mean breaking strength of the new bag is at least 23 kg, the manufacturer randomly selects a sample of n bags and calculates the mean $\bar{x}$ of the breaking strengths of these bags. If the sample mean so obtained is at least 23 kg, this provides some evidence that the mean breaking strength of all new bags is at least 23 kg.

Suppose that (unknown to the manufacturer) the breaking strengths of the new 130-L bag are normally distributed with a mean of $\mu = 22.9$ kg and a standard deviation of $\sigma = 0.7$ kg.

a. Find an interval containing 95.44 percent of all possible sample means if the sample size employed is $n = 5$.

b. Find an interval containing 95.44 percent of all possible sample means if the sample size employed is $n = 40$.

c. If the trash bag manufacturer hopes to obtain a sample mean that is at least 23 kg (so that it can provide evidence that the population mean breaking strength of the new bags is at least 23 kg), which sample size ($n = 5$ or $n = 40$) would be best? Explain why.

6.38 A computer supply house receives a large shipment of CD-ROMs each week. Past experience has shown that the number of flaws per CD can be described by the following probability distribution:

Number of Flaws per CD	Probability
0	0.65
1	0.2
2	0.1
3	0.05

a. Calculate the mean and standard deviation of the number of flaws per CD.

b. Suppose that we randomly select a sample of 100 CDs. Describe the shape of the sampling distribution of the sample mean $\bar{x}$. Then compute the mean and the standard deviation of the sampling distribution of $\bar{x}$.

c. Sketch the sampling distribution of the sample mean $\bar{x}$ and compare it to the distribution describing the number of flaws on a single CD.

d. The supply house's managers are worried that the CDs being received have an excessive number of flaws. Because of this, a random sample of 100 disks is drawn from each shipment and the shipment is rejected (sent back to the supplier) if the average number of flaws per disk for the 100 sample disks is greater than 0.75. Suppose that the mean number of flaws per disk for this week's entire shipment is actually 0.55. What is the probability that this shipment will be rejected and sent back to the supplier?

6.39 Most Canadian parents would consider themselves to be positive role models for their children when it comes to finances. However, it appears as though parents need to spend more time talking about the management of finances with their children. On August 31, 2006, Ipsos Reid released the results of a poll concerning this topic. The poll results were based on an online survey of 1338 Canadian households from August 8 to 14, 2006. The results state that 46 percent of Canadian teenagers would like to learn more about budgeting, while only 13 percent say that their parents have planned a back-to-school budget with them.[9]

a. Suppose we want to use these results to test a claim. Assume that we believe that half of Canadian teens would like to learn more about budgeting (that is, $p = 0.5$). Calculate the probability of observing a sample proportion of 0.46 or lower. That is, calculate $P(\hat{p} \le 0.46)$.

b. Based on the probability you calculated in part a, does it seem very likely that less than half of Canadian teens would like to learn more about budgeting? Explain.

6.40 On January 7, 2000, the Gallup Organization released the results of a poll comparing lifestyles of today with those of yesteryear. The poll results were based on telephone interviews with a randomly selected national sample of 1,031 adults, 18 years and older, conducted

December 20 to 21, 1999. One question asked if the respondent had vacationed for six days or longer within the last 12 months.

a. Suppose that we will attempt to use the poll's results to justify the claim that more than 40 percent of U.S. adults have vacationed for six days or longer within the last 12 months. The poll actually found that 42 percent of the respondents had done so.[10] If we assume that 40 percent of U.S. adults have vacationed for six days or longer within the last 12 months (that is, $p = 0.4$), calculate the probability of observing a sample proportion of 0.42 or more; that is, calculate $P(\hat{p} \ge 0.42)$.

b. Based on the probability you computed in part a, would you conclude that more than 40 percent of U.S. adults have vacationed for six days or longer within the last 12 months? Explain.

6.41 **THE INTERNATIONAL BUSINESS TRAVEL EXPENSE CASE**

Suppose that a large international corporation wants to assess whether the mean, μ, of all one-day travel expenses in Moscow exceeds $500. Recall that the mean of a random sample of 35 one-day travel expenses is $\bar{x} = \$538$ (Chapter 2, page 83), and assume that σ is known to equal $40.

a. Assuming that μ equals $500 and the sample size is 35, what is the probability of observing a sample mean that is greater than or equal to $538?

b. Based on your answer in part a, do you think that the mean of all one-day travel expenses in Moscow exceeds $500? Explain.

6.42 **THE U.K. INSURANCE CASE**

Suppose that we wish to assess whether more than 60 percent of all U.K. households spent on life insurance in 1993. That is, we wish to assess whether the proportion, p, of all U.K. households that spent on life insurance in 1993 exceeds 0.60. Assume here that the U.K. insurance survey is based on 1,000 randomly selected households and that 640 of these households spent on life insurance in 1993.

a. Assuming that p equals 0.60 and the sample size is 1,000, what is the probability of observing a sample proportion that is at least 0.64?

b. Based on your answer in part a, do you think more than 60 percent of all U.K. households spent on life insurance in 1993? Explain.

6.43 **INTERNET EXERCISE**

The best way to observe, first-hand, the concepts of sampling distributions is to conduct sampling experiments with real data. However, sampling experiments can be prohibitively time-consuming and tedious. An excellent alternative is to conduct computer-assisted sampling experiments or simulations. *Visual Statistics* by Doane, Mathieson, and Tracy (Irwin/McGraw-Hill) includes a simulation module to illustrate sampling distributions and the central limit theorem. In this exercise, we will download and install the central limit theorem demonstration module from *Visual Statistics* and use the software to demonstrate the central limit theorem.

From the Irwin/McGraw-Hill Business Statistics Centre (http://www.mhhe.com/business/opsci/bstat/), select in turn—"Visual Statistics and Other Data Visualization Tools" : "Visual Statistics by Doane" : "Free Stuff"—and download both the CLT module and the Worktext. When the download is complete, install the CLT module by double-clicking the installation file (vs_setup.exe). Study the overview and orientation sections of the work text and work through the first four learning exercises on the Width of Car Hood example.

[9]Source: World Wide Web, http://www.ipsos-na.com/news/pressrelease.cfm?id=3173, "Canadian parents consider themselves positive financial role models for their children," August 31, 2006.

[10]Source: World Wide Web, http://www.gallup.com/poll/releases/, The Gallup Organization, January 4, 2000.

CHAPTER **7**

Confidence Intervals

LEARNING OBJECTIVES

After reading this chapter, you should be able to

- understand the concept of a confidence interval
- calculate a confidence interval for a population mean both when the population standard deviation (σ) is known and when it is not known
- explain when a z value should be used and when a t value should be used
- define what is meant by a *margin of error*
- explain how a confidence interval is constructed for a finite population
- define what is meant by *sampling with replacement*
- compare and contrast a confidence interval with a tolerance interval

CHAPTER OUTLINE

7.1 z-Based Confidence Intervals for a Population Mean: σ Known

7.2 t-Based Confidence Intervals for a Population Mean: σ Unknown

7.3 Sample Size Determination

7.4 Confidence Intervals for a Population Proportion

7.5 Confidence Intervals for Parameters of Finite Populations (Optional)

7.6 A Comparison of Confidence Intervals and Tolerance Intervals (Optional)

In Chapter 6, we discussed the idea of sampling from a population in order to make inferences about that population. We used point estimates to estimate these population parameters. We learned in Chapter 6 that in the long run the expected value of these point estimates would equal the population parameter of interest. This illustrated the concept of an unbiased estimator. These individual estimates on their own are not very useful for making inferences. Instead, we will construct intervals using these point estimates. These intervals will be used to make inferences about the underlying population of interest. We will use the statistical theory learned in Chapter 6 to learn how to construct these intervals.

As an election draws near, you are very likely to hear on your TV or radio or read in the newspaper some results from a poll. These polls are excellent examples of the

concepts discussed in Chapter 6. We are sampling from the population in order to find out information about that population. We know that these polls are never completely accurate. We would have to speak to the entire population in order to achieve greater accuracy, and even then, there would be no guarantees. People change their minds all the time, and the data collector and data entry person could make mistakes quite easily with so much information to sift through. When the results from these polls are announced, you usually hear or read something like, "This poll is said to be accurate to within plus or minus 3 percentage points, 19 times out of 20." You may have ignored that part of the poll, but that is statistics at work. By the end of the chapter, you should be able to understand exactly what that sentence means.

In the **Loonie Case**, we use a confidence interval to provide strong evidence that the mean coin mass exceeds the required 7 g.

In the **Payment Time Case**, we use a confidence interval to more completely assess the reduction in mean payment time that was achieved by the new billing system.

In the **Cheese Spread Case**, we use a confidence interval to provide strong evidence that less than 10 percent of all current purchasers will stop buying the cheese spread if the new spout is used and, therefore, that it is reasonable to use the new spout.

Sections 7.1 through 7.4 present confidence intervals for population means and proportions. These intervals are appropriate when the sampled population is either infinite or finite and **much larger** than (say, at least 20 times as large as) the size of the sample. The appropriate procedures to use when the population is not large compared to the sample are explained in optional Section 7.5. Finally, optional Section 7.6 compares confidence intervals and tolerance intervals.

7.1 *z*-Based Confidence Intervals for a Population Mean: σ Known

An example of calculating and interpreting a confidence interval for μ We have seen that we use the sample mean as the point estimate of the population mean. A **confidence interval** for the population mean is an interval constructed around the sample mean so that we are reasonably sure, or confident, that this interval contains the population mean. For example, suppose in the loonie case we wish to calculate a confidence interval for the mean μ of the population of all Canadian loonies produced in 1989. To do this, we use the random sample of $n = 200$ masses given in Table 1.7 (page 15). Before using this sample, consider calculating a confidence interval for μ using a smaller sample of $n = 5$ coins. We will take three separate samples, each of size $n = 5$, to illustrate the concept of a confidence interval. For each sample, we will calculate the sample mean $\bar{x}$. Recall from Chapter 6 that the distribution of coin masses was approximately normal with mean $\mu = 7$ g. We also stated that we knew that $\sigma = 0.06$ g. It followed that the sampling distribution of $\bar{x}$ was also approximately normal with mean $\mu_{\bar{x}} = \mu$ and standard deviation $\sigma_{\bar{x}} = \sigma / \sqrt{n}$. To obtain a confidence interval for μ, we use $\bar{x}$ and $\sigma_{\bar{x}}$ to calculate the interval using the following formula:

$$[\bar{x} \pm 2\sigma_{\bar{x}}] = \left[\bar{x} \pm 2\frac{\sigma}{\sqrt{n}} \right]$$

$$= \left[\bar{x} - 2\frac{\sigma}{\sqrt{5}}, \bar{x} + 2\frac{\sigma}{\sqrt{5}} \right].$$

Note: This formula will make more sense later in the chapter when we discuss its origin in more detail. For now, we will use the formula to construct confidence intervals. Recall that we said earlier that we knew the true population proportion, $\sigma = 0.06$ g. This is unrealistic, but assume that we know this value for now. We will not usually know the value of σ. Later on in this chapter, we will see that we can calculate a confidence interval without knowing σ. Assuming, for now, that $\sigma = 0.06$ g, we will calculate the interval

$$\left[\bar{x} \pm 2\frac{0.06}{\sqrt{5}} \right] = [\bar{x} \pm 0.0537].$$

It is easy to see that each confidence interval of size $n = 5$ that we construct will depend on the value of $\bar{x}$. Each confidence interval will be unique, because each $\bar{x}$ we obtain will be different. This relates to the fact that we view the sample mean $\bar{x}$ as a random variable. The sample mean varies from sample to sample. Some of the confidence intervals will then contain the value of μ, and some will not. In our case, as long as the sample mean is within 0.0537 of the value of μ, then the interval will contain μ. Suppose for now that the true value of μ (which is also unknown) is $\mu = 7$ g. We then see in Table 7.1 that all three intervals contain this true value of μ. We will now discuss the interpretation of a confidence interval.

In the formula above, we see that the interval is given by $[\bar{x} \pm 2(0.06/\sqrt{5})]$ or $[\bar{x} \pm 2\sigma_{\bar{x}}]$ in general. Where does the 2 come from? We are making use of the **empirical rule**. This will all make sense a little later. To try to understand confidence intervals in general, consider the following:

1 The empirical rule for a normally distributed population implies that the probability is 0.9544 that $\bar{x}$ will be within plus or minus

TABLE **7.1**   The Sample Mean $\bar{x}$ and the Interval [$\bar{x} \pm 0.0537$] Given by Each of Three Samples

Sample	Sample	Sample
$x_1 = 7.0654$	$x_1 = 7.0467$	$x_1 = 7.0974$
$x_2 = 7.0018$	$x_2 = 7.0519$	$x_2 = 6.9815$
$x_3 = 7.0405$	$x_3 = 7.0697$	$x_3 = 6.9516$
$x_4 = 7.0412$	$x_4 = 7.1735$	$x_4 = 7.0212$
$x_5 = 7.0193$	$x_5 = 6.9784$	$x_5 = 6.9793$
$\bar{x} = 7.0336$	$\bar{x} = 7.0640$	$\bar{x} = 7.0062$
$\mu = [\bar{x} \pm 0.0537]$	$\mu = [\bar{x} \pm 0.0537]$	$\mu = [\bar{x} \pm 0.0537]$
$= [7.0336 \pm 0.0537]$	$= [7.0640 \pm 0.0537]$	$= [7.0062 \pm 0.0537]$
$= [6.9799, 7.0873]$	$= [7.0103, 7.1177]$	$= [6.9525, 7.0599]$

$$2\sigma_{\bar{x}} = 2\frac{\sigma}{\sqrt{n}} = 2\frac{0.06}{\sqrt{5}} = 0.0537$$

of μ. This is illustrated in Figure 7.1.

2   In this case, if we repeatedly took samples of $n = 5$ from this population, each interval would have the form

$$\bar{x} \pm 0.0537.$$

Some intervals would contain the true value of μ and some would not, but what proportion of the intervals would contain μ?

3   Combining (1) and (2), we come up with the concept of a confidence interval. That is, if we repeatedly sampled from this population, then we would expect that 95.44 percent of the intervals would contain the true value of μ and 4.56 percent of the intervals would not contain the true value of μ. In practice, we will never know if our interval contains μ or not. If we did know this, then we would not need a confidence interval. The three cases illustrated in Table 7.1 are all examples of 95.44 percent confidence intervals. Later on, we will see that 95 percent is the value that is used most of the time.

FIGURE **7.1**   Three 95.44 Percent Confidence Intervals for μ

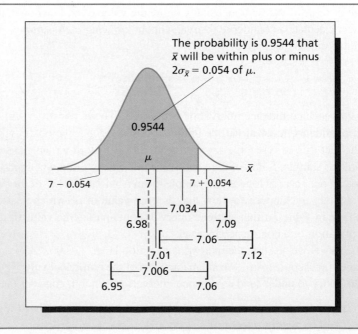

A general confidence interval formula A little later in this section, we will see how to make practical use of confidence intervals. First, however, we present a general formula for finding a confidence interval using the empirical rule:

$$[\bar{x} \pm 2\sigma_{\bar{x}}] = \left[\bar{x} \pm 2\frac{\sigma}{\sqrt{n}}\right].$$

We make use of the two-standard-deviation part of the empirical rule, and this makes the above interval a 95.44 percent confidence interval. In general, the level of confidence in the interval is expressed as $100(1 - \alpha)$ percent. We will refer to this value as the **confidence coefficient**. The complement of this confidence coefficient is, of course, $100(\alpha)$ percent. For now, we will not need to know what α specifically represents. At this point, we will say that α represents the probability of an error. This error will be discussed in Chapter 8 (Hypothesis Testing).

The following box summarizes the formula used in calculating a $100(1 - \alpha)$ percent confidence interval for a population mean μ.

A Confidence Interval for a Population Mean μ: σ Known

Suppose that the sampled population is normally distributed. Then a **100(1 − α) percent confidence interval for μ is**

This interval is also approximately correct for non-normal populations if the sample size is large (at least 30).

$$\left[\bar{x} \pm z_{\alpha/2}\frac{\sigma}{\sqrt{n}}\right] = \left[\bar{x} - z_{\alpha/2}\frac{\sigma}{\sqrt{n}}, \bar{x} + z_{\alpha/2}\frac{\sigma}{\sqrt{n}}\right].$$

To find a general formula for a confidence interval for a population mean μ, we assume that the sampled population is normally distributed, or the sample size n is large. Under these conditions, the sampling distribution of the sample mean $\bar{x}$ is exactly (or approximately, by the central limit theorem) a normal distribution with mean $\mu_{\bar{x}} = \mu$ and standard deviation $\sigma_{\bar{x}} = \sigma/\sqrt{n}$. Then, in order to obtain a confidence interval that has a $(1 - \alpha)$ probability of containing μ, we find the point $z_{\alpha/2}$ that gives a right-hand tail area under the standard normal curve equal to $\alpha/2$, and we find the point $-z_{\alpha/2}$ that gives a left-hand tail area under this curve equal to $\alpha/2$ (see Figure 7.2). Noting from Figure 7.2 that the area under the standard normal curve between $-z_{\alpha/2}$ and $z_{\alpha/2}$ is $(1 - \alpha)$, it can be shown that the probability is $(1 - \alpha)$ that the sample mean $\bar{x}$ will be within plus or minus $z_{\alpha/2}\sigma_{\bar{x}}$ units of the population mean μ. The quantity $z_{\alpha/2}\sigma_{\bar{x}}$ is called the **margin of error** when estimating μ by $\bar{x}$. If this margin of error is added to and subtracted from $\bar{x}$ to form the interval

$$[\bar{x} \pm z_{\alpha/2}\sigma_{\bar{x}}] = \left[\bar{x} \pm z_{\alpha/2}\frac{\sigma}{\sqrt{n}}\right],$$

FIGURE **7.2** The Point $z_{\alpha/2}$

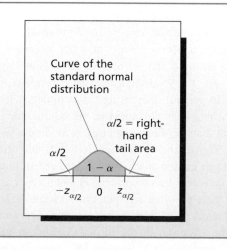

Curve of the standard normal distribution

$\alpha/2$ = right-hand tail area

$\alpha/2$

$1 - \alpha$

$-z_{\alpha/2}$ 0 $z_{\alpha/2}$

FIGURE **7.3** The Point $z_{0.025}$

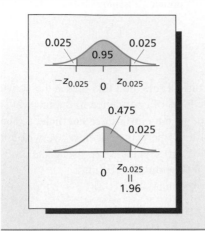

FIGURE **7.4** The Point $z_{0.005}$

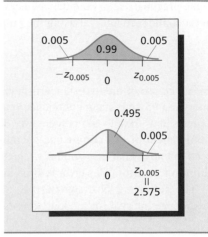

then the level of confidence that this interval will contain the population mean is $(1 - \alpha)$. In other words, this interval is a confidence interval for μ based on a confidence coefficient of $(1 - \alpha)$, and hence we call this interval a **$100(1 - \alpha)$ percent confidence interval for the population mean**. Here **$100(1 - \alpha)$ percent** is called the **confidence level** associated with the confidence interval.

For example, suppose we wish to find a 95 percent confidence interval for the population mean. Since the confidence level is 95 percent, we have $100(1 - \alpha) = 95$. This implies that the confidence coefficient is $(1 - \alpha) = 0.95$, which implies that $\alpha = 0.05$ and $\alpha/2 = 0.025$. Therefore, we need to find the point $z_{0.025}$. As shown in Figure 7.3, the area under the standard normal curve between $-z_{0.025}$ and $z_{0.025}$ is 0.95, and the area under this curve between 0 and $z_{0.025}$ is 0.475. Looking up the area 0.475 in Table A.3, we find that $z_{0.025} = 1.96$. It follows that the interval

$$[\bar{x} \pm z_{0.025}\sigma_{\bar{x}}] = \left[\bar{x} \pm 1.96 \frac{\sigma}{\sqrt{n}} \right]$$

is a 95 percent confidence interval for the population mean μ. This means that if all possible samples were used to calculate this interval, 95 percent of the resulting intervals would contain μ.

As another example, consider a 99 percent confidence interval for the population mean. Because the confidence level is 99 percent, we have $100(1 - \alpha) = 99$, and the confidence coefficient is $(1 - \alpha) = 0.99$. This implies that $\alpha = 0.01$ and $\alpha/2 = 0.005$. Therefore, we need to find the point $z_{0.005}$. As shown in Figure 7.4, the area under the standard normal curve between $-z_{0.005}$ and $z_{0.005}$ is 0.99, and the area under this curve between 0 and $z_{0.005}$ is 0.495. Looking up the area 0.495 in Table A.3, we find that $z_{0.005} = 2.575$. It follows that the interval

$$[\bar{x} \pm z_{0.005}\sigma_{\bar{x}}] = \left[\bar{x} \pm 2.575 \frac{\sigma}{\sqrt{n}} \right]$$

is a 99 percent confidence interval for the population mean μ. This means that if all possible samples were used to calculate this interval, 99 percent of the resulting intervals would contain μ.

To compare the 95 percent and 99 percent confidence intervals, notice that the margin of error $2.575(\sigma/\sqrt{n})$ used to compute the 99 percent interval is larger than the margin of error $1.96(\sigma/\sqrt{n})$ used to compute the 95 percent interval. Therefore, the 99 percent interval is the longer of these intervals. In general, increasing the confidence level (1) has the advantage of making us more confident that μ is contained in the confidence interval, but (2) has the disadvantage of increasing the margin of error and thus providing a less precise estimate of the true value of μ. Frequently, 95 percent confidence intervals are used to make conclusions. If conclusions based on stronger evidence are desired, 99 percent intervals are sometimes used.

Table 7.2 shows the confidence levels 95 percent and 99 percent, as well as two other confidence levels—90 percent and 98 percent—that are sometimes used to calculate confidence intervals. In addition, this table gives the values of α, $\alpha/2$, and $z_{\alpha/2}$ that correspond to these confidence levels.

A confidence interval for μ is based on the normal distribution and requires that the true value of the population standard deviation σ be known. Of course in almost all real-world situations

TABLE 7.2   The Point $z_{\alpha/2}$ for Various Levels of Confidence

100(1 − α) percent	α	α/2	Normal Point $z_{\alpha/2}$
90% = 100(1 − 0.10)%	0.10	0.05	$z_{0.05} = 1.645$
95% = 100(1 − 0.05)%	0.05	0.025	$z_{0.025} = 1.96$
98% = 100(1 − 0.02)%	0.02	0.01	$z_{0.01} = 2.33$
99% = 100(1 − 0.01)%	0.01	0.005	$z_{0.005} = 2.575$

this value is not known. However, the concepts and calculations related to confidence intervals are most easily illustrated using the normal distribution. Therefore, in this section we will assume that through extensive experience with the population or process under consideration, we know σ. When σ is unknown, we construct a confidence interval for μ by using the t distribution. In Section 7.2, we study t-based confidence intervals for μ, and we will revisit the examples of this section assuming that σ is unknown.

Example 7.1 The Mass of a Loonie

We will now construct a 95 percent confidence interval for the true mean mass of the loonies produced in 1989. We assumed that we knew the population standard deviation. It was given as $\sigma = 0.06$ g. Our sample of size $n = 200$ gave a sample mean of $\bar{x} = 7.012$ g. As illustrated in Figure 7.3, in order to construct a 95 percent confidence interval, we use the normal point $z_{\alpha/2} = z_{0.05/2} = z_{0.025} = 1.96$. Thus, the 95 percent confidence interval for μ is

$$\left[\bar{x} \pm z_{0.025} \frac{\sigma}{\sqrt{n}} \right] = \left[7.012 \pm 1.96 \frac{0.06}{\sqrt{200}} \right]$$
$$= [7.012 \pm 0.008]$$
$$= [7.004, 7.020].$$

We are 95 percent confident that the true mean mass of the population of loonies in 1989 is between 7.004 g and 7.020 g.

Suppose we wanted to have a higher level of confidence. Suppose we wanted to construct a 99 percent confidence interval for μ. As illustrated in Figure 7.4, we would use the point $z_{\alpha/2} = z_{0.005} = 2.575$. This yields

$$\left[\bar{x} \pm z_{0.005} \frac{\sigma}{\sqrt{n}} \right] = \left[7.012 \pm 2.575 \frac{0.06}{\sqrt{200}} \right]$$
$$= [7.012 \pm 0.010]$$
$$= [7.001, 7.023].$$

We are 99 percent confident that the true mean mass of the population of loonies in 1989 is between 7.001 g and 7.023 g. Note that by increasing the level of confidence, the interval becomes wider, but just slightly wider in our case. This is because our sample size is large. In general, though, as the level of confidence increases, so does the width of the confidence interval. Precision or accuracy is lost as the level of confidence increases.

Example 7.2 The Payment Time Case

Recall from Example 6.3 on page 189 that a management consulting firm has installed a new computer-based, electronic billing system in a trucking company. The mean payment time using the trucking company's old billing system was approximately equal to, but no less than, 39 days. In order to assess whether the mean payment time, μ, using the new billing system is substantially less than 39 days, the consulting firm will use a sample of $n = 65$ payment times to

find a 95 percent confidence interval for μ. The mean of the 65 payment times is $\bar{x} = 18.1077$. Using the point $z_{\alpha/2} = z_{0.025} = 1.96$, and assuming that σ is known to equal 4.2, it follows that the 95 percent confidence interval for μ is

$$\left[\bar{x} \pm z_{0.025}\frac{\sigma}{\sqrt{n}}\right] = \left[18.1077 \pm 1.96\frac{4.2}{\sqrt{65}}\right]$$
$$= [18.1077 \pm 1.021]$$
$$= [17.1, 19.1].$$

Recalling that the mean payment time using the old billing system is 39 days, the point estimate $\bar{x} = 18.1$ says we estimate that the new billing system reduces the mean payment time by 20.9 days. Because the interval says that we are 95 percent confident that the mean payment time using the new billing system is between 17.1 days and 19.1 days, we are 95 percent confident that the new billing system reduces the mean payment time by at most 21.9 days and by at least 19.9 days.

Example 7.3 Coffee Fills

Suppose that data were collected on medium coffee served at Phil Moore's coffee shop. A medium coffee should contain about 312.5 mL (10 ounces). Suppose that it is known that the standard deviation of medium coffee fills at Phil Moore's is $\sigma = 1$ mL. A random sample of 30 medium cups of coffee is obtained from this location and it is found that the sample mean is $\bar{x} = 312$. Constructing a 95 percent confidence interval for μ, the average volume of coffee served in the medium cups, we have

$$\left[\bar{x} \pm z_{0.025}\frac{\sigma}{\sqrt{n}}\right] = \left[312 \pm 1.96\frac{1}{\sqrt{30}}\right]$$
$$= [312 \pm 0.3578]$$
$$= [311.6422, 312.3578].$$

With 95 percent confidence, we say that the average volume of coffee in a medium coffee at Phil Moore's is somewhere between 311.6422 and 312.3578. So, if we repeatedly sampled from this population (store), say, 1000 times, then we would **expect** that 95 percent of the intervals, or 950 intervals, would contain the true average volume and 50 intervals would not contain this true average. We may find that 947 intervals contain μ, and 53 do not. Remember, we **expect** 95 percent of the intervals to contain μ in the long run. In the next chapter, we will use hypothesis testing to determine whether or not $\mu = 312.5$ mL.

The derivation of the confidence interval formula   To show why the interval

$$\left[\bar{x} \pm z_{\alpha/2}\frac{\sigma}{\sqrt{n}}\right]$$

is a $100(1 - \alpha)$ percent confidence interval for μ, recall that if the sampled population is normally distributed or the sample size n is large, then the sampling distribution of $\bar{x}$ is (exactly or approximately) a normal distribution with mean $\mu_{\bar{x}} = \mu$ and standard deviation $\sigma_{\bar{x}} = \sigma/\sqrt{n}$. It follows that the sampling distribution of

$$z = \frac{\bar{x} - \mu}{\sigma/\sqrt{n}}$$

is (exactly or approximately) a standard normal distribution. Therefore, the probability that we will obtain a sample mean $\bar{x}$ such that z is between $-z_{\alpha/2}$ and $z_{\alpha/2}$ is $1 - \alpha$ (see Figure 7.5). That is, we can say that the probability that

$$-z_{\alpha/2} \leq \frac{\bar{x} - \mu}{\sigma/\sqrt{n}} \leq z_{\alpha/2}$$

FIGURE 7.5 A Probability for Deriving a Confidence Interval for the Population Mean

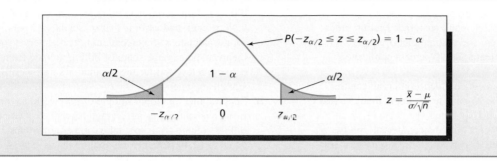

equals $1 - \alpha$. Using some algebraic manipulations, we can show that this is equivalent to saying that the probability that

$$\bar{x} - z_{\alpha/2}\frac{\sigma}{\sqrt{n}} \leq \mu \leq \bar{x} + z_{\alpha/2}\frac{\sigma}{\sqrt{n}}$$

equals $1 - \alpha$. This probability statement says that the probability is $1 - \alpha$ (for example, 0.95) that we will obtain a sample mean $\bar{x}$ such that the interval

$$\left[\bar{x} \pm z_{\alpha/2}\frac{\sigma}{\sqrt{n}}\right]$$

contains μ. In other words, this interval is a $100(1 - \alpha)$ percent confidence interval for μ.

Exercises for Section 7.1

CONCEPTS

7.1 Explain why it is important to calculate a confidence interval in addition to calculating a point estimate of a population parameter.

7.2 Write a paragraph explaining exactly what the term "95 percent confidence" means in the context of calculating a 95 percent confidence interval for a population mean.

7.3 For each of the following changes, indicate whether a confidence interval for μ will have a larger or smaller margin of error:
   a. An increase in the level of confidence.
   b. An increase in the sample size.
   c. A decrease in the level of confidence.
   d. A decrease in the sample size.

METHODS AND APPLICATIONS

7.4 For each of the following confidence levels, $100(1 - \alpha)$ percent, find the $z_{\alpha/2}$ point needed to compute a confidence interval for μ:
   a. 95%.   **c.** 99.73%.   **e.** 97%.
   b. 99%.   **d.** 80%.   **f.** 92%.

7.5 Suppose that, for a sample of size $n = 100$ measurements, we find that $\bar{x} = 50$. Assuming that σ equals 2, calculate confidence intervals for the population mean μ with the following confidence levels:
   a. 95%.   **c.** 97%.   **e.** 99.73%.
   b. 99%.   **d.** 80%.

7.6 THE TRASH BAG CASE

Consider the trash bag problem. Suppose that an independent laboratory has tested trash bags and has found that no 130-L bags that are currently on the market have a mean breaking strength of 23 kg or more. On the basis of these results, the producer of the new, improved trash bag feels sure that its 130-L bag will be the strongest such bag on the market if the new trash bag's mean breaking strength can be shown to be at least 23 kg. The mean of the sample of 40 trash bag breaking strengths is $\bar{x} = 22.9$ kg. Let μ denote the mean of the breaking strengths of all possible trash bags of the new type and assume that σ equals 0.7.
   a. Calculate 95 percent and 99 percent confidence intervals for μ.
   b. Using the 95 percent confidence interval, can we be 95 percent confident that μ is at least 23 kg? Explain.
   c. Using the 99 percent confidence interval, can we be 99 percent confident that μ is at least 23 kg? Explain.
   d. Based on your answers to parts b and c, how convinced are you that the new 130-L trash bag is the strongest such bag on the market?

7.7 THE BANK CUSTOMER WAITING TIME CASE
   ● WaitTime

Recall from Exercise 1.9 on page 10 that a bank manager has developed a new system to reduce the time customers spend waiting to be served by tellers during peak business hours. The mean waiting time during peak business hours under the current system is roughly 9 to 10 minutes. The bank manager hopes that the new system will have a mean waiting time that is less than six minutes. The mean of the sample of 100 bank customer waiting times is $\bar{x} = 5.46$. Let μ denote the mean of all possible bank customer waiting times using the new system and assume that σ equals 2.47.

a. Calculate 95 percent and 99 percent confidence intervals for μ.

b. Using the 95 percent confidence interval, can the bank manager be 95 percent confident that μ is less than six minutes? Explain.

c. Using the 99 percent confidence interval, can the bank manager be 99 percent confident that μ is less than six minutes? Explain.

d. Based on your answers to parts b and c, how convinced are you that the new mean waiting time is less than six minutes?

7.8 The average cost of a sample of $n = 50$ cell phone calling plans per month from the Payless cell phone company is $\bar{x} = \$48$. Let μ denote the mean cost of calling plans used by all customers who use the Payless calling plans and suppose that $\sigma = \$5$.

a. Calculate 95 and 99 percent confidence intervals for μ.

b. Using the 95 percent confidence interval, can we be 95 percent confident that μ is $\$50$?

c. Using the 99 percent confidence interval, can we be 99 percent confident that μ is $\$50$?

d. Based on your answers to parts b and c, how confident are you that μ is $\$50$?

7.9 In an article in the *Journal of Management*, Morris, Avila, and Allen studied innovation by surveying firms to find (among other things) the number of new products introduced by the firms. Suppose a random sample of 100 firms is selected and each firm is asked to report the number of new products it has introduced during the last year. The sample mean is found to be $\bar{x} = 5.68$. Assume that σ equals 8.70.

a. Calculate a 98 percent confidence interval for the population mean number of new products introduced in the last year.

b. Based on your confidence interval, find a reasonable estimate for the smallest value that the mean number of new products might be. Explain.

7.10 In an article in *Marketing Science*, Silk and Berndt investigate the output of advertising agencies. They describe ad agency output by finding the shares of dollar billing volume coming from various media categories, such as network television, spot television, newspapers, and radio.

a. Suppose that a random sample of 400 world advertising agencies gives an average percentage share of billing volume from network television equal to 7.46 percent, and assume that σ equals 1.42 percent. Calculate a 95 percent confidence interval for the mean percentage share of billing volume from network television for the population of all world advertising agencies.

b. Suppose that a random sample of 400 world advertising agencies gives an average percentage share of billing volume from spot television commercials equal to 12.44 percent, and assume that σ equals 1.55 percent. Calculate a 95 percent confidence interval for the mean percentage share of billing volume from spot television commercials for the population of all world advertising agencies.

c. Compare the confidence intervals in parts a and b. Does it appear that the mean percentage share of billing volume from spot television commercials for world advertising agencies is greater than the mean percentage share of billing volume from network television? Explain.

7.11 A random sample of $n = 20$ detached two-storey house prices was taken in Vancouver in December 2006. The sample mean is $\bar{x} = \$581,393$. Suppose it is known that $\sigma = \$75,000$.

a. Calculate a 95 percent confidence interval for the population mean detached two-storey house price in Vancouver.

b. Calculate a 99 percent confidence interval for the population mean detached two-storey house price in Vancouver.

c. Based on your answers in parts a and b, how confident are you that the average house price in Vancouver is at least $\$620,000$?

7.12 A random sample of $n = 60$ detached two-storey house prices was taken in Toronto in December 2006. The sample mean is $\bar{x} = \$425,196$. Suppose it is known that $\sigma = \$55,000$. A random sample of $n = 40$ detached two-storey house prices was taken in Calgary in December 2006. The sample mean is $\bar{x} = \$398,459$. Suppose it is known that $\sigma = \$55,000$.

a. Calculate a 99 percent confidence interval for the population mean detached two-storey house price in Toronto.

b. Calculate a 99 percent confidence interval for the population mean detached two-storey house price in Calgary.

7.2 *t*-Based Confidence Intervals
for a Population Mean: σ Unknown

If we do not know σ (which is usually the case), we can use the sample standard deviation s to help construct a confidence interval for μ. The interval is based on the sampling distribution of

$$t = \frac{\bar{x} - \mu}{s/\sqrt{n}}.$$

If the sampled population is normally distributed, then for any sample size n, this sampling distribution is what is called a *t* **distribution**. The *t* distribution was named after William Gossett. While he was doing research at the Guinness brewery in Dublin, Ireland, Gossett used his statistical knowledge to help the brewery select the best-yielding varieties of barley. Another researcher at the brewery had previously published a paper containing some of the brewery's trade secrets, so Guinness prohibited its employees from publishing any papers. Gossett was then unable to publish any works under his name, so he used the pseudonym Student for his publications. This explains why this distribution is referred to as the Student *t* distribution. It may have otherwise been called the Gossett *t* distribution.

The curve of the *t* distribution has a shape similar to that of the standard normal curve. Two *t* curves and a standard normal curve are illustrated in Figure 7.6. A *t* curve is symmetrical about zero, which is the mean of any *t* distribution. However, the *t* distribution is more spread out, or variable, than the standard normal distribution. Since the above *t* statistic is a function of two random variables, $\bar{x}$ and s, it is logical that the sampling distribution of this statistic is more variable than the sampling distribution of the z statistic, which is a function of only one random variable, $\bar{x}$. The exact spread, or standard deviation, of the *t* distribution depends on a parameter that is called the **number of degrees of freedom (denoted *df*)**. The degrees of freedom *df* varies depending on the problem. In this situation, the sampling distribution of *t* has a number of degrees of freedom that equals the sample size minus 1. We say that this sampling distribution is a *t* **distribution with** $n - 1$ **degrees of freedom**. As the sample size n (and thus the number of degrees of freedom) increases, the spread of the *t* distribution decreases (see Figure 7.6). Furthermore, as the number of degrees of freedom approaches infinity, the curve of the *t* distribution approaches (that is, becomes shaped more and more like) the curve of the standard normal distribution. In fact, when the sample size n is at least 30 and thus the number of degrees of freedom $n - 1$ is at least 29, the curve of the *t* distribution is very similar to the standard normal curve.

In order to use the *t* distribution, we employ a *t* **point that is denoted** t_α. As illustrated in Figure 7.7, t_α **is the point on the horizontal axis under the curve of the *t* distribution that gives a right-hand tail area equal to** α. The value of t_α in a particular situation depends upon the right-hand tail area α and the number of degrees of freedom of the *t* distribution. Values of t_α are tabulated in a *t* **table**. Such a table is given in Table A.4 of Appendix A, and a portion of Table A.4 is reproduced in this chapter as Table 7.3. In this *t* table, the rows correspond to the different numbers of degrees of freedom (denoted *df*). The values of *df* are listed down the left side of the table, while the columns designate the right-hand tail area α. For example, suppose we wish to find the *t* point that gives a right-hand tail area of 0.025 under a *t* curve with $df = 14$ degrees of freedom. To do this, we look in Table 7.3 at the row labelled 14 and the column labelled $t_{0.025}$. We find that this $t_{0.025}$ point is 2.145 (also see

FIGURE **7.6** **As the Number of Degrees of Freedom Increases, the Spread of the *t* Distribution Decreases and the *t* Curve Approaches the Standard Normal Curve**

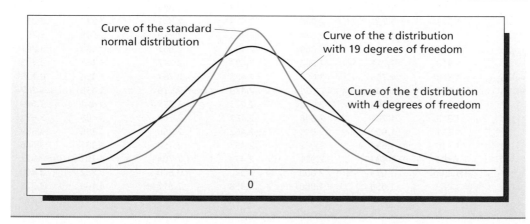

FIGURE **7.7** An Example of a *t* Point Giving a Specified Right-Hand Tail Area
(This *t* Point Gives a Right-Hand Tail Area Equal to α)

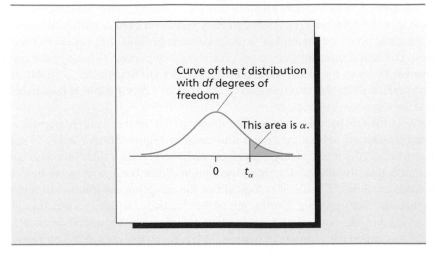

TABLE **7.3** A *t* Table

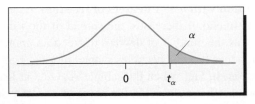

df	$t_{0.100}$	$t_{0.050}$	$t_{0.025}$	$t_{0.01}$	$t_{0.005}$	$t_{0.001}$	$t_{0.0005}$
1	3.078	6.314	12.706	31.821	63.657	318.31	636.62
2	1.886	2.920	4.303	6.965	9.925	22.326	31.598
3	1.638	2.353	3.182	4.541	5.841	10.213	12.924
4	1.533	2.132	2.776	3.747	4.604	7.173	8.610
5	1.476	2.015	2.571	3.365	4.032	5.893	6.869
6	1.440	1.943	2.447	3.143	3.707	5.208	5.959
7	1.415	1.895	2.365	2.998	3.499	4.785	5.408
8	1.397	1.860	2.306	2.896	3.355	4.501	5.041
9	1.383	1.833	2.262	2.821	3.250	4.297	4.781
10	1.372	1.812	2.228	2.764	3.169	4.144	4.587
11	1.363	1.796	2.201	2.718	3.106	4.025	4.437
12	1.356	1.782	2.179	2.681	3.055	3.930	4.318
13	1.350	1.771	2.160	2.650	3.012	3.852	4.221
14	1.345	1.761	2.145	2.624	2.977	3.787	4.140
15	1.341	1.753	2.131	2.602	2.947	3.733	4.073
16	1.337	1.746	2.120	2.583	2.921	3.686	4.015
17	1.333	1.740	2.110	2.567	2.898	3.646	3.965
18	1.330	1.734	2.101	2.552	2.878	3.610	3.922
19	1.328	1.729	2.093	2.539	2.861	3.579	3.883
20	1.325	1.725	2.086	2.528	2.845	3.552	3.850
21	1.323	1.721	2.080	2.518	2.831	3.527	3.819
22	1.321	1.717	2.074	2.508	2.819	3.505	3.792
23	1.319	1.714	2.069	2.500	2.807	3.485	3.767
24	1.318	1.711	2.064	2.492	2.797	3.467	3.745
25	1.316	1.708	2.060	2.485	2.787	3.450	3.725
26	1.315	1.706	2.056	2.479	2.779	3.435	3.707
27	1.314	1.703	2.052	2.473	2.771	3.421	3.690
28	1.313	1.701	2.048	2.467	2.763	3.408	3.674
29	1.311	1.699	2.045	2.462	2.756	3.396	3.659
30	1.310	1.697	2.042	2.457	2.750	3.385	3.646
40	1.303	1.684	2.021	2.423	2.704	3.307	3.551
60	1.296	1.671	2.000	2.390	2.660	3.232	3.460
120	1.289	1.658	1.980	2.358	2.617	3.160	3.373
∞	1.282	1.645	1.960	2.326	2.576	3.090	3.291

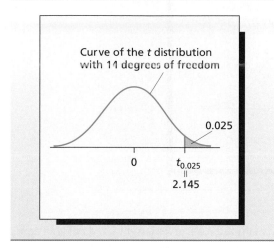

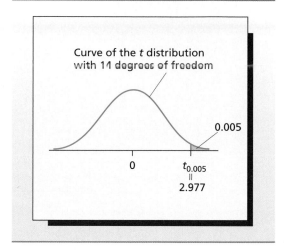

Figure 7.8). Similarly, when there are $df = 14$ degrees of freedom, we find that $t_{0.005} = 2.977$ (see Table 7.3 and Figure 7.9).

Table 7.3 gives *t* points for degrees of freedom *df* from 1 to 30. The table also gives *t* points for 40, 60, 120, and an infinite number of degrees of freedom. Looking at this table, it is useful to realize that the normal points (*z* values) giving the various right-hand tail areas are listed in the row of the *t* table corresponding to an infinite (∞) number of degrees of freedom. Looking at the row corresponding to ∞, we see that, for example, $z_{0.025} = 1.96$ and $z_{0.005} = 2.576$. Therefore, we can use this row in the *t* table as an alternative to using the normal table when we need to find normal points (*z* values) (such as $z_{\alpha/2}$ in Section 7.1).

Table A.4 of Appendix A gives *t* points for selected values of *df* ranging from 1 to infinity. We can use a computer to find *t* points based on values of *df* greater than 100. Alternatively, because a *t* curve based on more than 100 degrees of freedom is approximately the shape of the standard normal curve, *t* points based on values of *df* greater than 100 can be approximated by their corresponding *z* points. That is, when performing hand calculations, it is reasonable to approximate values of t_α by z_α when *df* is greater than 100.

We now present the formula for a $100(1 - \alpha)$ percent confidence interval for a population mean μ based on the *t* distribution.

A *t*-Based $100(1 - \alpha)$ Percent Confidence Interval for a Population Mean μ: σ Unknown

If the sampled population is normally distributed with mean μ, then a **$100(1 - \alpha)$ percent confidence interval for μ** is

$$\left[\bar{x} \pm t_{\alpha/2} \frac{s}{\sqrt{n}} \right].$$

Here *s* is the sample standard deviation, $t_{\alpha/2}$ is the *t* point giving a right-hand tail area of $\alpha/2$ under the *t* curve with $n - 1$ degrees of freedom, and *n* is the sample size.

VS

CHAPTER 9

Before presenting an example, we need to make a few comments. First, it has been shown that this confidence interval is approximately valid for many populations that are not exactly normally distributed. In particular, this interval is approximately valid for a mound-shaped, or single-peaked, population, even if the population is somewhat skewed to the right or left. Second, this

FIGURE **7.10**   The Point $t_{\alpha/2}$ with $n-1$ Degrees of Freedom

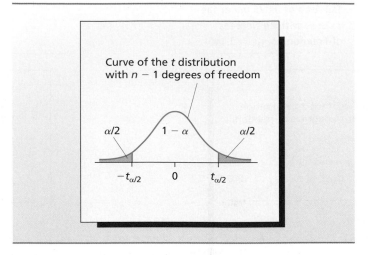

interval employs the point $t_{\alpha/2}$, which, as shown in Figure 7.10, gives a right-hand tail area equal to $\alpha/2$ under the t curve with $n-1$ degrees of freedom. Here $\alpha/2$ is determined from the desired confidence level $100(1-\alpha)$ percent.

Example 7.4

One measure of a company's financial health is its **debt-to-equity ratio.** This quantity is defined to be the ratio of the company's corporate debt to the company's equity. If this ratio is too high, it is one indication of financial instability. For obvious reasons, banks often monitor the financial health of companies to which they have extended commercial loans. Suppose that, in order to reduce risk, a large bank has decided to initiate a policy limiting the mean debt-to-equity ratio for its portfolio of commercial loans to 1.5. In order to estimate the mean debt-to-equity ratio of its loan portfolio, the bank randomly selects a sample of 15 of its commercial loan accounts. Audits of these companies result in the following debt-to-equity ratios:

1.31	1.05	1.45	1.21	1.19
1.78	1.37	1.41	1.22	1.11
1.46	1.33	1.29	1.32	1.65

```
1.0 | 5
1.1 | 1 9
1.2 | 1 2 9
1.3 | 1 2 3 7
1.4 | 1 5 6
1.5 |
1.6 | 5
1.7 | 8
```

● DebtEq

A stem-and-leaf display of these ratios is given in the page margin, and a box plot of the ratios is given below. The stem-and-leaf display looks reasonably mound-shaped, and both the stem-and-leaf display and the box plot look reasonably symmetrical. Furthermore, the sample mean and standard deviation of the ratios can be calculated to be $\bar{x} = 1.343$ and $s = 0.192$.

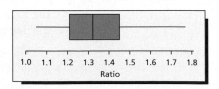

Suppose the bank wishes to calculate a 95 percent confidence interval for the loan portfolio's mean debt-to-equity ratio, μ. Because the bank has taken a sample of size $n = 15$, we have $n - 1 = 15 - 1 = 14$ degrees of freedom, and the level of confidence $100(1 - \alpha)\% = 95\%$ implies that $\alpha = 0.05$. Therefore, we use the t point $t_{\alpha/2} = t_{0.05/2} = t_{0.025} = 2.145$ (see Table 7.3). It follows that the 95 percent confidence interval for μ is

$$\left[\bar{x} \pm t_{0.025} \frac{s}{\sqrt{n}} \right] = \left[1.343 \pm 2.145 \frac{0.192}{\sqrt{15}} \right]$$

$$= [1.343 \pm 0.106]$$

$$= [1.237, 1.449]$$

This interval says the bank is 95 percent confident that the mean debt-to-equity ratio for its portfolio of commercial loan accounts is between 1.237 and 1.449. Based on this interval, the bank has strong evidence that the portfolio's mean ratio is less than 1.5 (or that the bank is in compliance with its new policy).

Recall that in the cases discussed in Section 7.1 we calculated *z*-based confidence intervals for μ by assuming that the population standard deviation σ is known. If σ is actually not known (which is usually true), we should compute *t*-based confidence intervals. Furthermore, recall that in each of these cases the sample size is large (at least 30). In general, it can be shown that if the sample size is large, the *t*-based confidence interval for μ is approximately valid even if the sampled population is not normally distributed (or mound-shaped). Therefore, consider the sample of 65 payment times, which has mean $\bar{x} = 18.1077$ and standard deviation $s = 3.9612$. The 95 percent *t*-based confidence interval for the population mean payment time μ is $[18.1077 \pm 1.998(3.9612/\sqrt{65})] = [17.1, 19.1]$, where $t_{0.025} = 1.998$ is based on $n - 1 = 65 - 1 = 64$ degrees of freedom—see Table A.4. This interval is (within rounding) the same as the 95 percent *z*-based interval computed earlier in this chapter. As a third example, the sample of 60 bottle design ratings (see Chapter 1) has mean $\bar{x} = 30.35$ and standard deviation $s = 3.1073$. The 95 percent *t*-based confidence interval for the population mean bottle design rating μ is $[30.35 \pm 2.001(3.1073/\sqrt{60})] = [29.5, 31.2]$, where $t_{0.025} = 2.001$ is based on $n - 1 = 60 - 1 = 59$ degrees of freedom—see Table A.4. This interval is very close to the 95 percent *z*-based interval [29.6, 31.1].

In summary, the *t*-based 95 percent confidence intervals computed using $\bar{x}$ and s for the samples of payment times and bottle design ratings do not differ by much from the *z*-based intervals computed in Section 7.1. Therefore, the practical conclusions reached in Section 7.1 using *z*-based intervals would also be reached using the *t*-based intervals discussed here.

Confidence intervals for μ can be computed using MINITAB, Excel, and MegaStat. For example, Figure 7.11(a) gives the Excel output of the sample mean and the margin of error for the *t*-based 95 percent confidence interval for μ computed using the sample of $n = 15$ debt-to-equity ratios in Example 7.4. Figure 7.12(a) gives the MINITAB output of the *t*-based 95 percent confidence interval for the mean debt-to-equity ratio, which (as hand calculated in Example 7.4) is [1.2369, 1.4497]. The MINITAB output also gives the sample mean $\bar{x}$, as well as the sample standard deviation s and the quantity $s/\sqrt{n}$, which is called the **standard error of the estimate** $\bar{x}$ and denoted "SE Mean" on the MINITAB output (note that $s/\sqrt{n}$ is given on the Excel output as "Standard Error"). Finally, the MINITAB output gives a box plot of the sample of 15 debt-to-equity ratios and graphically illustrates under the box plot the 95 percent confidence interval for the mean debt-to-equity ratio. Figure 7.12(b) gives the MegaStat output of the 95 percent confidence interval for the mean debt-to-equity ratio.

To conclude this section, we note that, if the sample size n is small and the sampled population is not mound-shaped or is highly skewed, the *t*-based confidence interval for the population mean might not be valid. In this case, we can use a **nonparametric method**—a method that makes no assumption about the shape of the sampled population and is valid for any sample size—to find a confidence interval for the **population median**. For example, Figure 7.11(b) gives the MINITAB output of a 95 percent confidence interval for the population **median** payment time using the new electronic billing system. This figure also shows the 95 percent *t*-based confidence interval for the population mean. Because the histogram of payment times is mound-shaped and not highly skewed to the right, both the population mean and the population median are reasonable measures of central tendency. The confidence

FIGURE 7.11   Excel and MINITAB Outputs for the Debt-to-Equity Ratio Example and the Payment Time Case

(a) Excel output in the debt-to-equity ratio example

STATISTICS	
Mean	1.343333
Standard Error	0.049595
Median	1.32
Mode	#N/A
Standard Deviation	0.192081
Sample Variance	0.036895
Kurtosis	0.833414
Skewness	0.805013
Range	0.73
Minimum	1.05
Maximum	1.78
Sum	20.15
Count	15
Confidence Level (95.0%)	0.106371

(b) MINITAB output of the payment time case

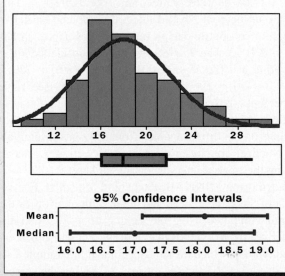

Summary for Payment Times

Anderson-Darling Normality Test	
A-Squared	0.92
P-Value	0.018
Mean	18.108
StDev	3.961
Variance	15.691
Skewness	0.600799
Kurtosis	0.033812
N	65
Minimum	10.000
1st Quartile	15.000
Median	17.000
3rd Quartile	21.000
Maximum	29.000
95% Confidence Interval for Mean	
17.126	19.089
95% Confidence Interval for Median	
16.000	18.879

95% Confidence Intervals

FIGURE 7.12   MINITAB and MegaStat Outputs of a *t*-Based 95 Percent Confidence Interval for the Mean Debt-to-Equity Ratio

(a) The MINITAB output

Variable	N	Mean	StDev	SE Mean	95% CI
Ratio	15	1.3433	0.1921	0.0496	(1.2370, 1.4497)

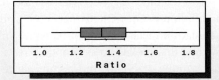

(b) The MegaStat output

Confidence interval - mean

1.3433 mean	15 n	**1.4497 upper confidence limit**
0.1921 std. dev	2.145 t (df = 14)	**1.2369 lower confidence limit**

interval for the population median is particularly useful if the sampled population is highly skewed and is valid even if the sample size is small.

Exercises for Section 7.2

CONCEPTS

7.13 Explain the effect on each of the following as the **number of degrees of freedom** describing a *t* curve **increases**:
   a. The standard deviation of the *t* curve.
   b. The points t_α and $t_{\alpha/2}$.

7.14 Discuss when it is appropriate to use the *t*-based confidence interval for μ.

METHODS AND APPLICATIONS

7.15 Using Table 7.3, find $t_{0.10}$, $t_{0.025}$, and $t_{0.001}$ based on 11 degrees of freedom. Also, find these *t* points based on six degrees of freedom.

7.16 Suppose that for a sample of $n = 11$ measurements, we find that $\bar{x} = 72$ and $s = 5$. Assuming normality, compute confidence intervals for the population mean μ with the following levels of confidence:
   a. 95%. **c.** 80%. **e.** 98%.
   b. 99%. **d.** 90%. **f.** 99.8%.

7.17 The **bad debt ratio** for a financial institution is defined to be the dollar value of loans defaulted divided by the total dollar value of all loans made. Suppose a random sample of seven Ontario banks is selected and that the bad debt ratios (written as percentages) for these banks are 7 percent, 4 percent, 6 percent, 7 percent, 5 percent, 4 percent, and 9 percent. Assuming the bad debt ratios are approximately normally distributed, the MINITAB output of a 95 percent confidence interval for the mean bad debt ratio of all banks in Ontario is as follows: ⬤ BadDebt

Variable	N	Mean	StDev
D-Ratio	7	6.00000	1.82574

SE Mean	95% CI
0.69007	(4.31147, 7.68853)

   a. Using the $\bar{x}$ and s on the MINITAB output, verify the calculation of the 95 percent confidence interval, and calculate a 99 percent confidence interval for the mean bad debt ratio.
   b. Banking officials claim the mean bad debt ratio for all banks in Canada is 3.5 percent and that the mean bad debt ratio for banks in Ontario is higher. Using the 95 percent confidence interval, can we be 95 percent confident that this claim is true? Using the 99 percent confidence interval, can we be 99 percent confident that this claim is true?

7.18 Suppose that a random sample of $n = 15$ gas stations in the city of Edmonton was sampled during the week of March 6, 2007. The following prices (in cents) for a litre of regular unleaded gasoline were observed: 91.0, 93.7, 94.1, 92.7, 90.9, 90.6, 92.4, 93.7, 95.1, 90.2, 94.5, 91.4, 96.2, 91.3, 90.5. Assume that the prices are approximately normally distributed.
   a. Calculate a 95 percent confidence interval for the average price of a litre of gasoline in Edmonton during the week of March 6, 2007.

   b. Calculate a 99 percent confidence interval for the average price of a litre of gasoline in Edmonton during the week of March 6, 2007.

7.19 A federal agency wishes to assess the effectiveness of a new air traffic control display panel. The mean time required for air traffic controllers to stabilize an air traffic emergency in which two aircraft have been assigned to the same air space is known to be roughly equal to, but no less than, 17 seconds when the current display panel is used. In order to test the new display panel, 20 air traffic controllers are randomly selected and each is trained to use the new panel. When each randomly selected controller uses the new display panel to stabilize a simulated emergency in which two aircraft have been assigned to the same air space, the mean and standard deviation of the 20 stabilization times so obtained are $\bar{x} = 13.8$ seconds and $s = 1.57$ seconds.

   a. Assuming that stabilization times are approximately normally distributed, find a 95 percent confidence interval for the true mean time required to stabilize the emergency situation using the new display panel.
   b. Are we 95 percent confident that the mean stabilization time using the new display panel is less than the 17 seconds for the current display panel? Explain.

7.20 Whole Foods is an all-natural grocery chain that has 50,000-square-foot (4,600-m²) stores, up from the industry average of 34,000 square feet (3,200 m²). Sales per square foot of supermarkets average just under $400 per square foot, as reported by *USA Today* in an article called "A whole new ballgame in grocery shopping." Suppose that sales per square foot in the most recent fiscal year are recorded for a random sample of 10 Whole Foods supermarkets. The data (sales dollars per square foot) are as follows: 854, 858, 801, 892, 849, 807, 894, 863, 829, 815. Using the fact that $\bar{x} = 846.2$ and $s = 32.866$, find a 95 percent confidence interval for the true mean sales dollars per square foot for all Whole Foods supermarkets during the most recent fiscal year. Are we 95 percent confident that this mean is greater than $800, the historical average for Whole Foods? ⬤ WholeFoods

7.21 A production supervisor at a major chemical company wishes to determine whether a new catalyst, catalyst XA-100, increases the mean hourly yield of a chemical process beyond the current mean hourly yield, which is known to be roughly equal to, but no more than, 750 g per hour. To test the new catalyst, five trial runs using catalyst XA-100 are made. The resulting yields for the trial runs (in grams per hour) are 801, 814, 784, 836, and 820. Assuming that all factors affecting yields of the process have been held as constant as possible during the test runs, it is reasonable to regard the five yields obtained using the new catalyst as a random sample from the population of all possible yields that would be obtained by using the new catalyst. Furthermore, we will assume that this population is approximately normally distributed.   ChemYield

a. Using the Excel output in Figure 7.13, find a 95 percent confidence interval for the mean of all possible yields obtained using catalyst XA-100.

b. Based on the confidence interval, can we be 95 percent confident that the mean yield using catalyst XA-100 exceeds 750 g per hour? Explain.

7.22 The mean and the standard deviation of a sample of 40 coffee-maker price points are $\bar{x} = 50.575$ and $s = 1.6438$. Calculate a t-based 95 percent confidence interval for μ, the mean of the prices of all possible coffeemakers. Also find this interval using the Excel output in Figure 7.14. Are we 95 percent confident that μ is at least $50?

7.23 THE BANK CUSTOMER WAITING TIME CASE
   WaitTime

The mean and the standard deviation of the sample of 100 bank customer waiting times (see Chapter 1, Exercise 1.9) are $\bar{x} = 5.46$ and $s = 2.475$. Calculate a t-based 95 percent confidence interval for μ, the mean of all possible bank customer waiting times using the new system. Also find this interval using the MINITAB output in Figure 7.15. Are we 95 percent confident that μ is less than six minutes?

FIGURE **7.13**   Excel Output for Exercise 7.21

STATISTICS	
Mean	811
Standard Error	8.786353
Median	814
Mode	#N/A
Standard Deviation	19.64688
Sample Variance	386
Kurtosis	−0.12472
Skewness	−0.23636
Range	52
Minimum	784
Maximum	836
Sum	4055
Count	5
Confidence Level (95.0%)	24.39488

FIGURE **7.14**   Excel Output for Exercise 7.22

STATISTICS	
Mean	50.575
Standard Error	0.2599
Median	50.65
Mode	50.9
Standard Deviation	1.643753
Sample Variance	2.701923
Kurtosis	−0.2151
Skewness	−0.05493
Range	7.2
Minimum	46.8
Maximum	54
Sum	2023
Count	40
Confidence Level (95.0%)	0.525697

FIGURE **7.15**   MINITAB Output for Exercise 7.23

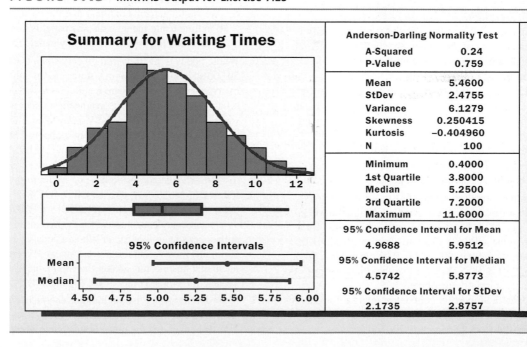

7.24 THE VIDEO GAME SATISFACTION RATING CASE
  ◑ VideoGame

The mean and the standard deviation of the sample of $n = 65$ customer satisfaction ratings (see Chapter 1, Exercise 1.8) are $\bar{x} = 42.95$ and $s = 2.6424$. Calculate a t-based 95 percent confidence interval for μ, the mean of all possible customer satisfaction ratings for the XYZ-Box video game system. Are we 95 percent confident that μ is at least 42, the minimal rating given by a very satisfied customer?

7.3 Sample Size Determination

We will now explain how to find the size of the sample that will be needed to make the margin of error in a confidence interval for μ as small as we wish. In order to develop a formula for the needed sample size, we will initially assume that we know σ. Then, if the population is normally distributed or the sample size is large, the z-based $100(1 - \alpha)$ percent confidence interval for μ is

$$\left[\bar{x} \pm z_{\alpha/2} \frac{\sigma}{\sqrt{n}} \right].$$

To find the needed sample size, we set $z_{\alpha/2}\,(\sigma/\sqrt{n})$ equal to the desired margin of error and solve for n. Letting E denote the desired margin of error, we obtain

$$z_{\alpha/2} \frac{\sigma}{\sqrt{n}} = E.$$

Multiplying both sides of this equation by $\sqrt{n}$ and dividing both sides by E, we obtain

$$\sqrt{n} = \frac{z_{\alpha/2}\sigma}{E}.$$

Squaring both sides of this result gives us the formula for n.

Determining the Sample Size for a Confidence Interval for μ: σ Known

A sample of size

$$n = \left(\frac{z_{\alpha/2}\sigma}{E} \right)^2$$

makes the margin of error in a $100(1 - \alpha)$ percent confidence interval for μ equal to E. That is, this sample size makes us $100(1 - \alpha)$ percent confident that $\bar{x}$ is within E units of μ. If the calculated value of n is not a whole number, round this value up to the next whole number (so that the margin of error is at least as small as desired).

If we consider the formula for the sample size n, it intuitively follows that the value E is the farthest that the user is willing to allow $\bar{x}$ to be from μ at a given level of confidence, and the normal point $z_{\alpha/2}$ follows directly from the given level of confidence. Furthermore, because the population standard deviation σ is in the numerator of the formula for n, it follows that the more variable the individual population measurements are, the larger is the sample size needed to estimate μ with a specified accuracy.

In order to use this formula for n, either we must know σ (which is unlikely) or we must compute an estimate of σ. Often we estimate σ by using a **preliminary sample**. In this case, we modify the above formula for n by replacing σ by the standard deviation s of the preliminary sample and by replacing $z_{\alpha/2}$ by $t_{\alpha/2}$. Thus, we obtain

$$n = \left(\frac{t_{\alpha/2}\,s}{E} \right)^2,$$

where the number of degrees of freedom for the $t_{\alpha/2}$ point is the size of the preliminary sample minus 1. Intuitively, using $t_{\alpha/2}$ compensates for the fact that the preliminary sample's value of s might underestimate σ.

Example 7.5 Sample Size Determination (with σ Known)

A manufacturer of pharmaceutical products analyzes a specimen from each batch of a product to verify the concentration of the active ingredient. It has been determined that results of repeated measurements follow a normal distribution quite closely. The standard deviation σ is known to be 0.0068 g/L. Suppose that management asks the laboratory to produce results accurate to within ± 0.005 with 95 percent confidence. We can calculate how many measurements must be averaged to comply with this request:

$$n = \left(\frac{z_{0.025}\sigma}{E} \right)^2 = \left(\frac{1.96(0.0068)}{0.005} \right)^2 = 7.11.$$

Rounding this value up to the next integer, we see that a sample size of at least 8 is needed here. A larger sample would also do here, but the point of this exercise is to find the smallest sample size that will achieve the desired accuracy.

When the value of σ is not known (which is usually the case), it is very difficult to determine the exact sample size needed in order to be within a desired margin of error. Why is this? When σ is unknown, we substitute s in its place, and we use $t_{\alpha/2}$ instead of $z_{\alpha/2}$. But in order to find the value of $t_{\alpha/2}$, we need to know the number of degrees of freedom, which of course depends on the sample size. So, when we have sample information, as a rough approximation, we may want to use the corresponding value of $z_{\alpha/2}$ along with s.

In general, the purpose behind replacing $z_{\alpha/2}$ by $t_{\alpha/2}$ when we are using a preliminary sample to obtain an estimate of σ is to be **conservative**, so that we compute a sample size that is **at least as large as needed**. Because of this, we often obtain a margin of error that is even smaller than we have requested.

Finally, sometimes we do not have a preliminary sample that can be used to estimate σ. In this case, we have two alternatives. First, we might estimate σ by using our knowledge about a similar population or process. For instance, an automaker might believe that the standard deviation of the fuel efficiency values for this year's midsize model is about the same as the standard deviation of the fuel efficiency values for last year's model. Thus, it might be reasonable to use the best available estimate of σ for last year's model as a preliminary estimate of σ for this year's model. Second, it can be shown that, if we can make a reasonable guess of the range of the population being studied, a conservatively large estimate of σ is this estimated range divided by 4. For example, if the automaker's design engineers feel that almost all of its midsize cars should get fuel efficiency values within a range of 1.1 L/100 km, then a conservatively large estimate of σ is $1.1/4 = 0.275$ L/100 km. When employing such an estimate of σ, it is sufficient to use the z-based sample size formula $n = (z_{\alpha/2}\sigma/E)^2$, because a conservatively large estimate of σ will give us a conservatively large sample size.

Exercises for Section 7.3

CONCEPTS

7.25 Explain what is meant by the margin of error for a confidence interval. What error are we talking about in the context of an interval for μ?

7.26 Explain exactly what we mean when we say that a sample of size n makes us 99 percent confident that $\bar{x}$ is within E units of μ.

7.27 Why do we usually need to take a preliminary sample when determining the size of the sample needed to make the margin of error of a confidence interval equal to E?

METHODS AND APPLICATIONS

7.28 Consider a population with a standard deviation equal to 10. We wish to estimate the mean of this population.
   a. How large a random sample is needed to construct a 95.44 percent confidence interval for the mean of this population with a margin of error equal to 1?
   b. Suppose that we now take a random sample of the size we have determined in part a. If we obtain a sample mean equal to 295, calculate the 95.44 percent confidence interval for the population mean. What is the interval's margin of error?

7.29 Consider a random sample of $n = 20$ detached two-storey house prices in Vancouver for which the sample standard deviation $s = \$72,500$.
  a. How large a random sample of house prices is needed to make us 95 percent confident that $\bar{x}$, the sample mean house price, is within a margin of error of $\$25,000$ of μ, the true mean house price in Vancouver?
  b. Suppose that we now take a random sample of the size we have determined in part a. If we obtain a sample mean equal to $\$580,000$ and a sample standard deviation, $s = \$75,000$, calculate the 95 percent confidence interval for the population mean. What is the interval's margin of error?

7.30 Consider a random sample of $n = 60$ detached two-storey house prices in Calgary for which the sample standard deviation $s = \$72,500$. How large a random sample of house prices is needed to make us
  a. 95 percent confident that $\bar{x}$, the sample mean house price, is within a margin of error of $\$29,000$ of μ, the true mean house price in Calgary?
  b. 99 percent confident that $\bar{x}$, the sample mean house price, is within a margin of error of $\$29,000$ of μ, the true mean house price in Calgary?

7.31 Referring to Exercise 7.21, regard the sample of five trial runs for which $s = 19.65$ (see Figure 7.13) as a preliminary sample. Determine the number of trial runs of the chemical process needed to make us
  a. 95 percent confident that $\bar{x}$, the sample mean hourly yield, is within a margin of error of 8 g of the true mean hourly yield μ when catalyst XA-100 is used.
  b. 99 percent confident that $\bar{x}$ is within a margin of error of 5 g of μ. ● ChemYield

7.32 Referring to Exercise 7.20, regard the sample of 10 sales figures for which $s = 32.866$ as a preliminary sample. How large a sample of sales figures is needed to make us 95 percent confident that $\bar{x}$, the sample mean sales dollars per square foot, is within a margin of error of $\$10$ of μ, the true mean sales dollars per square foot for all Whole Foods supermarkets?

7.33 Referring to Exercise 7.19, regard the sample of 20 stabilization times for which $s = 1.57$ as a preliminary sample. Determine the sample size needed to make us 95 percent confident that $\bar{x}$, the sample mean time required to stabilize the emergency situation, is within a margin of error of 0.5 seconds of μ, the true mean time required to stabilize the emergency situation using the new display panel.

7.4 Confidence Intervals for a Population Proportion

In Chapter 6, the soft cheese spread producer decided to replace its current spout with the new spout if p, the true proportion of all current purchasers who would stop buying the cheese spread if the new spout were used, is less than 0.10. Suppose that when 1,000 current purchasers are randomly selected and are asked to try the new spout, 63 say they would stop buying the spread if the new spout were used. The point estimate of the population proportion p is the sample proportion $\hat{p} = 63/1,000 = 0.063$. This sample proportion says we estimate that 6.3 percent of all current purchasers would stop buying the cheese spread if the new spout were used. Since $\hat{p}$ equals 0.063, we have some evidence that p is less than 0.10.

In order to see if there is strong evidence that p is less than 0.10, we can calculate a confidence interval for p. As explained in Chapter 6, if the sample size n is large, then the sampling distribution of the sample proportion $\hat{p}$ is approximately a normal distribution with mean $\mu_{\hat{p}} = p$ and standard deviation $\sigma_{\hat{p}} = \sqrt{p(1 - p)/n}$. Using the same logic we used in developing confidence intervals for μ, it follows that a $100(1 - \alpha)$ percent confidence interval for p is

$$\left[\hat{p} \pm z_{\alpha/2}\sqrt{\frac{p(1 - p)}{n}} \right].$$

Estimating $p(1 - p)$ by $\hat{p}(1 - \hat{p})$, it follows that a $100(1 - \alpha)$ percent confidence interval for p can be calculated as summarized below:

A Large Sample $100(1 - \alpha)$ Percent Confidence Interval for a Population Proportion p

If the sample size n is large, a $100(1 - \alpha)$ percent confidence interval for the population proportion p is

$$\left[\hat{p} \pm z_{\alpha/2}\sqrt{\frac{\hat{p}(1 - \hat{p})}{n}} \right].$$

Here n should be considered large if both $n\hat{p}$ and $n(1 - \hat{p})$ are at least 5.[1]

---

[1] Some statisticians suggest using the more conservative rule that both $n\hat{p}$ and $n(1 - \hat{p})$ must be at least 10. Furthermore, because $\hat{p}(1 - \hat{p})/(n - 1)$ is an unbiased point estimate of $p(1 - p)/n$, a more correct $100(1 - \alpha)$ percent confidence interval for p is $[\hat{p} \pm z_{\alpha/2} \sqrt{\hat{p}(1 - \hat{p})/(n - 1)}]$. However, because n is large, there is little difference between intervals obtained by using this formula and those obtained by using the formula in the above box.

Example 7.6 The Cheese Spread Case

In the cheese spread situation, consider calculating a confidence interval for p, the population proportion of purchasers who would stop buying the cheese spread if the new spout were used. In order to see whether the sample size $n = 1,000$ is large enough to enable us to use the confidence interval formula just given, recall that the point estimate of p is $\hat{p} = 63/1,000 = 0.063$. Therefore, because $n\hat{p} = 1,000(0.063) = 63$ and $n(1 - \hat{p}) = 1,000(0.937) = 937$ are both greater than 5, we can use the confidence interval formula. For example, a 95 percent confidence interval for p is

$$\left[\hat{p} \pm z_{0.025} \sqrt{\frac{\hat{p}(1 - \hat{p})}{n}} \right] = \left[0.063 \pm 1.96 \sqrt{\frac{(0.063)(0.937)}{1,000}} \right]$$
$$= [0.063 \pm 0.0151]$$
$$= [0.0479, 0.0781].$$

This interval says that we are 95 percent confident that between 4.79 percent and 7.81 percent of all current purchasers would stop buying the cheese spread if the new spout were used. Below we give the MegaStat output of this interval.

Confidence interval - proportion

1,000 n	95% confidence level	**0.078 upper confidence limit**
1.960 z	0.063 proportion	**0.048 lower confidence limit**

A 99 percent confidence interval for p is

$$\left[\hat{p} \pm z_{0.005} \sqrt{\frac{\hat{p}(1 - \hat{p})}{n}} \right] = \left[0.063 \pm 2.575 \sqrt{\frac{(0.063)(0.937)}{1,000}} \right]$$
$$= [0.063 \pm 0.0198]$$
$$= [0.0432, 0.0828].$$

The upper limits of both the 95 percent and 99 percent intervals are less than 0.10. Therefore, we have very strong evidence that the true proportion p of all current purchasers who would stop buying the cheese spread is less than 0.10. Based on this result, it seems reasonable to use the new spout.

In the cheese spread example, a sample of 1,000 purchasers gives us a 95 percent confidence interval for p—[0.063 ± 0.0151]—with a reasonably small margin of error of 0.0151. Generally speaking, quite a large sample is needed in order to make the margin of error in a confidence interval for p reasonably small. The next two examples demonstrate that a sample size of 200, which most people would consider quite large, does not necessarily give a 95 percent confidence interval for p with a small margin of error.

Example 7.7

Antibiotics occasionally cause nausea as a side effect. Scientists working for a major drug company have developed a new antibiotic called Phe-Mycin. The company wishes to estimate p, the proportion of all patients who would experience nausea as a side effect when being treated with Phe-Mycin. Suppose that a sample of 200 patients is randomly selected. When these patients are treated with Phe-Mycin, 35 experience nausea. The point estimate of the population proportion p is the sample proportion $\hat{p} = 35/200 = 0.175$. This sample proportion says that we estimate that 17.5 percent of all patients would experience nausea as a side effect of taking Phe-Mycin. Furthermore, because $n\hat{p} = 200(0.175) = 35$ and $n(1 - \hat{p}) = 200(0.825) = 165$ are both at least 5, we can use the previously given formula to calculate a confidence interval for p. Doing this, we find that a 95 percent confidence interval for p is

$$\left[\hat{p} \pm z_{0.025}\sqrt{\frac{\hat{p}(1 - \hat{p})}{n}} \right] = \left[0.175 \pm 1.96\sqrt{\frac{(0.175)(0.825)}{200}} \right]$$

$$= [0.175 \pm 0.053]$$

$$= [0.122, 0.228].$$

This interval says we are 95 percent confident that between 12.2 percent and 22.8 percent of all patients would experience nausea as a side effect of taking Phe-Mycin. Notice that the margin of error (0.053) in this interval is rather large. Therefore, this interval is fairly long, and it does not provide a very precise estimate of p.

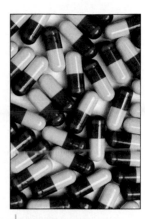

Example 7.8

According to an Ipsos Reid poll conducted from November 7 to 9, 2006, nearly half (49.05 percent) of Canadians currently do not have a passport.[2] Since January 2007, Canadians travelling by air to the United States have been required to have a valid passport. One thousand one Canadians were surveyed in this poll. The point estimate of p is the sample proportion $\hat{p} = 0.4905$. Because $n\hat{p} = 491$ and $n(1 - \hat{p}) = 511$ are both at least 5, it follows that a 95 percent confidence interval is

$$\left[\hat{p} \pm z_{0.025}\sqrt{\frac{\hat{p}(1 - \hat{p})}{n}} \right] = \left[0.4905 \pm 1.96\sqrt{\frac{(0.4905)(0.5095)}{1,001}} \right]$$

$$= [0.4905 \pm 0.0310]$$

$$= [0.4595, 0.5215].$$

This interval says that we are 95 percent confident that between 45.95 percent and 52.15 percent of Canadians do not have a valid Canadian passport and thus cannot travel to the United States by air. That would explain the long lines at passport offices in late 2006 and early 2007!

In order to find the size of the sample needed to estimate a population proportion, we consider the theoretically correct interval

$$\left[\hat{p} \pm z_{\alpha/2}\sqrt{\frac{p(1 - p)}{n}} \right].$$

To obtain the sample size needed to make the margin of error in this interval equal to E, we set

$$z_{\alpha/2}\sqrt{\frac{p(1 - p)}{n}} = E$$

and solve for n. When we do this, we get the following result:

Determining the Sample Size for a Confidence Interval for p

A sample of size

$$n = p(1 - p)\left(\frac{z_{\alpha/2}}{E}\right)^2$$

makes the margin of error in a $100(1 - \alpha)$ percent confidence interval for p equal to E. That is, this sample size makes us $100(1 - \alpha)$ percent confident that $\hat{p}$ is within E units of p. If the calculated value of n is not a whole number, round this value up to the next whole number.

[2] Source: World Wide Web, http://www.ipsos-na.com/news/pressrelease.cfm?id=3285, "The Annual Expedia Winter Survey," November 28, 2007.

FIGURE **7.16**　The Graph of $p(1 - p)$ versus p

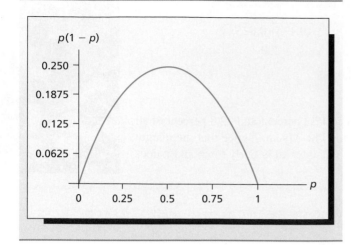

FIGURE **7.17**　MegaStat Output of a
Sample Size Calculation

Sample size - proportion
0.02 E, error tolerance
0.5 estimated population proportion
95% confidence level
1.960 z
2,400.905 sample size
2,401 rounded up

Looking at this formula, we see that the larger $p(1 - p)$ is, the larger n will be. To make sure n is large enough, consider Figure 7.16, which is a graph of $p(1 - p)$ versus p. This figure shows that $p(1 - p)$ equals 0.25 when p equals 0.5. Furthermore, $p(1 - p)$ is never larger than 0.25. Therefore, if the true value of p could be near 0.5, we should set $p(1 - p)$ equal to 0.25. This will ensure that n is as large as needed to make the margin of error as small as desired. For example, suppose we wish to estimate the proportion p of all registered U.S. voters who currently favour a particular candidate for President of the United States. If this candidate is the nominee of a major political party, or if the candidate enjoys broad popularity for some other reason, then p could be near 0.5. Furthermore, suppose we wish to make the margin of error in a 95 percent confidence interval for p equal to 0.02. If the sample to be taken is random, it should consist of

$$n = p(1 - p)\left(\frac{z_{\alpha/2}}{E}\right)^2 = 0.25\left(\frac{1.96}{0.02}\right)^2 = 2,401$$

registered voters. The MegaStat output of the results of this calculation is shown in Figure 7.17. In reality, a list of all registered voters in the United States is not available to polling organizations. Therefore, it is not feasible to take a (technically correct) random sample of registered voters in that country. For this reason, U.S. polling organizations actually employ other (more complicated) kinds of samples. We have explained some of the basic ideas behind these more complex samples in Section 1.6. For now, we consider the samples taken by these polling organizations to be approximately random. Suppose, then, that when the sample of voters is actually taken, the proportion $\hat{p}$ of sampled voters who favour the candidate turns out to be greater than 0.52. It follows, because the sample is large enough to make the margin of error in a 95 percent confidence interval for p equal to 0.02, that the lower limit of such an interval is greater than 0.50. This says we have strong evidence that a majority of all registered voters favour the candidate. For instance, if the sample proportion $\hat{p}$ equals 0.53, we are 95 percent confident that the proportion of all registered voters who favour the candidate is between 0.51 and 0.55.

Major polling organizations conduct public opinion polls concerning many kinds of issues. Whereas making the margin of error in a 95 percent confidence interval for p equal to 0.02 requires a sample size of 2,401, making the margin of error in such an interval equal to 0.03 requires a sample size of only

$$n = p(1 - p)\left(\frac{z_{\alpha/2}}{E}\right)^2 = 0.25\left(\frac{1.96}{0.03}\right)^2 = 1,067.1,$$

or 1,068 (rounding up). Of course these calculations assume that the proportion p being estimated could be near 0.5. However, for any value of p, increasing the margin of error from 0.02 to 0.03 substantially decreases the needed sample size and thus saves considerable time and money. For this reason, although the most accurate public opinion polls use a margin of error of 0.02, the vast majority of public opinion polls use a margin of error of 0.03 or larger.

When the news media report the results of a public opinion poll, they express the margin of error in a 95 percent confidence interval for p **in percentage points**. For instance, if the margin of error is 0.03, the media would say the poll's margin of error is 3 percentage points. The media seldom report the level of confidence, but almost all polling results are based on 95 percent confidence. Sometimes the media make a vague reference to the level of confidence. For instance, if the margin of error is 3 percentage points, the media might say that "the sample result will be within 3 percentage points of the population value in 19 out of 20 samples." Here the "19 out of 20 samples" is a reference to the level of confidence, which is $100(19/20) = 100(0.95) = 95$ percent.

As an example, suppose a news report says a recent poll finds that 34 percent of the public favours military intervention in an international crisis, and suppose the poll's margin of error is reported to be 3 percentage points. This means the sample taken is large enough to make us 95 percent confident that the sample proportion $\hat{p} = 0.34$ is within 0.03 (that is, 3 percentage points) of the true proportion p of the entire public that favours military intervention. That is, we are 95 percent confident that p is between 0.31 and 0.37.

If the population proportion we are estimating is substantially different from 0.5, setting p equal to 0.5 will give a sample size that is much larger than is needed. In this case, we should use our intuition or previous sample information—along with Figure 7.16—to determine the largest reasonable value for $p(1 - p)$. Figure 7.16 implies that for any range of reasonable values of p that does not contain 0.5, the quantity $p(1 - p)$ is maximized by the reasonable value of p that is closest to 0.5. Therefore, **when we are estimating a proportion that is substantially different from 0.5, we use the reasonable value of p that is closest to 0.5 to calculate the sample size needed to obtain a specified margin of error**.

Example 7.9

Again consider estimating the proportion of all patients who would experience nausea as a side effect of taking the new antibiotic Phe-Mycin. Suppose the drug company wishes to find the size of the random sample that is needed in order to obtain a 2 percent margin of error with 95 percent confidence. In Example 7.7, we employed a sample of 200 patients to compute a 95 percent confidence interval for p. This interval, which is [0.122, 0.228], makes us very confident that p is between 0.122 and 0.228. As shown in Figure 7.18, because 0.228 is the reasonable value of p that is closest to 0.5, the largest reasonable value of $p(1 - p)$ is $0.228(1 - 0.228) = 0.1760$, and thus the drug company should take a sample of

$$n = p(1 - p)\left(\frac{z_{\alpha/2}}{B}\right)^2 = 0.1760\left(\frac{1.96}{0.02}\right)^2 = 1691 \text{ (rounded up)}$$

patients.

FIGURE **7.18** The Largest Reasonable Value for $p(1 - p)$ in the Antibiotic Example Is $(0.228)(1 - 0.228) = 0.1760$

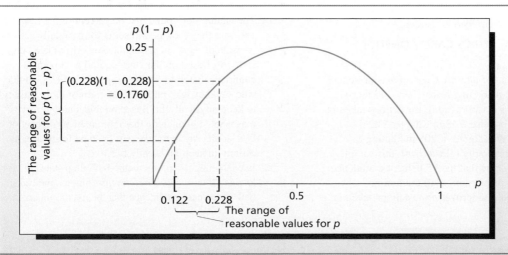

Finally, as a last example of choosing p for sample size calculations, suppose that experience indicates that a population proportion p is at least 0.75. Then, 0.75 is the reasonable value of p that is closest to 0.5, and we would use the largest reasonable value of $p(1 - p)$, which is $0.75(1 - 0.75) = 0.1875$.

Exercises for Section 7.4

CONCEPTS

7.34 **a.** What does a population proportion tell us about the population?
  b. Explain the difference between p and $\hat{p}$.
  c. What is meant when a public opinion poll's **margin of error** is 0.03?

7.35 Suppose we are using the sample size formula in the box on page 221 to find the sample size needed to make the margin of error in a confidence interval for p equal to E. In each of the following situations, explain what value of p would be used in the formula for finding n:
  a. We have no idea what value p is—it could be any value between 0 and 1.
  b. Past experience tells us that p is no more than 0.3.
  c. Past experience tells us that p is at least 0.8.

METHODS AND APPLICATIONS

7.36 In each of the following cases, determine whether the sample size n is large enough to use the large sample formula presented in the box on page 219 to compute a confidence interval for p.
  a. $\hat{p} = 0.1$, $n = 30$.   **d.** $\hat{p} = 0.8$, $n = 400$.
  b. $\hat{p} = 0.1$, $n = 100$.   **e.** $\hat{p} = 0.9$, $n = 30$.
  c. $\hat{p} = 0.5$, $n = 50$.   **f.** $\hat{p} = 0.99$, $n = 200$.

7.37 In each of the following cases, compute 95 percent, 98 percent, and 99 percent confidence intervals for the population proportion p.
  a. $\hat{p} = 0.4$ and $n = 100$.   **c.** $\hat{p} = 0.9$ and $n = 100$.
  b. $\hat{p} = 0.1$ and $n = 300$.   **d.** $\hat{p} = 0.6$ and $n = 50$.

7.38 On May 10, 2007, Ipsos Reid reported that 74 percent of Canadian consumers say that good customer service is the best way for companies to express appreciation for their patronage.[3] Suppose that these results are based on an online sample of 1,000 adult Canadians (aged 18 or older). Find a 95 percent confidence interval for the true proportion of Canadian adults who believe this to be true. Are we 95 percent confident that this proportion would exceed 80 percent?

7.39 **THE MARKETING ETHICS CASE: CONFLICT OF INTEREST**

  Recall that a conflict of interest scenario was presented to a sample of 205 marketing researchers and that 111 of these researchers disapproved of the actions taken in the scenario (see Exercise 2.48 in Chapter 2).
  a. Assuming that the sample of 205 marketing researchers was randomly selected, use this sample information to show that the 95 percent confidence interval for the proportion of all marketing researchers who disapprove of the actions taken in

the conflict of interest scenario is as given in the MINITAB output below. Interpret this interval.

CI for One Proportion

```
   X    N   Sample p        95% CI
 111  205  0.541463  (0.473254, 0.609673)
```

  b. On the basis of this interval, is there convincing evidence that a majority of all marketing researchers disapprove of the actions taken in the conflict of interest scenario? Explain.

7.40 Consider a two-way election race between Willie Win and Betty Wont to elect a new student council president at a Canadian university. Suppose that 500 students were randomly selected from the population of students. Suppose that 237 students said they would vote for Betty.
  a. Find a point estimate of and a 95 percent confidence interval for p, the proportion of all students who will vote for Betty.
  b. Based on your interval, can we be 95 percent confident that Betty will win the election?

7.41 On January 7, 2000, the Gallup Organization released the results of a poll comparing the lifestyles of today with yesteryear. The survey results were based on telephone interviews with a randomly selected sample of 1,031 U.S. adults, 18 years and older, conducted December 20 to 21, 1999.[4]
  a. The Gallup poll found that 42 percent of the respondents said that they spend less than three hours watching TV on an average weekday. Based on this finding, calculate a 99 percent confidence interval for the proportion of U.S. adults who say that they spend less than three hours watching TV on an average weekday. Based on this interval, is it reasonable to conclude that more than 40 percent of U.S. adults say they spend less than three hours watching TV on an average weekday?
  b. The Gallup poll found that 60 percent of the respondents said they took part in some form of daily activity (outside of work, including housework) to keep physically fit. Based on this finding, find a 95 percent confidence interval for the proportion of U.S. adults who say they take part in some form of daily activity to keep physically fit. Based on this interval, is it reasonable to conclude that more than 50 percent of U.S. adults say they take part in some form of daily activity to keep physically fit?
  c. In explaining its survey methods, Gallup states the following: "For results based on this sample, one can say with 95 percent confidence that the maximum error

[3]Source: World Wide Web, http://www.ipsos-na.com/news/pressrelease.cfm?id=3482, "Good customer service best way to show customer appreciation," May 10, 2007.

[4]Source: World Wide Web, http://www.gallup.com/poll/releases/, The Gallup Organization, January 7, 2000.

attributable to sampling and other random effects is plus or minus 3 percentage points." Explain how your calculations for part b verify that this statement is true.

7.42 In an article in the *Journal of Advertising*, Weinberger and Spotts compare the use of humour in television ads in the United States and the United Kingdom. They found that a substantially greater percentage of U.K. ads use humour.

  a. Suppose that a random sample of 400 television ads in the United Kingdom reveals that 142 of these ads use humour. Show that the point estimate and 95 percent confidence interval for the proportion of all U.K. television ads that use humour are as given in the MegaStat output below.

Confidence interval - proportion

400 n	95% confidence level	0.402 upper confidence limit
1.960 z	0.355 proportion	0.308 lower confidence limit

  b. Suppose a random sample of 500 television ads in the United States reveals that 122 of these ads use humour. Find a point estimate of and a 95 percent confidence interval for the proportion of all U.S. television ads that use humour.

  c. Do the confidence intervals you computed in parts a and b suggest that a greater percentage of U.K. ads use humour? Explain. How might an ad agency use this information?

7.43 In an article in *CA Magazine*, Fitzgerald surveyed Scottish business customers concerning their satisfaction with aspects of their banking relationships. Fitzgerald reports that, in 418 telephone interviews conducted by George Street Research, 67 percent of the respondents gave their banks a high rating for overall satisfaction.

  a. Assuming that the sample is randomly selected, calculate a 99 percent confidence interval for the proportion of Scottish business customers who give their banks a high rating for overall satisfaction.

  b. Based on this interval, can we be 99 percent confident that more than 60 percent of Scottish business customers give their banks a high rating for overall satisfaction?

7.44 In the March 16, 1998, issue of *Fortune* magazine, the results of a survey of 2,221 MBA students from across the United States conducted by the Stockholm-based academic consulting firm Universum showed that only 20 percent of MBA students expect to stay at their first job five years or more.[5] Assuming that a random sample was employed, find a 95 percent confidence interval for the proportion of all U.S. MBA students who expect to stay at their first job five years or more. Based on this interval, is there strong evidence that less than one fourth of all U.S. MBA students expect to stay?

7.45 *Consumer Reports* (January 2005) indicates that profit margins on extended warranties are much greater than on the purchase of most products.[6] In this exercise, we consider a major electronics retailer that wishes to increase the proportion of customers who buy extended warranties on digital cameras. Historically, 20 percent of digital camera customers have purchased the retailer's extended war-

ranty. To increase this percentage, the retailer has decided to offer a new warranty that is less expensive and more comprehensive. Suppose that three months after starting to offer the new warranty, a random sample of 500 customer sales invoices shows that 152 of 500 digital camera customers purchased the new warranty. Find a 95 percent confidence interval for the proportion of all digital camera customers who have purchased the new warranty. Are we 95 percent confident that this proportion exceeds 0.20?

7.46 The manufacturer of the ColourSmart-5000 television set claims 95 percent of its sets last at least five years without needing a single repair. In order to test this claim, a consumer group randomly selects 400 consumers who have owned a ColourSmart-5000 television set for five years. Of these 400 consumers, 316 say their ColourSmart-5000 television sets did not need a repair, whereas 84 say their ColourSmart-5000 television sets did need at least one repair.

  a. Find a 99 percent confidence interval for the proportion of all ColourSmart-5000 television sets that have lasted at least five years without needing a single repair.

  b. Does this confidence interval provide strong evidence that the percentage of ColourSmart-5000 television sets that last at least five years without a single repair is less than the 95 percent claimed by the manufacturer? Explain.

7.47 In the book *Cases in Finance*, Nunnally and Plath present a case in which the estimated percentage of uncollectible accounts varies with the age of the account. Here the age of an unpaid account is the number of days elapsed since the invoice date.

Suppose an accountant believes the percentage of accounts that will be uncollectible increases as the ages of the accounts increase. To test this theory, the accountant randomly selects 500 accounts with ages between 31 and 60 days from the accounts receivable ledger dated one year ago. The accountant also randomly selects 500 accounts with ages between 61 and 90 days from the accounts receivable ledger dated one year ago.

  a. If 10 of the 500 accounts with ages between 31 and 60 days were eventually classified as uncollectible, find a point estimate of and a 95 percent confidence interval for the proportion of all accounts with ages between 31 and 60 days that will be uncollectible.

  b. If 27 of the 500 accounts with ages between 61 and 90 days were eventually classified as uncollectible, find a point estimate of and a 95 percent confidence interval for the proportion of all accounts with ages between 61 and 90 days that will be uncollectible.

  c. Based on these intervals, is there strong evidence that the percentage of accounts aged between 61 and 90 days that will be uncollectible is higher than the percentage of accounts aged between 31 and 60 days that will be uncollectible? Explain.

7.48 Consider Exercise 7.41b and suppose we wish to find the sample size n needed in order to be 95 percent confident that $\hat{p}$, the sample proportion of respondents who said they took part in some sort of daily activity to keep physically fit, is within a margin of error of 0.02 of p, the true proportion of all U.S. adults who say that

---

[5]Source: Shelly Branch, "MBAs: What do they really want," *Fortune* (March 16, 1998), p. 167.

[6]Source: *Consumer Reports*, January 2005, page 51.

they take part in such activity. In order to find an appropriate value for $p(1 - p)$, note that the 95 percent confidence interval for p that you calculated in Exercise 7.41b was [0.57, 0.63]. This indicates that the reasonable value for p that is closest to 0.5 is 0.57, and thus the largest reasonable value for $p(1 - p)$ is $0.57(1 - 0.57) = 0.2451$. Calculate the required sample size n.

7.49 Referring to Exercise 7.46, determine the sample size needed in order to be 99 percent confident that $\hat{p}$, the sample proportion of ColourSmart-5000 television sets that last at least five years without a single repair, is

within a margin of error of 0.03 of p, the true proportion of sets that last at least five years without a single repair.

7.50 Suppose we conduct a poll to estimate the proportion of voters who favour a particular political party. Assuming that 50 percent of the electorate could be in favour of the party, determine the sample size needed so that we are 95 percent confident that $\hat{p}$, the sample proportion of voters who favour the party, is within a margin of error of 0.01 of p, the true proportion of all voters who are in favour of the party.

7.5 Confidence Intervals for Parameters of Finite Populations (Optional)

It is best to use the confidence intervals presented in Sections 7.1 through 7.4 when the sampled population is either infinite or finite and **much larger than** (say, at least 20 times as large as) the sample. Although these previously discussed intervals are sometimes used when a finite population is not much larger than the sample, better methods exist for handling such situations. We present these methods in this section.

As we have explained, we often wish to estimate a population mean. Sometimes we also wish to estimate a **population total**.

A **population total** is the sum of the values of all the population measurements.

For example, companies in financial trouble have sometimes falsified their accounts receivable invoices in order to mislead stockholders. For this reason, independent auditors are often asked to estimate a company's true total sales for a given period. The auditor randomly selects a sample of invoices from the population of all invoices and then independently determines the actual amount of each sale by contacting the purchasers. The sample results are used to estimate the company's total sales, and this estimate can then be compared with the total sales reported by the company.

In order to estimate **a population total, which we denote as τ** (tau), we note that the population mean μ is the population total divided by the number, N, of population measurements. That is, we have $\mu = \tau/N$, which implies that $\tau = N\mu$. It follows, because a point estimate of the population mean μ is the sample mean $\bar{x}$, that

A **point estimate of a population total τ** is $N\bar{x}$, where N is the size of the population.

Example 7.10

A company sells and installs satellite dishes and receivers for both private individuals and commercial establishments (bars, restaurants, and so forth). The company accumulated 2,418 sales invoices last year. The total of the sales amounts listed on these invoices (that is, the total sales claimed by the company) is $5,127,492.17. In order to estimate the true total sales, τ, for last year, an independent auditor randomly selects 242 of the invoices and determines the actual sales amounts by contacting the purchasers. When the sales amounts are averaged, the mean of the actual sales amounts for the 242 sampled invoices is $\bar{x} = \$1,843.93$. This says that a point estimate of the true total sales τ is

$$N\bar{x} = 2,418(\$1,843.93) = \$4,458,622.70.$$

This point estimate is considerably lower than the claimed total sales of $5,127,492.17. However, we cannot expect the point estimate of τ to exactly equal the true total sales, so we need to calculate a confidence interval for τ before drawing any unwarranted conclusions.

In order to find a confidence interval for the mean and total of a finite population, we consider the sampling distribution of the sample mean $\bar{x}$. It can be shown that, if we randomly select a large sample of n measurements without replacement from a finite population of N measurements, the sampling distribution of $\bar{x}$ is approximately normal with mean $\mu_{\bar{x}} = \mu$ and standard deviation

$$\sigma_{\bar{x}} = \frac{\sigma}{\sqrt{n}}\sqrt{\frac{N-n}{N-1}}.$$

It can also be shown that the appropriate point estimate of $\sigma_{\bar{x}}$ is $(s/\sqrt{n})(\sqrt{(N-n)/N})$, where s is the sample standard deviation. This point estimate of $\sigma_{\bar{x}}$ is used in the confidence intervals for μ and τ, which we summarize as follows:

Confidence Intervals for the Population Mean and Population Total for a Finite Population

Suppose we randomly select a sample of n measurements **without replacement from a finite population of N measurements**. Then, if n is large (say, at least 30),

1 A $100(1 - \alpha)$ percent confidence interval for the population mean μ is

$$\left[\bar{x} \pm z_{\alpha/2}\frac{s}{\sqrt{n}}\sqrt{\frac{N-n}{N}}\right].$$

2 A $100(1 - \alpha)$ percent confidence interval for the population total τ is found by multiplying the lower and upper limits of the $100(1 - \alpha)$ percent confidence interval for μ by N.

The quantity $\sqrt{(N-n)/N}$ in the confidence intervals for μ and τ is called the **finite population correction**. If the population size N is much larger than (say, at least 20 times as large as) the sample size n, then the finite population correction is approximately equal to 1. For example, if we randomly select (without replacement) a sample of 1,000 from a population of 1 million, then the finite population correction is $\sqrt{(1,000,000 - 1,000)/1,000,000} = 0.9995$. In such a case, many people believe it is not necessary to include the finite population correction in the confidence interval calculations. This is because the correction is not far enough below 1 to meaningfully shorten the confidence intervals for μ and τ. However, **if the population size N is not much larger than the sample size n (say, if n is more than 5 percent of N), then the finite population correction is substantially less than 1 and should be included** in the confidence interval calculations.

Example 7.11

Recall that the satellite dish dealer claims that its total sales τ for last year were \$5,127,492.17. Since the company accumulated 2,418 invoices during last year, the company is claiming that μ, the mean sales amount per invoice, is \$5,127,492.17/2,418 = \$2,120.55. Suppose, when the independent auditor randomly selects a sample of $n = 242$ invoices, that the mean and standard deviation of the actual sales amounts for these invoices are $\bar{x} = 1,843.93$ and $s = 516.42$. Here the sample size $n = 242$ is $(242/2,418)100 = 10.008$ percent of the population size $N = 2,418$. Because n is more than 5 percent of N, we should include the finite population correction in our confidence interval calculations. It follows that a 95 percent confidence interval for the mean sales amount μ per invoice is

$$\left[\bar{x} \pm z_{0.025}\frac{s}{\sqrt{n}}\sqrt{\frac{N-n}{N}}\right] = \left[1,843.93 \pm 1.96\frac{516.42}{\sqrt{242}}\sqrt{\frac{2,418-242}{2,418}}\right]$$

$$= [1,843.93 \pm 61.723812]$$

$$= [1,782.21, 1,905.65].$$

The upper limit of this interval is less than the mean amount of \$2,120.55 claimed by the company, so we have strong evidence that the company is overstating its mean sales per invoice for last year. A 95 percent confidence interval for the total sales τ last year is found by multiplying the lower and upper limits of the 95 percent confidence interval for μ by $N = 2,418$. Therefore,

this interval is [1,782.21(2,418), 1,905.65(2,418)], or [4,309,383.8, 4,607,861.7]. Because the upper limit of this interval is more than $500,000 below the total sales amount of $5,127,492.17 claimed by the company, we have strong evidence that the satellite dealer is substantially over-stating its total sales for last year.

We sometimes estimate the total number, τ, of population units that fall into a particular category. For instance, the auditor of Examples 7.10 and 7.11 might wish to estimate the total num-ber of the 2,418 invoices with incorrect sales amounts. Here the proportion, p, of the population units that fall into a particular category is the total number, τ, of population units that fall into the category divided by the number, N, of population units. That is, $p = \tau/N$, which implies that $\tau = Np$. Therefore, since a point estimate of the population proportion p is the sample proportion $\hat{p}$, a point estimate of the population total τ is $N\hat{p}$. For example, suppose that 34 of the 242 sampled invoices have incorrect sales amounts. Because the sample proportion is $\hat{p} = 34/242 = 0.1405$, a point estimate of the total number of the 2,418 invoices that have incorrect sales amounts is

$$N\hat{p} = 2,418(0.1405) = 339.729.$$

We now summarize how to find confidence intervals for p and τ.

Confidence Intervals for the Proportion of and Total Number of Units in a Category When Sampling a Finite Population

Suppose that we randomly select a sample of n units without replacement from a finite population of N units. Then, if n is large, we have the following:

1   A 100(1 − α) percent confidence interval for the population proportion p is

$$\left[\hat{p} \pm z_{\alpha/2}\sqrt{\frac{\hat{p}(1-\hat{p})}{n-1}\left(\frac{N-n}{N}\right)}\right].$$

2   A 100(1 − α) percent confidence interval for the population total τ is found by multiplying the lower and upper limits of the 100(1 − α) percent confidence interval for p by N.

Example 7.12

Recall that in Examples 7.10 and 7.11 we found that 34 of the 242 sampled invoices have in-correct sales amounts. Since $\hat{p} = 34/242 = 0.1405$, a 95 percent confidence interval for the proportion of the 2418 invoices that have incorrect sales amounts is

$$\left[\hat{p} \pm z_{0.025}\sqrt{\frac{\hat{p}(1-\hat{p})}{n-1}\left(\frac{N-n}{N}\right)}\right] = \left[0.1405 \pm 1.96\sqrt{\frac{(0.1405)(0.8595)}{241}\left(\frac{2,418-242}{2,418}\right)}\right]$$

$$= [0.1405 \pm 0.0416208]$$

$$= [0.0989, \ 0.1821].$$

This interval says we are 95 percent confident that between 9.89 percent and 18.21 percent of the invoices have incorrect sales amounts. A 95 percent confidence interval for the total number of the 2,418 invoices that have incorrect sales amounts is found by multiplying the lower and upper limits of the 95 percent confidence interval for p by $N = 2,418$. Therefore, this interval is [0.0989(2,418), 0.1821(2,418)], or [239.14, 440.32], and we are 95 percent confident that be-tween (roughly) 239 and 440 of the 2,418 invoices have incorrect sales amounts.

Finally, we can determine the sample size that is needed to make the margin of error in a con-fidence interval for μ, p, or τ equal to a desired size E by setting the appropriate margin of error formula equal to E and by solving the resulting equation for the sample size n (the procedure is the same as illustrated in Sections 7.3 and 7.4). Exercise 7.57 gives the reader an opportunity to use the sample size formulas that are obtained.

Exercises for Section 7.5

CONCEPTS

7.51 Define a population total. Give an example of a population total that will interest you in your career when you graduate from university.

7.52 Explain why the finite population correction $\sqrt{(N-n)/N}$ is unnecessary when the population is at least 20 times as large as the sample. Give an example using numbers.

METHODS AND APPLICATIONS

7.53 A retailer that sells home entertainment systems accumulated 10,451 sales invoices during the previous year. The total of the sales amounts listed on these invoices (that is, the total sales claimed by the company) is $6,384,675. In order to estimate the true total sales for last year, an independent auditor randomly selects 350 of the invoices and determines the actual sales amounts by contacting the purchasers. The mean and the standard deviation of the 350 sampled sales amounts are $\bar{x} = \$532$ and $s = \$168$.
   a. Find a 95 percent confidence interval for μ, the true mean sales amount per invoice on the 10,451 invoices.
   b. Find a point estimate of and a 95 percent confidence interval for τ, the true total sales for the previous year.
   c. What does this interval say about the company's claim that the true total sales were $6,384,675? Explain.

7.54 A company's manager is considering simplifying a travel voucher form. In order to assess the costs associated with erroneous travel vouchers, the manager must estimate the total number of such vouchers that were filled out incorrectly in the last month. In a random sample of 100 vouchers drawn without replacement from the 1,323 travel vouchers submitted in the last month, 31 vouchers were filled out incorrectly.
   a. Find a point estimate of and a 95 percent confidence interval for the true proportion of travel vouchers that were filled out incorrectly in the last month.
   b. Find a point estimate of and a 95 percent confidence interval for the total number of travel vouchers that were filled out incorrectly in the last month.
   c. If it costs the company $10 to correct an erroneous travel voucher, find a reasonable estimate of the minimum cost of correcting all of last month's erroneous travel vouchers. Would it be worthwhile to spend $5,000 to design a simplified travel voucher that could be used for at least a year?

7.55 A personnel manager is estimating the total number of person-days lost to unexcused absences by hourly workers in the last year. In a random sample of 50 employees drawn without replacement from the 687 hourly workers at the company, records show that the 50 sampled workers had an average of $\bar{x} = 4.3$ days of unexcused absences over the past year with a standard deviation of $s = 1.26$.
   a. Find a point estimate of and a 95 percent confidence interval for the total number of unexcused absences by hourly workers in the last year.

   b. Can the personnel manager be 95 percent confident that more than 2,500 person-days were lost to unexcused absences last year? Can the manager be 95 percent confident that more than 3,000 person-days were lost to unexcused absences last year? Explain.

7.56 An auditor randomly samples 32 accounts receivable without replacement from a firm's 600 accounts and checks to verify that all documents for the accounts comply with company procedures. Ten of the 32 accounts are found to have documents not in compliance. Find a point estimate of and a 95 percent confidence interval for the total number of accounts with documents that do not comply with company procedures.

7.57 SAMPLE SIZES WHEN SAMPLING FINITE POPULATIONS

   a. *Estimating μ and τ*
   Consider randomly selecting a sample of n measurements without replacement from a finite population consisting of N measurements and having variance σ^2. Also consider the sample size given by the formula

   $$n = \frac{N\sigma^2}{(N-1)D + \sigma^2}.$$

   Then, it can be shown that this sample size makes the margin of error in a $100(1 - \alpha)$ percent confidence interval for μ equal to E if we set D equal to $(E/z_{\alpha/2})^2$. It can also be shown that this sample size makes the margin of error in a $100(1 - \alpha)$ percent confidence interval for τ equal to E if we set D equal to $[E/(z_{\alpha/2}N)]^2$. Now consider Exercise 7.55. Using $s^2 = (1.26)^2$, or 1.5876, as an estimate of σ^2, determine the sample size that makes the margin of error in a 95 percent confidence interval for the **total number** of person-days lost to unexcused absences last year equal to 100 days.

   b. *Estimating p and τ*
   Consider randomly selecting a sample of n units without replacement from a finite population consisting of N units and having a proportion p of these units fall into a particular category. Also consider the sample size given by the formula

   $$n = \frac{Np(1 - p)}{(N-1)D + p(1 - p)}.$$

   It can be shown that this sample size makes the margin of error in a $100(1 - \alpha)$ percent confidence interval for p equal to E if we set D equal to $(E/z_{\alpha/2})^2$. It can also be shown that this sample size makes the margin of error in a $100(1 - \alpha)$ percent confidence interval for τ equal to E if we set D equal to $[E/(z_{\alpha/2}N)]^2$. Now consider Exercise 7.54. Using $\hat{p} = 0.31$ as an estimate of p, determine the sample size that makes the margin of error in a 95 percent confidence interval for the **proportion** of the 1,323 vouchers that were filled out incorrectly equal to 0.04.

7.6 A Comparison of Confidence Intervals and Tolerance Intervals (Optional)

In this section, we compare confidence intervals with tolerance intervals. We saw in Chapter 2 that a tolerance interval is an interval that is meant to contain a specified percentage (often 68.26 percent, 95.44 percent, or 99.73 percent) of the **individual** population measurements. By contrast, a confidence interval for the population mean μ is an interval that is meant to contain one thing—the population mean μ—and the confidence level associated with the confidence interval expresses how sure we are that this interval contains μ. Often we choose the confidence level to be 95 percent or 99 percent because such a confidence level is usually considered high enough to provide convincing evidence about the true value of μ.

Example 7.13 DVD Prices

The mean and the standard deviation of a sample of 49 DVD price points (see Chapter 2) are $\bar{x} = 31.5531$ and $s = 0.7992$. Also it was found that the estimated tolerance intervals $[\bar{x} \pm s] = [30.8, \ 32.4]$, $[\bar{x} \pm 2s] = [30.0, \ 33.2]$, and $[\bar{x} \pm 3s] = [29.2, \ 34.0]$ imply that approximately (1) 68.26 percent of all individual DVDs will cost between \$30.80 and \$32.40, (2) 95.44 percent of all individual DVDs will cost between \$30.00 and \$33.20, and (3) 99.73 percent of all individual DVDs will cost between \$29.20 and \$34.00. A 95 percent t-based confidence interval for the mean, μ, of the prices of all individual DVDs is $[\bar{x} \pm 2.011(s/\sqrt{49})] = [31.32, \ 31.78]$. This interval says that we are 95 percent confident that μ is between \$31.32 and \$31.78. Figure 7.19 graphically depicts the three estimated tolerance

FIGURE 7.19   A Comparison of Confidence Intervals and Tolerance Intervals

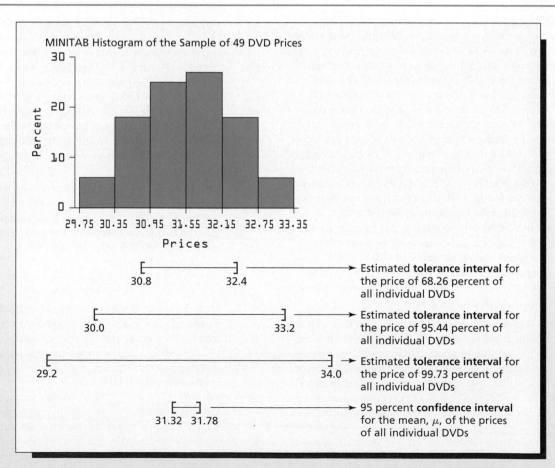

intervals and the 95 percent confidence interval, which are shown below a MINITAB histogram of the 49 prices. Note that the estimated tolerance intervals, which are meant to contain the **many** prices that make up specified percentages of all individual DVDs, are longer than the 95 percent confidence interval, which is meant to contain the **single** population mean μ.

Exercises for Section 7.6

CONCEPTS

7.58 What is a tolerance interval meant to contain?

7.59 What is a confidence interval for the population mean meant to contain?

7.60 Intuitively, why is a tolerance interval longer than a confidence interval?

METHODS AND APPLICATIONS

In Exercises 7.61 through 7.63, we give the mean and the standard deviation of a sample that has been randomly selected from a population. For each exercise, find estimated tolerance intervals that contain approximately 68.26 percent, 95.44 percent, and 99.73 percent of the individual population measurements. Also find a 95 percent confidence interval for the population mean. Interpret the estimated tolerance intervals and the confidence interval in the context of the situation related to the exercise.

7.61 THE TRASH BAG CASE 🔵 TrashBag

The mean and the standard deviation of the sample of 40 trash bag breaking strengths are $\bar{x} = 22.990$ and $s = 0.7428$.

7.62 THE BANK CUSTOMER WAITING TIME CASE 🔵 WaitTime

The mean and the standard deviation of the sample of 100 bank customer waiting times are $\bar{x} = 5.46$ and $s = 2.475$.

7.63 THE VIDEO GAME SATISFACTION RATING CASE 🔵 VideoGame

The mean and the standard deviation of the sample of 65 customer satisfaction ratings are $\bar{x} = 42.95$ and $s = 2.6424$.

CHAPTER SUMMARY

In this chapter, we discussed **confidence intervals** for population **means**, **proportions**, and **totals**. We began by assuming that the population is either infinite or much larger than (say, at least 20 times as large as) the sample. First, we studied how to compute a confidence interval for a **population mean**. We saw that when the population standard deviation σ is known, we can use the **normal distribution** to compute a confidence interval for a population mean. When σ is not known, if the population is normally distributed (or at least mound-shaped) or if the sample size n is large, we use the t **distribution** to compute this interval. We also studied how to find the size of the sample needed if we wish to compute a confidence interval for a mean with a prespecified **confidence level** and with a prespecified **margin of error**. Figure 7.20 is a flowchart summarizing our discussions concerning how to compute an appropriate confidence interval for a population mean.

Next we saw that we are often interested in estimating the proportion of population units falling into a category of interest. We showed how to compute a large sample confidence interval for a **population proportion**, and we saw how to find the sample size needed to estimate a population proportion with a prespecified **confidence level** and with a prespecified **margin of error**.

In optional Section 7.5, we continued by studying how to compute confidence intervals for parameters of **finite populations** that are not much larger than the sample. We saw how to compute confidence intervals for a population mean and total when we are sampling **without replacement**. We also saw how to compute confidence intervals for a population proportion and for the total number of units in a category when sampling a finite population. In optional Section 7.6, we concluded this chapter by comparing confidence intervals with tolerance intervals.

GLOSSARY OF TERMS

confidence coefficient: The (before-sampling) probability that a confidence interval for a population parameter will contain the population parameter. (page 203)

confidence interval: An interval of numbers computed so that we can be very confident (say, 95 percent confident) that a population parameter is contained in the interval. (page 201)

confidence level: The percentage of time that a confidence interval would contain a population parameter if all possible samples were used to calculate the interval. (page 204)

degrees of freedom (for a t curve): A parameter that describes the exact spread of the curve of a t distribution. (page 209)

margin of error: The quantity that is added to and subtracted from a point estimate of a population parameter to obtain a confidence interval for the parameter. It gives the maximum distance between the population parameter of interest and its point estimate when we assume the parameter is inside the confidence interval. (page 203)

population total: The sum of the values of all the population measurements. (page 226)

standard error of the estimate $\bar{x}$: The point estimate of $\sigma_{\bar{x}}$. (page 213)

t distribution: A commonly used continuous probability distribution that is described by a distribution curve similar to

FIGURE **7.20**   **Computing an Appropriate Confidence Interval for a Population Mean**

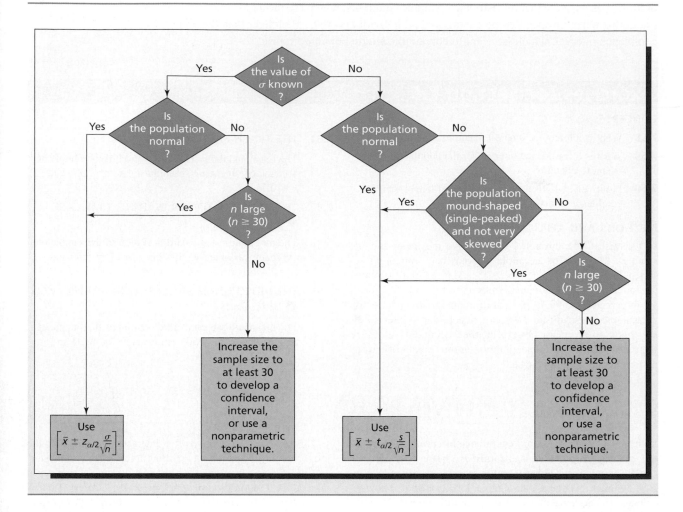

a normal curve. The *t* curve is symmetrical about zero and is more spread out than a standard normal curve. (page 209)

t point, t_α: The point on the horizontal axis under a *t* curve that gives a right-hand tail area equal to α. (page 209)

t table: A table of *t* point values listed according to the area in the tail of the *t* curve and according to values of the degrees of freedom. (pages 209–211)

IMPORTANT FORMULAS

A *z*-based confidence interval for a population mean μ with σ known: page 203

A *t*-based confidence interval for a population mean μ with σ unknown: page 211

Sample size when estimating μ: page 217

A large sample confidence interval for a population proportion *p*: page 219

Sample size when estimating *p*: page 221

Estimation of a mean and a total for a finite population: page 227

Estimation of a proportion and a total for a finite population: page 228

SUPPLEMENTARY EXERCISES

7.64   In an article in the *Journal of Accounting Research*, Ashton, Willingham, and Elliott studied audit delay (the length of time from a company's fiscal year-end to the date of the auditor's report) for industrial and financial companies. In the study, a random sample of 250 industrial companies yielded a mean audit delay of 68.04 days with a standard deviation of 35.72 days, while a random sample of 238 financial companies yielded a mean audit delay of 56.74 days with a standard deviation of 34.87 days. Use these sample results to do the following:

a. Calculate a 95 percent confidence interval for the mean audit delay for all industrial companies. Note: $t_{0.025} = 1.97$ when $df = 249$.

b. Calculate a 95 percent confidence interval for the mean audit delay for all financial companies. Note: $t_{0.025} = 1.97$ when $df = 237$.

c. Compare the 95 percent confidence intervals you calculated in parts a and b. Is there strong evidence that the mean audit delay for financial companies is shorter than the mean audit delay for industrial companies? Explain.

7.65 In an article in *Accounting and Business Research*, Beattie and Jones investigate the use and abuse of graphic presentations in the annual reports of U.K. firms. The authors found that 65 percent of the sampled companies graph at least one key financial variable, but that 30 percent of the graphics are materially distorted (nonzero vertical axis, exaggerated trend, or the like). Results for U.S. firms have been found to be similar.

a. Suppose that in a random sample of 465 graphics from the annual reports of U.K. firms, 142 of the graphics are found to be distorted. Find a point estimate of and a 95 percent confidence interval for the proportion of U.K. annual report graphics that are distorted.

b. Based on this interval, can we be 95 percent confident that more than 25 percent of all graphics appearing in the annual reports of U.K. firms are distorted? Explain. Does this suggest that auditors should understand proper graphing methods?

c. Determine the sample size needed in order to be 95 percent confident that $\hat{p}$, the sample proportion of U.K. annual report graphics that are distorted, is within a margin of error of 0.03 of p, the true proportion of U.K. annual report graphics that are distorted.

7.66 On November 3, 2006, Ipsos Reid conducted a survey on behalf of LG Electronics Canada to ask Canadians about their cell phone attitudes. Apparently size does matter! The study found that 82 percent indicated that size was an extremely important attribute for a cell phone. For this particular poll, 1,428 Canadians aged 18 or older who owned or were considering purchasing a cell phone in the next six months were surveyed.[7]

a. Based on these findings, calculate a 95 percent confidence interval for the proportion of all Canadians aged 18 or older who own or are considering purchasing a cell phone in the next six months who believe that size is important.

b. In explaining the survey methods, Ipsos Reid stated the following: "For results based on a sample of this size, the results are considered to be accurate to within ±2.6 percentage points." Explain how your calculations in part a verify that this statement is true.

7.67 The manager of a chain of discount department stores wishes to estimate the total number of erroneous discounts allowed by sales clerks during the last month.

A random sample of 200 of the chain's 57,532 transactions for the last month reveals that erroneous discounts were allowed on eight of the transactions. Use this sample information to find a point estimate of and a 95 percent confidence interval for the total number of erroneous discounts allowed during the last month.

7.68 Canadian Motor Products has equipped the ZX-900 with a new disc brake system. We define the stopping distance for a ZX-900 to be the distance (in metres) required to bring the automobile to a complete stop from a speed of 50 km/h under normal driving conditions using this new brake system. In addition, we define μ to be the mean stopping distance of all ZX-900s. One of the ZX-900's major competitors is advertised to achieve a mean stopping distance of 18 m. Canadian Motor Products would like to claim in a new advertising campaign that the ZX-900 achieves a shorter mean stopping distance.

Suppose that Canadian Motor Products randomly selects a sample of $n = 81$ ZX-900s. The company records the stopping distance of each automobile and calculates the mean and standard deviation of the sample of $n = 81$ stopping distances to be $\bar{x} = 17.6$ m and $s = 1.83$ m.

a. Calculate a 95 percent confidence interval for μ. Can Canadian Motor Products be 95 percent confident that μ is less than 18 m? Explain.

b. Using the sample of $n = 81$ stopping distances as a preliminary sample, find the sample size necessary to make Canadian Motor Products 95 percent confident that $\bar{x}$ is within a margin of error of 0.3 m of μ.

7.69 A large construction contractor is building 257 homes, which are in various stages of completion. For tax purposes, the contractor needs to estimate the total dollar value of its inventory due to construction in progress. The contractor randomly selects (without replacement) a sample of 40 of the 257 houses and determines the accumulated costs (the amount of money tied up in inventory) for each sampled house. The contractor finds that the sample mean accumulated cost is $\bar{x} = \$75,162.70$ and that the sample standard deviation is $s = \$28,865.04$.

a. Find a point estimate of and a 99 percent confidence interval for the total accumulated costs (total amount of money tied up in inventory) for all 257 homes that are under construction.

b. Using the confidence interval as the basis for your answer, find a reasonable estimate of the largest possible total dollar value of the contractor's inventory due to construction in progress.

7.70 In an article in the *Journal of Retailing*, Blodgett, Granbois, and Walters investigated negative word-of-mouth consumer behaviour. In a random sample of 201 consumers, 150 reported that they engaged in negative word-of-mouth behaviour (for instance, they vowed never to patronize a retailer again). In addition, the 150 respondents who engaged in such behaviour, on average, told 4.88 people about their dissatisfying experience (with a standard deviation equal to 6.11).

[7]Source: World Wide Web, http://www.ipsos-na.com/news/pressrelease.cfm?id=3248, "When it comes to cell phones size does matter," November 3, 2006.

a. Use these sample results to compute a 95 percent confidence interval for the proportion of all consumers who engage in negative word-of-mouth behaviour. On the basis of this interval, would it be reasonable to claim that more than 70 percent of all consumers engage in such behaviour? Explain.

b. Use the sample results to compute a 95 percent confidence interval for the mean number of people who are told about a dissatisfying experience by consumers who engage in negative word-of-mouth behaviour. On the basis of this interval, would it be reasonable to claim that these dissatisfied consumers tell, on average, at least three people about their bad experience? Explain. Note: $t_{0.025} = 1.98$ when $df = 149$.

7.71 A random sample of 50 perceived age estimates for a model in a liquor advertisement in a particular country showed that $\bar{x} = 26.22$ years and that $s = 3.7432$ years.   ◐ ModelAge

a. Use this sample to calculate a 95 percent confidence interval for the population mean age estimate for all viewers of the ad.

b. The liquor industry in this country requires that models must appear at least 25 years old. Does the confidence interval make us 95 percent confident that the mean perceived age estimate is at least 25? Is the mean perceived age estimate much more than 25? Explain.

7.72 In an article in the *Journal of Management Information Systems*, Mahmood and Mann investigate how information technology (IT) investment relates to company performance. In particular, Mahmood and Mann obtain sample data concerning IT investment for companies that effectively use information systems. Among the variables studied are the company's IT budget as a percentage of company revenue, percentages of the IT budget spent on staff and training, and number of PCs and terminals as a percentage of total employees.

a. Suppose a random sample of 15 companies considered to effectively use information systems yields a sample mean IT budget as a percentage of company revenue of $\bar{x} = 2.73$ with a standard deviation of $s = 1.64$. Assuming that IT budget percentages are approximately normally distributed, calculate a 99 percent confidence interval for the mean IT budget as a percentage of company revenue for all firms that effectively use information systems. Does this interval provide evidence that a firm can successfully use information systems with an IT budget that is less than 5 percent of company revenue? Explain.

b. Suppose a random sample of 15 companies considered to effectively use information systems yields a sample mean number of PCs and terminals as a percentage of total employees of $\bar{x} = 34.76$ with a standard deviation of $s = 25.37$. Assuming approximate normality, calculate a 99 percent confidence interval for the mean number of PCs and terminals as a percentage of total employees for all firms that effectively use information systems. Why is this interval so wide? What can we do to obtain a narrower (more useful) confidence interval?

7.73 THE INVESTMENT CASE

Suppose that random samples of 50 returns for each of the following investment classes give the indicated sample mean and sample standard deviation:

Fixed annuities: $\bar{x} = 7.83\%$, $s = 0.51\%$

Domestic large cap stocks: $\bar{x} = 13.42\%$, $s = 15.17\%$

Domestic midcap stocks: $\bar{x} = 15.03\%$, $s = 18.44\%$

Domestic small cap stocks: $\bar{x} = 22.51\%$, $s = 21.75\%$

a. For each investment class, compute a 95 percent confidence interval for the population mean return.

7.74 THE INTERNATIONAL BUSINESS TRAVEL EXPENSE CASE

Recall (see Exercise 2.77 on page 83) that the mean and the standard deviation of a random sample of 35 one-day travel expenses in Moscow are $\bar{x} = \$538$ and $s = \$41$. Find a 95 percent confidence interval for the mean, μ, of all one-day travel expenses in Moscow.

7.75 THE U.K. INSURANCE CASE

Assume that the U.K. insurance survey is based on 1,000 randomly selected U.K. households and that 640 of these households spent on life insurance in 1993. Find a 95 percent confidence interval for the proportion, p, of all U.K. households that spent on life insurance in 1993.

7.76 A local factory is responsible for bagging and shipping 1-kg bags of sugar. A random sample of sixteen 1-kg bags of sugar is obtained and the actual masses of the bags are measured. The sample mean is 1.051 kg with a sample standard deviation of $s = 0.06$ kg. The masses are approximately normally distributed. Calculate a 99 percent confidence interval for the average mass of all bags of sugar produced at this factory. Is it plausible that the true average mass of all bags produced at this factory is actually 1.02 kg and not 1 kg? Explain.

7.77 In Chapter 2, Exercise 2.8, we briefly described a series of international quality standards called ISO 9000. In the results of a Quality Systems Update/Deloitte & Touche survey of ISO 9000 registered companies published by CEEM Information Systems, 515 of 620 companies surveyed reported that they are encouraging their suppliers to pursue ISO 9000 registration.[8]

a. Using these survey results, compute a 95.44 percent confidence interval for the proportion of all ISO 9000 registered companies that encourage their suppliers to pursue ISO 9000 registration. Assume here that the survey participants were randomly selected.

b. Based on this interval, is there conclusive evidence that more than 75 percent of all ISO 9000 registered companies encourage their suppliers to pursue ISO 9000 registration?

---

[8]Source: *Is ISO 9000 for You?* (Fairfax, VA: CEEM Information Services).

7.78   INTERNET EXERCISE

What is the average selling price of a home? The Data and Story Library (DASL) contains data, including the sale price, for a random sample of 117 homes sold in Albuquerque, New Mexico. Go to the DASL Web site (http://lib.stat.cmu.edu/DASL/) and retrieve the home price data set (http://lib.stat.cmu.edu/DASL/Datafiles/homedat.html). Use MINITAB, Excel, or MegaStat to produce appropriate graphical (histogram, stem-and-leaf plot, box plot) and numerical summaries of the price data. Identify, from your numerical summaries, the sample mean and standard deviation. Use these summaries to construct a 99 percent confidence interval for μ, the mean sale price. Use statistical software (MINITAB, Excel, or MegaStat) to compute a 99 percent confidence interval for μ. Do the results of your hand calculations agree with those from your statistical software?

Technical Note: There are many ways to capture the home price data from the DASL site. One simple way is to select just the rows containing the data values (and not the labels), copy, paste directly into an Excel or MINITAB worksheet, add your own variable labels, and save the resulting worksheet. It is possible to copy the variable labels from DASL as well, but the differences in alignment and the intervening blank line add to the difficulty.   AlbHome

CHAPTER **8**

Hypothesis Testing

LEARNING OBJECTIVES

After reading this chapter, you should be able to

- define and contrast the null hypothesis (H_0) and the research (or alternative; H_a) hypothesis

- explain the difference between and define Type I (α) and Type II (β) errors

- understand which error type is the one most researchers are concerned about

- describe the steps involved in conducting a hypothesis test using a rejection point

- conduct hypothesis tests and take appropriate action or make appropriate decisions based on the results

- explain what is meant by the term *statistical significance*

- describe a situation in which a finding may be statistically significant but not practically significant

CHAPTER OUTLINE

8.1 The Null and Alternative Hypotheses and Errors in Hypothesis Testing

8.2 Type I and Type II Errors and Their Probabilities

8.3 z Tests about a Population Mean (σ Known): One-Sided Alternatives

8.4 z Tests about a Population Mean (σ Known): Two-Sided Alternatives

8.5 t Tests about a Population Mean (σ Unknown)

8.6 z Tests about a Population Proportion

Imagine that you are walking down railway tracks and listening to a digital music player with your headphones on. You hear a noise, and you are not sure what it is. It might be a train, but it might not be. You have two choices to make. You could ignore the sound, and keep walking on the tracks, or you could jump away from the tracks and look behind you. You have, in effect, just conducted your own hypothesis test. In this test, there are two errors to consider. One of these errors is harmless (jumping off when no train is coming) and one could be fatal (ignoring the noise, but that noise is actually a train coming). In this chapter, we discuss testing hypotheses about population means, proportions, and variances.

In order to illustrate how hypothesis testing works, we revisit several cases introduced in previous chapters.

The Payment Time Case. The consulting firm uses hypothesis testing to provide strong evidence that the new electronic billing system has reduced the mean payment time by more than 50 percent.

The Cheese Spread Case. The cheese spread producer uses hypothesis testing to supply extremely strong evidence that less than 10 percent of all current purchasers would stop buying the cheese spread if the new spout were used.

The Electronic Article Surveillance Case. A company that sells and installs electronic article surveillance (EAS) systems claims that no more than 5 percent of all consumers would say they would never shop in a store again if the store subjected them to a false EAS alarm. A store considering the purchase of such a system uses hypothesis testing to provide extremely strong evidence that this claim is not true.

In addition, we introduce two new cases that illustrate how to test a hypothesis:

The Beer Case. A beer drinker uses hypothesis testing to support a claim that the mean volume of beer in the bottle is less than 341 mL. As a result, the consumer will file a complaint with the brewery (and maybe get some free beer).

The Camshaft Case. An automobile manufacturer uses hypothesis testing to study an important quality characteristic affecting V6 engine camshafts. It finds that the mean "hardness depth" differs from its desired target value and that this problem is one reason why some of the hardness depths fail to meet specifications.

8.1 The Null and Alternative Hypotheses and Errors in Hypothesis Testing

CHAPTER 9

One of the authors' former students is employed by a major television network in the standards and practices division. One of the division's responsibilities is to reduce the chances that advertisers will make false claims in commercials run on the network. To test claims, the network uses a statistical methodology called **hypothesis testing**.

To see how this might be done, suppose that a company wishes to advertise a claim, and suppose that the network has reason to doubt that this claim is true. The network assumes that **the claim is not valid**. This assumption is called the **null hypothesis** (denoted H_0). The statement that **the claim is valid** is called the **alternative**, or **research**, **hypothesis** (denoted H_a). The network will run the commercial only if the company making the claim provides **sufficient sample evidence** to reject the null hypothesis that the claim is not valid in favour of the alternative hypothesis that the claim is valid.

The Null Hypothesis and the Alternative Hypothesis

In hypothesis testing:

1   The **null hypothesis**, denoted H_0, is the statement being tested. Usually this statement represents the status quo and is not rejected unless there is convincing sample evidence that it is false.

2   The **alternative**, or **research**, **hypothesis**, denoted H_a, is a statement that will be accepted only if there is convincing sample evidence that it is true.

Setting up the null and alternative hypotheses in a practical situation can be tricky. In some situations, there is a condition for which we need to attempt to find supportive evidence. We then formulate (1) the alternative hypothesis to be the statement that this condition exists and (2) the null hypothesis to be the statement that this condition does not exist. To illustrate this, we consider the following case study.

Example 8.1 The Payment Time Case

Recall (see Example 6.3 on page 189) that a management consulting firm has installed a new computer-based, electronic billing system in a trucking company. Because of the system's advantages, and because the trucking company's clients are receptive to using this system, the management consulting firm believes that the new system will reduce the mean bill payment time by more than 50 percent. The mean payment time using the old billing system was approximately equal to, but no less than, 39 days. Therefore, if μ denotes the mean payment time using the new system, the consulting firm believes that μ will be less than 19.5 days. Because it is hoped that the new billing system **reduces** mean payment time, we formulate the alternative hypothesis as H_a: $\mu < 19.5$ and the null hypothesis as H_0: $\mu \geq 19.5$. The consulting firm will randomly select a sample of n invoices and determine how much evidence their payment times provide to reject H_0 in favour of H_a. The firm will use the results of the hypothesis test to demonstrate the benefits of the new

billing system both to the company and to other trucking companies that are considering using such a system. Note, however, that a potential user will decide whether to install the new system by considering factors beyond the results of the hypothesis test. For example, the cost of the new billing system and the receptiveness of the company's clients to using the new system are other factors that must be considered. In complex business and industrial situations such as this, hypothesis testing is used to accumulate knowledge about and understand the problem at hand. The ultimate decision (such as whether to adopt the new billing system) is made on the basis of non-statistical considerations, intuition, and the results of one or more hypothesis tests.

Example 8.2 **The Camshaft Case**

On March 8, 1999, Coltec Industries of Charlotte, North Carolina, made an alarming discovery. A Coltec quality control study revealed that the company had supplied Consolidated Edison–Indian Point 2 nuclear power plant with inadequately hardened engine camshafts. The suspect camshafts were a significant safety hazard because they could cause failure of FM-ALCO 251 engines, which the power plant used to run emergency standby power generators. Although Coltec was not aware of any engine failures in nuclear power plants, such failures had occurred in commercial applications after approximately 200 hours of operation. Coltec immediately reported its conclusions to the U.S. Nuclear Regulatory Commission, and a crisis was averted at the Consolidated Edison plant. Coltec also substantially improved its camshaft inspection process so that the problem would not occur again. (Source: http://www.nrc.gov/reading-rm/doc-collections/event-status/part21/1999/1999161.html.)

In general, an engine camshaft is an important engine part used in a variety of commercial and industrial applications. For example, the camshaft of a V6 automobile engine is illustrated in Figure 8.1. Positioned on this (or any) camshaft are metal disks called **eccentrics**. As the camshaft turns, these eccentrics repeatedly make contact with **engine lifters** and thus must have the appropriate hardness to wear properly. To harden the eccentrics, the camshaft is heat treated, and a hardened layer is produced on the surface of the camshaft. The depth of this layer is called the **hardness depth** of the camshaft. If the hardness depth of a camshaft is within given specifications, the camshaft will wear properly, resulting in long engine life.

FIGURE **8.1** **A Camshaft and Related Parts**

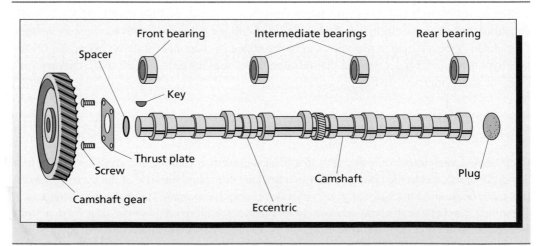

To illustrate how we might use a hypothesis test to study camshaft hardness, we consider an automobile manufacturer that is having problems properly hardening the camshaft of a V6 automobile engine. The **optimal**, or **target**, hardness depth of this camshaft is 4.5 mm, and specifications state that, in order for the camshaft to wear properly, the hardness depth must be between 3.0 mm and 6.0 mm. Unfortunately, however, the hardening process has been producing too many out-of-specification camshafts. To investigate why this is so, a quality control analyst randomly selects n camshafts from the population of all camshafts produced on a particular day and measures the hardness depth of each sampled camshaft. Then, letting μ denote the population mean hardness depth of all camshafts produced that day, the analyst will evaluate whether μ differs from the target value of 4.5 mm by testing the null hypothesis H_0: $\mu = 4.5$ versus the alternative hypothesis H_a: $\mu \neq 4.5$. Of course, μ differing from 4.5 is not the only reason the hardness depths of the camshafts produced on the particular day might be out of specification. Another reason might be that the variation of the hardness depths is too large.

We next summarize the sets of null and alternative hypotheses that we have thus far considered.

$$H_0: \mu \geq 19.5 \qquad\qquad H_0: \mu = 4.5$$
$$\text{versus} \qquad\qquad\qquad \text{versus}$$
$$H_a: \mu < 19.5 \qquad\qquad H_a: \mu \neq 4.5$$

In general, H_a: $\mu > x$ is called a **one-sided, greater than** alternative hypothesis; H_a: $\mu < x$ is called a **one-sided, less than** alternative hypothesis; and H_a: $\mu \neq x$ is called a **two-sided, not equal to** alternative hypothesis. Many of the alternative hypotheses we consider in this book are one of these three types. Also note that each null hypothesis we have considered involves an **equality**. For example, the null hypothesis H_0: $\mu \geq 19.5$ says that μ is either greater than or **equal to** 19.5. We will see that, in general, the approach we use to test a null hypothesis versus an alternative hypothesis requires that the null hypothesis involve an equality.

The idea of a test statistic   Suppose that in the electronic billing case the consultant randomly selects a sample of $n = 40$ new invoices. The sample mean $\bar{x}$ of the 40 payment times is calculated. In order to test H_0: $\mu \geq 19.5$ versus H_a: $\mu < 19.5$, we utilize the **test statistic**

$$z = \frac{\bar{x} - 19.5}{\sigma_{\bar{x}}} = \frac{\bar{x} - 19.5}{\sigma / \sqrt{n}}.$$

The test statistic z measures the distance between $\bar{x}$ and 19.5. The division by $\sigma_{\bar{x}}$ says that this distance is measured in units of the standard deviation of all possible sample means. For example, a value of z equal to, say, 2.4 would tell us that $\bar{x}$ is 2.4 standard deviations above 19.5. In general, the value of the test statistic is less than or equal to zero when $\bar{x}$ is less than or equal to μ, and the value of the test statistic is greater than zero when $\bar{x}$ is greater than μ. Furthermore, the farther the value of the test statistic is from 0 (the farther $\bar{x}$ is away from μ), the stronger is the evidence to support rejecting H_0 in favour of H_a.

Hypothesis testing and the legal system   If the value of the test statistic z is far enough from 0, we reject H_0 in favour of H_a. To see how large z must be in order to reject H_0, we must understand that **a hypothesis test rejects a null hypothesis H_0 only if there is strong statistical evidence against H_0.** This is similar to our legal system, which rejects the innocence of the accused only if evidence of guilt is beyond a reasonable doubt. A test statistic that is only slightly greater than or less than 0 might not be convincing enough. However, because such a test statistic would result from a sample mean $\bar{x}$ that is slightly different from μ, it would provide some evidence to support rejecting H_0, and it certainly would not provide strong evidence supporting H_0. Therefore, if the value of the test statistic is not large enough to convince us to reject H_0, **we do not say that we accept H_0. Rather we say that we do not reject H_0** (or we fail to reject H_0) because the evidence against H_0 is not strong enough. Again this is similar to our legal system, where the lack of evidence of guilt beyond a reasonable doubt results in a verdict of **not guilty** but does not prove that the accused is innocent.

Example 8.3 The Beer Case

Suppose that we believe that our favourite beer supplier is underfilling its 341-mL bottles of beer. We want to use hypothesis testing to provide strong evidence that this is true. In order to test this hypothesis, we randomly sample $n = 30$ bottles of beer. Suppose that it is known that the standard deviation of the volume of beer in each bottle is $\sigma = 2$ mL. We determine that $\bar{x} = 340.1$ mL for our sample. We will use the appropriate test to determine if our belief is valid.

We will test $H_0: \mu = 341$ mL versus $H_a: \mu < 341$ mL.

We will first calculate the test statistic

$$
\begin{aligned}
z &= \frac{\bar{x} - 341}{\sigma/\sqrt{n}} \\
&= \frac{340.1 - 341}{2/\sqrt{30}} \\
&= -2.46.
\end{aligned}
$$

Since we are 2.46 standard deviations away from the mean, this provides evidence that we can reject H_0. Later in the chapter, we will learn how to calculate a p value based on this test statistic, and this p value will allow us to make our decision based on a predetermined value of α.

For now, we will say that our data suggest that there is little evidence to support H_0. Therefore, we reject H_0.

8.2 Type I and Type II Errors and Their Probabilities

To determine exactly how much statistical evidence is required to reject H_0, we consider the errors and the correct decisions that can be made in hypothesis testing. These errors and correct decisions are summarized in Table 8.1. Across the top of the table are listed the two possible **states of nature**. Either H_0 is true or H_0 is false. Down the left side of each table are listed the two possible decisions we can make in the hypothesis test. Using the sample data, we will either reject H_0 or we will not reject H_0.

TABLE **8.1** Type I and Type II Errors

Decision	State of Nature	
	H_0 **True**	H_0 **False**
Reject H_0	Type I error	Correct decision
Do not reject H_0	Correct decision	Type II error

In general, the two types of errors that can be made in hypothesis testing are defined here:

Type I and Type II Errors

If we reject H_0 when it is true, this is a **Type I error**.
If we do not reject H_0 when it is false, this is a **Type II error**.

As can be seen in Table 8.1, if we commit a Type I error, we will make a false claim. If we commit a Type II error, we will fail to make a true claim.

We now let the symbol α (alpha) **denote the probability of a Type I error**, and we let β (beta) **denote the probability of a Type II error**. Obviously, we would like both α and β to be small. A common (but not the only) procedure is to base a hypothesis test on taking a sample of a fixed size (for example, $n = 40$ surveys) and on setting α equal to a small prespecified value. Setting α low means there is only a small chance of rejecting H_0 when it is true. This implies that we are requiring strong evidence against H_0 before we reject it.

We sometimes choose α as high as 0.10, but we usually choose α between 0.05 and 0.01. A frequent choice for α is 0.05. Since a Type I error is deciding that H_a is valid when it is not, the policy of setting α equal to 0.05 says that, in the long run, only 5 percent of all claims made will be false.

One might wonder why researchers do not set α lower—say at 0.01. One reason is that **it can be shown that, for a fixed sample size, the lower we set α, the higher is β, and the higher we set α, the lower is β**. Setting α at 0.05 means that β, the probability of failing to make a true claim (a Type II error), will be smaller than it would be if α were set at 0.01. As long as (1) the claim is plausible and (2) the consequences of making the claim even if it is false are not terribly serious, then it is reasonable to set α equal to 0.05. However, if either (1) or (2) is not true, then we might set α lower than 0.05. For example, suppose a pharmaceutical company wishes to advertise that it has developed an effective treatment for a disease that has formerly been very resistant to treatment. Such a claim may be difficult to believe. Moreover, if the claim is false, patients suffering from the disease would be subjected to false hope and needless expense. In such a case, it might be reasonable for the company to set α at 0.01 because this would lower the chance of advertising the claim if it is false. We usually do not set α lower than 0.01 because doing so often leads to an unacceptably large value of β. However, β can be difficult or impossible to calculate in many situations, and we often must rely on our intuition when deciding how to set α.

One additional point to be made about Type II (β) errors is that they are typically theoretical in nature. Knowing β suggests that we know what the "real world" (the population) is actually like, and if we really knew this, then we would probably not be taking a sample (because samples are taken to estimate what is happening in the population). A Type I (α) error, on the other hand, is a greater issue. Making a claim that there is an effect or rejecting the null hypothesis (the status quo) is a bigger deal than playing it safe and saying there is no effect or failing to reject H_0. Because of this, the Type I (α) error is a more applied issue (as opposed to the more theoretical Type II error).

Exercises for Sections 8.1 and 8.2

CONCEPTS

8.1 Which hypothesis (the null hypothesis, H_0, or the alternative hypothesis, H_a) is the status quo hypothesis (that is, the hypothesis that states that things are remaining as is)? Which hypothesis is the hypothesis that says that a "hoped for" or "suspected" condition exists?

8.2 Which hypothesis (H_0 or H_a) is not rejected unless there is convincing sample evidence that it is false? Which hypothesis (H_0 or H_a) will be accepted only if there is convincing sample evidence that it is true?

8.3 Define each of the following:
  a. Type I error.   **c.** α.
  b. Type II error.   **d.** β.

8.4 For each of the following situations, indicate whether an error has occurred and, if so, indicate what kind of error (Type I or Type II) has occurred. Try not to refer to Table 8.1.
  a. We do not reject H_0 and H_0 is true.
  b. We reject H_0 and H_0 is true.
  c. We do not reject H_0 and H_0 is false.
  d. We reject H_0 and H_0 is false.

8.5 If we reject H_0, what is the only type of error that we could be making? Explain.

8.6 If we do not reject H_0, what is the only type of error that we could be making? Explain.

8.7 When testing a hypothesis, why do we not set the probability of a Type I error to be extremely small? Explain.

METHODS AND APPLICATIONS

8.8 THE VIDEO GAME SATISFACTION RATING CASE ⓢ VideoGame

Recall from Exercise 1.8 on pages 9–10 that "very satisfied" customers give the XYZ-Box video game system a rating that is at least 42. Suppose that the manufacturer of the XYZ-Box wishes to use the 65 satisfaction ratings to provide evidence supporting the claim that the mean composite satisfaction rating for the XYZ-Box exceeds 42.
  a. Letting μ represent the mean composite satisfaction rating for the XYZ-Box, set up the null and alternative hypotheses needed if we wish to attempt to provide evidence supporting the claim that μ exceeds 42.
  b. In the context of this situation, interpret making a Type I error; interpret making a Type II error.

8.9 THE BANK CUSTOMER WAITING TIME CASE ⓢ WaitTime

Recall from Exercise 1.9 on page 10 that a bank manager has developed a new system to reduce the time customers spend waiting for teller service during peak hours. The manager hopes the new system will reduce waiting times from the current 9 to 10 minutes to less than 6 minutes.

Suppose the manager wishes to use the 100 waiting times to support the claim that the mean waiting time under the new system is shorter than six minutes.
  a. Letting μ represent the mean waiting time under the new system, set up the null and alternative hypotheses

needed if we wish to attempt to provide evidence supporting the claim that μ is shorter than six minutes.

b. In the context of this situation, interpret making a Type I error; interpret making a Type II error.

8.10 An automobile parts supplier owns a machine that produces a cylindrical engine part. This part is supposed to have an outside diameter of 3 cm. Parts with diameters that are too small or too large do not meet customer requirements and must be rejected. Lately, the company has experienced problems meeting customer requirements. The technical staff feels that the mean diameter produced by the machine is off target. In order to verify this, a special study will randomly sample 100 parts produced by the machine. The 100 sampled parts will be measured, and if the results obtained cast a substantial amount of doubt on the hypothesis that the mean diameter equals the target value of 3 cm, the company will assign a problem-solving team to intensively search for the causes of the problem.

a. The parts supplier wishes to set up a hypothesis test so that the problem-solving team will be assigned when the null hypothesis is rejected. Set up the null and alternative hypotheses for this situation.

b. In the context of this situation, interpret making a Type I error; interpret making a Type II error.

c. Suppose it costs the company $3,000 a day to assign the problem-solving team to a project. Is this $3,000 figure the daily cost of a Type I error or a Type II error? Explain.

8.11 The Classic Bottling Company has just installed a new bottling process that will fill 355-mL cans of its Classic Cola soft drink. Both overfilling and underfilling cans are undesirable: Underfilling leads to customer complaints and overfilling costs the company considerable money. In order to verify that the filler is set up correctly, the company wishes to see whether the mean can fill, μ, is close to the target fill of 355 mL. To this end, a random sample of 36 filled cans is selected from the output of a test filler run. If the sample results cast a substantial amount of doubt on the hypothesis that the mean can fill is the desired 355 mL, then the filler's initial setup will be adjusted.

a. The bottling company wants to set up a hypothesis test so that the filler will be adjusted if the null hypothesis is rejected. Set up the null and alternative hypotheses for this hypothesis test.

b. In the context of this situation, interpret making a Type I error; interpret making a Type II error.

8.12 A large electric power utility has just built a modern nuclear power plant. This plant discharges waste water that is allowed to flow into a lake. The Ministry of the Environment has ordered that the waste water not be excessively warm so that thermal pollution of the marine environment near the plant can be avoided. Because of this order, the waste water is allowed to cool in specially constructed ponds and is then released into the lake. This cooling system works properly if the mean temperature of waste water discharged is 15°C or less. The utility is required to monitor the temperature of the waste water. A sample of 100 temperature readings will be obtained each day, and if the sample results cast a substantial amount of doubt on the hypothesis that the cooling system is working properly (the mean temperature of waste water discharged is 15°C or less), then the plant must be shut down and appropriate actions must be taken to correct the problem.

a. The utility wishes to set up a hypothesis test so that the power plant will be shut down when the null hypothesis is rejected. Set up the null and alternative hypotheses that should be used.

b. In the context of this situation, interpret making a Type I error; interpret making a Type II error.

c. The ministry periodically conducts spot checks to determine whether the waste water being discharged is too warm. Suppose the ministry has the power to impose very severe penalties (for example, very heavy fines) when the waste water is excessively warm. Other things being equal, should the utility set the probability of a Type I error equal to $\alpha = 0.01$ or $\alpha = 0.05$? Explain.

d. Suppose the utility has been experiencing technical problems with the cooling system. Because the system has been unreliable, the company feels it must take precautions to avoid failing to shut down the plant when its waste water is too warm. Other things being equal, should the utility set the probability of a Type I error equal to $\alpha = 0.01$ or $\alpha = 0.05$? Explain.

8.13 THE DISC BRAKE CASE

Canadian Motor Products has equipped the ZX-900 with a new disc brake system. We define the stopping distance for a ZX-900 as the distance (in metres) required to bring the automobile to a complete stop from a speed of 50 km/h under normal driving conditions using this new brake system. In addition, we define μ to be the mean stopping distance of all ZX-900s. One of the ZX-900's major competitors is advertised to achieve a mean stopping distance of 18 m. Canadian Motor Products would like to claim in a new television commercial that the ZX-900 achieves a shorter mean stopping distance. The standards and practices division of a major television network will permit Canadian Motor Products to run the commercial if $H_0: \mu \geq 18$ can be rejected in favour of $H_a: \mu < 18$ by setting $\alpha = 0.05$. Interpret what it means to set α at 0.05.

8.3 z Tests about a Population Mean (σ Known): One-Sided Alternatives

CHAPTER 9

In this (and the next) section, we discuss hypothesis tests about a population mean that are **based on the normal distribution**. These tests are called z **tests**, and they require that the **true value of the population standard deviation σ be known**. Of course in almost all real-world situations the true value of σ is not known. However, the concepts and calculations of hypothesis testing are most easily illustrated using the normal distribution. Therefore, in this (and the next) section, we will assume that, through extensive experience with the population or process under consideration, we know σ. When σ is unknown, we test hypotheses about a population mean by using the *t* **distribution**. In Section 8.5, we study *t* **tests**, and we will revisit the examples of this (and the next) section assuming that σ is unknown.

Testing a "greater than" alternative hypothesis by using a rejection point rule   In Sections 8.1 and 8.2, we explained how to set up appropriate null and alternative hypotheses. We also discussed how to specify a value for α, the probability of a Type I error (also called the **level of significance**) of the hypothesis test, and we introduced the idea of a test statistic. We can use these concepts to begin developing a seven-step hypothesis testing procedure. We will introduce these steps in the context of monthly cable TV subscriptions costs and testing a "greater than" alternative hypothesis.

A marketing company has suggested that the cost of monthly cable TV subscriptions has risen dramatically, which is causing more people to use illegal satellite dishes. Cable TV companies claim that their full cable package subscriptions cost on average $50 a month. The marketing company wants to demonstrate that the cost is significantly greater than $50 and randomly selects 40 cable TV subscribers and determines the price they pay for their monthly cable.

Step 1: State the null hypothesis H_0 and the alternative hypothesis H_a. In this case, we will test H_0: $\mu \leq 50$ versus H_a: $\mu > 50$. Here μ is the mean subscription cost.
Step 2: Specify the level of significance α. The marketing company will be able to support its claim that cable subscription costs have risen if we can reject H_0: $\mu \leq 50$ in favour of H_a: $\mu > 50$ by setting α equal to 0.05.
Step 3: Select the test statistic. In order to test H_0: $\mu \leq 50$ versus H_a: $\mu > 50$, we will test the modified null hypothesis H_0: $\mu = 50$ versus H_a: $\mu > 50$. The idea here is that if there is sufficient evidence to reject the hypothesis that μ equals 50 in favour of $\mu > 50$, then there is certainly also sufficient evidence to reject the hypothesis that μ is less than or equal to 50. In order to test H_0: $\mu = 50$ versus H_a: $\mu > 50$, we randomly select a sample of $n = 40$ subscribers and calculate the mean $\bar{x}$ of the monthly costs. We will then utilize the **test statistic**

$$z = \frac{\bar{x} - 50}{\sigma_{\bar{x}}} = \frac{\bar{x} - 50}{\sigma/\sqrt{n}}.$$

A positive value of this test statistic results from an $\bar{x}$ that is greater than 50 and thus provides evidence against H_0: $\mu = 50$ and in favour of H_a: $\mu > 50$.
Step 4: Determine the rejection point rule for deciding whether to reject H_0. To decide how large the test statistic must be to reject H_0 in favour of H_a by setting the probability of a Type I error equal to α, we do the following:

- Place the probability of a Type I error, α, in the right-hand tail of the standard normal curve and use the normal table (see Table A.3) to find the normal point z_α. Here z_α, which we call a **rejection point** (or **critical point**), is the point on the horizontal axis under the standard normal curve that gives a right-hand tail area equal to α.

- **Reject H_0: $\mu = 50$ in favour of H_a: $\mu > 50$ if and only if the test statistic z is greater than the rejection point z_α.** This is the **rejection point rule**.

Figure 8.2 illustrates that since we have set α equal to 0.05, we should use the rejection point $z_\alpha = z_{0.05} = 1.645$ (see Table A.3). This says that we should reject H_0 if $z > 1.645$ and we should not reject H_0 if $z \leq 1.645$.

To more fully explain what it means to set α equal to 0.05 and to use the rejection point rule, we consider the sampling distribution of the test statistic z. Because the sample size $n = 40$ is moderately large, the central limit theorem tells us that the sampling distribution of $(\bar{x} - \mu)/\sigma_{\bar{x}}$ is (approximately) a standard normal distribution. It follows that if the null hypothesis H_0: $\mu = 50$ is true, then the sampling distribution of the test statistic $z = (\bar{x} - 50)/\sigma_{\bar{x}}$ is (approximately) a standard normal distribution. Therefore, examining the standard normal curve in Figure 8.2, we can see that the areas under this curve imply the following:

- If H_0: $\mu = 50$ is true, 95 percent of all possible values of the test statistic z are less than or equal to $z_{0.05} = 1.645$ and thus would tell us not to reject H_0: $\mu = 50$—a correct decision.

FIGURE 8.2   The Rejection Point for Testing $H_0: \mu = 50$ versus $H_a: \mu > 50$ by Setting $\alpha =$

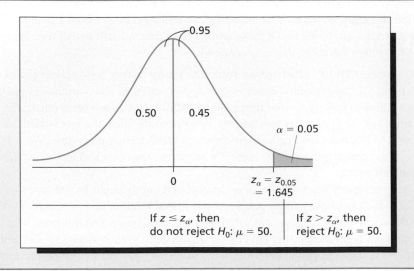

- If $H_0: \mu = 50$ is true, 5 percent of all possible values of the test statistic z are greater than $z_{0.05} = 1.645$ and thus would tell us to reject $H_0: \mu = 50$: a Type I error.

These two statements explain what it means to set α equal to 0.05 and to use the rejection point rule.
Step 5: Collect the sample data and compute the value of the test statistic. When the sample of $n = 40$ subscriptions is randomly selected, the mean of the cable costs is calculated to be $\bar{x} = 50.575$. Assuming that σ is known to equal 1.65, the value of the test statistic is

$$ z = \frac{\bar{x} - 50}{\sigma/\sqrt{n}} = \frac{50.575 - 50}{1.65/\sqrt{40}} = 2.20. $$

Step 6: Decide whether to reject H_0 by using the test statistic value and the rejection point rule. Since the test statistic value $z = 2.20$ is greater than the rejection point $z_{0.05} = 1.645$, we can reject $H_0: \mu = 50$ in favour of $H_a: \mu > 50$ by setting α equal to 0.05. Furthermore, we can be intuitively confident that $H_0: \mu = 50$ is false and $H_a: \mu > 50$ is true. This is because, since we have rejected H_0 by setting α equal to 0.05, we have rejected H_0 by using a test that allows only a 5 percent chance of wrongly rejecting H_0. In general, if we can reject a null hypothesis in favour of an alternative hypothesis by setting the probability of a Type I error equal to α, we say that we have **statistical significance at the α level**.
Step 7: Interpret the statistical results in managerial (real-world) terms and assess their practical importance. Since we have rejected $H_0: \mu = 50$ in favour of $H_a: \mu > 50$ by setting α equal to 0.05, we conclude (at an α of 0.05) that the average monthly cable subscription cost exceeds \$50. Note, however, that the point estimate of μ, $\bar{x} = 50.575$, indicates that μ is not much larger than 50. Therefore, the marketing company can claim only that cable subscription costs are slightly higher than is claimed by cable companies. This difference between what cable companies claim are the average monthly subscription costs and the sample mean value may be of importance to cable subscribers. Some subscribers may find that any subscription cost greater than \$50 a month is too high and will then look for alternative sources for their television programs. Other subscribers may feel that the difference of \$0.575 (or 58 cents) is trivial and will stick with their cable TV subscriptions. This illustrates that, in general, a finding of statistical significance (that is, concluding that the alternative hypothesis is true) can be practically important to some people but not to others. Notice that the point estimate of the parameter involved in a hypothesis test can help us to assess practical importance. We can also use confidence intervals to help assess practical importance, as will be illustrated in Section 8.4.

Considerations in setting α   We have reasoned above that the marketing company has set α equal to 0.05 rather than 0.01 because doing so means that β, the probability of failing to make

FIGURE 8.3 The Rejection Points for Testing the Average Cable Subscription Cost $H_0: \mu = 50$ versus $H_a: \mu > 50$ by Setting $\alpha = 0.05$ and 0.01

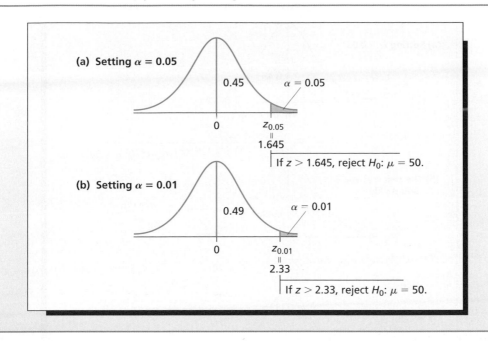

a true claim (a Type II error), will be smaller than it would be if α were set at 0.01. It is informative, however, to see what would have happened if the company had set α equal to 0.01. Figure 8.3 illustrates that as we decrease α from 0.05 to 0.01, the rejection point z_α increases from $z_{0.05} = 1.645$ to $z_{0.01} = 2.33$. Because the test statistic value $z = 2.20$ is less than $z_{0.01} = 2.33$, we cannot reject $H_0: \mu = 50$ in favour of $H_a: \mu > 50$ by setting α equal to 0.01. This illustrates the point that, the smaller we set α, the larger is the rejection point, and thus the stronger is the statistical evidence that we are requiring to reject the null hypothesis H_0. Some statisticians have concluded (somewhat subjectively) that (1) **if we set α equal to 0.05, then we are requiring strong evidence to reject H_0,** and (2) **if we set α equal to 0.01, then we are requiring very strong evidence to reject H_0.**

A *p* value for testing a "greater than" alternative hypothesis To decide whether to reject the null hypothesis H_0 at level of significance α, steps 4, 5, and 6 of the seven-step hypothesis testing procedure compare the test statistic value with a rejection point. Another way to make this decision is to calculate a *p* **value,** which measures the likelihood of the sample results if the null hypothesis H_0 is true. Sample results that are not likely if H_0 is true are evidence that H_0 is not true. To test H_0 by using a *p* value, we use the following steps 4, 5, and 6:

Step 4: Collect the sample data and compute the value of the test statistic. In the cable subscription example, we have computed the value of the test statistic to be $z = 2.20$.

Step 5: Calculate the *p* value by using the test statistic value. The *p* value for testing H_0: $\mu = 50$ versus $H_a: \mu > 50$ is the area under the standard normal curve to the right of the test statistic value $z = 2.20$. As illustrated in Figure 8.4(b), this area is $0.5 - 0.4861 = 0.0139$. The *p* value is the probability, computed assuming that $H_0: \mu = 50$ is true, of observing a value of the test statistic that is greater than or equal to the value $z = 2.20$ that we have actually computed from the sample data. The *p* value of 0.0139 says that, if $H_0: \mu = 50$ is true, only 139 in 10 000 of all possible test statistic values are at least as large, or extreme, as the value $z = 2.20$. That is, if we are to believe that H_0 is true, we must believe that we have observed a test statistic value that can be described as a 139 in 10,000 chance. Because it is difficult to believe that we have observed a 139 in 10,000 chance, we intuitively have strong evidence that $H_0: \mu = 50$ is false and $H_a: \mu > 50$ is true.

FIGURE 8.4   Testing H_0: $\mu = 50$ versus H_a: $\mu > 50$ by Using Rejection Points and the p Value

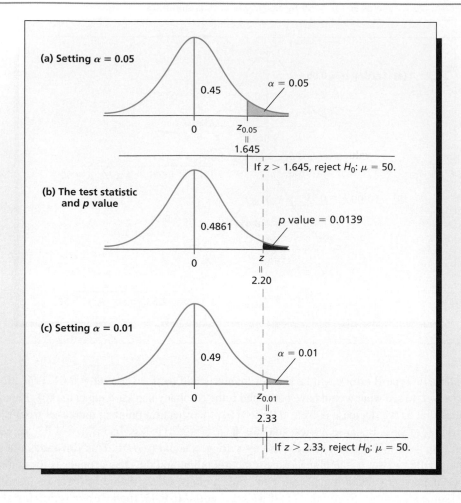

Step 6: Reject H_0 if the p value is less than α. Recall that the marketing company has set α equal to 0.05. **The p value of 0.0139 is less than the α of 0.05.** Comparing the two normal curves in Figure 8.4(a) and (b), we see that this implies that the test statistic value $z = 2.20$ is greater than the rejection point $z_{0.05} = 1.645$. Therefore, **we can reject H_0 by setting α equal to 0.05.** As another example, suppose that the marketing company had set α equal to 0.01. **The p value of 0.0139 is greater than the α of 0.01.** Comparing the two normal curves in Figure 8.4(b) and (c), we see that this implies that the test statistic value $z = 2.20$ is less than the rejection point $z_{0.01} = 2.33$. Therefore, **we cannot reject H_0 by setting α equal to 0.01.** Generalizing these examples, we conclude that the value of the test statistic z will be greater than the rejection point z_α if and only if the p value is less than α. That is, we can reject H_0 in favour of H_a at level of significance α if and only if the p value is less than α.

Comparing the rejection point and p value methods   Thus far we have considered two methods for testing H_0: $\mu = 50$ versus H_a: $\mu > 50$ at the 0.05 and 0.01 values of α. Using the first method, we determine if the test statistic value $z = 2.20$ is greater than the rejection points $z_{0.05} = 1.645$ and $z_{0.01} = 2.33$. Using the second method, we determine if the p value of 0.0139 is less than 0.05 and 0.01. Whereas the rejection point method requires that we look up a different rejection point for each different α value, the p value method requires only that we calculate a single p value and compare it directly with the different α values. It follows that the p value method is the most efficient way to test a hypothesis at different α values. This can be useful when there are different decision makers who might use different α values. For example, marketing companies do not always evaluate advertising claims by setting α equal to 0.05. The reason is that the consequences of a Type I error (advertising a false claim) are more serious for some claims than for others. For example, the consequences of a Type I error would be fairly serious for a claim about the effectiveness of a drug or for the superiority of one product over another. However, these consequences might not be as serious for a noncomparative claim about an inexpensive and safe product, such as a cosmetic. Companies sometimes use α values between 0.01 and 0.04 for claims with more serious Type I error consequences, and they sometimes use α values between 0.06 and 0.10 for claims with less serious Type I error consequences. Furthermore, one company's policies for setting α can differ somewhat from those of another. As a result, reporting a claim's *p* value to each company is the most efficient way to tell the company whether to allow the claim to be advertised.

Because a single *p* value can help different decision makers to make their own independent decisions, statistical software packages use *p* values to report the results of hypothesis tests (as we will begin to see in Section 8.5). However, the rejection point approach also has advantages. One is that understanding rejection points helps us to better understand the probability of a Type I error (and the probability of a Type II error). Furthermore, in some situations (for example, in Section 8.5), statistical tables are not complete enough to calculate the *p* value, and a computer software package or an electronic calculator with statistical capabilities is needed. If these tools are not immediately available, rejection points can be used to carry out hypothesis tests, because statistical tables are almost always complete enough to give the needed rejection points. Throughout this book, we will continue to present both the rejection point and the *p* value approaches to hypothesis testing.

Testing a "less than" alternative hypothesis   We next consider the payment time case and testing a "less than" alternative hypothesis:

Step 1: State the null hypothesis H_0 and the alternative hypothesis H_a. In order to study whether the new electronic billing system reduces the mean bill payment time by more than 50 percent, the management consulting firm will test H_0: $\mu \geq 19.5$ versus H_a: $\mu < 19.5$.

Step 2: Specify the level of significance α. The management consulting firm wants to be very sure that it truthfully describes the benefits of the new system both to the company in which it has been installed and to other companies that are considering installing such a system. Therefore, the firm will require very strong evidence to conclude that μ is less than 19.5, which implies that it will test H_0: $\mu \geq 19.5$ versus H_a: $\mu < 19.5$ by setting α equal to 0.01.

Step 3: Select the test statistic. In order to test H_0: $\mu \geq 19.5$ versus H_a: $\mu < 19.5$, we will test the modified null hypothesis H_0: $\mu = 19.5$ versus H_a: $\mu < 19.5$. The idea here is that if there is sufficient evidence to reject the hypothesis that μ equals 19.5 in favour of $\mu < 19.5$, then there is certainly also sufficient evidence to reject the hypothesis that μ is greater than or equal to 19.5. In order to test H_0: $\mu = 19.5$ versus H_a: $\mu < 19.5$, we will randomly select a sample of $n = 65$ invoices paid using the billing system and calculate the mean $\bar{x}$ of the payment times of these invoices. Since the sample size is large, the central limit theorem applies, and we will utilize the test statistic

$$z = \frac{\bar{x} - 19.5}{\sigma/\sqrt{n}}.$$

A value of the test statistic z that is less than zero results when $\bar{x}$ is less than 19.5. This provides evidence to support rejecting H_0 in favour of H_a because the point estimate $\bar{x}$ indicates that μ might be less than 19.5.

Step 4: Determine a rejection point rule for deciding whether to reject H_0. To decide how much less than zero the test statistic must be to reject H_0 in favour of H_a by setting the probability of a Type I error equal to α, we do the following:

- Place the probability of a Type I error, α, in the left-hand tail of the standard normal curve and use the normal table to find the rejection point $-z_\alpha$. Here $-z_\alpha$ is the negative of the normal point z_α. That is, $-z_\alpha$ is the point on the horizontal axis under the standard normal curve that gives a left-hand tail area equal to α.

FIGURE **8.5**   Testing H_0: $\mu = 19.5$ versus H_a: $\mu < 19.5$ by Using Rejection Points and the p Value

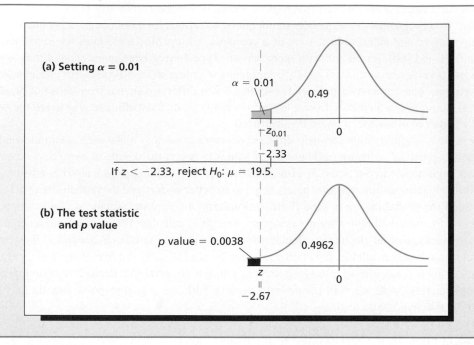

(a) Setting $\alpha = 0.01$

$\alpha = 0.01$ 0.49

$-z_{0.01}$
$\|$
-2.33

If $z < -2.33$, reject H_0: $\mu = 19.5$.

(b) The test statistic and p value

p value $= 0.0038$ 0.4962

z
$\|$
-2.67

- **Reject H_0: $\mu = 19.5$ in favour of H_a: $\mu < 19.5$ if and only if the test statistic z is less than the rejection point $-z_\alpha$.** Because α equals 0.01, the rejection point $-z_\alpha$ is $-z_{0.01} = -2.33$ (see Figure 8.5(a)).

Step 5: Collect the sample data and compute the value of the test statistic. When the sample of $n = 65$ invoices is randomly selected, the mean of the payment times of these invoices is calculated to be $\bar{x} = 18.1077$. Assuming that σ is known to equal 4.2, the value of the test statistic is

$$z = \frac{\bar{x} - 19.5}{\sigma/\sqrt{n}} = \frac{18.1077 - 19.5}{4.2/\sqrt{65}} = -2.67.$$

Step 6: Decide whether to reject H_0 by using the test statistic value and the rejection point rule. Since the test statistic value $z = -2.67$ is less than the rejection point $-z_{0.01} = -2.33$, we can reject H_0: $\mu = 19.5$ in favour of H_a: $\mu < 19.5$ by setting α equal to 0.01.

Step 7: Interpret the statistical results in managerial (real-world) terms and assess their practical importance. We conclude (at an α of 0.01) that the mean payment time for the new electronic billing system is less than 19.5 days. This, along with the fact that the sample mean $\bar{x} = 18.1077$ is slightly less than 19.5, implies that it is reasonable for the management consulting firm to conclude that the new electronic billing system has reduced the mean payment time by slightly more than 50 percent (a substantial improvement over the old system).

A p value for testing a "less than" alternative hypothesis   To test H_0: $\mu = 19.5$ versus H_a: $\mu < 19.5$ in the payment time case by using a p value, we use the following steps 4, 5, and 6:

Step 4: Collect the sample data and compute the value of the test statistic. We have computed the value of the test statistic in the payment time case to be $z = -2.67$.

Step 5: Calculate the p value by using the test statistic value. The p value for testing H_0: $\mu = 19.5$ versus H_a: $\mu < 19.5$ is the area under the standard normal curve to the left of the test statistic value $z = -2.67$. As illustrated in Figure 8.5(b), this area is $0.5 - 0.4962 = 0.0038$. The p value is the probability, computed assuming that H_0: $\mu = 19.5$ is true, of observing a value of the test statistic that is less than or equal to the value $z = -2.67$ that we have actually computed from the sample data. The p value of 0.0038 says that, if H_0: $\mu = 19.5$ is true, only 38 in 10,000 of all possible test statistic values are at least as negative, or extreme, as the value $z = -2.67$. That is, if we are to believe that H_0 is true, we must believe that we have observed a test statistic value that can be described as a 38 in 10,000 chance.

Step 6: Reject H_0 if the p value is less than α. The management consulting firm has set α equal to 0.01. **The p value of 0.0038 is less than the α of 0.01.** Comparing the two normal curves in Figure 8.5(a) and (b), we see that this implies that the test statistic value $z = -2.67$ is less than the rejection point $-z_{0.01} = -2.33$. Therefore, **we can reject H_0 by setting α equal to 0.01.** In general, the value of the test statistic z will be less than the rejection point $-z_\alpha$ if and only if the p value is less than α. That is, we can reject H_0 in favour of H_a at level of significance α if and only if the p value is less than α.

Example 8.4 The Beer Case

Recall that we were testing H_0: $\mu = 341$ mL versus H_a: $\mu < 341$ mL.
 We found the test statistic

$$z = \frac{\bar{x} - 341}{\sigma/\sqrt{n}} = -2.46.$$

Thus, our p value is $P(z < -2.46) = 0.0069$.
 This means that there is very little support for H_0, so we are very likely to reject H_0. If $\alpha = 0.05$, we reject H_0 since our p value is less than 0.05.
 Using a rejection point, we need to reject H_0 at $\alpha = 0.05$ if $z < -1.645$. Since $z = -2.46$, we indeed reject H_0 at $\alpha = 0.05$.

A summary of testing a one-sided alternative hypothesis   As illustrated in the previous examples, we can test two types of one-sided alternative hypotheses. First, we sometimes test hypotheses of the form H_0: $\mu = \mu_0$ versus H_a: $\mu > \mu_0$, where μ_0 is a specific number that depends on the problem. In this case, if we can reject H_0, we have evidence that $\mu > \mu_0$ and that μ is not less than or equal to μ_0. Second, we sometimes test H_0: $\mu = \mu_0$ versus H_a: $\mu < \mu_0$. In this case, if we can reject H_0, we have evidence that $\mu < \mu_0$ and that μ is not greater than or equal to μ_0. To summarize, we may think of testing a one-sided alternative hypothesis about a population mean as testing H_0: $\mu = \mu_0$ versus H_a: $\mu > \mu_0$ or as testing H_0: $\mu = \mu_0$ versus H_a: $\mu < \mu_0$. In addition, as illustrated in the previous examples, a rejection point rule and a p value tell us whether we can reject H_0: $\mu = \mu_0$ in favour of a particular one-sided alternative hypothesis **at level of significance α.** We summarize the rejection point rules and the p values in the following box:

A Hypothesis Test about a Population Mean: Testing H_0: $\mu = \mu_0$ versus a One-Sided Alternative Hypothesis when σ Is Known

Define the test statistic

$$z = \frac{\bar{x} - m_0}{\sigma/\sqrt{n}}$$

and assume that the population sampled is normally distributed, or that the sample size n is large. We can test H_0: $\mu = \mu_0$ versus a particular alternative hypothesis at level of significance α by using the appropriate rejection point rule or, equivalently, the corresponding p value.

Alternative Hypothesis	Rejection Point Rule: Reject H_0 if	p Value (Reject H_0 if p Value $< \alpha$)
H_a: $\mu > \mu_0$	$z > z_\alpha$	The area under the standard normal curve to the right of z
H_a: $\mu < \mu_0$	$z < -z_\alpha$	The area under the standard normal curve to the left of z

When using this summary box, it is vital to understand that the **alternative hypothesis** being tested **determines the rejection point rule and the p value** that should be used to perform the hypothesis test. For example, consider the cable subscription cost example and testing H_0: $\mu = 50$ versus H_a: $\mu > 50$ at level of significance α. Since the alternative hypothesis H_a: $\mu > 50$ is of the form H_a: $\mu > \mu_0$ (that is, it is a "greater than" alternative hypothesis), the summary box tells us that (1) we should reject H_0 if $z > z_\alpha$ and (2) the p value is the area under the standard normal curve to the right of z. When we tested H_0: $\mu = 50$ versus H_a: $\mu > 50$, we illustrated using this rejection point rule and this p value. As another example, consider the payment time case and testing H_0: $\mu = 19.5$ versus H_a: $\mu < 19.5$ at level of significance α. Since the alternative hypothesis H_a: $\mu < 19.5$ is of the form H_a: $\mu < \mu_0$ (that is, it is a "less than" alternative hypothesis), the summary box tells us that (1) we should reject H_0 if $z < -z_\alpha$ and (2) the p value is the area under the standard normal curve to the left of z. When we tested H_0: $\mu = 19.5$ versus H_a: $\mu < 19.5$, we illustrated using this rejection point rule and this p value. For most future hypothesis tests that we will consider, we will present hypothesis testing summary boxes. Therefore, we now present the seven-step hypothesis testing procedure in a way that emphasizes using a summary box to determine an appropriate rejection point rule and an appropriate p value.

The Seven Steps of Hypothesis Testing

1   State the null hypothesis H_0 and the alternative hypothesis H_a.
2   Specify the level of significance α.
3   Select the test statistic.

Using a rejection point rule:

4   Use the summary box to find the rejection point rule corresponding to the alternative hypothesis. Use the specified value of α to find the rejection point given in the rejection point rule.
5   Collect the sample data and compute the value of the test statistic.
6   Decide whether to reject H_0 by using the test statistic value and the rejection point rule.

Using a p value:

4   Collect the sample data and compute the value of the test statistic.
5   Use the summary box to find the p value corresponding to the alternative hypothesis. Calculate the p value by using the test statistic value.
6   Reject H_0 at level of significance α if the p value is less than α.

7   Interpret your statistical results in managerial (real-world) terms and assess their practical importance.

Measuring the weight of evidence against the null hypothesis   In general, the decision to take an action is sometimes based solely on whether there is sufficient sample evidence to reject a null hypothesis (H_0: $\mu = 50$) by setting α equal to a single, prespecified value (0.05). In such situations, it is often also useful to know all of the information—called the **weight of evidence**—that the hypothesis test provides against the null hypothesis and in favour of the alternative hypothesis. For example, a drug manufacturer would almost certainly wish to know **how much** evidence there is that its new medication is more effective than its former medication. Furthermore, although we tested a hypothesis in the payment time case by setting α equal to a single, prespecified value, the hypothesis test did not immediately lead to a decision as to whether to take an action. In a situation such as this, when hypothesis testing is used more as a way to achieve evolving understanding of an industrial or scientific process, it is particularly important to know the weight of evidence against the null hypothesis and in favour of the alternative hypothesis.

The most informative way to measure the weight of evidence is to use the p value. For every hypothesis test considered in this book, we can interpret the p value to be the **probability, computed** assuming that the null hypothesis H_0 is true, of observing a value of the test statistic that is at least as extreme, in the direction of H_a, as the value actually computed from the sample data. The smaller the p value is, the less likely are the sample results if the null hypothesis H_0 is true and therefore the stronger is the evidence that H_0 is false and that the alternative hypothesis H_a is true. We can use the p value to test H_0 versus H_a at level of significance α as follows:

We reject H_0 in favour of H_a at level of significance α if and only if the p value is less than α.

Experience with hypothesis testing has resulted in statisticians making the following (somewhat subjective) conclusions:

Interpreting the Weight of Evidence against the Null Hypothesis

If the p value for testing H_0 is less than

- 0.10, we have **some evidence** that H_0 is false.
- 0.05, we have **strong evidence** that H_0 is false.

- 0.01, we have **very strong evidence** that H_0 is false.
- 0.001, we have **extremely strong evidence** that H_0 is false.

For example, recall that the p value for testing H_0: $\mu = 50$ versus H_a: $\mu > 50$ in the cable subscription cost example is 0.0139. This p value is less than 0.05 but not less than 0.01. Therefore, we have strong evidence, but not very strong evidence, that H_0: $\mu = 50$ is false and H_a: $\mu > 50$ is true. That is, we have strong evidence that the mean monthly subscription costs exceed \$50. As another example, the p value for testing H_0: $\mu = 19.5$ versus H_a: $\mu < 19.5$ in the payment time case is 0.0038. This p value is less than 0.01 but not less than 0.001. Therefore, we have very strong evidence, but not extremely strong evidence, that H_0: $\mu = 19.5$ is false and H_a: $\mu < 19.5$ is true. That is, we have very strong evidence that the new billing system has reduced the mean payment time to less than 19.5 days.

To conclude this section, we note that, while many statisticians believe in assessing the weight of evidence, other statisticians do not. Those who do not might be called **decision theorists**. They contend that measuring the weight of evidence lets the results of a single sample bias our view too much as to the relative validity of H_0 and H_a. Decision theorists state that, even in establishing your own personal belief, you should make a choice between H_0 and H_a by setting α equal to a single value that is prespecified before the sample is taken. Even for decision theorists, however, the p value has the advantage of being the most efficient way to report the results of a hypothesis test to different decision makers who might use different prespecified values of α. In this book, we will continue to assess the weight of evidence, and the decision theorist can regard the p value as simply an efficient way to report the results of a hypothesis test.

Exercises for Section 8.3

CONCEPTS

8.14 Explain what a rejection point is, and explain how it is used to test a hypothesis.

8.15 Explain what a p value is, and explain how it is used to test a hypothesis.

METHODS AND APPLICATIONS

In Exercises 8.16 through 8.22, we consider using a random sample of 100 measurements to test H_0: $\mu = 80$ versus H_a: $\mu > 80$.

8.16 If $\bar{x} = 85$ and $\sigma = 20$, calculate the value of the test statistic z.

8.17 Use a rejection point to test H_0 versus H_a by setting α equal to 0.10.

8.18 Use a rejection point to test H_0 versus H_a by setting α equal to 0.05.

8.19 Use a rejection point to test H_0 versus H_a by setting α equal to 0.01.

8.20 Use a rejection point to test H_0 versus H_a by setting α equal to 0.001.

8.21 Calculate the p value and use it to test H_0 versus H_a at each of $\alpha = 0.10, 0.05, 0.01$, and 0.001.

8.22 How much evidence is there that H_0: $\mu = 80$ is false and H_a: $\mu > 80$ is true?

In Exercises 8.23 through 8.29, we consider using a random sample of 49 measurements to test H_0: $\mu = 20$ versus H_a: $\mu < 20$.

8.23 If $\bar{x} = 18$ and $\sigma = 7$, calculate the value of the test statistic z.

8.24 Use a rejection point to test H_0 versus H_a by setting α equal to 0.10.

8.25 Use a rejection point to test H_0 versus H_a by setting α equal to 0.05.

8.26 Use a rejection point to test H_0 versus H_a by setting α equal to 0.01.

8.27 Use a rejection point to test H_0 versus H_a by setting α equal to 0.001.

8.28 Calculate the p value and use it to test H_0 versus H_a at each of $\alpha = 0.10, 0.05, 0.01$, and 0.001.

8.29 How much evidence is there that H_0: $\mu = 20$ is false and H_a: $\mu < 20$ is true?

8.30 THE VIDEO GAME SATISFACTION RATING CASE
◆ VideoGame

Recall (See Exercise 8.8) that "very satisfied" customers give the XYZ-Box video game system a rating that is at least 42. Letting μ be the mean composite satisfaction rating for the XYZ-Box, we found in Exercise 8.8 that we should test H_0: $\mu \le 42$ versus H_a: $\mu > 42$ in order to attempt to provide evidence supporting the claim that μ exceeds 42. The random sample of 65 satisfaction ratings yields a sample mean of $\bar{x} = 42.954$. Assume that σ equals 2.64.

a. Use rejection points to test H_0 versus H_a at each of $\alpha = 0.10, 0.05, 0.01$, and 0.001.

b. Calculate the p value and use it to test H_0 versus H_a at each of $\alpha = 0.10, 0.05, 0.01$, and 0.001.

c. How much evidence is there that the mean composite satisfaction rating exceeds 42?

8.31 THE BANK CUSTOMER WAITING TIME CASE
◆ WaitTime

Letting μ be the mean waiting time under the new system, we found in Exercise 8.9 that we should test H_0: $\mu \ge 6$ versus H_a: $\mu < 6$ in order to attempt to provide evidence that μ is less than six minutes. The random sample of 100 waiting times yields a sample mean of $\bar{x} = 5.46$ minutes. Moreover, Figure 8.6 gives the MINITAB output obtained when we use the waiting time data to test H_0: $\mu = 6$ versus H_a: $\mu < 6$. On this output, the label "SE Mean," which stands for "the standard error of the mean," denotes the quantity $\sigma/\sqrt{n}$, and the label "Z" denotes the calculated test statistic. Assume that σ equals 2.47.

a. Use rejection points to test H_0 versus H_a at each of $\alpha = 0.10, 0.05, 0.01$, and 0.001.

b. Calculate the p value and verify that it equals 0.014, as shown on the MINITAB output. Use the p value

to test H_0 versus H_a at each of $\alpha = 0.10, 0.05, 0.01$, and 0.001.

c. How much evidence is there that the new system has reduced the mean waiting time to below six minutes?

8.32 A "secret shopper" was sent to a local fast food restaurant to determine whether or not the drive-through service standards at that store were being met. It is currently believed that the store is not meeting the required service time standards. In order to meet the current standards, the store's drive-through service time must be 30 seconds or less. This store has two service windows. The time at the second window was recorded. A random sample of 100 service times was recorded throughout various times of the day during one week. This random sample yielded a sample mean of 29.17 seconds. Assume that it is known that $\sigma = 4$ seconds. Formulate the null hypothesis H_0 and the alternative hypothesis H_a that would be used to determine how much evidence there is that the mean service time at this store is indeed less than 30 seconds. Calculate a p value for this test and draw any conclusions at $\alpha = 0.05$.

8.33 Consider the electric power utility waste water situation in Exercise 8.12 and recall that the power plant will be shut down and corrective action will be taken on the cooling system if the null hypothesis H_0: $\mu \le 15°C$ is rejected in favour of H_a: $\mu > 15°C$. Suppose the utility decides to use a level of significance of $\alpha = 0.05$, and suppose a random sample of 100 temperature readings is obtained. For each of the following sample results, determine whether the power plant should be shut down and the cooling system repaired. In each case, assume that $\sigma = 2$.

a. $\bar{x} = 15.482$. **b.** $\bar{x} = 15.262$. **c.** $\bar{x} = 15.618$.

8.34 THE DISC BRAKE CASE

Recall that the television network will permit Canadian Motor Products to claim that the ZX-900 achieves a shorter mean stopping distance than a competitor if H_0: $\mu \ge 18$ m can be rejected in favour of H_a: $\mu < 18$ m by setting α equal to 0.05 (see Exercise 8.13). If the stopping distances of a random sample of $n = 81$ ZX-900s have a mean of $\bar{x} = 17.6$ m, will Canadian Motor Products be allowed to run the commercial? Assume here that $\sigma = 1.83$ m. Calculate a 95 percent confidence interval for μ. Do the point estimate of μ and confidence interval for μ indicate that μ might be far enough below 18 m to suggest that we have a practically important result?

FIGURE 8.6 MINITAB Output of the Test of H_0: $\mu = 6$ versus H_a: $\mu < 6$ in the Bank Customer Waiting Time Case

```
Test of mu = 6 vs < 6.   The assumed standard deviation = 2.47

Variable    N     Mean    StDev   SE Mean      Z      P
WaitTime   100  5.46000  2.47546  0.24700   -2.19  0.014
```

Note: Because the test statistic z has a denominator $\sigma/\sqrt{n}$ that uses the population standard deviation σ, MINITAB makes the user specify an assumed value for σ.

8.4 *z* Tests about a Population Mean (σ Known): Two-Sided Alternatives

Testing a "not equal to" alternative hypothesis   We next consider the camshaft case and testing a "not equal to" alternative hypothesis:

Step 1: State the null hypothesis H_0 and the alternative hypothesis H_a. The quality control analyst will test H_0: $\mu = 4.5$ versus H_a: $\mu \neq 4.5$. Here μ is the mean of the population of the hardness depths of all camshafts produced on a particular day.

Step 2: Specify the level of significance α. The quality control analyst will set α equal to 0.05. To understand this choice of α, recall that the camshaft hardening process has not been meeting specifications. For this reason, the analyst has decided that it is very important to avoid committing a Type II error. That is, it is very important to avoid failing to reject H_0: $\mu = 4.5$ if μ for the day's production does differ from 4.5 mm. Setting α equal to 0.05 rather than 0.01 makes the probability of this Type II error smaller than it would be if α were set at 0.01.

Step 3: Select the test statistic. The quality control analyst will randomly select $n = 35$ camshafts from the day's production of camshafts and calculate the mean $\bar{x}$ of the hardness depths of these camshafts. Since the sample size is large, the central limit theorem applies, and we will utilize the test statistic

$$z = \frac{\bar{x} - 4.5}{\sigma/\sqrt{n}}.$$

A value of the test statistic that is greater than 0 results when $\bar{x}$ is greater than 4.5. This provides evidence to support rejecting H_0 in favour of H_a because the point estimate $\bar{x}$ indicates that μ might be greater than 4.5. Similarly, a value of the test statistic that is less than 0 results when $\bar{x}$ is less than 4.5. This also provides evidence to support rejecting H_0 in favour of H_a because the point estimate $\bar{x}$ indicates that μ might be less than 4.5.

Step 4: Determine a rejection point rule for deciding whether to reject H_0. To decide how different from zero (positive or negative) the test statistic must be in order to reject H_0 in favour of H_a by setting the probability of a Type I error equal to α, we do the following:

- Divide the probability of a Type I error, α, into two equal parts, and place the area $\alpha/2$ in the right-hand tail of the standard normal curve and the area $\alpha/2$ in the left-hand tail of the standard normal curve. Then use the normal table to find the rejection points $z_{\alpha/2}$ and $-z_{\alpha/2}$. Here $z_{\alpha/2}$ is the point on the horizontal axis under the standard normal curve that gives a right-hand tail area equal to $\alpha/2$, and $-z_{\alpha/2}$ is the point giving a left-hand tail area equal to $\alpha/2$.

- **Reject H_0: $\mu = 4.5$ in favour of H_a: $\mu \neq 4.5$ if and only if the test statistic z is greater than the rejection point $z_{\alpha/2}$ or less than the rejection point $-z_{\alpha/2}$.** Note that this is equivalent to saying that we should **reject H_0 if and only if the absolute value of the test statistic, $|z|$, is greater than the rejection point $z_{\alpha/2}$.** Because α equals 0.05, the rejection points are (see Figure 8.7(a))

$$z_{\alpha/2} = z_{0.05/2} = z_{0.025} = 1.96 \quad \text{and} \quad -z_{\alpha/2} = -z_{0.025} = -1.96.$$

Step 5: Collect the sample data and compute the value of the test statistic. When the sample of $n = 35$ camshafts is randomly selected, the mean of the hardness depths of these camshafts is calculated to be $\bar{x} = 4.26$. Assuming that σ is known to equal 0.47, the value of the test statistic is

$$z = \frac{\bar{x} - 4.5}{\sigma/\sqrt{n}} = \frac{4.26 - 4.5}{0.47/\sqrt{35}} = -3.02.$$

Step 6: Decide whether to reject H_0 by using the test statistic value and the rejection point rule. Since the test statistic value $z = -3.02$ is less than $-z_{0.025} = -1.96$ (or, equivalently, since $|z| = 3.02$ is greater than $z_{0.025} = 1.96$), we can reject H_0: $\mu = 4.5$ in favour of H_a: $\mu \neq 4.5$ by setting α equal to 0.05.

FIGURE **8.7**   Testing H_0: $\mu = 4.5$ versus H_a: $\mu \neq 4.5$ by Using Rejection Points and the *p* Value

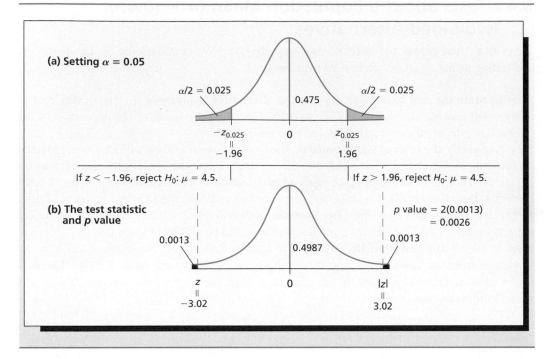

Step 7: Interpret the statistical results in managerial (real-world) terms and assess their practical importance. We conclude (at an α of 0.05) that the mean camshaft hardness depth μ differs from 4.5 mm. To help determine whether the difference between μ and 4.5 mm is practically important, recall that specifications state that each individual camshaft hardness depth should be between 3 mm and 6 mm. Using $\bar{x} = 4.26$ and $\sigma = 0.47$, we estimate that 99.73 percent of all individual camshaft hardness depths are in the interval $[\bar{x} \pm 3\sigma] = [4.26 \pm 3(0.47)] = [2.85, 5.67]$. This estimated tolerance interval says that, because of a somewhat small $\bar{x}$ of 4.26, we estimate that we are producing some hardness depths that are below the lower specification limit of 3 mm. This is a practically important result. Clearly, the automobile manufacturer must modify the camshaft heat treatment process so that it produces hardness depths with an average value nearer the 4.5-mm target.

A *p* value for testing a "not equal to" alternative hypothesis   To test H_0: $\mu = 4.5$ versus H_a: $\mu \neq 4.5$ in the camshaft case by using a *p* value, we use the following steps 4, 5, and 6:

Step 4: Collect the sample data and compute the value of the test statistic. We have computed the value of the test statistic in the camshaft case to be $z = -3.02$.

Step 5: Calculate the *p* value by using the test statistic value. Note from Figure 8.7(b) that the area under the standard normal curve to the right of $|z| = 3.02$ is 0.0013. Twice this area—that is, $2(0.0013) = 0.0026$—is the *p* value for testing H_0: $\mu = 4.5$ versus H_a: $\mu \neq 4.5$. To interpret the *p* value as a probability, note that the symmetry of the standard normal curve implies that twice the area under the curve to the right of $|z| = 3.02$ equals the area under this curve to the right of 3.02 plus the area under the curve to the left of -3.02 (see Figure 8.7(b)). Also note that since both positive and negative test statistic values count against H_0: $\mu = 4.5$, a test statistic value that is either greater than or equal to 3.02 or less than or equal to -3.02 is at least as extreme as the observed test statistic value $z = -3.02$. It follows that the *p* value of 0.0026 says that, if H_0: $\mu = 4.5$ is true, then only 26 in 10,000 of all possible test statistic values are at least as extreme as $z = -3.02$. That is, if we are to believe that H_0 is true, we must believe that we have observed a test statistic value that can be described as a 26 in 10,000 chance.

Step 6: Reject H_0 if the *p* value is less than α. The quality control analyst has set α equal to 0.05. Since **the *p* value of 0.0026 is less than the α of 0.05**, one half the *p* value = 0.0013 is less than

$\alpha/2 = 0.025$. Comparing the two normal curves in Figure 8.7(a) and (b), we see that this implies that $|z| = 3.02$ is greater than the rejection point $z_{0.025} = 1.96$. Therefore, **we can reject H_0 by setting α equal to 0.05**. In general, the absolute value of the test statistic *z* will be greater than the rejection point $z_{\alpha/2}$ if and only if the *p* value is less than α. That is, we can reject H_0 in favour of H_a at level of significance α if and only if the *p* value is less than α. For example, the *p* value of 0.0026 is less than an α of 0.01 but not less than an α of 0.001. It follows that we have very strong evidence, but not extremely strong evidence, that $H_0: \mu = 4.5$ is false and $H_a: \mu \neq 4.5$ is true. That is, we have very strong evidence that the mean camshaft hardness depth differs from 4.5 mm.

A summary of testing $H_0: \mu = \mu_0$ In the rest of this chapter and in Chapter 9, we will present most of the hypothesis testing examples using the seven steps and hypothesis testing summary boxes. However, to be more concise, we will not formally label each step. Rather, for each of the first six steps, we will set out in boldface font a key phrase that indicates that the step is being carried out. Then we will highlight the seventh step—the business improvement conclusion—as we highlight all business improvement conclusions in this book. After Chapter 9, we will continue to use hypothesis testing summary boxes, and we will more informally use the seven steps. In the following box, we summarize how to test $H_0: \mu = \mu_0$ versus $H_a: \mu > \mu_0$, $H_a: \mu < \mu_0$, or $H_a: \mu \neq \mu_0$:

Testing a Hypothesis about a Population Mean: Testing $H_0: \mu = \mu_0$ when σ Is Known

Define the test statistic

$$z = \frac{\bar{x} - m_0}{\sigma/\sqrt{n}}$$

and assume that the population sampled is normally distributed or that the sample size *n* is large. We can test $H_0: \mu = \mu_0$ versus a particular alternative hypothesis at level of significance α by using the appropriate rejection point rule or, equivalently, the corresponding *p* value.

Alternative Hypothesis	Rejection Point Rule: Reject H_0 if	*p* Value (Reject H_0 if *p* Value $< \alpha$)
$H_a: \mu > \mu_0$	$z > z_\alpha$	The area under the standard normal curve to the right of *z*
$H_a: \mu < \mu_0$	$z < -z_\alpha$	The area under the standard normal curve to the left of *z*
$H_a: \mu \neq \mu_0$	$|z| > z_{\alpha/2}$—that is, $z > z_{\alpha/2}$ or $z < -z_{\alpha/2}$	Twice the area under the standard normal curve to the right of $|z|$

In many future examples, we will first use a rejection point rule to test the hypotheses under consideration at a fixed value of α, and we will then use a *p* value to assess the weight of evidence against the null hypothesis. For example, suppose that airline flights between Toronto and Vancouver have routinely experienced delays for the last several years. Last year, these delayed flights were an average of 35 minutes late. A consumer advocacy group wishes to assess whether this average has changed. To do this, the consumer group will test a hypothesis about the mean delay time, μ, of flights that were delayed over the last two months. **The null hypothesis to be tested is $H_0: \mu = 35$, and the alternative hypothesis is $H_a: \mu \neq 35$.** If H_0 can be rejected in favour of H_a at the **0.05 level of significance**, the consumer group will conclude that the mean delay time over the last two months differs from last year's 35-minute mean delay time. To perform the hypothesis test, we will randomly select $n = 36$ flights that were delayed over the last two months and use their delay times to calculate the value of the **test statistic *z* in the summary box**. Then, since $H_a: \mu \neq 35$ is of the form $H_a: \mu \neq \mu_0$, we will **reject $H_0: \mu = 35$ if the absolute value of *z* is greater than $z_{\alpha/2} = z_{0.025} = 1.96$**. Suppose that when the sample is randomly selected, the mean of the delay times of the $n = 36$ flights is calculated to be $\bar{x} = 33$ minutes. Assuming that σ is known to equal 12, the **value of the test statistic** is

$$z = \frac{\bar{x} - 35}{\sigma/\sqrt{n}} = \frac{33 - 35}{12/\sqrt{36}} = -1.$$

Since $|z| = 1$ is less than $z_{0.025} = 1.96$, we cannot reject H_0: $\mu = 35$ in favour of H_a: $\mu \neq 35$. That is, we cannot conclude (at an α of 0.05) that the mean delay time over the last two months differs from last year's 35-minute mean delay time. The p value for testing H_0: $\mu = 35$ versus H_a: $\mu \neq 35$ is twice the area under the standard normal curve to the right of $|z| = 1$. Using Table A.3, we find that this p value equals $2(0.5 - 0.3413) = 2(0.1587) = 0.3174$. Since the p value of 0.3174 is greater than any reasonable value of α, we have little evidence against H_0: $\mu = 35$ and in favour of H_a: $\mu \neq 35$. That is, we have little evidence that the mean delay time over the last two months differs from last year's 35-minute mean delay time.

Using confidence intervals to test hypotheses   Confidence intervals can be used to test hypotheses. Specifically, we can reject H_0: $\mu = \mu_0$ in favour of H_a: $\mu \neq \mu_0$ by setting the probability of a Type I error equal to α if and only if the $100(1 - \alpha)$ percent confidence interval for μ does not contain μ_0. For example, consider the camshaft case and testing H_0: $\mu = 4.5$ versus H_a: $\mu \neq 4.5$ by setting α equal to 0.05. To do this, we use the mean $\bar{x} = 4.26$ of the sample of $n = 35$ camshafts to calculate the 95 percent confidence interval for μ to be

$$\left[\bar{x} \pm z_{\alpha/2} \frac{\sigma}{\sqrt{n}} \right] = \left[4.26 \pm 1.96 \frac{0.47}{\sqrt{35}} \right] = [4.10, 4.42].$$

Because this interval does not contain 4.5, we can reject H_0: $\mu = 4.5$ in favour of H_a: $\mu \neq 4.5$ by setting α equal to 0.05.

Whereas we can use the **two-sided** confidence intervals of this book to test "not equal to" alternative hypotheses, we must use **one-sided** confidence intervals to test "greater than" or "less than" alternative hypotheses. However, it should be emphasized that we do not need to use confidence intervals (one-sided or two-sided) to test hypotheses. We can test hypotheses by using test statistics and rejection points or p values. Furthermore, confidence intervals can help us to evaluate practical importance after we have established statistical significance by using a hypothesis test. This is illustrated in the next section.

The effect of sample size   If we can reject a null hypothesis by setting the probability of a Type I error equal to α, we say that we have **statistical significance at the α level**. Whether we have statistical significance at a given level often depends greatly on the size of the sample we have selected. To see this, recall that the marketing company wishes to test H_0: $\mu \leq 50$ versus H_a: $\mu > 50$ and has obtained the sample mean $\bar{x} = 50.575$ based on a sample of $n = 40$ cable TV subscriptions. Assuming that σ is known to equal 1.65, the p value associated with

$$z = \frac{\bar{x} - 50}{\sigma/\sqrt{n}} = \frac{50.575 - 50}{1.65/\sqrt{40}} = \frac{0.575}{0.26089} = 2.20$$

is 0.0139. It follows that we have statistical significance at the 0.05 level but not at the 0.01 level. However, suppose that the manufacturer had obtained the same $\bar{x}$ based on a larger sample of $n = 100$ subscriptions. The test statistic value is then

$$z = \frac{\bar{x} - 50}{\sigma/\sqrt{n}} = \frac{50.575 - 50}{1.65/\sqrt{100}} = \frac{0.575}{0.165} = 3.48,$$

and the p value is the area under the standard normal curve to the right of $z = 3.48$. Looking at the normal table (see Table A.3), we see that the area to the right of 3.09 is $0.5 - 0.4990 = 0.001$. Therefore, because 3.48 is greater than 3.09, the p value is less than 0.001, and we have statistical significance at the 0.001 level. What has happened here is that the numerator of the test statistic has remained the same, while the larger sample size makes the denominator of the test statistic smaller. This results in a larger and more statistically significant value of the test statistic. Understand, however, that the highly statistically significant test statistic value means only that we have extremely strong evidence that μ is greater than 50. It does not necessarily mean that the difference between μ and 50 is large enough to be practically important to cable TV subscribers. In fact, the sample mean $\bar{x} = 50.575$ indicates that μ is not much larger than 50. A difference of about 58 cents would not represent a large increase in cost to potential subscribers.

Exercises for Section 8.4

CONCEPTS

8.35 Suppose we are carrying out a two-sided hypothesis test about a population mean.
 a. Give the rejection point rule for rejecting H_0: $\mu = \mu_0$.
 b. Explain how the *p* value and *α* tell us whether H_0: $\mu = \mu_0$ should be rejected.

8.36 Discuss how we assess the practical importance of a statistically significant result.

METHODS AND APPLICATIONS

In Exercises 8.37 through 8.43, we consider using a random sample of $n = 81$ measurements to test H_0: $\mu = 40$ versus H_a: $\mu \neq 40$. Suppose that $\bar{x} = 34$ and $\sigma = 18$.

8.37 Calculate the value of the test statistic *z*.

8.38 Use rejection points to test H_0 versus H_a by setting *α* equal to 0.10.

8.39 Use rejection points to test H_0 versus H_a by setting *α* equal to 0.05.

8.40 Use rejection points to test H_0 versus H_a by setting *α* equal to 0.01.

8.41 Use rejection points to test H_0 versus H_a by setting *α* equal to 0.001.
 Hint: $z_{0.0005}$ can be shown to equal 3.29.

8.42 Calculate the *p* value and use it to test H_0 versus H_a at each of *α* = 0.10, 0.05, 0.01, and 0.001.

8.43 How much evidence is there that H_0: $\mu = 40$ is false and H_a: $\mu \neq 40$ is true?

8.44 Consider the automobile parts supplier in Exercise 8.10. Suppose that a problem-solving team will be assigned to rectify the process producing cylindrical engine parts if the null hypothesis H_0: $\mu = 3$ can be rejected in favour of H_a: $\mu \neq 3$ by setting *α* equal to 0.05.
 a. A sample of 40 parts yields a sample mean diameter of $\bar{x} = 3.006$ cm. Assuming *σ* equals 0.016, use rejection points and a *p* value to test H_0 versus H_a by setting *α* equal to 0.05. Should the problem-solving team be assigned?
 b. Suppose that product specifications state that each and every part must have a diameter between 2.95 cm and 3.05 cm—that is, the specifications are

3 cm ± 0.05 cm. Use the sample information given in part a to estimate an interval that contains almost all (99.73 percent) of the diameters. Compare this estimated interval with the specification limits. Are the specification limits being met, or are some diameters outside the specification limits? Explain.

8.45 Consider the Classic Bottling Company fill process in Exercise 8.11. Recall that the initial setup of the filler will be adjusted if the null hypothesis H_0: $\mu = 355$ mL is rejected in favour of H_a: $\mu \neq 355$ mL. Suppose that Classic Bottling Company decides to use a level of significance of *α* = 0.01, and suppose a random sample of 36 can fills is obtained from a test run of the filler. For each of the following sample results, determine whether the filler's initial setup should be adjusted. In each case, use a rejection point and a *p* value, and assume that *σ* equals 0.1.
 a. $\bar{x} = 355.05$.   **c.** $\bar{x} = 355.02$.
 b. $\bar{x} = 354.96$.

8.46 Use the sample information in part a of Exercise 8.45 and a confidence interval to test H_0: $\mu = 355$ versus H_a: $\mu \neq 355$ by setting *α* equal to 0.05. What considerations would help you to decide whether the result has practical importance?

8.47 In an article in the *Journal of Marketing*, Bayus studied the mean numbers of auto dealers visited by two types of buyers.
 a. Letting *μ* be the mean number of dealers visited by the first type of buyer, suppose that we wish to test H_0: $\mu = 4$ versus H_a: $\mu \neq 4$. A random sample of 800 of these buyers yields a mean number of dealers visited of $\bar{x} = 3.3$. Assuming *σ* equals 0.71, calculate the *p* value and test H_0 versus H_a. Do we estimate that *μ* is less than 4 or greater than 4?
 b. Letting *μ* be the mean number of dealers visited by the second type of buyer, suppose that we wish to test H_0: $\mu = 4$ versus H_a: $\mu \neq 4$. A random sample of 500 of these buyers yields a mean number of dealers visited of $\bar{x} = 4.3$. Assuming *σ* equals 0.66, calculate the *p* value and test H_0 versus H_a. Do we estimate that *μ* is less than 4 or greater than 4?

8.5 *t* Tests about a Population Mean (*σ* Unknown)

If we do not know *σ* (which is usually the case), we can base a hypothesis test about *μ* on the sampling distribution of

$$\frac{\bar{x} - \mu}{s/\sqrt{n}}.$$

If the sampled population is normally distributed, then this sampling distribution is a *t* **distribution with** $n - 1$ **degrees of freedom**. This leads to the following results:

A t Test about a Population Mean: Testing $H_0: \mu = \mu_0$ when σ Is Unknown

Define the test statistic

$$t = \frac{\bar{x} - m_0}{\sigma/\sqrt{n}}$$

and assume that the population sampled is normally distributed. We can test $H_0: \mu = \mu_0$ versus a particular alternative hypothesis at level of significance α by using the appropriate rejection point rule or, equivalently, the corresponding p value.

Alternative Hypothesis	Rejection Point Rule: Reject H_0 if
$H_a: \mu > \mu_0$	$t > t_\alpha$
$H_a: \mu < \mu_0$	$t < -t_\alpha$
$H_a: \mu \neq \mu_0$	$\lvert t \rvert > t_{\alpha/2}$—that is, $t > t_{\alpha/2}$ or $t < -t_{\alpha/2}$

p Value (Reject H_0 if p Value $< \alpha$)

The area under the t distribution curve to the right of t

The area under the t distribution curve to the left of t

Twice the area under the t distribution curve to the right of $\lvert t \rvert$

Here t_α, $t_{\alpha/2}$, and the p values are based on $n - 1$ degrees of freedom.

Example 8.5

In 2001, the average interest rate charged by Canadian credit card issuers was 18.8 percent. Since that time, there has been a proliferation of new credit cards affiliated with retail stores, oil companies, alumni associations, and so on. A financial officer wishes to study whether the increased competition in the credit card business has reduced interest rates. To do this, the officer will test a hypothesis about the current mean interest rate, μ, charged by Canadian credit card issuers. **The null hypothesis to be tested is $H_0: \mu = 18.8\%$, and the alternative hypothesis is $H_a: \mu < 18.8\%$.** If H_0 can be rejected in favour of H_a at the **0.05 level of significance**, the officer will conclude that the current mean interest rate is less than the 18.8 percent mean interest rate charged in 2001. To perform the hypothesis test, suppose that we randomly select $n = 15$ credit cards and determine their current interest rates. The interest rates for the 15 sampled cards are given in Table 8.2. A stem-and-leaf display and MINITAB box plot are given in Figure 8.8. The stem-and-leaf display looks reasonably mound-shaped, and both the stem-and-leaf display and the box plot look reasonably symmetrical. It follows that it is appropriate to calculate the value of the **test statistic t in the summary box**. Furthermore, since $H_a: \mu < 18.8\%$ is of the form $H_a: \mu < \mu_0$, we should **reject $H_0: \mu = 18.8\%$ if the value of t is less than the rejection point $-t_\alpha = -t_{0.05} = -1.761$. Here $-t_{0.05} = -1.761$ is based on $n - 1 = 15 - 1 = 14$ degrees of freedom, and this rejection point is

TABLE 8.2   **Interest Rates Charged by 15 Randomly Selected Credit Cards**

15.6%	15.3%	19.2%
17.8	16.4	15.8
14.6	18.4	18.1
17.3	17.6	16.6
18.7	14.0	17.0

FIGURE 8.8   **Stem-and-Leaf Display and Box Plot of the Interest Rates**

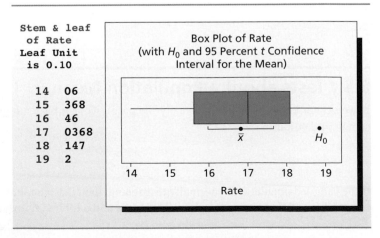

```
Stem & leaf
 of Rate
Leaf Unit
 is 0.10

  14   06
  15   368
  16   46
  17   0368
  18   147
  19   2
```

FIGURE 8.9   Testing H_0: $\mu = 18.8\%$ versus H_a: $\mu < 18.8\%$ by Using a Rejection Point and a *p* Value

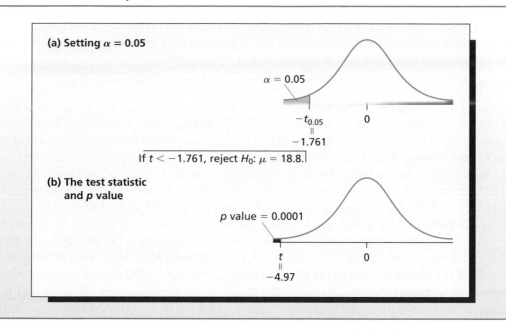

(a) Setting $\alpha = 0.05$

$\alpha = 0.05$

$-t_{0.05}$
||
-1.761

0

If $t < -1.761$, reject H_0: $\mu = 18.8$.

(b) The test statistic and *p* value

p value = 0.0001

t
||
-4.97

0

illustrated in Figure 8.9(a). The mean and the standard deviation of the $n = 15$ interest rates in Table 8.2 are $\bar{x} = 16.827$ and $s = 1.538$. This implies that the **value of the test statistic** is

$$t = \frac{\bar{x} - 18.8}{s/\sqrt{n}} = \frac{16.827 - 18.8}{1.538/\sqrt{15}} = -4.97.$$

Since $t = -4.97$ is less than $-t_{0.05} = -1.761$, we reject H_0: $\mu = 18.8\%$ in favour of H_a: $\mu < 18.8\%$. That is, we conclude (at an α of 0.05) that the current mean credit card interest rate is lower than 18.8 percent, the mean interest rate in 2001. Furthermore, the sample mean $\bar{x} = 16.827$ says that we estimate the mean interest rate is $18.8\% - 16.827\% = 1.973\%$ lower than it was in 2001.

The *p* value for testing H_0: $\mu = 18.8\%$ versus H_a: $\mu < 18.8\%$ is the area under the curve of the *t* distribution with 14 degrees of freedom to the left of $t = -4.97$. Tables of *t* points (such as Table A.4) are not complete enough to give such areas for most *t* statistic values, so we use computer software packages to calculate *p* values that are based on the *t* distribution. For example, the MINITAB output in Figure 8.10(a) and the MegaStat output in Figure 8.11 tell us that the *p* value for testing H_0: $\mu = 18.8\%$ versus H_a: $\mu < 18.8\%$ is 0.0001. This is also noted in Figure 8.9(b). Notice that both MINITAB and MegaStat round *p* values to three or four decimal places. The Excel output in Figure 8.10(b) gives the slightly more accurate value of 0.000103 for the *p* value.

FIGURE 8.10   The MINITAB and Excel Outputs for Testing H_0: $\mu = 18.8\%$ versus H_a: $\mu < 18.8\%$

(a) The MINITAB output   (b) The Excel output

```
Test of mu = 18.8 vs < 18.8
```

Variable	N	Mean	StDev	SE Mean	T	P
Rate	15	16.8267	1.5378	0.3971	-4.97	0.000

t-statistic
-4.97
p-value
0.000103

FIGURE 8.11   The MegaStat Output for Testing H_0: $\mu = 18.8\%$ versus H_a: $\mu < 18.8\%$

Hypothesis Test: Mean vs. Hypothesized Value

18.8000 hypothesized value	1.5378 std. dev.	15 n	-4.97 t
16.8267 mean Rate	0.3971 std. error	14 df	0.0001 p-value (one-tailed, lower)

     = Significant at 0.05 level   = Significant at 0.01 level

Because this p value is less than 0.05, 0.01, and 0.001, we can reject H_0 at the 0.05, 0.01, and 0.001 levels of significance. As a probability, the p value of 0.0001 says that if we are to believe that H_0: $\mu = 18.8\%$ is true, we must believe that we have observed a t statistic value ($t = -4.97$) that can be described as a 1 in 10,000 chance. In summary, we have extremely strong evidence that H_0: $\mu = 18.8\%$ is false and H_a: $\mu < 18.8\%$ is true. That is, we have extremely strong evidence that the current mean credit card interest rate is less than 18.8 percent.

Recall that in three cases discussed in Sections 8.3 and 8.4 we tested hypotheses by assuming that the population standard deviation σ is known and by using z tests. If σ is actually not known in these cases (which would probably be true), we should test the hypotheses under consideration by using t tests. Furthermore, recall that in each case the sample size is large (at least 30). In general, it can be shown that if the sample size is large, the t test is approximately valid even if the sampled population is not normally distributed (or mound-shaped). Therefore, consider the camshaft case and testing H_0: $\mu = 4.5$ versus H_a: $\mu \neq 4.5$ at the **0.05 level of significance**. To perform the hypothesis test, assume that we will randomly select $n = 35$ camshafts and use their hardness depths to calculate the value of the **test statistic t in the summary box**. Then, since the alternative hypothesis H_a: $\mu \neq 4.5$ is of the form H_a: $\mu \neq \mu_0$, we will **reject H_0: $\mu = 4.5$ if the absolute value of t is greater than $t_{\alpha/2} = t_{0.025} = 2.032$ (based on $n - 1 = 34$ degrees of freedom)**. Suppose that when the sample is randomly selected, the mean and the standard deviation of the hardness depths of the $n = 35$ camshafts are calculated to be $\bar{x} = 4.26$ and $s = 0.49$. The **value of the test statistic** is

$$t = \frac{\bar{x} - 4.5}{s/\sqrt{n}} = \frac{4.26 - 4.5}{0.49/\sqrt{35}} = -2.8977.$$

Since $|t| = 2.8977$ is greater than $t_{0.025} = 2.032$, we can reject H_0: $\mu = 4.5$ at α equal to 0.05. The p value for the hypothesis test is twice the area under the t distribution curve with 34 degrees of freedom to the right of $|t| = 2.8977$. Using a computer, we find that this p value is 0.0066.

In summary, the p values obtained for the cases using t tests do not differ by much from the corresponding p values using z tests. Therefore, the practical conclusions reached in Sections 8.3 and 8.4 using z tests would also be reached using the t tests discussed here. Finally, if the sample size is small (< 30) and the sampled population is not mound-shaped, or if the sampled population is highly skewed, then it might be appropriate to use a **nonparametric test about the population median**. Such a test is discussed in Chapter 13.

Exercises for Section 8.5

CONCEPTS

8.48 What assumptions must be met in order to carry out the test about a population mean based on the t distribution?

8.49 How do we decide whether to use a z test or a t test when testing a hypothesis about a population mean?

METHODS AND APPLICATIONS

8.50 Suppose that a random sample of 16 measurements from a normally distributed population gives a sample mean of $\bar{x} = 13.5$ and a sample standard deviation of $s = 6$. Use rejection points to test H_0: $\mu \leq 10$ versus H_a: $\mu > 10$ using levels of significance $\alpha = 0.10$, $\alpha = 0.05$, $\alpha = 0.01$, and $\alpha = 0.001$. What do you conclude at each value of α?

8.51 Suppose that a random sample of nine measurements from a normally distributed population gives a sample mean of $\bar{x} = 2.57$ and a sample standard deviation of $s = 0.3$. Use rejection points to test H_0: $\mu = 3$ versus H_a: $\mu \neq 3$ using levels of significance $\alpha = 0.10$, $\alpha = 0.05$, $\alpha = 0.01$, and $\alpha = 0.001$. What do you conclude at each value of α?

8.52 The **bad debt ratio** for a financial institution is defined to be the dollar value of loans defaulted divided by the total dollar value of all loans made. Suppose that a random sample of seven Ontario banks is selected and that the bad debt ratios (written as percentages) for these banks are 7%, 4%, 6%, 7%, 5%, 4%, and 9%.
⬤ BadDebt
a. Banking officials claim that the mean bad debt ratio for all Canadian banks is 3.5 percent and that the mean bad debt ratio for Ontario banks is higher. Set up the null and alternative hypotheses needed to attempt to provide evidence supporting the claim that the mean bad debt ratio for Ontario banks exceeds 3.5 percent.
b. Assuming that bad debt ratios for Ontario banks are approximately normally distributed, use rejection points and the given sample information to test the hypotheses you set up in part a by setting α equal to 0.10, 0.05, 0.01, and 0.001. How much evidence is there that the mean bad debt ratio for Ontario banks

FIGURE 8.12   MegaStat and MINITAB Output for Exercises 8.53, 8.55, and 8.57

(a) MINITAB output of the test statistic and *p* value for Exercise 8.53

```
Test of mu = 3.5 vs > 3.5
Variable   N    Mean    StDev   SE Mean     T      P
d-ratio    7    6.000   1.82574  0.69007   3.62   0.006
```

(b) MegaStat output of the test statistic and *p* value and Excel output of the *p* value for Exercise 8.55

Hypothesis Test: Mean vs. Hypothesized Value

750.000 hypothesized value   19.647 std. dev.   5 n   6.94 t
811.000 mean Hourly Yield   8.786 std. error   4 df   0.0023 p-value (two-tailed)

t-statistic
6.942585
p-value
0.002261

(c) MINITAB output for Exercise 8.57

```
Test of mu = 800 vs > 800

Variable    N     Mean    StDev   SE Mean    T      P
SqFtSales  10   846.200  32.866   10.393   4.45   0.001
```

exceeds 3.5 percent? What does this say about the banking official's claim?

8.53 Consider Exercise 8.52. in Figure 8.12(a), we give the MINITAB output of the test statistic and *p* value for testing H_0: $\mu = 3.5$ versus H_a: $\mu > 3.5$.   ● BadDebt

   a. Use the *p* value to test H_0 versus H_a by setting α equal to 0.10, 0.05, 0.01, and 0.001. What do you conclude at each value of α?

   b. How much evidence is there that the mean bad debt ratio for Ontario banks exceeds 3.5 percent?

8.54 In the book *Business Research Methods*, Cooper and Emory discuss using hypothesis testing to study receivables outstanding. To quote Cooper and Emory:

> . . . the controller of a large retail chain may be concerned about a possible slowdown in payments by the company's customers. She measures the rate of payment in terms of the average number of days receivables outstanding. Generally, the company has maintained an average of about 50 days with a standard deviation of 10 days. Since it would be too expensive to analyze all of a company's receivables frequently, we normally resort to sampling.

   a. Set up the null and alternative hypotheses needed to attempt to show that there has been a slowdown in payments by the company's customers (there has been a slowdown if the average days outstanding exceeds 50).

   b. Assume approximate normality and suppose that a random sample of 25 accounts gives an average days outstanding of $\bar{x} = 54$ with a standard deviation of $s = 8$. Use rejection points to test the hypotheses you set up in part a at levels of significance $\alpha = 0.10$, $\alpha = 0.05$, $\alpha = 0.01$, and $\alpha = 0.001$. How much evidence is there of a slowdown in payments?

   c. Are you qualified to decide whether this result has practical importance? Who would be?

8.55 Consider a chemical company that wishes to determine whether a new catalyst, catalyst XA-100, changes the

mean hourly yield of its chemical process from the historical process mean of 750 g per hour. When five trial runs are made using the new catalyst, the following yields (in grams per hour) are recorded: 801, 814, 784, 836, and 820.   ● ChemYield

   a. Let μ be the mean of all possible yields using the new catalyst. Assuming that chemical yields are approximately normally distributed, the MegaStat output of the test statistic and *p* value and the Excel output of the *p* value for testing H_0: $\mu = 750$ versus H_a: $\mu \neq 750$ are as in Figure 8.12(b). (In Figure 8.12(b), we had Excel calculate twice the area under the *t* distribution curve with four degrees of freedom to the right of 6.942585.) Use the sample data to verify that the values of $\bar{x}$, s, and t given on the output are correct.

   b. Use the test statistic and rejection points to test H_0 versus H_a by setting α equal to 0.10, 0.05, 0.01, and 0.001.

8.56 Consider Exercise 8.55. Use the *p* value to test H_0: $\mu = 750$ versus H_a: $\mu \neq 750$ by setting α equal to 0.10, 0.05, 0.01, and 0.001. How much evidence is there that the new catalyst changes the mean hourly yield?

8.57 Whole Foods is an all-natural grocery chain that has 50,000-square-foot (4,600-m^2) stores, up from the industry average of 34,000 square feet (3,200 m^2). Sales per square foot of supermarkets average just under \$400 per square foot, as reported by *USA Today* in an article called "A whole new ballgame in grocery shopping." Suppose that sales per square foot in the most recent fiscal year are recorded for a random sample of 10 Whole Foods supermarkets. The data (sales dollars per square foot) are as follows: 854, 858, 801, 892, 849, 807, 894, 863, 829, 815. Let μ denote the mean sales dollars per square foot for all Whole Foods supermarkets during the most recent fiscal year, and note that the historical mean sales dollars per square foot for Whole Foods supermarkets in previous years has been \$800. In Figure 8.12(c), we present the MINITAB output obtained by using the sample data to test H_0: $\mu = 800$ versus H_a: $\mu > 800$.   ● WholeFoods

a. Use the p value to test H_0 versus H_a by setting α equal to 0.10, 0.05, 0.01, and 0.001.

b. How much evidence is there that μ exceeds $800?

8.58 Consider Exercise 8.57. Do you think that the difference between the sample mean of $846.20 and the historical average of $800 has practical importance?

8.59 **THE VIDEO GAME SATISFACTION RATING CASE**
    ● VideoGame

The mean and the standard deviation of the sample of $n = 65$ customer satisfaction ratings in Chapter 1 are $\bar{x} = 42.95$ and $s = 2.6424$. Let μ denote the mean of all possible customer satisfaction ratings for the XYZ-Box video game system, and consider testing $H_0: \mu = 42$

versus $H_a: \mu > 42$. Perform a t test of these hypotheses by setting α equal to 0.05 and using a rejection point. Also interpret the p value of 0.0025 for the hypothesis test.

8.60 **THE BANK CUSTOMER WAITING TIME CASE**
    ● WaitTime

The mean and the standard deviation of the sample of 100 bank customer waiting times in Chapter 1, Exercise 1.9, are $\bar{x} = 5.46$ and $s = 2.475$. Let μ denote the mean of all possible bank customer waiting times using the new system and consider testing $H_0: \mu = 6$ versus $H_a: \mu < 6$. Perform a t test of these hypotheses by setting α equal to 0.05 and using a rejection point. Also, interpret the p value of 0.0158 for the hypothesis test.

8.6 z Tests about a Population Proportion

In this section, we study a large sample hypothesis test about a population proportion (that is, about the fraction of population units that possess some qualitative characteristic). We begin with an example.

Example 8.6 The Cheese Spread Case

Recall that the soft cheese spread producer has decided that replacing the current spout with the new spout is profitable only if p, the true proportion of all current purchasers who would stop buying the cheese spread if the new spout were used, is less than 0.10. The producer feels that it is unwise to change the spout unless it has very strong evidence that p is less than 0.10. Therefore, the spout will be changed if and only if the null hypothesis $H_0: p = 0.10$ can be rejected in favour of the alternative hypothesis $H_a: p < 0.10$ at the 0.01 level of significance.

In order to see how to test this kind of hypothesis, remember that when n is large, the sampling distribution of

$$\frac{\hat{p} - p}{\sqrt{\dfrac{p(1 - p)}{n}}}$$

is approximately a standard normal distribution. Let p_0 denote a specified value between 0 and 1 (its exact value will depend on the problem), and consider testing the null hypothesis $H_0: p = p_0$. We then have the following result:

A Large Sample Test about a Population Proportion: Testing $H_0: p = p_0$

Define the test statistic

$$z = \frac{\hat{p} - p_0}{\sqrt{\dfrac{p_0(1 - p_0)}{n}}}.$$

If the sample size n is large, we can test $H_0: p = p_0$ versus a particular alternative hypothesis at level of significance α by using the appropriate rejection point rule or, equivalently, the corresponding p value.

Alternative Hypothesis	Rejection Point Rule: Reject H_0 if	p Value (Reject H_0 if p Value $< \alpha$)
$H_a: p > p_0$	$z > z_\alpha$	The area under the standard normal curve to the right of z
$H_a: p < p_0$	$z < -z_\alpha$	The area under the standard normal curve to the left of z
$H_a: p \neq p_0$	$\lvert z \rvert > z_{\alpha/2}$—that is, $z > z_{\alpha/2}$ or $z < -z_{\alpha/2}$	Twice the area under the standard normal curve to the right of $\lvert z \rvert$

Here n should be considered large if both np_0 and $n(1 - p_0)$ are at least 5.[1]

---

[1]Some statisticians suggest using the more conservative rule that both np_0 and $n(1 - p_0)$ must be at least 10.

Example 8.7 The Cheese Spread Case

We have seen that the cheese spread producer wishes to test $H_0: p = 0.10$ versus $H_a: p < 0.10$, where p is the proportion of all current purchasers who would stop buying the cheese spread if the new spout were used. The producer will use the new spout if H_0 can be rejected in favour of H_a at the **0.01 level of significance**. To perform the hypothesis test, we will randomly select $n = 1{,}000$ current purchasers of the cheese spread, find the proportion ($\hat{p}$) of these purchasers who would stop buying the cheese spread if the new spout were used, and calculate the value of the **test statistic z in the summary box**. Then, since the alternative hypothesis $H_a: p < 0.10$ is of the form $H_a: p < p_0$, we will **reject $H_0: p = 0.10$ if the value of z is less than $-z_\alpha = -z_{0.01} = -2.33$**. (Note that using this procedure is valid because $np_0 = 1{,}000(0.10) = 100$ and $n(1 - p_0) = 1{,}000(1 - 0.10) = 900$ are both at least 5.) Suppose that when the sample is randomly selected, we find that 63 of the 1,000 current purchasers say they would stop buying the cheese spread if the new spout were used. Since $\hat{p} = 63/1{,}000 = 0.063$, the **value of the test statistic is**

$$z = \frac{\hat{p} - p_0}{\sqrt{\dfrac{p_0(1 - p_0)}{n}}} = \frac{0.063 - 0.10}{\sqrt{\dfrac{0.10(1 - 0.10)}{1{,}000}}} = -3.90.$$

Because $z = -3.90$ is less than $-z_{0.01} = -2.33$, we reject $H_0: p = 0.10$ in favour of $H_a: p < 0.10$. That is, we conclude (at an α of 0.01) that the proportion of current purchasers who would stop buying the cheese spread if the new spout were used is less than 0.10. It follows that the company will use the new spout. Furthermore, the point estimate $\hat{p} = 0.063$ says we estimate that 6.3 percent of all current customers would stop buying the cheese spread if the new spout were used.

Although the cheese spread producer has made its decision by setting α equal to a single, pre-chosen value (0.01), it would probably also wish to know the weight of evidence against H_0 and in favour of H_a. The p value is the area under the standard normal curve to the left of $z = -3.90$. Since Table A.3 tells us that the area to the left of -3.09 is 0.001, and since -3.90 is less than -3.09, the p value is less than 0.001. Therefore, we have extremely strong evidence that $H_a: p < 0.10$ is true. That is, we have extremely strong evidence that less than 10 percent of current purchasers would stop buying the cheese spread if the new spout were used.

Example 8.8

Recent medical research has sought to develop drugs that lessen the severity and duration of viral infections. Virol, a relatively new drug, has been shown to provide relief for 70 percent of all patients suffering from viral upper respiratory infections. A major drug company is developing a competing drug called Phantol. The drug company wishes to investigate whether Phantol is more effective than Virol. To do this, the drug company will test a hypothesis about the true proportion, p, of all patients whose symptoms would be relieved by Phantol. **The null hypothesis to be tested is $H_0: p = 0.70$, and the alternative hypothesis is $H_a: p > 0.70$.** If H_0 can be rejected in favour of H_a at the **0.05 level of significance**, the drug company will conclude that Phantol helps more than the 70 percent of patients helped by Virol. To perform the hypothesis test, we will randomly select $n = 300$ patients with viral upper respiratory infections, find the proportion ($\hat{p}$) of these patients whose symptoms are relieved by Phantol, and calculate the value of the **test statistic z in the summary box**. Then, since the alternative hypothesis $H_a: p > 0.70$ is of the form $H_a: p > p_0$, we will **reject $H_0: p = 0.70$ if the value of z is greater than $z_\alpha = z_{0.05} = 1.645$**. (Note that using this procedure is valid because $np_0 = 300(0.70) = 210$ and $n(1 - p_0) = 300(1 - 0.70) = 90$ are both at least 5.) Suppose that when the sample is randomly selected, we find that Phantol provides relief for 231 of the 300 patients. Since $\hat{p} = 231/300 = 0.77$, the **value of the test statistic is**

$$z = \frac{\hat{p} - p_0}{\sqrt{\dfrac{p_0(1 - p_0)}{n}}} = \frac{0.77 - 0.70}{\sqrt{\dfrac{(0.70)(1 - 0.70)}{300}}} = 2.65.$$

Because $z = 2.65$ is greater than $z_{0.05} = 1.645$, we reject H_0: $p = 0.70$ in favour of H_a: $p > 0.70$. That is, we conclude (at an α of 0.05) that Phantol will provide relief for more than 70 percent of all patients suffering from viral upper respiratory infections. More specifically, the point estimate $\hat{p} = 0.77$ of p says that we estimate that Phantol will provide relief for 77 percent of all such patients. Comparing this estimate to the 70 percent of patients whose symptoms are relieved by Virol, we conclude that Phantol is somewhat more effective.

The p value for testing H_0: $p = 0.70$ versus H_a: $p > 0.70$ is the area under the standard normal curve to the right of $z = 2.65$. This p value is $(0.5 - 0.4960) = 0.004$ (see Table A.3), and it provides very strong evidence against H_0: $p = 0.70$ and in favour of H_a: $p > 0.70$. That is, we have very strong evidence that Phantol will provide relief for more than 70 percent of all patients suffering from viral upper respiratory infections.

Example 8.9   The Electronic Article Surveillance Case

Suppose that a company selling electronic article surveillance (EAS) devices claims that the proportion, p, of all consumers who would say they would never shop in a store again if the store subjected them to a false alarm is no more than 0.05. A store considering installing such a device is concerned that p is greater than 0.05 and wishes to test H_0: $p = 0.05$ versus H_a: $p > 0.05$. To perform the hypothesis test, the store will calculate a p value and use it to measure the **weight of evidence** against H_0 and in favour of H_a. Recall from Example 2.11 on page 64 that 40 out of 250 consumers in a systematic sample said they would never shop in a store again if the store subjected them to a false alarm. Therefore, the sample proportion of lost consumers is $\hat{p} = 40/250 = 0.16$. Since $np_0 = 250(0.05) = 12.5$ and $n(1 - p_0) = 250(1 - 0.05) = 237.5$ are both at least 5, we can use the **test statistic z in the summary box. The value of the test statistic** is

$$z = \frac{\hat{p} - p_0}{\sqrt{\dfrac{p_0(1 - p_0)}{n}}} = \frac{0.16 - 0.05}{\sqrt{\dfrac{(0.05)(0.95)}{250}}} = 7.98.$$

Noting that H_a: $p > 0.05$ is of the form H_a: $p > p_0$, **the p value is the area under the standard normal curve to the right of $z = 7.98$. The normal table tells us that the area under the standard normal curve to the right of 3.09 is 0.001. Therefore, the p value is less than 0.001** and provides **extremely strong evidence against H_0: $p = 0.05$ and in favour of H_a: $p > 0.05$.** That is, we have extremely strong evidence that the proportion of all consumers who say they would never shop in a store again if the store subjected them to a false alarm is greater than 0.05. Furthermore, the point estimate $\hat{p} = 0.16$ says we estimate that the percentage of such consumers is 11 percentage points more than the 5 percent maximum claimed by the company selling the EAS devices. We will further investigate the results by looking at a 95 percent confidence interval for p:

$$\left[\hat{p} \pm z_{0.025} \sqrt{\frac{\hat{p}(1 - \hat{p})}{n}}\right] = \left[0.16 \pm 1.96 \sqrt{\frac{(0.16)(0.84)}{250}}\right]$$

$$= [0.1146, 0.2054].$$

This interval says we are 95 percent confident that the percentage of consumers who would say they would never shop in a store again if the store subjected them to a false alarm is between 6.46 and 15.54 percentage points more than the 5 percent maximum claimed by the company selling the EAS devices. The rather large increases over the claimed 5 percent maximum implied by the point estimate and the confidence interval would mean substantially more lost customers and thus are practically important. Figure 8.13 gives the MegaStat output for testing H_0: $p = 0.05$ versus H_a: $p > 0.05$. Note that this output includes a 95 percent confidence interval for p. Also notice that MegaStat expresses the p value for this test in scientific notation. In general, when a p value is less than 0.0001, MegaStat (and also Excel)

FIGURE **8.13** The MegaStat Output for Testing H_0: $p = 0.05$ versus H_a: $p > 0.05$

Hypothesis test for proportion vs hypothesized value

Observed	Hypothesized		
0.16	0.05 p (as decimal)	0.0138 std. error	0.1146 confidence interval 95.% lower
40/250	13/250 p (as fraction)	7.98 z	0.2054 confidence interval 95.% upper
40.	12.5 X	7.77E-16 p-value	0.0454 half-width
250	250 n	(one-tailed upper)	

expresses the *p* value in scientific notation. Here the *p* value of 7.77 E-16 says that we must move the decimal point 16 places to the left to obtain the decimal equivalent. That is, the *p* value is 0.000000000000000777.

Exercises for Section 8.6

CONCEPTS

8.61 If we test a hypothesis to provide evidence supporting the claim that a majority of voters prefer a political party, explain the difference between p and $\hat{p}$.

8.62 If we test a hypothesis to provide evidence supporting the claim that more than 30 percent of all consumers prefer a particular brand of beer, explain the difference between p and $\hat{p}$.

8.63 If we test a hypothesis to provide evidence supporting the claim that less than 5 percent of the units produced by a process are defective, explain the difference between p and $\hat{p}$.

8.64 What condition must be satisfied in order to appropriately use the methods of this section?

METHODS AND APPLICATIONS

8.65 For each of the following sample sizes and hypothesized values of the population proportion p, determine whether the sample size is large enough to use the large sample test about p given in this section:
   a. $n = 400$ and $p_0 = 0.5$.
   b. $n = 100$ and $p_0 = 0.01$.
   c. $n = 10,000$ and $p_0 = 0.01$.
   d. $n = 100$ and $p_0 = 0.2$.
   e. $n = 256$ and $p_0 = 0.7$.
   f. $n = 200$ and $p_0 = 0.98$.
   g. $n = 1,000$ and $p_0 = 0.98$.
   h. $n = 25$ and $p_0 = 0.4$.

8.66 Suppose we wish to test H_0: $p \leq 0.8$ versus H_a: $p > 0.8$ and that a random sample of $n = 400$ gives a sample proportion $\hat{p} = 0.86$.
   a. Test H_0 versus H_a at the 0.05 level of significance by using a rejection point. What do you conclude?
   b. Find the *p* value for this test.
   c. Use the *p* value to test H_0 versus H_a by setting α equal to 0.10, 0.05, 0.01, and 0.001. What do you conclude at each value of α?

8.67 Suppose we test H_0: $p = 0.3$ versus H_a: $p \neq 0.3$ and that a random sample of $n = 100$ gives a sample proportion $\hat{p} = 0.20$.
   a. Test H_0 versus H_a at the 0.01 level of significance by using a rejection point. What do you conclude?

   b. Find the *p* value for this test.
   c. Use the *p* value to test H_0 versus H_a by setting α equal to 0.10, 0.05, 0.01, and 0.001. What do you conclude at each value of α?

8.68 Suppose we are testing H_0: $p \leq 0.5$ versus H_a: $p > 0.5$, where p is the proportion of all beer drinkers who have tried at least one brand of beer from a craft brewery. If a random sample of 500 beer drinkers has been taken and if $\hat{p}$ equals 0.57, how many beer drinkers in the sample have tried at least one brand of beer from a craft brewery?

8.69 **THE MARKETING ETHICS CASE: CONFLICT OF INTEREST**

   Recall that a conflict of interest scenario was presented to a sample of 205 marketing researchers and that 111 of these researchers disapproved of the actions taken (see Exercise 2.48 on page 67).
   a. Let p be the proportion of all marketing researchers who disapprove of the actions taken in the conflict of interest scenario. Set up the null and alternative hypotheses needed to attempt to provide evidence supporting the claim that a majority (more than 50 percent) of all marketing researchers disapprove of the actions taken.
   b. Assuming that the sample of 205 marketing researchers has been randomly selected, use rejection points and the previously given sample information to test the hypotheses you set up in part a at the 0.10, 0.05, 0.01, and 0.001 levels of significance. How much evidence is there that a majority of all marketing researchers disapprove of the actions taken?
   c. Suppose a random sample of 1,000 marketing researchers reveals that 540 of the researchers disapprove of the actions taken in the conflict of interest scenario. Use rejection points to determine how much evidence there is that a majority of all marketing researchers disapprove of the actions taken.
   d. Note that in parts b and c the sample proportion $\hat{p}$ is (essentially) the same. Explain why the results of the hypothesis tests in parts b and c differ.

8.70 Last year, television station CXYZ's share of the 11 P.M. news audience was approximately equal to, but no

FIGURE **8.14** **MINITAB Output for Exercise 8.70**

```
Test of p = 0.25 vs p > 0.25

   Sample    X    N     Sample p     Z-Value    P-Value
     1      146   400    0.365000      5.31       0.000
```

greater than, 25 percent. The station's management believes that the current audience share is higher than last year's 25 percent share. In an attempt to substantiate this belief, the station surveyed a random sample of 400 11 P.M. news viewers and found that 146 watched CXYZ.

a. Let p be the current proportion of all 11 P.M. news viewers who watch CXYZ. Set up the null and alternative hypotheses needed to attempt to provide evidence supporting the claim that the current audience share for CXYZ is higher than last year's 25 percent share.

b. Use rejection points and the MINITAB output in Figure 8.14 to test the hypotheses you set up in part a at the 0.10, 0.05, 0.01, and 0.001 levels of significance. How much evidence is there that the current audience share is higher than last year's 25 percent share?

c. Calculate the p value for the hypothesis test in part b. Use the p value to carry out the test by setting α equal to 0.10, 0.05, 0.01, and 0.001. Interpret your results.

d. Do you think that the result of the station's survey has practical importance? Why or why not?

8.71 In the book *Essentials of Marketing Research*, Dillon, Madden, and Firtle discuss a marketing research proposal to study day-after recall for a brand of mouthwash. To quote the authors:

> The ad agency has developed a TV ad for the introduction of the mouthwash. The objective of the ad is to create awareness of the brand. The objective of this research is to evaluate the awareness generated by the ad measured by aided- and unaided-recall scores.
>
>   A minimum of 200 respondents who claim to have watched the TV show in which the ad was aired the night before will be contacted by telephone in 20 cities.
>
>   The study will provide information on the incidence of unaided and aided recall.

Suppose a random sample of 200 respondents shows that 46 of the people interviewed were able to recall the commercial without any prompting (unaided recall).

a. In order for the ad to be considered successful, the percentage of unaided recall must be above the category norm for a TV commercial for the product class. If this norm is 18 percent, set up the null and alternative hypotheses needed to attempt to provide evidence that the ad is successful.

b. Use the previously given sample information to compute the p value for the hypothesis test you set up in part a. Use the p value to carry out the test by setting α equal to 0.10, 0.05, 0.01, and 0.001. How much evidence is there that the TV commercial is successful?

c. Do you think the result of the ad agency's survey has practical importance? Explain your opinion.

8.72 *Quality Progress*, February 2005, reports on the results achieved by Bank of America in improving customer satisfaction and customer loyalty by listening to the "voice of the customer." A key measure of customer satisfaction is the response on a scale from 1 to 10 to the question, "Considering all the business you do with Bank of America, what is your overall satisfaction with Bank of America?"[2] Suppose that a random sample of 350 current customers results in 195 customers with a response of 9 or 10 representing "customer delight."

a. Let p denote the true proportion of all current Bank of America customers who would respond with a 9 or a 10, and note that the historical proportion of customer delight for Bank of America has been 0.48. Calculate the p value for testing H_0: $p = 0.48$ versus H_a: $p > 0.48$. How much evidence is there that p exceeds 0.48?

b. Bank of America has a base of nearly 30 million customers. Do you think that the sample results have practical importance? Explain your opinion.

8.73 The manufacturer of the ColourSmart-5000 television set claims that 95 percent of its sets last at least five years without needing a single repair. In order to test this claim, a consumer group randomly selects 400 consumers who have owned a ColourSmart-5000 television set for five years. Of these 400 consumers, 316 say that their ColourSmart-5000 television sets did not need repair, while 84 say that their ColourSmart-5000 television sets did need at least one repair.

a. Letting p be the proportion of ColourSmart-5000 television sets that last five years without a single repair, set up the null and alternative hypotheses that the consumer group should use to attempt to show that the manufacturer's claim is false.

b. Use rejection points and the previously given sample information to test the hypotheses you set up in part a by setting α equal to 0.10, 0.05, 0.01, and 0.001. How much evidence is there that the manufacturer's claim is false?

c. Do you think the results of the consumer group's survey have practical importance? Explain your opinion.

---

[2]Source: "Driving organic growth at Bank of America," *Quality Progress*, February 2005, pp. 23–27.

FIGURE **8.15**   Selecting an Appropriate Test Statistic to Test a Hypothesis about a Population Mean

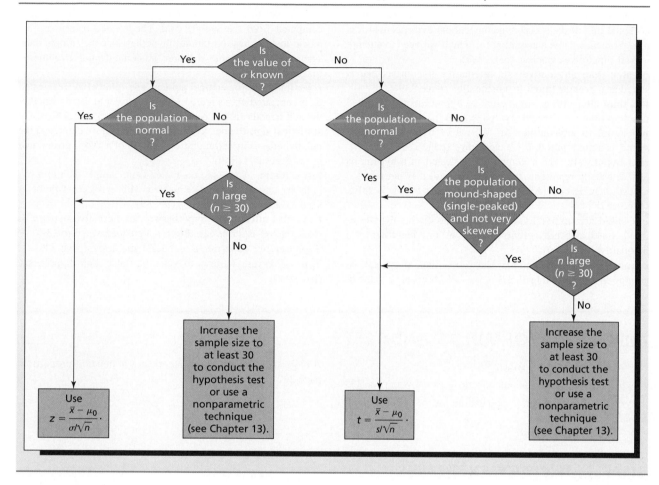

CHAPTER SUMMARY

We began this chapter by learning about the two hypotheses that make up the structure of a hypothesis test. The **null hypothesis** is the statement being tested. Usually it represents the status quo and is not rejected unless there is convincing sample evidence that it is false. The **alternative**, or **research**, **hypothesis** is a statement that is accepted only if there is convincing sample evidence that it is true and that the null hypothesis is false. In some situations, the alternative hypothesis is a condition for which we need to attempt to find supportive evidence. We also learned that two types of errors can be made in a hypothesis test. A **Type I error** occurs when we reject a true null hypothesis, and a **Type II error** occurs when we do not reject a false null hypothesis.

We studied two commonly used ways to conduct a hypothesis test. The first involves comparing the value of a test statistic with what is called a **rejection point**, and the second employs what is called a **p value**. The p value measures the weight of evidence against the null hypothesis. The smaller the p value, the more we doubt the null hypothesis. We learned

that, if we can reject the null hypothesis with the probability of a Type I error equal to α, then we say that the test result has **statistical significance at the α level**. However, we also learned that, even if the result of a hypothesis test tells us that statistical significance exists, we must carefully assess whether the result is practically important. One good way to do this is to use a point estimate and confidence interval for the parameter of interest.

The specific hypothesis tests we covered in this chapter all dealt with a hypothesis about one population parameter. First, we studied a test about a **population mean** that is based on the assumption that the population standard deviation σ **is known**. This test employs the **normal distribution**. Second, we studied a test about a population mean that assumes that σ **is unknown**. We learned that this test is based on the *t* **distribution**. Figure 8.15 presents a flowchart summarizing how to select an appropriate test statistic to test a hypothesis about a population mean. Finally, we presented a test about a **population proportion** that is based on the **normal distribution**.

GLOSSARY OF TERMS

alternative (research) hypothesis: A statement that will be accepted only if there is convincing sample evidence that it is true. Sometimes it is a condition for which we need to attempt to find supportive evidence. (page 237)

greater than alternative: An alternative hypothesis that is stated as a **greater than** (>) inequality. (page 239)

less than alternative: An alternative hypothesis that is stated as a **less than** (<) inequality. (page 239)

not equal to alternative: An alternative hypothesis that is stated as a **not equal to** (≠) inequality. (page 239)

null hypothesis: The statement being tested in a hypothesis test. It usually represents the status quo and it is not rejected unless there is convincing sample evidence that it is false. (page 237)

one-sided alternative hypothesis: An alternative hypothesis that is stated as either a **greater than** (>) or a **less than** (<) inequality. (page 239)

p value (probability value): The probability, computed assuming that the null hypothesis is true, of observing a value of the test statistic that is at least as extreme as the value actually computed from the sample data. The p value measures how much doubt is cast on the null hypothesis by the sample data. The smaller the p value, the more we doubt the null hypothesis. (pages 245, 248, 250, 254)

rejection point (or critical point): The value of the test statistic is compared with a rejection point in order to decide whether the null hypothesis can be rejected. (pages 243, 247, 253)

statistical significance at the α level: When we can reject the null hypothesis by setting the probability of a Type I error equal to α. (pages 244, 256)

test statistic: A statistic computed from sample data in a hypothesis test. It is either compared with a rejection point or used to compute a p value. (page 239)

two-sided alternative hypothesis: An alternative hypothesis that is stated as a **not equal to** (≠) inequality. (page 239)

Type I error: Rejecting a true null hypothesis. (page 240)

Type II error: Failing to reject a false null hypothesis. (page 240)

IMPORTANT FORMULAS AND TESTS

Hypothesis testing steps: page 250

A hypothesis test about a population mean (σ known): page 255

A hypothesis test about a population mean (σ unknown): page 258

A large sample hypothesis test about a population proportion: page 262

SUPPLEMENTARY EXERCISES

8.74 The auditor for a large corporation routinely monitors cash disbursements. As part of this process, the auditor examines cheque request forms to determine whether they have been properly approved. Improper approval can occur in several ways. For instance, the cheque may have no approval, the cheque request might be missing, the approval might be written by an unauthorized person, or the dollar limit of the authorizing person might be exceeded.

    a. Last year, the corporation experienced a 5 percent improper cheque request approval rate. Since this was considered unacceptable, efforts were made to reduce the rate of improper approvals. Letting p be the proportion of all cheques that are now improperly approved, set up the null and alternative hypotheses needed to attempt to demonstrate that the current rate of improper approvals is lower than last year's rate of 5 percent.

    b. Suppose that the auditor selects a random sample of 625 cheques that have been approved in the last month. The auditor finds that 18 of these 625 cheques have been improperly approved. Use rejection points and this sample information to test the hypotheses you set up in part a at the 0.10, 0.05, 0.01, and 0.001 levels of significance. How much evidence is there that the rate of improper approvals has been reduced below last year's 5 percent rate?

    c. Find the p value for the test of part b. Use the p value to carry out the test by setting α equal to 0.10, 0.05, 0.01, and 0.001. Interpret your results.

    d. Suppose the corporation incurs a $10 cost to detect and correct an improperly approved cheque. If the corporation disburses at least 2 million cheques per year, does the observed reduction of the rate of improper approvals seem to have practical importance? Explain your opinion.

8.75 In an article in the *Journal of Retailing*, Kumar, Kerwin, and Pereira study factors affecting merger and acquisition activity in retailing. As part of the study, the authors compare the characteristics of "target firms" (firms targeted for acquisition) and "bidder firms" (firms attempting to make acquisitions). Among the variables studied in the comparison were earnings per share, debt-to-equity ratio, growth rate of sales, market share, and extent of diversification.

    a. Let μ be the mean growth rate of sales for all target firms (firms that have been targeted for acquisition in the last five years and that have not bid on other firms), and assume growth rates are approximately normally distributed. Furthermore, suppose a random sample of 25 target firms yields a sample mean sales growth rate of $\bar{x} = 0.16$ with a standard deviation of $s = 0.12$. Use rejection points and this sample information to test H_0: $\mu \leq 0.10$

versus H_a: $\mu > 0.10$ by setting α equal to 0.10, 0.05, 0.01, and 0.001. How much evidence is there that the mean growth rate of sales for target firms exceeds 0.10 (that is, exceeds 10 percent)?

b. Now let μ be the mean growth rate of sales for all firms that are bidders (firms that have bid to acquire at least one other firm in the last five years), and again assume growth rates are approximately normally distributed. Furthermore, suppose a random sample of 25 bidders yields a sample mean sales growth rate of $\bar{x} = 0.12$ with a standard deviation of $s = 0.09$. Use rejection points and this sample information to test H_0: $\mu \le 0.10$ versus H_a: $\mu > 0.10$ by setting α equal to 0.10, 0.05, 0.01, and 0.001. How much evidence is there that the mean growth rate of sales for bidders exceeds 0.10 (that is, exceeds 10 percent)?

8.76 A consumer electronics firm has developed a new type of remote control button that is designed to operate longer before becoming intermittent. A random sample of 35 of the new buttons is selected and each is tested in continuous operation until becoming intermittent. The resulting lifetimes are found to have a sample mean of $\bar{x} = 1{,}241.2$ hours and a sample standard deviation of $s = 110.8$.

a. Independent tests reveal that the mean lifetime (in continuous operation) of the best remote control button on the market is 1,200 hours. Letting μ be the mean lifetime of the population of all new remote control buttons that will or could potentially be produced, set up the null and alternative hypotheses needed to attempt to provide evidence that the new button's mean lifetime exceeds the mean lifetime of the best remote button currently on the market.

b. Using the previously given sample results, use rejection points to test the hypotheses you set up in part a by setting α equal to 0.10, 0.05, 0.01, and 0.001. What do you conclude for each value of α?

c. Suppose that $\bar{x} = 1{,}241.2$ and $s = 110.8$ had been obtained by testing a sample of 100 buttons. Use rejection points to test the hypotheses you set up in part a by setting α equal to 0.10, 0.05, 0.01, and 0.001. Which sample (the sample of 35 or the sample of 100) gives a more statistically significant result? That is, which sample provides stronger evidence that H_a is true?

d. If we define practical importance to mean that μ exceeds 1,200 by an amount that would be clearly noticeable to most consumers, do you think that the result has practical importance? Explain why the samples of 35 and 100 both indicate the same degree of practical importance.

e. Suppose that further research and development effort improves the new remote control button and that a random sample of 35 buttons gives $\bar{x} = 1{,}524.6$ hours and $s = 102.8$ hours. Test your hypotheses of part a by setting α equal to 0.10, 0.05, 0.01, and 0.001.

   (1) Do we have a highly statistically significant result? Explain.

   (2) Do you think we have a practically important result? Explain.

8.77 Again consider the remote control button lifetime situation discussed in Exercise 8.76. Using the sample information given in the introduction to Exercise 8.76, the p value for testing H_0 versus H_a can be calculated to be 0.0174.

a. Determine whether H_0 would be rejected at each of $\alpha = 0.10$, $\alpha = 0.05$, $\alpha = 0.01$, and $\alpha = 0.001$.

b. Describe how much evidence we have that the new button's mean lifetime exceeds the mean lifetime of the best remote button currently on the market.

8.78 Calculate and use an appropriate 95 percent confidence interval to help evaluate practical importance as it relates to the hypothesis test in each of the following situations discussed in previous supplementary exercises. Explain what you think each confidence interval says about practical importance.

a. The cheque approval situation of Exercise 8.74.

b. The remote control button situation of Exercise 8.76a, c, and e.

8.79 Several industries located along the Ohio River discharge a toxic substance called carbon tetrachloride into the river. The state Environmental Protection Agency monitors the amount of carbon tetrachloride pollution in the river. Specifically, the agency requires that the carbon tetrachloride contamination must average no more than 10 parts per million. In order to monitor the carbon tetrachloride contamination in the river, the agency takes a daily sample of 100 pollution readings at a specified location. If the mean carbon tetrachloride reading for this sample casts substantial doubt on the hypothesis that the average amount of carbon tetrachloride contamination in the river is at most 10 parts per million, the agency must issue a shutdown order. In the event of such a shutdown order, industrial plants along the river must be closed until the carbon tetrachloride contamination is reduced to a more acceptable level. Assume that the state Environmental Protection Agency decides to issue a shutdown order if a sample of 100 pollution readings implies that H_0: $\mu \le 10$ can be rejected in favour of H_a: $\mu > 10$ by setting $\alpha = 0.01$. If σ equals 2, and a sample mean of 10.37 was recorded, calculate the p value and determine whether or not a shutdown order should be given.

8.80 THE INVESTMENT CASE

Suppose that random samples of 50 returns for each of the following investment classes give the indicated sample mean and sample standard deviation:

Fixed annuities: $\bar{x} = 7.83\%$, $s = 0.51\%$
Domestic large-cap stocks: $\bar{x} = 13.42\%$, $s = 15.17\%$
Domestic midcap stocks: $\bar{x} = 15.03\%$, $s = 18.44\%$
Domestic small-cap stocks: $\bar{x} = 22.51\%$, $s = 21.75\%$

a. For each investment class, set up the null and alternative hypotheses needed to test whether the current mean return differs from the historical (1970 to 1994) mean return given in the InvestRet data set on the student CD-ROM.

b. Test each hypothesis you set up in part a at the 0.05 level of significance. What do you conclude? For which investment classes does the current mean return differ from the historical mean?

8.81   THE U.K. INSURANCE CASE

Assume that the U.K. insurance survey (see Exercise 6.42 on page 199) is based on 1,000 randomly selected U.K. households and that 640 of these households spent on life insurance in 1993.

a. If p denotes the proportion of all U.K. households that spent on life insurance in 1993, set up the null and alternative hypotheses needed to attempt to justify the claim that more than 60 percent of U.K. households spent on life insurance in 1993.

b. Test the hypotheses you set up in part a by setting $\alpha = 0.10, 0.05, 0.01,$ and 0.001. How much evidence is there that more than 60 percent of U.K. households spent on life insurance in 1993?

8.82 A local factory is responsible for bagging and shipping 1-kg bags of sugar. A production manager suspects that the bags are being overfilled. In order to test the claim, a random sample of sixteen 1-kg bags of sugar is obtained and the actual masses of the bags are measured. The sample mean is 1.051 kg with a sample standard deviation of $s = 0.06$ kg. Suppose it is also known that the masses of the bags of sugar have an approximately normal distribution. Use this information to test $H_0: \mu = 1$ kg versus $H_a: \mu > 1$ kg at $\alpha = 0.01$. Is there evidence to support the production manager's claim at the 0.01 level of significance?

8.83 *Consumer Reports* (January 2005) indicates that profit margins on extended warranties are much greater than on the purchase of most products.[3] In this exercise, we consider a major electronics retailer that wishes to increase the proportion of customers

who buy extended warranties on digital cameras. Historically, 20 percent of digital camera customers have purchased the retailer's extended warranty. To increase this percentage, the retailer has decided to offer a new warranty that is less expensive and more comprehensive. Suppose that three months after the company starts to offer the new warranty, a random sample of 500 customer sales invoices shows that 152 out of 500 digital camera customers purchased the new warranty. Letting p denote the proportion of all digital camera customers who have purchased the new warranty, calculate the p value for testing $H_0: p = 0.20$ versus $H_a: p > 0.20$. How much evidence is there that p exceeds 0.20? Does the difference between $\hat{p}$ and 0.2 seem to be practically important? Explain your opinion.

8.84 Business magazines periodically report on the rise of fees and expenses charged by stock funds.

a. Suppose that 10 years ago the average annual expense for stock funds was 1.19 percent. Let μ be the current mean annual expense for all stock funds, and assume that stock fund annual expenses are approximately normally distributed. If a random sample of 12 stock funds gives a sample mean annual expense of $\bar{x} = 1.63\%$ with a standard deviation of $s = 0.31\%$, use rejection points and this sample information to test $H_0: \mu \leq 1.19\%$ versus $H_a: \mu > 1.19\%$ by setting α equal to 0.10, 0.05, 0.01, and 0.001. How much evidence is there that the current mean annual expense for stock funds exceeds the average of 10 years ago?

b. Do you think that the result in part a has practical importance? Explain your opinion.

8.85   INTERNET EXERCISE

Are Canadian consumers comfortable using their credit cards to make purchases over the Internet? Suppose that a noted authority suggests that credit cards will be firmly established on the Internet once the 80 percent barrier is broken, that is, as soon as more than 80 percent of those who make purchases over the Internet are willing to use a credit card to pay for their transactions. Suppose that a recent poll was conducted in which $n = 504$ Internet purchasers were surveyed and it was found that 386 have paid for Internet purchases using a credit card in the past year. According to these results, is there sufficient evidence to suggest that the proportion of Internet purchasers willing to use a credit card now exceeds 80 percent?

Set up the appropriate null and alternative hypotheses, and test at the 0.05 and 0.01 levels of significance using a p value.

Go to the Ipsos Reid Web site (http://www.ipsos-na.com/news) and find the index of recent poll results (http://www.ipsos-na.com/news/results.cfm). Select an interesting current poll and prepare a brief written summary of the poll or some aspect thereof. Include a statistical test for the significance of a proportion (you may have to make up your own value for the hypothesized proportion p_0) as part of your report. For example, you might select a political poll and test whether a particular party is preferred by a majority of voters ($p > 0.50$).

---

[3]*Consumer Reports,* January 2005, page 51.

CHAPTER 9

Statistical Inferences Based on Two Samples

LEARNING OBJECTIVES

After reading this chapter, you should be able to

- calculate a confidence interval for a difference in population means both when the population standard deviation (σ) is known and when σ is not known

- understand the difference between independent and dependent (paired) samples

- calculate a confidence interval for a difference in population proportions when large, independent samples are used

- identify the appropriate formula to use to test your hypothesis (equal variances, unequal variances, variances known, variances unknown)

- conduct a hypothesis test for differences in population means using a rejection/critical point and *p* value

- conduct a hypothesis test for differences in population proportions using a rejection/critical point and *p* value

- determine the difference between a one-tailed test and a two-tailed test

- understand the difference between the *z* test and the *t* test, and when you should use each

- conduct an *F* test and use it to compare population variances

CHAPTER OUTLINE

A local university offers two sections of an Introductory Business Statistics course, one in the morning and one in the afternoon. Both sections are taught by the same professor. The average course grades for each section are calculated. Students may be interested in the historical difference in averages. This could affect which section they enroll in. Could it be that the average in the morning class is higher than that in the afternoon class, or is it the other way around?

In this chapter, we discuss using confidence intervals and hypothesis tests to **compare two populations**. Specifically, we compare two population means, two population variances, and two population proportions. We make these comparisons by studying **differences**

and **ratios**. For instance, to compare two population means, say μ_1 and μ_2, we consider the difference between these means, $\mu_1 - \mu_2$. If, for example, we use a confidence interval or hypothesis test to conclude that $\mu_1 - \mu_2$ is a positive number, then we conclude that μ_1 is greater than μ_2. On the other hand, if a confidence interval or hypothesis test shows that $\mu_1 - \mu_2$ is a negative number, then we conclude that μ_1 is less than μ_2. As another example, if we compare two population variances, say σ_1^2 and σ_2^2, we might consider the ratio σ_1^2/σ_2^2. If this ratio exceeds 1, then we can conclude that σ_1^2 is greater than σ_2^2.

We explain many of this chapter's methods in the context of three new cases:

The Coffee Cup Case. The production supervisor of a plant that produces coffee cups uses confidence intervals and hypothesis tests for the difference between two population means to determine which production process yields higher average hourly output, measured in kilograms of coffee cups. By maximizing average hourly output, the plant can increase productivity and improve its profitability.

The Repair Cost Comparison Case. In order to reduce the costs of automobile accident claims, an insurance company uses confidence intervals and hypothesis

tests for the difference between two population means to compare repair cost estimates for damaged cars at two different garages.

The Advertising Media Case. An advertising agency is test marketing a new product by using one advertising campaign in Toronto, Ontario, and a different campaign in Vancouver, British Columbia. The agency uses confidence intervals and hypothesis tests for the difference between two population proportions to compare the effectiveness of the two advertising campaigns.

**PART 1
Confidence
Intervals**

9.1 Comparing Two Population Means by Using Independent Samples: Variances Known

A bank manager has developed a new system to reduce the time customers spend waiting to be served by tellers during peak business hours. We let μ_1 denote the mean customer waiting time during peak business hours under the current system. To estimate μ_1, the manager randomly selects $n_1 = 100$ customers and records the length of time each customer spends waiting for service. The manager finds that the sample mean waiting time for these 100 customers is $\bar{x}_1 = 8.79$ minutes. We let μ_2 denote the mean customer waiting time during peak business hours for the new system. During a trial run, the manager finds that the mean waiting time for a random sample of $n_2 = 100$ customers is $\bar{x}_2 = 5.14$ minutes.

In order to compare μ_1 and μ_2, the manager estimates $\mu_1 - \mu_2$, the difference between μ_1 and μ_2. Intuitively, a logical point estimate of $\mu_1 - \mu_2$ is the difference between the sample means

$$\bar{x}_1 - \bar{x}_2 = 8.79 - 5.14 = 3.65 \text{ minutes.}$$

This says we estimate that the current mean waiting time is 3.65 minutes longer than the mean waiting time under the new system. That is, we estimate that the new system reduces the mean waiting time by 3.65 minutes.

To compute a confidence interval for $\mu_1 - \mu_2$ (or to test a hypothesis about $\mu_1 - \mu_2$), we need to know the properties of the sampling distribution of $\bar{x}_1 - \bar{x}_2$. To understand this sampling distribution, consider randomly selecting a sample[1] of n_1 measurements from a population with mean μ_1 and variance σ_1^2. Let $\bar{x}_1$ be the mean of this sample. Also consider randomly selecting

---

[1]Each sample in this chapter is a **random** sample. As has been our practice throughout this book, for brevity we sometimes refer to "random samples" as "samples."

FIGURE **9.1** The Sampling Distribution of $\bar{x}_1 - \bar{x}_2$ Has Mean $\mu_1 - \mu_2$ and Standard Deviation $\sigma_{\bar{x}_1 - \bar{x}_2}$

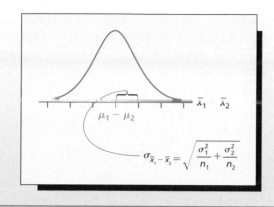

a sample of n_2 measurements from another population with mean μ_2 and variance σ_2^2. Let $\bar{x}_2$ be the mean of this sample. Different samples from the first population would give different values of $\bar{x}_1$, and different samples from the second population would give different values of $\bar{x}_2$—so different pairs of samples from the two populations would give different values of $\bar{x}_1 - \bar{x}_2$. In the following box, we describe the sampling distribution of $\bar{x}_1 - \bar{x}_2$, which is the probability distribution of all possible values of $\bar{x}_1 - \bar{x}_2$:

CHAPTER 10

The Sampling Distribution of $\bar{x}_1 - \bar{x}_2$

If the randomly selected samples are **independent** of each other,[2] then the population of all possible values of $\bar{x}_1 - \bar{x}_2$

1 Is normally distributed if each sampled population has a normal distribution, or has approximately a normal distribution if the sampled

populations are not normally distributed and each of the sample sizes n_1 and n_2 is large.

2 Has mean $\mu_{\bar{x}_1 - \bar{x}_2} = \mu_1 - \mu_2$.

3 Has standard deviation $\sigma_{\bar{x}_1 - \bar{x}_2} = \sqrt{\dfrac{\sigma_1^2}{n_1} + \dfrac{\sigma_2^2}{n_2}}$.

Figure 9.1 illustrates the sampling distribution of $\bar{x}_1 - \bar{x}_2$. Using this sampling distribution, we can find a confidence interval for and test a hypothesis about $\mu_1 - \mu_2$. Although the interval and test assume that the true values of the population variances σ_1^2 and σ_2^2 are known, we believe that they are worth presenting because they provide a simple introduction to the basic idea of comparing two population means. Readers who wish to proceed more quickly to the more practical t-based procedures of the next section may skip the rest of this section without loss of continuity.

A z-Based Confidence Interval for $\mu_1 - \mu_2$, the Difference between Two Population Means, when σ_1 and σ_2 are Known

Let $\bar{x}_1$ be the mean of a sample of size n_1 that has been randomly selected from a population with mean μ_1 and standard deviation σ_1, and let $\bar{x}_2$ be the mean of a sample of size n_2 that has been randomly selected from a population with mean μ_2 and standard deviation σ_2. Furthermore, suppose that each sampled population is normally distrib-

uted, or that each of the sample sizes n_1 and n_2 is large. Then, if the samples are independent of each other, a **100(1 − α) percent confidence interval for $\mu_1 - \mu_2$** is

$$\left[(\bar{x}_1 - \bar{x}_2) \pm z_{\alpha/2} \sqrt{\frac{\sigma_1^2}{n_1} + \frac{\sigma_2^2}{n_2}} \right].$$

---

[2]This means that there is no relationship between the measurements in one sample and the measurements in the other sample.

Example 9.1 The Bank Customer Waiting Time Case

Suppose the random sample of $n_1 = 100$ waiting times observed under the current system gives a sample mean $\bar{x}_1 = 8.79$ and the random sample of $n_2 = 100$ waiting times observed during the trial run of the new system yields a sample mean $\bar{x}_2 = 5.14$. Assuming that σ_1^2 is known to equal 4.7 and σ_2^2 is known to equal 1.9, and noting that each sample is large, a 95 percent confidence interval for $\mu_1 - \mu_2$ is

$$\left[(\bar{x}_1 - \bar{x}_2) \pm z_{0.025}\sqrt{\frac{\sigma_1^2}{n_1} + \frac{\sigma_2^2}{n_2}} \right] = \left[(8.79 - 5.14) \pm 1.96\sqrt{\frac{4.7}{100} + \frac{1.9}{100}} \right]$$

$$= [3.65 \pm 0.5035]$$

$$= [3.15, \ 4.15].$$

With 95 percent confidence, we believe that the true difference in mean waiting times between the old system and the new system is somewhere between 3.15 minutes and 4.15 minutes. In this case, we have strong evidence that the new system has reduced the mean waiting time.

Exercises for Section 9.1

CONCEPTS

9.1 Suppose we compare two population means, μ_1 and μ_2, and consider the difference $\mu_1 - \mu_2$. In each case, indicate how μ_1 relates to μ_2 (that is, is μ_1 greater than, less than, equal to, or not equal to μ_2)?
  a. $\mu_1 - \mu_2 < 0$.   **d.** $\mu_1 - \mu_2 > 0$.
  b. $\mu_1 - \mu_2 = 0$.   **e.** $\mu_1 - \mu_2 > 20$.
  c. $\mu_1 - \mu_2 < -10$.   **f.** $\mu_1 - \mu_2 \neq 0$.

9.2 Suppose we compute a 95 percent confidence interval for $\mu_1 - \mu_2$. If the interval is
  a. [3, 5], can we be 95 percent confident that μ_1 is greater than μ_2? Why or why not?
  b. [3, 5], can we be 95 percent confident that μ_1 is not equal to μ_2? Why or why not?
  c. [−20, −10], can we be 95 percent confident that μ_1 is not equal to μ_2? Why or why not?
  d. [−20, −10], can we be 95 percent confident that μ_1 is greater than μ_2? Why or why not?
  e. [−3, 2], can we be 95 percent confident that μ_1 is not equal to μ_2? Why or why not?
  f. [−10, 10], can we be 95 percent confident that μ_1 is less than μ_2? Why or why not?
  g. [−10, 10], can we be 95 percent confident that μ_1 is greater than μ_2? Why or why not?

9.3 Suppose that we calculate a 95 percent confidence interval for $\mu_1 - \mu_2$ to be [1, 15]. Answer each of the following statements with "true," "false," or "cannot say for sure."
  a. The difference in sample means is 8.
  b. The difference in population means is 8.
  c. The difference in population means is somewhere between 1 and 15.
  d. Sampling again from the same population, the difference in sample means lies in the interval [1, 15].
  e. Changing the confidence level to 90 percent would cause the confidence interval to become wider.

  f. Everything else being equal, decreasing the sample sizes would cause the confidence interval to become narrower.

9.4 In order to employ the formulas of this section, the samples that have been randomly selected from the populations being compared must be independent of each other. In such a case, we say that we are performing an **independent samples experiment**. In your own words, explain what it means when we say that samples are independent of each other.

9.5 Describe the assumptions that must be met in order to validly use the methods of Section 9.1.

METHODS AND APPLICATIONS

9.6 Suppose we randomly select two independent samples from populations with means μ_1 and μ_2. If $\bar{x}_1 = 25$, $\bar{x}_2 = 20$, $\sigma_1 = 3$, $\sigma_2 = 4$, $n_1 = 100$, and $n_2 = 100$, calculate a 95 percent confidence interval for $\mu_1 - \mu_2$. Can we be 95 percent confident that μ_1 is greater than μ_2? Explain.

9.7 Suppose we select two independent random samples from populations with means μ_1 and μ_2. If $\bar{x}_1 = 151$, $\bar{x}_2 = 162$, $\sigma_1 = 6$, $\sigma_2 = 8$, $n_1 = 625$, and $n_2 = 625$, calculate a 95 percent confidence interval for $\mu_1 - \mu_2$. Can we be 95 percent confident that μ_2 is greater than μ_1? By how much? Explain.

9.8 Some grocery stores have self-serve checkouts. Most people who use the self-serve checkouts do not have a large number of items. We will compare the service times of the express checkout with the service times of the self-serve checkout and see if there is a difference in average service times. Let μ_1 be the average service time for the express checkout and let μ_2 be the average service time for the self-serve checkout. Suppose that a random sample of 100 service times in the express checkout gave an average time of 3.7 minutes and suppose that a random sample of 100 service times in the self-serve checkout gave an average time of 4.2 minutes. Assuming that the samples are independent and that $\sigma_1 = 0.9$ minutes and $\sigma_2 = 1.6$ minutes, calculate a 95 percent confidence interval for the difference in mean service time between the two checkout methods. Based on this interval, can we be 95 percent confident that the mean service time for those who use the express checkout is less than the mean service time for those who use the self-serve checkout? If so, by how much?

9.9 Who drinks more coffee on average, second-year students at the University of Western Ontario or second-year students at the University of Alberta? Let μ_1 be the average number of cups of coffee drunk per day by University of Western Ontario students and let μ_2 be the average number of cups of coffee drunk per day by University of Alberta students. To determine the answer to this question, a random sample of 50 second-year students was taken from each university and the average number of cups of coffee drunk per day was recorded. The results are as follows:

University of Western Ontario	University of Alberta
$\bar{x}_1 = 2.1$	$\bar{x}_2 = 2.9$
$\sigma_1 = 1.0$	$\sigma_2 = 0.8$
$n_1 = 50$	$n_2 = 50$

Calculate a 95 percent confidence interval for the mean difference in cups of coffee drunk by the second-year students at these universities. Based on this interval, can we be 95 percent confident that the mean number of cups of coffee drunk by second-year students at the University of Alberta is higher than the average number drunk at the University of Western Ontario?

9.10 An Ontario university wishes to demonstrate that car ownership is detrimental to academic achievement. A random sample of 100 students who do not own cars had a mean grade point average (GPA) of 2.68, while a random sample of 100 students who own cars had a mean GPA of 2.55.

a. Assuming that the independence assumption holds, and letting μ_1 be the mean GPA for all students who do not own cars and μ_2 be the mean GPA for all students who own cars, use the above data to compute a 95 percent confidence interval for $\mu_1 - \mu_2$. Assume here that $\sigma_1 = 0.7$ and $\sigma_2 = 0.6$.

b. On the basis of the interval calculated in part a, can the university statistically justify that car ownership harms academic achievement? That is, can the university justify that μ_1 is greater than μ_2? Explain.

9.11 In the *Journal of Marketing*, Bayus studied differences between "early replacement buyers" and "late replacement buyers."[3] Suppose that a random sample of 800 early replacement buyers yields a mean number of automobile dealers visited of $\bar{x}_1 = 3.3$ and a random sample of 500 late replacement buyers yields a mean number of dealers visited of $\bar{x}_2 = 4.5$. Assuming that these samples are independent, let μ_1 be the mean number of dealers visited by early replacement buyers, and let μ_2 be the mean number of dealers visited by late replacement buyers. Calculate a 95 percent confidence interval for $\mu_2 - \mu_1$. Assume here that $\sigma_1 = 0.71$ and $\sigma_2 = 0.66$. Based on this interval, can we be 95 percent confident that on average late replacement buyers visit more dealers than do early replacement buyers?

9.12 Students in a large statistics course at a British Columbia university were concerned that the average test scores were much lower on their second term test than on their first term test. Suppose that it was known that the standard deviations for the first and second term tests were $\sigma_1 = 8$ and $\sigma_1 = 10$, respectively. Independent random samples of 45 test scores were taken from the first and second tests and the means were 72 and 65, respectively.

Let μ_1 be the mean score from the first test and let μ_2 be the mean score from the second test. Construct a 95 percent confidence interval for $\mu_1 - \mu_2$. Based on this interval, can we be 95 percent confident that the test scores were lower on the second test?

9.2 Comparing Two Population Means by Using Independent Samples: Variances Unknown

Suppose that (as is usually the case) the true values of the population variances σ_1^2 and σ_2^2 are not known. We then estimate σ_1^2 and σ_2^2 by using s_1^2 and s_2^2, the variances of the samples randomly selected from the populations being compared. There are two approaches to doing this. The first approach assumes that the population variances σ_1^2 and σ_2^2 are equal. Denoting the common value of these variances as σ^2, it follows that

CHAPTER 10

$$\sigma_{\bar{x}_1 - \bar{x}_2} = \sqrt{\frac{\sigma_1^2}{n_1} + \frac{\sigma_2^2}{n_2}} = \sqrt{\frac{\sigma^2}{n_1} + \frac{\sigma^2}{n_2}} = \sqrt{\sigma^2 \left(\frac{1}{n_1} + \frac{1}{n_2} \right)}.$$

[3]Early replacement buyers are consumers who replace a product during the early part of its lifetime, while late replacement buyers make replacement purchases late in the product's lifetime. In particular, Bayus studied automobile replacement purchases. Consumers who traded in cars with ages of zero to three years and mileages of no more than 35 000 miles (57 000 km) were classified as early replacement buyers. Consumers who traded in cars with ages of seven or more years and mileages of more than 73 000 miles (120 000 km) were classified as late replacement buyers.

Because we are assuming that $\sigma_1^2 = \sigma_2^2 = \sigma^2$, we do not need separate estimates of σ_1^2 and σ_2^2. Instead, we combine the results of the two independent random samples to compute a single estimate of σ^2. This estimate is called the **pooled estimate** of σ^2, and it is a weighted average of the two sample variances s_1^2 and s_2^2. Denoting the pooled estimate as s_p^2, we compute it using the formula

$$s_p^2 = \frac{(n_1 - 1)s_1^2 + (n_2 - 1)s_2^2}{n_1 + n_2 - 2}.$$

Using s_p^2, the estimate of $\sigma_{\bar{x}_1 - \bar{x}_2}$ is

$$\sqrt{s_p^2\left(\frac{1}{n_1} + \frac{1}{n_2}\right)},$$

and we form the statistic

$$\frac{(\bar{x}_1 - \bar{x}_2) - (\mu_1 - \mu_2)}{\sqrt{s_p^2\left(\frac{1}{n_1} + \frac{1}{n_2}\right)}}.$$

It can be shown that, if we have randomly selected independent samples from two normally distributed populations with equal variances, the sampling distribution of this statistic is a t distribution with $(n_1 + n_2 - 2)$ degrees of freedom. Therefore, we can obtain the following confidence interval for $\mu_1 - \mu_2$:

A t-Based Confidence Interval for $\mu_1 - \mu_2$, the Difference between Two Population Means, when $\sigma_1^2 = \sigma_2^2$

Suppose we have randomly selected independent samples from two normally distributed populations with equal variances. Then, a **100(1 − α) percent confidence interval for $\mu_1 - \mu_2$** is

$$\left[(\bar{x}_1 - \bar{x}_2) \pm t_{\alpha/2}\sqrt{s_p^2\left(\frac{1}{n_1} + \frac{1}{n_2}\right)}\right],$$

where

$$s_p^2 = \frac{(n_1 - 1)s_1^2 + (n_2 - 1)s_2^2}{n_1 + n_2 - 2}$$

and $t_{\alpha/2}$ is based on $(n_1 + n_2 - 2)$ degrees of freedom.

Example 9.2 The Coffee Cup Case

A production supervisor at a coffee cup production plant must determine which of two production processes, Java and Joe, maximizes the hourly yield for coffee cup production. In order to compare the mean hourly yields obtained by using the two processes, the supervisor runs the process using each method for five one-hour periods. The resulting yields (in kilograms of cups per hour) for each method, along with the means, variances, and box plots of the yields,[4] are given in Table 9.1. Assuming that all other factors affecting the production of the cups have been held as constant as possible during the test runs, it seems reasonable to regard the five observed yields for each production process as a random sample from the population of all possible hourly yields for the cups. Furthermore, since the sample variances $s_1^2 = 386$ and $s_2^2 = 484.2$ do not differ substantially (notice that $s_1 = 19.65$ and $s_2 = 22.00$ differ by even less), it might be reasonable to conclude that the population variances are approximately equal.[5] It follows that the pooled estimate

$$s_p^2 = \frac{(n_1 - 1)s_1^2 + (n_2 - 1)s_2^2}{n_1 + n_2 - 2}$$

$$= \frac{(5 - 1)(386) + (5 - 1)(484.2)}{5 + 5 - 2} = 435.1$$

is a point estimate of the common variance σ^2.

---

[4]All of the box plots presented in this chapter and in Chapter 10 have been obtained using MINITAB.

[5]We describe how to test the equality of two variances in Section 9.10 (although, as we will explain, this test has drawbacks).

TABLE 9.1   **Coffee Cup Production Using Two Methods**   ● CoffeeCup

Java	Joe	
801	752	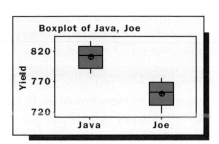
814	718	
784	776	
836	742	
820	763	
$\bar{x}_1 = 811$	$\bar{x}_2 = 750.2$	
$s_1^2 = 386$	$s_2^2 = 484.2$	

We define μ_1 as the mean hourly yield obtained by using the Java process, and we define μ_2 as the mean hourly yield obtained by using the Joe process. If the populations of all possible hourly yields for the production methods are normally distributed, then a 95 percent confidence interval for $\mu_1 - \mu_2$ is

$$\left[(\bar{x}_1 - \bar{x}_2) \pm t_{0.025} \sqrt{s_p^2 \left(\frac{1}{n_1} + \frac{1}{n_2} \right)} \right]$$

$$= \left[(811 - 750.2) \pm 2.306 \sqrt{435.1 \left(\frac{1}{5} + \frac{1}{5} \right)} \right]$$

$$= [60.8 \pm 30.4217]$$

$$= [30.38, \; 91.22].$$

Here $t_{0.025} = 2.306$ is based on $n_1 + n_2 - 2 = 5 + 5 - 2 = 8$ degrees of freedom. This interval tells us that we are 95 percent confident that the mean hourly yield obtained by using the Java process is between 30.38 kg and 91.22 kg higher than the mean hourly yield obtained by using the Joe process.

Now we will consider the case where the underlying population variances are not known and are also not equal. Later in this chapter, we will learn about a test that is used to determine whether two variances are statistically equal or not. For now, unless we know that the underlying variances are equal, we must use the unequal variances procedures.

When the sampled populations are normally distributed and the population variances σ_1^2 and σ_2^2 differ, the following can be shown:

t-Based Confidence Intervals for $\mu_1 - \mu_2$

1   When the sample sizes n_1 and n_2 are equal, the equal variances t-based confidence interval given in the preceding box is approximately valid even if the population variances σ_1^2 and σ_2^2 differ substantially. As a rough rule of thumb, if the larger sample variance is not more than three times the smaller sample variance when the sample sizes are equal, we can use the equal variances interval.

2   Suppose that the larger sample variance is more than three times the smaller sample variance when the sample sizes are equal, or suppose that both the sample sizes and the sample variances differ substantially. Then, we can use an approximate procedure that is sometimes called

an "unequal variances" procedure. This procedure says that an **approximate 100(1 − α) percent confidence interval** for $\mu_1 - \mu_2$ is

$$\left[(\bar{x}_1 - \bar{x}_2) \pm t_{\alpha/2} \sqrt{\frac{s_1^2}{n_1} + \frac{s_2^2}{n_2}} \right].$$

For the above confidence interval, the degrees of freedom are equal to

$$df = \frac{(s_1^2/n_1 + s_2^2/n_2)^2}{\dfrac{(s_1^2/n_1)^2}{n_1 - 1} + \dfrac{(s_2^2/n_2)^2}{n_2 - 1}}.$$

Here, if df is not a whole number, we can round df down to the next smallest whole number.

In general, both the equal variances and the unequal variances procedures have been shown to be approximately valid when the sampled populations are only approximately normally distributed (say, if they are mound-shaped). Furthermore, although the above summary box might seem to imply that we should use the unequal variances procedure only if we cannot use the equal variances procedure, this is not necessarily true. In fact, since the unequal variances procedure can be shown to be a very accurate approximation whether or not the population variances are equal and for most sample sizes (here, both n_1 and n_2 should be at least 5), **many statisticians believe that it is best to use the unequal variances procedure in almost every situation**. If each of n_1 and n_2 is large (at least 30), both the equal variances procedure and the unequal variances procedure are approximately valid, no matter what probability distributions describe the sampled populations.

To illustrate the unequal variances procedure, consider the bank customer waiting time situation, and recall that $\mu_1 - \mu_2$ is the difference between the mean customer waiting time under the current system and the mean customer waiting time under the new system. Because of cost considerations, the bank manager wants to implement the new system only if it reduces the mean waiting time by more than three minutes.

To find a 95 percent confidence interval for $\mu_1 - \mu_2$, note that we can use a computer to find that $t_{0.025}$ based on 163 degrees of freedom is 1.97. It follows that the 95 percent confidence interval for $\mu_1 - \mu_2$ is

$$\left[(\bar{x}_1 - \bar{x}_2) \pm t_{0.025}\sqrt{\frac{s_1^2}{n_1} + \frac{s_2^2}{n_2}} \right] = \left[(8.79 - 5.14) \pm 1.97\sqrt{\frac{4.8237}{100} + \frac{1.7927}{100}} \right]$$
$$= [3.65 \pm 0.50792]$$
$$= [3.14, 4.16].$$

This interval says that we are 95 percent confident that the new system reduces the mean customer waiting time by between 3.14 minutes and 4.16 minutes. Because the entire 95 percent confidence interval contains values greater than 3, we are 95 percent confident that the new system reduces waiting time by more than three minutes.

Using the degrees of freedom formula given previously, we would actually obtain a value of 163.657. Notice that in the previous example, $df = 163$ was used. When using that degrees of freedom formula, we should always round the answer down, ignoring the decimal part. Rounding down will give a smaller value (unless your answer was an exact integer to start) for the degrees of freedom. Smaller values for df lead to slightly larger values of t. This will give slightly larger confidence intervals. Rounding down will give a slightly more conservative answer.

In general, the degrees of freedom for the unequal variances procedure will always be less than or equal to $n_1 + n_2 - 2$, the degrees of freedom for the equal variances procedure. For example, if we use the unequal variances procedure to analyze the coffee cup data in Table 9.1, we can calculate df to be 7.9. This is slightly less than $n_1 + n_2 - 2 = 5 + 5 - 2 = 8$, the degrees of freedom for the equal variances procedure. Figure 9.2 gives the MINITAB output of the unequal variances analysis of the coffee cup comparison data. Note that MINITAB rounds df down to 7 and finds that a 95 percent confidence interval for $\mu_1 - \mu_2$ is [29.6049, 91.9951].

FIGURE 9.2   MINITAB Output of the Unequal Variances Procedure for the Coffee Cup Case

Two-Sample T-Test and CI: Java, Joe

	N	Mean	StDev	SE Mean
Java	5	811.0	19.6	8.8
Joe	5	750.2	22.0	9.8

Difference = mu (Java) - mu (Joe)
Estimate for difference: 60.8000
95% CI for difference: (29.6049, 91.9951)
T-Test of difference = 0 (vs not =):
   T-Value = 4.61   P-Value = 0.002 DF = 7

To conclude this section, it is important to point out that if the sample sizes n_1 and n_2 are not large (at least 30), and if we fear that the sampled populations might be far from normally distributed, we can use a **nonparametric method**. One nonparametric method for comparing populations when using independent samples is the **Wilcoxon rank sum test**. This test is discussed in Section 13.2 (pages 508–511).

Exercises for Section 9.2

CONCEPTS

For both the formulas described below, list the assumptions that must be satisfied in order to validly use the formula.

9.13 The confidence interval formula in the formula box on page 276.

9.14 The confidence interval formula in the formula box on page 277.

METHODS AND APPLICATIONS

Suppose we have taken independent, random samples of sizes $n_1 = 7$ and $n_2 = 7$ from two normally distributed populations with means μ_1 and μ_2, and suppose we obtain $\bar{x}_1 = 240$, $\bar{x}_2 = 210$, $s_1 = 5$, and $s_2 = 6$.

9.15 Using the equal variances procedure, calculate a 95 percent confidence interval for $\mu_1 - \mu_2$. Can we be 95 percent confident that $\mu_1 - \mu_2$ is greater than 20? Explain why we can use the equal variances procedure here.

9.16 Now calculate a 95 percent confidence interval using the unequal variances procedure. Compare your results to those obtained using the equal variances procedure.

9.17 The October 7, 1991, issue of *Fortune* magazine reported on the rapid rise of fees and expenses charged by mutual funds. Assuming that stock fund expenses and municipal bond fund expenses are each approximately normally distributed, suppose a random sample of 12 stock funds gives a mean annual expense of 1.63 percent with a standard deviation of 0.31 percent, and an independent random sample of 12 municipal bond funds gives a mean annual expense of 0.89 percent with a standard deviation of 0.23 percent. Let μ_1 be the mean annual expense for stock funds, and let μ_2 be the mean annual expense for municipal bond funds. Answer the following question first using the equal variances procedure and then using the unequal variances procedure. Compare the two confidence intervals.

Calculate a 95 percent confidence interval for the difference between the mean annual expenses for stock funds and municipal bond funds. Can we be 95 percent confident that the mean annual expense for stock funds exceeds that for municipal bond funds by more than 0.5 percentage points? Explain.

9.18 A manager at a local electronics store wishes to compare the effectiveness of two methods for training new salespeople. The experiment is described as follows:

The company selects 22 sales trainees who are randomly divided into two experimental groups of equal size—one receives type *A* and the other type *B* training. The trainees are then assigned and managed without regard to the training they have received. At the year's end, the manager reviews the

performances of trainees in these groups and finds the following results:

	A Group	B Group
Average Weekly Sales	$\bar{x}_1 = \$1{,}500$	$\bar{x}_2 = \$1{,}300$
Standard Deviation	$s_1 = 225$	$s_2 = 251$

Use the equal variances procedure to calculate a 95 percent confidence interval for the difference between the mean weekly sales obtained when type *A* training is used and the mean weekly sales obtained when type *B* training is used. Interpret this interval.

9.19 A large discount chain compares the performance of its credit managers in Alberta and Ontario by comparing the mean dollar amounts owed by customers with delinquent charge accounts in these two provinces. Here a small mean dollar amount owed is desirable because it indicates that bad credit risks are not being extended large amounts of credit. Two independent, random samples of delinquent accounts are selected from the populations of delinquent accounts in Alberta and Ontario. The first sample, which consists of 10 randomly selected delinquent accounts in Alberta, gives a mean dollar amount of $524 with a standard deviation of $68. The second sample, which consists of 20 randomly selected delinquent accounts in Ontario, gives a mean dollar amount of $473 with a standard deviation of $22.

Assuming that the normality assumption holds, calculate a 95 percent confidence interval for the difference between the mean dollar amounts owed in Alberta and Ontario. Based on this interval, do you think that these mean dollar amounts differ in a practically important way?

9.20 A loan officer compares the interest rates for 48-month fixed-rate auto loans and 48-month variable-rate auto loans. Two independent, random samples of auto loan rates are selected. A sample of eight 48-month fixed-rate auto loans had the following loan rates:

◆ AutoLoan

| 10.29% | 9.75% | 9.50% | 9.99% |
| 9.75% | 9.99% | 11.40% | 10.00% |

A sample of five 48-month variable-rate auto loans had loan rates as follows:

| 9.59% | 8.75% | 8.99% | 8.50% | 9.00% |

Calculate a 95 percent confidence interval for the difference between the mean rates for fixed- and variable-rate 48-month auto loans. Can we be 95 percent confident that the difference between these means is 0.4 percentage points or more? Explain.

9.3 Comparing Two Population Means by Using Paired Differences

Example 9.3 The Repair Cost Comparison Case

Forest City Casualty, specializing in automobile insurance, wishes to compare the repair costs of moderately damaged cars (repair costs between $700 and $1,400) at two garages. One way to study these costs would be to take two independent samples (here we arbitrarily assume that each sample is of size $n = 7$). First we would randomly select seven moderately damaged cars that have recently been in accidents. Each of these cars would be taken to the first garage (garage 1), and repair cost estimates would be obtained. Then we would randomly select seven **different** moderately damaged cars, and repair cost estimates for these cars would be obtained at the second garage (garage 2). This sampling procedure would give us independent samples because the cars taken to garage 1 differ from those taken to garage 2. However, because the repair costs for moderately damaged cars can range from $700 to $1,400, there can be substantial differences in damages to moderately damaged cars. These differences might tend to conceal any real differences between repair costs at the two garages. For example, suppose the repair cost estimates for the cars taken to garage 1 are higher than those for the cars taken to garage 2. This difference might exist because garage 1 charges customers more for repair work than does garage 2. However, the difference could also arise because the cars taken to garage 1 are more severely damaged than the cars taken to garage 2.

To overcome this difficulty, we can perform a **paired difference experiment**. Here we could randomly select one sample of $n = 7$ moderately damaged cars. The cars in this sample would be taken to both garages, and a repair cost estimate for each car would be obtained at each garage. The advantage of the paired difference experiment is that the repair cost estimates at the two garages are obtained for the same cars. Thus, any true differences in the repair cost estimates would not be concealed by possible differences in the severity of damages to the cars.

Suppose that when we perform the paired difference experiment, we obtain the repair cost estimates in Table 9.2 (these estimates are given in units of $100). To analyze these data, we calculate the difference between the repair cost estimates at the two garages for each car. The resulting **paired differences** are given in the last column of Table 9.2. The mean of the sample of $n = 7$ paired differences is

$$\bar{d} = \frac{-0.8 + (-1.1) + (-1.2) + \cdots + (-1.4)}{7} = -0.8,$$

TABLE **9.2** A Sample of $n = 7$ Paired Differences of the Repair Cost Estimates at Garages 1 and 2 (Cost Estimates in Hundreds of Dollars) ● Repair

Sample of $n = 7$ Damaged Cars	Repair Cost Estimates at Garage 1	Repair Cost Estimates at Garage 2	Sample of $n = 7$ Paired Differences
Car 1	$ 7.1	$ 7.9	$d_1 = -0.8$
Car 2	9.0	10.1	$d_2 = -1.1$
Car 3	11.0	12.2	$d_3 = -1.2$
Car 4	8.9	8.8	$d_4 = 0.1$
Car 5	9.9	10.4	$d_5 = -0.5$
Car 6	9.1	9.8	$d_6 = -0.7$
Car 7	10.3	11.7	$d_7 = -1.4$
	$\bar{x}_1 = 9.329$	$\bar{x}_2 = 10.129$	$\bar{d} = -0.8 - \bar{x}_1 \cdot \bar{x}_2$
			$s_d^2 = 0.2533$
			$s_d = 0.5033$

which equals the difference between the sample means of the repair cost estimates at the two garages:

$$\bar{x}_1 - \bar{x}_2 = 9.329 - 10.129 = -0.8.$$

Furthermore, $\bar{d} = -0.8$ (that is, $-\$80$) is the point estimate of

$$\mu_d = \mu_1 - \mu_2,$$

the mean of the population of all possible paired differences of the repair cost estimates (for all possible moderately damaged cars) at garages 1 and 2—which is equivalent to μ_1, the mean of all possible repair cost estimates at garage 1, minus μ_2, the mean of all possible repair cost estimates at garage 2. This says we estimate that the mean of all possible repair cost estimates at garage 1 is $80 less than the mean of all possible repair cost estimates at garage 2.

In addition, the variance and standard deviation of the sample of $n = 7$ paired differences,

$$s_d^2 = \frac{\sum\limits_{i=1}^{7}(d_i - \bar{d})^2}{7 - 1} = 0.2533$$

and

$$s_d = \sqrt{0.2533} = 0.5033,$$

are the point estimates of σ_d^2 and σ_d, the variance and standard deviation of the population of all possible paired differences.

In general, suppose we wish to compare two population means, μ_1 and μ_2. Also suppose that we have obtained two different measurements (for example, repair cost estimates) on the same n units (for example, cars), and suppose we have calculated the n paired differences between these measurements. Let $\bar{d}$ and s_d be the mean and the standard deviation of these n paired differences. If it is reasonable to assume that the paired differences have been randomly selected from a normally distributed (or at least mound-shaped) population of paired differences with mean μ_d and standard deviation σ_d, then the sampling distribution of

$$\frac{\bar{d} - \mu_d}{s_d/\sqrt{n}}$$

is a t distribution with $n - 1$ degrees of freedom. This implies that we have the following confidence interval for μ_d:

A Confidence Interval for the Mean, μ_d, of a Population of Paired Differences

Let μ_d be the mean of a **normally distributed population of paired differences**, and let $\bar{d}$ and s_d be the mean and standard deviation of a sample of n paired differences that have been randomly selected from the population. Then, a **100(1 − α) percent** confidence interval for $\mu_d = \mu_1 - \mu_2$ is

$$\left[\bar{d} \pm t_{\alpha/2}\frac{s_d}{\sqrt{n}}\right].$$

Here $t_{\alpha/2}$ is based on $(n - 1)$ degrees of freedom.

Example 9.4 The Repair Cost Comparison Case

Using the data in Table 9.2, and assuming that the population of paired repair cost differences is normally distributed, a 95 percent confidence interval for $\mu_d = \mu_1 - \mu_2$ is

$$\left[\bar{d} \pm t_{0.025}\frac{s_d}{\sqrt{n}}\right] = \left[-0.8 \pm 2.447\frac{0.5033}{\sqrt{7}}\right]$$

$$= [-0.8 \pm 0.4654]$$

$$= [-1.2654, -0.3346].$$

Here $t_{0.025} = 2.447$ is based on $n - 1 = 7 - 1 = 6$ degrees of freedom. This interval says that Forest City Casualty can be 95 percent confident that μ_d, the mean of all possible paired differences of the repair cost estimates at garages 1 and 2, is between $-\$126.54$ and $-\$33.46$. That is, we are 95 percent confident that μ_1, the mean of all possible repair cost estimates at garage 1, is between \$126.54 and \$33.46 less than μ_2, the mean of all possible repair cost estimates at garage 2.

In general, an experiment in which we have obtained two different measurements on the same n units is called a **paired difference experiment**. The idea of this type of experiment is to remove the variability due to the variable (for example, the amount of damage to a car) on which the observations are paired. In many situations, a paired difference experiment will provide more information than an independent samples experiment. As another example, suppose that we wish to assess which of two different machines produces a higher hourly output. If we randomly select 10 machine operators and randomly assign 5 of these operators to test machine 1 and the others to test machine 2, we would be performing an independent samples experiment. This is because different machine operators test machines 1 and 2. However, any difference in machine outputs could be obscured by differences in the abilities of the machine operators. For instance, if the observed hourly outputs are higher for machine 1 than for machine 2, we might not be able to tell whether this is due to (1) the superiority of machine 1 or (2) the possible higher skill level of the operators who tested machine 1. Because of this, it might be better to randomly select five machine operators, thoroughly train each operator to use both machines, and have each operator test both machines. We would then be **pairing on the machine operator**, and this would remove the variability due to the differing abilities of the operators.

The formulas we have given for analyzing a paired difference experiment are based on the t distribution. These formulas assume that the population of all possible paired differences is normally distributed (or at least mound-shaped). If the sample size is large (say, at least 30), the t-based interval of this section is approximately valid no matter what the shape of the population of all possible paired differences. If the sample size is small, and if we fear that the population of all paired differences might be far from normally distributed, we can use a nonparametric method. One nonparametric method for comparing two populations when using a paired difference experiment is the **Wilcoxon signed ranks test**, discussed in Section 13.3.

Exercises for Section 9.3

CONCEPTS

9.21 Explain how a paired difference experiment differs from an independent samples experiment in terms of how the data for these experiments are collected.

9.22 Why is a paired difference experiment sometimes more informative than an independent samples experiment? Give an example of a situation in which a paired difference experiment might be advantageous.

9.23 What assumptions must be satisfied to appropriately carry out a paired difference experiment? When can we carry out a paired difference experiment no matter what the shape of the population of all paired differences might be?

9.24 Suppose a company wishes to compare the hourly output of its employees before and after vacations. Explain how you would collect data for a paired difference experiment to make this comparison.

METHODS AND APPLICATIONS

9.25 Suppose a sample of 11 paired differences that has been randomly selected from a normally distributed population of paired differences yields a sample mean of $\bar{d} = 103.5$ and a sample standard deviation of $s_d = 5$. Calculate 95 percent and 99 percent confidence intervals for $\mu_d = \mu_1 - \mu_2$. Can we be 95 percent confident that the difference between μ_1 and μ_2 exceeds 100? Can we be 99 percent confident?

9.26 Suppose a sample of 49 paired differences that have been randomly selected from a normally distributed population of paired differences yields a sample mean of $\bar{d} = 5$ and a sample standard deviation of $s_d = 7$. Calculate a 95 percent confidence interval for $\mu_d = \mu_1 - \mu_2$. Can we be 95 percent confident that the difference between μ_1 and μ_2 is greater than 0?

9.27 In the book *Essentials of Marketing Research*, Dillon, Madden, and Firtle present preexposure and postexposure attitude scores from an advertising study involving 10 respondents. The data for the experiment are given in Table 9.3. Assuming that the differences between pairs of postexposure and preexposure scores are normally distributed, provide a good estimate for the minimum difference between the mean postexposure attitude score

TABLE **9.3** **Preexposure and Postexposure Attitude Scores for Exercise 9.27** ● AdStudy

Subject	Preexposure Attitudes (A_1)	Postexposure Attitudes (A_2)	Attitude Change (d_i)
1	50	53	3
2	25	27	2
3	30	38	8
4	50	55	5
5	60	61	1
6	80	85	5
7	45	45	0
8	30	31	1
9	65	72	7
10	70	78	8

Source: *Essentials of Marketing Research*, by W. R. Dillon, T. J. Madden, and N. H. Firtle (Burr Ridge, IL: Richard D. Irwin, 1993), p. 435. Copyright © 1993. Reprinted by permission of McGraw-Hill Companies, Inc.

and the mean preexposure attitude score. Justify your answer. ● AdStudy

9.28 Ten runners were asked to run a 5-km race in each of two consecutive weeks. The runners wore one brand of shoe in one race and a second brand in the other race. The brand worn in each race is randomly determined. The runners were timed and asked to do their best during each race. The results, in minutes, are given below:

Runner	Brand *A*	Brand *B*
1	15.74	15.99
2	14.98	14.87
3	16.11	15.87
4	15.44	15.93
5	15.37	15.79
6	14.83	14.66
7	15.15	15.49
8	16.02	16.36
9	15.29	15.12
10	14.76	15.01

Assume that the differences between pairs of race times are normally distributed.
a. Calculate a 95 percent confidence interval for the mean difference in race times for the two types of running shoes.

b. Can we be 95 percent confident that there is a difference in mean race times between shoe brands? Justify your answer. ● RaceShoes

9.29 To compare the fuel efficiency of two types of gasoline, five cars were randomly selected, the type of gasoline used was randomly determined, and the fuel efficiency obtained using each brand was recorded below (in L/100 km) for each car:

Car	Type *A*	Type *B*
1	8.4	7.9
2	7.8	7.1
3	11.3	10.9
4	8.1	7.3
5	6.6	5.7

Assume that the differences between pairs of fuel efficiencies are normally distributed.
a. Calculate a 95 percent confidence interval for the mean difference in fuel efficiency for the two types of gas.
b. Can we be 95 percent confident that there is a difference in mean fuel efficiency between the different gasoline types? Justify your answer. ● FuelEffic

9.30 Do students reduce study time in classes where they achieve a higher midterm score? In a *Journal of Economic Education* article (Winter 2005), Krohn and O'Connor studied student effort and performance in a class over a semester. In an intermediate macroeconomics course, they found that "students respond to higher midterm scores by reducing the number of hours they subsequently allocate to studying for the course."[6] Suppose that a random sample of $n = 8$ students who performed well on the midterm exam was taken and weekly study times before and after the exam were compared. The resulting data are given in Table 9.4. Assume that the population of all possible paired differences is normally distributed.
a. Calculate a 95 percent confidence interval for the mean difference in study times before and after the midterm exam. Estimate the minimum reduction in the mean study time from before to after the exams.
b. Can we be 95 percent confident that average study times are reduced after a student does well on a midterm exam?

TABLE **9.4** **Weekly Study Time Data for Students Who Perform Well on the MidTerm** ● StudyTime

Student	1	2	3	4	5	6	7	8
Before	15	14	17	17	19	14	13	16
After	9	9	11	10	19	10	14	10

[6]Source: "Student effort and performance over the semester," by Gregory Krohn and Catherine O'Connor, *Journal of Economic Education*, Winter 2005, pages 3–28.

9.4 Comparing Two Population Proportions by Using Large, Independent Samples

Example 9.5 The Advertising Media Case

Suppose a new product was test marketed in the Toronto, Ontario, and Vancouver, British Columbia, metropolitan areas. Equal amounts of money were spent on advertising in the two areas. However, different advertising media were employed in the two areas. Advertising in the Toronto area was done entirely on television, while advertising in the Vancouver area consisted of a mixture of television, radio, newspaper, and magazine ads. Two months after the advertising campaigns commenced, surveys were taken to estimate consumer awareness of the product. In the Toronto area, 631 out of 1,000 randomly selected consumers were aware of the product, whereas in the Vancouver area, 798 out of 1,000 randomly selected consumers were aware of the product. We define p_1 to be the true proportion of consumers in the Toronto area who are aware of the product and p_2 to be the true proportion of consumers in the Vancouver area who are aware of the product. It follows that, since the sample proportions of consumers who are aware of the product in the Toronto and Vancouver areas are

$$\hat{p}_1 = \frac{631}{1,000} = 0.631$$

and

$$\hat{p}_2 = \frac{798}{1,000} = 0.798,$$

a point estimate of $p_1 - p_2$ is

$$\hat{p}_1 - \hat{p}_2 = 0.631 - 0.798 = -0.167.$$

This says we estimate that p_1 is 0.167 less than p_2. That is, we estimate that the percentage of consumers who are aware of the product in the Vancouver area is 16.7 percentage points higher than the percentage in the Toronto area.

In order to find a confidence interval for and to carry out a hypothesis test about $p_1 - p_2$, we need to know the properties of the sampling distribution of $\hat{p}_1 - \hat{p}_2$. In general, therefore, consider randomly selecting n_1 units from a population, and assume that a proportion p_1 of all the units in the population fall into a particular category. Let $\hat{p}_1$ denote the proportion of units in the sample that fall into the category. Also consider randomly selecting a sample of n_2 units from a second population, and assume that a proportion p_2 of all the units in this population fall into the particular category. Let $\hat{p}_2$ denote the proportion of units in the second sample that fall into the category.

The Sampling Distribution of $\hat{p}_1 - \hat{p}_2$

If the randomly selected samples are independent of each other, then the population of all possible values of $\hat{p}_1 - \hat{p}_2$

1 Is approximately normal if each of the sample sizes n_1 and n_2 is large. Here n_1 and n_2 are large enough if $n_1 p_1$, $n_1(1 - p_1)$, $n_2 p_2$, and $n_2(1 - p_2)$ are all at least 5.

2 Has mean $\mu_{\hat{p}_1 - \hat{p}_2} = p_1 - p_2$.

3 Has standard deviation

$$\sigma_{\hat{p}_1 - \hat{p}_2} = \sqrt{\frac{p_1(1 - p_1)}{n_1} + \frac{p_2(1 - p_2)}{n_2}}.$$

If we estimate p_1 by $\hat{p}_1$ and p_2 by $\hat{p}_2$ in the expression for $\sigma_{\hat{p}_1 - \hat{p}_2}$, then the sampling distribution of $\hat{p}_1 - \hat{p}_2$ implies the following $100(1 - \alpha)$ percent confidence interval for $p_1 - p_2$:

A Large Sample Confidence Interval for $p_1 - p_2$, the Difference between Two Population Proportions[7]

Suppose we randomly select a sample of size n_1 from a population, and let $\hat{p}_1$ denote the proportion of units in this sample that fall into a category of interest. Also suppose we randomly select a sample of size n_2 from another population, and let $\hat{p}_2$ denote the proportion of units in this second sample that fall into the category of interest. Then, if each of the sample sizes n_1 and n_2 is large

$(n_1\hat{p}_1, n_1(1 - \hat{p}_1), n_2\hat{p}_2,$ and $n_2(1 - \hat{p}_2)$ must all be at least 5), and if the random samples are independent of each other, a **100(1 − α) percent confidence interval for $p_1 - p_2$** is

$$\left[(\hat{p}_1 - \hat{p}_2) \pm z_{\alpha/2}\sqrt{\frac{\hat{p}_1(1 - \hat{p}_1)}{n_1} + \frac{\hat{p}_2(1 - \hat{p}_2)}{n_2}} \right].$$

Example 9.6 The Advertising Media Case

Recall that in the advertising media situation described at the beginning of this section, 631 of 1,000 randomly selected consumers in Toronto were aware of the new product, while 798 of 1,000 randomly selected consumers in Vancouver were aware of the new product. Also recall that

$$\hat{p}_1 = \frac{631}{1,000} = 0.631$$

and

$$\hat{p}_2 = \frac{798}{1,000} = 0.798.$$

Because $n_1\hat{p}_1 = 1,000(0.631) = 631$, $n_1(1 - \hat{p}_1) = 1,000(1 - 0.631) = 369$, $n_2\hat{p}_2 = 1,000(0.798) = 798$, and $n_2(1 - \hat{p}_2) = 1,000(1 - 0.798) = 202$ are all at least 5, both n_1 and n_2 can be considered large. It follows that a 95 percent confidence interval for $p_1 - p_2$ is

$$\left[(\hat{p}_1 - \hat{p}_2) \pm z_{0.025}\sqrt{\frac{\hat{p}_1(1 - \hat{p}_1)}{n_1} + \frac{\hat{p}_2(1 - \hat{p}_2)}{n_2}} \right]$$

$$= \left[(0.631 - 0.798) \pm 1.96\sqrt{\frac{(0.631)(0.369)}{1,000} + \frac{(0.798)(0.202)}{1,000}} \right]$$

$$= [-0.167 \pm 0.0389]$$

$$= [-0.2059, -0.1281].$$

This interval says we are 95 percent confident that p_1, the proportion of all consumers in the Toronto area who are aware of the product, is between 0.2059 and 0.1281 less than p_2, the proportion of all consumers in the Vancouver area who are aware of the product. Thus, we have substantial evidence that advertising the new product by using a mixture of television, radio, newspaper, and magazine ads (as in Vancouver) is more effective than spending an equal amount of money on television commercials only.

There is a lot of material in this chapter, so to conclude this first part, we will take note of a few things. This will help us better understand the second part of the chapter. We need to make note of the similarities and differences between confidence intervals when the population standard deviation is known and when it is unknown (i.e., using z versus using t in the formula). The population standard deviation was not known when we looked at confidence intervals involving

---

[7]More correctly, because $\hat{p}_1(1 - \hat{p}_1)/(n_1 - 1)$ and $\hat{p}_2(1 - \hat{p}_2)/(n_2 - 1)$ are unbiased point estimates of $p_1(1 - p_1)/n_1$ and $p_2(1 - p_2)/n_2$, a point estimate of $\sigma_{\hat{p}_1 - \hat{p}_2}$ is

$$s_{\hat{p}_1 - \hat{p}_2} = \sqrt{\frac{\hat{p}_1(1 - \hat{p}_1)}{n_1 - 1} + \frac{\hat{p}_2(1 - \hat{p}_2)}{n_2 - 1}},$$

and a 100(1 − α) percent confidence interval for $p_1 - p_2$ is $[(\hat{p}_1 - \hat{p}_2) \pm z_{\alpha/2}s_{\hat{p}_1 - \hat{p}_2}]$. Because both n_1 and n_2 are large, there is little difference between the interval obtained by using this formula and that obtained by using the formula in the box above.

differences between means. It is important to know how to calculate the degrees of freedom in this case. It is also important to be able to tell the difference between a one-sided and a two-sided confidence interval (by noting the subscripted value of the t or the z in the formula). Also note the less than or greater than sign (one-sided) versus the equality sign (two-sided) for these confidence intervals. We finished this part of the chapter by looking at confidence intervals for differences between proportions. The nice thing about this section is that we will only deal with large samples, so note that any confidence interval formulas will only involve a z value.

Exercises for Section 9.4

CONCEPTS

9.31 Explain what population is described by the sampling distribution of $\hat{p}_1 - \hat{p}_2$.

9.32 What assumptions must be satisfied in order to use the methods presented in this section?

METHODS AND APPLICATIONS

9.33 Suppose that we have selected two independent random samples from populations with proportions p_1 and p_2 and that $\hat{p}_1 = 800/1{,}000 = 0.8$ and $\hat{p}_2 = 950/1{,}000 = 0.95$. Calculate a 95 percent confidence interval for $p_1 - p_2$. Interpret this interval. Can we be 95 percent confident that $p_1 - p_2$ is less than 0? That is, can we be 95 percent confident that p_1 is less than p_2? Explain.

9.34 A large Canadian university newspaper conducted a survey of faculty and students on campus to determine whether or not the parking is adequate. A random sample of 200 faculty members and a random sample of 500 students were selected. One hundred twenty-six of the faculty members and 277 of the students said that parking on campus is inadequate.

Calculate a 95 percent confidence interval for the difference between the proportion of faculty members and the proportion of students who believe that parking on campus is inadequate. On the basis of this interval, can we be 95 percent confident that these proportions differ? Explain.

9.35 Have the attitudes of young Canadian adults about smoking changed in recent years? In 1999, a random sample of 1,000 young adults aged 18 to 24 was taken and 576 of them said that they were smokers. In 2006, a random sample of 900 young adults aged 18 to 24 was taken and 459 of them said they were smokers.

Calculate a 95 percent confidence interval for the difference between the proportion of young adults who smoked in 1999 versus 2006. On the basis of this interval, can we be 95 percent confident that a smaller percentage of young adults are smoking in 2006 compared to those of the same age group in 1999? Explain.

9.36 The digital music players produced by a large Canadian manufacturer during the first two months of 2007 were of poor quality. A random sample of 100 players was obtained during this time and the players were tested. It was determined that 21 of them were defective. Quality control standards were then tightened. A random sample of 100 players was taken during the next two months. It was determined that 12 were defective.

Calculate a 95 percent confidence interval for the difference between the proportions of defective digital music players produced during the first two months and the second two months of 2007. On the basis of this interval, can we be 95 percent confident that the stricter quality control standards made a difference? Explain.

9.37 On January 7, 2000, the Gallup Organization released the results of a poll comparing the lifestyles of today with yesteryear. The survey results were based on telephone interviews with a randomly selected national sample of 1,031 adults, 18 years and older, conducted December 20 to 21, 1999. The poll asked several questions and compared the 1999 responses with the responses given in polls taken in previous years. In Figure 9.3, we summarize some of the poll's results.[8] Assume that each poll was based on a randomly selected national sample of 1,031 adults and that the samples in different years are independent.

a. Let p_1 be the December 1999 population proportion of U.S. adults who had taken a vacation lasting six days or more within the last 12 months, and let p_2 be the December 1968 population proportion who

FIGURE **9.3**   **Result of Gallup Survey for Exercise 9.37**

	Percentage of respondents	
1 Had taken a vacation lasting six days or more within the last 12 months:	December 1999 42%	December 1968 62%
2 Took part in some sort of daily activity to keep physically fit:	December 1999 60%	September 1977 48%
3 Watched TV more than four hours on an average weekday:	December 1999 28%	April 1981 25%
4 Drove a car or truck to work:	December 1999 87%	April 1971 81%

had taken such a vacation. Calculate a 99 percent confidence interval for the difference between p_1 and p_2. Interpret what this interval says about how these population proportions differ.

b. Let p_1 be the December 1999 population proportion of U.S. adults who drove a car or truck to work, and let p_2 be the April 1971 population proportion who did the same. Calculate a 95 percent confidence interval for the difference between p_1 and p_2. On the basis of this interval, can it be concluded that the 1999 and 1971 population proportions differ?

9.38 In a local municipal election to elect a mayor for the city of Melville, only two candidates are running for the position of mayor, Willie Gettin and Betty Wont. In

an attempt to see how the voters are voting by age group, a poll is conducted. One thousand citizens of the city aged 18 to 40 are randomly selected and are asked whom they would vote for, and 1,000 residents aged 41 and older are asked the same question. All 2,000 people sampled offered a response. Let $\hat{p}_1$ represent the proportion of voters aged 18 to 40 who said they would vote for Willie and let $\hat{p}_2$ represent the proportion of voters aged 41 and older who said that they would vote for Willie. The results are $\hat{p}_1 = 510/1,000$ and $\hat{p}_2 = 550/1,000$.

Calculate a 95 percent confidence interval for $\hat{p}_1 - \hat{p}_2$ and decide whether or not age makes a difference. That is, is there a difference in the support level for Willie between the two age groups?

9.5 z Tests about a Difference in Population Means: One-Tailed Alternative

**PART 2
Hypothesis
Tests: Two
Samples**

Consider the bank customer waiting time example. Recall that μ_1 represents the mean waiting time during peak business hours under the current system and μ_2 denotes the mean waiting time for customers under the new system. Random samples of $n_1 = n_2 = 100$ are drawn, and the sample means for the first and second samples are 8.79 minutes and 5.14 minutes, respectively. This yields a difference of 3.65 minutes. Because we know the properties of the sampling distribution of $\bar{x}_1 - \bar{x}_2$, we can easily test a hypothesis about the difference between mean waiting times.

Now suppose we wish to conduct a one-sided hypothesis test about $\mu_1 - \mu_2$. In the following box, we describe how we test the null hypothesis $H_0: \mu_1 - \mu_2 = D_0$ versus the other two one-sided scenarios, $H_a: \mu_1 - \mu_2 < D_0$ and $H_a: \mu_1 - \mu_2 < D_0$. The value of D_0 varies depending on the situation.

A One-Tailed z Test about the Difference between Two Population Means: Testing $H_0: \mu_1 - \mu_2 = D_0$ when σ_1 and σ_2 Are Known

Define the test statistic

$$z = \frac{(\bar{x}_1 - \bar{x}_2) - D_0}{\sqrt{\dfrac{\sigma_1^2}{n_1} + \dfrac{\sigma_2^2}{n_2}}}.$$

Assume that each sampled population is normally distributed, or that each of the sample sizes n_1 and n_2 is large. Then, if the samples are independent of each other, we can test $H_0: \mu_1 - \mu_2 = D_0$ versus a particular alternative hypothesis at level of significance α by using the appropriate rejection point rule or, equivalently, the corresponding p value.

Alternative Hypothesis	Rejection Point Rule: Reject H_0 if	p Value (Reject H_0 if p Value $< \alpha$)
$H_a: \mu_1 - \mu_2 > D_0$	$z > z_\alpha$	The area under the standard normal curve to the right of z
$H_a: \mu_1 - \mu_2 < D_0$	$z < -z_\alpha$	The area under the standard normal curve to the left of z

Often D_0 will be the number 0. In such a case, the null hypothesis $H_0: \mu_1 - \mu_2 = 0$ says there is **no difference** between the population means μ_1 and μ_2. For example, in the bank customer waiting time situation, the null hypothesis $H_0: \mu_1 - \mu_2 = 0$ says there is no difference between the mean customer waiting times under the current and new systems. When D_0 is 0, each alternative hypothesis in the box implies that the population means μ_1 and μ_2 differ. For instance, in the bank customer waiting time situation, the alternative hypothesis $H_a: \mu_1 - \mu_2 > 0$ says that the current mean customer waiting time is longer than the new mean customer waiting time. That is, this alternative hypothesis says that the new system reduces the mean customer waiting time.

Example 9.7   The Bank Customer Waiting Time Case

To attempt to provide evidence supporting the claim that the new system reduces the mean bank customer waiting time, we will test $H_0: \mu_1 - \mu_2 = 0$ versus $H_a: \mu_1 - \mu_2 > 0$ at the **0.05 level of significance**. To perform the hypothesis test, we will use the sample information in Example 9.1 to calculate the value of the **test statistic z in the summary box**. Then, since $H_a: \mu_1 - \mu_2 > 0$ is of the form $H_a: \mu_1 - \mu_2 > D_0$, we will **reject $H_0: \mu_1 - \mu_2 = 0$ if the value of z is greater than $z_\alpha = z_{0.05} = 1.645$**. Assuming that $\sigma_1^2 = 4.7$ and $\sigma_2^2 = 1.9$, the **value of the test statistic is**

$$z = \frac{(\bar{x}_1 - \bar{x}_2) - D_0}{\sqrt{\dfrac{\sigma_1^2}{n_1} + \dfrac{\sigma_2^2}{n_2}}} = \frac{(8.79 - 5.14) - 0}{\sqrt{\dfrac{4.7}{100} + \dfrac{1.9}{100}}} = \frac{3.65}{0.2569} = 14.21.$$

Because $z = 14.21$ is greater than $z_{0.05} = 1.645$, we reject $H_0: \mu_1 - \mu_2 = 0$ in favour of H_a: $\mu_1 - \mu_2 > 0$. We conclude (at an α of 0.05) that $\mu_1 - \mu_2$ is greater than 0 and, therefore, that the new system reduces the mean customer waiting time. Furthermore, the point estimate $\bar{x}_1 - \bar{x}_2 = 3.65$ says we estimate that the new system reduces mean waiting time by 3.65 minutes. The p value for the test is the area under the standard normal curve to the right of $z = 14.21$. Since this p value is less than 0.001, it provides extremely strong evidence that H_0 is false and that H_a is true. That is, we have extremely strong evidence that $\mu_1 - \mu_2$ is greater than 0 and, therefore, that the new system reduces the mean customer waiting time.

Next suppose that because of cost considerations the bank manager wants to implement the new system only if it reduces mean waiting time by more than three minutes. In order to demonstrate that $\mu_1 - \mu_2$ is greater than 3, the manager (setting D_0 equal to 3) will attempt to reject the null hypothesis $H_0: \mu_1 - \mu_2 = 3$ in favour of the alternative hypothesis $H_a: \mu_1 - \mu_2 > 3$ at the 0.05 level of significance. To perform the hypothesis test, we compute

$$z = \frac{(\bar{x}_1 - \bar{x}_2) - 3}{\sqrt{\dfrac{\sigma_1^2}{n_1} + \dfrac{\sigma_2^2}{n_2}}} = \frac{(8.79 - 5.14) - 3}{\sqrt{\dfrac{4.7}{100} + \dfrac{1.9}{100}}} = \frac{0.65}{0.2569} = 2.53.$$

Because $z = 2.53$ is greater than $z_{0.05} = 1.645$, we can reject $H_0: \mu_1 - \mu_2 = 3$ in favour of H_a: $\mu_1 - \mu_2 > 3$. The p value for the test is the area under the standard normal curve to the right of $z = 2.53$. Table A.3 tells us that this area is $0.5 - 0.4943 = 0.0057$. Therefore, we have very strong evidence against $H_0: \mu_1 - \mu_2 = 3$ and in favour of $H_a: \mu_1 - \mu_2 > 3$. In other words, we have very strong evidence that the new system reduces mean waiting time by more than three minutes.

Exercises for Section 9.5

CONCEPTS

9.39 Suppose we want to compare two means, μ_1 and μ_2, using a one-sided hypothesis test. Consider each of the following situations and decide whether or not H_0 would be rejected at $\alpha = 0.05$:
  a. $H_a: \mu_1 - \mu_2 < 0; z = -1.79$.
  b. $H_a: \mu_1 - \mu_2 > 0; z = 1.79$.
  c. $H_a: \mu_1 - \mu_2 > 4; z = -2.01$.
  d. $H_a: \mu_1 - \mu_2 > 0; z = 2.17$.
  e. $H_a: \mu_1 - \mu_2 < 0; z = -1.24$.
  f. $H_a: \mu_1 - \mu_2 < 4; z = -1.15$.

9.40 Determine the significance level, α, of the one-sided hypothesis test for $H_0: \mu_1 - \mu_2 = D_0$ given the following information:
  a. $H_a: \mu_1 - \mu_2 < 1; z_\alpha = -1.75$.

  b. $H_a: \mu_1 - \mu_2 > 5; z_\alpha = 1.75$.
  c. $H_a: \mu_1 - \mu_2 < 0; z_\alpha = -2.05$.
  d. $H_a: \mu_1 - \mu_2 > 10; z_\alpha = 2.33$.
  e. $H_a: \mu_1 - \mu_2 > 0; z_\alpha = 1.96$.
  f. $H_a: \mu_1 - \mu_2 > 31; z_\alpha = 1.88$.

METHODS AND APPLICATIONS

9.41 Suppose we randomly select two independent samples from populations with means μ_1 and μ_2. Suppose $\bar{x}_1 = 25$, $\bar{x}_2 = 20$, $\sigma_1 = 3$, $\sigma_2 = 4$, $n_1 = 100$, and $n_2 = 100$.
  a. Test the null hypothesis $H_0: \mu_1 - \mu_2 = 0$ versus H_a: $\mu_1 - \mu_2 > 0$ by setting $\alpha = 0.05$. What do you conclude about how μ_1 compares to μ_2?

b. Find the *p* value for testing $H_0: \mu_1 - \mu_2 = 4$ versus $H_a: \mu_1 - \mu_2 > 4$. Use the *p* value to test these hypotheses by setting α equal to 0.10, 0.05, 0.01, and 0.001.

9.42 Suppose we select two independent random samples from populations with means μ_1 and μ_2, and suppose that $\bar{x}_1 = 151$, $\bar{x}_2 = 162$, $\sigma_1 = 6$, $\sigma_2 = 8$, $n_1 = 625$, and $n_2 = 625$.
a. Test the null hypothesis $H_0: \mu_1 - \mu_2 = -10$ versus $H_a: \mu_1 - \mu_2 < -10$ by setting $\alpha = 0.05$. What do you conclude?
b. Test the null hypothesis $H_0: \mu_1 - \mu_2 = -10$ versus $H_a: \mu_1 - \mu_2 > -10$ by setting α equal to 0.01. What do you conclude?
c. Find the *p* value for testing $H_0: \mu_1 - \mu_2 = -10$ versus $H_a: \mu_1 - \mu_2 < -10$. Use the *p* value to test these hypotheses by setting α equal to 0.10, 0.05, 0.01, and 0.001.

9.43 Use the information in Exercise 9.8 to answer the following questions:
a. Let μ_1 be the true average service time in the express checkout and let μ_2 be the true average service time in the self-serve checkout. Consider testing the null hypothesis $H_0: \mu_1 - \mu_2 = 0$ versus $H_a: \mu_1 - \mu_2 < 0$. Interpret (in practical terms) each of H_0 and H_a.
b. Use a rejection point to test H_0 at the 0.05 level of significance. Based on this test, what do you conclude about how μ_1 and μ_2 compare? Write your conclusion in practical terms.
c. Use a *p* value to test H_0 by setting $\alpha = 0.10$, 0.05, 0.01, and 0.001. How much evidence is there that μ_1 is less than μ_2?

9.44 Use the information in Exercise 9.9 to answer the following questions:
a. Set up the null and alternative hypotheses needed to try to establish that the mean number of cups of coffee drunk by second-year students at the University of Alberta is greater than the mean number drunk by second-year students at the University of Western Ontario.
b. Use rejection points to test the hypotheses you set up in part a by setting α equal to 0.10, 0.05, 0.01, and 0.001. How much evidence is there that second-year students at the University of Alberta drink more coffee on average than their counterparts at the University of Western Ontario?

9.45 An Ontario university wishes to demonstrate that car ownership is detrimental to academic achievement. A random sample of 100 students who do not own cars had a mean grade point average (GPA) of 2.68, while a random sample of 100 students who own cars had a mean GPA of 2.55.
a. Set up the null and alternative hypotheses that should be used to attempt to justify that the mean GPA for non–car owners is higher than the mean GPA for car owners.
b. Test the hypotheses that you set up in part a with $\alpha = 0.05$. Assume that $\sigma_1 = 0.7$ and $\sigma_2 = 0.6$. Interpret the results of this test. That is, what do your results say about whether the university can statistically justify that car ownership hurts academic achievement?

9.46 In the *Journal of Marketing*, Bayus studied differences between "early replacement buyers" and "late replacement buyers." Suppose that a random sample of 800 early replacement buyers yields a mean number of automobile dealers visited of $\bar{x}_1 = 3.3$, and that a random sample of 500 late replacement buyers yields a mean number of dealers visited of $\bar{x}_2 = 4.5$. Assume that these samples are independent.
a. Set up the null and alternative hypotheses needed to attempt to show that the mean number of dealers visited by late replacement buyers exceeds the mean number of dealers visited by early replacement buyers by more than 1.
b. Test the hypotheses you set up in part a by using rejection points and by setting α equal to 0.10, 0.05, 0.01, and 0.001. How much evidence is there that H_0 should be rejected?
c. Find the *p* value for testing the hypotheses you set up in part a. Use the *p* value to test these hypotheses with α equal to 0.10, 0.05, 0.01, and 0.001. How much evidence is there that H_0 should be rejected? Explain your conclusion in practical terms.
d. Do you think that the results of the hypothesis tests in parts b and c have practical significance? Explain and justify your answer.

9.47 Use the information in Exercise 9.12 to answer the following questions:
a. Set up the null and alternative hypotheses needed to try to establish whether or not the average on the second term test was lower than the average on the first term test.
b. Use a rejection point to test the hypotheses you set up in part a by setting α equal to 0.01. How much evidence is there that the average on the second term test was lower than the average on the first term test?
c. Use a *p* value to test H_0 by setting $\alpha = 0.10$, 0.05, 0.01, and 0.001. How much evidence is there that the mean score from test two is lower than the mean score from test one?

9.6 *z* Tests about a Difference in Population Means: Two-Tailed Alternative

Suppose we wish to conduct a two-sided hypothesis test about $\mu_1 - \mu_2$. In the following box, we describe how this can be done. Here we test the null hypothesis $H_0: \mu_1 - \mu_2 = D_0$, where D_0 is a number whose value varies depending on the situation.

A Two-Tailed z Test about the Difference between Two Population Means: Testing $H_0: \mu_1 - \mu_2 = D_0$ when σ_1 and σ_2 Are Known

Define the test statistic

$$z = \frac{(\bar{x}_1 - \bar{x}_2) - D_0}{\sqrt{\dfrac{\sigma_1^2}{n_1} + \dfrac{\sigma_2^2}{n_2}}}.$$

Assume that each sampled population is normally distributed, or that each of the sample sizes n_1 and n_2

is large. Then, if the samples are independent of each other, we can test $H_0: \mu_1 - \mu_2 = D_0$ versus a particular alternative hypothesis at level of significance α by using the appropriate rejection point rule or, equivalently, the corresponding p value.

Alternative Hypothesis	Rejection Point Rule: Reject H_0 if	p Value (Reject H_0 if p Value $< \alpha$)
$H_a: \mu_1 - \mu_2 \neq D_0$	$\|z\| > z_{\alpha/2}$—that is, $z > z_{\alpha/2}$ or $z < -z_{\alpha/2}$	Twice the area under the standard normal curve to the right of $\|z\|$

It is often the case that D_0 will be 0. In such a case, the null hypothesis $H_0: \mu_1 - \mu_2 = 0$ says there is **no difference** between the underlying population means. For example, in the bank customer waiting time case, the alternative hypothesis $H_a: \mu_1 - \mu_2 \neq 0$ says that the mean waiting times are different from one another. Notice that this time we are not specifying that the difference is greater than or less than zero specifically. Now we are just saying that the mean waiting times are different. Now the alternative hypothesis says that the new system results in a different mean customer waiting time than the old system.

Example 9.8   The Bank Customer Waiting Time Case

To attempt to provide evidence supporting the claim that the new system produces a different mean bank customer waiting time, we will test $H_0: \mu_1 - \mu_2 = 0$ versus $H_a: \mu_1 - \mu_2 \neq 0$ at the **0.05 level of significance**. To perform the hypothesis test, we will use the sample information in Example 9.1 to calculate the value of the **test statistic z in the summary box**. Then, since $H_a: \mu_1 - \mu_2 \neq 0$ is of the form $H_a: \mu_1 - \mu_2 \neq D_0$, we will **reject $H_0: \mu_1 - \mu_2 = 0$ if the value of $\|z\|$ is greater than** $z_{\alpha/2} = z_{0.025} = 1.96$. Assuming that $\sigma_1^2 = 4.7$ and $\sigma_2^2 = 1.9$, the **value of the test statistic is**

$$z = \frac{(\bar{x}_1 - \bar{x}_2) - D_0}{\sqrt{\dfrac{\sigma_1^2}{n_1} + \dfrac{\sigma_2^2}{n_2}}} = \frac{(8.79 - 5.14) - 0}{\sqrt{\dfrac{4.7}{100} + \dfrac{1.9}{100}}} = \frac{3.65}{0.2569} = 14.21.$$

Because $z = 14.21$ is greater than $z_{0.025} = 1.96$, we reject $H_0: \mu_1 - \mu_2 = 0$ in favour of $H_a:$ $\mu_1 - \mu_2 \neq 0$. We conclude (at an α of 0.05) that $\mu_1 - \mu_2$ is not equal to 0 and, therefore, that the new system results in a different mean customer waiting time.

Exercises for Section 9.6

METHODS AND APPLICATIONS

9.48 Suppose we select two independent random samples from populations with means μ_1 and μ_2, and suppose that $\bar{x}_1 = 151$, $\bar{x}_2 = 162$, $\sigma_1 = 6$, $\sigma_2 = 8$, $n_1 = 625$, and $n_2 = 625$.

    a. Find the p value for testing $H_0: \mu_1 - \mu_2 = -10$ versus $H_a: \mu_1 - \mu_2 \neq -10$. Use the p value to test these hypotheses by setting α equal to 0.10, 0.05, 0.01, and 0.001.

9.49 In an article in the *Journal of Management*, Wright and Bonett study the relationship between voluntary organizational turnover and such factors as work

performance, work satisfaction, and company tenure. As part of the study, the authors compare work performance ratings for "stayers" (employees who stay in their organization) and "leavers" (employees who voluntarily quit their jobs). Suppose that a random sample of 175 stayers has a mean performance rating (on a 20-point scale) of $\bar{x}_1 = 12.8$ and that a random sample of 140 leavers has a mean performance rating of $\bar{x}_2 = 14.7$. Assume that these random samples are independent and $\sigma_1 = 3.7$ and $\sigma_2 = 4.5$.

a. Set up the null and alternative hypotheses needed to try to establish that the mean performance rating for leavers is different from the mean performance rating for stayers.

b. Use rejection points to test the hypotheses you set up in part a by setting α equal to 0.10, 0.05, 0.01, and 0.001. How much evidence is there that leavers have a different mean performance rating than do stayers?

9.50 In the book *Essentials of Marketing Research*, Dillon, Madden, and Firtle discuss a corporate image study designed to find out whether perceptions of technical support services vary depending on the position of the respondent in the organization. The management of a company that supplies telephone cable to telephone companies commissioned a media campaign primarily designed to

    (1) increase awareness of the company and (2) create favorable perceptions of the company's technical support. The campaign was targeted to purchasing managers and technical managers at independent telephone companies with greater than 10,000 trunk lines.

    Perceptual ratings were measured with a nine-point agree–disagree scale. Suppose the results of a telephone survey of 175 technical managers and 125 purchasing managers reveal that the mean perception score for technical managers is 7.3 and the mean perception score for purchasing managers is 8.2.

a. Let μ_1 be the mean perception score for all purchasing managers, and let μ_2 be the mean perception score for all technical managers. Set up the null and alternative hypotheses needed to establish whether the mean perception scores for purchasing managers and technical managers differ. Hint: If μ_1 and μ_2 do not differ, what does $\mu_1 - \mu_2$ equal?

b. Assuming that the samples of 175 technical managers and 125 purchasing managers are independent random samples, test the hypotheses you set up in part a by using a rejection point with $\alpha = 0.05$. Assume here that $\sigma_1 = 1.6$ and $\sigma_2 = 1.4$. What do you conclude about whether the mean perception scores for purchasing managers and technical managers differ?

c. Find the p value for testing the hypotheses you set up in part a. Use the p value to test these hypotheses by setting α equal to 0.10, 0.05, 0.01, and 0.001. How much evidence is there that the mean perception scores for purchasing managers and technical managers differ?

9.7 *t* Tests about a Difference in Population Means: One-Tailed Alternative

In Section 9.1, we learned how to calculate a confidence interval for $\mu_1 - \mu_2$ when the population variances were not known but were assumed to be equal. Now suppose we wish to test a hypothesis about $\mu_1 - \mu_2$ under these same circumstances. In the following box, we describe how this can be done using a one-tailed test.

Here we test the null hypothesis $H_0: \mu_1 - \mu_2 = D_0$, where D_0 is a number whose value varies depending on the situation. Often D_0 will be the number 0. In such a case, the null hypothesis $H_0: \mu_1 - \mu_2 = 0$ says there is **no difference** between the population means μ_1 and μ_2. In this case, each alternative hypothesis in the box implies that the population means μ_1 and μ_2 differ in a particular way.

A One-Tailed *t* Test about the Difference between Two Population Means: Testing $H_0: \mu_1 - \mu_2 = D_0$ when $\sigma_1^2 = \sigma_2^2$

Define the test statistic

$$t = \frac{(\bar{x}_1 - \bar{x}_2) - D_0}{\sqrt{s_p^2\left(\dfrac{1}{n_1} + \dfrac{1}{n_2}\right)}}$$

and assume that the sampled populations are normally distributed with equal variances. Then, if the samples are independent of each other, we can test $H_0: \mu_1 - \mu_2 = D_0$ versus a particular alternative hypothesis at level of significance α by using the appropriate rejection point rule or, equivalently, the corresponding p value.

Alternative Hypothesis	Rejection Point Rule: Reject H_0 if	p Value (Reject H_0 if p Value $< \alpha$)
$H_a: \mu_1 - \mu_2 > D_0$	$t > t_\alpha$	The area under the t distribution curve to the right of t
$H_a: \mu_1 - \mu_2 < D_0$	$t < -t_\alpha$	The area under the t distribution curve to the left of t

Here t_α and the p values are based on $n_1 + n_2 - 2$ degrees of freedom.

Example 9.9　The Coffee Cup Case

In order to compare the mean hourly yields obtained by using the Java and Joe production methods, we will test $H_0: \mu_1 - \mu_2 = 0$ versus $H_a: \mu_1 - \mu_2 > 0$ at the **0.05 level of significance**. To perform the hypothesis test, we will use the sample information in Table 9.1 to calculate the value of the **test statistic t in the summary box**. Then, since $H_a: \mu_1 - \mu_2 > 0$ is of the form $H_a: \mu_1 - \mu_2 > D_0$, we will **reject $H_0: \mu_1 - \mu_2 = 0$ if t is greater than $t_\alpha = t_{0.05} = 1.860$**. Here the t_α point is based on $n_1 + n_2 - 2 = 5 + 5 - 2 = 8$ degrees of freedom. Using the data in Table 9.1, the **value of the test statistic is**

$$t = \frac{(\bar{x}_1 - \bar{x}_2) - D_0}{\sqrt{s_p^2\left(\frac{1}{n_1} + \frac{1}{n_2}\right)}} = \frac{(811 - 750.2) - 0}{\sqrt{435.1\left(\frac{1}{5} + \frac{1}{5}\right)}} = 4.6087.$$

Because $t = 4.6087$ is greater than $t_{0.05} = 1.860$, we can reject $H_0: \mu_1 - \mu_2 = 0$ in favour of $H_a: \mu_1 - \mu_2 > 0$. We conclude (at an α of 0.05) that the mean hourly yields obtained by using the two production methods differ. Furthermore, the point estimate $\bar{x}_1 - \bar{x}_2 = 811 - 750.2 = 60.8$ says we estimate that the mean hourly yield obtained by using Java is 60.8 kg higher than the mean hourly yield obtained by using Joe.

Figure 9.4(a) and (b) gives the MegaStat and Excel outputs for testing H_0 versus H_a. The outputs tell us that $t = 4.61$ and that the associated p value is 0.001736 (rounded to 0.0017 on the MegaStat output). The very small p value tells us that we have very strong evidence against $H_0: \mu_1 - \mu_2 = 0$ and in favour of $H_a: \mu_1 - \mu_2 > 0$. In other words, we have very strong evidence that the mean hourly yields obtained by using the two production methods differ. Finally, notice that the MegaStat output gives the 95 percent confidence interval for $\mu_1 - \mu_2$, which is [30.378, 91.222].

FIGURE 9.4 **MegaStat and Excel Outputs for Testing the Equality of Means in the Coffee Cup Comparison Case Assuming Equal Variances**

(a) The MegaStat Output

Hypothesis Test: Independent Groups
(t-test, pooled variance)

Java	Joe			
811.00	750.20	mean	4.61	t
19.65	22.00	std. dev.	0.0017	p-value (two-tailed)
5	5	n	30.378	confidence interval 95% lower
			91.222	confidence interval 95% upper

8	df
60.800	difference (Java - Joe)
435.100	pooled variance
20.859	pooled std. dev.
13.192	standard error of difference
0	hypothesized difference

F-test for equality of variance

484.20	variance: Joe
386.00	variance: Java
1.25	F
0.8314	p-value

(b) The Excel Output

t-Test: Two-Sample Assuming Equal Variances

	Java	Joe
Mean	811	750.2
Variance	386	484.2
Observations	5	5
Pooled Variance	435.1	
Hypothesized Mean Diff	0	
df	8	
t Stat	4.608706	
P(T<=t) one-tail	0.000868	
t Critical one-tail	1.859548	
P(T<=t) two-tail	0.001736	
t Critical two-tail	2.306004	

When the sampled populations are normally distributed and the population variances σ_1^2 and σ_2^2 differ, the following can be shown:

A One-Tailed t Test of $H_0: \mu_1 - \mu_2 = D_0$ when $\sigma_1^2 \neq \sigma_2^2$

1　When the sample sizes n_1 and n_2 are equal, the equal variances hypothesis test given in the preceding box is approximately valid even if the population variances σ_1^2 and σ_2^2 differ substantially. As a rough rule of thumb, if the larger sample variance is not more than three times the smaller sample variance when the sample sizes are equal, we can use the equal variances test.

2 Suppose that the larger sample variance is more than three times the smaller sample variance when the sample sizes are equal, or suppose that both the sample sizes and the sample variances differ substantially. Then, we can use the approximate unequal variances procedure.

We can test $H_0: \mu_1 - \mu_2 = D_0$ by using the test statistic

$$t = \frac{(\bar{x}_1 - \bar{x}_2) - D_0}{\sqrt{\dfrac{s_1^2}{n_1} + \dfrac{s_2^2}{n_2}}}$$

and by using the previously given rejection point and *p* value conditions.

For the test, the degrees of freedom are equal to

$$df = \frac{(s_1^2/n_1 + s_2^2/n_2)^2}{\dfrac{(s_1^2/n_1)^2}{n_1 - 1} + \dfrac{(s_2^2/n_2)^2}{n_2 - 1}},$$

Here, if *df* is not a whole number, we can round it down to the next smallest whole number.

To illustrate the unequal variances procedure, consider the bank customer waiting time situation, and recall that $\mu_1 - \mu_2$ is the difference between the mean customer waiting time under the current system and the mean customer waiting time under the new system. Recall that the bank manager wants to implement the new system only if it reduces the mean waiting time by more than three minutes. Therefore, the manager will test the **null hypothesis $H_0: \mu_1 - \mu_2 = 3$ versus the alternative hypothesis $H_a: \mu_1 - \mu_2 > 3$.** If H_0 can be rejected in favour of H_a at the **0.05 level of significance**, the manager will implement the new system. Suppose that a random sample of $n_1 = 100$ waiting times observed under the current system gives a sample mean $\bar{x}_1 = 8.79$ and a sample variance $s_1^2 = 4.8237$. Further, suppose a random sample of $n_2 = 100$ waiting times observed during the trial run of the new system yields a sample mean $\bar{x}_2 = 5.14$ and a sample variance $s_2^2 = 1.7927$. Since each sample is large, we can use the **unequal variances test statistic *t* in the summary box**. The degrees of freedom for this statistic are

$$
\begin{aligned}
df &= \frac{(s_1^2/n_1 + s_2^2/n_2)^2}{\dfrac{(s_1^2/n_1)^2}{n_1 - 1} + \dfrac{(s_2^2/n_2)^2}{n_2 - 1}} \\
&= \frac{[(4.8237/100) + (1.7927/100)]^2}{\dfrac{(4.8237/100)^2}{99} + \dfrac{(1.7927/100)^2}{99}} \\
&= 163.657,
\end{aligned}
$$

which we will round down to 163. Therefore, since $H_a: \mu_1 - \mu_2 > 3$ is of the form $H_a: \mu_1 - \mu_2 > D_0$, we will **reject $H_0: \mu_1 - \mu_2 = 3$ if the value of the test statistic *t* is greater than $t_\alpha = t_{0.05} = 1.65$** (which is based on 163 degrees of freedom and was found using a computer). Using the sample data, the **value of the test statistic** is

$$t = \frac{(\bar{x}_1 - \bar{x}_2) - 3}{\sqrt{\dfrac{s_1^2}{n_1} + \dfrac{s_2^2}{n_2}}} = \frac{(8.79 - 5.14) - 3}{\sqrt{\dfrac{4.8237}{100} + \dfrac{1.7927}{100}}} = \frac{0.65}{0.25722} = 2.53.$$

Because $t = 2.53$ is greater than $t_{0.05} = 1.65$, we reject $H_0: \mu_1 - \mu_2 = 3$ in favour of $H_a: \mu_1 - \mu_2 > 3$. We conclude (at an α of 0.05) that $\mu_1 - \mu_2$ is greater than 3 and, therefore, that the new system reduces the mean customer waiting time by more than three minutes. Therefore, the bank manager will implement the new system. Furthermore, the point estimate $\bar{x}_1 - \bar{x}_2 = 3.65$ says that we estimate that the new system reduces mean waiting time by 3.65 minutes.

Figure 9.5 gives the MegaStat output of using the unequal variances procedure to test $H_0: \mu_1 - \mu_2 = 3$ versus $H_a: \mu_1 - \mu_2 > 3$. The output tells us that $t = 2.53$ and that the associated *p* value is 0.0062. The very small *p* value tells us that we have very strong evidence against $H_0: \mu_1 - \mu_2 = 3$ and in favour of $H_a: \mu_1 - \mu_2 > 3$. That is, we have very strong evidence that $\mu_1 - \mu_2$ is greater than 3 and, therefore, that the new system reduces the mean customer waiting

FIGURE **9.5**   **MegaStat Output of the Unequal Variances Procedure for the Bank Customer Waiting Time Situation**

Hypothesis Test: Independent Groups (t-test, unequal variance)

Current	New			
			163	df
8.79	5.14	mean	3.65000	difference (Current - New)
2.1963	1.3389	std. dev.	0.25722	standard error of difference
100	100	n	3	hypothesized difference
			2.53	t
F-test for equality of variance			0.0062	p-value (one-tailed, upper)
2.69	F		3.14208	confidence interval 95.% lower
1.46E-06	p-value		4.15792	confidence interval 95.% upper
			0.50792	half-width

time by more than three minutes. To find a 95 percent confidence interval for $\mu_1 - \mu_2$, note that we can use a computer to find that $t_{0.025}$ based on 163 degrees of freedom is 1.97.

We can also test a hypothesis about μ_d, the mean of a population of paired differences. We show how to test the null hypothesis

$$H_0: \mu_d = D_0$$

in the following box. Here the value of the constant D_0 depends on the particular problem. Often D_0 equals 0, and the null hypothesis $H_0: \mu_d = 0$ says that μ_1 and μ_2 do not differ.

A One-Tailed Hypothesis Test about the Mean, μ_d, of a Population of Paired Differences: Testing $H_0: \mu_d = D_0$

Assume that the population of paired differences is normally distributed, and consider testing

$$H_0: \mu_d = D_0$$

by using the test statistic

$$t = \frac{\overline{d} - D_0}{s_d / \sqrt{n}}.$$

We can test $H_0: \mu_d = D_0$ versus a particular alternative hypothesis at level of significance α by using the appropriate rejection point rule or, equivalently, the corresponding p value.

Alternative Hypothesis	Rejection Point Rule: Reject H_0 if	p Value (Reject H_0 if p Value $< \alpha$)
$H_a: \mu_d > D_0$	$t > t_\alpha$	The area under the t distribution curve to the right of t
$H_a: \mu_d < D_0$	$t < -t_\alpha$	The area under the t distribution curve to the left of t

Here t_α and the p values are based on $n - 1$ degrees of freedom.

Example 9.10 The Repair Cost Comparison Case

Forest City Casualty currently contracts to have moderately damaged cars repaired at garage 2. However, a local insurance agent suggests that garage 1 provides less expensive repair service that is of equal quality. Because it has done business with garage 2 for years, Forest City has decided to give some of its repair business to garage 1 only if it has very strong evidence that μ_1, the mean repair cost estimate at garage 1, is smaller than μ_2, the mean repair cost estimate at garage 2— that is, if $\mu_d = \mu_1 - \mu_2$ is less than zero. Therefore, we will test $H_0: \mu_d = 0$ or, equivalently, $H_0: \mu_1 - \mu_2 = 0$, versus $H_a: \mu_d < 0$ or, equivalently, $H_a: \mu_1 - \mu_2 < 0$, at the **0.01 level of significance**. To perform the hypothesis test, we will use the sample data in Table 9.2 to calculate the value of the **test statistic t in the summary box**. Since $H_a: \mu_d < 0$ is of the form $H_a: \mu_d < D_0$, we will **reject**

FIGURE 9.6 MINITAB and MegaStat Outputs of Testing H_0: $\mu_d = 0$

(a) MINITAB output of testing H_0: $\mu_d = 0$ versus H_a: $\mu_d < 0$

```
Paired T for Garage1 - Garage2

           N       Mean      StDev     SE Mean
Garage1    7     9.3286     1.2500      0.4724
Garage2    7    10.1286     1.5097      0.5706
Difference 7   -0.800000   0.503322    0.190238

T-Test of mean difference = 0 (vs < 0):
                  T-Value = -4.21      P-Value = 0.003
```

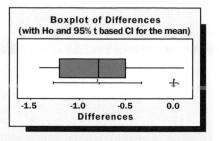

Boxplot of Differences
(with Ho and 95% t based CI for the mean)

(b) MegaStat output of testing H_0: $\mu_d = 0$ versus H_a: $\mu_d \neq 0$

Hypothesis Test: Paired Observations

```
    0.0000  hypothesized value
    9.3286  mean Garage1
   10.1286  mean Garage2
   -0.8000  mean difference (Garage1 - Garage2)
    0.5033  std. dev.
    0.1902  std. error
         7  n
         6  df

   -4.21  t
  0.0057  p-value (two-tailed)
```

H_0: $\mu_d = 0$ if the value of t is less than $-t_\alpha = -t_{0.01} = -3.143$. Here the t_α point is based on $n - 1 = 7 - 1 = 6$ degrees of freedom. Using the data in Table 9.2, the **value of the test statistic** is

$$t = \frac{\bar{d} - D_0}{s_d / \sqrt{n}} = \frac{-0.8 - 0}{0.5033 / \sqrt{7}} = -4.2053.$$

Because $t = -4.2053$ is less than $-t_{0.01} = -3.143$, we can reject H_0: $\mu_d = 0$ in favour of H_a: $\mu_d < 0$. We conclude (at an α of 0.01) that μ_1, the mean repair cost estimate at garage 1, is less than μ_2, the mean repair cost estimate at garage 2. As a result, Forest City will give some of its repair business to garage 1. Furthermore, Figure 9.6(a), which gives the MINITAB output of this hypothesis test, shows us that the p value for the test is 0.003. Since this p value is very small, we have very strong evidence that H_0 should be rejected and that μ_1 is less than μ_2.

To demonstrate testing a "not equal to" alternative hypothesis, Figure 9.6(b) gives the MegaStat output of testing H_0: $\mu_d = 0$ versus H_a: $\mu_d \neq 0$. The output shows that the p value for this two-tailed test is 0.0057. MegaStat will, of course, also perform the test of H_0: $\mu_d = 0$ versus H_a: $\mu_d < 0$. For this test (output not shown), MegaStat and MINITAB find that the p value is about 0.003 (with MegaStat giving us the two-tailed p value).

Exercises for Section 9.7

CONCEPTS

9.51 List all of the assumptions that must be satisfied in order to validly use the hypothesis test described in each of the formula boxes.

METHODS AND APPLICATIONS

Suppose we have taken independent, random samples of sizes $n_1 = 7$ and $n_2 = 7$ from two normally distributed populations

with means μ_1 and μ_2, and suppose we obtain $\bar{x}_1 = 240$, $\bar{x}_2 = 210$, $s_1 = 5$, and $s_2 = 6$.

9.52 Using the equal variances procedure, use rejection points to test the null hypothesis H_0: $\mu_1 - \mu_2 \leq 20$ versus the alternative hypothesis H_a: $\mu_1 - \mu_2 > 20$ by setting α equal to 0.10, 0.05, 0.01, and 0.001. How much evidence is there that the difference between μ_1 and μ_2 exceeds 20?

9.53 Repeat Exercise 9.52 using the unequal variances procedure. Compare your results to those obtained using the equal variances procedure.

9.54 The October 7, 1991, issue of *Fortune* magazine reported on the rapid rise of fees and expenses charged by mutual funds. Assuming that stock fund expenses and municipal bond fund expenses are each approximately normally distributed, suppose a random sample of 12 stock funds gives a mean annual expense of 1.63 percent with a standard deviation of 0.31 percent, and an independent random sample of 12 municipal bond funds gives a mean annual expense of 0.89 percent with a standard deviation of 0.23 percent. Let μ_1 be the mean annual expense for stock funds, and let μ_2 be the mean annual expense for municipal bond funds. Do parts a and b by using the equal variances procedure. Then repeat parts a and b using the unequal variances procedure. Compare your results.

  a. Set up the null and alternative hypotheses needed to attempt to establish that the mean annual expense for stock funds is larger than the mean annual expense for municipal bond funds. Test these hypotheses at the 0.05 level of significance. What do you conclude?

  b. Set up the null and alternative hypotheses needed to attempt to establish that the mean annual expense for stock funds exceeds the mean annual expense for municipal bond funds by more than 0.5 percentage points. Test these hypotheses at the 0.05 level of significance. What do you conclude?

9.55 Use the information in Exercise 9.18 to answer the following questions:

  a. Set up the null and alternative hypotheses needed to attempt to establish that type *A* training results in higher mean weekly sales than does type *B* training.

  b. Because different sales trainees are assigned to the two experimental groups, it is reasonable to believe that the two samples are independent. Assuming that the normality assumption holds, and using the equal variances procedure, test the hypotheses you set up in part a at levels of significance 0.10, 0.05, 0.01, and 0.001. How much evidence is there that type *A* training produces results that are superior to those of type *B*?

9.56 A loan officer compares the interest rates for 48-month fixed-rate auto loans and 48-month variable-rate auto loans. Two independent, random samples of auto loan rates are selected. A sample of eight 48-month fixed-rate auto loans had the following loan rates:

  ● AutoLoan

  > 10.29%   9.75%   9.50%   9.99%
  > 9.75%   9.99%   11.40% 10.00%

A sample of five 48-month variable-rate auto loans had loan rates as follows:

  > 9.59%   8.75%   8.99%   8.50%   9.00%

  a. Set up the null and alternative hypotheses needed to determine whether the mean rates for 48-month fixed-rate and variable-rate auto loans differ by more than 0.4 percentage points.

  b. Use a hypothesis test to establish that the difference between the mean rates for fixed- and variable-rate 48-month auto loans exceeds 0.4 percentage points. Use α equal to 0.05.

9.57 Suppose a sample of 11 paired differences that has been randomly selected from a normally distributed population of paired differences yields a sample mean of $\bar{d} = 103.5$ and a sample standard deviation of $s_d = 5$.

  a. Test the null hypothesis $H_0: \mu_d \leq 100$ versus $H_a: \mu_d > 100$ by setting α equal to 0.05 and 0.01. How much evidence is there that $\mu_d = \mu_1 - \mu_2$ exceeds 100?

  b. Test the null hypothesis $H_0: \mu_d \geq 110$ versus $H_a: \mu_d < 110$ by setting α equal to 0.05 and 0.01. How much evidence is there that $\mu_d = \mu_1 - \mu_2$ is less than 110?

9.58 Suppose a sample of 49 paired differences that have been randomly selected from a normally distributed population of paired differences yields a sample mean of $\bar{d} = 5$ and a sample standard deviation of $s_d = 7$. Find the *p* value for testing $H_0: \mu_d \leq 3$ versus $H_a: \mu_d > 3$. Use the *p* value to test these hypotheses with α equal to 0.10, 0.05, 0.01, and 0.001. How much evidence is there that μ_d exceeds 3? What does this say about the size of the difference between μ_1 and μ_2?

9.59 Use the information in Exercise 9.28 to answer the following questions:

  a. Set up the null and alternative hypotheses needed to attempt to establish that brand *A* shoes yield lower times than brand *B* shoes.

  b. Use a *p* value to test the hypotheses you set up in part a at the 0.10, 0.05, 0.01, and 0.001 levels of significance. How much evidence is there that brand *A* shoes yield lower times than brand *B* shoes?

9.60 Use the information in Exercise 9.29 to answer the following questions:

  a. Set up the null and alternative hypotheses needed to attempt to establish that type *B* gasoline provides better average fuel efficiency than type *A* gasoline.

  b. Use a *p* value to test the hypotheses you set up in part a at the 0.10, 0.05, 0.01, and 0.001 levels of significance. How much evidence is there that type *B* gasoline yields better fuel efficiency, on average, than type *A* gasoline?   ● FuelEffic

9.8 *t* Tests about a Difference in Population Means: Two-Tailed Alternative

In the last section, we learned how to conduct a one-sided *t* test for $\mu_1 - \mu_2$ when the population variances were unknown and equal and unknown and not equal. In the following box, we describe how this can be done using a two-tailed test:

A Two-Tailed *t* Test about the Difference between Two Population Means: Testing $H_0: \mu_1 - \mu_2 = D_0$ when $\sigma_1^2 = \sigma_2^2$

Define the test statistic

$$t = \frac{(\bar{x}_1 - \bar{x}_2) - D_0}{\sqrt{s_p^2\left(\frac{1}{n_1} + \frac{1}{n_2}\right)}}$$

and assume that the sampled populations are normally distributed with equal variances. Then, if

the samples are independent of each other, we can test $H_0: \mu_1 - \mu_2 = D_0$ versus a particular alternative hypothesis at level of significance α by using the appropriate rejection point rule or, equivalently, the corresponding *p* value.

Alternative Hypothesis	Rejection Point Rule: Reject H_0 if	*p* Value (Reject H_0 if *p* Value $< \alpha$)
$H_a: \mu_1 - \mu_2 \neq D_0$	$\lvert t \rvert > t_{\alpha/2}$—that is, $t > t_{\alpha/2}$ or $t < -t_{\alpha/2}$	Twice the area under the *t* distribution curve to the right of $\lvert t \rvert$

Here $t_{\alpha/2}$ and the *p* values are based on $n_1 + n_2 - 2$ degrees of freedom.

Example 9.11   The Coffee Cup Case

In order to compare the mean hourly yields obtained by using the Java and Joe methods, we will test $H_0: \mu_1 - \mu_2 = 0$ versus $H_a: \mu_1 - \mu_2 \neq 0$ at the **0.05 level of significance**. To perform the hypothesis test, we will use the sample information in Table 9.1 to calculate the value of the **test statistic *t* in the summary box**. Then, since $H_a: \mu_1 - \mu_2 \neq 0$ is of the form $H_a: \mu_1 - \mu_2 \neq D_0$, we will **reject $H_0: \mu_1 - \mu_2 = 0$ if the absolute value of *t* is greater than** $t_{\alpha/2} = t_{0.025} = 2.306$. Here the $t_{\alpha/2}$ point is based on $n_1 + n_2 - 2 = 5 + 5 - 2 = 8$ degrees of freedom. Using the data in Table 9.1, the **value of the test statistic is**

$$t = \frac{(\bar{x}_1 - \bar{x}_2) - D_0}{\sqrt{s_p^2\left(\frac{1}{n_1} + \frac{1}{n_2}\right)}} = \frac{(811 - 750.2) - 0}{\sqrt{435.1\left(\frac{1}{5} + \frac{1}{5}\right)}} = 4.6087.$$

Because $\lvert t \rvert = 4.6087$ is greater than $t_{0.025} = 2.306$, we can reject $H_0: \mu_1 - \mu_2 = 0$ in favour of $H_a: \mu_1 - \mu_2 \neq 0$. We conclude (at an α of 0.05) that the mean hourly yields obtained by using the two production methods differ. Furthermore, the point estimate $\bar{x}_1 - \bar{x}_2 = 811 - 750.2 = 60.8$ says we estimate that the mean hourly yield obtained by using Java is 60.8 kg higher than the mean hourly yield obtained by using Joe.

Figure 9.7(a) and (b) gives the MegaStat and Excel outputs for testing H_0 versus H_a. The outputs tell us that $t = 4.61$ and that the associated *p* value is 0.001736 (rounded to 0.0017

FIGURE 9.7   MegaStat and Excel Outputs for Testing the Equality of Means in the Coffee Cup Case Assuming Equal Variances

(a) The MegaStat Output

Hypothesis Test: Independent Groups (t-test, pooled variance)

Java	Joe			
811.00	750.20	mean	4.61	t
19.65	22.00	std. dev.	0.0017	p-value (two-tailed)
5	5	n	30.378	confidence interval 95% lower
			91.222	confidence interval 95% upper

8	df	
60.800	difference (Java - Joe)	**F-test for equality of variance**
435.100	pooled variance	484.20 variance: Joe
20.859	pooled std. dev.	386.00 variance: Java
13.192	standard error of difference	1.25 F
0	hypothesized difference	0.8314 p-value

(b) The Excel Output

t-Test: Two-Sample Assuming Equal Variances

	Java	Joe
Mean	811	750.2
Variance	386	484.2
Observations	5	5
Pooled Variance	435.1	
Hypothesized Mean Diff	0	
df	8	
t Stat	4.608706	
P(T<=t) one-tail	0.000868	
t Critical one-tail	1.859548	
P(T<=t) two-tail	0.001736	
t Critical two-tail	2.306004	

on the MegaStat output). The very small p value tells us that we have very strong evidence against H_0: $\mu_1 - \mu_2 = 0$ and in favour of H_a: $\mu_1 - \mu_2 \neq 0$. In other words, we have very strong evidence that the mean hourly yields obtained by using the two production methods differ.

When the sampled populations are normally distributed and the population variances σ_1^2 and σ_2^2 differ, the following can be shown:

A Two-Tailed t Test of H_0: $\mu_1 - \mu_2 = D_0$ when $\sigma_1^2 \neq \sigma_2^2$

When the sample sizes n_1 and n_2 are equal, the equal variances t-based hypothesis test given in the preceding box is approximately valid even if the population variances σ_1^2 and σ_2^2 differ substantially. As a rough rule of thumb, if the larger sample variance is not more than three times the smaller sample variance when the sample sizes are equal, we can use the equal variances interval test.

Furthermore, we can test H_0: $\mu_1 - \mu_2 = D_0$ by using the test statistic

$$t = \frac{(\bar{x}_1 - \bar{x}_2) - D_0}{\sqrt{\dfrac{s_1^2}{n_1} + \dfrac{s_2^2}{n_2}}}$$

and by using the previously given rejection point and p value conditions.

The degrees of freedom are equal to

$$df = \frac{(s_1^2/n_1 + s_2^2/n_2)^2}{\dfrac{(s_1^2/n_1)^2}{n_1 - 1} + \dfrac{(s_2^2/n_2)^2}{n_2 - 1}}.$$

Here, if df is not a whole number, we can round it down to the next smallest whole number.

Consider a two-tailed hypothesis test about μ_d, the mean of a population of paired differences. We will show how to test the null hypothesis

$$H_0: \mu_d = D_0$$

in the following box. Here the value of the constant D_0 depends on the particular problem. Often D_0 equals 0, and the null hypothesis H_0: $\mu_d = 0$ says that μ_1 and μ_2 do not differ.

A Two-Tailed Hypothesis Test about the Mean, μ_d, of a Population of Paired Differences: Testing H_0: $\mu_d = D_0$

Assume that the population of paired differences is normally distributed, and consider testing

$$H_0: \mu_d = D_0$$

by using the test statistic

$$t = \frac{\bar{d} - D_0}{s_d/\sqrt{n}}.$$

We can test H_0: $\mu_d = D_0$ versus a particular alternative hypothesis at level of significance α by using the appropriate rejection point rule or, equivalently, the corresponding p value.

Alternative Hypothesis	Rejection Point Rule: Reject H_0 if	p Value (Reject H_0 if p Value $< \alpha$)
H_a: $\mu_d \neq D_0$	$|t| > t_{\alpha/2}$—that is, $t > t_{\alpha/2}$ or $t < -t_{\alpha/2}$	Twice the area under the t distribution curve to the right of $|t|$

Here $t_{\alpha/2}$ and the p values are based on $n - 1$ degrees of freedom.

Exercises for Section 9.8

CONCEPTS

9.61 List all of the assumptions that must be satisfied in order to validly use the hypothesis test described in each of the formula boxes on pages 297 and 298.

METHODS AND APPLICATIONS

Suppose we have taken independent, random samples of sizes $n_1 = 7$ and $n_2 = 7$ from two normally distributed populations with means μ_1 and μ_2, and suppose we obtain $\bar{x}_1 = 240$, $\bar{x}_2 = 210$, $s_1 = 5$, and $s_2 = 6$.

9.62 Using the equal variances procedure, use rejection points to test the null hypothesis $H_0: \mu_1 - \mu_2 = 20$ versus the alternative hypothesis $H_a: \mu_1 - \mu_2 \neq 20$ by setting α equal to 0.10, 0.05, 0.01, and 0.001. How much evidence is there that the difference between μ_1 and μ_2 is not equal to 20?

9.63 Repeat Exercise 9.62 using the unequal variances procedure. Compare your results to those obtained using the equal variances procedure.

9.64 A marketing research firm wishes to compare the prices charged by two supermarket chains—Miller's and Albert's. The research firm, using a standardized one-week shopping plan (grocery list), makes identical purchases at 10 of each chain's stores. The stores for each chain are randomly selected, and all purchases are made during a single week.

The shopping expenses obtained at the two chains, along with box plots of the expenses, are as in Figure 9.8.   ● ShopExp

Because the stores in each sample are different stores in different chains, it is reasonable to assume that the samples are independent, and we assume that weekly expenses at each chain are normally distributed.

a. Letting μ_M be the mean weekly expense for the shopping plan at Miller's, and letting μ_A be the mean weekly expense for the shopping plan at Albert's, Figure 9.9 gives the MINITAB output of the test of $H_0: \mu_M - \mu_A = 0$ (that is, there is no difference between μ_M and μ_A) versus $H_a: \mu_M - \mu_A \neq 0$ (that is, μ_M and μ_A differ). Note that MINITAB has employed the equal variances procedure. Use the sample data to show that $\bar{x}_M = 121.92$, $s_M = 1.40$, $\bar{x}_A = 114.81$, $s_A = 1.84$, and $t = 9.73$.

b. Using the t statistic given on the output and rejection points, test H_0 versus H_a by setting α equal to 0.10, 0.05, 0.01, and 0.001. How much evidence is there that the mean weekly expenses at Miller's and Albert's differ?

c. Figure 9.9 gives the p value for testing H_0: $\mu_M - \mu_A = 0$ versus $H_a: \mu_M - \mu_A \neq 0$. Use the p value to test H_0 versus H_a by setting α equal to 0.10, 0.05, 0.01, and 0.001. How much evidence is there that the mean weekly expenses at Miller's and Albert's differ?

d. Set up the null and alternative hypotheses needed to attempt to establish that the mean weekly expense for the shopping plan at Miller's exceeds the mean weekly expense at Albert's by more than $5. Test the hypotheses at the 0.10, 0.05, 0.01, and 0.001 levels of significance. How much evidence is there that the mean weekly expense at Miller's exceeds that at Albert's by more than $5?

FIGURE 9.8 **Shopping Expenses at Miller's and Albert's for Exercise 9.64**

Miller's

$119.25	$121.32	$122.34	$120.14	$122.19
$123.71	$121.72	$122.42	$123.63	$122.44

Albert's

$111.99	$114.88	$115.11	$117.02	$116.89
$116.62	$115.38	$114.40	$113.91	$111.87

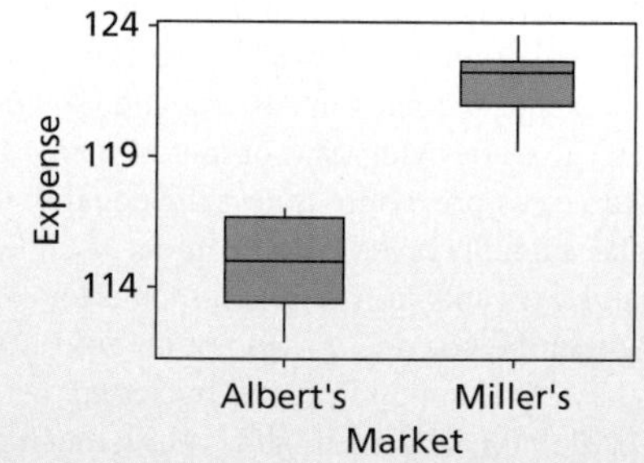

FIGURE 9.9 **MINITAB Output of Testing the Equality of Mean Weekly Expenses at Miller's and Albert's Supermarket Chains**

```
Two-sample T for Millers vs Alberts

             N     Mean    StDev   SE Mean
Millers     10    121.92    1.40     0.44
Alberts     10    114.81    1.84     0.58

Difference = mu(Millers)- mu(Alberts)   Estimate for difference: 7.10900
95% CI for difference:  (5.57350, 8.64450)
T-Test of diff = 0 (vs not =): T-Value = 9.73   P-Value = 0.000   DF = 18
Both use Pooled StDev = 1.6343
```

FIGURE 9.10 MegaStat Output of Testing the Equality of Mean Dollar Amounts Owed for Alberta and Ontario

Hypothesis Test: Independent Groups (t-test, unequal variance)

Alberta	Ontario	
524	473	mean
68	22	std. dev.
10	20	n

9 df
51.000 difference (Alberta - Ontario)
22.059 standard error of difference
0 hypothesized difference
2.31 t
0.0461 p-value (two-tailed)

FIGURE 9.11 MegaStat Output of Testing the Equality of Mean Loan Rates for Fixed and Variable 48-Month Auto Loans

Hypothesis Test: Independent Groups (t-test, pooled variance)

Fixed	Variable			
10.0838	8.9660	mean	11	df
0.5810	0.4046	std. dev.	1.11775	difference (Fixed - Variable)
8	5	n	0.27437	pooled variance

F-test for equality of variance   0.52381 pooled std. dev.
0.3376 variance: Fixed   0.29862 standard error of difference
0.1637 variance: Variable   0 hypothesized difference
2.06 F   3.74 t
0.5052 p-value   0.0032 p-value (two-tailed)

9.65 A large discount chain compares the performance of its credit managers in Alberta and Ontario by comparing the mean dollar amounts owed by customers with delinquent charge accounts in these two provinces. Here a small mean dollar amount owed is desirable because it indicates that bad credit risks are not being extended large amounts of credit. Two independent, random samples of delinquent accounts are selected from the populations of delinquent accounts in Alberta and Ontario, respectively. The first sample, which consists of 10 randomly selected delinquent accounts in Alberta, gives a mean dollar amount of $524 with a standard deviation of $68. The second sample, which consists of 20 randomly selected delinquent accounts in Ontario, gives a mean dollar amount of $473 with a standard deviation of $22.

a. Set up the null and alternative hypotheses needed to test whether there is a difference between the population mean dollar amounts owed by customers with delinquent charge accounts in Alberta and Ontario.

b. Figure 9.10 gives the MegaStat output of using the unequal variances procedure to test the equality of mean dollar amounts owed by customers with delinquent charge accounts in Alberta and Ontario. Assuming that the normality assumption holds, test the hypotheses you set up in part a by setting α equal to 0.10, 0.05, 0.01, and 0.001. How much evidence is there that the mean dollar amounts owed in Alberta and Ontario differ?

9.66 A loan officer compares the interest rates for 48-month fixed-rate auto loans and 48-month variable-rate auto loans. Two independent, random samples of auto loan rates are selected. A sample of eight 48-month fixed-rate auto loans had the following loan rates:

🌑 AutoLoan

10.29%   9.75%   9.50%   9.99%
9.75%   9.99%   11.40%   10.00%

A sample of five 48-month variable-rate auto loans had loan rates as follows:

9.59%   8.75%   8.99%   8.50%   9.00%

a. Set up the null and alternative hypotheses needed to determine whether the mean rates for 48-month fixed-rate and variable-rate auto loans differ.

b. Figure 9.11 gives the MegaStat output of using the equal variances procedure to test the hypotheses you set up in part a. Assuming that the normality and equal variances assumptions hold, use the MegaStat output and rejection points to test these hypotheses by setting α equal to 0.10, 0.05, 0.01, and 0.001. How much evidence is there that the mean rates for 48-month fixed- and variable-rate auto loans differ?

c. Figure 9.11 gives the p value for testing the hypotheses you set up in part a. Use the p value to test these hypotheses by setting α equal to 0.10, 0.05, 0.01, and 0.001. How much evidence is there that the mean rates for 48-month fixed- and variable-rate auto loans differ?

9.67 Suppose a sample of 49 paired differences that have been randomly selected from a normally distributed population of paired differences yields a sample mean of $\overline{d} = 5$ and a sample standard deviation of $s_d = 7$.

a. Test the null hypothesis $H_0: \mu_d = 0$ versus the alternative hypothesis $H_a: \mu_d \neq 0$ by setting α equal to 0.10, 0.05, 0.01, and 0.001. How much evidence is there that μ_d differs from 0? What does this say about how μ_1 and μ_2 compare?

b. Find the p value for testing $H_0: \mu_d = 3$ versus $H_a: \mu_d \neq 3$. Use the p value to test these hypotheses with α equal to 0.10, 0.05, 0.01, and 0.001. How much evidence is there that μ_d is different from 3?

9.68 On its Web site, the *Statesman Journal* newspaper (Salem, Oregon, 1999) reported mortgage loan interest rates for 30-year and 15-year fixed-rate mortgage loans for a number of Willamette Valley lending institutions. Of interest is whether there is any systematic difference between 30-year rates and 15-year rates (expressed as annual percentage rate or APR) and, if there is, what the size of that difference is. Table 9.5 displays mortgage loan rates and the difference between 30-year and 15-year rates for nine randomly selected lending institutions.

TABLE **9.5**   **1999 Mortgage Loan Interest Rates for Nine Randomly Selected Willamette Valley Lending Institutions**   ● Mortgage99

Lending Institution	Annual Percentage Rate		
	30-Year	15-Year	Difference
American Mortgage N.W. Inc.	6.715	6.599	0.116
City and Country Mortgage	6.648	6.367	0.281
Commercial Bank	6.740	6.550	0.190
Landmark Mortgage Co.	6.597	6.362	0.235
Liberty Mortgage, Inc.	6.425	6.162	0.263
MaPS Credit Union	6.880	6.583	0.297
Mortgage Brokers, Inc.	6.900	6.800	0.100
Mortgage First Corp.	6.675	6.394	0.281
Silver Eagle Mortgage	6.790	6.540	0.250

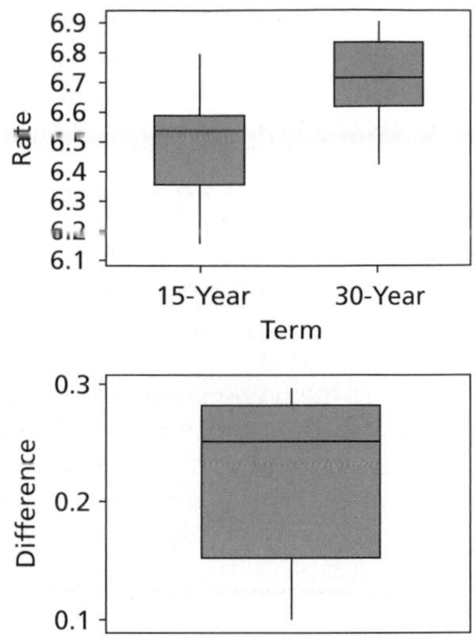

Source: World Wide Web, Salem Homeplace Mortgage Rates Directory, http://www.salemhomeplace. com/pages/finance/, *Statesman Journal Newspaper*, Salem, Oregon January 4, 1999.

FIGURE **9.12**   **MINITAB Paired Difference t Test of the Mortgage Loan Rate Data for Exercise 9.68**

```
Paired T for 30-Year - 15-Year

              N        Mean        StDev       SE Mean
30-Year       9        6.70778     0.14635     0.04878
15-Year       9        6.48411     0.18396     0.06132
Difference    9        0.223667    0.072750    0.024250

95% CI for mean difference: (0.167746, 0.279587)
T-Test of mean difference = 0 (vs not = 0):
                           T-Value = 9.22   P-Value = 0.000
```

Assume that the population of paired differences is normally distributed.   ● Mortgage99

a. Set up the null and alternative hypotheses needed to determine whether there is a difference between mean 30-year rates and mean 15-year rates.

b. Figure 9.12 gives the MINITAB output for testing the hypotheses that you set up in part a. Use the output and rejection points to test these hypotheses by setting α equal to 0.10, 0.05, 0.01, and 0.001. How much evidence is there that mean mortgage loan rates for 30-year and 15-year terms differ?

c. Figure 9.12 gives the *p* value for testing the hypotheses that you set up in part a. Use the *p* value to test these hypotheses by setting α equal to 0.10, 0.05, 0.01, and 0.001. How much evidence is there that mean mortgage loan rates for 30-year and 15-year terms differ?

9.69 National Paper Company must purchase a new machine for producing cardboard boxes. The company must choose between two machines. The machines produce boxes of equal quality, so the company will choose the machine that produces (on average) the most boxes. It is known that there are substantial differences in the abilities of the company's machine operators. Therefore, National Paper has decided to compare the machines using a paired difference experiment. Suppose that eight randomly selected machine operators produce boxes for one hour using machine 1 and for one hour using machine 2, with the following results: ● BoxYield

	Machine Operator							
	1	2	3	4	5	6	7	8
Machine 1	53	60	58	48	46	54	62	49
Machine 2	50	55	56	44	45	50	57	47

a. Assuming normality, perform a hypothesis test to determine whether there is a difference between the mean hourly outputs of the two machines. Use $\alpha = 0.05$.

b. Estimate the minimum and maximum differences between the mean outputs of the two machines. Justify your answer.

TABLE **9.6**   Weekly Study Time Data for Students Who Perform
Well on the MidTerm   ◐ StudyTime

Student	1	2	3	4	5	6	7	8
Before	15	14	17	17	19	14	13	16
After	9	9	11	10	19	10	14	10

FIGURE **9.13**   MINITAB Output for Exercise 9.70

Paired T-Test and CI: StudyBefore, StudyAfter

```
Paired T for StudyBefore - StudyAfter
              N      Mean     StDev   SE Mean
StudyBefore   8   15.6250    1.9955    0.7055
StudyAfter    8   11.5000    3.4226    1.2101
Difference    8    4.12500   2.99702   1.05961

95% CI for mean difference: (1.61943, 6.63057)
T-Test of mean difference = 0 (vs not = 0): T-Value = 3.89  P-Value = 0.006
```

9.70   Do students reduce study time in classes where they achieve a higher midterm score? In a *Journal of Economic Education* article (Winter 2005), Krohn and O'Connor studied student effort and performance in a class over a semester. In an intermediate macroeconomics course, they found that "students respond to higher midterm scores by reducing the number of hours they subsequently allocate to studying for the course."[9] Suppose that a random sample of $n = 8$ students who performed well on the midterm exam was taken and weekly study times before and after the exam were compared. The resulting data are given in Table 9.6. Assume that the population of all possible paired differences is normally distributed.

a. Set up the null and alternative hypotheses to test whether there is a difference in the true mean study time before and after the midterm exam.

b. In Figure 9.13, we present the MINITAB output for the paired differences test. Use the output and rejection points to test the hypotheses at the 0.10, 0.05, and 0.01 levels of significance. Has the true mean study time changed?

c. Use the p value to test the hypotheses at the 0.10, 0.05, and 0.01 levels of significance. How much evidence is there against the null hypothesis?

9.9 *z* Tests about a Difference in Population Proportions

In Section 9.4, we learned how to calculate a confidence interval for the difference between population proportions, $p_1 - p_2$. Now we wish to conduct a hypothesis test about the difference between two population proportions. In this text, we will only consider the case where n_1 and n_2 are large. This allows us to use a z test when conducting our hypothesis tests.

To test the null hypothesis $H_0: p_1 - p_2 = D_0$, we use the test statistic

$$z = \frac{(\hat{p}_1 - \hat{p}_2) - D_0}{\sigma_{\hat{p}_1 - \hat{p}_2}}.$$

A commonly employed special case of this hypothesis test is obtained by setting D_0 equal to 0. In this case, the null hypothesis $H_0: p_1 - p_2 = 0$ says there is **no difference** between the population proportions p_1 and p_2. When $D_0 = 0$, the best estimate of the common population proportion $p = p_1 = p_2$ is obtained by computing

$$\hat{p} = \frac{\text{the total number of units in the two samples that fall into the category of interest}}{\text{the total number of units in the two samples}}.$$

Therefore, the point estimate of $\sigma_{\hat{p}_1 - \hat{p}_2}$ is

$$s_{\hat{p}_1 - \hat{p}_2} = \sqrt{\frac{\hat{p}(1 - \hat{p})}{n_1} + \frac{\hat{p}(1 - \hat{p})}{n_2}}$$

$$= \sqrt{\hat{p}(1 - \hat{p})\left(\frac{1}{n_1} + \frac{1}{n_2}\right)}.$$

[9]Source: "Student effort and performance over the semester," by Gregory Krohn and Catherine O'Connor, *Journal of Economic Education*, Winter 2005, pages 3–28.

For the case where $D_0 \neq 0$, the point estimate of $\sigma_{\hat{p}_1 - \hat{p}_2}$ is obtained by estimating p_1 by $\hat{p}_1$ and p_2 by $\hat{p}_2$. With these facts in mind, we present the following procedure for testing $H_0: p_1 - p_2 = D_0$:

A Hypothesis Test about the Difference between Two Population Proportions: Testing $H_0: p_1 - p_2 = D_0$

Let $\hat{p}$ be as just defined. Furthermore, define the test statistic

$$z = \frac{(\hat{p}_1 - \hat{p}_2) - D_0}{\sigma_{\hat{p}_1 - \hat{p}_2}}$$

and assume that each of the sample sizes n_1 and n_2 is large. Then, if the samples are independent of each other, we can test $H_0: p_1 - p_2 = D_0$ versus a particular alternative hypothesis at level of significance α by using the appropriate rejection point rule or, equivalently, the corresponding p value.

Alternative Hypothesis	Rejection Point Rule: Reject H_0 if	p Value (Reject H_0 if p Value $< \alpha$)
$H_a: p_1 - p_2 > D_0$	$z > z_\alpha$	The area under the standard normal curve to the right of z
$H_a: p_1 - p_2 < D_0$	$z < -z_\alpha$	The area under the standard normal curve to the left of z
$H_a: p_1 - p_2 \neq D_0$	$\|z\| > z_{\alpha/2}$—that is, $z > z_{\alpha/2}$ or $z < -z_{\alpha/2}$	Twice the area under the standard normal curve to the right of $\|z\|$

Note:

1 If $D_0 = 0$, we estimate $\sigma_{\hat{p}_1 - \hat{p}_2}$ by

$$s_{\hat{p}_1 - \hat{p}_2} = \sqrt{\hat{p}(1 - \hat{p})\left(\frac{1}{n_1} + \frac{1}{n_2}\right)}.$$

2 If $D_0 \neq 0$, we estimate $\sigma_{\hat{p}_1 - \hat{p}_2}$ by

$$s_{\hat{p}_1 - \hat{p}_2} = \sqrt{\frac{\hat{p}_1(1 - \hat{p}_1)}{n_1} + \frac{\hat{p}_2(1 - \hat{p}_2)}{n_2}}.$$

Example 9.12 The Advertising Media Case

Recall that p_1 is the proportion of all consumers in the Toronto area who are aware of the new product and that p_2 is the proportion of all consumers in the Vancouver area who are aware of the new product. To test for the equality of these proportions, we will test $H_0: p_1 - p_2 = 0$ versus $H_a: p_1 - p_2 \neq 0$ at the **0.05 level of significance**. Because both of the Toronto and Vancouver samples are large (see Example 9.6), we will calculate the value of the **test statistic z in the summary box** (where $D_0 = 0$). Since $H_a: p_1 - p_2 \neq 0$ is of the form $H_a: p_1 - p_2 \neq D_0$, we will **reject $H_0: p_1 - p_2 = 0$ if the absolute value of z is greater than $z_{\alpha/2} = z_{0.05/2} = z_{0.025} = 1.96$**. Because 631 out of 1,000 randomly selected Toronto residents were aware of the product and 798 out of 1,000 randomly selected Vancouver residents were aware of the product, the estimate of $p = p_1 = p_2$ is

$$\hat{p} = \frac{631 + 798}{1,000 + 1,000} = \frac{1,429}{2,000} = 0.7145,$$

and the **value of the test statistic is**

$$z = \frac{(\hat{p}_1 - \hat{p}_2) - D_0}{\sqrt{\hat{p}(1 - \hat{p})(\frac{1}{n_1} + \frac{1}{n_2})}} = \frac{(0.631 - 0.798) - 0}{\sqrt{(0.7145)(0.2855)(\frac{1}{1,000} + \frac{1}{1,000})}} = \frac{-0.167}{0.0202} = -8.2673.$$

Because $\|z\| - 8.2673$ is greater than 1.96, we can reject $H_0: p_1 - p_2 = 0$ in favour of $H_a: p_1 - p_2 \neq 0$. We conclude (at an α of 0.05) that the proportions of consumers who are aware of the product in Toronto and Vancouver differ. Furthermore, the point estimate $\hat{p}_1 - \hat{p}_2 = 0.631 - 0.798 = -0.167$ says we estimate that the percentage of consumers who are aware of the product in Vancouver is 16.7 percentage points higher than the percentage of consumers who are aware of the product in Toronto. The p value for this test is twice the area under the standard normal curve to the right of $\|z\| = 8.2673$. Since the area under the standard

F I G U R E **9.14**   MegaStat Output of Statistical Inference in the Advertising Media Case

Testing H_0: $p_1 - p_2 = 0$ versus H_a: $p_1 - p_2 \neq 0$

Hypothesis test for two independent proportions

p1	p2	pc		
0.631	0.798	0.7145	−0.167	difference
631/1,000	798/1,000	1,429/2000	0.	hypothesized difference
631.	798.	1,429. X	0.0202	std. error
1,000	1,000	2,000 n	**−8.27**	z
			0.00E+00	p-value (two-tailed)

normal curve to the right of 3.29 is 0.0005, the p value for testing H_0 is less than 2(0.0005) = 0.001. It follows that we have extremely strong evidence that H_0: $p_1 - p_2 = 0$ should be rejected in favour of H_a: $p_1 - p_2 \neq 0$. That is, this small p value provides extremely strong evidence that p_1 and p_2 differ. Figure 9.14 presents the MegaStat output of the hypothesis test of H_0: $p_1 - p_2 = 0$ versus H_a: $p_1 - p_2 \neq 0$. A MINITAB output of the test is given in Appendix 9.1.

Before we move on to tests for equality of variance, we would like to conclude this part of the chapter in the same way we concluded the first part. The reason we are not including the equality of variances test in our conclusion is that the F test is somewhat different in form from the tests that we have seen in this part of the chapter.

In this chapter, we have learned how to conduct hypothesis tests using a z test statistic and a t test statistic. Why do we switch between using z and t? Think back to confidence intervals. Remember that z values were used in the confidence interval when the values of σ_1 and σ_2 were not known, or when the sample sizes were very large. The same is true when conducting hypothesis tests. We will use a z test statistic to conduct a hypothesis test when the σ's are known or when the sample sizes are large. We will use a t test statistic when the data are approximately normal, the sample sizes are small, and the values of σ are not known. The test statistic will take on the following form, in general:

$$\text{test statistic} = \frac{\text{estimated difference} - \text{difference under } H_0}{\text{standard error of the estimated difference}}.$$

Note that this form will not hold true in the next section of the text when we test for equality of variances.

Exercises for Section 9.9

CONCEPTS

9.71 What assumptions must be satisfied in order to use the methods presented in this section?

METHODS AND APPLICATIONS

In Exercises 9.72 and 9.73, we assume that we have selected two independent random samples from populations with proportions p_1 and p_2 and that $\hat{p}_1 = 800/1,000 = 0.8$ and $\hat{p}_2 = 950/1,000 = 9.5$.

9.72 Test H_0: $p_1 - p_2 = 0$ versus H_a: $p_1 - p_2 \neq 0$ by using rejection points and by setting α equal to 0.10, 0.05, 0.01, and 0.001. How much evidence is there that p_1 and p_2 differ? Explain. Hint: $z_{0.0005} = 3.29$.

9.73 Test H_0: $p_1 - p_2 \geq -0.12$ versus H_a: $p_1 - p_2 < -0.12$ by using a p value and by setting α equal to 0.10, 0.05, 0.01, and 0.001. How much evidence is there that p_2 exceeds p_1 by more than 0.12? Explain.

9.74 Use the information in Exercise 9.34 to answer the following questions:
   a. Set up the null and alternative hypotheses needed to determine whether the proportion of faculty members who believe that there is inadequate parking is different from the proportion of students who believe that there is inadequate parking.
   b. Test the hypotheses you set up in part a by using rejection points and by setting α equal to 0.10, 0.05,

FIGURE **9.15** **Results of Gallup Survey for Exercise 9.77**

	Percentage of respondents	
1 Had taken a vacation lasting six days or more within the last 12 months:	December 1999 42%	December 1968 62%
2 Took part in some sort of daily activity to keep physically fit:	December 1999 60%	September 1977 48%
3 Watched TV more than four hours on an average weekday:	December 1999 28%	April 1981 25%
4 Drove a car or truck to work:	December 1999 87%	April 1971 81%

0.01, and 0.001. How much evidence is there that the proportions are different?

c. Set up the null and alternative hypotheses needed to determine whether the difference between the proportion of faculty members and the proportion of students who believe that there is inadequate parking is more than 0.05 (five percentage points). Test these hypotheses by using a *p* value and by setting α equal to 0.10, 0.05, 0.01, and 0.001. How much evidence is there that the difference between the proportions exceeds 0.05?

9.75 Use the information in Exercise 9.35 to answer the following questions:

a. Let p_1 be the proportion of young adults who smoked in 1999 and let p_2 be the proportion of young adults who smoked in 2006. Set up the null and alternative hypotheses needed to determine whether the proportion of young adults who smoked in 1999 differs from the proportion who smoked in 2006.

b. Find the test statistic *z* and the *p* value for testing the hypotheses you set up in part a. Use the *p* value to test the hypotheses at the 0.10, 0.05, 0.01, and 0.001 levels of significance. How much evidence is there that the proportion of young adults who smoked in 1999 differs from the proportion who smoked in 2006?

9.76 Use the information in Exercise 9.36 to answer the following questions:

a. Let p_1 be the proportion of defective digital music players during the first two months of 2007 and let p_2 be the proportion of defective digital music players during the next two months. Set up the null and alternative hypotheses needed to determine whether the proportion of defective digital music players declined after the quality control standards were tightened.

b. Find the test statistic *z* and the *p* value for testing the hypotheses you set up in part a. Use the *p* value to test the hypotheses at the 0.10, 0.05, 0.01, and 0.001 levels of significance. How much evidence is there that the proportion of defective digital music players declined after the quality control standards were tightened?

9.77 On January 7, 2000, the Gallup Organization released the results of a poll comparing the lifestyles of today with yesteryear. The survey results were based on telephone interviews with a randomly selected national sample of 1,031 adults, 18 years and older, conducted December 20 to 21, 1999. The poll asked several questions and compared the 1999 responses with the responses given in polls taken in previous years. In Figure 9.15, we summarize some of the poll's results.[10] Assume that each poll was based on a randomly selected national sample of 1,031 adults and that the samples in different years are independent.

a. Let p_1 be the December 1999 population proportion of U.S. adults who took part in some sort of daily activity to keep physically fit, and let p_2 be the September 1977 population proportion who did the same. Carry out a hypothesis test to attempt to justify that the proportion who took part in such daily activity increased from September 1977 to December 1999. Use α = 0.05 and explain your result.

b. Let p_1 be the December 1999 population proportion of U.S. adults who watched TV more than four hours on an average weekday, and let p_2 be the April 1981 population proportion who did the same. Carry out a hypothesis test to determine whether these population proportions differ. Use α = 0.05 and interpret the result of your test.

9.10 *F* Tests about a Difference in Population Variances

Earlier in the chapter, we saw that we often wish to compare two population means. In addition, it is often useful to compare two population variances. For example, in the bank customer waiting time situation of Example 9.1, we might compare the variance of the waiting times experienced under the

CHAPTER 10

[10]Source: World Wide Web, http://www.galluppoll.com/content/?id=33528pg-1. The Gallup Poll, December 30, 1999.

FIGURE **9.16**   *F* Distribution Curves and *F* Points

(a) The point F_α corresponding to df_1 and df_2 degrees of freedom

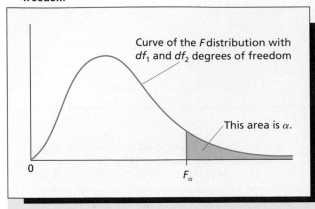

(b) The point $F_{0.05}$ corresponding to 4 and 7 degrees of freedom

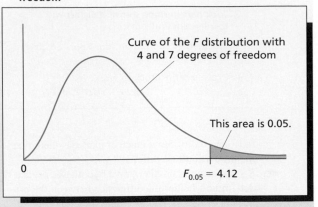

current and new systems. Or, as another example, we might wish to compare the variance of the coffee cup production obtained when using the Java method with that obtained when using the Joe method. Here the method that produces yields with the smaller variance is giving more consistent (or predictable) results.

If σ_1^2 and σ_2^2 are the population variances that we wish to compare, one approach is to test the null hypothesis

$$H_0:\ \sigma_1^2 = \sigma_2^2.$$

We might test H_0 versus an alternative hypothesis of, for instance,

$$H_a:\ \sigma_1^2 > \sigma_2^2.$$

Dividing by σ_2^2, we see that testing these hypotheses is equivalent to testing

$$H_0:\ \frac{\sigma_1^2}{\sigma_2^2} = 1 \qquad \text{versus} \qquad H_a:\ \frac{\sigma_1^2}{\sigma_2^2} > 1.$$

Intuitively, we would reject H_0 in favour of H_a if s_1^2/s_2^2 is significantly larger than 1. Here s_1^2 is the variance of a random sample of n_1 observations from the population with variance σ_1^2, and s_2^2 is the variance of a random sample of n_2 observations from the population with variance σ_2^2. To decide exactly how large s_1^2/s_2^2 must be in order to reject H_0, we need to consider the sampling distribution of s_1^2/s_2^2.[11]

It can be shown that, if the null hypothesis $H_0: \sigma_1^2/\sigma_2^2 = 1$ is true, then the population of all possible values of s_1^2/s_2^2 is described by what is called an **F distribution**. In general, as illustrated in Figure 9.16, the curve of the *F* distribution is skewed to the right. Moreover, the exact shape of this curve depends on two parameters that are called the **numerator degrees of freedom (denoted df_1)** and the **denominator degrees of freedom (denoted df_2)**. The values of df_1 and df_2 that describe the sampling distribution of s_1^2/s_2^2 are given in the following result:

---

[11]Note that we divide by σ_2^2 to form a null hypothesis of the form $H_0: \sigma_1^2/\sigma_2^2 = 1$ rather than subtracting σ_2^2 to form a null hypothesis of the form $H_0: \sigma_1^2 - \sigma_2^2 = 0$. This is because the population of all possible values of $s_1^2 - s_2^2$ has no known sampling distribution.

The Sampling Distribution of s_1^2/s_2^2

Suppose we randomly select independent samples from two normally distributed populations with variances σ_1^2 and σ_2^2. Then, if the null hypothesis H_0: $\sigma_1^2/\sigma_2^2 = 1$ is true, the population of all possible values of s_1^2/s_2^2 has an **F distribution** with $df_1 = (n_1 - 1)$ **numerator degrees of freedom** and $df_2 = (n_2 - 1)$ **denominator degrees of freedom**.

In order to use the F distribution, we employ an **F point**, which is denoted F_α. As illustrated in Figure 9.16(a), **F_α is the point on the horizontal axis under the curve of the F distribution that gives a right-hand tail area equal to α.** The value of F_α in a particular situation depends on the size of the right-hand tail area (the size of α) and on the numerator degrees of freedom (df_1) and the denominator degrees of freedom (df_2). Values of F_α are given in an **F table**. Tables A.5, A.6, A.7, and A.8 give values of $F_{0.10}$, $F_{0.05}$, $F_{0.025}$, and $F_{0.01}$, respectively. Each table tabulates values of F_α according to the appropriate numerator degrees of freedom (values listed across the top of the table) and the appropriate denominator degrees of freedom (values listed down the left side of the table). A portion of Table A.6, which gives values of $F_{0.05}$, is reproduced in this chapter as Table 9.7. For instance, suppose we wish to find the F point that gives a right-hand tail area of 0.05 under the curve of the F distribution with 4 numerator and 7 denominator degrees of freedom. To do this, we scan across the top of Table 9.7 until we find the column corresponding to 4 numerator degrees of freedom, and we scan down the left side of the table until we find the row corresponding to 7 denominator degrees of freedom. The table entry in this column and row is the desired F point. We find that the $F_{0.05}$ point is 4.12 (see Figure 9.16(b)).

We now present the procedure for testing the equality of two population variances when the alternative hypothesis is one-tailed:

Testing the Equality of Population Variances: Testing H_0: $\sigma_1^2 = \sigma_2^2$ versus a One-Tailed Alternative Hypothesis

Suppose we randomly select independent samples from two normally distributed populations— populations 1 and 2. Let s_1^2 be the variance of the random sample of n_1 observations from population 1, and let s_2^2 be the variance of the random sample of n_2 observations from population 2.

1   In order to test H_0: $\sigma_1^2 = \sigma_2^2$ versus H_a: $\sigma_1^2 > \sigma_2^2$, define the test statistic

$$F = \frac{s_1^2}{s_2^2}$$

and define the corresponding p value to be the area to the right of F under the curve of the F distribution with $df_1 = n_1 - 1$ numerator degrees of freedom and $df_2 = n_2 - 1$ denominator degrees of freedom. We can reject H_0 at level of significance α if and only if
   a. $F > F_\alpha$ or, equivalently,
   b. p value $< \alpha$.

Here F_α is based on $df_1 = n_1 - 1$ and $df_2 = n_2 - 1$ degrees of freedom.

2   In order to test H_0: $\sigma_1^2 = \sigma_2^2$ versus H_a: $\sigma_1^2 < \sigma_2^2$, define the test statistic

$$F = \frac{s_2^2}{s_1^2}$$

and define the corresponding p value to be the area to the right of F under the curve of the F distribution with $df_1 = n_2 - 1$ numerator degrees of freedom and $df_2 = n_1 - 1$ denominator degrees of freedom. We can reject H_0 at level of significance α if and only if
   a. $F > F_\alpha$ or, equivalently,
   b. p value $< \alpha$.

Here F_α is based on $df_1 = n_2 - 1$ and $df_2 = n_1 - 1$ degrees of freedom.

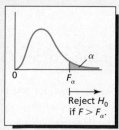

Reject H_0
if $F > F_\alpha$.

TABLE **9.7**   **A Portion of an *F* Table: Values of $F_{0.05}$**

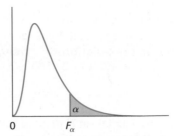

df_1	Numerator Degrees of Freedom, df_1								
df_2	1	2	3	4	5	6	7	8	9
1	161.4	199.5	215.7	224.6	230.2	234.0	236.8	238.9	240.5
2	18.51	19.00	19.16	19.25	19.30	19.33	19.35	19.37	19.38
3	10.13	9.55	9.28	9.12	9.01	8.94	8.89	8.85	8.81
4	7.71	6.94	6.59	6.39	6.26	6.16	6.09	6.04	6.00
5	6.61	5.79	5.41	5.19	5.05	4.95	4.88	4.82	4.77
6	5.99	5.14	4.76	4.53	4.39	4.28	4.21	4.15	4.10
7	5.59	4.71	4.25	4.12	3.97	3.87	3.79	3.73	3.68
8	5.32	4.46	4.07	3.84	3.69	3.58	3.50	3.44	3.39
9	5.12	4.26	3.86	3.63	3.48	3.37	3.29	3.23	3.18
10	4.96	4.10	3.71	3.48	3.33	3.22	3.14	3.07	3.02
11	4.84	3.98	3.59	3.36	3.20	3.09	3.01	2.95	2.90
12	4.75	3.89	3.49	3.26	3.11	3.00	2.91	2.85	2.80
13	4.67	3.81	3.41	3.18	3.03	2.92	2.83	2.77	2.71
14	4.60	3.74	3.34	3.11	2.96	2.85	2.76	2.70	2.65
15	4.54	3.68	3.29	3.06	2.90	2.79	2.71	2.64	2.59
16	4.49	3.63	3.24	3.01	2.85	2.74	2.66	2.59	2.54
17	4.45	3.59	3.20	2.96	2.81	2.70	2.61	2.55	2.49
18	4.41	3.55	3.16	2.93	2.77	2.66	2.58	2.51	2.46
19	4.38	3.52	3.13	2.90	2.74	2.63	2.54	2.48	2.42
20	4.35	3.49	3.10	2.87	2.71	2.60	2.51	2.45	2.39
21	4.32	3.47	3.07	2.84	2.68	2.57	2.49	2.42	2.37
22	4.30	3.44	3.05	2.82	2.66	2.55	2.46	2.40	2.34
23	4.28	3.42	3.03	2.80	2.64	2.53	2.44	2.37	2.32
24	4.26	3.40	3.01	2.78	2.62	2.51	2.42	2.36	2.30
25	4.24	3.39	2.99	2.76	2.60	2.49	2.40	2.34	2.28
26	4.23	3.37	2.98	2.74	2.59	2.47	2.39	2.32	2.27
27	4.21	3.35	2.96	2.73	2.57	2.46	2.37	2.31	2.25
28	4.20	3.34	2.95	2.71	2.56	2.45	2.36	2.29	2.24
29	4.18	3.33	2.93	2.70	2.55	2.43	2.35	2.28	2.22
30	4.17	3.32	2.92	2.69	2.53	2.42	2.33	2.27	2.21
40	4.08	3.23	2.84	2.61	2.45	2.34	2.25	2.18	2.12
60	4.00	3.15	2.76	2.53	2.37	2.25	2.17	2.10	2.04
120	3.92	3.07	2.68	2.45	2.29	2.17	2.09	2.02	1.96
∞	3.84	3.00	2.60	2.37	2.21	2.10	2.01	1.94	1.88

Denominator Degrees of Freedom, df_2

Source: "Tables of percentage points of the inverted beta (*F*) distribution," by M. Merrington and C. M. Thompson, *Biometrika*, Vol. 33 (1943), pp. 73–88. Reproduced by permission of Oxford University Press and *Biometrika* trustees.

Example 9.13   The Coffee Cup Case

Again consider the production comparison situation of Example 9.2, and suppose the production supervisor wishes to use the sample data in Table 9.1 to determine whether σ_1^2, the variance of the average production yields obtained by using the Java method, is smaller than σ_2^2, the variance of the yields obtained by using the Joe method. To do this, the supervisor will test the null hypothesis

$$H_0:\ \sigma_1^2 = \sigma_2^2,$$

FIGURE **9.17**   Excel Output for Testing H_0: $\sigma_1^2 = \sigma_2^2$ in the Coffee Cup Case

F-Test Two-Sample for Variances

	Joe	Java
Mean	750.2	811
Variance	484.2	386
Observations	5	5
df	4	4
F	1.254404	
P(F<=f) one-tail	0.415724	
F Critical one-tail	6.388234	

which says the methods produce yields with the same amount of variability, versus the alternative hypothesis

$$H_a: \sigma_1^2 < \sigma_2^2 \quad \text{or, equivalently,} \quad H_a: \sigma_2^2 > \sigma_1^2,$$

which says Java produces yields that are less variable (that is, more consistent) than the yields produced by Joe. Recall from Table 9.1 that $n_1 = n_2 = 5$, $s_1^2 = 386$, and $s_2^2 = 484.2$. In order to test H_0 versus H_a, we compute the test statistic

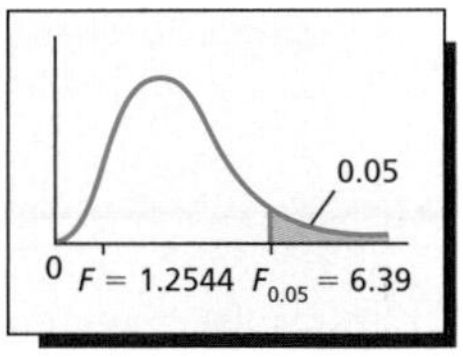

$$F = \frac{s_2^2}{s_1^2} = \frac{484.2}{386} = 1.2544,$$

and we compare this value with F_α based on $df_1 = n_2 - 1 = 5 - 1 = 4$ numerator degrees of freedom and $df_2 = n_1 - 1 = 5 - 1 = 4$ denominator degrees of freedom. If we test H_0 versus H_a at the 0.05 level of significance, then Table 9.7 tells us that when $df_1 = 4$ and $df_2 = 4$, we have $F_{0.05} = 6.39$. Because $F = 1.2544$ is not greater than $F_{0.05} = 6.39$, we cannot reject H_0 at the 0.05 level of significance. That is, at the 0.05 level of significance we cannot conclude that σ_1^2 is less than σ_2^2. This says that there is little evidence that Java produces yields that are more consistent than the yields produced by Joe.

The p value for testing H_0 versus H_a is the area to the right of $F = 1.2544$ under the curve of the F distribution with 4 numerator degrees of freedom and 4 denominator degrees of freedom. The Excel output in Figure 9.17 tells us that this p value equals 0.415724. Since this p value is large, we have little evidence to support rejecting H_0 in favour of H_a. That is, there is little evidence that Java produces yields that are more consistent than the yields produced by Joe.

Again considering the coffee cup comparison case, suppose we wish to test

$$H_0: \sigma_1^2 = \sigma_2^2 \quad \text{versus} \quad H_a: \sigma_1^2 \neq \sigma_2^2.$$

One way to carry out this test is to compute

$$F = \frac{s_1^2}{s_2^2} = \frac{386}{484.2} = 0.797.$$

As illustrated in Figure 9.18, if we set $\alpha = 0.10$, we compare F with the rejection points $F_{0.95}$ and $F_{0.05}$ under the curve of the F distribution with $n_1 - 1 = 4$ numerator and $n_2 - 1 = 4$ denominator degrees of freedom. We see that we can easily find the appropriate upper-tail rejection point to be $F_{0.05} = 6.39$. In order to find the lower-tail rejection point, $F_{0.95}$, we use the following relationship:

$$\frac{F_{(1-\alpha)} \text{ with } df_1 \text{ numerator and } df_2 \text{ denominator degrees of freedom}}{= \frac{1}{F_\alpha \text{ with } df_2 \text{ numerator and } df_1 \text{ denominator degrees of freedom}}.}$$

This says that for the F curve with 4 numerator and 4 denominator degrees of freedom, $F_{(1-0.05)} = F_{0.95} = 1/F_{0.05} = 1/6.39 = 0.1565$. Therefore, because $F = 0.797$ is not greater than

FIGURE **9.18**   Rejection Points for Testing $H_0: \sigma_1^2 = \sigma_2^2$ versus $H_a: \sigma_1^2 \neq \sigma_2^2$ with $\alpha = 0.10$

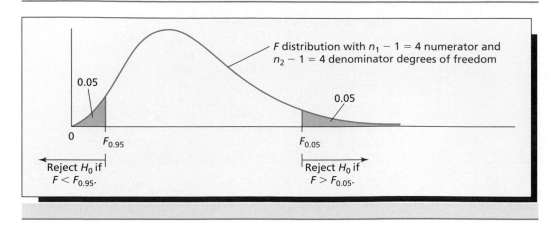

$F_{0.05} = 6.39$ and $F = 0.797$ is not less than $F_{0.95} = 0.1565$, we cannot reject H_0 in favour of H_a at the 0.10 level of significance.

Although we can calculate the lower-tail rejection point for this hypothesis test as just illustrated, it is common practice to compute the test statistic F so that its value is always greater than 1. This means that we will always compare F with the upper-tail rejection point when carrying out the test. This can be done by always calculating F to be the larger of s_1^2 and s_2^2 divided by the smaller of s_1^2 and s_2^2. We obtain the following result:

Testing the Equality of Population Variances: Testing $H_0: \sigma_1^2 = \sigma_2^2$ versus $H_a: \sigma_1^2 \neq \sigma_2^2$

Suppose we randomly select independent samples from two normally distributed populations and define all notation as in the previous box. Then, in order to test $H_0: \sigma_1^2 = \sigma_2^2$ versus $H_a: \sigma_1^2 \neq \sigma_2^2$, define the test statistic

$$F = \frac{\text{the larger of } s_1^2 \text{ and } s_2^2}{\text{the smaller of } s_1^2 \text{ and } s_2^2}$$

and let

$df_1 = \{$the size of the sample with the largest variance$\} - 1,$

$df_2 = \{$the size of the sample with the smallest variance$\} - 1.$

Also define the corresponding p value to be twice the area to the right of F under the curve of the F distribution with df_1 numerator degrees of freedom and df_2 denominator degrees of freedom.

We can reject H_0 at level of significance α if and only if

1   $F > F_{\alpha/2}$ or, equivalently,

2   p value $< \alpha$.

Here $F_{\alpha/2}$ is based on df_1 and df_2 degrees of freedom.

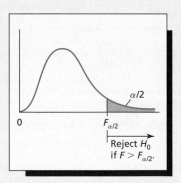

Example 9.14   The Coffee Cup Case

In the coffee cup comparison situation, we can reject $H_0: \sigma_1^2 = \sigma_2^2$ in favour of $H_a: \sigma_1^2 \neq \sigma_2^2$ at the 0.05 level of significance if

$$F = \frac{\text{the larger of } s_1^2 \text{ and } s_2^2}{\text{the smaller of } s_1^2 \text{ and } s_2^2} = \frac{484.2}{386} = 1.2544$$

is greater than $F_{\alpha/2} = F_{0.05/2} = F_{0.025}$. Here the degrees of freedom are

$$df_1 = \{\text{the size of the sample with the largest variance}\} - 1$$
$$= n_2 - 1 = 5 - 1 = 4$$

and

$$df_2 = \{\text{the size of the sample with the smallest variance}\} - 1$$
$$= n_1 - 1 = 5 - 1 = 4.$$

Table A.7 tells us that the appropriate $F_{0.025}$ point equals 9.60. Because $F = 1.2544$ is not greater than 9.60, we cannot reject H_0 at the 0.05 level of significance and thus we have little evidence that the consistencies of the yields produced by Java and Joe differ.

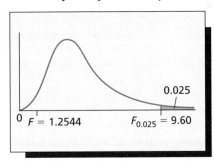

It has been suggested that the F test of $H_0: \sigma_1^2 = \sigma_2^2$ be used to choose between the equal variances and unequal variances t-based procedures when comparing two means. Certainly the F test is one approach to making this choice. However, studies have shown that the validity of the F test is very sensitive to violations of the normality assumption—much more sensitive, in fact, than the equal variances procedure is to violations of the equal variances assumption. While opinions vary, some statisticians believe that this is a serious problem and that the F test should never be used to choose between the equal variances and unequal variances procedures. Others feel that performing the test for this purpose is reasonable if the test's limitations are kept in mind.

As an example for those who believe that using the F test is reasonable, we found in Example 9.14 that we do not reject $H_0: \sigma_1^2 = \sigma_2^2$ at the 0.05 level of significance in the context of the coffee cup comparison situation. Further, the p value related to the F test, which equals 0.831, tells us that there is little evidence to suggest that the population variances differ. It follows that it might be reasonable to compare the mean yields of the production methods by using the equal variances procedure.

Exercises for Section 9.10

CONCEPTS

9.78 Explain what population is described by the sampling distribution of s_1^2/s_2^2.

9.79 Intuitively explain why a value of s_1^2/s_2^2 that is substantially greater than 1 provides evidence that σ_1^2 is not equal to σ_2^2.

METHODS AND APPLICATIONS

9.80 Use Table 9.7 to find the $F_{0.05}$ point for each of the following:
  a. $df_1 = 3$ numerator degrees of freedom and $df_2 = 14$ denominator degrees of freedom.
  b. $df_1 = 6$ and $df_2 = 10$.

  c. $df_1 = 2$ and $df_2 = 22$.
  d. $df_1 = 7$ and $df_2 = 5$.

9.81 Use Tables A.5, A.6, A.7, and A.8 to find the following F_α points:
  a. $F_{0.10}$ with $df_1 = 4$ numerator degrees of freedom and $df_2 = 7$ denominator degrees of freedom.
  b. $F_{0.01}$ with $df_1 = 3$ and $df_2 = 25$.
  c. $F_{0.025}$ with $df_1 = 7$ and $df_2 = 17$.
  d. $F_{0.05}$ with $df_1 = 9$ and $df_2 = 3$.

9.82 Suppose two independent random samples of sizes $n_1 = 9$ and $n_2 = 7$ that have been taken from two normally distributed populations with variances σ_1^2 and σ_2^2 give sample variances of $s_1^2 = 100$ and $s_2^2 = 20$.

a. Test H_0: $\sigma_1^2 = \sigma_2^2$ versus H_a: $\sigma_1^2 \neq \sigma_2^2$ with $\alpha = 0.05$. What do you conclude?

b. Test H_0: $\sigma_1^2 \leq \sigma_2^2$ versus H_a: $\sigma_1^2 > \sigma_2^2$ with $\alpha = 0.05$. What do you conclude?

9.83 Suppose two independent random samples of sizes $n_1 = 5$ and $n_2 = 16$ that have been taken from two normally distributed populations with variances σ_1^2 and σ_2^2 give sample standard deviations of $s_1 = 5$ and $s_2 = 9$.

a. Test H_0: $\sigma_1^2 = \sigma_2^2$ versus H_a: $\sigma_1^2 \neq \sigma_2^2$ with $\alpha = 0.05$. What do you conclude?

b. Test H_0: $\sigma_1^2 \geq \sigma_2^2$ versus H_a: $\sigma_1^2 < \sigma_2^2$ with $\alpha = 0.01$. What do you conclude?

9.84 Consider the situation of Exercise 9.19 (page 279). Use the sample information to test H_0: $\sigma_1^2 = \sigma_2^2$ versus H_a: $\sigma_1^2 \neq \sigma_2^2$ with $\alpha = 0.05$. Based on this test, does it make sense to believe that the unequal variances procedure is appropriate? Explain.

CHAPTER SUMMARY

We began this chapter by explaining how to compare two populations by using one-tailed and two-tailed confidence intervals. We discussed how to compare **two population means** by using **independent samples**. Here the measurements in one sample are not related to the measurements in the other sample. We saw that in the unlikely event that the population variances are known, a **z-based** confidence interval can be constructed. When these variances are unknown, **t-based** intervals are appropriate if the underlying populations are at least symmetric in nature. Both **equal variances** and **unequal variances t-based confidence intervals** were discussed. We learned that, because it can be difficult to compare the population variances, many statisticians believe that it is almost always best to use the unequal variances procedure, unless of course you have prior knowledge that the underlying variances are indeed equal.

Sometimes samples are not independent. We learned that one such case is what is called a **paired difference experiment**. In these types of experiments, we would obtain two different measurements on the same sample units, and we first learned that we can compare two population means by using a confidence interval using the differences between the pairs of measurements. We next explained how to compare **two population proportions** from **large, independent samples** using a confidence interval.

The second part of this chapter was devoted to hypothesis testing. We discussed how to conduct hypothesis tests under each scenario described above, using various **t tests** and **z tests**. We concluded the chapter by discussing how to compare **two population variances** by using independent samples, and we learned that this comparison is done by using a test based on the **F distribution**.

GLOSSARY OF TERMS

F distribution: A continuous probability curve with a shape that depends on two parameters—the numerator degrees of freedom, df_1, and the denominator degrees of freedom, df_2. (pages 306–307)

independent samples experiment: An experiment in which there is no relationship between the measurements in the different samples. (pages 273, 274)

paired difference experiment: An experiment in which two different measurements are taken on the same units and inferences are made using the differences between the pairs of measurements. (pages 280, 282)

sampling distribution of $\hat{p}_1 - \hat{p}_2$: The probability distribution that describes the population of all possible values of $\hat{p}_1 - \hat{p}_2$, where $\hat{p}_1$ is the sample proportion for a random sample taken

from one population and $\hat{p}_2$ is the sample proportion for a random sample taken from a second population. (page 284)

sampling distribution of s_1^2/s_2^2: The probability distribution that describes the population of all possible values of s_1^2/s_2^2, where s_1^2 is the sample variance of a random sample taken from one population and s_2^2 is the sample variance of a random sample taken from a second population. (page 307)

sampling distribution of $\bar{x}_1 - \bar{x}_2$: The probability distribution that describes the population of all possible values of $\bar{x}_1 - \bar{x}_2$, where $\bar{x}_1$ is the sample mean of a random sample taken from one population and $\bar{x}_2$ is the sample mean of a random sample taken from a second population. (page 273)

IMPORTANT FORMULAS AND TESTS

Sampling distribution of $\bar{x}_1 - \bar{x}_2$ (independent random samples): page 273

z-based confidence interval for $\mu_1 - \mu_2$: page 273

t-based confidence interval for $\mu_1 - \mu_2$ when $\sigma_1^2 = \sigma_2^2$: page 276

t-based confidence intervals for $\mu_1 - \mu_2$: page 277

Confidence interval for μ_d: page 281

Sampling distribution of $\hat{p}_1 - \hat{p}_2$ (independent random samples): page 284

Large sample confidence interval for $p_1 - p_2$: page 285

z test about $\mu_1 - \mu_2$: pages 287, 290

t test about $\mu_1 - \mu_2$ when $\sigma_1^2 = \sigma_2^2$: pages 291, 297

t test about $\mu_1 - \mu_2$ when $\sigma_1^2 \neq \sigma_2^2$: pages 292, 298

A hypothesis test about μ_d: pages 294, 298

Large sample hypothesis test about $p_1 - p_2$: page 303

Sampling distribution of s_1^2/s_2^2 (independent random samples): page 307

A hypothesis test about the equality of σ_1^2 and σ_2^2: pages 307, 310

SUPPLEMENTARY EXERCISES

9.85 In its February 2, 1998, issue, *Fortune* magazine published the results of a Yankelovich Partners survey of 600 adults that investigated their ideas about marriage, divorce, and the contributions of the corporate wife. The survey results are shown in Figure 9.19. For each statement in the figure, the proportions of men and women who agreed with the statement are given. Assume that the survey results were obtained from independent random samples of 300 men and 300 women.

a. For each statement, carry out a hypothesis test that tests the equality of the population proportions of men and women who agree with the statement. Use α equal to 0.10, 0.05, 0.01, and 0.001. How much evidence is there that the population proportions of men and women who agree with each statement differ?

b. For each statement, calculate a 95 percent confidence interval for the difference between the population proportion of men who agree with the statement and the population proportion of women who agree with the statement. Use the interval to help assess whether you feel that the difference between population proportions has practical significance.

Exercises 9.86 and 9.87 deal with the following situation:

In an article in the *Journal of Retailing*, Kumar, Kerwin, and Pereira study factors affecting merger and acquisition activity in retailing by comparing "target firms" and "bidder firms" with respect to several financial and marketing-related variables. If we consider two of the financial variables included in the study, suppose a random sample of 36 target firms gives a mean earnings per share of $1.52 with a standard deviation of $0.92, and that this sample gives a mean debt-to-equity ratio of 1.66 with a standard deviation of 0.82. Furthermore, an independent random sample of 36 bidder firms gives a mean earnings per share of $1.20 with a standard deviation of $0.84, and this sample gives a mean debt-to-equity ratio of 1.58 with a standard deviation of 0.81.

9.86 a. Set up the null and alternative hypotheses needed to test whether the mean earnings per share for all "target firms" differs from the mean earnings per share for all "bidder firms." Test these hypotheses at the 0.10, 0.05, 0.01, and 0.001 levels of significance. How much evidence is there that these means differ? Explain.

b. Calculate a 95 percent confidence interval for the difference between the mean earnings per share for target firms and bidder firms. Interpret the interval.

9.87 a. Set up the null and alternative hypotheses needed to test whether the mean debt-to-equity ratio for all target firms differs from the mean debt-to-equity ratio for all bidder firms. Test these hypotheses at the 0.10, 0.05, 0.01, and 0.001 levels of significance. How much evidence is there that these means differ? Explain.

b. Calculate a 95 percent confidence interval for the difference between the mean debt-to-equity ratios for target firms and bidder firms. Interpret the interval.

FIGURE **9.19** The Results of a Yankelovich Partners Survey of 600 Adults on Marriage, Divorce, and the Contributions of the Corporate Wife (All Respondents with Income $50,000 or More)

People were magnanimous on the general proposition:
- In a divorce in a long-term marriage where the husband works outside the home and the wife is not employed for pay, the wife should be entitled to half the assets accumulated during the marriage.
  93% of women agree
  85% of men agree

But when we got to the goodies, a gender gap began to appear . . .
- The pension accumulated during the marriage should be split evenly.
  80% of women agree
  68% of men agree
- Stock options granted during the marriage should be split evenly.
  77% of women agree
  62% of men agree

. . . and turned into a chasm over the issue of how important a stay-at-home wife is to a husband's success.
- Managing the household and child rearing are extremely important to a husband's success.
  57% of women agree
  41% of men agree
- A corporate wife who also must travel, entertain, and act as a sounding board is extremely important to the success of a high-level business executive.
  51% of women agree
  28% of men agree
- The lifestyle of a corporate wife is more of a job than a luxury.
  73% of women agree
  57% of men agree

Source: Reprinted from the February 2, 1998, issue of *Fortune*. Copyright © 1998 Time, Inc. Reprinted by permission.

FIGURE **9.20**   MINITAB Output for Exercise 9.88

Paired T-Test and CI: Before911, After911

```
Paired T for Before911 - After911
              N      Mean    StDev   SE Mean
Before911    12   117.333   26.976    7.787
After911     12    87.583   25.518    7.366
Difference   12   29.7500  10.3056   2.9750

T-Test of mean difference = 0 (vs > 0): T-Value = 10.00   P-Value = 0.000
```

c. Based on the results of this exercise and Exercise 9.86, does a firm's earnings per share or the firm's debt-to-equity ratio seem to have the most influence on whether a firm will be a target or a bidder? Explain.

9.88 What impact did the September 11, 2001, terrorist attack have on U.S. airline demand? An analysis was conducted by Ito and Lee, "Assessing the impact of the September 11 terrorist attacks on U.S. airline demand," in the *Journal of Economics and Business* (January–February 2005). They found a negative short-term effect of over 30 percent and an ongoing negative impact of over 7 percent. Suppose that we wish to test the impact by taking a random sample of 12 airline routes before and after September 11, 2001. Passenger miles (in millions) for the same routes were tracked for the 12 months prior to and the 12 months immediately following September 11, 2001. Assume that the population of all possible paired differences is normally distributed.

a. Set up the null and alternative hypotheses needed to determine whether there was a reduction in mean airline passenger demand.

b. In Figure 9.20, we present the MINITAB output for the paired differences test. Use the output and rejection points to test the hypotheses at the 0.10, 0.05, and 0.01 levels of significance. Has the true mean airline demand been reduced?

c. Use the *p* value to test the hypotheses at the 0.10, 0.05, and 0.01 levels of significance. How much evidence is there against the null hypothesis?

9.89 In the book *Essentials of Marketing Research*, Dillon, Madden, and Firtle discuss evaluating the effectiveness of a test coupon. Samples of 500 test coupons and 500 control coupons were randomly delivered to shoppers. The results indicated that 35 of the 500 control coupons were redeemed, while 50 of the 500 test coupons were redeemed.

a. In order to consider the test coupon for use, the marketing research organization required that the proportion of all shoppers who would redeem the test coupon be statistically shown to be greater than the proportion of all shoppers who would redeem the control coupon. Assuming that the two samples of shoppers are independent, carry out a hypothesis test at the 0.01 level of significance that will show whether this requirement is met by the test coupon. Explain your conclusion.

b. Use the sample data to find a point estimate and a 95 percent interval estimate of the difference between the proportions of all shoppers who would redeem the test coupon and the control coupon. What does this interval say about whether the test coupon should be considered for use? Explain.

c. Carry out the test of part a at the 0.10 level of significance. What do you conclude? Is your result statistically significant? Compute a 90 percent interval estimate instead of the 95 percent interval estimate of part b. Based on the interval estimate, do you feel that this result is practically important? Explain.

9.90 A marketing manager wishes to compare the mean prices charged for two brands of CD players. The manager conducts a random survey of retail outlets and obtains independent random samples of prices with the following results:

	Onkyo	JVC
Sample mean, $\bar{x}$	$189	$145
Sample standard deviation, s	$ 12	$ 10
Sample size	6	12

Assume normality and equal variances.

a. Use an appropriate hypothesis test to determine whether the mean prices for the two brands differ. How much evidence is there that the mean prices differ?

b. Use an appropriate 95 percent confidence interval to estimate the difference between the mean prices of the two brands of CD players. Do you think that the difference has practical importance?

c. Use an appropriate hypothesis test to provide evidence supporting the claim that the mean price of the Onkyo CD player is more than $30 higher than the mean price for the JVC CD player. Set α equal to 0.05.

9.91 Consider the situation of Exercise 9.90. Use the sample information to test $H_0: \sigma_1^2 = \sigma_2^2$ versus $H_a: \sigma_1^2 \neq \sigma_2^2$ with $\alpha = 0.05$. Based on this test, does it make sense to use the equal variances procedure? Explain.

9.92   INTERNET EXERCISE

Statistics Canada uses what they refer to as "Seasonal Adjustments" when determining the unemployment rates in Canada as a whole and for the provinces. Go to the Statistics Canada Web site (http://www.statcan.ca).

a. Determine what is meant by "seasonal adjustment."

b. Compare and contrast the employment rates in Alberta and Manitoba. What are the differences and why do you think these differences exist?

c. Compare and contrast the unemployment rates in your province and the national average. What are the differences and why do you think these differences exist?

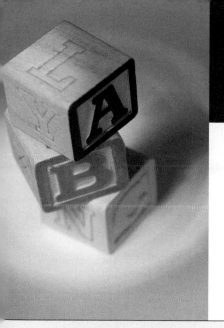

Experimental Design and Analysis of Variance

LEARNING OBJECTIVES

After reading this chapter, you should be able to

- define an independent variable (IV) and a dependent variable (DV)

- explain the difference between an experiment and an observational study

- compare one-way ANOVA designs with two-way ANOVA designs

- explain the term *randomized block design*

- list the statistics that appear in an ANOVA results table and understand how they are computed

- describe how pairwise comparisons are conducted

CHAPTER OUTLINE

10.1 Basic Concepts of Experimental Design

10.2 One-Way Analysis of Variance

10.3 The Randomized Block Design

10.4 Two-Way Analysis of Variance

In Chapter 9, we learned that business improvement often involves making **comparisons**. In that chapter, we presented several confidence intervals and several hypothesis-testing procedures for comparing two population means. However, business improvement often requires that we compare more than two means. For instance, we might compare the mean sales obtained by using three different advertising campaigns in order to improve a company's marketing process. Or, we might compare the mean production output obtained by using four different manufacturing process designs to improve productivity.

The Training Method Experiment Case. A camera manufacturer wants to improve the efficiency of packing by individuals (in terms of number of boxes packed per hour) by testing various training methods. The company uses **one-way ANOVA** to compare the effects of three different training methods to find the method that most increases packing efficiency.

The Commercial Response Case. Firms that run commercials on television want to make the best use of their advertising dollars. In this case, researchers use **one-way**

In this chapter, we extend the methods presented in Chapter 9 by considering statistical procedures for **comparing two or more means**. Each of the methods we discuss is called an **analysis of variance (ANOVA)** procedure. We also present some basic concepts of **experimental design**, which involves deciding how to collect data in a way that allows us to most effectively compare population means.

We explain the methods of this chapter in the context of four cases:

ANOVA to compare the effects of varying program content on a viewer's ability to recall brand names after watching TV commercials.

The Defective Cardboard Box Case. A paper company performs an experiment to investigate the effects of four production methods on the number of defective cardboard boxes produced in an hour. The company uses a **randomized block ANOVA** to determine which production method yields the smallest mean number of defective boxes.

The Shelf Display Case. A commercial bakery supplies many supermarkets. In order to improve the effectiveness of its supermarket shelf displays, the company wishes to compare the effects of shelf display height (bottom, mid- dle, or top) and width (regular or wide) on monthly de- mand. The bakery employs **two-way ANOVA** to find the display height and width combination that produces the highest monthly demand.

10.1 Basic Concepts of Experimental Design

In many statistical studies, researchers are interested in how a **factor** (the **independent variable** or **IV**) influences responses given by participants (the response measured is called the **dependent variable** or **DV**).[1] For example, a marketing company may be interested in the effects of a novel's cover on the likelihood that the novel will be purchased. The variable manipulated (cover appear- ance) is the independent variable and the self-reported likelihood that the individual would buy the book is the dependent variable. If we cannot control the factor(s) being studied, we say that the data obtained are **observational**. For example, suppose that in order to study how the size of a home re- lates to the sale price of the home, a real estate agent randomly selects 50 recently sold homes and records the sizes and sale prices of these homes. Because the real estate agent cannot control the sizes of the randomly selected homes, we say that the data are observational.

If we can control the factors being studied, we say that the data are **experimental**. Furthermore, in this case the values, or **levels**, of the factor (or combination of factors) are called **treatments**. The purpose of most experiments is **to compare and estimate the effects of the different treatments (IVs) on the response variable (DV)**. For example, suppose that an oil company wishes to study how three different gasoline types (A, B, and C) affect the fuel efficiency (L/100 km) obtained by a popular midsized automobile model. Here the response variable is fuel efficiency, and the company will study a single factor—gasoline type. Since the oil company can control which gasoline type is used in the midsized automobile, the data that it will collect are experimental. Furthermore, the treatments—the levels of the factor gasoline type—are gasoline types A, B, and C. This type of experimental design is also described as being a 1×3 design because there is one factor or IV (gasoline type) with three levels. The model's "dimensions" are given in the notation in that there is one row and three columns:

Gas A	Gas B	Gas C
x_1 L/100 km	x_2 L/100 km	x_3 L/100 km

In order to collect data in an experiment, the different treatments are assigned to objects (people, cars, animals, or the like) that are called **experimental units**. For example, in the fuel efficiency situation, gasoline types A, B, and C will be compared by conducting fuel ef- ficiency tests using a midsized automobile. The automobiles used in the tests are the experi- mental units.

In general, when a treatment is applied to more than one experimental unit, it is said to be **replicated**. Furthermore, when the analyst controls the treatments employed and how they are applied to the experimental units, a **designed experiment** is being carried out. A commonly used, simple experimental design is called the **completely randomized experimental design**.

In a **completely randomized experimental design**, independent random samples of experi- mental units are assigned to the treatments.

---

[1]The independent variable is called "independent" because in an experimental condition, the independent variable is the one that is manipulated by the experimenter and is therefore independent of what the subject (or participant in the study) does. The participant responses to the conditions set up by the experimenter are then termed as being "dependent" on the condition under which the participant was placed in the experiment.

Suppose we assign three experimental units to each of five treatments. We can achieve a completely randomized experimental design by assigning experimental units to treatments as follows. First, randomly select three experimental units and assign them to the first treatment. Next, randomly select three **different** experimental units from those remaining and assign them to the second treatment. That is, select these units from those not assigned to the first treatment. Third, randomly select three **different** experimental units from those not assigned to either the first or the second treatment. Assign these experimental units to the third treatment. Continue this procedure until the required number of experimental units have been assigned to each treatment.[2]

Once experimental units have been assigned to treatments, a value of the response variable is observed for each experimental unit. Thus, we obtain a **sample** of values of the response variable for each treatment. When we employ a completely randomized experimental design, we assume that each sample has been randomly selected from the population of all values of the response variable that could potentially be observed when using its particular treatment. We also assume that the different samples of response variable values are **independent** of each other. This is usually reasonable because the completely randomized design ensures that each different sample results from **different measurements** being taken on **different experimental units**. Thus, we sometimes say that we are conducting an **independent samples experiment**.

Example 10.1 Training Method Experiment Case

Great White North Cameras wants to increase the efficiency of their packers in terms of the number of camera boxes packed per hour. Clark, a human resources (HR) employee, suggests that they conduct an independent two-group design comparing passive video training (in which people watch a video about how to improve their efficiency) to interactive training (in which people actually pack boxes while receiving feedback from a trainer). Maggie (another HR employee) suggests adding in a third group, for comparison, that receives the basic training already used in the company (which consists of a booklet with photos explaining where the camera parts should be packed in the box and in what order). Clark agrees that this third group provides an excellent group to compare the other training methods to and in some ways acts as a control group. So the HR department decides upon a completely randomized experimental design with three conditions in which the IV is the training condition (three levels) and the DV is the number of boxes an individual can pack per hour the day after receiving the training.

Fifteen new employees are randomly selected from the pool of newly hired employees of Great White North Cameras. Of the fifteen individuals, five are randomly selected for the video training condition, five for the interactive training condition, and five for the standard training condition (the control group). In the following, the notation x_{ij} is used to denote j boxes packed per hour after receiving training type i. The data obtained are given in Table 10.1 and represent

TABLE **10.1** The Training Method Data ● Training

Video (Group A)	Interactive (Group B)	Standard (Group C)	
$x_{A1} = 34.0$	$x_{B1} = 35.3$	$x_{C1} = 33.3$	
$x_{A2} = 35.0$	$x_{B2} = 36.5$	$x_{C2} = 34.0$	
$x_{A3} = 34.3$	$x_{B3} = 36.4$	$x_{C3} = 34.7$	
$x_{A4} = 35.5$	$x_{B4} = 37.0$	$x_{C4} = 33.0$	
$x_{A5} = 35.8$	$x_{B5} = 37.6$	$x_{C5} = 34.9$	

[2]This method of sampling is also known as "sampling without replacement." In experimental designs, it is ideal to have the same number of experimental units (subjects) in each condition. In addition, because the selection of experimental units is random, this means that each unit has an equal probability of being assigned to any of the treatment conditions.

the average numbers of boxes packed per hour. Examining the box plots shown next to the data, we see some evidence that the interactive training method (*B*) may result in the greatest efficiency in packing camera parts.[3]

Example 10.2 The Shelf Display Case

The Tastee Bakery Company supplies a bakery product to many supermarkets in a metropolitan area. The company wishes to study the effect of the shelf display height employed by the supermarkets on monthly sales (measured in cases of 10 units each) for this product. Shelf display height, the factor to be studied, has three levels—bottom (*B*), middle (*M*), and top (*T*)—which are the treatments. To compare these treatments, the bakery uses a completely randomized experimental design. For each shelf height, six supermarkets (the experimental units) of equal sales potential are randomly selected, and each supermarket displays the product using its assigned shelf height for a month.[4] At the end of the month, sales of the bakery product (the response variable) at the 18 participating stores are recorded, giving the data in Table 10.2. Here we assume that the set of sales amounts for each display height is a sample randomly selected from the population of all sales amounts that could be obtained (at supermarkets of the given sales potential) at that display height. Examining the box plots that are shown next to the sales data, we seem to have evidence that a middle display height gives the highest bakery product sales (which supports the marketing finding that products at eye level for an adult are purchased more often than are products at the top or the bottom of the shelf display).

TABLE 10.2 The Bakery Product Sales Data ● BakeSale

Bottom (*B*)	Shelf Display Height Middle (*M*)	Top (*T*)
58.2	73.0	52.4
53.7	78.1	49.7
55.8	75.4	50.9
55.7	76.2	54.0
52.5	78.4	52.1
58.9	82.1	49.9

Example 10.3 The Commercial Response Case

Advertising research indicates that when a television program is involving, individuals exposed to commercials tend to have difficulty recalling the names of the products advertised. Therefore, in order for companies to make the best use of their advertising dollars, it is important to show their most original and memorable commercials during involving programs.

In an article in the *Journal of Advertising Research*, Soldow and Principe studied the effect of program content on the response to commercials. Program content, the factor studied, has three levels—more involving programs, less involving programs, and no program

---

[3]All of the box plots presented in this chapter were obtained using MINITAB.

[4]Note that pure design individuals would state that this model is not a true experiment because the individuals shopping at the supermarkets are **not** randomly assigned to the conditions (in other words, people are not assigned to shop in a certain store). Equating the stores in terms of sales potential is advantageous, but it could be argued that any differences between stores could be due to uncontrollable factors (also called "third factors" or "nuisance variables"), such as unexpected construction near a store decreasing the number of shoppers. True experimentalists would then refer to this design as "quasi-experimental."

(that is, commercials only)—which are the treatments. To compare these treatments, Soldow and Principe employed a completely randomized experimental design. For each program content level, 29 people were randomly selected and exposed to commercials in that program content level. Then a brand recall score (measured on a continuous scale) was obtained for each person. The 29 brand recall scores for each program content level are assumed to be a sample randomly selected from the population of all brand recall scores for that program content level. For this experiment, the summary statistics are presented in the exercises of Section 10.2.

Exercises for Section 10.1

CONCEPTS

10.1 Define the terms *response variable*, *factor*, *treatments*, and *experimental units*.

10.2 What is a completely randomized experimental design?

METHODS AND APPLICATIONS

10.3 A study compared three different display panels for use by air traffic controllers. Each display panel was tested in a simulated emergency condition; 12 highly trained air traffic controllers took part in the study. Four controllers were randomly assigned to each display panel. The time (in seconds) needed to stabilize the emergency condition was recorded. The results of the study

are given in Table 10.3. For this situation, identify the response variable, factor of interest, treatments, and experimental units. ● Display

10.4 A consumer preference study compares the effects of three different bottle designs (*A*, *B*, and *C*) on sales of a popular fabric softener. A completely randomized design is employed. Specifically, 15 supermarkets of equal sales potential are selected, and 5 of these supermarkets are randomly assigned to each bottle design. The number of bottles sold in 24 hours at each supermarket is recorded. The data obtained are displayed in Table 10.4. For this situation, identify the response variable, factor of interest, treatments, and experimental units. ● BottleDes

TABLE 10.3 Display Panel Study Data ● Display   **TABLE 10.4** Bottle Design Study Data ● BottleDes

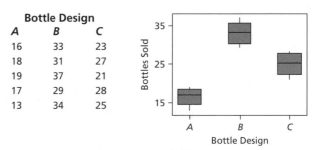

Display Panel		
A	*B*	*C*
21	24	40
27	21	36
24	18	35
26	19	32

Bottle Design		
A	*B*	*C*
16	33	23
18	31	27
19	37	21
17	29	28
13	34	25

10.2 One-Way Analysis of Variance

Suppose we wish to study the effects of p **treatments** (treatments $1, 2, \ldots, p$) on a **response variable**. For any particular treatment, say treatment i, we define μ_i and σ_i to be the mean and standard deviation of the population of all possible values of the response variable that could potentially be observed when using treatment i. Here we refer to μ_i as **treatment mean i**. The goal of **one-way ANOVA** is to estimate and compare the effects of the different treatments on the response variable. We do this by **estimating and comparing the treatment means** μ_1, $\mu_2, \ldots, \mu_p$. Here we assume that a sample has been randomly selected for each of the p treatments by employing a completely randomized experimental design. We let n_i denote the size of the sample that has been randomly selected for treatment i, and we let x_{ij} denote the jth value of the response variable that is observed when using treatment i. It then follows that the point estimate of μ_i is $\bar{x}_i$, the average of the sample of n_i values of the response variable observed when using treatment i. It further follows that the point estimate of σ_i is s_i, the standard deviation of the sample of n_i values of the response variable observed when using treatment i.

CHAPTER 12

Example 10.4 Training Method Experiment Case

Consider the training method case. We let μ_A, μ_B, and μ_C denote the means and σ_A, σ_B, and σ_C denote the standard deviations of the populations of all possible numbers of boxes packed per hour using training methods A (video), B (interactive), and C (reading only or control). To estimate these means and standard deviations, Great White North Cameras has employed a completely randomized experimental design and has obtained the samples of numbers of boxes packed per hour in Table 10.1. The means of these samples—$\bar{x}_A = 34.92$, $\bar{x}_B = 36.56$, and $\bar{x}_C = 33.98$—are the point estimates of μ_A, μ_B, and μ_C. The standard deviations of these samples—$s_A = 0.7662$, $s_B = 0.8503$, and $s_C = 0.8349$—are the point estimates of σ_A, σ_B, and σ_C. Using these point estimates, we will test to see whether there are any statistically significant differences between the treatment means μ_A, μ_B, and μ_C. If such differences exist, we will estimate their magnitudes. This will allow Great White North Cameras to judge whether these differences have practical importance.

The one-way ANOVA formulas allow us to test for significant differences between treatment means and to estimate differences between treatment means. The validity of these formulas requires that the following assumptions hold:

Assumptions for One-Way ANOVA

1 **Constant variance:** The p populations of values of the response variable associated with the treatments have equal variances.

2 **Normality:** The p populations of values of the response variable associated with the treatments all have normal distributions.

3 **Independence:** The samples of experimental units associated with the treatments are randomly selected, independent samples.

The one-way ANOVA results are not very sensitive to violations of the equal variances assumption. Studies have shown that this is particularly true when the sample sizes employed are equal (or nearly equal). Therefore, a good way to make sure that unequal variances will not be a problem is to take samples that are the same size. In addition, it is useful to compare the sample standard deviations $s_1, s_2, \ldots, s_p$ to see if they are reasonably equal. As a general rule, **the one-way ANOVA results will be approximately correct if the largest sample standard deviation is no more than twice the smallest sample standard deviation**. The variations of the samples can also be compared by constructing a box plot for each sample (as we have done for the box-packing data in Table 10.1). Several statistical texts also employ the sample variances to test the equality of the population variances (see Bowerman and O'Connell (1990) for two of these tests). However, these tests have some drawbacks—in particular, their results are very sensitive to violations of the normality assumption. Because of this, there is controversy over whether these tests should be performed.

The normality assumption says that each of the p populations is normally distributed. This assumption is not crucial. It has been shown that the one-way ANOVA results are approximately valid for mound-shaped distributions. It is useful to construct a box plot and/or a stem-and-leaf display for each sample. If the distributions are reasonably symmetric, and if there are no outliers, the ANOVA results can be trusted for sample sizes as small as 4 or 5. As an example, consider the box-packing experiment of Examples 10.1 and 10.4. The box plots of Table 10.1 suggest that the variability of the numbers of boxes packed per hour in each of the three samples is roughly the same. Furthermore, the sample standard deviations $s_A = 0.7662$, $s_B = 0.8503$, and $s_C = 0.8349$ are reasonably equal (the largest is not even close to twice the smallest). Therefore, it is reasonable to believe that the constant variance assumption is satisfied.

Moreover, because the sample sizes are the same, unequal variances would probably not be a serious problem anyway. Many small, independent factors influence packing efficiency, so the distributions of data points for training methods A, B, and C are probably mound-shaped. In addition, the box plots of Table 10.1 indicate that each distribution is roughly symmetric with no outliers. Thus, the normality assumption probably approximately holds. Finally, because Great White North Cameras has employed a completely randomized design, the independence assumption probably holds. This is because the packing rates in the different samples were obtained for **different** employees.

Testing for significant differences between treatment means   As a preliminary step in one-way ANOVA, we wish to determine whether there are any statistically significant differences between the treatment means $\mu_1, \mu_2, \ldots, \mu_p$. To do this, we test the null hypothesis

$$H_0: \mu_1 = \mu_2 = \cdots = \mu_p.$$

This hypothesis says that all the treatments have the same effect on the mean response. We test H_0 versus the alternative hypothesis

$$H_a: \text{at least two of } \mu_1, \mu_2, \ldots, \mu_p \text{ differ.}$$

This alternative says that at least two treatments have different effects on the mean response.

To carry out such a test, we compare what we call the **between-treatment variability** to the **within-treatment variability**. For instance, suppose we wish to study the effects of three training methods (A, B, and C) on mean packing efficiency, and consider Figure 10.1(a). This figure depicts three independent random samples of numbers of boxes packed per hour obtained using training methods A (video), B (interactive), and C (reading only or control). Observations obtained from training method A are plotted with blue dots (●), from method B with red dots (●), and from method C with green dots (●). Furthermore, the sample treatment means are labelled as "Method A mean," "Method B mean," and "Method C mean." We see that the variability of the sample treatment means—that is, the **between-treatment variability**—is not large compared to the variability within each sample (the **within-treatment variability**). In this case, the differences between the sample treatment means could quite easily be the result of sampling variation. Thus, we would not have sufficient evidence to reject

$$H_0: \mu_A = \mu_B = \mu_C.$$

FIGURE 10.1   **Comparing Between-Treatment Variability and Within-Treatment Variability**

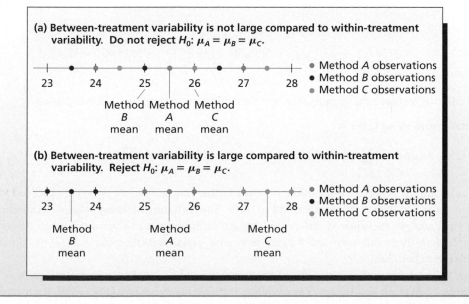

Next look at Figure 10.1(b), which depicts a different set of three independent random samples of packing efficiency. Here the variability of the sample treatment means (the between-treatment variability) is large compared to the variability within each sample. This would probably provide enough evidence to tell us to reject

$$H_0: \mu_A = \mu_B = \mu_C$$

in favour of

$$H_a: \text{at least two of } \mu_A, \mu_B, \text{ and } \mu_C \text{ differ.}$$

We would conclude that at least two of training methods A, B, and C have different effects on mean number of boxes packed per hour.

In order to numerically compare the between-treatment and within-treatment variability, we can define several **sums of squares** and **mean squares**. To begin, we define n to be the total number of experimental units employed in the one-way ANOVA, and we define $\bar{x}$ to be the overall mean of all observed values of the response variable. Then we define the following:

The **treatment sum of squares** is

$$SST = \sum_{i=1}^{p} n_i(\bar{x}_i - \bar{x})^2.$$

In order to compute the SST, we calculate the difference between each sample treatment mean $\bar{x}_i$ and the overall mean $\bar{x}$, we square each of these differences, we multiply each squared difference by the number of observations for that treatment, and we sum over all treatments. The SST measures the variability of the sample treatment means. For instance, if all the sample treatment means ($\bar{x}_i$ values) were equal, then the SST would be equal to 0. The more the $\bar{x}_i$ values vary, the larger will be the SST. In other words, the SST measures the amount of **between-treatment variability**.

As an example, consider the training method data in Table 10.1. In this experiment, we employ a total of

$$n = n_A + n_B + n_C = 5 + 5 + 5 = 15$$

experimental units. Furthermore, the overall mean of the 15 observed numbers of boxes packed per hour is

$$\bar{x} = \frac{34.0 + 35.0 + \cdots + 34.9}{15} = \frac{527.3}{15} = 35.153.$$

Then,

$$
\begin{aligned}
SST &= \sum_{i=A,B,C} n_i(\bar{x}_i - \bar{x})^2 \\
&= n_A(\bar{x}_A - \bar{x})^2 + n_B(\bar{x}_B - \bar{x})^2 + n_C(\bar{x}_C - \bar{x})^2 \\
&= 5(34.92 - 35.153)^2 + 5(36.56 - 35.153)^2 + 5(33.98 - 35.153)^2 \\
&= 17.0493.
\end{aligned}
$$

In order to measure the within-treatment variability, we define the following quantity:

The **error sum of squares** is

$$SSE = \sum_{j=1}^{n_1} (x_{1j} - \bar{x}_1)^2 + \sum_{j=1}^{n_2} (x_{2j} - \bar{x}_2)^2 + \cdots + \sum_{j=1}^{n_p} (x_{pj} - \bar{x}_p)^2.$$

Here x_{1j} is the jth observed value of the response in the first sample, x_{2j} is the jth observed value of the response in the second sample, and so forth. The formula above says that we compute the SSE by calculating the squared difference between each observed value of the response and its corresponding treatment mean and by summing these squared differences over all the observations in the experiment.

The SSE measures the variability of the observed values of the response variable around their respective treatment means. For example, if there were no variability within each sample, the *SSE* would be equal to 0. The more the values within the samples vary, the larger will be the *SSE*.

As an example, in the training method study, the sample treatment means are $\bar{x}_A = 34.92$, $\bar{x}_B = 36.56$, and $\bar{x}_C = 33.98$. It follows that

$$SSE = \sum_{j=1}^{n_A} (x_{Aj} - \bar{x}_A)^2 + \sum_{j=1}^{n_B} (x_{Bj} - \bar{x}_B)^2 + \sum_{j=1}^{n_C} (x_{Cj} - \bar{x}_C)^2$$

$$= [(34.0 - 34.92)^2 + (35.0 - 34.92)^2 + (34.3 - 34.92)^2 + (35.5 - 34.92)^2 + (35.8 - 34.92)^2]$$

$$+ [(35.3 - 36.56)^2 + (36.5 - 36.56)^2 + (36.4 - 36.56)^2 + (37.0 - 36.56)^2 + (37.6 - 36.56)^2]$$

$$+ [(33.3 - 33.98)^2 + (34.0 - 33.98)^2 + (34.7 - 33.98)^2 + (33.0 - 33.98)^2 + (34.9 - 33.98)^2]$$

$$= 8.028.$$

Finally, we define a sum of squares that measures the total amount of variability in the observed values of the response:

The **total sum of squares** is

$$SSTO = SST + SSE.$$

The variability in the observed values of the response must come from one of two sources—the between-treatment variability and the within-treatment variability. It follows that the *SSTO* equals the sum of the *SST* and the *SSE*. Therefore, the **SST and SSE are said to partition the SSTO**.

In the training method study, we see that

$$SSTO = SST + SSE = 17.0493 + 8.028 = 25.0773.$$

Using the *SST* and the *SSE*, we next define two **mean squares**:

The **treatment mean square** is

$$MST = \frac{SST}{p - 1}.$$

The **error mean square** is

$$MSE = \frac{SSE}{n - p}.$$

In order to decide whether there are any statistically significant differences between the treatment means, it makes sense to compare the amount of between-treatment variability to the amount of within-treatment variability. This comparison suggests the following *F* test:

An *F* Test for Differences between Treatment Means

Suppose that we wish to compare p treatment means $\mu_1, \mu_2, \ldots, \mu_p$ and consider testing

$H_0: \mu_1 = \mu_2 = \cdots = \mu_p$
(all treatment means are equal)

versus

H_a: at least two of $\mu_1, \mu_2, \ldots, \mu_p$ differ
(at least two treatment means differ).

Define the *F* statistic

$$F = \frac{MST}{MSE} = \frac{SST/(p - 1)}{SSE/(n - p)}$$

and its p value to be the area under the *F* curve with $p - 1$ and $n - p$ degrees of freedom to the right of *F*. We can reject H_0 in favour of H_a at level of significance α if either of the following equivalent conditions holds:

1 $F > F_\alpha$.   2 p value $< \alpha$.

Here the F_α point is based on $p - 1$ numerator and $n - p$ denominator degrees of freedom.

A large value of *F* results when the *SST*, which measures the between-treatment variability, is large compared to the *SSE*, which measures the within-treatment variability. If *F* is large enough, this implies that H_0 should be rejected. The rejection point F_α tells us when F is large enough to allow us to reject H_0 at level of significance α. When F is large, the associated p value is small. If this p value is less than α, we can reject H_0 at level of significance α.

Example 10.5 Training Method Experiment Case

From the data presented in Table 10.1, Great White North Cameras wishes to determine whether any of the training methods A, B, and C have different effects on the number of boxes packed per hour. That is, they are interested in whether or not there is a statistically significant difference between μ_A, μ_B, and μ_C. To do this, we test the null hypothesis

$$H_0: \mu_A = \mu_B = \mu_C,$$

which says that training methods A, B, and C have the same effects on mean packing efficiency. We test H_0 versus the alternative

$$H_a: \text{at least two of } \mu_A, \mu_B, \text{ and } \mu_C \text{ differ},$$

which says that at least two of training methods A, B, and C have different effects on mean packing efficiency.

Since we have previously computed the SST to be 17.0493 and the SSE to be 8.028, and because we are comparing $p = 3$ treatment means, we have

$$MST = \frac{SST}{p-1} = \frac{17.0493}{3-1} = 8.525$$

and

$$MSE = \frac{SSE}{n-p} = \frac{8.028}{15-3} = 0.669.$$

FIGURE 10.2 MINITAB and Excel Output of an ANOVA of the Training Method Data in Table 10.1

(a) The MINITAB output

```
One-way      ANOVA:  Method A,   Method B,   Method C           Tukey 95% Simultaneous
Source       DF       SS          MS          F         P        Confidence Intervals
Training Method  2 [1]  17.049 [4]  8.525 [7]  12.74 [9]  0.001 [10]
Error        12 [2]    8.028 [5]   0.669 [8]                    Method A subtracted from:
Total        14 [3]   25.077 [6]
                                   Individual 95%                          Lower    Centre   Upper
                                   CIs For Mean Based on Pooled StDev   Method B   0.2610  1.6400  3.0190
Level      N   Mean     StDev  ---+---------+---------+---------+------   Method C  -2.3190 -0.9400  0.439
Method A   5   34.920 [11]  0.766         (------*------)
Method B   5   36.560 [12]  0.850                    (------*-----)      Method B subtracted from:
Method C   5   33.980 [13]  0.835  (-----*------)                                  Lower    Centre   Upper
                                   ---+---------+---------+---------+------  Method C  -3.9590 -2.5800 -1.2010
Pooled StDev = 0.818                   33.6   34.8   36.0   37.2
```

(b) The Excel output

SUMMARY

Groups	Count	Sum	Average	Variance
Method A	5	174.6	34.92 [11]	0.587
Method B	5	182.8	36.56 [12]	0.723
Method C	5	169.9	33.98 [13]	0.697

ANOVA

Source of Variation	SS	df	MS	F	P-value	F crit
Between Groups	17.0493 [4]	2 [1]	8.5247 [7]	12.7424 [9]	0.0011 [10]	3.8853 [14]
Within Groups	8.0280 [5]	12 [2]	0.6690 [8]			
Total	25.0773 [6]	14 [3]				

| [1] $p-1$ | [2] $n-p$ | [3] $n-1$ | [4] SST | [5] SSE | [6] $SSTO$ | [7] MST | [8] MSE | [9] F statistic | [10] p value related to F | [11] $\bar{x}_A$ | [12] $\bar{x}_B$ | [13] $\bar{x}_C$ | [14] $F_{0.05}$ |

TABLE 10.5 ANOVA Table for Testing $H_0 : \mu_A = \mu_B = \mu_C$ in the Training Method Experiment ($p = 3$ Training Methods, $n = 15$ Observations)

Source	Degrees of Freedom	Sums of Squares	Mean Squares	F Statistic	p Value
Treatments	$p - 1 = 3 - 1$ $= 2$	$SST = 17.0493$	$MST = \dfrac{SST}{p - 1}$ $= \dfrac{17.0493}{3 - 1}$ $= 8.525$	$F = \dfrac{MST}{MSE}$ $= \dfrac{8.525}{0.669}$ $= 12.74$	0.001
Error	$n - p = 15 - 3$ $= 12$	$SSE = 8.028$	$MSE = \dfrac{SSE}{n - p}$ $= \dfrac{8.028}{15 - 3}$ $= 0.669$		
Total	$n - 1 = 15 - 1$ $= 14$	$SSTO = 25.0773$			

It follows that

$$F = \frac{MST}{MSE} = \frac{8.525}{0.669} = 12.74.$$

In order to test H_0 at the 0.05 level of significance, we use $F_{0.05}$ with $p - 1 = 3 - 1 = 2$ numerator and $n - p = 15 - 3 = 12$ denominator degrees of freedom. Table A.6 tells us that this F point equals 3.89, so we have

$$F = 12.74 > F_{0.05} = 3.89.$$

Therefore, we reject H_0 at the 0.05 level of significance. This says we have strong evidence that at least two of the treatment means μ_A, μ_B, and μ_C differ. In other words, we conclude that at least two of training methods A, B, and C have different effects on mean packing efficiency.

Figure 10.2 gives the MINITAB and Excel output of an ANOVA of the training method data. Note that each output gives the value $F = 12.74$ and the related p value, which equals 0.001 (rounded). Since this p value is less than 0.05, we reject H_0 at the 0.05 level of significance.

The results of an ANOVA are often summarized in what is called an **ANOVA table**. This table gives the sums of squares (SST, SSE, $SSTO$), the mean squares (MST and MSE), and the F statistic and its related p value for the ANOVA. The table also gives the degrees of freedom associated with each source of variation—treatments, error, and total. Table 10.5 gives the ANOVA table for the training method experiment. Notice that in the column labelled "Sums of Squares," the values of the SST and SSE sum to the $SSTO$. Also notice that the upper portion of the MINITAB output and the lower portion of the Excel output give the ANOVA table of Table 10.5.

Before we continue, note that if we use the ANOVA F statistic to test the equality of **two** population means, it can be shown that

1 F equals t^2, where t is the equal variances t statistic discussed in Section 9.2 (pages 364–365) used to test the equality of the two population means.

2 The rejection point F_α, which is based on $p - 1 = 2 - 1 = 1$ and $n - p = n_1 + n_2 - 2$ degrees of freedom, equals $t_{\alpha/2}^2$, where $t_{\alpha/2}$ is the rejection point for the equal variances t test and is based on $n_1 + n_2 - 2$ degrees of freedom.

Hence, the rejection conditions

$$F > F_\alpha \qquad \text{and} \qquad |t| > t_{\alpha/2}$$

are equivalent. It can also be shown that in this case, the p value related to F equals the p value related to t. Therefore, the ANOVA F test of the equality of p treatment means can be regarded as a generalization of the equal variances t test of the equality of two treatment means.

Pairwise comparisons   If the one-way ANOVA F test says that at least two treatment means differ, then we investigate which treatment means differ and we estimate how large the differences are. We do this by making what we call **pairwise comparisons** (that is, we compare treatment means **two at a time**). One way to make these comparisons is to compute point estimates of and confidence intervals for **pairwise differences**. For example, in the training method experiment, we might estimate the pairwise differences $\mu_A - \mu_B$, $\mu_A - \mu_C$, and $\mu_B - \mu_C$. Here, for instance, the pairwise difference $\mu_A - \mu_B$ can be interpreted as the change in mean packing efficiency achieved by changing from using training method B (interactive training) to using training method A (watching a video).

There are two approaches to calculating confidence intervals for pairwise differences. The first involves computing the usual, or **individual**, confidence interval for each pairwise difference. Here, if we are computing $100(1 - \alpha)$ percent confidence intervals, we are $100(1 - \alpha)$ percent confident that each individual pairwise difference is contained in its respective interval. That is, the confidence level associated with each (individual) comparison is $100(1 - \alpha)$ percent, and we refer to α as the **comparisonwise error rate**. However, we are less than $100(1 - \alpha)$ percent confident that all of the pairwise differences are simultaneously contained in their respective intervals. A more conservative approach is to compute **simultaneous** confidence intervals. Such intervals make us $100(1 - \alpha)$ percent confident that all of the pairwise differences are simultaneously contained in their respective intervals. That is, when we compute simultaneous intervals, the overall confidence level associated with all the comparisons being made in the experiment is $100(1 - \alpha)$ percent, and we refer to α as the **experimentwise error rate**.

Several kinds of simultaneous confidence intervals can be computed. In this book, we present what is called the **Tukey formula** for simultaneous intervals. We do this because, **if we are interested in studying all pairwise differences between treatment means, the Tukey formula yields the most precise (shortest) simultaneous confidence intervals**. In general, a Tukey simultaneous $100(1 - \alpha)$ percent confidence interval is longer than the corresponding individual $100(1 - \alpha)$ percent confidence interval. Thus, intuitively, we are paying a penalty for simultaneous confidence by obtaining longer intervals. One pragmatic approach to comparing treatment means is to first determine if we can use the more conservative Tukey intervals to make meaningful pairwise comparisons. If we cannot, then we might see what the individual intervals tell us. In the following box, we present both individual and Tukey simultaneous confidence intervals for pairwise differences. We also present the formula for a confidence interval for a single treatment mean, which we might use after we have used pairwise comparisons to determine the "best" treatment.

Estimation in One-Way ANOVA

1   Consider the **pairwise difference $\mu_i - \mu_h$**, which can be interpreted to be the change in the mean value of the response variable associated with changing from using treatment h to using treatment i. Then, a **point estimate of the difference $\mu_i - \mu_h$ is $\bar{x}_i - \bar{x}_h$**, where $\bar{x}_i$ and $\bar{x}_h$ are the sample treatment means associated with treatments i and h.

2   An **individual $100(1 - \alpha)$ percent confidence interval for $\mu_i - \mu_h$** is

$$\left[(\bar{x}_i - \bar{x}_h) \pm t_{\alpha/2} \sqrt{MSE\left(\frac{1}{n_i} + \frac{1}{n_h}\right)} \right].$$

Here the $t_{\alpha/2}$ point is based on $n - p$ degrees of freedom, and MSE is the previously defined error mean square found in the ANOVA table.

3   A **Tukey simultaneous $100(1 - \alpha)$ percent confidence interval for $\mu_i - \mu_h$** is

$$\left[(\bar{x}_i - \bar{x}_h) \pm q_\alpha \sqrt{\frac{MSE}{m}} \right].$$

Here the value q_α is obtained from Table A.9, which is a **table of percentage points of the studentized range**. In this table, q_α is listed corresponding to values of p and $n - p$. Furthermore, we assume that the sample sizes n_i and n_h are equal to the same value, which we denote as m. If n_i and n_h are not equal, we replace $q_\alpha \sqrt{MSE/m}$ by $(q_\alpha/\sqrt{2})\sqrt{MSE[(1/n_i) + (1/n_h)]}$.

4   A **point estimate of the treatment mean μ_i is $\bar{x}_i$** and an **individual $100(1 - \alpha)$ percent confidence interval for μ_i** is

$$\left[\bar{x}_i \pm t_{\alpha/2} \sqrt{\frac{MSE}{n_i}} \right].$$

Here the $t_{\alpha/2}$ point is based on $n - p$ degrees of freedom.

Example 10.6 Training Method Experiment Case

In the training method experiment, we are comparing $p = 3$ treatment means (μ_A, μ_B, and μ_C). Furthermore, each sample is of size $m = 5$, there are a total of $n = 15$ observed packing times, and the *MSE* found in Table 10.5 is 0.669. Because $q_{0.05} = 3.77$ is the entry found in Table A.9 corresponding to $p = 3$ and $n - p = 12$, a Tukey simultaneous 95 percent confidence interval for $\mu_B - \mu_A$ is

$$\left[(\bar{x}_B - \bar{x}_A) \pm q_{0.05}\sqrt{\frac{MSE}{m}}\right] = \left[(36.56 - 34.92) \pm 3.77\sqrt{\frac{0.669}{5}}\right]$$
$$= [1.64 \pm 1.379]$$
$$= [0.261, 3.019].$$

Similarly, Tukey simultaneous 95 percent confidence intervals for $\mu_A - \mu_C$ and $\mu_B - \mu_C$ are, respectively,

$$[(\bar{x}_A - \bar{x}_C) \pm 1.379] \qquad \text{and} \qquad [(\bar{x}_B - \bar{x}_C) \pm 1.379]$$
$$= [(34.92 - 33.98) \pm 1.379] \qquad\qquad = [(36.56 - 33.98) \pm 1.379]$$
$$= [-0.439, 2.319] \qquad\qquad\qquad = [1.201, 3.959].$$

These intervals make us simultaneously 95 percent confident that

1   using interactive training (method *B*) compared to watching a video (method *A*) increases the mean number of boxes packed per hour by between 0.261 and 3.019 boxes,

2   changing the training method from reading instructions only (method *C* or the control group method) to showing a video (method *A*) might decrease the mean number of boxes packed by as much as 0.439 or might increase the mean number of boxes packed by as much as 2.319, and

3   changing the training method from reading instructions only (method *C*) to interactive training (method *B*) increases the mean number of boxes packed by between 1.201 and 3.959.

The first and third of these intervals make us 95 percent confident that μ_B is at least 0.261 boxes greater than μ_A and at least 1.201 boxes greater than μ_C. Therefore, we have strong evidence that training method *B* yields the highest mean number of boxes packed of the training methods tested. Furthermore, noting that $t_{0.025}$ based on $n - p = 12$ degrees of freedom is 2.179, it follows that an individual 95 percent confidence interval for μ_B is

$$\left[\bar{x}_B \pm t_{0.025}\sqrt{\frac{MSE}{n_B}}\right] = \left[36.56 \pm 2.179\sqrt{\frac{0.669}{5}}\right]$$
$$= [35.763, 37.357].$$

This interval says we can be 95 percent confident that the mean number of boxes packed by using interactive training (method *B*) is between 35.763 and 37.357 boxes. Notice that this confidence interval is graphed on the MINITAB output of Figure 10.2. This output also shows the 95 percent confidence intervals for μ_A and μ_C and gives Tukey simultaneous 95 percent intervals. For example, consider finding the Tukey interval for $\mu_B - \mu_A$ on the MINITAB output. To do this, we look in the table corresponding to "Method *A* subtracted from" and find the row in this table labelled "Method *B*." This row gives the interval for "Method *A* subtracted from Method *B*"—that is, the interval for $\mu_B - \mu_A$. This interval is [0.261, 3.109], as calculated above. Finally, note that the half-length of the individual 95 percent confidence interval for a pairwise comparison is (because $n_A = n_B = n_C = 5$)

$$t_{0.025}\sqrt{MSE\left(\frac{1}{n_i} + \frac{1}{n_h}\right)} = 2.179\sqrt{0.669\left(\frac{1}{5} + \frac{1}{5}\right)} = 1.127.$$

This half-length implies that the individual intervals are shorter than the previously constructed Tukey intervals, which have a half-length of 1.379. Recall, however, that the Tukey intervals are short enough to allow us to conclude with 95 percent confidence that μ_B is greater than μ_A and μ_C.

We next consider testing $H_0: \mu_i - \mu_h = 0$ versus $H_a: \mu_i - \mu_h \neq 0$. The test statistic t for performing this test is calculated by dividing $\bar{x}_i - \bar{x}_h$ by $\sqrt{MSE\,[(1/n_i) + (1/n_h)]}$. For example, consider testing $H_0: \mu_B - \mu_A = 0$ versus $H_a: \mu_B - \mu_A \neq 0$. Since $\bar{x}_B - \bar{x}_A = 34.92 - 36.56 = 1.64$ and $\sqrt{MSE\,[(1/n_B) + (1/n_A)]} = \sqrt{0.669[(1/5) + (1/5)]} = 0.5173$, the test statistic t equals $1.64/0.5173 = 3.17$. This test statistic value is given in the table at the left of the following MegaStat output, as is the test statistic value for testing $H_0: \mu_B - \mu_C = 0$ ($t = 4.99$) and the test statistic value for testing $H_0: \mu_A - \mu_C = 0$ ($t = 1.82$):

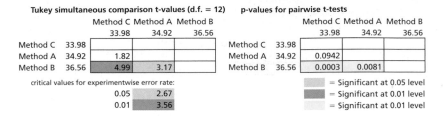

If we wish to use the Tukey simultaneous comparison procedure with an experimentwise error rate of α, we reject $H_0: \mu_i - \mu_h = 0$ in favour of $H_a: \mu_i - \mu_h \neq 0$ if the absolute value of t is greater than the rejection point $q_\alpha/\sqrt{2}$. Table A.9 tells us that $q_{0.05}$ is 3.77 and $q_{0.01}$ is 5.04. Therefore, the rejection points for experimentwise error rates of 0.05 and 0.01 are, respectively, $3.77/\sqrt{2} = 2.67$ and $5.04/\sqrt{2} = 3.56$ (see the MegaStat output). Suppose we set α equal to 0.05. Then, since the test statistic value for testing $H_0: \mu_B - \mu_A = 0$ ($t = 3.17$) and the test statistic value for testing $H_0: \mu_B - \mu_C = 0$ ($t = 4.99$) are greater than the rejection point 2.67, we reject both null hypotheses. This, along with the fact that $\bar{x}_B = 36.56$ is greater than $\bar{x}_A = 34.92$ and $\bar{x}_C = 33.98$, leads us to conclude that training method B yields the highest mean number of packed boxes of the training methods tested (note that the MegaStat output conveniently arranges the sample means in increasing order). Finally, note that the table at the right of the MegaStat output gives the p values for individual (rather than simultaneous) pairwise hypothesis tests. For example, the individual p value for testing $H_0: \mu_B - \mu_C = 0$ is 0.0003, and the individual p value for testing $H_0: \mu_B - \mu_A = 0$ is 0.0081.

In general, when we use a completely randomized experimental design, it is important to compare the treatments by using experimental units that are essentially the same with respect to the characteristic under study. For example, in the training method experiment, we have tested employees of the same type (new employees who have not received training) to compare the different training methods, and in the shelf display case we have used grocery stores of the same sales potential for the bakery product to compare the shelf display heights (the reader will analyze the data for this case in the exercises). Sometimes, however, it is not possible to use experimental units that are essentially the same with respect to the characteristic under study. For example, suppose a chain of stores that sells audio and video equipment wishes to compare the effects of street, mall, and downtown locations on the sales volume of its stores. The experimental units in this situation are the areas where the stores are located, but these areas are not of the same sales potential because each area is populated by a different number of households. In such a situation, we must explicitly account for the differences in the experimental units. One way to do this is to use **regression analysis**, which is discussed in Chapters 11 and 12. When we use regression analysis to explicitly account for a variable (such as the number of households in the store's area) that causes differences in the experimental units, we call the variable a **covariate**. Furthermore, we say that we are performing an **analysis of covariance**. Finally, another way to deal with differing experimental units is to employ a **randomized block design**. This experimental design is discussed in Section 10.3.

To conclude this section, we note that if we fear that the normality and/or equal variances assumptions for one-way ANOVA do not hold, we can use a nonparametric approach to compare several populations. One such approach is the Kruskal–Wallis H test, which is discussed in Section 13.4.

Exercises for Section 10.2

CONCEPTS

10.5 Explain the assumptions that must be satisfied in order to validly use the one-way ANOVA formulas.

10.6 Explain the difference between the between-treatment variability and the within-treatment variability when performing a one-way ANOVA.

10.7 Explain why we conduct pairwise comparisons of treatment means.

10.8 Explain the difference between individual and simultaneous confidence intervals for a set of several pairwise differences.

METHODS AND APPLICATIONS

10.9 THE SHELF DISPLAY CASE ● BakeSale

Consider Example 10.2, and let μ_B, μ_M, and μ_T represent the mean monthly sales when using the bottom, middle, and top shelf display heights, respectively. Figure 10.3 gives the MINITAB output of a one-way ANOVA of the bakery sales study data in Table 10.2 (page 318).

a. Test the null hypothesis that μ_B, μ_M, and μ_T are equal by setting $\alpha = 0.05$. On the basis of this test, can we conclude that the bottom, middle, and top shelf display heights have different effects on mean monthly sales?

b. Consider the pairwise differences $\mu_M - \mu_B$, $\mu_T - \mu_B$, and $\mu_T - \mu_M$. Find a point estimate of and a Tukey simultaneous 95 percent confidence interval for each pairwise difference. Interpret each interval in practical terms. Which display height maximizes mean sales?

c. Find an individual 95 percent confidence interval for each pairwise difference in part b. Interpret each interval.

d. Find 95 percent confidence intervals for μ_B, μ_M, and μ_T. Interpret each interval.

10.10 Consider the display panel situation in Exercise 10.3, and let μ_A, μ_B, and μ_C represent the mean times to stabilize the emergency condition when using display panels A, B, and C, respectively. Figure 10.4 gives the MINITAB output of a one-way ANOVA of the display panel data in Table 10.3 (page 319). ● Display

a. Test the null hypothesis that μ_A, μ_B, and μ_C are equal by setting $\alpha = 0.05$. On the basis of this test, can we conclude that display panels A, B, and C have different effects on the mean time to stabilize the emergency condition?

b. Consider the pairwise differences $\mu_B - \mu_A$, $\mu_C - \mu_A$, and $\mu_C - \mu_B$. Find a point estimate of and a Tukey simultaneous 95 percent confidence

FIGURE 10.3 MINITAB Output of a One-Way ANOVA of the Bakery Sales Study Data in Table 10.2

```
One-way ANOVA: Bakery Sales versus Display Height

Source           DF      SS       MS       F       P
Display Height    2  2273.88  1136.94  184.57   0.000
Error            15    92.40     6.16
Total            17  2366.28

                                 Individual 95%
                                 CIs For Mean Based on Pooled StDev
Level    N   Mean   StDev   --------+---------+---------+---------+-
Bottom   6  55.800  2.477         (--*-)
Middle   6  77.200  3.103
Top      6  51.500  1.648   (-*--)
                            --------+---------+---------+---------+-
 Pooled StDev = 2.482           56.0      64.0      72.0      80.0
```

```
Tukey 95% Simultaneous
Confidence Intervals

Bottom subtracted from:
             Lower    Center    Upper
Middle     17.681    21.400   25.119
Top        -8.019    -4.300   -0.581

Middle subtracted from:
             Lower    Center    Upper
Top       -29.419   -25.700  -21.981
```

(In the Individual 95% CI plot, Middle shows `(--*-)` at the right near 72–80.)

FIGURE 10.4 MINITAB Output of a One-Way ANOVA of the Display Panel Study Data in Table 10.3

```
One-way ANOVA: Time versus Display

Source   DF     SS      MS      F       P
Display   2  500.17  250.08  30.11   0.000
Error     9   74.75    8.31
Total    11  574.92

                              Individual 95%
                              CIs For Mean Based on Pooled StDev
Level   N   Mean   StDev   -+---------+---------+---------+--------
A       4  24.500  2.646          (-----*----)
B       4  20.500  2.646   (----*-----)
C       4  35.750  3.304                        (-----*----)
                          -+---------+---------+---------+--------
 Pooled StDev = 2.882     18.0      24.0      30.0      36.0
```

```
Tukey 95% Simultaneous
Confidence Intervals

A subtracted from:
        Lower   Center   Upper
B      -9.692   -4.000    1.692
C       5.558   11.250   16.942

B subtracted from:
        Lower   Center   Upper
C       9.558   15.250   20.942
```

FIGURE **10.5**   Excel Output of a One-Way ANOVA of the Bottle Design Study Data in Table 10.4

SUMMARY

Groups	Count	Sum	Average	Variance
DESIGN A	5	83	16.6	5.3
DESIGN B	5	164	32.8	9.2
DESIGN C	5	124	24.8	8.2

ANOVA

Source of Variation	SS	df	MS	F	P-Value	F crit
Between Groups	656.1333	2	328.0667	43.35683	3.23E-06	3.88529
Within Groups	90.8	12	7.566667			
Total	746.9333	14				

TABLE **10.6**   Golf Ball Durability Test Results and a MegaStat Plot of the Results   ● GolfBall

	Brand			
Alpha	**Best**	**Century**	**Divot**	
281	270	218	364	
220	334	244	302	
274	307	225	325	
242	290	273	337	
251	331	249	355	

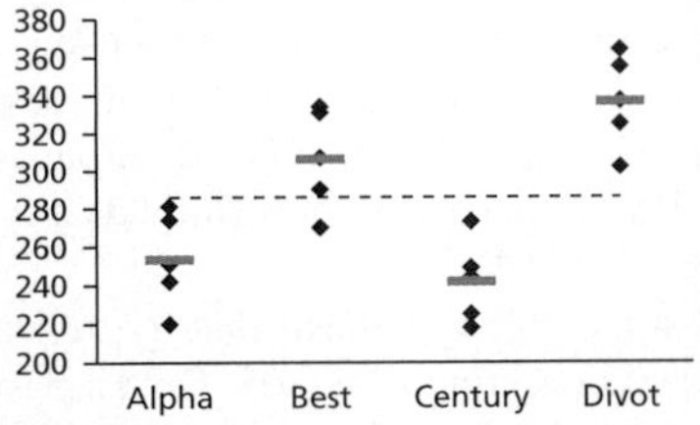

interval for each pairwise difference. Interpret the results by describing the effects of changing from using each display panel to using each of the other panels. Which display panel minimizes the time required to stabilize the emergency condition?

c. Find an individual 95 percent confidence interval for each pairwise difference in part b. Interpret the results.

10.11 Consider the bottle design study situation in Exercise 10.4, and let μ_A, μ_B, and μ_C represent mean daily sales using bottle designs A, B, and C, respectively. Figure 10.5 gives the Excel output of a one-way ANOVA of the bottle design study data in Table 10.4 (page 319).   ● BottleDes

a. Test the null hypothesis that μ_A, μ_B, and μ_C are equal by setting $\alpha = 0.05$. That is, test for statistically significant differences between these treatment means at the 0.05 level of significance. Based on this test, can we conclude that bottle designs A, B, and C have different effects on mean daily sales?

b. Consider the pairwise differences $\mu_B - \mu_A$, $\mu_C - \mu_A$, and $\mu_C - \mu_B$. Find a point estimate of and a Tukey simultaneous 95 percent confidence interval for each pairwise difference. Interpret the results in practical terms. Which bottle design maximizes mean daily sales?

c. Find an individual 95 percent confidence interval for each pairwise difference in part b. Interpret the results in practical terms.

d. Find a 95 percent confidence interval for each of the treatment means μ_A, μ_B, and μ_C. Interpret these intervals.

10.12 In order to compare the durability of four different brands of golf balls (Alpha, Best, Century, and Divot), the Canuck Golf Association randomly selects five balls of each brand and places each ball into a machine that exerts the force produced by a 250-yard drive. The number of simulated drives needed to crack or chip each ball is recorded. The results are given in Table 10.6. The MegaStat output of a one-way ANOVA of these data is shown in Figure 10.6. Test for statistically significant differences between the treatment means μ_{Alpha}, μ_{Best}, $\mu_{Century}$, and μ_{Divot}. Set $\alpha = 0.05$.   ● GolfBall

10.13 Perform pairwise comparisons of the treatment means in Exercise 10.12. Which brand(s) are most durable? Find a 95 percent confidence interval for each of the treatment means.

10.14 **THE COMMERCIAL RESPONSE CASE**

Recall from Example 10.3 that (1) 29 randomly selected subjects were exposed to commercials shown in more involving programs, (2) 29 randomly selected subjects were exposed to commercials shown in less involving programs, and (3) 29 randomly selected subjects watched commercials only (the control group). The mean brand recall scores for these three groups were, respectively, $\bar{x}_1 = 1.21$, $\bar{x}_2 = 2.24$, and $\bar{x}_3 = 2.28$. Furthermore, a one-way ANOVA of the data shows that $SST = 21.40$ and $SSE = 85.56$.

a. Define appropriate treatment means μ_1, μ_2, and μ_3. Then test for statistically significant differences between these treatment means. Set $\alpha = 0.05$.

FIGURE 10.6 MegaStat Output of a One-Way ANOVA of the Golf Ball Durability Data

ANOVA table

Source	SS		df	MS		F	6	p-value	7
Treatment	29,860.40	1	3	9,953.467	4	16.42		3.85E-05	
Error	9,698.40	2	16	606.150	5				
Total	39,558.80	3	19						

Mean	n	Std. Dev	
253.6	5	24.68	Alpha
306.4	5	27.21	Best
241.8	5	21.67	Century
336.6	5	24.60	Divot
284.6	20	45.63	Total

Tukey simultaneous comparison t-values (d.f. = 16)

		Century 241.8	Alpha 253.6	Best 306.4	Divot 336.6
Century	241.8				
Alpha	253.6	0.76			
Best	306.4	4.15	3.39		
Divot	336.6	6.09	5.33	1.94	

Critical values for experimentwise error rate:

0.05	2.86
0.01	3.67

p-values for pairwise t-tests

		Century 241.8	Alpha 253.6	Best 306.4	Divot 336.6
Century	241.8				
Alpha	253.6	0.4596			
Best	306.4	0.0008	0.0037		
Divot	336.6	1.57E-05	0.0001	0.0703	

1 SST	2 SSE	3 SSTO	4 MST	5 MSE	6 F	7 p value for F

b. Perform pairwise comparisons of the treatment means by computing a Tukey simultaneous 95 percent confidence interval for each of the pairwise differences $\mu_1 - \mu_2$, $\mu_1 - \mu_3$, and $\mu_2 - \mu_3$. Which type of program content results in the worst mean brand recall score?

10.3 The Randomized Block Design

Not all experiments employ a completely randomized design. For instance, suppose that when we employ a completely randomized design, we fail to reject the null hypothesis of equality of treatment means because the within-treatment variability (which is measured by the *SSE*) is large. This could happen because differences between the experimental units are concealing true differences between the treatments. We can often remedy this by using what is called a **randomized block design**.

Example 10.7 The Defective Cardboard Box Case

The Universal Paper Company manufactures cardboard boxes. The company wishes to investigate the effects of four production methods (methods 1, 2, 3, and 4) on the number of defective boxes produced in an hour. To compare the methods, the company could utilize a completely randomized design. For each of the four production methods, the company would select several (for example, three) machine operators, train each operator to use the production method to which they have been assigned, have each operator produce boxes for one hour, and record the number of defective boxes produced. The three operators using any one production method would be **different** from those using any other production method. That is, the completely randomized design would utilize a total of 12 machine operators. However, the abilities of the machine operators could differ substantially. These differences might tend to conceal any real differences between the production methods. To overcome this disadvantage, the company will employ a **randomized block experimental design**. This involves randomly selecting three machine operators and training each operator thoroughly to use all four production methods. Then each operator will produce boxes for one hour using each of the four production methods. The order in which each operator uses the four methods should be random. We record the number of defective boxes produced by each operator using each method. The advantage of the randomized block design is that the defective rates obtained by using the four methods result from employing the **same** three operators. Thus, any true differences in the effectiveness of the methods would not be concealed by differences in the operators' abilities.

TABLE 10.7 Numbers of Defective Cardboard Boxes Obtained by Production Methods 1, 2, 3, and 4 and Machine Operators 1, 2, and 3 ● CardBox

Treatment (Production Method)	Block (Machine Operator)			Sample Treatment Mean
	1	**2**	**3**	
1	9	10	12	10.3333
2	8	11	12	10.3333
3	3	5	7	5.0
4	4	5	5	4.6667
Sample Block Mean	6.0	7.75	9.0	$\bar{x} = 7.5833$

When Universal Paper employs the randomized block design, it obtains the 12 defective box counts in Table 10.7. We let x_{ij} denote the number of defective boxes produced by machine operator j using production method i. For example, $x_{32} = 5$ says that 5 defective boxes were produced by machine operator 2 using production method 3 (see Table 10.7). In addition to the 12 defective box counts, Table 10.7 gives the sample mean of these 12 observations, which is $\bar{x} = 7.5833$, and also gives **sample treatment means** and **sample block means**. The sample treatment means are the average defective box counts obtained when using production methods 1, 2, 3, and 4. Denoting these sample treatment means as $\bar{x}_{1\bullet}, \bar{x}_{2\bullet}, \bar{x}_{3\bullet}$, and $\bar{x}_{4\bullet}$, we see from Table 10.7 that $\bar{x}_{1\bullet} = 10.3333$, $\bar{x}_{2\bullet} = 10.3333, \bar{x}_{3\bullet} = 5.0$, and $\bar{x}_{4\bullet} = 4.6667$. Because $\bar{x}_{3\bullet}$ and $\bar{x}_{4\bullet}$ are less than $\bar{x}_{1\bullet}$ and $\bar{x}_{2\bullet}$, we estimate that the mean number of defective boxes produced per hour by production method 3 or 4 is less than the mean number of defective boxes produced per hour by production method 1 or 2. The sample block means are the average defective box counts obtained by machine operators 1, 2, and 3. Denoting these sample block means as $\bar{x}_{\bullet 1}, \bar{x}_{\bullet 2}$, and $\bar{x}_{\bullet 3}$, we see from Table 10.7 that $\bar{x}_{\bullet 1} = 6.0$, $\bar{x}_{\bullet 2} = 7.75$, and $\bar{x}_{\bullet 3} = 9.0$. Because $\bar{x}_{\bullet 1}, \bar{x}_{\bullet 2}$, and $\bar{x}_{\bullet 3}$ differ, we have evidence that the abilities of the machine operators differ and thus that using the machine operators as blocks is reasonable.

In general, a **randomized block design** compares p treatments (for example, production methods) by using b blocks (for example, machine operators). Each block is used exactly once to measure the effect of each and every treatment. The advantage of the randomized block design over the completely randomized design is that we are comparing the treatments by using the **same** experimental units. Thus, any true differences in the treatments will not be concealed by differences in the experimental units.

In some experiments, a block consists of **similar or matched sets of experimental units**. For example, suppose we wish to compare the performance of business majors, science majors, and fine arts majors on a graduate school admissions test. Here the blocks might be matched sets of students. Each matched set (block) would consist of a business major, a science major, and a fine arts major selected so that each is in their last year, attends the same university, and has the same grade point average. By selecting blocks in this fashion, any true differences between majors would not be concealed by differences between classes, universities, or grade point averages.

In order to analyze the data obtained in a randomized block design, we define

x_{ij} = the value of the response variable observed when block j uses treatment i,

$\bar{x}_{i\bullet}$ = the mean of the b values of the response variable observed when using treatment i,

$\bar{x}_{\cdot j}$ = the mean of the p values of the response variable observed when using block j,

$\bar{x}$ = the mean of the total of the bp values of the response variable that we have observed in the experiment.

The ANOVA procedure for a randomized block design partitions the **total sum of squares (SSTO)** into three components: the **treatment sum of squares (SST)**, the **block sum of squares (SSB)**, and the **error sum of squares (SSE)**. The formula for this partitioning is

$$SSTO = SST + SSB + SSE.$$

The steps for calculating these sums of squares, as well as what is measured by the sums of squares, can be summarized as follows:

Step 1: Calculate the SST, which measures the amount of between-treatment variability:

$$SST = b \sum_{i=1}^{p} (\bar{x}_{i\cdot} - \bar{x})^2.$$

Step 2: Calculate the SSB, which measures the amount of variability due to the blocks:

$$SSB = p \sum_{j=1}^{b} (\bar{x}_{\cdot j} - \bar{x})^2.$$

Step 3: Calculate the $SSTO$, which measures the total amount of variability:

$$SSTO = \sum_{i=1}^{p} \sum_{j=1}^{b} (x_{ij} - \bar{x})^2.$$

Step 4: Calculate the SSE, which measures the amount of variability due to the error:

$$SSE = SSTO - SST - SSB.$$

These sums of squares are shown in Table 10.8, which is the ANOVA table for a randomized block design. This table also gives the degrees of freedom associated with each source of variation—treatments, blocks, error, and total—as well as the mean squares and F statistics used to test the hypotheses of interest in a randomized block experiment.

Before discussing these hypotheses, we will illustrate how the entries in the ANOVA table are calculated. The sums of squares in the defective cardboard box case are calculated as follows (note that $p = 4$ and $b = 3$):

Step 1: $SST = 3[(\bar{x}_{1\cdot} - \bar{x})^2 + (\bar{x}_{2\cdot} - \bar{x})^2 + (\bar{x}_{3\cdot} - \bar{x})^2 + (\bar{x}_{4\cdot} - \bar{x})^2]$

$= 3[(10.3333 - 7.5833)^2 + (10.3333 - 7.5833)^2$

$+ (5.0 - 7.5833)^2 + (4.6667 - 7.5833)^2]$

$= 90.9167.$

Step 2: $SSB = 4[(\bar{x}_{\cdot 1} - \bar{x})^2 + (\bar{x}_{\cdot 2} - \bar{x})^2 + (\bar{x}_{\cdot 3} - \bar{x})^2]$

$= 4[(6.0 - 7.5833)^2 + (7.75 - 7.5833)^2 + (9.0 - 7.5833)^2]$

$= 18.1667.$

TABLE **10.8** ANOVA Table for the Randomized Block Design with p Treatments and b Blocks

Source of Variation	Degrees of Freedom	Sum of Squares	Mean Square	F
Treatments	$p - 1$	SST	$MST = \dfrac{SST}{p-1}$	$F(\text{treatments}) = \dfrac{MST}{MSE}$
Blocks	$b - 1$	SSB	$MSB = \dfrac{SSB}{b-1}$	$F(\text{blocks}) = \dfrac{MSB}{MSE}$
Error	$(p-1)(b-1)$	SSE	$MSE = \dfrac{SSE}{(p-1)(b-1)}$	
Total	$pb - 1$	SSTO		

Step 3: $SSTO = (9 - 7.5833)^2 + (10 - 7.5833)^2 + (12 - 7.5833)^2$
$$+ (8 - 7.5833)^2 + (11 - 7.5833)^2 + (12 - 7.5833)^2$$
$$+ (3 - 7.5833)^2 + (5 - 7.5833)^2 + (7 - 7.5833)^2$$
$$+ (4 - 7.5833)^2 + (5 - 7.5833)^2 + (5 - 7.5833)^2$$
$$= 112.9167.$$

Step 4: $SSE = SSTO - SST - SSB$
$$= 112.9167 - 90.9167 - 18.1667$$
$$= 3.8333.$$

Figure 10.7 gives the MINITAB output of a randomized block ANOVA of the defective box data. This figure shows the above-calculated sums of squares, as well as the degrees of freedom (recall that $p = 4$ and $b = 3$), the mean squares, and the F statistics (and associated p values) used to test the hypotheses of interest.

FIGURE 10.7 **MINITAB Output of a Randomized Block ANOVA of the Defective Box Data**

```
Rows: Method    Columns: Operator
                1          2          3          All
1           9.000     10.000     12.000      10.333
2           8.000     11.000     12.000      10.333
3           3.000      5.000      7.000       5.000
4           4.000      5.000      5.000       4.667
All         6.000      7.750      9.000       7.583

Two-way ANOVA: Rejects versus Method, Operator

Source      DF          SS              MS            F           P
Method       3      90.917 [1]      30.3056 [5]    47.43 [8]    0.000 [9]
Operator     2      18.167 [2]       9.0833 [6]    14.22 [10]   0.005 [11]
Error        6       3.833 [3]       0.6389 [7]
Total       11     112.917 [4]

Method      Mean              Operator    Mean
1        10.3333 [12]         1          6.00 [16]
2        10.3333 [13]         2          7.75 [17]
3         5.0000 [14]         3          9.00 [18]
4         4.6667 [15]
```

[1] SST	[2] SSB	[3] SSE	[4] SSTO	[5] MST	[6] MSB	[7] MSE	[8] F(treatments)	[9] p value for F(treatments)
[10] F(blocks)	[11] p value for F(blocks)	[12] $\bar{x}_{1\cdot}$	[13] $\bar{x}_{2\cdot}$	[14] $\bar{x}_{3\cdot}$	[15] $\bar{x}_{4\cdot}$	[16] $\bar{x}_{\cdot1}$	[17] $\bar{x}_{\cdot2}$	[18] $\bar{x}_{\cdot3}$

Of main interest is the test of the null hypothesis H_0 that **no differences exist between the treatment effects** on the mean value of the response variable versus the alternative hypothesis H_a that **at least two treatment effects differ**. We can reject H_0 in favour of H_a at level of significance α if

$$F(\text{treatments}) = \frac{MST}{MSE}$$

is greater than the F_α point based on $p - 1$ numerator and $(p - 1)(b - 1)$ denominator degrees of freedom. In the defective cardboard box case, $F_{0.05}$ based on $p - 1 = 3$ numerator and $(p - 1)(b - 1) = 6$ denominator degrees of freedom is 4.76 (see Table A.6). Because

$$F(\text{treatments}) = \frac{MST}{MSE} = \frac{30.306}{0.639} = 47.43$$

is greater than $F_{0.05} = 4.76$, we reject H_0 at the 0.05 level of significance. Therefore, we have strong evidence that at least two production methods have different effects on the mean number of defective boxes produced per hour. Alternatively, we can reject H_0 in favour of H_a at level of significance α if the p value is less than α. Here the p value is the area under the curve of the F distribution (with $p - 1$ and $(p - 1)(b - 1)$ degrees of freedom) to the right of

F(treatments). The MINITAB output in Figure 10.7 tells us that this p value is 0.000 (that is, less than 0.001) for the defective box data. Therefore, we have extremely strong evidence that at least two production methods have different effects on the mean number of defective boxes produced per hour.

It is also of interest to test the null hypothesis H_0 that **no differences exist between the block effects** on the mean value of the response variable versus the alternative hypothesis H_a that **at least two block effects differ**. We can reject H_0 in favour of H_a at level of significance α if

$$F(\text{blocks}) = \frac{MSB}{MSE}$$

is greater than the F_α point based on $b - 1$ numerator and $(p - 1)(b - 1)$ denominator degrees of freedom. In the defective cardboard box case, $F_{0.05}$ based on $b - 1 = 2$ numerator and $(p - 1)(b - 1) = 6$ denominator degrees of freedom is 5.14 (see Table A.6). Because

$$F(\text{blocks}) = \frac{MSB}{MSE} = \frac{9.083}{0.639} = 14.22$$

is greater than $F_{0.05} = 5.14$, we reject H_0 at the 0.05 level of significance. Therefore, we have strong evidence that at least two machine operators have different effects on the mean number of defective boxes produced per hour. Alternatively, we can reject H_0 in favour of H_a at level of significance α if the p value is less than α. Here the p value is the area under the curve of the F distribution (with $b - 1$ and $(p - 1)(b - 1)$ degrees of freedom) to the right of F(blocks). The MINITAB output tells us that this p value is 0.005 for the defective box data. Therefore, we have very strong evidence that at least two machine operators have different effects on the mean number of defective boxes produced per hour. This implies that using the machine operators as blocks is reasonable.

If, in a randomized block design, we conclude that at least two treatment effects differ, we can perform pairwise comparisons to determine how they differ.

Point Estimates and Confidence Intervals in a Randomized Block ANOVA

Consider the **difference between the effects of treatments i and h on the mean value of the response variable.**

1. A **point estimate** of this difference is $\bar{x}_{i\cdot} - \bar{x}_{h\cdot}$.

2. An **individual $100(1 - \alpha)$ percent confidence interval** for this difference is

$$\left[(\bar{x}_{i\cdot} - \bar{x}_{h\cdot}) \pm t_{\alpha/2}\, s\sqrt{\frac{2}{b}}\right].$$

Here $t_{\alpha/2}$ is based on $(p - 1)(b - 1)$ degrees of freedom, and s is the square root of the MSE found in the randomized block ANOVA table.

3. A **Tukey simultaneous $100(1 - \alpha)$ percent confidence interval** for this difference is

$$\left[(\bar{x}_{i\cdot} - \bar{x}_{h\cdot}) \pm q_\alpha \frac{s}{\sqrt{b}}\right].$$

Here the value q_α is obtained from Table A.9, which is a table of percentage points of the studentized range. In this table, q_α is listed corresponding to values of p and $(p - 1)(b - 1)$.

Example 10.8 The Defective Cardboard Box Case

We have previously concluded that we have extremely strong evidence that at least two production methods have different effects on the mean number of defective boxes produced per hour. We have also seen that the sample treatment means are $\bar{x}_{1\cdot} = 10.3333$, $\bar{x}_{2\cdot} = 10.3333$, $\bar{x}_{3\cdot} = 5.0$, and $\bar{x}_{4\cdot} = 4.6667$. Since $\bar{x}_{4\cdot}$ is the smallest sample treatment mean, we will use Tukey simultaneous 95 percent confidence intervals to compare the effect of production method 4 with the effects of production methods 1, 2, and 3. To compute these intervals, we first note that $q_{0.05} = 4.90$ is the entry in Table A.9 corresponding to $p = 4$ and $(p - 1)(b - 1) = 6$. Also note that the MSE found in the randomized block ANOVA table is 0.639 (see Figure 10.7), which implies that $s = \sqrt{0.639} = 0.7994$. It follows that a Tukey simultaneous 95 percent confidence interval for the difference between the effects of production methods 4 and 1 on the mean number of defective boxes produced per hour is

$$\left[(\bar{x}_{4\cdot} - \bar{x}_{1\cdot}) \pm q_{0.05} \frac{s}{\sqrt{b}} \right] = \left[(4.6667 - 10.3333) \pm 4.90 \left(\frac{0.7994}{\sqrt{3}} \right) \right]$$
$$= [-5.6666 \pm 2.2615]$$
$$= [-7.9281, -3.4051].$$

Furthermore, it can be verified that a Tukey simultaneous 95 percent confidence interval for the difference between the effects of production methods 4 and 2 on the mean number of defective boxes produced per hour is also $[-7.9281, -3.4051]$. Therefore, we can be 95 percent confident that changing from production method 1 or 2 to production method 4 decreases the mean number of defective boxes produced per hour by a machine operator by between 3.4051 and 7.9281 boxes. A Tukey simultaneous 95 percent confidence interval for the difference between the effects of production methods 4 and 3 on the mean number of defective boxes produced per hour is

$$[(\bar{x}_{4\cdot} - \bar{x}_{3\cdot}) \pm 2.2615] = [(4.6667 - 5) \pm 2.2615]$$
$$= [-2.5948, 1.9282].$$

This interval tells us (with 95 percent confidence) that changing from production method 3 to production method 4 might decrease the mean number of defective boxes produced per hour by as many as 2.5948 boxes or might increase this mean by as many as 1.9282 boxes. In other words, because this interval contains 0, we cannot conclude that the effects of production methods 4 and 3 differ.

Exercises for Section 10.3

CONCEPTS

10.15 In your own words, explain why we sometimes employ the randomized block design.

10.16 How can we test to determine if the blocks we have chosen are reasonable?

METHODS AND APPLICATIONS

10.17 A marketing organization wishes to study the effects of four sales methods on weekly sales of a product. The organization employs a randomized block design in which three salespeople use each sales method. The results obtained are given in Table 10.9. Figure 10.8 gives the Excel output of a randomized block ANOVA of the sales method data. ● SaleMeth

a. Test the null hypothesis H_0 that no differences exist between the effects of the sales methods (treatments) on mean weekly sales. Set $\alpha = 0.05$.

Can we conclude that the different sales methods have different effects on mean weekly sales?

b. Test the null hypothesis H_0 that no differences exist between the effects of the salespeople (blocks) on mean weekly sales. Set $\alpha = 0.05$. Can we conclude that the different salespeople have different effects on mean weekly sales?

c. Use Tukey simultaneous 95 percent confidence intervals to make pairwise comparisons of the sales method effects on mean weekly sales. Which sales method(s) maximize mean weekly sales?

10.18 A consumer preference study involving three different bottle designs (A, B, and C) for the jumbo size of a new liquid laundry detergent was carried out using a randomized block experimental design, with supermarkets as blocks. Specifically, four supermarkets

TABLE **10.9**   Results of a Sales Method Experiment Employing a Randomized Block Design   ● SaleMeth

Sales Method, i	Salesperson, j A	B	C
1	32	29	30
2	32	30	28
3	28	25	23
4	25	24	23

FIGURE **10.8** Excel Output of a Randomized Block ANOVA of the Sales Method Data Given in Table 10.9

Anova: Two-Factor Without Replication

SUMMARY	Count	Sum	Average	Variance
Method 1	3	91	30.3333 [12]	2.3333
Method 2	3	90	30 [13]	4
Method 3	3	76	25.3333 [14]	6.3333
Method 4	3	72	24 [15]	1
Salesperson A	4	117	29.25 [16]	11.5833
Salesperson B	4	108	27 [17]	8.6667
Salesperson C	4	104	26 [18]	12.6667

ANOVA

Source of Variation	SS	df	MS	F	P-value	F crit
Rows	93.5833 [1]	3	31.1944 [5]	36.2258 [8]	0.0003 [9]	4.7571
Columns	22.1667 [2]	2	11.0833 [6]	12.8710 [10]	0.0068 [11]	5.1433
Error	5.1667 [3]	6	0.8611 [7]			
Total	120.9167 [4]	11				

| [1] SST | [2] SSB | [3] SSE | [4] $SSTO$ | [5] MST | [6] MSB | [7] MSE | [8] F(treatments) | [9] p value for F(treatments) |
| [10] F(blocks) | [11] p value for F(blocks) | [12] $\bar{x}_1.$ | [13] $\bar{x}_2.$ | [14] $\bar{x}_3.$ | [15] $\bar{x}_4.$ | [16] $\bar{x}._1$ | [17] $\bar{x}._2$ | [18] $\bar{x}._3$ |

were supplied with all three bottle designs, which were priced the same. Table 10.10 gives the number of bottles of each design sold in a 24-hour period at each supermarket. If we use these data, the SST, SSB, and SSE can be calculated to be 586.1667, 421.6667, and 1.8333, respectively. ● BottleDes2

a. Test the null hypothesis H_0 that no differences exist between the effects of the bottle designs on mean daily sales. Set $\alpha = 0.05$. Can we conclude that the different bottle designs have different effects on mean sales?

b. Test the null hypothesis H_0 that no differences exist between the effects of the supermarkets on mean daily sales. Set $\alpha = 0.05$. Can we conclude that the different supermarkets have different effects on mean sales?

c. Use Tukey simultaneous 95 percent confidence intervals to make pairwise comparisons of the bottle design effects on mean daily sales. Which bottle design(s) maximize mean sales?

d. Thinking about the research design described above, what possible limitations to the design may affect the results?

10.19 To compare three brands of computer keyboards, four data entry specialists were randomly selected. Each specialist used all three keyboards to enter the same kind of

TABLE **10.10** Results of a Bottle Design Experiment
● BottleDes2

	Supermarket, j			
Bottle Design, i	1	2	3	4
A	16	14	1	6
B	33	30	19	23
C	23	21	8	12

text material for 10 minutes, and the number of words entered per minute was recorded. The data obtained are given in Table 10.11. If we use these data, the SST, SSB, and SSE can be calculated to be 392.6667, 143.5833, and 2.6667, respectively. ● Keyboard

a. Test the null hypothesis H_0 that no differences exist between the effects of the keyboard brands on the mean number of words entered per minute. Set $\alpha = 0.05$.

b. Test the null hypothesis H_0 that no differences exist between the effects of the data entry specialists on the mean number of words entered per minute. Set $\alpha = 0.05$.

c. Use Tukey simultaneous 95 percent confidence intervals to make pairwise comparisons of the keyboard brand effects on the mean number of words entered per minute. Which keyboard brand maximizes the mean number of words entered per minute?

TABLE **10.11** Results of a Keyboard Experiment
● Keyboard

	Keyboard Brand		
Data Entry Specialist	A	B	C
1	77	67	63
2	71	62	59
3	74	63	59
4	67	57	54

10.20 **OECD BROADBAND STATISTICS TO JUNE 2006**

The Organisation for Economic Co-operation and Development (OECD) collected statistics of broadband subscribers in 30 countries around the world. Options of accessing the Internet were DSL, Cable, and Other. The data, per 100 inhabitants, are presented in Table 10.12. ● Broadband

TABLE 10.12   Broadband Subscriber Statistics per 100 Inhabitants for Exercise 10.20

	DSL	Cable	Other	Rank		DSL	Cable	Other	Rank
Denmark	17.4	9	2.8	1	France	16.7	1	0	16
Netherlands	17.2	11.1	0.5	2	Australia	13.9	2.9	0.6	17
Iceland	26.5	0	0.7	3	Germany	14.7	0.3	0.1	18
Korea	13.2	8.8	4.5	4	Spain	10.5	3.1	0.1	19
Switzerland	16.9	9	0.4	5	Italy	12.6	0	0.6	20
Finland	21.7	3.1	0.2	6	Portugal	7.9	5	0	21
Norway	20.4	3.8	0.4	7	New Zealand	10.7	0.5	0.6	22
Sweden	14.4	4.3	4	8	Czech Republic	3.9	2	3.5	23
Canada	10.8	11.5	0.1	9	Ireland	6.8	1	1.4	24
United Kingdom	14.6	4.9	0	10	Hungary	4.8	2.9	0.1	25
Belgium	11.9	7.4	0	11	Poland	3.9	1.3	0.1	26
United States	8	9.8	1.4	12	Turkey	2.9	0	0	27
Japan	11.3	2.7	4.9	13	Slovak Republic	2.2	0.5	0.2	28
Luxembourg	16	1.9	0	14	Mexico	2.1	0.7	0	29
Austria	11.2	6.3	0.2	15	Greece	2.7	0	0	30

Source: OECD Broadband Statistics to June 2006; OECD, 2006, http://www.oecd.org/document/9/0,3343,en_2649_201185_37529673_1_1_1_1,00.html

To test whether or not there is a significant main effect for type of subscription, we can treat the data as a randomized block design where the treatments are the three types of subscriptions and the blocks are the 30 countries. Figure 10.9 gives the MegaStat output of a randomized block ANOVA of the broadband statistics.

a. Test the null hypothesis H_0 that no differences exist between the three subscription types. Do the three subscription types differ?

b. Make pairwise comparisons of the three subscription types. Which type is the most popular?

10.21 The Coca-Cola Company introduced new Coke in 1985. Within three months of this introduction, nega-

tive consumer reaction forced Coca-Cola to reintroduce the original formula of Coke as Coca-Cola classic. Suppose that two years later, in 1987, a marketing research firm in Vancouver compared the sales of Coca-Cola classic, new Coke, and Pepsi in public building vending machines. To do this, the marketing research firm randomly selected 10 public buildings in Vancouver with both a Coke machine (selling Coke classic and new Coke) and a Pepsi machine. The data—in number of cans sold over a given period of time—and a MegaStat randomized block ANOVA of the data are given in Figure 10.10.   ● Coke

FIGURE 10.9   MegaStat Output of a Randomized Block ANOVA of the Internet Data for Exercise 10.20

ANOVA table

Source	SS		df	MS		F		p-value	
Treatments	1,828.710	[1]	2	914.3551	[5]	58.13	[8]	1.40E-14	[9]
Blocks	659.182	[2]	29	22.7304	[6]	1.45	[10]	0.1162	[11]
Error	912.350	[3]	58	15.7302	[7]				
Total	3,400.242	[4]	89						

Post hoc analysis

Tukey simultaneous comparison t-values (d.f. = 58)

		OTHER 0.9133	CABLE 3.8267	DSL 11.5933
OTHER	0.9133			
CABLE	3.8267	2.84		
DSL	11.5933	10.43	7.58	

critical values for experimentwise error rate:

0.05	2.40
0.01	3.04

p-values for pairwise t-tests

		OTHER 0.9133	CABLE 3.8267	DSL 11.5933
OTHER	0.9133			
CABLE	3.8267	0.0061		
DSL	11.5933	6.39E-15	3.05E-10	

[1] *SST* [2] *SSB* [3] *SSE* [4] *SSTO* [5] *MST* [6] *MSB* [7] *MSE* [8] *F*(treatments) [9] *p* value for *F*(treatments) [10] *F*(blocks) [11] *p* value for *F*(blocks)

FIGURE 10.10   **MegaStat Output of a Randomized Block ANOVA of the Vending Machine Data for Exercise 10.21**

Building	1	2	3	4	5	6	7	8	9	10
Coke Classic	45	136	134	41	146	33	71	224	111	87
New Coke	6	114	56	14	39	20	42	156	61	140
Pepsi	24	90	100	43	51	42	68	131	74	107

ANOVA table

Source	SS	df	MS	F	p-value
Treatments	7,997.60	2	3,998.800	5.78	0.0115
Blocks	55,573.47	9	6,174.830	8.93	4.97E-05
Error	12,443.73	18	691.319		
Total	76,014.80	29			

Tukey simultaneous comparison t-values (d.f. = 18)

		New Coke	Pepsi	Coke Classic
		64.800	73.000	102.800
New Coke	64.800			
Pepsi	73.000	0.70		
Coke Classic	102.800	3.23	2.53	

critical values for experimentwise error rate:
0.05	2.55
0.01	3.32

p-values for pairwise t-tests

		New Coke	Pepsi	Coke Classic
		64.800	73.000	102.800
New Coke	64.800			
Pepsi	73.000	0.4945		
Coke Classic	102.800	0.0046	0.0208	

a. Test the null hypothesis H_0 that no differences exist between the mean sales of Coca-Cola classic, new Coke, and Pepsi in Vancouver public building vending machines. Set $\alpha = 0.05$.

b. Make pairwise comparisons of the mean sales of Coca-Cola classic, new Coke, and Pepsi in Vancouver public building vending machines.

c. By the mid-1990s, the Coca-Cola Company had discontinued making new Coke and had returned to making only its original product. Is there evidence in the 1987 study that this might happen? Explain your answer.

10.4 Two-Way Analysis of Variance

Many response variables are affected by more than one factor. Because of this, we must often conduct experiments in which we study the effects of several factors on the response. In this section, we consider studying the effects of **two factors** on a response variable. To begin, recall that in Example 10.2 we discussed an experiment in which the Tastee Bakery Company investigated the effect of shelf display height on monthly demand for one of its bakery products. This one-factor experiment is actually a simplification of a two-factor experiment carried out by the Tastee Bakery Company. We discuss this two-factor experiment in the following example.

Example 10.9 The Shelf Display Case

The Tastee Bakery Company supplies a bakery product to many supermarkets. The company wishes to study the effects of two factors—**shelf display height** and **shelf display width**—on **monthly demand** (measured in cases of 10 units each) for this product. The factor "display height" is defined to have three levels: B (bottom), M (middle), and T (top). The factor "display width" is defined to have two levels: R (regular) and W (wide). The **treatments** in this experiment are **display height and display width combinations**. This design is also referred to as a 3×2 design because there are three levels of the display height factor (rows) and two levels of the display width factor (columns). The design could also be referred to as a 2×3 design in which the two levels of IV_1 represent the display width factor and the three levels of IV_2 represent the display height factor. Again, as stated at the start of the chapter, this notation depicts what the experimental design in which there are two rows and three columns looks like:

	Display Height		
Display Width	**Bottom (B)**	**Middle (M)**	**Top (T)**
Regular (R)	RB	RM	RT
Wide (W)	WB	WM	WT

TABLE **10.13** Six Samples of Monthly Demands for a Bakery Product ● BakeSale2

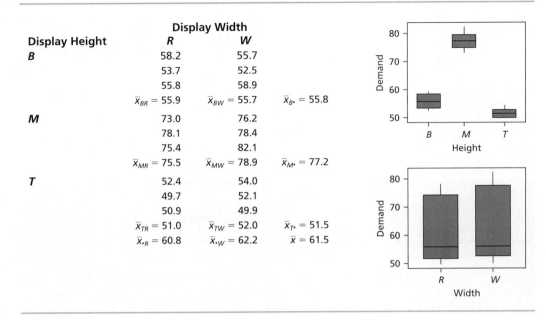

Display Height	Display Width		
	R	W	
B	58.2	55.7	
	53.7	52.5	
	55.8	58.9	
	$\bar{x}_{BR} = 55.9$	$\bar{x}_{BW} = 55.7$	$\bar{x}_{B\cdot} = 55.8$
M	73.0	76.2	
	78.1	78.4	
	75.4	82.1	
	$\bar{x}_{MR} = 75.5$	$\bar{x}_{MW} = 78.9$	$\bar{x}_{M\cdot} = 77.2$
T	52.4	54.0	
	49.7	52.1	
	50.9	49.9	
	$\bar{x}_{TR} = 51.0$	$\bar{x}_{TW} = 52.0$	$\bar{x}_{T\cdot} = 51.5$
	$\bar{x}_{\cdot R} = 60.8$	$\bar{x}_{\cdot W} = 62.2$	$\bar{x} = 61.5$

Here, for example, the notation *RB* denotes the treatment condition (cell) of regular width display on the bottom. For each display height and width combination, the company randomly selects a sample of $m = 3$ supermarkets (all supermarkets used in the study will be of equal sales potential). Each supermarket sells the product for one month using its assigned display height and width combination, and the month's demand for the product is recorded. The six samples obtained in this experiment are given in Table 10.13. We let $x_{ij,k}$ denote the monthly demand obtained at the *k*th supermarket that used display height *i* and display width *j*. For example, $x_{MW,2} = 78.4$ is the monthly demand obtained at the second supermarket that used a middle display height and a wide display.

In addition to giving the six samples, Table 10.13 gives the **sample treatment mean** for each display height and display width combination. For example, $\bar{x}_{BR} = 55.9$ is the mean of the sample of three demands observed at supermarkets using a bottom display height and a regular display width. The table also gives the sample mean demand for each level of display height (*B*, *M*, and *T*) and for each level of display width (*R* and *W*). Specifically,

$\bar{x}_{B\cdot} = 55.8 =$ the mean of the six demands observed when using a bottom display height,

$\bar{x}_{M\cdot} = 77.2 =$ the mean of the six demands observed when using a middle display height,

$\bar{x}_{T\cdot} = 51.5 =$ the mean of the six demands observed when using a top display height,

$\bar{x}_{\cdot R} = 60.8 =$ the mean of the nine demands observed when using a regular display width,

$\bar{x}_{\cdot W} = 62.2 =$ the mean of the nine demands observed when using a wide display.

Finally, Table 10.13 gives $\bar{x} = 61.5$, which is the overall mean of the total of 18 demands observed in the experiment. Because $\bar{x}_{M\cdot} = 77.2$ is considerably larger than $\bar{x}_{B\cdot} = 55.8$ and $\bar{x}_{T\cdot} = 51.5$, we estimate that mean monthly demand is highest when using a middle display height. Since $\bar{x}_{\cdot R} = 60.8$ and $\bar{x}_{\cdot W} = 62.2$ do not differ by very much, we estimate that there is little difference between the effects of a regular display width and a wide display on mean monthly demand.

Figure 10.11 presents a graphical analysis of the bakery demand data. In this figure, we plot, for each display width (*R* and *W*), the change in the sample treatment mean demand associated with changing the display height from bottom (*B*) to middle (*M*) to top (*T*). Note that, for both the regular display width (*R*) and the wide display (*W*), the middle display height (*M*) gives the highest mean monthly demand. Also note that, for either a bottom, middle, or top display height, there is little difference between the effects of a regular display width and a wide display on mean monthly demand. This sort of graphical analysis is useful in determining whether a condition called **interaction** exists.

FIGURE 10.11 Graphical Analysis of the Bakery Demand Data

(a) Plotting the treatment means

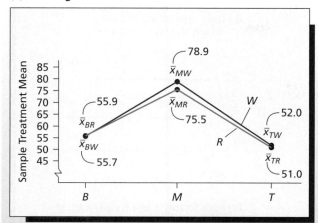

(b) A MINITAB output of the graphical analysis

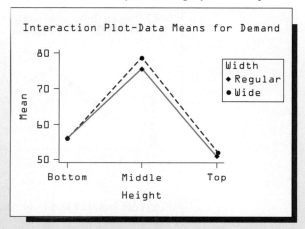

Interaction effects In general, suppose we wish to study the effects of two factors on a response variable. We assume that the first factor, which we refer to as **factor 1** (or IV_1), has **a** **levels** (levels 1, 2, . . . , a). Further, we assume that the second factor, which we will refer to as **factor 2** (or IV_2), has **b** **levels** (levels 1, 2, . . . , b). Here a **treatment** is considered to be a **combination of a level of factor 1 and a level of factor 2**. It follows that there are a total of *ab* treatments, and we assume that we will employ a **completely randomized experimental design** in which we will assign *m* experimental units to each treatment. This procedure results in our observing *m* values of the response variable for each of the *ab* treatments, and in this case we say that we are performing a **two-factor factorial experiment**.

The method we will explain for analyzing the results of a two-factor factorial experiment is called **two-way ANOVA**. This method requires that the following assumptions hold:

Assumptions for Two-Way ANOVA

1 We have obtained a random sample corresponding to each and every treatment, and the sample sizes in all the cells are equal (as described above).

2 **Independence:** The samples are independent because we have employed a completely randomized experimental design.

3 **Normality:** The populations of values of the response variable associated with the treatments have normal distributions with equal variances.

In order to understand the various ways in which factor 1 and factor 2 might affect the mean response, consider Figure 10.12. It is possible that only factor 1 significantly affects the mean response (see Figure 10.12(a)). On the other hand, it is possible that only factor 2 significantly affects the mean response (see Figure 10.12(b)). It is also possible that both factors 1 and 2 significantly affect the mean response. If this is so, these factors might affect the mean response independently (see Figure 10.12(c)), or these factors might **interact** as they affect the mean response (see Figure 10.12(d)). In general, we say that **there is interaction between factors 1 and 2 if the relationship between the mean response and one of the factors depends upon the level of the other factor**. This is clearly true in Figure 10.12(d). Note here that at levels 1 and 3 of factor 1, level 1 of factor 2 gives the highest mean response, whereas at level 2 of factor 1, level 2 of factor 2 gives the highest mean response. On the other hand, the **parallel** line plots in Figure 10.12(a), (b), and (c) indicate a lack of interaction between factors 1 and 2. To graphically check for interaction, we can plot

FIGURE 10.12   Different Possible Treatment Effects in Two-Way ANOVA

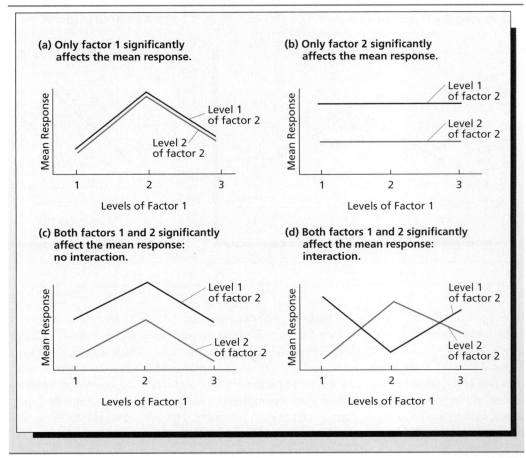

the sample treatment means, as we have done in Figure 10.11. If we obtain essentially parallel line plots, then it might be reasonable to conclude that there is little or no interaction between factors 1 and 2 (this is true in Figure 10.11). On the other hand, if the line plots are not parallel (the two lines intersect), then it might be reasonable to conclude that factors 1 and 2 interact.

In addition to graphical analysis, ANOVA is a useful tool for analyzing the data from a two-factor factorial experiment. To explain the ANOVA approach for analyzing such an experiment, we define

$\bar{x}_{ij,k}$ = the kth value of the response variable observed when using level i of factor 1 and level j of factor 2,

$\bar{x}_{ij}$ = the mean of the m values observed when using the ith level of factor 1 and the jth level of factor 2,

$\bar{x}_{i\bullet}$ = the mean of the bm values observed when using the ith level of factor 1,

$\bar{x}_{\bullet j}$ = the mean of the am values observed when using the jth level of factor 2,

$\bar{x}$ = the mean of the total of abm values that we have observed in the experiment.

The ANOVA procedure for a two-factor factorial experiment partitions the **total sum of squares (SSTO)** into four components: the **factor 1 sum of squares, $SS(1)$**; the **factor 2 sum of squares, $SS(2)$**; the **interaction sum of squares, $SS(\text{int})$**; and the **error sum of squares, SSE**. The formula for this partitioning is

$$SSTO = SS(1) + SS(2) + SS(\text{int}) + SSE.$$

The steps for calculating these sums of squares, as well as what is measured by the sums of squares, can be summarized as follows:

Step 1: Calculate the *SSTO*, which measures the total amount of variability:

$$SSTO = \sum_{i=1}^{a} \sum_{j=1}^{b} \sum_{k=1}^{m} (x_{ij,k} - \bar{x})^2.$$

Step 2: Calculate the *SS*(1), which measures the amount of variability due to the different levels of factor 1:

$$SS(1) = bm \sum_{i=1}^{a} (\bar{x}_{i\bullet} - \bar{x})^2.$$

Step 3: Calculate the *SS*(2), which measures the amount of variability due to the different levels of factor 2:

$$SS(2) = am \sum_{j=1}^{b} (\bar{x}_{\bullet j} - \bar{x})^2.$$

Step 4: Calculate the *SS*(interaction), which measures the amount of variability due to the interaction between factors 1 and 2:

$$SS(\text{int}) = m \sum_{i=1}^{a} \sum_{j=1}^{b} (\bar{x}_{ij} - \bar{x}_{i\bullet} - \bar{x}_{\bullet j} + \bar{x})^2.$$

Step 5: Calculate the *SSE*, which measures the amount of variability due to the error:

$$SSE = SSTO - SS(1) - SS(2) - SS(\text{int}).$$

These sums of squares are shown in Table 10.14, which is called a **two-way ANOVA table**. This table also gives the degrees of freedom associated with each source of variation—factor 1, factor 2, interaction, error, and total—as well as the mean squares and F statistics used to test the hypotheses of interest in a two-factor factorial experiment.

Before discussing these hypotheses, we will illustrate how the entries in the ANOVA table are calculated. The sums of squares in the shelf display case are calculated as follows (note that $a = 3$, $b = 2$, and $m = 3$):

Step 1: $SSTO = (58.2 - 61.5)^2 + (53.7 - 61.5)^2 + (55.8 - 61.5)^2$
$$+ (55.7 - 61.5)^2 + \cdots + (49.9 - 61.5)^2$$
$$= 2{,}366.28.$$

Step 2: $SS(1) = 2 \cdot 3[(\bar{x}_{B\bullet} - \bar{x})^2 + (\bar{x}_{M\bullet} - \bar{x})^2 + (\bar{x}_{T\bullet} - \bar{x})^2]$
$$= 6[(55.8 - 61.5)^2 + (77.2 - 61.5)^2 + (51.5 - 61.5)^2]$$
$$= 6(32.49 + 246.49 + 100)$$
$$= 2{,}273.88.$$

TABLE **10.14**   Two-Way ANOVA Table

Source of Variation	Degrees of Freedom	Sum of Squares	Mean Square	F
Factor 1	$a - 1$	$SS(1)$	$MS(1) = \dfrac{SS(1)}{a - 1}$	$F(1) = \dfrac{MS(1)}{MSE}$
Factor 2	$b - 1$	$SS(2)$	$MS(2) = \dfrac{SS(2)}{b - 1}$	$F(2) = \dfrac{MS(2)}{MSE}$
Interaction	$(a - 1)(b - 1)$	$SS(\text{int})$	$MS(\text{int}) = \dfrac{SS(\text{int})}{(a - 1)(b - 1)}$	$F(\text{int}) = \dfrac{MS(\text{int})}{MSE}$
Error	$ab(m - 1)$	SSE	$MSE = \dfrac{SSE}{ab(m - 1)}$	
Total	$abm - 1$	$SSTO$		

Step 3:
$$SS(2) = 3 \cdot 3[(\bar{x}_{\bullet R} - \bar{x})^2 + (\bar{x}_{\bullet W} - \bar{x})^2]$$
$$= 9[(60.8 - 61.5)^2 + (62.2 - 61.5)^2]$$
$$= 9(0.49 + 0.49)$$
$$= 8.82.$$

Step 4:
$$SS(\text{int}) = 3[(\bar{x}_{BR} - \bar{x}_{B\bullet} - \bar{x}_{\bullet R} + \bar{x})^2 + (\bar{x}_{BW} - \bar{x}_{B\bullet} - \bar{x}_{\bullet W} + \bar{x})^2$$
$$+ (\bar{x}_{MR} - \bar{x}_{M\bullet} - \bar{x}_{\bullet R} + \bar{x})^2 + (\bar{x}_{MW} - \bar{x}_{M\bullet} - \bar{x}_{\bullet W} + \bar{x})^2$$
$$+ (\bar{x}_{TR} - \bar{x}_{T\bullet} - \bar{x}_{\bullet R} + \bar{x})^2 + (\bar{x}_{TW} - \bar{x}_{T\bullet} - \bar{x}_{\bullet W} + \bar{x})^2]$$
$$= 3[(55.9 - 55.8 - 60.8 + 61.5)^2 + (55.7 - 55.8 - 62.2 + 61.5)^2$$
$$+ (75.5 - 77.2 - 60.8 + 61.5)^2 + (78.9 - 77.2 - 62.2 + 61.5)^2$$
$$+ (51.0 - 51.5 - 60.8 + 61.5)^2 + (52.0 - 51.5 - 62.2 + 61.5)^2]$$
$$= 3(3.36) = 10.08.$$

Step 5:
$$SSE = SSTO - SS(1) - SS(2) - SS(\text{int})$$
$$= 2366.28 - 2273.88 - 8.82 - 10.08$$
$$= 73.50.$$

Figure 10.13 gives the MINITAB output of a two-way ANOVA for the shelf display data. This figure shows the above-calculated sums of squares, as well as the degrees of freedom (recall that $a = 3$, $b = 2$, and $m = 3$), mean squares, and F statistics used to test the hypotheses of interest.

We first test the null hypothesis H_0 that **no interaction exists between factors 1 and 2** versus the alternative hypothesis H_a that **interaction does exist**. We can reject H_0 in favour of H_a at level of significance α if

$$F(\text{int}) = \frac{MS(\text{int})}{MSE}$$

is greater than the F_α point based on $(a - 1)(b - 1)$ numerator and $ab(m - 1)$ denominator degrees of freedom. In the shelf display case, $F_{0.05}$ based on $(a - 1)(b - 1) = 2$ numerator and

FIGURE 10.13   MINITAB Output of a Two-Way ANOVA of the Shelf Display Data

```
Rows : Height     Columns : Width        Cell Contents : Demand : Mean

                   Regular        Wide          All
         Bottom     55.90         55.70        55.80
         Middle     75.50         78.90        77.20
         Top        51.00         52.00        51.50
         All        60.80         62.20        61.50


Two-way ANOVA: Demand versus Height, Width

Source          DF           SS            MS           F           P
Height           2      2273.88 [1]    1136.94 [6]   185.62 [10]   0.000 [11]
Width            1         8.82 [2]       8.82 [7]     1.44 [12]    0.253 [13]
Interaction      2        10.08 [3]       5.04 [8]     0.82 [14]    0.462 [15]
Error           12        73.50 [4]       6.12 [9]
Total           17      2366.28 [5]


Height     Mean        Width       Mean
Bottom     55.8 [16]   Regular     60.8 [19]
Middle     77.2 [17]   Wide        62.2 [20]
Top        51.5 [18]
```

[1] SS(1)   [2] SS(2)   [3] SS(int)   [4] SSE   [5] SSTO   [6] MS(1)   [7] MS(2)   [8] MS(int)   [9] MSE   [10] F(1)   [11] p value for F(1)
[12] F(2)   [13] p value for F(2)   [14] F(int)   [15] p value for F(int)   [16] $\bar{x}_{B\bullet}$ [17] $\bar{x}_{M\bullet}$ [18] $\bar{x}_{T\bullet}$ [19] $\bar{x}_{\bullet R}$ [20] $\bar{x}_{\bullet W}$

$ab(m - 1) = 12$ denominator degrees of freedom is 3.89 (see Table A.6). Because

$$F(\text{int}) = \frac{MS(\text{int})}{MSE} = \frac{5.04}{6.12} = 0.82$$

is less than $F_{0.05} = 3.89$, we cannot reject H_0 at the 0.05 level of significance. We conclude that little or no interaction exists between shelf display height and shelf display width. That is, we conclude that the relationship between mean demand for the bakery product and shelf display height depends little (or not at all) on the shelf display width. Further, we conclude that the relationship between mean demand and shelf display width depends little (or not at all) on the shelf display height. Notice that these conclusions are suggested by the previously given plots of Figure 10.11 (page 341).

In general, when we conclude that little or no interaction exists between IV factors 1 and 2, we can (separately) test the significance of each of factors 1 and 2. We call this **testing the significance of the main effects** (what we do if we conclude that interaction does exist between factors 1 and 2 will be discussed at the end of this section).

To test the significance of factor 1 (the first IV), we test the null hypothesis H_0 **that no differences exist between the effects of the different levels of factor 1** on the mean response versus the alternative hypothesis H_a **that at least two levels of factor 1 have different effects**. We can reject H_0 in favour of H_a at level of significance α if

$$F(1) = \frac{MS(1)}{MSE}$$

is greater than the F_α point based on $a - 1$ numerator and $ab(m - 1)$ denominator degrees of freedom. In the shelf display case, $F_{0.05}$ based on $a - 1 = 2$ numerator and $ab(m - 1) = 12$ denominator degrees of freedom is 3.89. Because

$$F(1) = \frac{MS(1)}{MSE} = \frac{1136.94}{6.12} = 185.77$$

is greater than $F_{0.05} = 3.89$, we can reject H_0 at the 0.05 level of significance. Therefore, we have strong evidence that at least two of the bottom, middle, and top display heights have different effects on mean monthly demand.

To test the significance of factor 2 (the second IV), we test the null hypothesis H_0 **that no differences exist between the effects of the different levels of factor 2** on the mean response versus the alternative hypothesis H_a **that at least two levels of factor 2 have different effects**. We can reject H_0 in favour of H_a at level of significance α if

$$F(2) = \frac{MS(2)}{MSE}$$

is greater than the F_α point based on $b - 1$ numerator and $ab(m - 1)$ denominator degrees of freedom. In the shelf display case, $F_{0.05}$ based on $b - 1 = 1$ numerator and $ab(m - 1) = 12$ denominator degrees of freedom is 4.75. Because

$$F(2) = \frac{MS(2)}{MSE} = \frac{8.82}{6.12} = 1.44$$

is less than $F_{0.05} = 4.75$, we cannot reject H_0 at the 0.05 level of significance. Therefore, we do not have strong evidence that the regular display width and the wide display have different effects on mean monthly demand.

If, in a two-factor factorial experiment, we conclude that at least two levels of factor 1 have different effects or at least two levels of factor 2 have different effects, we can make pairwise comparisons to determine how the effects differ.

Point Estimates and Confidence Intervals in Two-Way ANOVA

1 Consider the **difference between the effects of levels i and i′ of factor 1 on the mean value of the response variable**.

a. A **point estimate** of this difference is $\bar{x}_{i\cdot} - \bar{x}_{i'\cdot}$.

b. An **individual 100(1 − α) percent confidence interval** for this difference is

$$\left[(\bar{x}_{i\cdot} - \bar{x}_{i'\cdot}) \pm t_{\alpha/2}\sqrt{MSE\left(\frac{2}{bm}\right)} \right],$$

where the $t_{\alpha/2}$ point is based on $ab(m - 1)$ degrees of freedom, and *MSE* is the error mean square found in the two-way ANOVA table.

c. A **Tukey simultaneous 100(1 − α) percent confidence interval** for this difference (in the set of all possible paired differences between the effects of the different levels of factor 1) is

$$\left[(\bar{x}_{i\cdot} - \bar{x}_{i'\cdot}) \pm q_{\alpha}\sqrt{MSE\left(\frac{1}{bm}\right)} \right],$$

where q_{α} is obtained from Table A.9, which is a table of percentage points of the studentized range. Here q_{α} is listed corresponding to values of *a* and $ab(m - 1)$.

2 Consider the **difference between the effects of levels j and j′ of factor 2 on the mean value of the response variable**.

a. A **point estimate** of this difference is $\bar{x}_{\cdot j} - \bar{x}_{\cdot j'}$.

b. An **individual 100(1 − α) percent confidence interval** for this difference is

$$\left[(\bar{x}_{\cdot j} - \bar{x}_{\cdot j'}) \pm t_{\alpha/2}\sqrt{MSE\left(\frac{2}{am}\right)} \right],$$

where the $t_{\alpha/2}$ point is based on $ab(m - 1)$ degrees of freedom.

c. A **Tukey simultaneous 100(1 − α) percent confidence interval** for this difference (in the set of all possible paired differences between the effects of the different levels of factor 2) is

$$\left[(\bar{x}_{\cdot j} - \bar{x}_{\cdot j'}) \pm q_{\alpha}\sqrt{MSE\left(\frac{1}{am}\right)} \right],$$

where q_{α} is obtained from Table A.9 and is listed corresponding to values of *b* and $ab(m - 1)$.

3 Let μ_{ij} denote the **mean value of the response variable obtained when using level i of factor 1 and level j of factor 2**. A point estimate of μ_{ij} is $\bar{x}_{ij}$, and an **individual 100(1 − α) percent confidence interval** for μ_{ij} is

$$\left[\bar{x}_{ij} \pm t_{\alpha/2}\sqrt{\frac{MSE}{m}} \right],$$

where the $t_{\alpha/2}$ point is based on $ab(m - 1)$ degrees of freedom.

Example 10.10 The Shelf Display Case

We have previously concluded that at least two of the bottom, middle, and top display heights have different effects on mean monthly demand. Since $\bar{x}_{M\cdot} = 77.2$ is greater than $\bar{x}_{B\cdot} = 55.8$ and $\bar{x}_{T\cdot} = 51.5$, we will use Tukey simultaneous 95 percent confidence intervals to compare the effect of a middle display height with the effects of the bottom and top display heights. To compute these intervals, we first note that $q_{0.05} = 3.77$ is the entry in Table A.9 corresponding to $a = 3$ and $ab(m - 1) = 12$. Also note that the *MSE* found in the two-way ANOVA table is 6.12 (see Figure 10.13). It follows that a Tukey simultaneous 95 percent confidence interval for the difference between the effects of a middle and a bottom display height on mean monthly demand is

$$\left[(\bar{x}_{M\cdot} - \bar{x}_{B\cdot}) \pm q_{0.05}\sqrt{MSE\left(\frac{1}{bm}\right)} \right] = \left[(77.2 - 55.8) \pm 3.77\sqrt{6.12\left(\frac{1}{2(3)}\right)} \right]$$

$$= [21.4 \pm 3.81]$$

$$= [17.59, 25.21],$$

and for the difference between the effects of a middle and a top display height on mean monthly demand is

$$[(\bar{x}_{M\cdot} - \bar{x}_{T\cdot}) \pm 3.81] = [(77.2 - 51.5) \pm 3.81]$$

$$= [21.89, 29.51].$$

Together, these intervals make us 95 percent confident that a middle shelf display height is, on average, at least 17.6 cases sold per month better than a bottom shelf display height and at least 21.9 cases sold per month better than a top shelf display height.[5]

Next, recall that previously conducted F tests suggest that there is little or no interaction between display height and display width and that there is little difference between using a regular display width and a wide display. However, intuitive and graphical analysis should always be used to supplement the results of hypothesis testing. In this case, note from Table 10.13 (page 340) that $\bar{x}_{MR} = 75.5$ and $\bar{x}_{MW} = 78.9$. This implies that we estimate that, when we use a middle display height, changing from a regular display width to a wide display increases mean monthly demand by 3.4 cases (or 34 units). This slight increase can be seen in Figure 10.11 (page 341) and suggests that it might be best (depending on what supermarkets charge for different display heights and widths) for the bakery to use a wide display with a middle display height. Since $t_{0.025}$ based on $ab(m - 1) = 12$ degrees of freedom is 2.179, an individual 95 percent confidence interval for μ_{MW}, the mean demand obtained when using a middle display height and a wide display, is

$$\left[\bar{x}_{MW} \pm t_{0.025}\sqrt{\frac{MSE}{m}} \right] = \left[78.9 \pm 2.179\sqrt{\frac{6.12}{3}} \right]$$
$$= [75.79, 82.01].$$

This interval says that, when we use a middle display height and a wide display, we can be 95 percent confident that mean demand for the bakery product will be between 75.8 and 82.0 cases per month.

If we conclude that an interaction exists between factors 1 and 2, the effects of changing the level of one IV will depend on the level of the other IV. In this case, we cannot separate the analysis of the effects of the levels of the two factors. One simple alternative procedure is to use one-way ANOVA (see Section 10.2) to compare all of the treatment means (the μ_{ij}'s) with the possible purpose of finding the best combination of levels of factors 1 and 2. For example, if there had been interaction in the shelf display case, we could have used one-way ANOVA to compare the six treatment means—μ_{BR}, μ_{BW}, μ_{MR}, μ_{MW}, μ_{TR}, and μ_{TW}—to find the best combination of display height and width. Alternatively, we could study the effects of the different levels of one factor at a specified level of the other factor. This is what we did at the end of the shelf display case, when we noticed that at a middle display height, a wide display seemed slightly more effective than a regular display width.

Finally, we might wish to study the effects of more than two factors on a response variable of interest. The ideas involved in such a study are an extension of those involved in a two-way ANOVA. Although studying more than two factors is beyond the scope of this text, a good reference is Neter, Kutner, Nachtsheim, and Wasserman (1996).

Exercises for Section 10.4

CONCEPTS

10.22 What is a treatment in the context of a two-factor factorial experiment?

10.23 Explain what we mean when we say that
  a. Interaction exists between factor 1 and factor 2.
  b. No interaction exists between the factors.

METHODS AND APPLICATIONS

10.24 An experiment is conducted to study the effects of two sales approaches—high-pressure (H) and low-pressure (L)—and to study the effects of two sales pitches (1 and 2) on the weekly sales of a product. The data in Table 10.15 are obtained by using a completely randomized design, and Figure 10.14 gives the Excel output of a two-way ANOVA of the sales experiment data. ● SaleMeth2
  a. Perform graphical analysis to check for interaction between sales pressure and sales pitch.
  b. Test for interaction by setting $\alpha = 0.05$.

---

[5]The 95 percent confidence level applies to all of the calculated confidence intervals simultaneously. If an interval is not included in an interpretation, then we are actually more than 95 percent confident in our statement.

TABLE 10.15 Results of the Sales Approach Experiment ● SaleMeth2

Sales Pressure	Sales Pitch 1	Sales Pitch 2
H	32	32
	29	30
	30	28
L	28	25
	25	24
	23	23

FIGURE 10.14 Excel Output of a Two-Way ANOVA of the Sales Approach Data

Anova: Two-Factor With Replication

SUMMARY	Pitch 1	Pitch 2	Total
High Pressure			
Count	3	3	6
Sum	91	90	181
Average	30.3333	30	30.1667 $\boxed{16}$
Variance	2.3333	4	2.5667
Low Pressure			
Count	3	3	6
Sum	76	72	148
Average	25.3333	24	24.6667 $\boxed{17}$
Variance	6.3333	1	3.4667
Total			
Count	6	6	
Sum	167	162	
Average	27.8333 $\boxed{18}$	27 $\boxed{19}$	
Variance	10.9667	12.8	

ANOVA

Source of Variation	SS	df	MS	F	P-value	F crit
Pressure	90.75 $\boxed{1}$	1	90.75 $\boxed{6}$	26.5610 $\boxed{10}$	0.0009 $\boxed{11}$	5.3177
Pitch	2.0833 $\boxed{2}$	1	2.0833 $\boxed{7}$	0.6098 $\boxed{12}$	0.4574 $\boxed{13}$	5.3177
Interaction	0.75 $\boxed{3}$	1	0.75 $\boxed{8}$	0.2195 $\boxed{14}$	0.6519 $\boxed{15}$	5.3177
Within	27.3333 $\boxed{4}$	8	3.4167 $\boxed{9}$			
Total	120.917 $\boxed{5}$	11				

$\boxed{1}$ $SS(1)$ $\boxed{2}$ $SS(2)$ $\boxed{3}$ $SS(\text{int})$ $\boxed{4}$ SSE $\boxed{5}$ $SSTO$
$\boxed{6}$ $MS(1)$ $\boxed{7}$ $MS(2)$ $\boxed{8}$ $MS(\text{int})$ $\boxed{9}$ MSE
$\boxed{10}$ $F(1)$ $\boxed{11}$ p value for $F(1)$ $\boxed{12}$ $F(2)$ $\boxed{13}$ p value for $F(2)$
$\boxed{14}$ $F(\text{int})$ $\boxed{15}$ p value for $F(\text{int})$ $\boxed{16}$ $\bar{x}_{H\bullet}$ $\boxed{17}$ $\bar{x}_{L\bullet}$ $\boxed{18}$ $\bar{x}_{\bullet 1}$ $\boxed{19}$ $\bar{x}_{\bullet 2}$

TABLE 10.16 Results of a Two-Factor Display Panel Experiment ● Display2

Display Panel	Emergency Condition 1	2	3	4
A	17	25	31	14
	14	24	34	13
B	15	22	28	9
	12	19	31	10
C	21	29	32	15
	24	28	37	19

c. Test for differences in the effects of the levels of sales pressure by setting $\alpha = 0.05$. That is, test the significance of sales pressure effects with $\alpha = 0.05$.

d. Calculate and interpret a 95 percent individual confidence interval for $\mu_{H\bullet} - \mu_{L\bullet}$.

e. Test for differences in the effects of the levels of sales pitch by setting $\alpha = 0.05$. That is, test the significance of sales pitch effects with $\alpha = 0.05$.

f. Calculate and interpret a 95 percent individual confidence interval for $\mu_{\bullet 1} - \mu_{\bullet 2}$.

g. Calculate a 95 percent individual confidence interval for mean sales when using high sales pressure and sales pitch 1. Interpret this interval.

10.25 A study compared three display panels used by air traffic controllers. Each display panel was tested for four different simulated emergency conditions. Twenty-four highly trained air traffic controllers were used in the study. Two controllers were randomly assigned to each display panel–emergency condition combination. The time (in seconds) required to stabilize the emergency condition was recorded. The data in Table 10.16 were observed. Figure 10.15 presents the MegaStat output of a two-way ANOVA of the display panel data. ● Display2

a. Interpret the MegaStat interaction plot in Figure 10.15. Then test for interaction with $\alpha = 0.05$.

b. Test the significance of display panel effects with $\alpha = 0.05$.

c. Test the significance of emergency condition effects with $\alpha = 0.05$.

d. Make pairwise comparisons of display panels A, B, and C.

e. Make pairwise comparisons of emergency conditions 1, 2, 3, and 4.

f. Which display panel minimizes the time required to stabilize an emergency condition? Does your answer depend on the emergency condition? Why?

g. Calculate a 95 percent individual confidence interval for the mean time required to stabilize emergency condition 4 using display panel B.

10.26 A telemarketing firm has studied the effects of two factors on the response to its television advertisements. The first factor is the time of day at which the ad is run, while the second is the position of the ad within the hour. The data in Table 10.16, which were obtained by using a completely randomized experimental design, give the number of calls placed to a toll-free number following a sample broadcast of the advertisement. If we use MegaStat to analyze these data, we obtain the output in Figure 10.16. ● TelMktResp

a. Perform graphical analysis to check for interaction between time of day and position of advertisement. Explain your conclusion. Then test for interaction with $\alpha = 0.05$.

b. Test the significance of time-of-day effects with $\alpha = 0.05$.

FIGURE 10.15 MegaStat Output of a Two-Way ANOVA of the Display Panel Data

Means:

		Factor 2				
		Condition 1	Condition 2	Condition 3	Condition 4	
Factor 1	Panel A	15.5	24.5	32.5	13.5	21.5
	Panel B	13.5	20.5	29.5	9.5	18.3
	Panel C	22.5	28.5	34.5	17.0	25.6
		17.2	24.5	32.2	13.3	21.8

ANOVA table

Source	SS	df	MS	F	p-value
Display Pane	218.58 [1]	2	109.292 [6]	26.49 [10]	3.96E-05 [11]
Emg Condition	1,247.46 [2]	3	415.819 [7]	100.80 [12]	8.91E-09 [13]
Interaction	16.42 [3]	6	2.736 [8]	0.66 [14]	0.6809 [15]
Error	49.50 [4]	12	4.125 [9]		
Total	1,531.96 [5]	23			

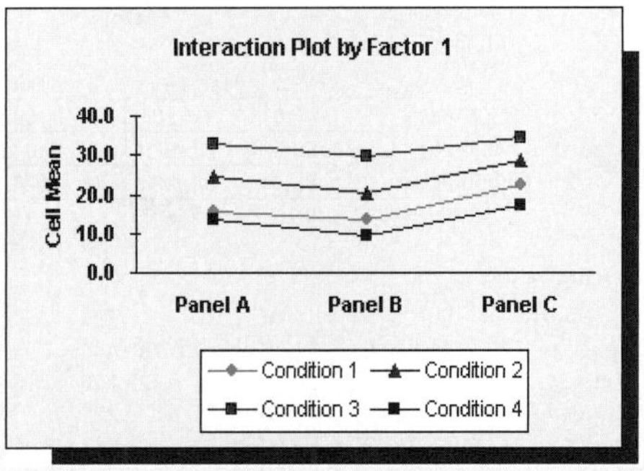

Interaction Plot by Factor 1

Condition 1 — Condition 2 — Condition 3 — Condition 4

Post hoc analysis for Factor 1
Tukey simultaneous comparison t-values (d.f. = 12)

		Panel B 18.3	Panel A 21.5	Panel C 25.6
Panel B	18.3			
Panel A	21.5	3.20		
Panel C	25.6	7.26	4.06	

critical values for experimentwise error rate:
| 0.05 | 2.67 |
| 0.01 | 3.56 |

Post hoc analysis for Factor 2
Tukey simultaneous comparison t-values (d.f. = 12)

		Condition 4 13.3	Condition 1 17.2	Condition 2 24.5	Condition 3 32.2
Condition 4	13.3				
Condition 1	17.2	3.27			
Condition 2	24.5	9.52	6.25		
Condition 3	32.2	16.06	12.79	6.54	

critical values for experimentwise error rate:
| 0.05 | 2.97 |
| 0.01 | 3.89 |

p-values for pairwise t-tests

		Panel B 18.3	Panel A 21.5	Panel C 25.6
Panel B	18.3			
Panel A	21.5	0.0076		
Panel C	25.6	9.98E-06	0.0016	

p-values for pairwise t-tests

		Condition 4 13.3	Condition 1 17.2	Condition 2 24.5	Condition 3 32.2
Condition 4	13.3				
Condition 1	17.2	0.0067			
Condition 2	24.5	6.06E-07	4.23E-05		
Condition 3	32.2	1.77E-09	2.36E-08	2.78E-05	

[1] $SS(1)$ [2] $SS(2)$ [3] $SS(\text{int})$ [4] SSE [5] $SSTO$ [6] $MS(1)$ [7] $MS(2)$ [8] $MS(\text{int})$
[9] MSE [10] $F(1)$ [11] p value for $F(1)$ [12] $F(2)$ [13] p value for $F(2)$ [14] $F(\text{int})$ [15] p value for $F(\text{int})$

TABLE 10.17 Results of a Two-Factor Telemarketing Response Experiment ● TelMktResp

Time of Day	Position of Advertisement			
	On the Hour	On the Half-Hour	Early in Program	Late in Program
10:00 morning	42	36	62	51
	37	41	68	47
	41	38	64	48
4:00 afternoon	62	57	88	67
	60	60	85	60
	58	55	81	66
9:00 evening	100	97	127	105
	96	96	120	101
	103	101	126	107

c. Test the significance of position of advertisement effects with $\alpha = 0.05$.

d. Make pairwise comparisons of the morning, afternoon, and evening times.

e. Make pairwise comparisons of the four ad positions.

f. Which time of day and advertisement position maximize consumer response? Compute a 95 percent individual confidence interval for the mean number of calls placed for this time of day–ad position combination.

10.27 A small builder of speculative homes builds three basic house designs and employs two supervisors. The builder has used each supervisor to build two houses of each design and has obtained the profits given in Table 10.18 (the profits are given in thousands of dollars). Figure 10.17 presents the MINITAB output of a two-way ANOVA of the house profitability data. ● HouseProf

FIGURE **10.16**   MegaStat Output of a Two-Way ANOVA of the Telemarketing Data

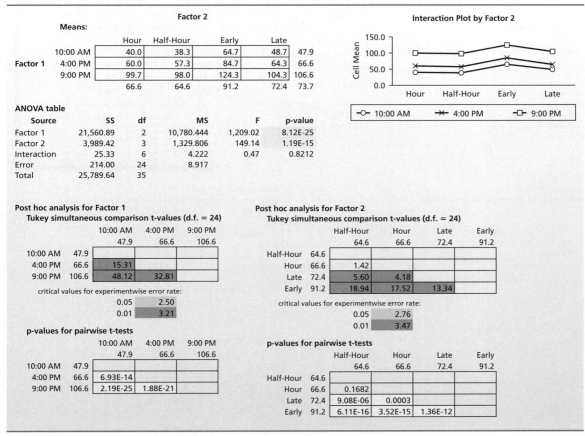

Means:

Factor 1	Hour	Half-Hour	Early	Late	
10:00 AM	40.0	38.3	64.7	48.7	47.9
4:00 PM	60.0	57.3	84.7	64.3	66.6
9:00 PM	99.7	98.0	124.3	104.3	106.6
	66.6	64.6	91.2	72.4	73.7

ANOVA table

Source	SS	df	MS	F	p-value
Factor 1	21,560.89	2	10,780.444	1,209.02	8.12E-25
Factor 2	3,989.42	3	1,329.806	149.14	1.19E-15
Interaction	25.33	6	4.222	0.47	0.8212
Error	214.00	24	8.917		
Total	25,789.64	35			

Post hoc analysis for Factor 1
Tukey simultaneous comparison t-values (d.f. = 24)

		10:00 AM	4:00 PM	9:00 PM
		47.9	66.6	106.6
10:00 AM	47.9			
4:00 PM	66.6	15.31		
9:00 PM	106.6	48.12	32.81	

critical values for experimentwise error rate:
0.05	2.50
0.01	3.21

p-values for pairwise t-tests

		10:00 AM	4:00 PM	9:00 PM
		47.9	66.6	106.6
10:00 AM	47.9			
4:00 PM	66.6	6.93E-14		
9:00 PM	106.6	2.19E-25	1.88E-21	

Post hoc analysis for Factor 2
Tukey simultaneous comparison t-values (d.f. = 24)

		Half-Hour	Hour	Late	Early
		64.6	66.6	72.4	91.2
Half-Hour	64.6				
Hour	66.6	1.42			
Late	72.4	5.60	4.18		
Early	91.2	18.94	17.52	13.34	

critical values for experimentwise error rate:
0.05	2.76
0.01	3.47

p-values for pairwise t-tests

		Half-Hour	Hour	Late	Early
		64.6	66.6	72.4	91.2
Half-Hour	64.6				
Hour	66.6	0.1682			
Late	72.4	9.08E-06	0.0003		
Early	91.2	6.11E-16	3.52E-15	1.36E-12	

TABLE **10.18**   Results of the House Profitability Study   ● HouseProf

Supervisor	House Design		
	A	B	C
1	10.2	12.2	19.4
	11.1	11.7	18.2
2	9.7	11.6	13.6
	10.8	12.0	12.7

a. Interpret the MINITAB interaction plot in Figure 10.17. Then test for interaction with $\alpha = 0.05$. Can we (separately) test for the significance of house design and supervisor effects? Explain why or why not.

b. Which house design–supervisor combination gives the highest profit? When we analyze the six house design–supervisor combinations using one-way ANOVA, we obtain $MSE = 0.390$. Compute a 95 percent individual confidence interval for mean profit when the best house design–supervisor combination is employed.

10.28 In the article "Humor in American, British, and German ads" (*Industrial Marketing Management*, vol. 22, 1993), McCullough and Taylor study humour in trade magazine advertisements. A sample of 665 ads were categorized according to two factors: nationality (American, British, or German) and industry (29 levels, ranging from accounting to travel). A panel of judges ranked the degree of humour in each ad on a five-point scale. When the resulting data were analyzed using two-way ANOVA, the p values for testing the significance of nationality, industry, and the interaction between nationality and industry were, respectively, 0.087, 0.000, and 0.046. Discuss why these p values agree with the following verbal conclusions of the authors: "British ads were more likely to be humorous than German or American ads in the graphics industry. German ads were least humorous in the grocery and mining industries, but funnier than American ads in the medical industry and funnier than British ads in the packaging industry."

FIGURE 10.17   MINITAB Output of a Two-Way ANOVA of the House Profitability Data

```
Rows: Supervisor    Columns: Design

            A       B       C      All
1         10.65   11.95   18.80   13.80
2         10.25   11.80   13.15   11.73
All       10.45   11.88   15.98   12.77

Cell Contents: Profit : Mean
```

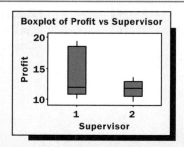

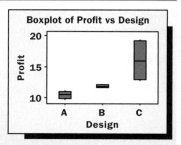

Two-way ANOVA: Profit versus Supervisor, Design

```
Source        DF      SS        MS       F      P
Supervisor     1    12.813   12.8133   32.85   0.001
Design         2    65.822   32.9108   84.39   0.000
Interaction    2    19.292    9.6458   24.73   0.001
Error          6     2.340    0.3900
Total         11   100.267

Supervisor  Mean         Design   Mean
1           13.8000      A        10.450
2           11.7333      B        11.875
                         C        15.975
```

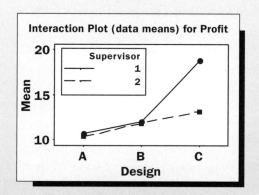

CHAPTER SUMMARY

We began this chapter by introducing some basic concepts of **experimental design**. We saw that we carry out an experiment by setting the values of one or more **factors** before the values of the **response variable** are observed. The different values (or levels) of a factor are called **treatments**, and the purpose of most experiments is to compare and estimate the effects of the various treatments on the response variable. We saw that the different treatments are assigned to **experimental units**, and we discussed the **completely randomized experimental design**. This design assigns independent, random samples of experimental units to the treatments.

We began studying how to analyze experimental data by discussing **one-way analysis of variance (ANOVA)**. Here we study how one factor (with p levels) affects the response variable. In particular, we learned how to use this methodology to test for differences between the **treatment means** and to estimate the size of pairwise differences between the treatment means.

Sometimes, even if we randomly select the experimental units, differences between the experimental units conceal differences between the treatments. In such a case, we learned that we can employ a **randomized block design**. Each **block** (experimental unit or set of experimental units) is used exactly once to measure the effect of each and every treatment. Because we are comparing the treatments by using the same experimental units, any true differences between the treatments will not be concealed by differences between the experimental units.

The last technique we studied in this chapter was **two-way ANOVA**. Here we study the effects of two factors by carrying out a **two-factor factorial experiment**. If there is little or no interaction between the two factors, then we are able to separately study the significance of each of the two factors. On the other hand, if substantial interaction exists between the two factors, we study the nature of the differences between the treatment means.

GLOSSARY OF TERMS

analysis of variance (ANOVA) table: A table that summarizes the sums of squares, mean squares, F statistic(s), and p value(s) for an ANOVA. (pages 325, 333, and 343)

completely randomized experimental design: An experimental design in which independent, random samples of experimental units are assigned to the treatments. (page 316)

experimental units: The entities (objects, people, and so on) to which the treatments are assigned. (page 316)

factor: A variable that might influence the response variable; an independent variable (IV). (page 316)

interaction: When the relationship between the mean response and one factor depends on the level of the other factor. (page 341)

one-way ANOVA: A method used to estimate and compare the effects of the different levels of a single factor on a response variable. (page 319)

randomized block design: An experimental design that compares p treatments by using b blocks (experimental units or sets of experimental units). Each block is used exactly once to measure the effect of each and every treatment. (page 332)

replication: When a treatment is applied to more than one experimental unit. (page 316)

response variable: The variable of interest in an experiment; the dependent variable (DV). (page 316)

treatment: A value (or level) of a factor (or combination of factors). (page 316)

treatment mean: The mean value of the response variable obtained by using a particular treatment. (page 319)

two-factor factorial experiment: An experiment in which we randomly assign m experimental units to each combination of levels of two factors. (page 341)

two-way ANOVA: A method used to study the effects of two factors on a response variable. (page 341)

IMPORTANT FORMULAS AND TESTS

One-way ANOVA sums of squares: pages 322–323

One-way ANOVA F test: page 323

One-way ANOVA table: page 325

Estimation in one-way ANOVA: page 326

Randomized block sums of squares: page 333

Randomized block ANOVA table: page 333

Estimation in a randomized block experiment: page 335

Two-way ANOVA sums of squares: page 343

Two-way ANOVA table: page 343

Estimation in two-way ANOVA: page 346

SUPPLEMENTARY EXERCISES

10.29 A drug company wishes to compare the effects of three different drugs (X, Y, and Z) that are being developed to reduce cholesterol levels. Each drug is administered to six patients at the recommended dosage for six months. At the end of this period, the reduction in cholesterol level is recorded for each patient. The results are given in Table 10.19. Completely analyze these data using one-way ANOVA. Use the MegaStat output in Figure 10.18.   ◗ CholRed

10.30 In an article in *Accounting and Finance* (the journal of the Accounting Association of Australia and New Zealand), Church and Schneider report on a study concerning auditor objectivity. A sample of 45 auditors was randomly divided into three groups: (1) the 15 auditors in group 1 designed an audit program for accounts receivable and evaluated an audit program for accounts payable designed by somebody else, (2) the 15 auditors in group 2 did the reverse, (3) the 15 auditors in group 3 (the control group) evaluated the audit programs for both accounts. All 45 auditors were then instructed to spend an additional 15 hours investigating suspected irregularities in either or both of the audit programs. The mean additional number of hours allocated to the accounts receivable audit

program by the auditors in groups 1, 2, and 3 were $\bar{x}_1 = 6.7$, $\bar{x}_2 = 9.7$, and $\bar{x}_3 = 7.6$. Furthermore, a one-way ANOVA of the data shows that $SST = 71.51$ and $SSE = 321.3$.

a. Define appropriate treatment means μ_1, μ_2, and μ_3. Then test for statistically significant differences between these treatment means. Set $\alpha = 0.05$. Can we conclude that the different auditor groups have different effects on the mean additional time allocated to investigating the accounts receivable audit program?

b. Perform pairwise comparisons of the treatment means by computing a Tukey simultaneous 95 percent confidence interval for each of the pairwise differences $\mu_1 - \mu_2$, $\mu_1 - \mu_3$, and $\mu_2 - \mu_3$. Interpret the results. What do your results imply about the objectivity of auditors? What are the practical implications of this result?

10.31 The loan officers at a large bank can use three different methods for evaluating loan applications. Loan decisions can be based on (1) the applicant's balance sheet (B), (2) examination of key financial ratios (F), or (3) use of a new decision support system (D). In order to compare these three methods, four of the bank's loan officers are randomly selected. Each officer employs each of the evaluation methods for one month (the methods are employed in randomly selected orders). After a year has passed, the percentage of bad loans for each loan officer and evaluation method is determined. The data obtained by using this randomized block design are given in Table 10.20. Completely analyze the data using randomized block ANOVA.   ◗ LoanEval

10.32 In an article in the *Accounting Review*, Brown and Solomon study the effects of two factors—confirmation of accounts receivable and verification of sales transactions—on account misstatement risk by auditors. Both factors had two levels—completed

TABLE 10.19   Reduction of Cholesterol Levels
◗ CholRed

	Drug	
X	*Y*	*Z*
22	40	15
31	35	9
19	47	14
27	41	11
25	39	21
18	33	5

FIGURE 10.18 MegaStat Output of an ANOVA of the Cholesterol Reduction Data

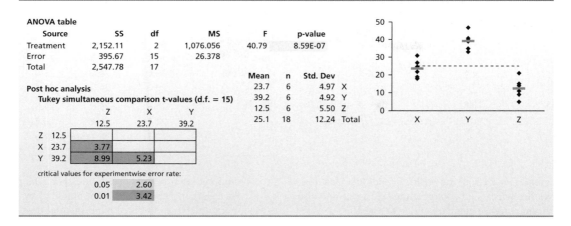

TABLE 10.20 Results of a Loan Evaluation Experiment ⬤ LoanEval

Loan Officer	Loan Evaluation Method		
	B	F	D
1	8	5	4
2	6	4	3
3	5	2	1
4	4	1	0

FIGURE 10.19 Line Plot for Exercise 10.32

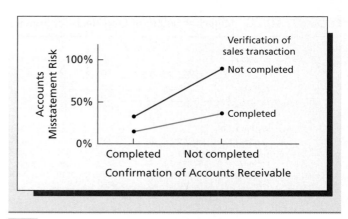

Source: "Configural information processing in auditing: The role of domain-specific knowledge," by C. E. Brown and I. Solomon, *The Accounting Review,* 66, no. 1 (January 1991), p. 105 (Figure 1). Copyright © 1991 American Accounting Association. Used with permission.

or not completed—and a line plot of the treatment mean misstatement risks is shown in Figure 10.19. This line plot makes it appear that interaction exists between the two factors. In your own words, explain what the interaction means in practical terms.

10.33 In an article in the *Academy of Management Journal,* Hicks and Klimoski studied the effects of two factors—degree of attendance choice and prior information—on managers' evaluation of a two-day workshop concerning performance reviews. Degree of attendance choice had two levels: high (little pressure from supervisors to attend) and low (mandatory attendance). Prior information also had two levels: realistic preview and traditional announcement. Twenty-one managers were randomly assigned to the four treatment combinations. At the end of the program, each manager was asked to rate the workshop on a seven-point scale (1 = no satisfaction, 7 = extreme satisfaction). The following sample treatment means were obtained:

Degree of Attendance Choice	Prior Information	
	Realistic Preview	Traditional Announcement
High	6.20	6.06
Low	5.33	4.82

Source: "Entry into training programs and its effects on training outcomes: A field experiment," by W. D. Hicks and R. J. Klimoski, *Academy, of Management Journal,* 30, no. 3 (September 1987), p. 548.

In addition, the $SS(1)$, $SS(2)$, $SS(int)$, and SSE were calculated to be, respectively, 22.26, 1.55, 0.61, and 114.4. Here factor 1 is degree of choice and factor 2 is prior information. Completely analyze this situation using two-way ANOVA.

10.34 An information systems manager wishes to compare the execution speed (in seconds) for a standard statistical software package using three different compilers. The manager tests each compiler using three different computer models, and the data in Table 10.21 are obtained. Completely analyze the data (using a

TABLE 10.21 Results of an Execution Speed Experiment for Three Compilers (Seconds) ● ExecSpd

Computer	Compiler 1	Compiler 2	Compiler 3
Model 235	9.9	8.0	7.1
Model 335	12.5	10.6	9.1
Model 435	10.8	9.0	7.8

TABLE 10.22 Results of a Two-Factor Wheat Yield Experiment ● Wheat

Fertilizer Type	Wheat Type M	N	O	P
A	19.4	25.0	24.8	23.1
	20.6	24.0	26.0	24.3
	20.0	24.5	25.4	23.7
B	22.6	25.6	27.6	25.4
	21.6	26.8	26.4	24.5
	22.1	26.2	27.0	26.3

computer package if you wish). In particular, test for compiler effects and computer model effects, and also perform pairwise comparisons. ● ExecSpd

10.35 A research team at a school of agriculture carried out an experiment to study the effects of two fertilizer types (A and B) and four wheat types (M, N, O,

and P) on crop yields (in tonnes per 5-ha plot). The data in Table 10.22 were obtained by using a completely randomized experimental design. Analyze these data by using the MegaStat output in Figure 10.20. ● Wheat

FIGURE 10.20 MegaStat Output of Crop Yields for Exercise 10.35

Means:

Factor 1	M	N	O	P	
A	20.00	24.50	25.40	23.70	23.40
B	22.10	26.20	27.00	25.40	25.18
	21.05	25.35	26.20	24.55	24.29

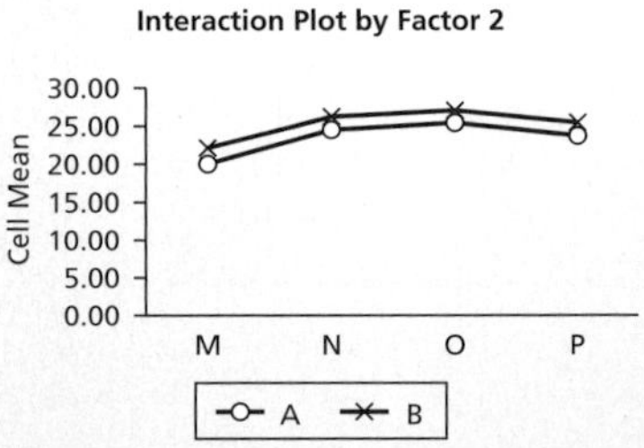

Interaction Plot by Factor 2

ANOVA table

Source	SS	df	MS	F	p-value
Factor 1	18.904	1	18.9038	48.63	3.14E-06
Factor 2	92.021	3	30.6738	78.90	8.37E-10
Interaction	0.221	3	0.0737	0.19	0.9019
Error	6.220	16	0.3888		
Total	117.366	23			

Post hoc analysis for Factor 1
Tukey simultaneous comparison t-values (d.f. = 16)

		A 23.40	B 25.18
A	23.40		
B	25.18	6.97	

critical values for experimentwise error rate:
| 0.05 | 2.12 |
| 0.01 | 2.92 |

p-values for pairwise t-tests

		A 23.40	B 25.18
A	23.40		
B	25.18	3.14E-06	

Post hoc analysis for Factor 2
Tukey simultaneous comparison t-values (d.f. = 16)

		M 21.05	P 24.55	N 25.35	O 26.20
M	21.05				
P	24.55	9.72			
N	25.35	11.95	2.22		
O	26.20	14.31	4.58	2.36	

critical values for experimentwise error rate:
| 0.05 | 2.86 |
| 0.01 | 3.67 |

p-values for pairwise t-tests

		M 21.05	P 24.55	N 25.35	O 26.20
M	21.05				
P	24.55	4.06E-08			
N	25.35	2.20E-09	0.0410		
O	26.20	1.55E-10	0.0003	0.0312	

10.36 INTERNET EXERCISE

Recently, because of rising gasoline prices, people have been concerned about the fuel consumption of their vehicles. One common belief is that larger vehicles are far less fuel efficient than are smaller vehicles. Natural Resources Canada lists the most fuel-efficient vehicles for 2007 on their Web site: http://oee.nrcan.gc.ca/transportation/personal/pdfs/most-efficient-vehicles-2007.pdf.

Group the vehicles into three groups: (1) two-seater, subcompact, and compact (n = 3), (2) mid-size, full-size,

and station wagon (n = 3), and (3) pickup trucks and special purpose (n = 3). Compute the mean fuel consumption values for each group for city driving and for highway driving separately. Conduct a one-way ANOVA on the city driving values. What do the results tell you? Conduct a one-way ANOVA on the highway driving values. What do the results tell you? Based on the findings of the two analyses, make a conclusion about the claim that larger vehicles are much less fuel efficient.

CHAPTER **11**

Correlation Coefficient and Simple Linear Regression Analysis

Managers often make decisions by studying the relationships between variables, and process improvements can often be made by understanding how changes in one or more variables affect the process output. The basic statistic for understanding how two variables are related is the correlation coefficient (r), which is also known as the Pearson-product-moment correlation, named after its creator Karl Pearson (1857–1936). This nifty little statistic describes two properties of the linear relationship between variables: the direction (positive or negative) and the strength (from zero, or no relationship, to one, or a perfect relationship). The correlation coefficient is briefly discussed in this chapter. Following the discussion of the correlation statistic (note that r was originally chosen as an abbreviation for "regression"), regression analysis is covered.

Regression analysis is a statistical technique in which we use observed data to relate a variable of interest, which is called the **dependent** (or **response** or **criterion**) **variable**, to one or more **independent** (or **predictor**) **variables**. The objective is to build a **regression model**, or **prediction equation**, that can be used to **describe**, **predict**, and **control** the dependent variable on the basis of the independent variables. For example, a company might wish to improve its marketing process. After collecting data concerning the demand for a product, the product's price, and the advertising expenditures made to promote the product, the company might use regression analysis to develop an equation to predict demand on the basis of price and advertising expenditure. Predictions of demand for various price–advertising expenditure combinations can then be used to evaluate potential changes in the company's marketing strategies. As another example, a manufacturer might use regression analysis to describe the relationship between several input variables and an important output variable. Understanding the relationships between these variables would allow the manufacturer to identify **control variables** that can be used to improve the process performance.

In this chapter, we present the simple linear regression model. Using this technique is appropriate when we are relating a dependent variable to a single independent variable and when a **straight-line model** describes the relationship between these two variables. We explain many of the methods of this chapter in the context of a new case:

The QHIC Case. The marketing department at Quality Home Improvement Centre (QHIC) uses simple linear regression analysis to predict home upkeep expenditure on the basis of home value.

Predictions of home upkeep expenditures are used to help determine which homes should be sent advertising brochures promoting QHIC's products and services.

11.1 Correlation Coefficient

In Chapter 2, we discussed how to use a scatter plot to explore the relationship between a dependent variable y and an independent variable x. To construct a scatter plot, a sample of n pairs of values of x and y—$(x_1, y_1), (x_2, y_2), \ldots, (x_n, y_n)$—is collected. Then each value of y is plotted against the corresponding value of x. If the plot points seem to fluctuate around a straight line, we say that there is a **linear relationship** between x and y. For example, suppose that 10 sales regions of equal sales potential for a company were randomly selected. The advertising expenditures (in units of $10,000) in these 10 sales regions were purposely set in July of last year at the values given in the second column of Table 11.1. The sales volumes (in units of $10,000) were then recorded for the 10 sales regions and found to be as given in the third column of Table 11.1. A scatter plot of sales volume, y, versus advertising expenditure, x, is given in Figure 11.1 and shows a linear relationship between x and y.

A measure of the **strength of the linear relationship** between x and y is the **covariance**. The **sample covariance** is calculated by using the sample of n pairs of observed values of x and y. This sample covariance is denoted as s_{xy} and is defined as follows:

$$s_{xy} = \frac{\sum_{i=1}^{n} (x_i - \bar{x})(y_i - \bar{y})}{n - 1}.$$

To use this formula, we first find the mean $\bar{x}$ of the n observed values of x and the mean $\bar{y}$ of the n observed values of y. For each observed (x_i, y_i) combination, we then multiply the deviation of x_i from $\bar{x}$ by the deviation of y_i from $\bar{y}$ to form the product $(x_i - \bar{x})(y_i - \bar{y})$. Finally, we add together the n products $(x_1 - \bar{x})(y_1 - \bar{y})$, $(x_2 - \bar{x})(y_2 - \bar{y})$, $\ldots$, $(x_n - \bar{x})(y_n - \bar{y})$ and divide the resulting sum by $n - 1$. For example, the mean of the 10 advertising expenditures in Table 11.1 is $\bar{x} = 9.5$, and the mean of the 10 sales volumes in Table 11.1 is $\bar{y} = 108.3$. It follows that the numerator of s_{xy} is the sum of the values of $(x_i - \bar{x})(y_i - \bar{y}) = (x_i - 9.5)(y_i - 108.3)$. Table 11.2 shows that this sum equals 365.50, which implies that the sample covariance is

$$s_{xy} = \frac{\sum (x_i - \bar{x})(y_i - \bar{y})}{n - 1} = \frac{365.50}{9} = 40.61111.$$

To interpret the covariance, consider Figure 11.2(a). This figure shows the scatter plot of Figure 11.1 with a vertical blue line drawn at $\bar{x} = 9.5$ and a horizontal red line drawn at $\bar{y} = 108.3$. The lines divide the scatter plot into four quadrants. Points in quadrant I correspond to x_i greater than $\bar{x}$ and y_i greater than $\bar{y}$ and thus give a value of $(x_i - \bar{x})(y_i - \bar{y})$ greater than 0. Points in quadrant III correspond to x_i less than $\bar{x}$ and y_i less than $\bar{y}$ and thus also give a value of $(x_i - \bar{x})(y_i - \bar{y})$ greater than 0. It follows that if s_{xy} is positive, the points with the greatest

TABLE 11.1 The Sales Volume Data

Sales Region	Advertising Expenditure, x	Sales Volume, y
1	5	89
2	6	87
3	7	98
4	8	110
5	9	103
6	10	114
7	11	116
8	12	110
9	13	126
10	14	130

FIGURE 11.1 A Scatter Plot of Sales Volume versus Advertising Expenditure

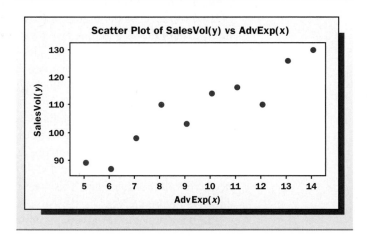

TABLE 11.2 The Calculation of the Numerator of s_{xy}

	x_i	y_i	$(x_i - 9.5)$	$(y_i - 108.3)$	$(x_i - 9.5)(y_i - 108.3)$
	5	89	−4.5	−19.3	86.85
	6	87	−3.5	−21.3	74.55
	7	98	−2.5	−10.3	25.75
	8	110	−1.5	1.7	−2.55
	9	103	−0.5	−5.3	2.65
	10	114	0.5	5.7	2.85
	11	116	1.5	7.7	11.55
	12	110	2.5	1.7	4.25
	13	126	3.5	17.7	61.95
	14	130	4.5	21.7	97.65
Totals	95	1,083	0	0	365.50

FIGURE 11.2 Interpretation of the Sample Covariance

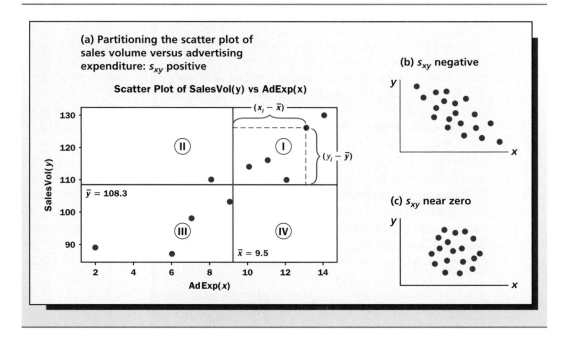

influence on $\Sigma(x_i - \bar{x})(y_i - \bar{y})$ and thus on s_{xy} must be in quadrants I and III. Therefore, a positive value of s_{xy} (as in the sales volume example) indicates a positive linear relationship between x and y. That is, as x increases, y increases.

If we further consider Figure 11.2, we see that points in quadrant II correspond to x_i less than $\bar{x}$ and y_i greater than $\bar{y}$ and thus give a value of $(x_i - \bar{x})(y_i - \bar{y})$ less than 0. Points in quadrant IV correspond to x_i greater than $\bar{x}$ and y_i less than $\bar{y}$ and thus also give a value of $(x_i - \bar{x})(y_i - \bar{y})$ less than 0. It follows that if s_{xy} is negative, the points with the greatest influence on $\Sigma(x_i - \bar{x})(y_i - \bar{y})$ and thus on s_{xy} must be in quadrants II and IV. Therefore, a negative value of s_{xy} indicates a negative linear relationship between x and y. That is, as x increases, y decreases, as shown in Figure 11.2(b). For example, a negative linear relationship might exist between average hourly outdoor temperature (x) in a city during a week and the city's natural gas consumption (y) during the week. That is, as the average hourly outdoor temperature increases, the city's natural gas consumption would decrease. Finally, note that if s_{xy} is near zero, the (x_i, y_i) points would be fairly evenly distributed across all four quadrants. This would indicate little or no linear relationship between x and y, as shown in Figure 11.2(c).[1]

From the previous discussion, it might seem that a large positive value for the covariance indicates that x and y have a strong positive linear relationship and a large negative value for the covariance indicates that x and y have a strong negative linear relationship. However, one problem with using the covariance as a measure of the strength of the linear relationship between x and y is that the value of the covariance depends on the units in which x and y are measured. A measure of the strength of the linear relationship between x and y that does not depend on the units in which x and y are measured is the **correlation coefficient**. The **simple correlation coefficient** is denoted as r and is defined as follows:

$$r = \frac{s_{xy}}{s_x s_y}.$$

Here s_{xy} is the previously defined sample covariance, s_x is the sample standard deviation of the sample of x values, and s_y is the sample standard deviation of the sample of y values. For the sales volume data,

$$s_x = \sqrt{\frac{\sum_{i=1}^{10}(x_i - \bar{x})^2}{9}} = 3.02765 \quad \text{and} \quad s_y = \sqrt{\frac{\sum_{i=1}^{10}(y_i - \bar{y})^2}{9}} = 14.30656.$$

Therefore, the sample correlation coefficient is

$$r = \frac{s_{xy}}{s_x s_y} = \frac{40.61111}{(3.02765)(14.30656)} = 0.93757.$$

It can be shown that the sample correlation coefficient r is always between -1 and 1. A value of r near 0 implies little linear relationship between x and y. A value of r close to 1 says that x and y have a strong tendency to move together in a straight-line fashion with a positive slope and, therefore, that x and y are highly related and **positively correlated**. A value of r close to -1 says that x and y have a strong tendency to move together in a straight-line fashion with a negative slope and, therefore, that x and y are highly related and **negatively correlated**. Note that if $r = 1$, the (x, y) points fall exactly on a positively sloped straight line, and, if $r = -1$, the (x, y) points fall exactly on a negatively sloped straight line. For example, since $r = 0.93757$ in the sales volume example, we conclude that advertising expenditure (x) and sales volume (y) have a strong tendency to move together in a straight-line fashion with a positive slope. That is, x and y have a strong positive linear relationship. In general, however, note that a strong positive or a strong negative linear relationship between an independent variable x and a dependent variable y does not necessarily mean that we can accurately **predict** y on the basis of x. We consider predicting y on the basis of x later in this chapter.

---

[1]One way to remember the zero correlation is that the scatter plot looks like a circle or a zero.

The sample covariance s_{xy} is the point estimate of the **population covariance**, which we denote as σ_{xy}, and the sample correlation coefficient r is the point estimate of the **population correlation coefficient**, which we denote as ρ. To define σ_{xy} and ρ, let μ_x and σ_x denote the mean and the standard deviation of the population of all possible x values, and let μ_y and σ_y denote the mean and the standard deviation of the population of all possible y values. Then, σ_{xy} is the average of all possible values of $(x - \mu_x)(y - \mu_y)$, and ρ equals $\sigma_{xy}/(\sigma_x \sigma_y)$. Similar to r, ρ is always between -1 and 1.

Another nifty statistic derived from the correlation coefficient (r) is the simple coefficient of determination or eta squared (eta^2) or r squared (r^2). Eta^2 is simply the squared correlation value as a percentage and tells you the amount of variance overlap between the two variables x and y. For example, if the correlation between self-reported altruistic behaviour and charity donations is 0.24, then eta^2 is $0.24 \times 0.24 = 0.0576$. Expressing this number as a percentage gives 5.76 percent. From this value, it can be concluded that 5.76 percent of the variance in charity donations overlaps with the variance in self-reported altruistic behaviour. More about r^2 and variance overlap and predicting y from x is discussed in Section 11.7.

Exercises for Section 11.1

METHODS AND APPLICATIONS

11.1 Recall from Example 2.12 (page 68) that chemical XB-135 is used in the production of a chemical product, and chemists feel that the amount of chemical XB-135 may be related to the viscosity of the chemical product. Also recall that to verify and quantify this relationship, 24 batches of the product are produced. The amount (x) of chemical XB-135 (in kilograms) is varied from batch to batch, and the viscosity (y) obtained for each batch is measured. Table 2.11 (page 69) gives (in time order) the values of x and the corresponding values of y for the 24 batches. Using the facts that

$$\sum_{i=1}^{24} (x_i - \bar{x})(y_i - \bar{y}) = 10.2281,$$

$$s_x = 0.7053, \text{ and } s_y = 0.6515,$$

calculate the sample covariance s_{xy} and the sample correlation coefficient r. Interpret r. What can we say about the strength of the linear relationship between x and y?

11.2 Statistics Canada (http://www.statcan.ca) collects data on the social behaviour of Canadians. One activity for which data are collected deals with donations to chari-

ties. Average donations (in dollars) are reported by Statistics Canada by age groups of Canadians for the year 2000, and the values are provided below for adults aged 15 and over.

Age Group	Average Donation ($)
15–24 years	118
25–34 years	229
35–44 years	242
45–54 years	338
55–64 years	316
65 years and over	308

Source: http://www40.statcan.ca/l01/cst01/famil104.htm.

For these data, compute the correlation value and interpret r (here, use a single number to represent each age group, such as 1, 2, 3, etc.). Also compute r^2 (eta^2). Based on the r^2 (eta^2) value, what percentage of variance overlap is found between age and average donation amount?

11.2 The Simple Linear Regression Model

The **simple linear regression model** assumes that the relationship between the **dependent variable, which is denoted** y, and the **independent variable, denoted** x, can be approximated by a straight line. We can tentatively decide whether there is an approximate straight-line relationship between y and x by making a **scatter diagram**, or **scatter plot**, of y versus x. First, data concerning the two variables are observed in pairs. To construct the scatter plot, each value of y is plotted against its corresponding value of x. If the y values tend to increase or decrease in a straight-line fashion as the x values increase, and if there is a scattering of the (x, y) points around the straight line, then it is reasonable to describe the relationship between y and x by using the simple linear regression model.

We suppose that we have gathered n observations—each observation consists of an observed value of x and its corresponding value of y. Then, we have the following:

The Simple Linear Regression Model

The **simple linear (or straight-line) regression model** is $y = \mu_{y|x} + \varepsilon = \beta_0 + \beta_1 x + \varepsilon$.

1   $\mu_{y|x} = \beta_0 + \beta_1 x$ is the **mean value** of the dependent variable y when the value of the independent variable is x.

2   β_0 is the **y intercept**. β_0 is the mean value of y when x equals zero.

3   β_1 is the **slope**. β_1 is the change (amount of increase or decrease) in the mean value of y associated with a one-unit increase in x. If β_1 is positive, the mean value of y increases as x increases. If β_1 is negative, the mean value of y decreases as x increases.

4   ε is an error term that describes the effects on y of all factors other than the value of the independent variable x.

This model is illustrated in Figure 11.3 (note that x_0 in this figure denotes a specific value of the independent variable x). The y intercept β_0 and the slope β_1 are called **regression parameters**. Because we do not know the true values of these parameters, we must use the sample data to estimate them. We see how this is done in the next section. In later sections, we show how to use these estimates to predict y.

FIGURE **11.3**   **The Simple Linear Regression Model (Here the Slope β_1 Is Positive)**

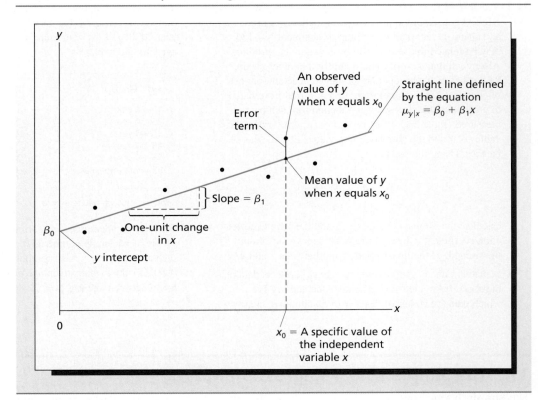

Example 11.1   The QHIC Case

Quality Home Improvement Centre (QHIC) operates five stores in a large metropolitan area. The marketing department at QHIC wishes to study the relationship between x, home value (in thousands of dollars), and y, yearly expenditure on home upkeep (in dollars). A random sample of 40 homeowners is taken and asked to estimate their expenditures during the previous year on the types of home upkeep products and services offered by QHIC. Public city records are used to obtain the previous year's assessed values of the homeowner's homes. The resulting x and y

TABLE 11.3   The QHIC Upkeep Expenditure Data   ◉ QHIC

(a) The data

Home	Value of Home, x (Thousands of Dollars)	Upkeep Expenditure, y (Dollars)	Home	Value of Home, x (Thousands of Dollars)	Upkeep Expenditure, y (Dollars)
1	237.00	1,412.08	21	153.04	849.14
2	153.08	797.20	22	232.18	1,313.84
3	184.86	872.48	23	125.44	602.06
4	222.06	1,003.42	24	169.82	642.14
5	160.68	852.90	25	177.28	1,038.80
6	99.68	288.48	26	162.82	697.00
7	229.04	1,288.46	27	120.44	324.34
8	101.78	423.08	28	191.10	965.10
9	257.86	1,351.74	29	158.78	920.14
10	96.28	378.04	30	178.50	950.90
11	171.00	918.08	31	272.20	1,670.32
12	231.02	1,627.24	32	48.90	125.40
13	228.32	1,204.76	33	104.56	479.78
14	205.90	857.04	34	286.18	2,010.64
15	185.72	775.00	35	83.72	368.36
16	168.78	869.26	36	86.20	425.60
17	247.06	1,396.00	37	133.58	626.90
18	155.54	711.50	38	212.86	1,316.94
19	224.20	1,475.18	39	122.02	390.16
20	202.04	1,413.32	40	198.02	1,090.84

(b) MINITAB Plot of Upkeep Expenditure versus Value of Home

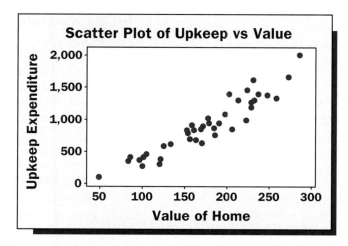

values are given in Table 11.3(a). Because the 40 observations are for the same year (for different homes), **these data are cross-sectional** (data observed at a single point in time as opposed to time series data, which are longitudinal).

The MINITAB output of a scatter plot of y versus x is given in Table 11.3(b). We see that the observed values of y tend to increase in a straight-line (or slightly curved) fashion as x increases. Assuming that $\mu_{y|x}$ and x have a straight-line relationship, it is reasonable to relate y to x by using the simple linear regression model with a positive slope ($\beta_1 > 0$)

$$y = \beta_0 + \beta_1 x + \varepsilon.$$

The slope β_1 is the change (increase) in mean dollar yearly upkeep expenditure associated with each \$1,000 increase in home value. In later examples, the marketing department at QHIC will use predictions given by this simple linear regression model to help determine which homes should be sent advertising brochures promoting QHIC's products and services.

We have interpreted the slope β_1 of the simple linear regression model to be the change in the mean value of y associated with a one-unit increase in x. We sometimes refer to this change as **the effect of the independent variable x on the dependent variable y**. However, we cannot prove that a **change in an independent variable causes a change in the dependent variable**. Rather, regression can be used only to establish that the two variables move together and that the independent variable contributes information for predicting the dependent variable. For instance, regression analysis might be used to establish that as liquor sales have increased over the years, university professors' salaries have also increased. However, this does not prove that increases in liquor sales cause increases in university professors' salaries. Rather, both variables are influenced by a third variable—long-run growth in the economy.

Exercises for Section 11.2

CONCEPTS

11.3 When does the scatter plot of the values of a dependent variable y versus the values of an independent variable x suggest that the simple linear regression model

$$y = \mu_{y|x} + \varepsilon$$
$$= \beta_0 + \beta_1 x + \varepsilon$$

might appropriately relate y to x?

11.4 In the simple linear regression model, what are y, $\mu_{y|x}$, and ε?

11.5 In the simple linear regression model, define the slope β_1 and the y intercept β_0.

11.6 What is the difference between time series data and cross-sectional data?

METHODS AND APPLICATIONS

11.7 THE SERVICE TIME CASE ◐ SrvcTime

Accu-Copiers, sells and services the Accu-500 copying machine. As part of its standard service contract, the company agrees to perform routine service on this copier. To obtain information about the time it takes to perform routine service, Accu-Copiers has collected data for 11 service calls. The data are as in Figure 11.4. Using the scatter plot (from MINITAB) of y versus x, discuss why the simple linear regression model might appropriately relate y to x.

11.8 THE SERVICE TIME CASE ◐ SrvcTime

Consider the simple linear regression model describing the service time data in Exercise 11.7.
a. Interpret $\mu_{y|x=4} = \beta_0 + \beta_1(4)$.
b. Interpret $\mu_{y|x=6} = \beta_0 + \beta_1(6)$.
c. Interpret the slope parameter β_1.
d. Interpret the y intercept β_0. Does this interpretation make practical sense?
e. The error term ε describes the effects of many factors on service time. What are these factors? Give two specific examples.

11.9 THE FRESH DETERGENT CASE ◐ Fresh

Enterprise Industries produces Fresh, a brand of liquid laundry detergent. In order to study the relationship between price and demand for the large bottle of Fresh, the company has gathered data concerning demand for Fresh over the last 30 sales periods (each sales period is four weeks). Here, for each sales period,

> y = demand for the large bottle of Fresh (in hundreds of thousands of bottles) in the sales period, and

> x = the difference between the average industry price (in dollars) of competitors' similar detergents and the price (in dollars) of Fresh as offered by Enterprise Industries in the sales period.

FIGURE 11.4 Routine Copier Service Times for Exercise 11.7

Service Call	Number of Copiers Serviced, x	Number of Minutes Required, y	
1	4	109	
2	2	58	
3	5	138	
4	7	189	
5	1	37	
6	3	82	
7	4	103	
8	5	134	
9	2	68	
10	4	112	
11	6	154	

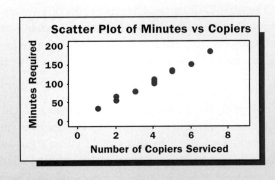

TABLE **11.4** Data for Exercises 11.11 and 11.13

(a) Direct labour cost data ● DirLab

Direct Labour Cost, y ($100s)	Batch Size, x
71	5
663	62
381	35
138	12
861	83
145	14
493	46
548	52
251	23
1024	100
435	41
772	75

(b) Real estate sales price data
● RealEst

Sales Price (y)	Home Size (x)
180	23
98.1	11
173.1	20
136.5	17
141	15
165.9	21
193.5	24
127.8	13
163.5	19
172.5	25

Source: Reprinted with permission from *The Real Estate Appraiser and Analyst*, Spring 1986 issue. Copyright © 1986 by the Appraisal Institute, Chicago, Illinois.

Referring to the variable x as the "price difference" for brevity's sake, the data are as follows:

Fresh Detergent Demand Data

Sales Period	y	x	Sales Period	y	x
1	7.38	−0.05	16	8.87	0.30
2	8.51	0.25	17	9.26	0.50
3	9.52	0.60	18	9.00	0.50
4	7.50	0	19	8.75	0.40
5	9.33	0.25	20	7.95	−0.05
6	8.28	0.20	21	7.65	−0.05
7	8.75	0.15	22	7.27	−0.10
8	7.87	0.05	23	8.00	0.20
9	7.10	−0.15	24	8.50	0.10
10	8.00	0.15	25	8.75	0.50
11	7.89	0.20	26	9.21	0.60
12	8.15	0.10	27	8.27	−0.05
13	9.10	0.40	28	7.67	0
14	8.86	0.45	29	7.93	0.05
15	8.90	0.35	30	9.26	0.55

Using the scatter plot (from MINITAB) of y versus x shown below, discuss why the simple linear regression model might appropriately relate y to x.

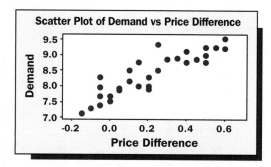

11.10 THE FRESH DETERGENT CASE ● Fresh

Consider the simple linear regression model relating demand, y, to the price difference, x, and the Fresh demand data of Exercise 11.9.

a. Interpret $\mu_{y|x=0.10} = \beta_0 + \beta_1(0.10)$.
b. Interpret $\mu_{y|x=-0.05} = \beta_0 + \beta_1(-0.05)$.
c. Interpret the slope parameter β_1.
d. Interpret the y intercept β_0. Does this interpretation make practical sense?
e. What factors are represented by the error term in this model? Give two specific examples.

11.11 THE DIRECT LABOUR COST CASE ● DirLab

An accountant wishes to predict direct labour cost (y) on the basis of the batch size (x) of a product produced in a job shop. Data for 12 production runs are given in Table 11.4(a).

a. Construct a scatter plot of y versus x.
b. Discuss whether the scatter plot suggests that a simple linear regression model might appropriately relate y to x.

11.12 THE DIRECT LABOUR COST CASE ● DirLab

Consider the simple linear regression model describing the direct labour cost data of Exercise 11.11.

a. Interpret $\mu_{y|x=60} = \beta_0 + \beta_1(60)$.
b. Interpret $\mu_{y|x=30} = \beta_0 + \beta_1(30)$.
c. Interpret the slope parameter β_1.
d. Interpret the y intercept β_0. Does this interpretation make practical sense?
e. What factors are represented by the error term in this model? Give two specific examples of these factors.

11.13 THE REAL ESTATE SALES PRICE CASE
● RealEst

A real estate agency collects data concerning $y =$ the sales price of a house (in thousands of dollars), and $x =$ the home size (in hundreds of square feet). The data are given in Table 11.4(b).

a. Construct a scatter plot of y versus x.
b. Discuss whether the scatter plot suggests that a simple linear regression model might appropriately relate y to x.

11.14   THE REAL ESTATE SALES PRICE CASE

🔴 RealEst

Consider the simple linear regression model describing the sales price data of Exercise 11.13.

a. Interpret $\mu_{y|x=20} = \beta_0 + \beta_1(20)$.

b. Interpret $\mu_{y|x=18} = \beta_0 + \beta_1(18)$.

c. Interpret the slope parameter β_1.

d. Interpret the y intercept β_0. Does this interpretation make practical sense?

e. What factors are represented by the error term in this model? Give two specific examples.

11.3 The Least Squares Estimates, and Point Estimation and Prediction

The true values of the y intercept (β_0) and slope (β_1) in the simple linear regression model are unknown. Therefore, it is necessary to use observed data to compute estimates of these regression parameters.

Consider the data and scatter plot of y versus x in Table 11.5 and Figure 11.4. This figure suggests that the simple linear regression model appropriately relates y to x. We now wish to use the data in Table 11.5 to estimate the intercept β_0 and the slope β_1 of the line of means. To do this, it might be reasonable to estimate the line of means by "fitting" the "best" straight line to the plotted data in Figure 11.4. But how do we fit the best straight line? One approach would be to simply "eyeball" a line through the points. Then we could read the y intercept and slope off the visually fitted line and use these values as the estimates of β_0 and β_1. For example, Figure 11.5 shows a line that has been visually fitted to the plot of the data. We see that this line intersects the y axis at $y = 15$. Therefore, the **y intercept** of the line is 15. In addition, the figure shows that the **slope** of the line is

$$\frac{\text{change in } y}{\text{change in } x} = \frac{12.8 - 13.8}{20 - 10} = \frac{-1}{10} = -0.1.$$

Therefore, based on the visually fitted line, we estimate that β_0 is 15 and that β_1 is -0.1.

In order to evaluate how "good" our point estimates of β_0 and β_1 are, consider using the visually fitted line to predict y. Denoting such a **prediction** as $\hat{y}$ (y hat), a reasonable prediction of y when x is a certain value is simply the point on the visually fitted line corresponding to x. For instance, when x is 28,

$$\hat{y} = 15 - 0.1x = 15 - 0.1(28) = 12.2,$$

as shown in Figure 11.6. We can evaluate how well the visually determined line fits the points on the scatter plot by comparing each observed value of y with the corresponding predicted value of y given by the fitted line. We do this by computing the **residual** $y - \hat{y}$. For instance, looking at the first observation in Table 11.5, we observe $y = 12.4$ and $x = 28.0$. Since the predicted y value when x equals 28 is $\hat{y} = 12.2$, the residual $y - \hat{y}$ equals $12.4 - 12.2 = 0.2$.

Table 11.6 gives the values of y, x, $\hat{y}$, and $y - \hat{y}$ for each observation in Table 11.5. Geometrically, the residuals for the visually fitted line are the vertical distances between the

TABLE 11.5   Data

Observation	x	y
1	28.0	12.4
2	28.0	11.7
3	32.5	12.4
4	39.0	10.8
5	45.9	9.4
6	57.8	9.5
7	58.1	8.0
8	62.5	7.5

FIGURE 11.4   Excel Output of a Scatter Plot of y versus x

FIGURE **11.5** Visually Fitting a Line

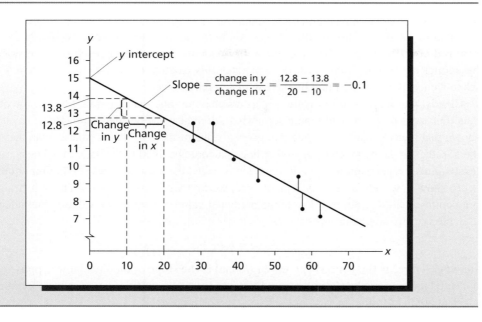

FIGURE **11.6** Using the Visually Fitted Line to Predict y When x = 28

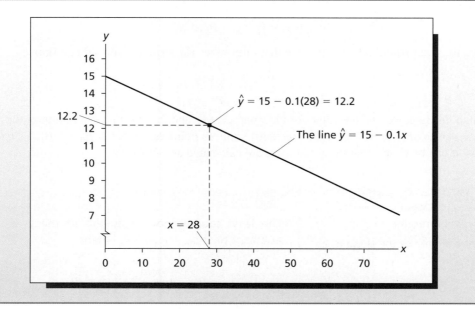

TABLE **11.6** Calculation of the *SSE* for a Line Visually Fitted to the Sample Data

y	x	$\hat{y} = 15 - 0.1x$	$y - \hat{y}$
12.4	28.0	15 − 0.1(28.0) = 12.2	12.4 − 12.2 = 0.2
11.7	28.0	15 − 0.1(28.0) = 12.2	11.7 − 12.2 = −0.5
12.4	32.5	15 − 0.1(32.5) = 11.75	12.4 − 11.75 = 0.65
10.8	39.0	15 − 0.1(39.0) = 11.1	10.8 − 11.1 = −0.3
9.4	45.9	15 − 0.1(45.9) = 10.41	9.4 − 10.41 = −1.01
9.5	57.8	15 − 0.1(57.8) = 9.22	9.5 − 9.22 = 0.28
8.0	58.1	15 − 0.1(58.1) = 9.19	8.0 − 9.19 = −1.19
7.5	62.5	15 − 0.1(62.5) = 8.75	7.5 − 8.75 = −1.25

$$SSE = \sum(y - \hat{y})^2 = (0.2)^2 + (-0.5)^2 + (0.65)^2 + \cdots + (-1.25)^2 = 4.8796$$

observed y values and the predictions obtained using the fitted line, which are depicted as the eight line segments in Figure 11.5.

If the visually determined line fits the data well, the residuals will be small. To obtain an overall measure of the quality of the fit, we compute the **sum of squared residuals** or **sum of squared errors**, denoted **SSE**. This quantity is obtained by squaring each of the residuals and by adding the results. Table 11.6 demonstrates this calculation and shows that $SSE = 4.8796$ when we use the visually fitted line to calculate predictions.

Clearly, the line shown in Figure 11.5 is not the only line that could be fitted to the observed data. Different people would obtain somewhat different visually fitted lines. However, it can be shown that there is exactly one line that gives a value of the SSE that is smaller than the value of the SSE that would be given by any other line that could be fitted to the data. This line is called the **least squares regression line** and its equation is called the **least squares prediction equation**.

To show how to find the least squares line, we first write the **general form** of a straight-line prediction equation. Letting $\hat{y}$ denote the predicted value of y when the value of the independent variable is x, we write this equation as

$$\hat{y} = b_0 + b_1 x.$$

Here b_0 (b zero) **is the y intercept** and b_1 (b one) **is the slope** of the line. Now suppose we have collected n observations $(x_1, y_1), (x_2, y_2), \ldots, (x_n, y_n)$ and consider a particular observation (x_i, y_i). The predicted value of y_i is

$$\hat{y}_i = b_0 + b_1 x_i$$

and the residual for this observation is

$$e_i = y_i - \hat{y}_i = y_i - (b_0 + b_1 x_i).$$

Then, the **least squares line** is the line that **minimizes the sum of squared residuals**

$$SSE = \sum_{i=1}^{n} (y_i - (b_0 + b_1 x_i))^2.$$

To find this line, we find the values of the y intercept b_0 and the slope b_1 that minimize the SSE. These values of b_0 and b_1 are called the **least squares point estimates** of β_0 and β_1. Using calculus, it can be shown that these estimates are calculated as follows:[2]

The Least Squares Point Estimates

For the simple linear regression model:

1 The **least squares point estimate of the slope β_1** is

$$b_1 = \frac{SS_{xy}}{SS_{xx}}, \text{ where}$$

$$SS_{xy} = \sum (x_i - \bar{x})(y_i - \bar{y}) = \sum x_i y_i - \frac{\left(\sum x_i\right)\left(\sum y_i\right)}{n}$$

and $SS_{xx} = \sum (x_i - \bar{x})^2 = \sum x_i^2 - \frac{\left(\sum x_i\right)^2}{n}.$

2 The **least squares point estimate of the y intercept β_0** is $b_0 = \bar{y} - b_1 \bar{x}$, where

$$\bar{y} = \frac{\sum y_i}{n} \quad \text{and} \quad \bar{x} = \frac{\sum x_i}{n}.$$

Here n is the number of observations (an observation is an observed value of x and its corresponding value of y).

Using the data in Table 11.5, we illustrate below how to calculate these point estimates and how to use them to estimate mean values and predict individual values of the dependent variable. Note that the quantities SS_{xy} and SS_{xx} used to calculate the least squares point estimates are also used throughout this chapter to perform other important calculations.

---

[2]In order to simplify notation, we will often drop the limits on summations in this and subsequent chapters. That is, instead of using the summation $\sum_{i=1}^{n}$, we will simply write $\sum$.

Part 1: Calculating the least squares point estimates To compute the least squares point estimates of the regression parameters β_0 and β_1, we first calculate the following preliminary summations:

y_i	x_i	x_i^2	$x_i y_i$
12.4	28.0	$(28.0)^2 = 784$	$(28.0)(12.4) = 347.2$
11.7	28.0	$(28.0)^2 = 784$	$(28.0)(11.7) = 327.6$
12.4	32.5	$(32.5)^2 = 1{,}056.25$	$(32.5)(12.4) = 403$
10.8	39.0	$(39.0)^2 = 1{,}521$	$(39.0)(10.8) = 421.2$
9.4	45.9	$(45.9)^2 = 2{,}106.81$	$(45.9)(9.4) = 431.46$
9.5	57.8	$(57.8)^2 = 3{,}340.84$	$(57.8)(9.5) = 549.1$
8.0	58.1	$(58.1)^2 = 3{,}375.61$	$(58.1)(8.0) = 464.8$
7.5	62.5	$(62.5)^2 = 3{,}906.25$	$(62.5)(7.5) = 468.75$
$\sum y_i = 81.7$	$\sum x_i = 351.8$	$\sum x_i^2 = 16{,}874.76$	$\sum x_i y_i = 3{,}413.11$

Using these summations, we calculate SS_{xy} and SS_{xx} as follows:

$$SS_{xy} = \sum x_i y_i - \frac{\left(\sum x_i\right)\left(\sum y_i\right)}{n}$$

$$= 3{,}413.11 - \frac{(351.8)(81.7)}{8} = -179.6475,$$

$$SS_{xx} = \sum x_i^2 - \frac{\left(\sum x_i\right)^2}{n}$$

$$= 16{,}874.76 - \frac{(351.8)^2}{8} = 1{,}404.355.$$

It follows that the least squares point estimate of the slope β_1 is

$$b_1 = \frac{SS_{xy}}{SS_{xx}} = \frac{-179.6475}{1{,}404.355} = -0.1279.$$

Furthermore, because

$$\bar{y} = \frac{\sum y_i}{8} = \frac{81.7}{8} = 10.2125 \quad \text{and} \quad \bar{x} = \frac{\sum x_i}{8} = \frac{351.8}{8} = 43.98,$$

the least squares point estimate of the y intercept β_0 is

$$b_0 = \bar{y} - b_1\bar{x} = 10.2125 - (-0.1279)(43.98) = 15.84.$$

Because $b_1 = -0.1279$, we estimate that y decreases (since b_1 is negative) by 0.1279 when x increases by 1. Because $b_0 = 15.84$, we estimate that y is 15.84 when x is 0.

Table 11.7 gives predictions of y for each observation obtained by using the least squares line (or prediction equation)

$$\hat{y} = b_0 + b_1 x = 15.84 - 0.1279x.$$

The table also gives each of the residuals and the sum of squared residuals ($SSE = 2.568$) obtained by using this prediction equation. Notice that the SSE here, which was obtained using the least squares point estimates, is smaller than the SSE of Table 11.6, which was obtained using the visually fitted line $\hat{y} = 15 - 0.1x$. In general, it can be shown that the SSE obtained by using the least squares point estimates is smaller than the value of the SSE that would be obtained by using any other estimates of β_0 and β_1. Figure 11.7(a) illustrates the eight observed y values (the dots in the figure) and the eight predicted y values (the squares in the figure) given by the least squares line. The distances between the observed and predicted fuel consumptions are the residuals. Therefore, when we say that the least squares point estimates minimize the SSE, we are saying that these estimates position the least squares line so as to minimize the sum of the squared distances between the observed and predicted y values. In this sense, the least squares

TABLE **11.7**   Calculation of the *SSE* Obtained by Using the Least Squares Point Estimates

y_i	x_i	$\hat{y}_i = 15.84 - 0.1279x_i$	$y_i - \hat{y}_i = $ residual
12.4	28.0	$15.84 - 0.1279(28.0) = 12.2588$	$12.4 - 12.2588 = 0.1412$
11.7	28.0	$15.84 - 0.1279(28.0) = 12.2588$	$11.7 - 12.2588 = -0.5588$
12.4	32.5	$15.84 - 0.1279(32.5) = 11.68325$	$12.4 - 11.68325 = 0.71675$
10.8	39.0	$15.84 - 0.1279(39.0) = 10.8519$	$10.8 - 10.8519 = -0.0519$
9.4	45.9	$15.84 - 0.1279(45.9) = 9.96939$	$9.4 - 9.96939 = -0.56939$
9.5	57.8	$15.84 - 0.1279(57.8) = 8.44738$	$9.5 - 8.44738 = 1.05262$
8.0	58.1	$15.84 - 0.1279(58.1) = 8.40901$	$8.0 - 8.40901 = -0.40901$
7.5	62.5	$15.84 - 0.1279(62.5) = 7.84625$	$7.5 - 7.84625 = -0.34625$

$$SSE = \sum (y_i - \hat{y}_i)^2 = (0.1412)^2 + (-0.5588)^2 + \cdots + (-0.346\,25)^2 = 2.568$$

line is the best straight line that can be fitted to the eight observed y values. Figure 11.7(b) gives the MINITAB output of this best fit line. Note that this output gives the least squares estimates $b_0 = 15.84$ and $b_1 = -0.1279$. In general, we will rely on MINITAB, Excel, and MegaStat to compute the least squares estimates (and to perform many other regression calculations).

Part 2: Estimating a mean y value and predicting an individual y value.   We define the **experimental region** to be the range of the previously observed values of x. Referring to Table 11.5, we see that the experimental region consists of the range of x values from 28 to 62.5. The simple linear regression model relates y to x for values of x that are in the experimental region. For such values of x, the least squares line is the estimate of the line of means.

We now consider finding a point estimate of

$$\mu_{y|x} = \beta_0 + \beta_1 x,$$

which is the mean of all of the y values that could be observed for x. Because the least squares line is the estimate of the line of means, the point estimate of $\mu_{y|x}$ is the point on the least squares line that corresponds to the average x value:

$$\hat{y} = b_0 + b_1 x$$
$$= 15.84 - 0.1279x.$$

This point estimate is intuitively logical because it is obtained by replacing the unknown parameters β_0 and β_1 in the expression for $\mu_{y|x}$ by their least squares estimates b_0 and b_1.

FIGURE **11.7**   The Least Squares Line for the Sample Data

(a) The observed and predicted y values

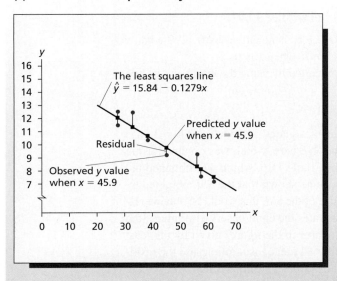

(b) The MINITAB output of the least squares line

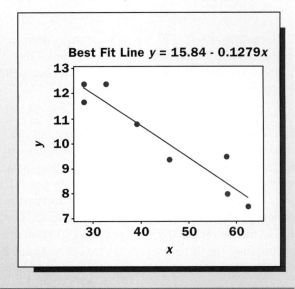

The quantity $\hat{y}$ is also the point prediction of the individual value

$$y = \beta_0 + \beta_1 x + \varepsilon,$$

which is the y value corresponding to the average value of x. To understand why $\hat{y}$ is the point prediction of y, note that y is the sum of the mean $\beta_0 + \beta_1 x$ and the error term ε. We have already seen that $\hat{y} = b_0 + b_1 x$ is the point estimate of $\beta_0 + \beta_1 x$. We will now explain why **we should use a value of 0 for the error term**, ε. Recall that we are using the average value of all the y's for a given value of x to estimate a single value of $\hat{y}$, so, logically, it would make sense to use the average value of all of the errors to estimate a single error. This allows us to use the average value of the errors, or 0, in place of the error term when using $\hat{y}$ as the point estimate of a single value of y. In the next section, we will discuss several assumptions concerning the simple linear regression model.

Now suppose a forecasted average x value is 40. Because 40 is in the experimental region,

$$\hat{y} = 15.84 - 0.1279(40)$$
$$= 10.72$$

is (1) the point estimate of y when the average x value is 40 and (2) the point prediction of an individual y value when the average x value is 40. This says that (1) we estimate that the average of all y values that could be observed when x is 40 equals 10.72, and (2) we predict that y in a single observation when $x = 40$ will be 10.72. Note that Figure 11.8 illustrates $\hat{y} = 10.72$ as a square on the least squares line.

To conclude, note that Figure 11.9 illustrates the potential danger of using the least squares line to predict outside the experimental region. In the figure, we extrapolate the least squares line far beyond the experimental region to obtain a prediction for $x = -10$. As shown in Figure 11.4 (page 364), for values of x in the experimental region the observed values of y tend to decrease in a straight-line fashion as the values of x increase. However, for x values lower than 28, the relationship between y and x might become curved. If it does, extrapolating the straight-line prediction equation to obtain a prediction for $x = -10$ might badly underestimate y (see Figure 11.9).

The previous situation illustrates that when we are using a least squares regression line, we should not estimate a mean value or predict an individual value unless the corresponding value of x is in the **experimental region**—the range of the previously observed values of x. Often the value $x = 0$ is not in the experimental region. In such a situation, it would not be appropriate to interpret the y intercept b_0 as the estimate of the mean value of y when x equals 0. For example, Figure 11.9 illustrates that $x = 0$ is not in the experimental region. Therefore, it would not be

FIGURE 11.8   Point Estimation and Point Prediction

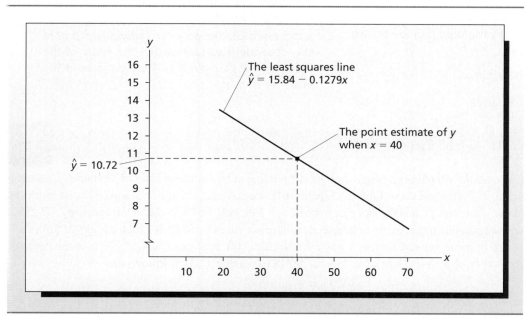

FIGURE **11.9**   **The Danger of Extrapolation Outside the Experimental Region**

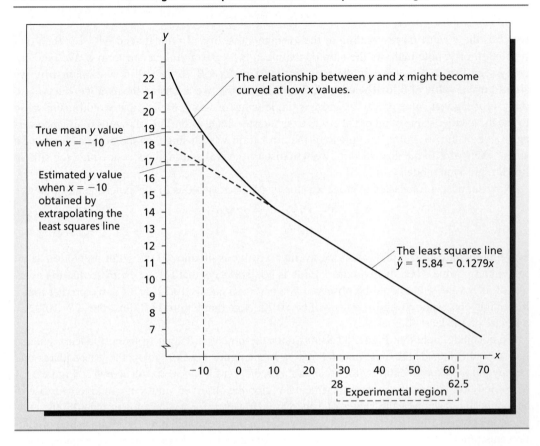

appropriate to use $b_0 = 15.84$ as the point estimate of y when $x = 0$. Because it is not meaningful to interpret the y intercept in many regression situations, we often omit such interpretations.

We now present a general procedure for estimating a mean value and predicting an individual value:

Point Estimation and Point Prediction in Simple Linear Regression

Let b_0 and b_1 be the least squares point estimates of the y intercept β_0 and the slope β_1 in the simple linear regression model, and suppose that x_0, a specified value of the independent variable x, is inside the experimental region. Then

$$\hat{y} = b_0 + b_1 x_0$$

1   is the **point estimate** of the **mean value of the dependent variable** when the value of the independent variable is x_0.

2   is the **point prediction** of an **individual value of the dependent variable** when the value of the independent variable is x_0. Here we predict the error term to be 0.

Example 11.2 The QHIC Case

Consider the simple linear regression model relating yearly home upkeep expenditure, y, to home value, x. Using the data in Table 11.3 (page 361), we can calculate the least squares point estimates of the y intercept β_0 and the slope β_1 to be $b_0 = -348.3921$ and $b_1 = 7.2583$. Because $b_1 = 7.2583$, we estimate that mean yearly upkeep expenditure increases by \$7.26 for each additional \$1,000 increase in home value. Consider a home worth \$220,000, and note that $x_0 = 220$ is in the range of previously observed values of x: 48.9 to 286.18 (see Table 11.3). It follows that

$$\hat{y} = b_0 + b_1 x_0$$
$$= -348.3921 + 7.2583(220)$$
$$= 1248.43 \text{ (or \$1,248.43)}$$

is the point estimate of the mean yearly upkeep expenditure for all homes worth $220,000 and is the point prediction of a yearly upkeep expenditure for an individual home worth $220,000.

The marketing department at QHIC wishes to determine which homes should be sent advertising brochures promoting QHIC's products and services. The prediction equation $\hat{y} = b_0 + b_1 x$ implies that the home value x corresponding to a predicted upkeep expenditure of $\hat{y}$ is

$$x = \frac{\hat{y} - b_0}{b_1} = \frac{\hat{y} - (-348.3921)}{7.2583} = \frac{\hat{y} + 348.3921}{7.2583}.$$

For instance, if we set predicted upkeep expenditure $\hat{y}$ equal to $500, we have

$$x = \frac{\hat{y} + 348.3921}{7.2583} = \frac{500 + 348.3921}{7.2583} = 116.886 \ (\$116,886).$$

Therefore, if QHIC wishes to send an advertising brochure to any home with a predicted upkeep expenditure of at least $500, then QHIC should send this brochure to any home with a value of at least $116,886.

Exercises for Section 11.3

CONCEPTS

11.15 What does the *SSE* measure?

11.16 What is the least squares regression line, and what are the least squares point estimates?

11.17 How do we obtain a point estimate of the mean value of the dependent variable and a point prediction of an individual value of the dependent variable?

11.18 Why is it dangerous to extrapolate outside the experimental region?

METHODS AND APPLICATIONS

11.19 THE SERVICE TIME CASE ● SrvcTime

The following output is obtained when Excel is used to fit a least squares line to the service time data given in Exercise 11.7 (page 362).
   a. Find the least squares point estimates b_0 and b_1 on the computer output and report their values. Interpret b_0 and b_1. Does the interpretation of b_0 make practical sense?
   b. Use the least squares line to compute a point estimate of the mean time to service four copiers and a point prediction of the time to service four copiers on a single call.

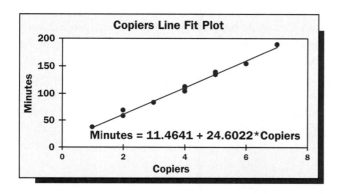

Copiers Line Fit Plot

Minutes = 11.4641 + 24.6022*Copiers

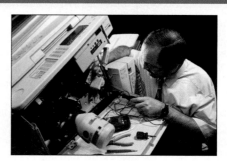

11.20 THE FRESH DETERGENT CASE ● Fresh

The following output is obtained when MINITAB is used to fit a least squares line to the Fresh detergent demand data given in Exercise 11.9 (pages 362 to 363).

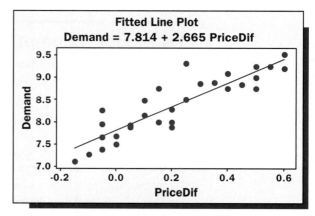

Fitted Line Plot
Demand = 7.814 + 2.665 PriceDif

   a. Find the least squares point estimates b_0 and b_1 on the computer output and report their values. Interpret b_0 and b_1. Does the interpretation of b_0 make practical sense?
   b. Use the least squares line to compute a point estimate of the mean demand in all sales periods when the price difference is 0.10 and a point prediction of the actual demand in an individual sales period when the price difference is 0.10.

c. If Enterprise Industries wishes to maintain a price difference that corresponds to a predicted demand of 850,000 bottles (that is, $\hat{y} = 8.5$), what should this price difference be?

11.21   THE DIRECT LABOUR COST CASE   ● DirLab

The following output is obtained when Excel is used to fit a least squares line to the direct labour cost data given in Exercise 11.11 (page 363).

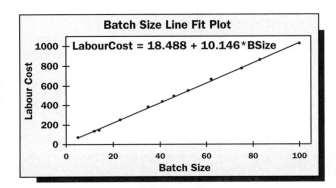

a. By using the formulas illustrated in this section and the data of Exercise 11.11, verify that $b_0 = 18.488$ and $b_1 = 10.146$, as shown on the Excel output.
b. Interpret b_0 and b_1. Does the interpretation of b_0 make practical sense?
c. Write the least squares prediction equation.
d. Use the least squares line to obtain a point estimate of the mean direct labour cost for all batches of size 60 and a point prediction of the direct labour cost for an individual batch of size 60.

11.22   THE REAL ESTATE SALES PRICE CASE   ● RealEst

The following output is obtained when MINITAB is used to fit a least squares line to the real estate sales price data given in Exercise 11.13 (page 363).

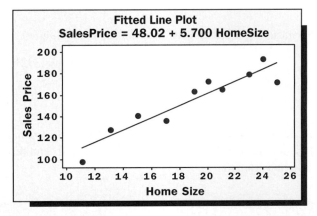

a. By using the formulas illustrated on pages 367 to 369 and the data of Exercise 11.13, verify that $b_0 = 48.02$ and $b_1 = 5.700$, as shown on the MINITAB output.
b. Interpret b_0 and b_1. Does the interpretation of b_0 make practical sense?
c. Write the least squares prediction equation.
d. Use the least squares line to obtain a point estimate of the mean sales price of all houses with 2000 square feet (about 180 m²) and a point prediction of the sales price of an individual house with 2000 square feet.

11.4 Model Assumptions and the Standard Error

Model assumptions   In order to perform hypothesis tests and set up various types of intervals when using the simple linear regression model

$$y = \mu_{y|x} + \varepsilon$$
$$= \beta_0 + \beta_1 x + \varepsilon,$$

we need to make certain assumptions about the error term ε. At any given value of x, there is a population of error term values that could potentially occur. These error term values describe the different potential effects on y of all factors other than the value of x. Therefore, these error term values explain the variation in the y values that could be observed when the independent variable is x. Our statement of the simple linear regression model assumes that $\mu_{y|x}$, the mean of the population of all y values that could be observed when the independent variable is x, is $\beta_0 + \beta_1 x$. This model also implies that $\varepsilon = y - (\beta_0 + \beta_1 x)$, so this is equivalent to assuming that the mean of the corresponding population of potential error term values is 0. In total, we make four assumptions—called the **regression assumptions**—about the simple linear regression model. These assumptions can be stated in terms of potential y values or, equivalently, in terms of potential error term values. Following tradition, we begin by stating these assumptions in terms of potential error term values:

1   At any given value of x, the population of potential error term values has a **mean equal to 0**.

2   **Constant variance assumption:** At any given value of x, the population of potential error term values has a variance that does not depend on the value of x. That is, the different populations of potential error term values corresponding to different values of x have **equal variances**. We denote the **constant variance as σ^2**.

3   **Normality assumption:** At any given value of x, the population of potential error term values has a **normal distribution**.

4   **Independence assumption:** Any one value of the error term ε is **statistically independent** of any other value of ε. That is, the value of the error term ε corresponding to an observed value of y is statistically independent of the value of the error term corresponding to any other observed value of y.

Taken together, the first three assumptions say that, at any given value of x, the population of potential error term values is **normally distributed** with **mean zero** and a **variance σ^2 that does not depend on the value of x**. Because the potential error term values cause the variation in the potential y values, these assumptions imply that the population of all y values that could be observed when the independent variable is x is **normally distributed** with **mean $\beta_0 + \beta_1 x$** and **a variance σ^2 that does not depend on x**. These three assumptions are illustrated in Figure 11.10 (based on the data in Table 11.5). Specifically, this figure depicts the populations of y values corresponding to two x values—32.5 and 45.9. Note that these populations are shown to be normally distributed with different means (each of which is on the line of means) and with the same variance (or spread).

The independence assumption is most likely to be violated when time series data are being utilized in a regression study. Intuitively, this assumption says that there is no pattern of positive error terms being followed (in time) by other positive error terms, and there is no pattern of positive error terms being followed by negative error terms. That is, there is no pattern of higher than average y values being followed by other higher than average y values, and there is no pattern of higher than average y values being followed by lower than average y values.

It is important to point out that the regression assumptions very seldom, if ever, hold exactly in any practical regression problem. However, it has been found that regression results are not extremely sensitive to mild departures from these assumptions. In practice, only pronounced departures from these assumptions require attention. For the examples in this chapter, we will suppose that the assumptions are valid.

In Section 11.3, we stated that, when we predict an individual value of the dependent variable, we predict the error term to be 0. To see why we do this, note that the regression

FIGURE **11.10**   An Illustration of the Model Assumptions

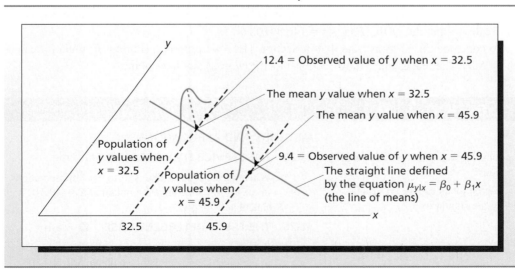

assumptions state that, at any given value of the independent variable, the population of all error term values that can potentially occur is normally distributed with a mean equal to 0. Since we also assume that successive error terms (observed over time) are statistically independent, each error term has a 50 percent chance of being positive and a 50 percent chance of being negative. Therefore, it is reasonable to predict any particular error term value to be 0.

The mean square error and the standard error   To present statistical inference formulas in later sections, we need to be able to compute point estimates of σ^2 and σ, the constant variance and standard deviation of the error term populations. The point estimate of σ^2 is called the **mean square error** and the point estimate of σ is called the **standard error**. In the following box, we show how to compute these estimates:

The Mean Square Error and the Standard Error

If the regression assumptions are satisfied and the SSE is the sum of squared residuals:

1   The point estimate of σ^2 is the **mean square error**

$$s^2 = \frac{SSE}{n - 2}.$$

2   The point estimate of σ is the **standard error**

$$s = \sqrt{\frac{SSE}{n - 2}}.$$

In order to understand these point estimates, recall that σ^2 is the variance of the population of y values (for a given value of x) around the mean value $\mu_{y|x}$. Because $\hat{y}$ is the point estimate of this mean, it seems natural to use

$$SSE = \sum (y_i - \hat{y}_i)^2$$

to help construct a point estimate of σ^2. We divide the SSE by $n - 2$ because it can be proven that doing so makes the resulting s^2 an unbiased point estimate of σ^2. Here we call $n - 2$ the **number of degrees of freedom** associated with the SSE.

Consider the data from Table 11.5 (page 364) and recall that in Table 11.7 (page 368) we calculated the sum of squared residuals to be $SSE = 2.568$. It follows, because we have $n = 8$ observations, that the point estimate of σ^2 is the mean square error

$$s^2 = \frac{SSE}{n - 2} = \frac{2.568}{8 - 2} = 0.428.$$

This implies that the point estimate of σ is the standard error

$$s = \sqrt{s^2} = \sqrt{0.428} = 0.6542.$$

As another example, it can be verified that the standard error for the simple linear regression model describing the QHIC data is $s = 146.8970$.

To conclude this section, note that in Section 11.11 we present a shortcut formula for calculating SSE. The reader may study Section 11.11 now or at any later point.

Exercises for Section 11.4

CONCEPTS

11.23   What four assumptions do we make about the simple linear regression model?

11.24   What is estimated by the mean square error, and what is estimated by the standard error?

METHODS AND APPLICATIONS

11.25   **THE SERVICE TIME CASE**   ● SrvcTime

When a least squares line is fit to the 11 observations in the service time data, we obtain $SSE = 191.7017$. Calculate s^2 and s.

11.26   **THE FRESH DETERGENT CASE**   ● Fresh

When a least squares line is fit to the 30 observations in the Fresh detergent data, we obtain $SSE = 2.806$. Calculate s^2 and s.

11.27 THE DIRECT LABOUR COST CASE ⬡ DirLab

When a least squares line is fit to the 12 observations in the labour cost data, we obtain $SSE = 746.7624$. Calculate s^2 and s.

11.28 THE REAL ESTATE SALES PRICE CASE
⬡ RealEst

When a least squares line is fit to the 10 observations in the real estate sales price data, we obtain $SSE = 896.8$. Calculate s^2 and s.

11.29 Ten sales regions of equal sales potential for a company were randomly selected. The advertising expenditures (in units of \$10,000) in these 10 sales regions were purposely set during July of last year at, respectively, 5, 6, 7, 8, 9, 10, 11, 12, 13, and 14. The sales volumes (in units of \$10,000) were then recorded for the 10 sales regions and found to be, respectively, 89, 87, 98, 110, 103, 114, 116, 110, 126, and 130. Assuming that the simple linear regression model is appropriate, it can be shown that $b_0 = 66.2121$, $b_1 = 4.4303$, and $SSE = 222.8242$. Calculate s^2 and s. ⬡ SalesVol

11.30 A Canadian youth training program tested 27 undergraduate students to examine the relationship between age and errors made on a flight simulator test. The average age of the participants was 20 years and the ages ranged from 18 to 26 years. The number of errors made was found for each individual. The data are presented in the Figure 11.11(a). In Figure 11.11(b) and (c) are the scatter plot of the resulting data and the regression results from MegaStat. From the results given:
a. Explain the relationship between age and errors.
b. Compute s^2 and s.
c. Find the values of b_0 and b_1. ⬡ FlightSim

FIGURE 11.11   Flight Simulator Test Results for Exercise 11.30

(a) Flight simulator test results

Age	Errors	Age	Errors
19	7	20	8
19	8	23	5
21	6	19	3
24	5	26	2
20	6	19	7
19	7	19	8
19	8	18	7
19	6	19	6
22	3	20	9
19	9	22	9
19	9	18	8
19	8	21	9
19	6	19	6
19	4		

(b) Scatter plot of flight simulator test results

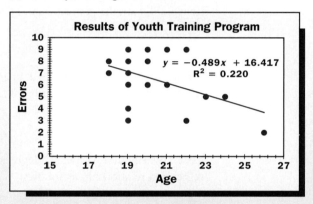

(c) MegaStat regression analysis of flight simulator test results

Regression Analysis

r^2 0.220	n 27
r −0.469	k 1
Std. Error 1.786	Dep. Var. Errors

ANOVA table

Source	SS	df	MS	F	p-value
Regression	22.5106	1	22.5106	7.05	0.0136
Residual	79.7857	25	3.1914		
Total	102.2963	26			

Regression output   confidence interval

variables	coefficients	std. error	t (df=25)	p-value	95% lower	95% upper	std. coeff.
Intercept	16.4169	3.7012	4.436	0.0002	8.7941	24.0396	0.000
Age	−0.4894	0.1843	−2.656	0.0136	−0.8688	−0.1099	−0.469

11.5 Testing the Significance of the Slope and *y* Intercept

Testing the significance of the slope   A simple linear regression model is not likely to be useful unless there is a **significant relationship between *y* and *x*.** In order to judge the significance of the relationship between *y* and *x*, we test the null hypothesis

$$H_0: \beta_1 = 0,$$

which says that there is no change in the mean value of y associated with an increase in x, versus the alternative hypothesis

$$H_a: \beta_1 \neq 0,$$

which says that there is a (positive or negative) change in the mean value of y associated with an increase in x. It would be reasonable to conclude that x is significantly related to y if we can be quite certain that we should reject H_0 in favour of H_a.

In order to test these hypotheses, recall that we compute the least squares point estimate b_1 of the true slope β_1 by using a sample of n observed values of the dependent variable y. Different samples of n observed y values would yield different values of the least squares point estimate b_1. It can be shown that, if the regression assumptions hold, the population of all possible values of b_1 is normally distributed with a mean of β_1 and a standard deviation of

$$\sigma_{b_1} = \frac{\sigma}{\sqrt{SS_{xx}}}.$$

The standard error s is the point estimate of σ, so it follows that a point estimate of σ_{b_1} is

$$s_{b_1} = \frac{s}{\sqrt{SS_{xx}}},$$

which is called the **standard error of the estimate b_1**. Furthermore, if the regression assumptions hold, then the population of all values of

$$\frac{b_1 - \beta_1}{s_{b_1}}$$

has a t distribution with $n - 2$ degrees of freedom. It follows that, if the null hypothesis $H_0: \beta_1 = 0$ is true, the population of all possible values of the test statistic

$$t = \frac{b_1}{s_{b_1}}$$

has a t distribution with $n - 2$ degrees of freedom. Therefore, we can test the significance of the regression relationship as follows:

Testing the Significance of the Regression Relationship: Testing the Significance of the Slope

Define the test statistic

$$t = \frac{b_1}{s_{b_1}}, \quad \text{where} \quad s_{b_1} = \frac{s}{\sqrt{SS_{xx}}},$$

and suppose that the regression assumptions hold. Then, we can test $H_0: \beta_1 = 0$ versus a particular alternative hypothesis at significance level α (that is, by setting the probability of a Type I error equal to α) by using the appropriate rejection point rule or, equivalently, the corresponding p value.

Alternative Hypothesis	Rejection Point Condition: Reject H_0 if	p Value (Reject H_0 if p Value $< \alpha$)
$H_a: \beta_1 \neq 0$	$\lvert t \rvert > t_{\alpha/2}$	Twice the area under the t curve to the right of $\lvert t \rvert$
$H_a: \beta_1 > 0$	$t > t_\alpha$	The area under the t curve to the right of t
$H_a: \beta_1 < 0$	$t < -t_\alpha$	The area under the t curve to the left of t

Here $t_{\alpha/2}$, t_α, and all p values are based on $n - 2$ degrees of freedom. **If we can reject $H_0: \beta_1 = 0$ at a given value of α, then we conclude that the slope** (or, equivalently, the regression relationship) is significant at the α level.

We usually use the two-sided alternative $H_a: \beta_1 \neq 0$ for this test of significance. However, sometimes a one-sided alternative is appropriate. For example, we could say that if the slope β_1

is not 0, then it must be negative. A negative β_1 would say that the *y* values decrease as *x* increases. Because of this, it would be appropriate to decide that *x* is significantly related to *y* if we can reject H_0: $\beta_1 = 0$ in favour of the one-sided alternative H_a: $\beta_1 < 0$. Most computer packages (such as MINITAB and Excel) present results for testing a two-sided alternative hypothesis. For these reasons, we will emphasize the two-sided test.

The following should also be noted:

1 **If we can decide that the slope is significant at the 0.05 significance level**, then we have concluded that *x* is significantly related to *y* by using a test that allows only a 0.05 probability of concluding that *x* is significantly related to *y* when it is not. **This is usually regarded as strong evidence that the regression relationship is significant.**

2 **If we can decide that the slope is significant at the 0.01 significance level, this is usually regarded as very strong evidence that the regression relationship is significant.**

3 The smaller the significance level α at which H_0 can be rejected, the stronger is the evidence that the regression relationship is significant.

In addition to testing the significance of the slope, it is often useful to calculate a confidence interval for β_1. We show how this is done in the following box:

A Confidence Interval for the Slope

If the regression assumptions hold, a $100(1 - \alpha)$ percent confidence interval for the true slope β_1 is $[b_1 \pm t_{\alpha/2}s_{b_1}]$. Here $t_{\alpha/2}$ is based on $n - 2$ degrees of freedom.

Example 11.3 The QHIC Case

Figure 11.12 presents the MegaStat output of a simple linear regression analysis of the QHIC data. We summarize some important quantities from the output as follows: $b_0 = -348.3921$, $b_1 = 7.2583$, $s = 146.897$, $s_{b_1} = 0.4156$, and $t = b_1/s_{b_1} = 17.466$. Since the *p* value related to $t = 17.466$ is less than 0.001 (see the MegaStat output), we can reject H_0: $\beta_1 = 0$ in favour of

FIGURE 11.12   MegaStat Output of a Simple Linear Regression Analysis of the QHIC Data

Regression Analysis	r^2 0.889 [9]				n 40		
	r 0.943				k 1		
	Std. Error 146.897 [8]				Dep. Var. Upkeep		

ANOVA table

Source	SS	df	MS	F [13]	p-value [14]		
Regression	6,582,759.6972 [10]	1	6,582,759.6972	305.06	9.49E-20		
Residual	819,995.5427 [11]	38	21,578.8301				
Total	7,402,755.2399 [12]	39					

Regression output

variables	coefficients	std. error	t (df=38)	p-value [7]	confidence interval 95% lower	95% upper
Intercept	-348.3921 [1]	76.1410 [3]	-4.576 [5]	4.95E-05	-502.5314	-194.2527
Value	7.2583 [2]	0.4156 [4]	17.466 [6]	9.49E-20	6.4170 [19]	8.0995 [19]

Predicted values for: Upkeep

Value	Predicted [15]	95% Confidence Interval [16] lower	upper	95% Prediction Interval [17] lower	upper	Leverage [18]
220	1,248.42597	1,187.78944	1,309.06251	944.92879	1,551.92315	0.042

[1] b_0 = point estimate of the y intercept [2] b_1 = point estimate of the slope [3] s_{b_0} = standard error of the estimate b_0 [4] s_{b_1} = standard error of the estimate b_1 [5] t for testing significance of the y intercept [6] t for testing significance of the slope [7] p values for t statistics [8] s = standard error [9] r^2 (eta²) [10] Explained variation [11] SSE = unexplained variation [12] Total variation [13] F(model) statistic [14] p value for F(model) [15] $\hat{y}$ = point prediction when x = 220 [16] 95% confidence interval when x = 220 [17] 95% prediction interval when x = 220 [18] distance value [19] 95% confidence interval for the slope β_1

H_a: $\beta_1 \neq 0$ at the 0.001 level of significance. It follows that we have extremely strong evidence that the regression relationship is significant. The MegaStat output also tells us that a 95 percent confidence interval for the true slope β_1 is [6.4170, 8.0995]. This interval says we are 95 percent confident that mean yearly upkeep expenditure increases by between \$6.42 and \$8.10 for each additional \$1,000 increase in home value.

Testing the significance of the y intercept   We can also test the significance of the y intercept β_0. We do this by testing the null hypothesis H_0: $\beta_0 = 0$ versus the alternative hypothesis H_a: $\beta_0 \neq 0$. **If we can reject H_0 in favour of H_a by setting the probability of a Type I error equal to α, we conclude that the intercept β_0 is significant at the α level.** To carry out the hypothesis test, we use the test statistic

$$ t = \frac{b_0}{s_{b_0}}, \quad \text{where} \quad s_{b_0} = s\sqrt{\frac{1}{n} + \frac{\bar{x}^2}{SS_{xx}}}. $$

Here the rejection point and p value conditions for rejecting H_0 are the same as those given previously for testing the significance of the slope, except that t is calculated as b_0/s_{b_0}. For example, consider a set of data for which $b_0 = 15.8379$, $s_{b_0} = 0.8018$, $t = 19.75$, and p value = 0.000. Because $t = 19.75 > t_{0.025} = 2.447$ and p value < 0.05, we can reject H_0: $\beta_0 = 0$ in favour of H_a: $\beta_0 \neq 0$ at the 0.05 level of significance. In fact, because p value < 0.001, we can also reject H_0 at the 0.001 level of significance. This provides extremely strong evidence that the y intercept β_0 does not equal 0 and thus is significant.

In general, if we fail to conclude that the intercept is significant at a level of significance of 0.05, it might be reasonable to drop the y intercept from the model. However, remember that β_0 equals the mean value of y when x equals 0. If, logically speaking, the mean value of y would not equal 0 when x equals 0, then it is common practice to include the y intercept whether or not H_0: $\beta_0 = 0$ is rejected. In fact, experience suggests that it is definitely safest, when in doubt, to include the intercept β_0.

Exercises for Section 11.5

CONCEPTS

11.31   What do we conclude if we can reject H_0: $\beta_1 = 0$ in favour of H_a: $\beta_1 \neq 0$ by setting
  a. α equal to 0.05?
  b. α equal to 0.01?

11.32   Give an example of a practical application of the confidence interval for β_1.

METHODS AND APPLICATIONS

In Exercises 11.33 through 11.36, we refer to MINITAB, MegaStat, and Excel output of simple linear regression analyses of the data sets related to four case studies introduced in the exercises for Section 11.2. Using the appropriate output for each case study,

a. Find the least squares point estimates b_0 and b_1 of β_0 and β_1 on the output and report their values.

b. Find the SSE and s on the computer output and report their values.

c. Find s_{b_1} and the t statistic for testing the significance of the slope on the output and report their values. Show how t was calculated by using b_1 and s_{b_1} from the computer output.

d. Using the t statistic and appropriate rejection point, test H_0: $\beta_1 = 0$ versus H_a: $\beta_1 \neq 0$ by setting α equal to 0.05. Is

the slope (regression relationship) significant at the 0.05 level?

e. Using the t statistic and appropriate rejection point, test H_0: $\beta_1 = 0$ versus H_a: $\beta_1 \neq 0$ by setting α equal to 0.01. Is the slope (regression relationship) significant at the 0.01 level?

f. Find the p value for testing H_0: $\beta_1 = 0$ versus H_a: $\beta_1 \neq 0$ on the output and report its value. Using the p value, determine whether we can reject H_0 by setting α equal to 0.10, 0.05, 0.01, and 0.001. How much evidence is there that the slope (regression relationship) is significant?

g. Calculate the 95 percent confidence interval for β_1 using numbers on the output. Interpret the interval.

h. Calculate the 99 percent confidence interval for β_1 using numbers on the output.

i. Find s_{b_0} and the t statistic for testing the significance of the y intercept on the output and report their values. Show how t was calculated by using b_0 and s_{b_0} from the computer output.

j. Find the p value for testing H_0: $\beta_0 = 0$ versus H_a: $\beta_0 \neq 0$. Using the p value, determine whether we can reject H_0 by setting α equal to 0.10, 0.05, 0.01, and 0.001. What do you conclude?

k. Using the appropriate data set and s from the computer output, hand calculate SS_{xx}, s_{b_0}, and s_{b_1}.

FIGURE 11.13   MegaStat Output of a Simple Linear Regression Analysis of the Service Time Data

Regression		r^2 0.990			n 11		
Analysis		r 0.995			k 1		
		Std. Error 4.615			Dep. Var. **Minutes (y)**		

ANOVA table						
Source	SS	df	MS	F	p-value	
Regression	19,918.8438	1	19,918.8438	935.15	2.09E-10	
Residual	191.7017	9	21.3002			
Total	20,110.5455	10				

Regression output					confidence interval	
variables	coefficients	std. error	t (df=9)	p-value	95% lower	95% upper
Intercept	11.4641	3.4390	3.334	0.0087	3.6845	19.2437
Copiers (x)	24.6022	0.8045	30.580	2.09E-10	22.7823	26.4221

Predicted values for: Minutes (y)

		95% Confidence Intervals		95% Prediction Intervals		
Copiers (x)	Predicted	lower	upper	lower	upper	Leverage
1	36.066	29.907	42.226	23.944	48.188	0.348
2	60.669	55.980	65.357	49.224	72.113	0.202
3	85.271	81.715	88.827	74.241	96.300	0.116
4	109.873	106.721	113.025	98.967	120.779	0.091
5	134.475	130.753	138.197	123.391	145.559	0.127
6	159.077	154.139	164.016	147.528	170.627	0.224
7	183.680	177.233	190.126	171.410	195.950	0.381

FIGURE 11.14   MINITAB Output of a Simple Linear Regression Analysis of the Fresh Detergent Demand Data

```
The regression equation is
Demand = 7.81 + 2.67 PriceDif

Predictor    Coef   SE Coef     T      P
Constant   7.81409  0.07988  97.82  0.000
PriceDif    2.6652  0.2585   10.31  0.000

S = 0.316561   R-Sq = 79.2%   R-Sq(adj) = 78.4%

Analysis of Variance
Source          DF      SS      MS      F      P
Regression       1   10.653  10.653  106.30  0.000
Residual Error  28    2.806   0.100
Total           29   13.459

Values of Predictors for New Obs     Predicted Values for New Observations
New Obs   PriceDif                   New Obs    Fit   SE Fit     95% CI            95% PI
      1     0.100                          1  8.0806  0.0648  (7.9479, 8.2133)  (7.4187, 8.7425)
      2     0.250                          2  8.4804  0.0586  (8.3604, 8.6004)  (7.8209, 9.1398)
```

11.33   THE SERVICE TIME CASE   ● SrvcTime

The MegaStat output of a simple linear regression analysis of the data set for this case is given in Figure 11.13.

11.34   THE FRESH DETERGENT CASE   ● Fresh

The MINITAB output of a simple linear regression analysis of the data set for this case is given in Figure 11.14.

11.35   THE DIRECT LABOUR COST CASE   ● DirLab

The Excel and MegaStat output of a simple linear regression analysis of the data set for this case is given in Figure 11.15.

11.36   THE REAL ESTATE SALES PRICE CASE
   ● RealEst

The MINITAB output of a simple linear regression analysis of the data set for this case is given in Figure 11.16.

11.37   Find and interpret a 95 percent confidence interval for the slope β_1 of the simple linear regression model describing the sales volume data in Exercise 11.29 (page 375).   ● SalesVol

FIGURE **11.15**   Excel and MegaStat Output of a Simple Linear Regression Analysis of the Direct Labour Cost Data

(a) The Excel Output

Regression Statistics

Multiple R	0.9996
R Square	0.9993
Adjusted R Square	0.9992
Standard Error	8.6415
Observations	12

ANOVA	df	SS	MS	F	Significance F
Regression	1	1,024,592.9043	1,024,592.9043	13,720.4677	5.04E-17
Residual	10	746.7624	74.6762		
Total	11	1,025,339.6667			

	Coefficients	Standard Error	t Stat	P-value	Lower 95%	Upper 95%
Intercept	18.4875	4.6766	3.9532	0.0027	8.0674	28.9076
BatchSize (x)	10.1463	0.0866	117.1344	5.04E-17	9.9533	10.3393

(b) Prediction Using MegaStat

Predicted values for: LabourCost (y)

BatchSize (x)	Predicted	95% Confidence Interval lower	95% Confidence Interval upper	95% Prediction Interval lower	95% Prediction Interval upper	Leverage
60	627.263	621.054	633.472	607.032	647.494	0.104

FIGURE **11.16**   MINITAB Output of a Simple Linear Regression Analysis of the Real Estate Sales Price Data

```
The regression equation is
SPrice = 48.0 + 5.70 HomeSize

Predictor    Coef   SE Coef      T      P
Constant    48.02     14.41   3.33  0.010
HomeSize   5.7003    0.7457   7.64  0.000

S = 10.5880     R-Sq = 88.0%      R-Sq(adj) = 86.5%

Analysis of Variance
Source          DF       SS      MS      F      P
Regression       1   6550.7  6550.7  58.43  0.000
Residual Error   8    896.8   112.1
Total            9   7447.5

Values of Predictors for New Obs      Predicted Values for New Observations
New Obs   HomeSize                    New Obs     Fit  SE Fit       95% CI            95% PI
      1       20.0                          1  162.03    3.47  (154.04, 170.02)  (136.34, 187.72)
```

11.6 Confidence and Prediction Intervals

The point on the least squares line corresponding to a particular value x_0 of the independent variable x is

$$\hat{y} = b_0 + b_1 x_0.$$

Unless we are very lucky, $\hat{y}$ will not exactly equal either the mean value of y when x equals x_0 or a particular individual value of y when x equals x_0. Therefore, we need to place bounds on how far $\hat{y}$ might be from these values. We can do this by calculating a **confidence interval for the mean value of y** and a **prediction interval for an individual value of y**.

Both of these intervals employ a quantity called the **distance value**. For simple linear regression, this quantity is calculated as follows:

The Distance Value for Simple Linear Regression

In simple linear regression, the **distance value** for a particular value x_0 of x is

$$\text{Distance value} = \frac{1}{n} + \frac{(x_0 - \bar{x})^2}{SS_{xx}}.$$

This quantity is given its name because it is a measure of the distance between the value x_0 of x and $\bar{x}$, the average of the previously observed values of x. Notice from the above formula that the farther x_0 is from $\bar{x}$, which can be regarded as the centre of the experimental region, the larger is the distance value. The significance of this fact will become apparent shortly.

We now consider establishing a confidence interval for the mean value of y when x equals a particular value x_0 (for later reference, we call this mean value $\mu_{y|x_0}$). Because each possible sample of n values of the dependent variable gives values of b_0 and b_1 that differ from the values given by other samples, different samples give different values of the point estimate

$$\hat{y} = b_0 + b_1 x_0.$$

It can be shown that, if the regression assumptions hold, the population of all possible values of $\hat{y}$ is normally distributed with mean $\mu_{y|x_0}$ and standard deviation

$$\sigma_{\hat{y}} = \sigma\sqrt{\text{Distance value}}.$$

The point estimate of $\sigma_{\hat{y}}$ is

$$s_{\hat{y}} = s\sqrt{\text{Distance value}},$$

which is called the **standard error of the estimate $\hat{y}$**. Using this standard error, we form a confidence interval as follows:

A Confidence Interval for a Mean Value of y

If the regression assumptions hold, a **100(1 − α) percent confidence interval for the mean value of y** when the value of the independent variable is x_0 is

$$[\hat{y} \pm t_{\alpha/2} s\sqrt{\text{Distance value}}].$$

Here $t_{\alpha/2}$ is based on $n - 2$ degrees of freedom.

For the data in Table 11.5 (page 364), suppose we wish to compute a 95 percent confidence interval for the y value when $x_0 = 40$. From page 369, the point estimate of this mean is

$$\begin{aligned}
\hat{y} &= b_0 + b_1 x_0 \\
&= 15.84 - 0.1279(40) \\
&= 10.72.
\end{aligned}$$

Furthermore, using the information on pages 367 and 368, we compute

$$\begin{aligned}
\text{Distance value} &= \frac{1}{n} + \frac{(x_0 - \bar{x})^2}{SS_{xx}} \\
&= \frac{1}{8} + \frac{(40 - 43.98)^2}{1{,}404.355} \\
&= 0.1363.
\end{aligned}$$

Because $s = 0.6542$ (see page 374) and $t_{\alpha/2} = t_{0.025}$ based on $n - 2 = 8 - 2 = 6$ degrees of freedom equals 2.447, it follows that the desired 95 percent confidence interval is

$$\begin{aligned}
[\hat{y} \pm t_{\alpha/2} s\sqrt{\text{Distance value}}] &= [10.72 \pm 2.447(0.6542)\sqrt{0.1363}] \\
&= [10.72 \pm 0.59] \\
&= [10.13, 11.31].
\end{aligned}$$

This interval says we are 95 percent confident that the y value that would be observed in all observations where $x = 40$ is between 10.13 and 11.31.

We develop an interval for an individual value of y when x equals a particular value x_0 by considering the **prediction error** $y - \hat{y}$. After observing each possible sample and calculating the point prediction based on that sample, we could observe any one of an infinite number of different individual values of y (because of different possible error terms). Therefore, an infinite number of different prediction errors could be observed. If the regression assumptions hold, it can be shown that the population of all possible prediction errors is normally distributed with mean 0 and standard deviation

$$\sigma_{(y-\hat{y})} = \sigma\sqrt{1 + \text{Distance value}}.$$

The point estimate of $\sigma_{(y-\hat{y})}$ is

$$s_{(y-\hat{y})} = s\sqrt{1 + \text{Distance value}},$$

which is called the **standard error of the prediction error**. Using this quantity, we obtain a **prediction interval** as follows:

A Prediction Interval for an Individual Value of y

If the regression assumptions hold, a **100(1 − α) percent prediction interval for an individual value of y** when the value of the independent variable is x_0 is

$$[\hat{y} \pm t_{\alpha/2}s\sqrt{1 + \text{Distance value}}].$$

Here $t_{\alpha/2}$ is based on $n - 2$ degrees of freedom.

In general, the prediction interval is useful if it is important to predict an individual value of the dependent variable. A confidence interval is useful if it is important to estimate the mean value, such as when observations are affected by a very large number of values of the dependent variable when the independent variable equals a particular value. We illustrate this in the following example.

Example 11.4 The QHIC Case

Consider a home worth \$220,000. We have seen that the predicted yearly upkeep expenditure for such a home is

$$\begin{aligned} \hat{y} &= b_0 + b_1x_0 \\ &= -348.3921 + 7.2583(220) \\ &= 1248.43 \text{ (that is, \$1,248.43)}. \end{aligned}$$

This predicted value is given at the bottom of the MegaStat output in Figure 11.12 (page 377), which we repeat here:

Predicted values for: Upkeep

Value	Predicted	95% Confidence Interval		95% Prediction Interval		Leverage
		lower	upper	lower	upper	
220	1,248.42597	1,187.78944	1,309.06251	944.92879	1,551.92315	0.042

In addition to giving $\hat{y} = 1,248.43$, the MegaStat output also tells us that the distance value, which is given under the heading "Leverage" on the output, equals 0.042. Therefore, since s equals 146.897 (see Figure 11.12), it follows that a 95 percent prediction interval for the yearly upkeep expenditure of an individual home worth \$220,000 is calculated as follows:

$$\begin{aligned} &[\hat{y} \pm t_{0.025}\,s\sqrt{1 + \text{Distance value}}] \\ &= [1,248.43 \pm 2.024(146.897)\sqrt{1.042}] \\ &= [944.93, 1,551.93]. \end{aligned}$$

Here $t_{0.025}$ is based on $n - 2 = 40 - 2 = 38$ degrees of freedom. Note that this interval is given on the MegaStat output.

Because there are many homes worth roughly $220,000 in the metropolitan area, QHIC is more interested in the mean upkeep expenditure for all such homes than in the individual upkeep expenditure for one such home. The MegaStat output tells us that a 95 percent confidence interval for this mean upkeep expenditure is [1,187.79, 1,309.06]. This interval says that QHIC is 95 percent confident that the mean upkeep expenditure for all homes worth $220,000 is at least $1,187.79 and is no more than $1,309.06.

Exercises for Section 11.6

CONCEPTS

11.38 What does the distance value measure?

11.39 What is the difference between a confidence interval and a prediction interval?

11.40 Discuss how the distance value affects the length of a confidence interval and a prediction interval.

METHODS AND APPLICATIONS

11.41 THE SERVICE TIME CASE ● SrvcTime

The partial MegaStat regression output in Figure 11.17 for the service time data relates to predicting service times for 1, 2, 3, 4, 5, 6, and 7 copiers.
a. Report (as shown on the computer output) a point estimate of and a 95 percent confidence interval for the mean time to service four copiers.
b. Report (as shown on the computer output) a point prediction of and a 95 percent prediction interval for the time to service four copiers on a single call.
c. For this case, $n = 11$, $b_0 = 11.4641$, $b_1 = 24.6022$, and $s = 4.615$. Using this information and a distance value from the MegaStat output, hand calculate (within rounding) the confidence interval of part a and the prediction interval of part b.
d. If we examine the service time data, we see that there was at least one call on which Accu-Copiers serviced each of 1, 2, 3, 4, 5, 6, and 7 copiers. The 95 percent confidence intervals for the mean service times on these calls might be used to schedule future service calls. To understand this, note that a person making service calls will (in, say, a year or more) make a very large number of service calls. Some of the person's individual service times will

be below, and some will be above, the corresponding mean service times. However, since the very large number of individual service times will average out to the mean service times, it seems fair to both the efficiency of the company and the person making service calls to schedule service calls by using estimates of the mean service times. Therefore, suppose we wish to schedule a call to service five copiers. Examining the MegaStat output, we see that a 95 percent confidence interval for the mean time to service five copiers is [130.753, 138.197]. Since the mean time might be 138.197 minutes, it would seem fair to allow 138 minutes to make the service call. Now suppose we wish to schedule a call to service four copiers. Determine how many minutes to allow for the service call.

11.42 THE FRESH DETERGENT CASE ● Fresh

The partial MINITAB regression output in Figure 11.18(a) for the Fresh detergent data relates to predicting demand for future sales periods in which the price difference will be 0.10 (see New Obs 1) and 0.25 (see New Obs2).
a. Report (as shown on the computer output) a point estimate of and a 95 percent confidence interval for the mean demand for Fresh in all sales periods when the price difference is 0.10.
b. Report (as shown on the computer output) a point prediction of and a 95 percent prediction interval for the actual demand for Fresh in an individual sales period when the price difference is 0.10.
c. Remembering that $s = 0.316561$ and that the distance value equals $(s_{\hat{y}}/s)^2$, use $s_{\hat{y}}$ from the

FIGURE **11.17** Partial MegaStat Regression Output for Exercise 11.41

Predicted values for: Minutes (y)

Copiers (x)	Predicted	95% Confidence Intervals lower	upper	95% Prediction Intervals lower	upper	Leverage
1	36.066	29.907	42.226	23.944	48.188	0.348
2	60.669	55.980	65.357	49.224	72.113	0.202
3	85.271	81.715	88.827	74.241	96.300	0.116
4	109.873	106.721	113.025	98.967	120.779	0.091
5	134.475	130.753	138.197	123.391	145.559	0.127
6	159.077	154.139	164.016	147.528	170.627	0.224
7	183.680	177.233	190.126	171.410	195.950	**0.381**

FIGURE **11.18**   **MINITAB and MegaStat Output for Exercises 11.42, 11.44, and 11.43**

(a) MINITAB output of the Fresh detergent data for Exercise 11.42

```
Predicted Values for New Observations
New Obs    Fit   SE Fit       95% CI           95% PI
      1  8.0806  0.0648  (7.9479, 8.2133)  (7.4187, 8.7425)
      2  8.4804  0.0586  (8.3604, 8.6004)  (7.8209, 9.1398)
```

(b) MegaStat output of the labour cost data for Exercise 11.43

Predicted values for: LabourCost (y)

BatchSize (x)	Predicted	95% Confidence Interval		95% Prediction Interval		Leverage
		lower	upper	lower	upper	
60	627.263	621.054	633.472	607.032	647.494	0.104

(c) MINITAB output of the real estate data for Exercise 11.44

```
Predicted Values for New Observations
New Obs    Fit   SE Fit        95% CI              95% PI
      1  162.03   3.47  (154.04, 170.02)  (136.34, 187.72)
```

computer output to hand calculate the distance value when $x = 0.10$.

d. For this case, $n = 30$, $b_0 = 7.81409$, $b_1 = 2.6652$, and $s = 0.316561$. Using this information and your result from part c, find 99 percent confidence and prediction intervals for mean and individual demands when $x = 0.10$.

e. Repeat parts a, b, c, and d when $x = 0.25$.

11.43   THE DIRECT LABOUR COST CASE   ● DirLab

The partial MegaStat regression output in Figure 11.18(b) for the direct labour cost data relates to predicting direct labour cost when the batch size is 60.

a. Report (as shown on the MegaStat output) a point estimate of and a 95 percent confidence interval

for the mean direct labour cost of all batches of size 60.

b. Report (as shown on the MegaStat output) a point prediction of and a 95 percent prediction interval for the actual direct labour cost of an individual batch of size 60.

c. For this case, $n = 12$, $b_0 = 18.4875$, $b_1 = 10.1463$, and $s = 8.6415$. Use this information and the distance value from the MegaStat output to compute 99 percent confidence and prediction intervals for the mean and individual labour costs when $x = 60$.

11.44   THE REAL ESTATE SALES PRICE CASE   ● RealEst

The partial MINITAB regression output in Figure 11.18(c) for the real estate sales price data relates to predicting the sales price of a home with 2000 square feet (about 180 m^2).

a. Report (as shown on the MINITAB output) a point estimate of and a 95 percent confidence interval for the mean sales price of all houses with 2000 square feet.

b. Report (as shown on the MINITAB output) a point prediction of and a 95 percent prediction interval for the sales price of an individual house with 2000 square feet.

c. If you were purchasing a home with 2000 square feet, which of the above intervals would you find to be most useful? Explain.

11.45   Using the sales volume data in Exercise 11.29 (page 375) find a point prediction of and a 95 percent prediction interval for sales volume when advertising expenditure is 11 (that is, \$110,000).   ● SalesVol

---

11.7 Simple Coefficients of Determination and Correlation

The simple coefficient of determination   The **simple coefficient of determination** (r^2 **or eta**^{2}) is a measure of the usefulness of a simple linear regression model. Suppose we have observed n values of the dependent variable y. However, we choose to predict y without using a predictor (independent) variable x. In such a case, the only reasonable prediction of a specific value of y, say y_i, would be $\bar{y}$, which is simply the average of the n observed values $y_1, y_2, \ldots, y_n$. Here the error of prediction in predicting y_i would be $y_i - \bar{y}$ and represents the prediction errors obtained when we do not use the information provided by the independent variable x.

If we decide to employ the predictor variable x and observe the values $x_1, x_2, \ldots, x_n$ corresponding to the observed values of y, then the prediction of y_i is

$$\hat{y}_i = b_0 + b_1 x_i$$

and the prediction error is $y_i - \hat{y}_i$. Using the predictor variable x decreases the prediction error in predicting y_i from $(y_i - \bar{y})$ to $(y_i - \hat{y}_i)$, or by an amount equal to

$$(y_i - \bar{y}) - (y_i - \hat{y}_i) = (\hat{y}_i - \bar{y}).$$

It can be shown that in general

$$\sum (y_i - \bar{y})^2 - \sum (y_i - \hat{y}_i)^2 = \sum (\hat{y}_i - \bar{y})^2.$$

The sum of squared prediction errors obtained when we do not employ the predictor variable x, $\sum (y_i - \bar{y})^2$, is called the **total variation**. Intuitively, this quantity measures the total amount of variation exhibited by the observed values of y. The sum of squared prediction errors obtained when we use the predictor variable x, $\sum (y_i - \hat{y}_i)^2$, is called the **unexplained variation** (this is another name for the *SSE*). Intuitively, this quantity measures the amount of variation in the values of y that is not explained by the predictor variable. The quantity $\sum (\hat{y}_i - \bar{y})^2$ is called the **explained variation**. Using these definitions and the above equation involving these summations, we see that

$$\text{Total variation} - \text{Unexplained variation} = \text{Explained variation}.$$

It follows that the explained variation is the reduction in the sum of squared prediction errors that has been accomplished by using the predictor variable x to predict y. It also follows that

$$\text{Total variation} = \text{Explained variation} + \text{Unexplained variation}.$$

Intuitively, this equation implies that the explained variation represents the amount of the total variation in the observed values of y that is explained by the predictor variable x (and the simple linear regression model).

We now define the **simple coefficient of determination** to be

$$\text{eta}^2 = r^2 = \frac{\text{Explained variation}}{\text{Total variation}}.$$

That is, r^2 (or eta^2) is the proportion of the total variation in the n observed values of y that is explained by the simple linear regression model. Neither the explained variation nor the total variation can be negative (both quantities are sums of squares). Therefore, r^2 is greater than or equal to 0. Because the explained variation must be less than or equal to the total variation, r^2 cannot be greater than 1. The nearer r^2 is to 1, the larger is the proportion of the total variation that is explained by the model, and the greater is the utility of the model in predicting y. If the value of r^2 is not reasonably close to 1, the independent variable in the model does not provide accurate predictions of y. In such a case, a different predictor variable must be found in order to accurately predict y. It is also possible that no regression model employing a single predictor variable will accurately predict y. In this case, the model must be improved by including more than one independent variable. We see how to do this in Chapter 12.

In the following box, we summarize the results of this section:

The Simple Coefficient of Determination, r^2

For the simple linear regression model:

1   **Total variation** $= \sum (y_i - \bar{y})^2$.

2   **Explained variation** $= \sum (\hat{y}_i - \bar{y})^2$.

3   **Unexplained variation** $= \sum (y_i - \hat{y}_i)^2$.

4   **Total variation = Explained variation + Unexplained variation.**

5   **(eta^2) The simple coefficient of determination is**
$$r^2 = \frac{\text{Explained variation}}{\text{Total variation}}.$$

6   r^2 is the proportion of the total variation in the n observed values of the dependent variable that is explained by the simple linear regression model.

Example 11.5   The QHIC Case

In the QHIC case, it can be shown that Total variation = 7,402,755.2399, Explained variation = 6,582,759.6972, SSE = Unexplained variation = 819,995.5427, and

$$r^2 = \frac{\text{Explained variation}}{\text{Total variation}} = \frac{6,582,759.6972}{7,402,755.2399} = 0.889.$$

This value of r^2 (eta^2) says that the simple linear regression model that employs home value as a predictor variable explains 88.9 percent of the total variation in the 40 observed home upkeep expenditures.

In Section 11.11, we present some shortcut formulas for calculating the total, explained, and unexplained variations. In the previous section, r^2, the explained variation, the unexplained variation, and the total variation were calculated by MINITAB, Excel, and MegaStat.

Exercises for Section 11.7

CONCEPTS

11.46   Discuss the meanings of the total variation, the unexplained variation, and the explained variation.

11.47   What does the simple coefficient of determination measure?

METHODS AND APPLICATIONS

In Exercises 11.48 through 11.51, we give the total variation, the unexplained variation (SSE), and the least squares point estimate b_1 that are obtained when simple linear regression is used to analyze the data set related to each of four previously discussed case studies. Using the information given in each exercise, find the explained variation, the simple coefficient of

determination (r^2 or eta^2), and the simple correlation coefficient (r). Interpret r^2.

11.48   **THE SERVICE TIME CASE**   ● SrvcTime
Total variation = 20,110.5455, SSE = 191.7017, b_1 = 24.6022.

11.49   **THE FRESH DETERGENT CASE**   ● Fresh
Total variation = 13.459, SSE = 2.806, b_1 = 2.6652.

11.50   **THE DIRECT LABOUR COST CASE**   ● DirLab
Total variation = 1,025,339.6667, SSE = 746.7624, b_1 = 10.1463.

11.51   **THE REAL ESTATE SALES PRICE CASE**   ● RealEst
Total variation = 7,447.5, SSE = 896.8, b_1 = 5.7003.

11.8 Testing the Significance of the Population Correlation Coefficient

The simple correlation coefficient measures the linear relationship between the observed values of x and the observed values of y that make up the sample. A similar coefficient of linear correlation can be defined for the population of **all possible combinations of observed values of x and y**. We call this coefficient the **population correlation coefficient** and denote it by the symbol ρ (rho). We use r as the point estimate of ρ. In addition, we can carry out a hypothesis test. Here we test the null hypothesis $H_0: \rho = 0$, **which says there is no linear relationship**

between x and y, against the alternative H_a: $\rho \neq 0$, **which says there is a positive or negative linear relationship between x and y**. This test employs the test statistic

$$t = \frac{r\sqrt{n-2}}{\sqrt{1-r^2}}$$

and is based on the assumption that the population of all possible observed combinations of values of x and y has a **bivariate normal probability distribution** (see Wonnacott and Wonnacott (1981) for a discussion of this distribution). It can be shown that the preceding test statistic t and the p value used to test H_0: $\rho = 0$ versus H_a: $\rho \neq 0$ are equal to, respectively, the test statistic $t = b_1/s_{b_1}$ and the p value used to test H_0: $\beta_1 = 0$ versus H_a: $\beta_1 \neq 0$, where β_1 is the slope in the simple linear regression model. Keep in mind, however, that although the mechanics involved in these hypothesis tests are the same, these tests are based on different assumptions (remember that the test for significance of the slope is based on the regression assumptions). If the bivariate normal distribution assumption for the test concerning ρ is badly violated, we can use a nonparametric approach to correlation. One such approach is **Spearman's rank correlation coefficient**. This approach is discussed in Section 13.5.

Exercises for Section 11.8

CONCEPTS

11.52 Explain what is meant by the population correlation coefficient ρ.

11.53 Explain how we test H_0: $\rho = 0$ versus H_a: $\rho \neq 0$. What do we conclude if we reject H_0: $\rho = 0$?

METHODS AND APPLICATIONS

11.54 THE SERVICE TIME CASE   ● SrvcTime

Consider testing H_0: $\beta_1 = 0$ versus H_a: $\beta_1 \neq 0$. Figure 11.13 (page 379) tells us that $t = 30.580$ and that the

related p value is less than 0.001. Assuming that the bivariate normal probability distribution assumption holds, test H_0: $\rho = 0$ versus H_a: $\rho \neq 0$ by setting α equal to 0.05, 0.01, and 0.001. What do you conclude about how x and y are related?

11.9 An *F* Test for the Model

In this section, we discuss an F test that can be used to test the significance of the regression relationship between x and y (sometimes referred to as testing the significance of the simple linear regression model). For simple linear regression, this test is another way to test the null hypothesis H_0: $\beta_1 = 0$ (the relationship between x and y is not significant) versus H_a: $\beta_1 \neq 0$ (the relationship between x and y is significant). If we can reject H_0 at level of significance α, we often say that **the simple linear regression model is significant at level of significance α**.

An *F* Test for the Simple Linear Regression Model

Suppose that the regression assumptions hold, and define the **overall *F* statistic** to be

$$F(\text{model}) = \frac{\text{Explained variation}}{(\text{Unexplained variation})/(n-2)}.$$

Also define the p value related to $F(\text{model})$ to be the area under the curve of the F distribution (with 1 numerator and $n - 2$ denominator degrees of freedom) to the right of $F(\text{model})$—see Figure 11.19(b).

We can reject H_0: $\beta_1 = 0$ in favour of H_a: $\beta_1 \neq 0$ at level of significance α if either of the following equivalent conditions holds:

1. $F(\text{model}) > F_\alpha$.

2. p value $< \alpha$.

Here the point F_α is based on 1 numerator and $n - 2$ denominator degrees of freedom.

The first condition in the box says we should reject H_0: $\beta_1 = 0$ (and conclude that the relationship between x and y is significant) when $F(\text{model})$ is large. This is intuitive because a large overall F statistic would be obtained when the explained variation is large compared to the unexplained variation. This would occur if x is significantly related to y, which would imply that the slope β_1 is not equal to 0. Figure 11.19(a) illustrates that we reject H_0 when $F(\text{model})$ is greater than F_α. As can be seen in Figure 11.19(b), when $F(\text{model})$ is large, the related p value is small.

FIGURE **11.19**   An *F* Test for the Simple Linear Regression Model

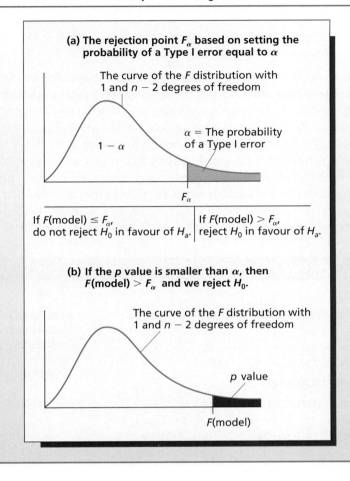

When the *p* value is small enough (resulting from an *F*(model) statistic that is large enough), we reject H_0. Figure 11.19(b) illustrates that the second condition in the box (*p* value $<$ α) is an equivalent way to carry out this test.

For example, a partial MINITAB output of a simple linear regression analysis relating *y* to *x* is given below:

```
Analysis of Variance
Source                  DF          SS          MS          F          P
Regression               1      22.981      22.981      53.69      0.000
Residual Error           6       2.568       0.428
Total                    7      25.549
```

Looking at this output, we see that the explained variation is 22.981 and the unexplained variation is 2.568. It follows that

$$F(\text{model}) = \frac{\text{Explained variation}}{(\text{Unexplained variation})/(n-2)}$$

$$= \frac{22.981}{2.568/(8-2)} = \frac{22.981}{0.428}$$

$$= 53.69.$$

Note that this overall *F* statistic is given on the MINITAB output and is also given on the following partial Excel output:

ANOVA	df	SS	MS	F	Significance F
Regression	1	22.9808	22.9808	53.6949	0.0003
Residual	6	2.5679	0.4280		
Total	7	25.5488			

The p value related to F(model) is the area to the right of 53.69 under the curve of the F distribution with 1 numerator and 6 denominator degrees of freedom. This p value is given on both the MINITAB output (labelled "P") and the Excel output (labelled "Significance F") and is less than 0.001. If we wish to test the significance of the regression relationship with level of significance $\alpha = 0.05$, we use the rejection point $F_{0.05}$ based on 1 numerator and 6 denominator degrees of freedom. Using Table A.6, we find that $F_{0.05} = 5.99$. Since F(model) $= 53.69 > F_{0.05} = 5.99$, we can reject H_0: $\beta_1 = 0$ in favour of H_a: $\beta_1 \neq 0$ at level of significance 0.05. Alternatively, since the p value is smaller than 0.05, 0.01, and 0.001, we can reject H_0 at level of significance 0.05, 0.01, or 0.001. Therefore, we have extremely strong evidence that H_0: $\beta_1 = 0$ should be rejected and that the regression relationship between x and y is significant. That is, we might say that we have extremely strong evidence that the simple linear model relating y to x is significant.

As another example, consider the following partial MegaStat output:

ANOVA table

Source	SS	df	MS	F	p-value
Regression	6,582,759.6972	1	6,582,759.6972	305.06	9.49E-20
Residual	819,995.5427	38	21,578.8301		
Total	7,402,755.2399	39			

This output tells us that for the QHIC simple linear regression model, F(model) is 305.06 and the related p value is less than 0.001. Because the p value is less than 0.001, we have extremely strong evidence that the regression relationship is significant.

Testing the significance of the regression relationship between y and x by using the overall F statistic and its related p value is equivalent to doing this test by using the t statistic and its related p value. Specifically, it can be shown that $(t)^2 = F$(model) and that $(t_{\alpha/2})^2$ based on $n - 2$ degrees of freedom equals F_α based on 1 numerator and $n - 2$ denominator degrees of freedom. It follows that the rejection point conditions

$$|t| > t_{\alpha/2} \quad \text{and} \quad F(\text{model}) > F_\alpha$$

are equivalent. Furthermore, the p values related to t and F(model) can be shown to be equal. Because these tests are equivalent, it would be logical to ask why we have presented the F test. There are two reasons. First, most standard regression computer packages include the results of the F test as a part of the regression output. Second, the F test has a useful generalization in multiple regression analysis (where we employ more than one predictor variable). The F test in multiple regression is not equivalent to a t test. This is further explained in Chapter 12.

Exercises for Section 11.9

CONCEPTS

11.55 What are the null and alternative hypotheses for the F test in simple linear regression?

11.56 The F test in simple linear regression is equivalent to what other test?

METHODS AND APPLICATIONS

In Figure 11.20, we give MINITAB, MegaStat, and Excel outputs of simple linear regression analyses of the data sets related to four previously discussed case studies. Use the appropriate computer output to do the following for Exercises 11.57 through 11.60:

a. Use the explained variation and the unexplained variation as given on the computer output to calculate the F(model) statistic.

b. Use the F(model) statistic and the appropriate rejection point to test H_0: $\beta_1 = 0$ versus H_a: $\beta_1 \neq 0$ by setting α equal to 0.05. What do you conclude about the regression relationship between y and x?

c. Use the F(model) statistic and the appropriate rejection point to test H_0: $\beta_1 = 0$ versus H_a: $\beta_1 \neq 0$ by setting α equal to 0.01. What do you conclude about the regression relationship between y and x?

d. Find the p value related to F(model) on the computer output and report its value. Using the p value, test the significance of the regression model at the 0.10, 0.05, 0.01, and 0.001 levels of significance. What do you conclude?

e. Show that the F(model) statistic is (within rounding) the square of the t statistic for testing H_0: $\beta_1 = 0$ versus H_a: $\beta_1 \neq 0$. Also show that the $F_{0.05}$ rejection point is the square of the $t_{0.025}$ rejection point.

Note that in the lower right-hand corner of each output we give (in parentheses) the number of observations, n, used to perform the regression analysis and the t statistic for testing H_0: $\beta_1 = 0$ versus H_a: $\beta_1 \neq 0$.

11.57   THE SERVICE TIME CASE   ⬥ SrvcTime

The MegaStat output for this case is given in Figure 11.20(a).

11.58   THE FRESH DETERGENT CASE   ⬥ Fresh

The MINITAB output for this case is given in Figure 11.20(b).

11.59   THE DIRECT LABOUR COST CASE   ⬥ DirLab

The Excel output for this case is given in Figure 11.20(c).

11.60   THE REAL ESTATE SALES PRICE CASE
⬥ RealEst

The MINITAB output for this case is given in Figure 11.20(d).

FIGURE 11.20   MINITAB, MegaStat, and Excel Outputs for Exercises 11.57 through 11.60

(a) MegaStat output for Exercise 11.57

ANOVA table

Source	SS	df	MS	F	p-value
Regression	19,918.8438	1	19,918.8438	935.15	2.09E-10
Residual	191.7017	9	21.3002		
Total	20,110.5455	10			

(n=11; t=30.580)

(b) MINITAB output for Exercise 11.58

```
Analysis of Variance
Source           DF       SS       MS       F       P
Regression        1   10.653   10.653   106.30   0.000
Residual Error   28    2.806    0.100
Total            29   13.459            (n=30; t=10.31)
```

(c) Excel output for Exercise 11.59

ANOVA	df	SS	MS	F	Significance F
Regression	1	1,024,592.9043	1,024,592.9043	13,720.4677	5.04E-17
Residual	10	746.7624	74.6762		
Total	11	1,025,339.6667			

(n=12; t=117.1344)

(d) MINITAB output for Exercise 11.60

```
Analysis of Variance
Source           DF       SS       MS       F       P
Regression        1    6550.7   6550.7   58.43   0.000
Residual Error    8     896.8    112.1
Total             9    7447.5           (n=10; t=7.64)
```

11.10 Residual Analysis

CHAPTER 16

In this section, we explain how to check the validity of the regression assumptions. The required checks are carried out by analyzing the **regression residuals**. The residuals are defined as follows:

For any particular observed value of y, the corresponding **residual** is

$$e = y - \hat{y} = (\text{observed value of } y - \text{predicted value of } y),$$

where the predicted value of y is calculated using the **least squares prediction equation**

$$\hat{y} = b_0 + b_1 x.$$

The linear regression model $y = \beta_0 + \beta_1 x + \varepsilon$ implies that the error term ε is given by the equation $\varepsilon = y - (\beta_0 + \beta_1 x)$. Since $\hat{y}$ in the previous box is clearly the point estimate of $\beta_0 + \beta_1 x$, we see that the residual $e = y - \hat{y}$ is the point estimate of the error term ε. If the regression assumptions are valid, then, for any given value of the independent variable, the population of potential error term values will be normally distributed with mean 0 and variance σ^2 (see the regression assumptions in Section 11.4 on page 373). Furthermore, the different error terms will be statistically independent. Because the residuals provide point estimates of the error terms, we have the following:

If the regression assumptions hold, the residuals should look like they have been randomly and independently selected from normally distributed populations with mean 0 and variance σ^2.

In any real regression problem, the regression assumptions will not hold exactly. In fact, it is important to point out that mild departures from the regression assumptions do not seriously hinder our ability to use a regression model to make statistical inferences. Therefore, we are looking for pronounced, rather than subtle, departures from the regression assumptions. Because of this, we will require that the residuals only approximately fit the description just given.

Residual plots   One useful way to analyze residuals is to plot them versus various criteria. The resulting plots are called **residual plots**. To construct a residual plot, we compute the residual for each observed y value. The calculated residuals are then plotted versus some criterion. To validate the regression assumptions, we make residual plots against (1) values of the independent variable x, (2) values of $\hat{y}$, the predicted value of the dependent variable, and (3) the time order in which the data have been observed (if the regression data are time series data).

We next look at an example of constructing residual plots. Then we explain how to use these plots to check the regression assumptions.

Example 11.6 The QHIC Case

Figure 11.21 gives the QHIC upkeep expenditure data and a scatter plot of the data. If we use a simple linear regression model to describe the QHIC data, we find that the least squares point estimates of β_0 and β_1 are $b_0 = -348.3921$ and $b_1 = 7.2583$. The MegaStat output in

FIGURE 11.21   **The QHIC Upkeep Expenditure Data and a Scatter Plot of the Data**   ● QHIC

Home	Value of Home, x (Thousands of Dollars)	Upkeep Expenditure, y (Dollars)	Home	Value of Home, x (Thousands of Dollars)	Upkeep Expenditure, y (Dollars)
1	237.00	1,412.08	21	153.04	849.14
2	153.08	797.20	22	232.18	1,313.84
3	184.86	872.48	23	125.44	602.06
4	222.06	1,003.42	24	169.82	642.14
5	160.68	852.90	25	177.28	1,038.80
6	99.68	288.48	26	162.82	697.00
7	229.04	1,288.46	27	120.44	324.34
8	101.78	423.08	28	191.10	965.10
9	257.86	1,351.74	29	158.78	920.14
10	96.28	378.04	30	178.50	950.90
11	171.00	918.08	31	272.20	1,670.32
12	231.02	1,627.24	32	48.90	125.40
13	228.32	1,204.76	33	104.56	479.78
14	205.90	857.04	34	286.18	2,010.64
15	185.72	775.00	35	83.72	368.36
16	168.78	869.26	36	86.20	425.60
17	247.06	1,396.00	37	133.58	626.90
18	155.54	711.50	38	212.86	1,316.94
19	224.20	1,475.18	39	122.02	390.16
20	202.04	1,413.32	40	198.02	1,090.84

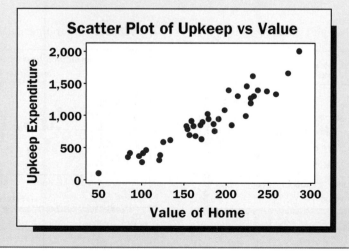

Figure 11.22(a) presents the predicted home upkeep expenditures and residuals that are given by the simple linear regression model. Here each residual is computed as

$$e = y - \hat{y} = y - (b_0 + b_1x) = y - (-348.3921 + 7.2583x).$$

For instance, for the first observation (home), when $y = 1412.08$ and $x = 237.00$ (see Figure 11.21), the residual is

$$e = 1,412.08 - (-348.3921 + 7.2583(237))$$
$$= 1,412.08 - 1,371.816 = 40.264.$$

The MINITAB output in Figure 11.22(b) and (c) gives plots of the residuals for the QHIC simple linear regression model against values of x and $\hat{y}$. To understand how these plots are constructed, recall that for the first observation (home), $y = 1,412.08$, $x = 237.00$, $\hat{y} = 1,371.816$, and the residual is 40.264. It follows that the point plotted in Figure 11.22(b) corresponding to the first observation has a horizontal axis coordinate of the x value 237.00 and a vertical axis coordinate of the residual 40.264. It also follows that the point plotted in Figure 11.22(c) corresponding to the first observation has a horizontal axis coordinate of the

FIGURE 11.22   MegaStat and MINITAB Output of the Residuals and Residual Plots for the QHIC
Simple Linear Regression Model

(a) MegaStat output of the residuals

Observation	Upkeep	Predicted	Residual	Observation	Upkeep	Predicted	Residual
1	1,412.080	1,371.816	40.264	21	849.140	762.413	86.727
2	797.200	762.703	34.497	22	1,313.840	1,336.832	−22.992
3	872.480	993.371	−120.891	23	602.060	562.085	39.975
4	1,003.420	1,263.378	−259.958	24	642.140	884.206	−242.066
5	852.900	817.866	35.034	25	1,038.800	938.353	100.447
6	288.480	375.112	−86.632	26	697.000	833.398	−136.398
7	1,288.460	1,314.041	−25.581	27	324.340	525.793	−201.453
8	423.080	390.354	32.726	28	965.100	1,038.662	−73.562
9	1,351.740	1,523.224	−171.484	29	920.140	804.075	116.065
10	378.040	350.434	27.606	30	950.900	947.208	3.692
11	918.080	892.771	25.309	31	1,670.320	1,627.307	43.013
12	1,627.240	1,328.412	298.828	32	125.400	6.537	118.863
13	1,204.760	1,308.815	−104.055	33	479.780	410.532	69.248
14	857.040	1,146.084	−289.044	34	2,010.640	1,728.778	281.862
15	775.000	999.613	−224.613	35	368.360	259.270	109.090
16	869.260	876.658	−7.398	36	425.600	277.270	148.330
17	1,396.000	1,444.835	−48.835	37	626.900	621.167	5.733
18	711.500	780.558	−69.058	38	1,316.940	1,196.602	120.338
19	1,475.180	1,278.911	196.269	39	390.160	537.261	−147.101
20	1,413.320	1,118.068	295.252	40	1,090.840	1,088.889	1.951

(b) MINITAB output of residual plot versus x

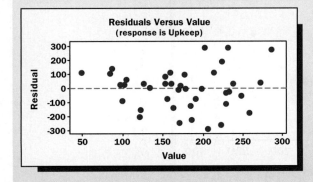

(c) MINITAB output of residual plot versus $\hat{y}$

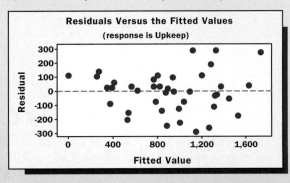

$\hat{y}$ value 1,371.816 and a vertical axis coordinate of the residual 40.264. Finally, note that the QHIC data are cross-sectional data, not time series data. Therefore, we cannot make a residual plot versus time.

The constant variance assumption To check the validity of the constant variance assumption, we examine plots of the residuals against values of x, $\hat{y}$, and time (if the regression data are time series data). When we look at these plots, the pattern of the residuals' fluctuation around 0 tells us about the validity of the constant variance assumption. A residual plot that "fans out" (as in Figure 11.23(a)) suggests that the error terms are becoming more spread out as the horizontal plot value increases and that the constant variance assumption is violated. Here we would say that an **increasing error variance** exists. A residual plot that "funnels in" (as in Figure 11.23(b)) suggests that the spread of the error terms is decreasing as the horizontal plot value increases and that again the constant variance assumption is violated. In this case, we would say that a **decreasing error variance** exists. A residual plot with a "horizontal band appearance" (as in Figure 11.23(c)) suggests that the spread of the error terms around 0 is not changing much as the horizontal plot value increases. Such a plot tells us that the constant variance assumption (approximately) holds.

As an example, consider the QHIC case and the residual plot in Figure 11.22(b). This plot appears to fan out as x increases, indicating that the spread of the error terms is increasing as x increases. That is, an increasing error variance exists. This is equivalent to saying that the variance of the population of potential yearly upkeep expenditures for houses worth x (thousand dollars) appears to increase as x increases. The reason is that the model $y = \beta_0 + \beta_1 x + \varepsilon$ says that the variation of y is the same as the variation of ε. For example, the variance of the population of potential yearly upkeep expenditures for houses worth \$200,000 would be larger than the variance of the population of potential yearly upkeep expenditures for houses worth \$100,000. Increasing variance makes some intuitive sense because people with more expensive homes generally have more discretionary income. These people can choose to spend either a substantial amount or a much smaller amount on home upkeep, thus causing a relatively large variation in upkeep expenditures.

Another residual plot showing the increasing error variance in the QHIC case is Figure 11.22(c). This plot tells us that the residuals appear to fan out as $\hat{y}$ (predicted y) increases, which is logical because $\hat{y}$ is an increasing function of x. Also note that the scatter plot of y versus x in Figure 11.21 shows the increasing error variance—the y values appear to fan out as x increases. In fact, one might ask why we need to consider residual plots when we can simply look

FIGURE 11.23   **Residual Plots and the Constant Variance Assumption**

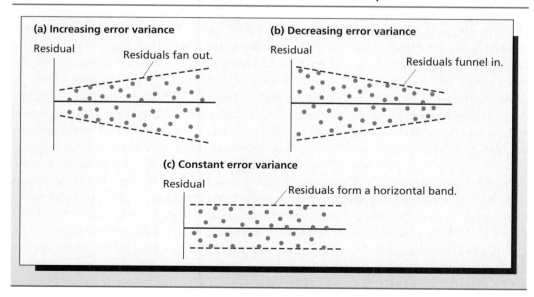

(a) Increasing error variance
Residual
Residuals fan out.

(b) Decreasing error variance
Residual
Residuals funnel in.

(c) Constant error variance
Residual
Residuals form a horizontal band.

at scatter plots of y versus x. One answer is that, in general, because of possible differences in scaling between residual plots and scatter plots of y versus x, one of these types of plots might be more informative in a particular situation. Therefore, we should always consider both types of plots.

When the constant variance assumption is violated, we cannot use the formulas of this chapter to make statistical inferences. Later in this section, we discuss how we can make statistical inferences when a nonconstant error variance exists.

The assumption of correct functional form   If the functional form of a regression model is incorrect, the residual plots constructed by using the model often display a pattern suggesting the form of a more appropriate model. For instance, if we use a simple linear regression model when the true relationship between y and x is curved, the residual plot will have a curved appearance. For example, the scatter plot of upkeep expenditure, y, versus home value, x, in Figure 11.21 (page 391) has either a straight-line or a slightly curved appearance. We used a simple linear regression model to describe the relationship between y and x, but note that there is a "dip," or slightly curved appearance, in the upper left portion of each residual plot in Figure 11.22. Therefore, both the scatter plot and residual plots indicate that there might be a slightly curved relationship between y and x. Later in this section, we discuss one way to model curved relationships.

The normality assumption   If the normality assumption holds, a histogram and/or a stem-and-leaf display of the residuals should look reasonably bell-shaped and reasonably symmetric about 0. Figure 11.24(a) gives the MINITAB output of a stem-and-leaf display of the residuals from the simple linear regression model describing the QHIC data. The stem-and-leaf display looks fairly bell-shaped and symmetric about 0. However, the tails of the display look somewhat long and "heavy" or "thick," indicating a possible violation of the normality assumption.

Another way to check the normality assumption is to construct a **normal plot** of the residuals. To make a normal plot, we first arrange the residuals in order from smallest to largest. Letting the ordered residuals be denoted as $e_{(1)}, e_{(2)}, \ldots, e_{(n)}$, we denote the ith residual in the ordered listing as $e_{(i)}$. We plot $e_{(i)}$ on the vertical axis against a point called $z_{(i)}$ on the horizontal axis. Here $z_{(i)}$ is defined to be the point on the horizontal axis under the standard normal curve so that the area under this curve to the left of $z_{(i)}$ is $(3i - 1)/(3n + 1)$. For example, recall in the QHIC case that there are $n = 40$ residuals given in Figure 11.22(a). It follows that, when $i = 1$,

$$\frac{3i - 1}{3n + 1} = \frac{3(1) - 1}{3(40) + 1} = \frac{2}{121} = 0.0165.$$

Therefore, $z_{(1)}$ is the normal point with an area of 0.0165 under the standard normal curve to its left. This implies that the area under the standard normal curve between $z_{(1)}$ and 0 is $0.5 - 0.0165 = 0.4835$. Thus, as illustrated in Figure 11.24(b), $z_{(1)}$ equals -2.13. Because the smallest residual in Figure 11.22(a) is -289.044, the first point plotted is $e_{(1)} = -289.044$ on the vertical scale versus $z_{(1)} = -2.13$ on the horizontal scale. When $i = 2$, it can be verified that $(3i - 1)/(3n + 1)$ equals 0.0413 and thus that $z_{(2)} = -1.74$. Therefore, because the second-smallest residual in Figure 11.22(a) is -259.958, the second point plotted is $e_{(2)} = -259.958$ on the vertical scale versus $z_{(2)} = -1.74$ on the horizontal scale. This process is continued until the entire normal plot is constructed. The MegaStat output of this plot is given in Figure 11.24(c).

An equivalent plot is shown in Figure 11.24(d), which is a MINITAB output. In this figure, we plot the percentage $p_{(i)}$ of the area under the standard normal curve to the left of $z_{(i)}$ on the vertical axis. Thus, the first point plotted in this normal plot is $e_{(1)} = -289.044$ on the horizontal scale versus $p_{(1)} = (0.0165)(100) = 1.65$ on the vertical scale, and the second point plotted is $e_{(2)} = -259.958$ on the horizontal scale versus $p_{(2)} = (0.0413)(100) = 4.13$ on the vertical scale. It is important to note that the scale on the vertical axis does not have the usual spacing between the percentages. The spacing reflects the distance between the z scores that correspond to the percentages in the standard normal distribution. Hence, if we wished to create the plot in Figure 11.24(d) by hand, we would need special graphing paper with this vertical scale.

It can be proven that, if the normality assumption holds, the expected value of the ith ordered residual $e_{(i)}$ is proportional to $z_{(i)}$. Therefore, a plot of the $e_{(i)}$ values on the horizontal scale versus the $z_{(i)}$ values on the vertical scale (or, equivalently, the $e_{(i)}$ values on the horizontal scale versus

FIGURE **11.24**   **Stem-and-Leaf Display and Normal Plots of the Residuals from the Simple Linear Regression Model Describing the QHIC Data**

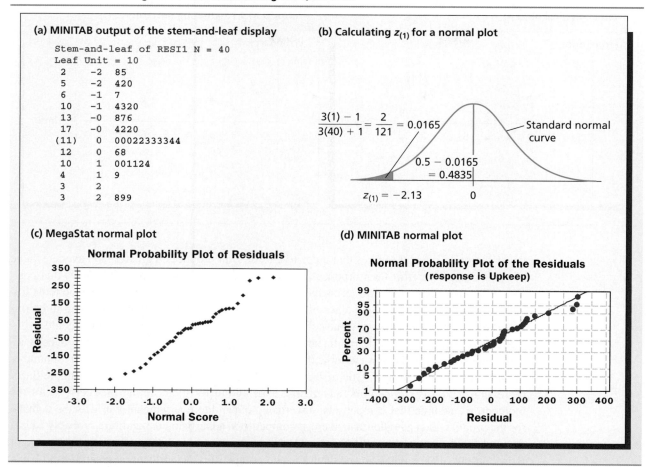

(a) MINITAB output of the stem-and-leaf display

```
Stem-and-leaf of RESI1  N = 40
Leaf Unit = 10
  2     -2   85
  5     -2   420
  6     -1   7
 10     -1   4320
 13     -0   876
 17     -0   4220
(11)     0   00022333344
 12      0   68
 10      1   001124
  4      1   9
  3      2
  3      2   899
```

(b) Calculating $z_{(1)}$ for a normal plot

$$\frac{3(1) - 1}{3(40) + 1} = \frac{2}{121} = 0.0165$$

Standard normal curve

$$0.5 - 0.0165 = 0.4835$$

$$z_{(1)} = -2.13 \qquad 0$$

(c) MegaStat normal plot

Normal Probability Plot of Residuals

Residual (y-axis: -350 to 350)
Normal Score (x-axis: -3.0 to 3.0)

(d) MINITAB normal plot

Normal Probability Plot of the Residuals (response is Upkeep)

Percent (y-axis: 1 to 99)
Residual (x-axis: -400 to 400)

the $p_{(i)}$ values on the vertical scale) should have a straight-line appearance. That is, if the normality assumption holds, then the normal plot should have a straight-line appearance. A normal plot that does not look like a straight line (admittedly a subjective decision) indicates that the normality assumption is violated. Since the normal plots in Figure 11.24 have some curvature (particularly in the upper right portion), there is a possible violation of the normality assumption.

It is important to realize that violations of the constant variance and correct functional form assumptions can often cause a histogram and/or a stem-and-leaf display of the residuals to look nonnormal and can cause the normal plot to have a curved appearance. Because of this, it is usually a good idea to use residual plots to check for nonconstant variance and incorrect functional form before making any final conclusions about the normality assumption. Later in this section, we discuss a procedure that sometimes remedies simultaneous violations of the constant variance, correct functional form, and normality assumptions.

The independence assumption   The independence assumption is most likely to be violated when the regression data are **time series data**—that is, data that have been collected in a time sequence. For such data, the time-ordered error terms can be **autocorrelated**. Intuitively, we say that error terms occurring over time have **positive autocorrelation** if a positive error term in time period i tends to produce, or be followed by, another positive error term in time period $i + k$ (some later time period) and if a negative error term in time period i tends to produce, or be followed by, another negative error term in time period $i + k$. In other words, positive autocorrelation exists when positive error terms tend to be followed over time by positive error terms and when negative error terms tend to be followed over time by negative error terms. Positive autocorrelation in the error terms is depicted in Figure 11.25(a), which illustrates that **positive autocorrelation can produce a cyclical error term pattern over time**. The simple

FIGURE **11.25**   **Positive and Negative Autocorrelation**

(a) Positive autocorrelation in the error terms: Cyclical pattern

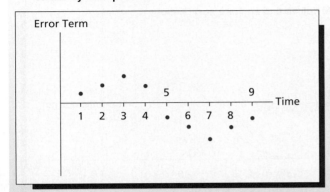

(b) Negative autocorrelation in the error terms: Alternating pattern

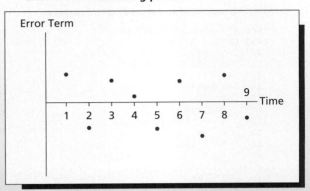

linear regression model implies that a positive error term produces a greater than average value of y and a negative error term produces a smaller than average value of y. It follows that positive autocorrelation in the error terms means that greater than average values of y tend to be followed by greater than average values of y, and smaller than average values of y tend to be followed by smaller than average values of y. An example of positive autocorrelation could hypothetically be provided by a simple linear regression model relating demand for a product to advertising expenditure. Here we assume that the data are time series data observed over a number of consecutive sales periods. One of the factors included in the error term of the simple linear regression model is competitors' advertising expenditure for their similar products. If, for the moment, we assume that competitors' advertising expenditure significantly affects the demand for the product, then a higher than average competitors' advertising expenditure probably causes demand for the product to be lower than average and hence probably causes a negative error term. On the other hand, a lower than average competitors' advertising expenditure probably causes the demand for the product to be higher than average and hence probably causes a positive error term. If, then, competitors tend to spend money on advertising in a cyclical fashion—spending large amounts for several consecutive sales periods (during an advertising campaign) and then spending lesser amounts for several consecutive sales periods—a negative error term in one sales period will tend to be followed by a negative error term in the next sales period, and a positive error term in one sales period will tend to be followed by a positive error term in the next sales period. In this case, the error terms would display positive autocorrelation, and thus these error terms would not be statistically independent.

Intuitively, error terms occurring over time have **negative autocorrelation** if a positive error term in time period i tends to produce, or be followed by, a negative error term in time period $i + k$ and if a negative error term in time period i tends to produce, or be followed by, a positive error term in time period $i + k$. In other words, negative autocorrelation exists when positive error terms tend to be followed over time by negative error terms and negative error terms tend to be followed over time by positive error terms. An example of negative autocorrelation in the error terms is depicted in Figure 11.25(b), which illustrates that **negative autocorrelation in the error terms can produce an alternating pattern over time**. It follows that negative autocorrelation in the error terms means that greater than average values of y tend to be followed by smaller than average values of y and smaller than average values of y tend to be followed by greater than average values of y. An example of negative autocorrelation might be provided by a retailer's weekly stock orders. Here a larger than average stock order one week might result in an oversupply and hence a smaller than average order the next week.

The **independence assumption** basically says that the time-ordered error terms display no positive or negative autocorrelation. This says that **the error terms occur in a random pattern over time**. Such a random pattern would imply that the error terms (and their corresponding y values) are statistically independent.

Because the residuals are point estimates of the error terms, a residual plot versus time is used to check the independence assumption. If a residual plot versus the data's time sequence has a cyclical appearance, the error terms are positively autocorrelated and the independence assumption is violated. If a plot of the time-ordered residuals has an alternating pattern, the error terms are negatively autocorrelated, and again the independence assumption is violated. However, if a plot of the time-ordered residuals displays a random pattern, the error terms have little or no autocorrelation. In such a case, it is reasonable to conclude that the independence assumption holds.

Example 11.7

Figure 11.26(a) presents data concerning weekly sales at Folio Bookstore (Sales), Folio's weekly advertising expenditure (Adver), and the weekly advertising expenditure of Folio's main competitor (Compadv). Here the sales values are expressed in thousands of dollars, and the advertising expenditure values are expressed in hundreds of dollars. Figure 11.26(a) also gives the residuals that are obtained when MegaStat is used to perform a simple linear regression analysis relating Folio's sales to Folio's advertising expenditure. These residuals are plotted versus time in Figure 11.26(b). We see that the residual plot has a cyclical pattern. This tells us that the

FIGURE 11.26   Folio Bookstore Sales and Advertising Data, and Residual Analysis

(a) The data and the MegaStat output of the residuals from a simple linear regression relating
    Folio's sales to Folio's advertising expenditure   ● BookSales

Observation	Adver	Compadv	Sales	Predicted	Residual
1	18	10	22	18.7	3.3
2	20	10	27	23.0	4.0
3	20	15	23	23.0	−0.0
4	25	15	31	33.9	−2.9
5	28	15	45	40.4	4.6
6	29	20	47	42.6	4.4
7	29	20	45	42.6	2.4
8	28	25	42	40.4	1.6
9	30	35	37	44.7	−7.7
10	31	35	39	46.9	−7.9
11	34	35	45	53.4	−8.4
12	35	30	52	55.6	−3.6
13	36	30	57	57.8	−0.8
14	38	25	62	62.1	−0.1
15	41	20	73	68.6	4.4
16	45	20	84	77.3	6.7

Durbin-Watson = 0.65

(b) MegaStat output of a plot of the residuals in
    Figure 11.26(a) versus time

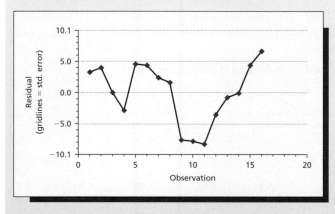

error terms for the model are positively autocorrelated and the independence assumption is violated. Furthermore, there tend to be positive residuals when the competitor's advertising expenditure is lower (in weeks 1 through 8 and weeks 12 through 16) and negative residuals when the competitor's advertising expenditure is higher (in weeks 9 through 11). Therefore, the competitor's advertising expenditure seems to be causing the positive autocorrelation.

To conclude this example, note that the simple linear regression model relating Folio's sales to Folio's advertising expenditure has a standard error, s, of 5.038. The MegaStat residual plot in Figure 11.26(b) includes grid lines that are placed one and two standard errors above and below the residual mean of 0. All MegaStat residual plots use such grid lines to help better diagnose potential violations of the regression assumptions.

When the independence assumption is violated, various remedies can be employed. One approach is to identify which independent variable left in the error term (for example, competitors' advertising expenditure) is causing the error terms to be autocorrelated. We can then remove this independent variable from the error term and insert it directly into the regression model, forming a **multiple regression model**. (Multiple regression models are discussed in Chapter 12.)

The Durbin–Watson test   One type of positive or negative autocorrelation is called **first-order autocorrelation**. It says that ε_t, the error term in time period t, is related to ε_{t-1}, the error term in time period $t-1$. To check for first-order autocorrelation, we can use the **Durbin–Watson statistic**

$$d = \frac{\sum_{t=2}^{n} (e_t - e_{t-1})^2}{\sum_{t=1}^{n} e_t^2},$$

where $e_1, e_2, \ldots, e_n$ are the time-ordered residuals.

Small values of d lead us to conclude that there is positive autocorrelation. This is because, if d is small, the differences $(e_t - e_{t-1})$ are small. This indicates that the adjacent residuals e_t and e_{t-1} are of the same magnitude, which in turn says that the adjacent error terms ε_t and ε_{t-1} are positively correlated. Consider testing the null hypothesis H_0 **that the error terms are not autocorrelated** versus the alternative hypothesis H_a **that the error terms are positively autocorrelated**. Durbin and Watson have shown that there are points (denoted $d_{L,\alpha}$ and $d_{U,\alpha}$) such that, if α is the probability of a Type I error, we have the following:

1   If $d < d_{L,\alpha}$, we reject H_0.

2   If $d > d_{U,\alpha}$, we do not reject H_0.

3   If $d_{L,\alpha} \leq d \leq d_{U,\alpha}$, the test is inconclusive.

So that the Durbin–Watson test may be easily done, tables containing the points $d_{L,\alpha}$ and $d_{U,\alpha}$ have been constructed. These tables give the appropriate $d_{L,\alpha}$ and $d_{U,\alpha}$ points for various values of α; k, the number of independent variables used by the regression model; and n, the number of observations. Tables A.10, A.11, and A.12 give these points for $\alpha = 0.05$, $\alpha = 0.025$, and $\alpha = 0.01$. A portion of Table A.10 is given in Table 11.8. Note that when we are considering a simple linear regression model, which uses **one** independent variable, we look up the points $d_{L,\alpha}$ and $d_{U,\alpha}$ under

TABLE **11.8**   Critical Values for the Durbin–Watson d Statistic ($\alpha = 0.05$)

	$k = 1$		$k = 2$		$k = 3$		$k = 4$	
n	$d_{L,0.05}$	$d_{U,0.05}$	$d_{L,0.05}$	$d_{U,0.05}$	$d_{L,0.05}$	$d_{U,0.05}$	$d_{L,0.05}$	$d_{U,0.05}$
15	1.08	1.36	0.95	1.54	0.82	1.75	0.69	1.97
16	1.10	1.37	0.98	1.54	0.86	1.73	0.74	1.93
17	1.13	1.38	1.02	1.54	0.90	1.71	0.78	1.90
18	1.16	1.39	1.05	1.53	0.93	1.69	0.82	1.87
19	1.18	1.40	1.08	1.53	0.97	1.68	0.86	1.85
20	1.20	1.41	1.10	1.54	1.00	1.68	0.90	1.83

the heading "$k = 1$." Other values of k are used when we study multiple regression models in Chapter 12. Using the residuals in Figure 11.26(a), we can calculate the Durbin–Watson statistic for the simple linear regression model relating Folio's sales to Folio's advertising expenditure to be

$$d = \frac{\sum\limits_{t=2}^{16} (e_t - e_{t-1})^2}{\sum\limits_{t=1}^{16} e_t^2}$$

$$= \frac{(4.0 - 3.3)^2 + (0.0 - 4.0)^2 + \cdots + (6.7 - 4.4)^2}{(3.3)^2 + (4.0)^2 + \cdots + (6.7)^2}$$

$$= 0.65.$$

A MegaStat output of the Durbin–Watson statistic is given at the bottom of Figure 11.26(a). To test for positive autocorrelation, we note that there are $n = 16$ observations and the regression model uses $k = 1$ independent variable. Therefore, if we set $\alpha = 0.05$, Table 11.8 tells us that $d_{L,0.05} = 1.10$ and $d_{U,0.05} = 1.37$. Since $d = 0.65$ is less than $d_{L,0.05} = 1.10$, we reject the null hypothesis of no autocorrelation. That is, we conclude (at an α of 0.05) that there is positive (first-order) autocorrelation.

It can be shown that the Durbin–Watson statistic d is always between 0 and 4. Large values of d (and hence small values of $4 - d$) lead us to conclude that there is negative autocorrelation because if d is large, this indicates that the differences $(e_t - e_{t-1})$ are large. This says that the adjacent error terms ε_t and ε_{t-1} are negatively autocorrelated. Consider testing the null hypothesis H_0 that the error terms are not autocorrelated versus the alternative hypothesis H_a that the error terms are negatively autocorrelated. Durbin and Watson have shown that based on setting the probability of a Type I error equal to α, the points $d_{L,\alpha}$ and $d_{U,\alpha}$ are such that we have the following:

1. If $(4 - d) < d_{L,\alpha}$, we reject H_0.
2. If $(4 - d) > d_{U,\alpha}$, we do not reject H_0.
3. If $d_{L,\alpha} \leq (4 - d) \leq d_{U,\alpha}$, the test is inconclusive.

As an example, for the Folio sales simple linear regression model, we see that

$$(4 - d) = (4 - 0.65) = 3.35 > d_{U,0.05} = 1.37.$$

Therefore, on the basis of setting α equal to 0.05, we do not reject the null hypothesis of no autocorrelation. That is, there is no evidence of negative (first-order) autocorrelation.

We can also use the Durbin–Watson statistic to test for positive or negative autocorrelation. Specifically, consider testing the null hypothesis H_0 that the error terms are not autocorrelated versus the alternative hypothesis H_a that the error terms are positively or negatively autocorrelated. Durbin and Watson have shown that, based on setting the probability of a Type I error equal to α, we have the following:

1. If $d < d_{L,\alpha/2}$ or if $(4 - d) < d_{L,\alpha/2}$, we reject H_0.
2. If $d > d_{U,\alpha/2}$ and if $(4 - d) > d_{U,\alpha/2}$, we do not reject H_0.
3. If $d_{L,\alpha/2} \leq d \leq d_{U,\alpha/2}$ or if $d_{L,\alpha/2} \leq (4 - d) \leq d_{U,\alpha/2}$, the test is inconclusive.

For example, consider testing for positive or negative autocorrelation in the Folio sales model. If we set α equal to 0.05, then $\alpha/2 = 0.025$, and we need to find the points $d_{L,0.025}$ and $d_{U,0.025}$ when $n = 16$ and $k = 1$. Looking up these points in Table A.11, we find that $d_{L,0.025} = 0.98$ and $d_{U,0.025} = 1.24$. Since $d = 0.65$ is less than $d_{L,0.025} = 0.98$, we reject the null hypothesis of no autocorrelation. That is, we conclude (at an α of 0.05) that there is first-order autocorrelation.

Although we have used the Folio sales model in these examples to demonstrate the Durbin–Watson tests for (1) positive autocorrelation, (2) negative autocorrelation, and (3) positive or negative autocorrelation, we must in practice choose one of these Durbin–Watson tests in a particular situation. Since positive autocorrelation is more common in real time series data than negative autocorrelation, the Durbin–Watson test for positive autocorrelation is used more often than the other two tests. Also note that each Durbin–Watson test assumes that the population of all possible residuals at any time t has a normal distribution.

Transforming the dependent variable: A possible remedy for violations of the constant variance, correct functional form, and normality assumptions   In general, if a data or residual plot indicates that the error variance of a regression model increases as an independent variable or the predicted value of the dependent variable increases, then we can sometimes remedy the situation by transforming the dependent variable. One transformation that works well is to take each y value to a fractional power. As an example, we might use a transformation in which we take the square root (or one-half power) of each y value. Letting y^* denote the value obtained when the transformation is applied to y, we would write the **square root transformation** as

$$y^* = \sqrt{y} = y^{0.5}.$$

Another commonly used transformation is the **quartic root transformation**. Here we take each y value to the one-fourth power. That is,

$$y^* = y^{0.25}.$$

In addition, we sometimes use the **logarithmic transformation**

$$y^* = \ln y,$$

which takes the natural logarithm of each y value. In general, when we take a fractional power (including the natural logarithm) of the dependent variable, the transformation not only tends to equalize the error variance but also tends to "straighten out" certain types of nonlinear data plots. Specifically, if a data plot indicates that the dependent variable is increasing at an increasing rate (as in Figure 11.21 on page 391), then a fractional power transformation tends to straighten out the data plot. A fractional power transformation can also help to remedy a violation of the normality assumption. Because we cannot know which fractional power to use before we actually take the transformation, we recommend taking all of the square root, quartic root, and natural logarithm transformations and seeing which one best equalizes the error variance and (possibly) straightens out a nonlinear data plot.

Example 11.8   The QHIC Case

Consider the QHIC upkeep expenditures. In Figures 11.27, 11.28, and 11.29, we show the plots that result when we take the square root, quartic root, and natural logarithmic transformations of the upkeep expenditures and plot the transformed values versus the home values. The square root transformation seems to best equalize the error variance and straighten out the curved data plot in Figure 11.21. Note that the natural logarithm transformation seems to "overtransform" the data—the error variance tends to decrease as the home value increases and the data plot seems to "bend down." The plot of the quartic roots indicates that the quartic root transformation also seems to overtransform the data (but not by as much as the logarithmic transformation). In general, as the fractional power gets smaller, the transformation gets stronger. Different fractional powers are best in different situations.

Since the plot in Figure 11.27 of the square roots of the upkeep expenditures versus the home values has a straight-line appearance, we consider the model

$$y^* = \beta_0 + \beta_1 x + \varepsilon, \quad \text{where } y^* = y^{0.5}.$$

The MINITAB output of a regression analysis using this transformed model is given in Figure 11.30, and the MINITAB output of an analysis of the model's residuals is given in Figure 11.31. Note that the residual plot versus x for the transformed model in Figure 11.31(a) has a horizontal band appearance. It can also be verified that the transformed model's residual plot versus $\hat{y}$, which we do not give here, has a similar horizontal band appearance. Therefore, we conclude that the constant variance and the correct functional form assumptions approximately hold for the transformed model. Next, note that the histogram of the transformed model's residuals in Figure 11.31(b) looks reasonably bell-shaped and symmetric, and note that the normal plot of these residuals in Figure 11.31(c) looks straighter than the normal plot for the untransformed

FIGURE **11.27** MINITAB Plot of the Square Roots of the Upkeep Expenditures versus the Home Values

FIGURE **11.28** MINITAB Plot of the Quartic Roots of the Upkeep Expenditures versus the Home Values

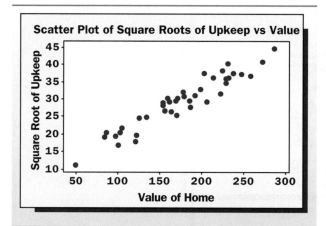

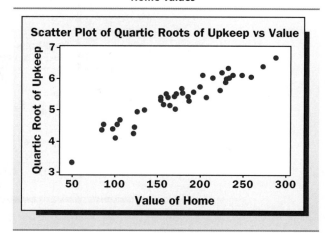

FIGURE **11.29** MINITAB Plot of the Natural Logarithms of the Upkeep Expenditures versus the Home Values

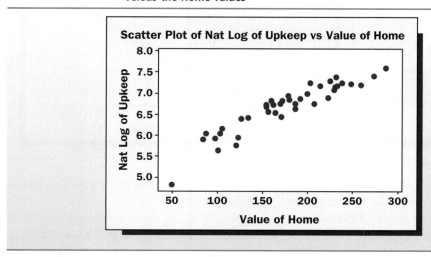

FIGURE **11.30** MINITAB Output of a Regression Analysis of the Upkeep Expenditure Data by Using the Model $y^* = \beta_0 + \beta_1 x + \varepsilon$, where $y^* = y^{0.5}$

```
The regression equation is
SqRtUpkeep = 7.20 + 0.127 Value

Predictor       Coef    SE Coef       T      P
Constant       7.201      1.205    5.98  0.000
Value       0.127047   0.006577   19.32  0.000

S = 2.32479   R-Sq = 90.8%   R-Sq(adj) = 90.5%

Analysis of Variance
Source          DF       SS       MS       F      P
Regression       1   2016.8   2016.8  373.17  0.000
Residual Error  38    205.4      5.4
Total           39   2222.2

Values of Predictors for New Obs     Predicted Values for New Observations
New Obs   Value                      New Obs    Fit   SE Fit      95% CI              95% PI
      1     220                            1  35.151   0.474  (34.191, 36.111)  (30.348, 39.954)
```

FIGURE **11.31** **MINITAB Output of Residual Analysis for the Upkeep Expenditure Model**
$y^* = \beta_0 + \beta_1 x + \varepsilon$, where $y^* = y^{0.5}$

(a) Residual plot versus x

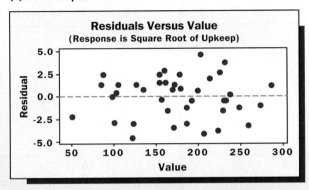

(b) Histogram of the residuals

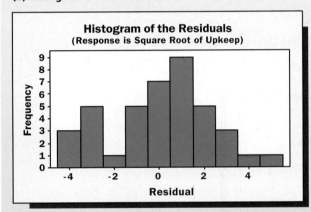

(c) Normal plot of the residuals

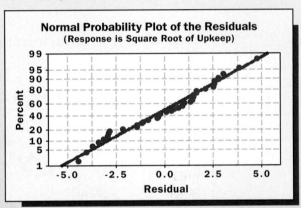

model (see Figure 11.24 on page 395). Therefore, we also conclude that the normality assumption approximately holds for the transformed model.

Because the regression assumptions approximately hold for the transformed regression model, we can use this model to make statistical inferences. Consider a home worth $220,000. Using the least squares point estimates on the MINITAB output in Figure 11.30, it follows that a point prediction of y^* for such a home is

$$\hat{y}^* = 7.201 + 0.127047(220)$$
$$= 35.151.$$

This point prediction is given at the bottom of the MINITAB output, as is the 95 percent prediction interval for y^*, which is [30.348, 39.954]. It follows that a point prediction of the upkeep expenditure for a home worth $220,000 is $(35.151)^2 = \$1,235.59$ and that a 95 percent prediction interval for this upkeep expenditure is $[(30.348)^2, (39.954)^2] = [\$921.00, \$1,596.32]$. Suppose that QHIC wishes to send an advertising brochure to any home that has a predicted upkeep expenditure of at least $500. Solving the prediction equation $\hat{y}^* = b_0 + b_1 x$ for x, and noting that a predicted upkeep expenditure of $500 corresponds to a $\hat{y}^*$ of $\sqrt{500} = 22.36068$, we obtain

$$x = \frac{\hat{y}^* - b_0}{b_1} = \frac{22.36068 - 7.201}{0.127047} = 119.3234 \text{ (or } \$119,323).$$

It follows that QHIC should send the advertising brochure to any home that has a value of at least $119,323.

Recall that because there are many homes of a particular value in the metropolitan area, QHIC is interested in estimating the mean upkeep expenditure corresponding to this value. Consider all homes worth, for example, $220,000. The MINITAB output in Figure 11.30 tells us that a point estimate of the mean of the square roots of the upkeep expenditures for all such homes is 35.151 and that a 95 percent confidence interval for this mean is [34.191, 36.111]. Unfortunately, because it can be shown that the mean of the square root is not the square root of the mean, we cannot transform the results for the mean of the square roots back into a result for the mean of the original upkeep expenditures. This is a major drawback to transforming the dependent variable and one reason why many statisticians avoid doing this unless the regression assumptions are badly violated. In Chapter 12, we discuss other remedies for violations of the regression assumptions that do not have some of the drawbacks of transforming the dependent variable. Some of these remedies involve transforming the independent variable. Furthermore, if we reconsider the residual analysis of the original, untransformed, QHIC model in Figures 11.22 (page 392) and 11.24 (page 395), we might conclude that the regression assumptions are not badly violated for the untransformed model. Also note that the point prediction, 95 percent prediction interval, and value of x obtained here using the transformed model are not very different from the results obtained in Examples 11.2 (pages 370 to 371) and 11.4 (pages 382 to 383) using the untransformed model. This implies that it might be reasonable to rely on the results obtained using the untransformed model, or to at least rely on the results for the mean upkeep expenditures obtained using the untransformed model.

Exercises for Section 11.10

CONCEPTS

11.61 In a regression analysis, what variables should the residuals be plotted against? What types of patterns in residual plots indicate violations of the regression assumptions?

11.62 In regression analysis, how do we check the normality assumption?

11.63 What is one possible remedy for violations of the constant variance, correct functional form, and normality assumptions?

METHODS AND APPLICATIONS

11.64 THE FRESH DETERGENT CASE ◐ Fresh

Figure 11.32 gives the MINITAB output of residual diagnostics that are obtained when the simple linear regression model is fit to the Fresh detergent demand data. Interpret the diagnostics and determine if they indicate any violations of the regression assumptions.

FIGURE **11.32** MINITAB Residual Diagnostics for Exercise 11.64

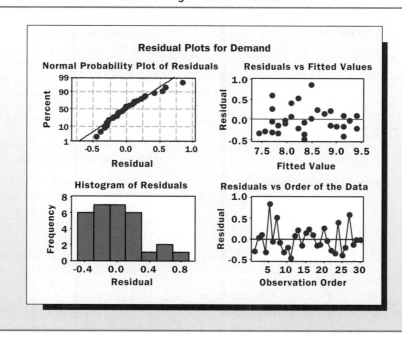

FIGURE **11.33**   **MegaStat Output of the Residuals for the Service Time Model**

Observation	Minutes	Predicted	Residual
1	109.0	109.9	−0.9
2	58.0	60.7	−2.7
3	138.0	134.5	3.5
4	189.0	183.7	5.3
5	37.0	36.1	0.9
6	82.0	85.3	−3.3
7	103.0	109.9	−6.9
8	134.0	134.5	−0.5
9	68.0	60.7	7.3
10	112.0	109.9	2.1
11	154.0	159.1	−5.1

TABLE **11.9**   **Ordered Residuals and Normal Plot Calculations**

i	Ordered Residual, $e_{(i)}$	$\dfrac{3i-1}{3n+1}$	$z_{(i)}$
1	−6.9	0.0588	−1.565
2	−5.1	0.1470	−1.05
3	−3.3	0.2353	−0.72
4	−2.7	0.3235	−0.46
5	−0.9	0.4118	−0.22
6	−0.5	0.5000	0
7	0.9	0.5882	0.22
8	2.1	0.6765	0.46
9	3.5	0.7647	0.72
10	5.3	0.8529	1.05
11	7.3	0.9412	1.565

11.65   THE SERVICE TIME CASE   ◓ SrvcTime

The MegaStat output of the residuals given by the service time model is given in Figure 11.33 and MegaStat output of residual plots versus x and $\hat{y}$ is given in Figure 11.34(a) and (b). Do the plots indicate any violations of the regression assumptions?

FIGURE **11.34**   **MegaStat Residual Plots for the Service Time Model**

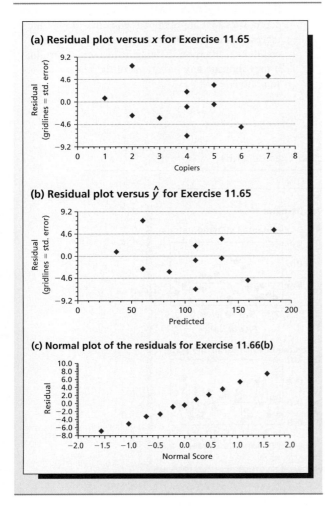

(a) Residual plot versus x for Exercise 11.65

(b) Residual plot versus ŷ for Exercise 11.65

(c) Normal plot of the residuals for Exercise 11.66(b)

11.66   THE SERVICE TIME CASE   ◓ SrvcTime

Figure 11.33 gives the MegaStat output of the residuals from the simple linear regression model describing the service time data.

a. In this exercise, we construct a normal plot of the residuals from the simple linear regression model. To construct this plot, we must first arrange the residuals in order from smallest to largest. These ordered residuals are given in Table 11.9. Denoting the ith ordered residual as $e_{(i)}$ ($i = 1, 2, \ldots, 11$), we next compute for each value of i the point $z_{(i)}$. These computations are summarized in Table 11.9. Show how $z_{(4)} = -0.46$ and $z_{(10)} = 1.05$ were obtained.

b. The ordered residuals (the $e_{(i)}$'s) are plotted against the $z_{(i)}$'s on the MegaStat output of Figure 11.34(c). Does this figure indicate a violation of the normality assumption?

11.67   A simple linear regression model is employed to analyze the 24 monthly observations given in Table 11.10. Residuals are computed and are plotted versus time. The resulting residual plot is shown in Figure 11.35. Discuss why the residual plot suggests the existence of positive autocorrelation. The Durbin–Watson statistic d can be calculated to be 0.473. Test for positive (first-order) autocorrelation at $\alpha = 0.05$, and test for negative (first-order) autocorrelation at $\alpha = 0.05$.   ◓ SalesAdv

11.68   USING A NATURAL LOGARITHM TRANSFORMATION   ◓ WestStk

Western Steakhouses, a fast-food chain, opened 15 years ago. Each year since then, the number of steakhouses in operation, y, has been recorded. An analyst for the firm wishes to use these data to predict the number of steakhouses that will be in operation next year. The data are given in Figure 11.36(a), and a plot of the data is given in Figure 11.36(b). Examining the data plot, we see that the number of steakhouse openings has increased over time at an increasing rate and with increasing variation. A plot of the natural logarithms of the steakhouse values versus time (see Figure 11.36(c))

TABLE **11.10** Sales and Advertising Data for Exercise 11.67 ● SalesAdv

Month	Monthly Total Sales, y	Advertising Expenditures, x	Month	Monthly Total Sales, y	Advertising Expenditures, x
1	202.66	116.44	13	260.51	129.85
2	232.91	119.58	14	266.34	122.65
3	272.07	125.74	15	281.24	121.64
4	290.97	124.55	16	286.19	127.24
5	299.09	122.35	17	271.97	132.35
6	296.95	120.44	18	265.01	130.86
7	279.49	123.24	19	274.44	122.90
8	255.75	127.55	20	291.81	117.15
9	242.78	121.19	21	290.91	109.47
10	255.34	118.00	22	264.95	114.34
11	271.58	121.81	23	228.40	123.72
12	268.27	126.54	24	209.33	130.33

Source: "Sales and advertising data," by S. Makridakis, S. C. Wheelwright, and V. E. McGee, *Forecasting: Methods and Applications* (Copyright © 1983 John Wiley & Sons, Inc.). Reprinted by permission of John Wiley & Sons, Inc.

FIGURE **11.35** Residual Plot for Exercise 11.67

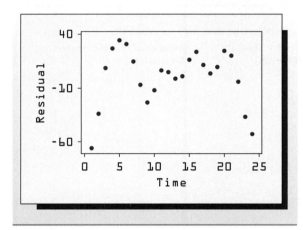

FIGURE **11.36** The Data and Data Plots for Exercise 11.68 ● WestStk

(a) Western Steakhouse Openings for the Last 15 Years

Year, t	Steakhouse Openings, y	Year, t	Steakhouse Openings, y
1	11	9	82
2	14	10	99
3	16	11	119
4	22	12	156
5	28	13	257
6	36	14	284
7	46	15	403
8	67		

(b) Time Series Plot of y versus t

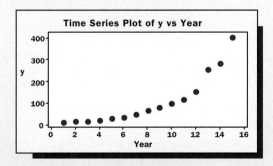

has a straight-line appearance with constant variation. Therefore, we consider the model

$$\ln y_t = \beta_0 + \beta_1 t + \varepsilon_t.$$

If we use MINITAB, we find that the least squares point estimates of β_0 and β_1 are $b_0 = 2.07012$ and $b_1 = 0.256880$. We also find that a point prediction of and a 95 percent prediction interval for the natural logarithm of the number of steakhouses in operation next year (year 16) are 6.1802 and [5.9945, 6.3659]. See the MINITAB output in Figure 11.37.

a. Use the least squares point estimates to verify the point prediction.

b. By exponentiating the point prediction and prediction interval—that is, by calculating $e^{6.1802}$ and $[e^{5.9945}, e^{6.3659}]$—find a point prediction of and a 95 percent prediction interval for the number of steakhouses in operation next year.

c. Use the Durbin–Watson statistic on the MINITAB output to test for positive autocorrelation at the 0.05 level of significance.

(c) Time Series Plot of Natural Logarithm of y versus t

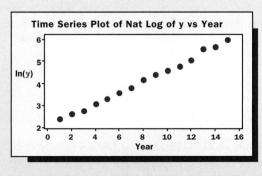

FIGURE 11.37 **MINITAB Output of a Regression Analysis of the Steakhouse Data Using the Model**
$y^* = \beta_0 + \beta_1 x + \varepsilon$, where $y^* = \ln y$

```
The regression equation is
ln(y) = 2.07 + 0.257 Year

Predictor         Coef      SE Coef         T          P
Constant       2.07012      0.04103     50.45      0.000
Year           0.256880     0.004513    56.92      0.000

S = 0.0755161    R-Sq = 99.6%    R-Sq(adj) = 99.6%    Durbin-Watson statistic = 1.87643

Analysis of Variance
Source          DF          SS         MS          F         P
Regression       1      18.477     18.477    3239.97     0.000
Residual Error  13       0.074      0.006
Total           14      18.551

Values of Predictors for New Obs    Predicted Values for New Observations
New Obs   Year                      Obs    Fit   SE Fit        95% CI             95% PI
    1     16                          1  6.1802  0.0410  (6.0916, 6.2689)  (5.9945, 6.3659)
```

d. The model $\ln y_t = \beta_0 + \beta_1 t + \varepsilon_t$ is called a **growth curve model** because it implies that

$$y_t = e^{(\beta_0 + \beta_1 t + \varepsilon_t)} = (e^{\beta_0})(e^{\beta_1 t})(e^{\varepsilon_t}) = \alpha_0 \alpha_1^t \eta_t,$$

where $\alpha_0 = e^{\beta_0}$, $\alpha_1 = e^{\beta_1}$, and $\eta_t = e^{\varepsilon_t}$. Here $\alpha_1 = e^{\beta_1}$ is called the **growth rate** of the y values. Noting that the least squares point estimate of β_1 is $b_1 = 0.256880$, estimate the growth rate α_1. Also interpret this growth rate by using the fact that $y_t = \alpha_0 \alpha_1^t \eta_t = (\alpha_0 \alpha_1^{t-1})\alpha_1 \eta_t \approx (y_{t-1})\alpha_1 \eta_t$. This says that y_t is expected to be approximately α_1 times y_{t-1}.

11.69 THE UNEQUAL VARIANCES SERVICE TIME CASE ● SrvcTime2

Figure 11.38(a) presents data concerning the time, y, required to perform service and the number of microcomputers serviced, x, for 15 service calls. Figure 11.38(b) gives a plot of y versus x, and Figure 11.38(c) gives the Excel output of a plot of the residuals versus x for a simple linear regression model. What regression assumption appears to be violated?

11.70 THE UNEQUAL VARIANCES SERVICE TIME CASE ● SrvcTime2

Consider the simple linear regression model describing the service time data in Figure 11.38(a). Figure 11.38(c) shows that the residual plot versus x for this model fans out, indicating that the error term ε tends to become larger in magnitude as x increases. To remedy this violation of the constant variance assumption, we divide all terms in the simple linear regression model by x. This gives the transformed model

$$\frac{y}{x} = \beta_0\left(\frac{1}{x}\right) + \beta_1 + \frac{\varepsilon}{x} \quad \text{or, equivalently,}$$

$$\frac{y}{x} = \beta_0 + \beta_1\left(\frac{1}{x}\right) + \frac{\varepsilon}{x}.$$

Figure 11.39 and Figure 11.40 give a regression output and a residual plot versus x, respectively, for this model.

a. Does the residual plot indicate that the constant variance assumption holds for the transformed model?

FIGURE 11.38 **The Data, Data Plot, and Residual Plot for Exercise 11.69** ● SrvcTime2

(a) Service time data for 15 service calls

Service Time, y (Minutes)	Number of Microcomputers Serviced, x
92	3
63	2
126	6
247	8
49	2
90	4
119	5
114	6
67	2
115	4
188	6
298	11
77	3
151	10
27	1

(b) Plot of y versus x

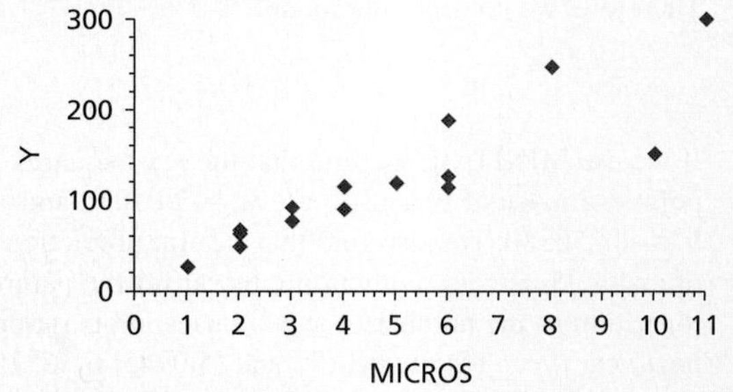

(c) The Excel residual plot

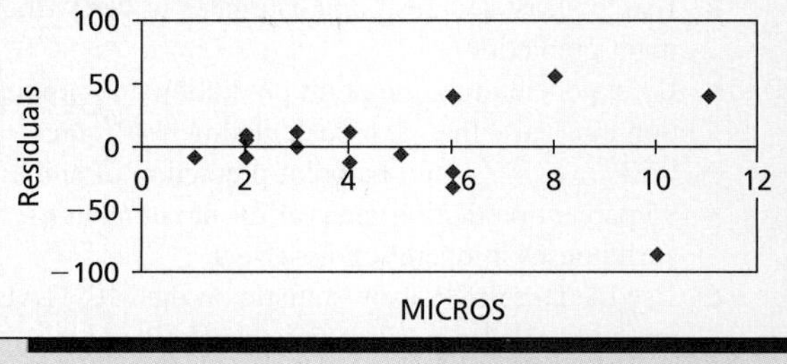

FIGURE **11.39** MegaStat Output of a Regression Analysis of the Service Time Data Using the Model $y/x = \beta_0 + \beta_1(1/x) + \varepsilon/x$

Regression Analysis

	r^2 0.095		n 15	
	r 0.308		k 1	
	Std. Error 5.158		Dep. Var. Y/X	

ANOVA table

Source	SS	df	MS	F	p-value
Regression	36.2685	1	36.2685	1.36	0.2640
Residual	345.8857	13	26.6066		
Total	382.1542	14			

Regression output

variables	coefficients	std. error	t (df = 13)	p-value	confidence interval 95% lower	95% upper
Intercept	24.0406	2.2461	10.703	8.13E-08	19.1883	28.8929
1/X	6.7642	5.7936	1.168	0.2640	−5.7521	19.2804

Predicted values for: Y/X

1/X	Predicted	95% Confidence Intervals lower	upper	95% Prediction Intervals lower	upper	Leverage
0.1429	25.0069	21.4335	28.5803	13.3044	36.7094	0.103

b. Consider a future service call on which seven micro-computers will be serviced. Let μ_0 represent the mean service time for all service calls on which seven microcomputers will be serviced, and let y_0 represent the actual service time for an individual service call on which seven microcomputers will be serviced. The bottom of the MegaStat output in Figure 11.39 tells us that

$$\frac{\hat{y}}{7} = 24.0406 + 6.7642\left(\frac{1}{7}\right) = 25.0069$$

is a point estimate of $\mu_0/7$ and a point prediction of $y_0/7$. Multiply this result by 7 to obtain $\hat{y}$. Multiply the ends of the confidence interval and prediction interval shown on the MegaStat output by 7. This will give a 95 percent confidence interval for μ_0 and a 95 percent prediction interval for y_0. If the number of minutes we will allow for the future service call is the upper limit of the 95 percent confidence interval for μ_0, how many minutes will we allow?

FIGURE **11.40** MegaStat Residual Plot for Exercise 11.70

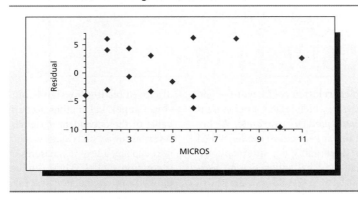

11.11 Some Shortcut Formulas

Calculating the sum of squared residuals   A shortcut formula for the sum of squared residuals is

$$SSE = SS_{yy} - \frac{SS_{xy}^2}{SS_{xx}},$$

where

$$SS_{yy} = \sum (y_i - \bar{y})^2 = \sum y_i^2 - \frac{\left(\sum y_i\right)^2}{n}.$$

For example, consider the data below. If we square each of the eight observed y values and add up the resulting squared values, we find that $\sum y_i^2 = 859.91$. Also, for these data, it has been found that $\sum y_i = 81.7$, $SS_{xy} = -179.6475$, and $SS_{xx} = 1,404.355$. It follows that

$$SS_{yy} = \sum y_i^2 - \frac{\left(\sum y_i\right)^2}{n}$$

$$= 859.91 - \frac{(81.7)^2}{8} = 25.549$$

and

$$SSE = SS_{yy} - \frac{SS_{xy}^2}{SS_{xx}} = 25.549 - \frac{(-179.6475)^2}{1,404.355}$$

$$= 25.549 - 22.981 = 2.568.$$

Finally, note that SS_{xy}^2/SS_{xx} equals $b_1 SS_{xx}$. However, we recommend using the first of these expressions, because doing so usually gives less round-off error.

Observation	x	y
1	28.0	12.4
2	28.0	11.7
3	32.5	12.4
4	39.0	10.8
5	45.9	9.4
6	57.8	9.5
7	58.1	8.0
8	62.5	7.5

Calculating the total, explained, and unexplained variations   The **unexplained variation** is the SSE, and thus the shortcut formula for the SSE is a shortcut formula for the unexplained variation. The quantity SS_{yy} is the **total variation**, and thus the shortcut formula for SS_{yy} is a shortcut formula for the total variation. Lastly, it can be shown that the expression SS_{xy}^2/SS_{xx} equals the **explained variation** and thus is a shortcut formula for this quantity.

CHAPTER SUMMARY

This chapter has discussed the **correlation coefficient (r)**, and **simple linear regression analysis**, which relates a **dependent variable** to a single **independent** (predictor) **variable**. We began by considering the **simple linear regression model**, which employs two parameters: the **slope** and the **y intercept**. We next discussed how to compute the **least squares point estimates** of these parameters and how to use these estimates to calculate a **point estimate of the mean value of the dependent variable** and a **point prediction of an individual value** of the dependent variable. Then, after considering the assumptions behind the simple linear regression model, we

discussed **testing the significance of the regression relationship (slope)**, calculating a **confidence interval** for the mean value of the dependent variable, and calculating a **prediction interval** for an individual value of the dependent variable. We next explained several measures of the utility of the simple linear regression model. These include the **simple coefficient of determination** and an **F test for the simple linear model**. We concluded this chapter by discussing using **residual analysis** to detect violations of the regression assumptions. We learned that we can sometimes remedy violations of these assumptions by **transforming** the dependent variable.

GLOSSARY OF TERMS

correlation coefficient (r): A measure of the strength of the linear relationship between x and y that does not depend on the units in which x and y are measured. (page 358)
cross-sectional data: Data that are observed at a single point in time. (page 361)

dependent variable: The variable that is being described, predicted, or controlled. (page 359)
distance value: A measure of the distance between a particular value x_0 of the independent variable x and $\bar{x}$, the average of the previously observed values of x (the centre of the experimental region). (pages 380–381)

experimental region: The range of the previously observed values of the independent variable. (page 368)

independent variable: A variable used to describe, predict, and control the dependent variable. (page 359)

least squares point estimates: The point estimates of the slope and y intercept of the simple linear regression model that minimize the sum of squared residuals. (pages 366–368)

negative autocorrelation: The situation in which positive error terms tend to be followed over time by negative error terms and negative error terms tend to be followed over time by positive error terms. (page 396)

normal plot: A residual plot that is used to check the normality assumption. (page 394)

positive autocorrelation: The situation in which positive error terms tend to be followed over time by positive error terms and negative error terms tend to be followed over time by negative error terms. (page 395)

residual: The difference between the observed value of the dependent variable and the corresponding predicted value of the dependent variable. (pages 364, 390)

residual plot: A plot of the residuals against some criterion. The plot is used to check the validity of one or more regression assumptions. (page 391)

simple coefficient of determination: The proportion of the total variation in the observed values of the dependent variable that is explained by the simple linear regression model. (pages 359, 384)

simple correlation coefficient: A measure of the linear association between two variables. (page 358)

simple linear regression model: An equation that describes the straight-line relationship between a dependent variable and an independent variable. (pages 359–360)

slope (of the simple linear regression model): The change in the mean value of the dependent variable that is associated with a one-unit increase in the value of the independent variable. (page 364)

time series data: Data that are observed in time sequence. (page 395)

y intercept (of the simple linear regression model): The mean value of the dependent variable when the value of the independent variable is 0. (page 364)

IMPORTANT FORMULAS AND TESTS

Simple correlation coefficient: page 358
Simple linear regression model: page 360
Least squares point estimates of β_0 and β_1: pages 366–368
Least squares line (prediction equation): page 366
The predicted value of y_i: page 366
Sum of squared residuals: pages 366, 407
The residual: pages 369, 390
Point estimate of a mean value of y: page 370
Point prediction of an individual value of y: page 370
Mean square error: page 374
Standard error: page 374
Sampling distribution of b_1: page 376
Standard error of the estimate b_1: page 376
Testing the significance of the slope: page 376

Confidence interval for the slope: page 377
Testing the significance of the y intercept: page 378
Sampling distribution of $\hat{y}$: page 381
Standard error of $\hat{y}$: page 381
Confidence interval for a mean value of y: page 381
Prediction interval for an individual value of y: page 382
Explained variation: page 385
Unexplained variation: page 385
Total variation: page 385
Simple coefficient of determination: page 386
Testing the significance of the population correlation coefficient: page 386–387
An F test for the simple linear regression model: page 387
Durbin–Watson test: pages 398–399

SUPPLEMENTARY EXERCISES

11.71 Consider the following data concerning the demand (y) and price (x) of a consumer product.
⬤ Demand

Demand, y	252	244	241	234	230	223
Price, x	$2.00	$2.20	$2.40	$2.60	$2.80	$3.00

a. Plot y versus x. Does it seem reasonable to use the simple linear regression model to relate y to x?

b. Calculate the least squares point estimates of the parameters in the simple linear regression model.

c. Write the least squares prediction equation. Graph this equation on the plot of y versus x.

d. Test the significance of the regression relationship between y and x.

e. Find a point prediction of and a 95 percent prediction interval for the demand corresponding to each of the prices $2.10, $2.75, and $3.10.

11.72 In an article in *Public Roads* (1983), Bissell, Pilkington, Mason, and Woods study bridge safety (measured in accident rates per 100 million vehicles) and the difference between the width of the bridge and the width of the roadway approach (road plus shoulder):[3] ⬤ AutoAcc

WidthDiff.	−6	−4	−2	0	2	4	6	8	10	12
Accident	120	103	87	72	58	44	31	20	12	7

The MINITAB output of a simple linear regression analysis relating accident to width difference is as in Figure 11.41.

---

[3]Source: "Roadway cross section and alignment," by H. H. Bissell, G. B. Pilkington II, J. M. Mason, and D. L. Woods, *Public Roads*, 46 (March 1983), pp. 132–141.

FIGURE 11.41   MINITAB Output for Exercise 11.72

```
The regression equation is
Accident Rate = 74.7 - 6.44 WidthDif

Predictor        Coef      SE Coef         T        P
Constant       74.727        1.904     39.25    0.000
WidthDif       -6.4424       0.2938    -21.93    0.000

S = 5.33627    R-Sq = 98.4%    R-Sq(adj) = 98.2%

Analysis of Variance
Source          DF         SS        MS        F        P
Regression       1      13697     13697    480.99    0.000
Residual Error   8        228        28
Total            9      13924
```

Using the MINITAB output,

a. Identify and interpret the least squares point estimate of the slope of the simple linear regression model.

b. Identify and interpret the p value for testing H_0: $\beta_1 = 0$ versus H_a: $\beta_1 \neq 0$.

c. Identify and interpret r^2 (eta^2).

11.73 In an article in the *Journal of Accounting Research*, Barlev and Levy consider relating accounting rates on stocks and market returns. Fifty-four companies were selected. For each company, the authors recorded values of x, the mean yearly accounting rate for the period 1959 to 1974, and y, the mean yearly market return rate for the period 1959 to 1974. The data in Table 11.11 were obtained. Here the accounting rate can be interpreted to represent input into investment and therefore is a logical predictor of market return. Use the simple linear regression model and a computer to do the following: ● AcctRet

a. Find a point estimate of and a 95 percent confidence interval for the mean market return rate of all stocks with an accounting rate of 15.00.

b. Find a point prediction of and a 95 percent prediction interval for the market return rate of an individual stock with an accounting rate of 15.00.

TABLE 11.11   Accounting Rates on Stocks and Market Returns for 54 Companies   ● AcctRet

Company	Market Rate	Accounting Rate	Company	Market Rate	Accounting Rate
McDonnell Douglas	17.73	17.96	Philips Petroleum	10.81	10.06
NCR	4.54	8.11	FMC	5.71	13.30
Honeywell	3.96	12.46	Caterpillar Tractor	13.38	17.66
TRW	8.12	14.70	Georgia Pacific	13.43	14.59
Raytheon	6.78	11.90	Minnesota Mining & Manufacturing	10.00	20.94
W. R. Grace	9.69	9.67	Standard Oil (Ohio)	16.66	9.62
Ford Motors	12.37	13.35	American Brands	9.40	16.32
Textron	15.88	16.11	Aluminum Company of America	0.24	8.19
Lockheed Aircraft	−1.34	6.78	General Electric	4.37	15.74
Getty Oil	18.09	9.41	General Tire	3.11	12.02
Atlantic Richfield	17.17	8.96	Borden	6.63	11.44
Radio Corporation of America	6.78	14.17	American Home Products	14.73	32.58
Westinghouse Electric	4.74	9.12	Standard Oil (California)	6.15	11.89
Johnson & Johnson	23.02	14.23	International Paper	5.96	10.06
Champion International	7.68	10.43	National Steel	6.30	9.60
R. J. Reynolds	14.32	19.74	Republic Steel	0.68	7.41
General Dynamics	−1.63	6.42	Warner Lambert	12.22	19.88
Colgate-Palmolive	16.51	12.16	U.S. Steel	0.90	6.97
Coca-Cola	17.53	23.19	Bethlehem Steel	2.35	7.90
International Business Machines	12.69	19.20	Armco Steel	5.03	9.34
			Texaco	6.13	15.40
Allied Chemical	4.66	10.76	Shell Oil	6.58	11.95
Uniroyal	3.67	8.49	Standard Oil (Indiana)	14.26	9.56
Greyhound	10.49	17.70	Owens Illinois	2.60	10.05
Cities Service	10.00	9.10	Gulf Oil	4.97	12.11
Philip Morris	21.90	17.47	Tenneco	6.65	11.53
General Motors	5.86	18.45	Inland Steel	4.25	9.92
			Kraft	7.30	12.27

Source: Reprinted by permission from "On the variability of accounting income numbers," by Benzion Barlev and Haim Levy, *Journal of Accounting Research* (Autumn 1979), pp. 305–315. Copyright © 1979. Used with permission of Blackwell Publishers.

TABLE 11.12 Annualized Investment Risk and Credit Rating for 40 Countries   InvRisk

Country	Annualized Investment Risk	Credit Rating	Country	Annualized Investment Risk	Credit Rating
Argentina	87.0	31.8	Malaysia	26.7	64.4
Australia	26.9	78.2	Mexico	46.3	43.3
Austria	26.3	83.8	Netherlands	18.5	87.6
Belgium	22.0	78.4	New Zealand	26.3	68.9
Brazil	64.8	36.2	Nigeria	41.4	30.6
Canada	19.2	87.1	Norway	28.3	83.0
Chile	31.6	38.6	Pakistan	24.4	26.4
Colombia	31.5	44.4	Philippines	38.4	29.6
Denmark	20.6	72.6	Portugal	47.5	56.7
Finland	26.1	76.0	Singapore	26.4	77.6
France	23.8	85.3	Spain	24.8	70.8
Germany	23.0	93.4	Sweden	24.5	79.5
Greece	39.6	51.9	Switzerland	19.6	94.7
Hong Kong	34.3	69.6	Taiwan	53.7	72.9
India	30.0	46.6	Thailand	27.0	55.8
Ireland	23.4	66.4	Turkey	74.1	32.6
Italy	28.0	75.5	United Kingdom	21.8	87.6
Japan	25.7	94.5	United States	15.4	93.4
Jordan	17.6	33.6	Venezuela	46.0	45.0
Korea	30.7	62.2	Zimbabwe	35.6	24.5

Source: "Country risk and global equity selection," by C. B. Erb, C. R. Harvey, and T. E. Viskanta, *Journal of Portfolio Management*, Vol. 21, No. 2, p. 76. This copyrighted material is reprinted with permission from *The Journal of Portfolio Management*, a publication of Institutional Investor, Inc., 488 Madison Ave., New York, NY 10022.

11.74 In an article in the *Journal of Portfolio Management*, Erb, Harvey, and Viskanta present the data in Table 11.12 concerning the annualized investment risk, y, and the credit rating, x, for each of 40 countries. If we use simple linear regression to analyze these data, we obtain the least squares prediction equation that is plotted, along with the observed combinations of x and y, in Figure 11.42. In this figure, we have circled the observations that might be considered outliers with respect to the regression relationship.

We discuss in Chapter 12 more precise ways to identify such outliers, as well as how to interpret the outliers. For now, answer the following simple questions: InvRisk

a. Which countries have an investment risk that is substantially larger than would be suggested by their credit rating?

b. Which countries have an investment risk that is substantially smaller than would be suggested by their credit rating?

FIGURE 11.42 Plot of the Least Squares Prediction Equation for the Investment Risk Data

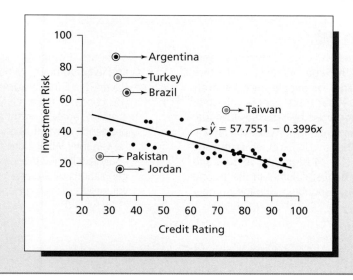

11.75 In analyzing the stock market, we sometimes use the model $y = \beta_0 + \beta_1 x + \varepsilon$ to relate y, the rate of return on a particular stock, to x, the rate of return on the overall stock market. When using the preceding model, we can interpret β_1 to be the percentage point change in the mean (or expected) rate of return on the particular stock that is associated with an increase of one percentage point in the rate of return on the overall stock market.

If regression analysis can be used to conclude (at a high level of confidence) that β_1 is greater than 1 (for example, if the 95 percent confidence interval for β_1 is [1.1826, 1.4723]), this indicates that the mean rate of return on the particular stock changes more quickly than the rate of return on the overall stock market. Such a stock is called an **aggressive stock** because gains for such a stock tend to be greater than overall market gains (which occur when the market is bullish). However, losses for such a stock tend to be greater than overall market losses (which occur when the market is bearish). Aggressive stocks should be purchased if you expect the market to rise and avoided if you expect the market to fall.

If regression analysis can be used to conclude (at a high level of confidence) that β_1 is less than 1 (for example, if the 95 percent confidence interval for β_1 is [0.4729, 0.7861]), this indicates that the mean rate of return on the particular stock changes more slowly than the rate of return on the overall stock market. Such a stock is called a **defensive stock**. Losses for such a stock tend to be less than overall market losses, whereas gains for such a stock tend to be less than overall market gains. Defensive stocks should be held if you expect the market to fall and sold if you expect the market to rise.

If the least squares point estimate b_1 of β_1 is nearly equal to 1, and if the 95 percent confidence interval for β_1 contains 1, this might indicate that the mean rate of return on the particular stock changes at roughly the same rate as the rate of return on the overall stock market. Such a stock is called a **neutral stock**.

In a 1984 article in *Financial Analysts Journal*, Levy considers how a stock's value of β_1 depends on the length of time for which the rate of return is calculated. Levy calculated estimated values of β_1 for return length times varying from 1 to 30 months for each of 38 aggressive stocks, 38 defensive stocks, and 68 neutral stocks. Each estimated value was based on data from 1946 to 1975. In the following table, we present the average estimate of β_1 for each stock type for different return length times:

Return Length Time	Average Estimate of β_1 🌑 Beta		
	Aggressive Stocks	Defensive Stocks	Neutral Stocks
1	1.37	0.50	0.98
3	1.42	0.44	0.95
6	1.53	0.41	0.94
9	1.69	0.39	1.00
12	1.83	0.40	0.98
15	1.67	0.38	1.00
18	1.78	0.39	1.02
24	1.86	0.35	1.14
30	1.83	0.33	1.22

Source: Reprinted by permission from "Measuring risk and performance over alternative investment horizons," by H. Levy, *Financial Analysts Journal* (March–April 1984), pp. 61–68. Copyright © 1984, CFA Institute. Reproduced and modified from *Financial Analysts Journal* with permission of CFA Institute.

Let y = average estimate of β_1 and x = return length time, and consider relating y to x for each stock type by using the simple linear regression model

$$y = \beta_0^* + \beta_1^* x + \varepsilon.$$

Here β_0^* and β_1^* are regression parameters relating y to x. We use the asterisks to indicate that these regression parameters are different from β_0 and β_1. Calculate a 95 percent confidence interval for β_1^* for each stock type. Carefully interpret each interval.

11.76   INTERNET EXERCISE 🖱️

Organizations that depend on volunteers can gain information about the age, income, and other personal characteristics of people and the average number of hours that these people volunteer from the statistics reported by Statistics Canada. Go to the data file at http://www40.statcan.ca/l01/cst01/famil103.htm. In Excel, enter the age groups from 1 to 6 (15–24 is group 1 and 65 and older is group 6) in the first column. In the second column, enter the corresponding average number of hours. Compute the correlation between age and average hours. What does this value tell you? Compute r^2 (eta^2) from the correlation. What can you conclude from this value? Also run a linear regression analysis with average hours as the dependent (y) variable and age as the independent (x) variable. What does the result of the regression analysis tell you? If you were asked by volunteer organizations which age groups to target to look for volunteers, which group would you suggest?

CHAPTER 12

Multiple Regression and Model Building

LEARNING OBJECTIVES

After reading this chapter, you should be able to

- explain what is meant by the *least squares point estimate* of a model parameter

- compute an *F* test from the results output

- define the multiple coefficient of determination

- explain the steps that can be taken when the assumption of linearity is not supported

- understand a multiple regression output and how to interpret the values given

- define backward, stepwise, and logistic regression

- appreciate how an outlier can influence the regression results

CHAPTER OUTLINE

Important Note:

Part 1 of this chapter discusses basic multiple regression analysis and is the only prerequisite for Optional Part 2, for Optional Part 3, and for any section of Optional Part 4. Parts 2, 3, and 4 cover more advanced regression topics and can be read independently of each other. They can be covered in any order without loss of continuity.

Often we can more accurately describe, predict, and control a dependent variable by using a regression model that employs more than one independent variable, such as when deciding on whom to hire for a position. In this situation, multiple pieces of information are preferable to a single question and answer. For example, a job candidate's past employment experience may be a good indicator of future work behaviour. If an interviewer can also add information such as a work sample or personality–job fit measures, then the hiring decision will be more sound. Such a model is called a **multiple regression model**, which is the subject of this chapter.

In order to explain the ideas of this chapter, we consider the following two cases:

The Sales Territory Performance Case. A sales manager evaluates the performance of sales representatives by using a multiple regression model that predicts sales performance on the basis of five independent variables. Salespeople whose actual performance is far worse than predicted performance will get extra training to help improve their sales techniques.

The Fresh Detergent Case. Enterprise Industries predicts future demand for Fresh liquid laundry detergent by using a multiple regression model that employs as independent variables the advertising expenditures used to promote Fresh and the difference between the price of Fresh and the average price of competing detergents.

**PART 1
Basic Multiple
Regression**

12.1 The Multiple Regression Model

Regression models that employ more than one independent variable are called **multiple regression models**.

CHAPTER 17

Part 1: The data and a regression model   In Chapter 11, we used a single predictor variable x to predict y. We now consider predicting y using an additional variable, x_2.

Consider the data in Table 12.1. Figure 12.1 presents a scatter plot of y versus x_1. This plot shows that y tends to decrease in a straight-line fashion as x_1 increases. This suggests that, if we wish to predict y on the basis of x_1 only, the simple linear regression model

$$y = \beta_0 + \beta_1 x_1 + \varepsilon$$

relates y to x_1. Figure 12.2 presents a scatter plot of y versus x_2. This plot shows that y tends to increase in a straight-line fashion as x_2 increases. This suggests that, if we wish to predict y on the basis of x_2 only, the simple linear regression model

$$y = \beta_0 + \beta_1 x_2 + \varepsilon$$

relates y to x_2. If we wish to predict y on the basis of both x_1 and x_2, it seems reasonable to combine these models to form the model

$$y = \beta_0 + \beta_1 x_1 + \beta_2 x_2 + \varepsilon$$

**TABLE 12.1
Sample Data**

x_1	x_2	y
28.0	18	12.4
28.0	14	11.7
32.5	24	12.4
39.0	22	10.8
45.9	8	9.4
57.8	16	9.5
58.1	1	8.0
62.5	0	7.5

to relate y to x_1 and x_2. Here we have arbitrarily placed the $\beta_1 x_1$ term first and the $\beta_2 x_2$ term second, and we have renumbered β_1 and β_2 to be consistent with the subscripts on x_1 and x_2. This regression model says that

1   β_0, β_1, and β_2 are regression parameters relating the mean value of y to x_1 and x_2.

2   ε is an error term that describes the effects on y of all factors other than x_1 and x_2.

Part 2: Interpreting the regression parameters β_0, β_1, and β_2   The exact interpretations of the parameters β_0, β_1, and β_2 are quite simple. First suppose that $x_1 = 0$ and $x_2 = 0$. Then

$$\beta_0 + \beta_1 x_1 + \beta_2 x_2 = \beta_0 + \beta_1(0) + \beta_2(0) = \beta_0.$$

So β_0 is the mean y value when $x_1 = 0$ and $x_2 = 0$. The parameter β_0 is called the **intercept** in the regression model. One might wonder whether β_0 has any practical interpretation, since it

FIGURE 12.1 Plot of *y* versus *x₁*

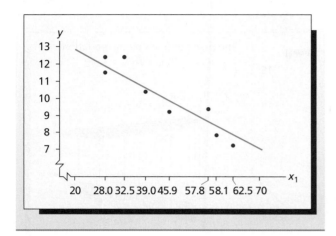

FIGURE 12.2 Plot of *y* versus *x₂*

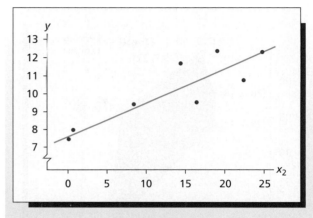

might be unlikely that x_1 and x_2 equal zero. Indeed, sometimes the parameter β_0 and other parameters in a regression analysis do not have practical interpretations because the situations related to the interpretations would not be likely to occur in practice. In fact, sometimes each parameter does not, by itself, have much practical importance. Rather, the parameters relate the mean of the dependent variable to the independent variables in an overall sense.

We next interpret β_1 and β_2 individually. To examine the interpretation of β_1, consider two observations. Suppose that for x_1, the value is *c,* and for x_2, the value is *d.* The mean *y* value is then

$$\beta_0 + \beta_1(c) + \beta_2(d).$$

For the second observation, suppose that the x_1 value is $c + 1$ and the x_2 value is *d.* The mean *y* value is

$$\beta_0 + \beta_1(c + 1) + \beta_2(d).$$

It is easy to see that the difference between these mean *y* values is β_1 because the two observations only differ in that x_1 is one greater in the second observation than in the first. In the following, we can interpret the parameter β_1 as the change in *y* associated with a one-point increase in x_1 (note that x_2 did not change in value).

The interpretation of β_2 can be established similarly. We can interpret β_2 as the change in mean *y* values that is associated with a one-unit increase in x_2 when x_1 does not change.

Part 3: A geometric interpretation of the regression model To interpret a multiple regression model geometrically, we begin by defining the **experimental region** to be the range of the combinations of the observed values of x_1 and x_2. From the data in Table 12.1, it is reasonable to depict the experimental region as the shaded region in Figure 12.3. Here the combinations of x_1 and x_2 values are the ordered pairs in the figure.

We next write the mean value of *y* when IV_1 (independent variable one) is x_1 and IV_2 is x_2 as $\mu_{y|x_1, x_2}$ (mu of *y* given x_1 and x_2) and consider the equation

$$\mu_{y|x_1, x_2} = \beta_0 + \beta_1 x_1 + \beta_2 x_2,$$

which relates mean *y* values to x_1 and x_2. Because this is a linear equation with two variables, geometry tells us that this equation is the equation of a plane in three-dimensional space. We sometimes refer to this plane as the **plane of means**, and we illustrate the portion of this plane corresponding to the (x_1, x_2) combinations in the experimental region in Figure 12.4. As illustrated in this figure, the model

$$y = \mu_{y|x_1, x_2} + \varepsilon$$
$$= \beta_0 + \beta_1 x_1 + \beta_2 x_2 + \varepsilon$$

FIGURE **12.3**   **The Experimental Region**

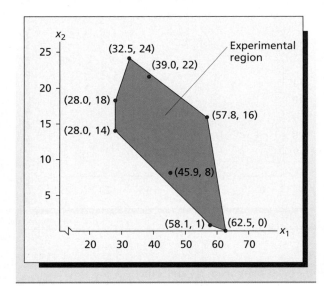

FIGURE **12.4**   **A Geometrical Interpretation of the Regression Model Relating y to x_1 and x_2**

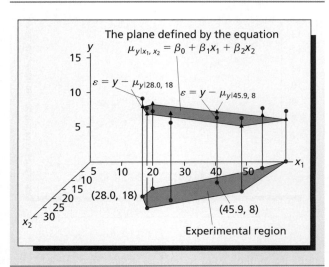

says that the error terms cause the observed y values (the red dots in the upper portion of the figure) to deviate from the mean y values (the triangles in the figure), which exactly lie on the plane of means

$$\mu_{y|x_1, x_2} = \beta_0 + \beta_1 x_1 + \beta_2 x_2.$$

For example, consider the first row of data in Table 12.1 ($y = 12.4$, $x_1 = 28.0$, $x_2 = 18$). Figure 12.4 shows that the error term for this observation is positive, causing y to be higher than $\mu_{y|28.0, 18}$ (mean y value when $x_1 = 28$ and $x_2 = 18$). Here factors other than x_1 and x_2 have resulted in a positive error term. As another example, the error term for row 5 in Table 12.1 ($y = 9.4$, $x_1 = 45.9$, $x_2 = 8$) is negative, so y is lower than $\mu_{y|45.9, 8}$ (mean y value when $x_1 = 45.9$ and $x_2 = 8$). Here factors other than x_1 and x_2 have resulted in a negative error term.

The model above expresses the dependent variable as a function of two independent variables. In general, we can use a multiple regression model to express a dependent variable as a function of any number of independent variables. For example, hiring decisions could be based on four independent variables, such as education, past work experience, personality, and a current work sample. The general form of a multiple regression model expresses the dependent variable y as a function of k independent variables $x_1, x_2, \ldots, x_k$. We express this general form in the following box. Here we assume that we have obtained n observations, with each observation consisting of an observed value of y and corresponding observed values of $x_1, x_2, \ldots, x_k$.

The Multiple Regression Model

The multiple regression model relating y to x_1, $x_2, \ldots, x_k$ is

$$\begin{aligned} y &= \mu_{y|x_1, x_2, \ldots, x_k} + \varepsilon \\ &= \beta_0 + \beta_1 x_1 + \beta_2 x_2 + \cdots + \beta_k x_k + \varepsilon. \end{aligned}$$

Here

1 $\mu_{y|x_1, x_2, \ldots, x_k} = \beta_0 + \beta_1 x_1 + \beta_2 x_2 + \cdots + \beta_k x_k$ is the mean value of the dependent variable y when the values of the independent variables are $x_1, x_2, \ldots, x_k$.

2 $\beta_0, \beta_1, \beta_2, \ldots, \beta_k$ are (unknown) **regression parameters** relating the mean value of y to x_1, $x_2, \ldots, x_k$.

3 ε is an **error term** that describes the effects on y of all factors other than the values of the independent variables $x_1, x_2, \ldots, x_k$.

Example 12.1 The Sales Territory Performance Case

Suppose the sales manager of a company wishes to evaluate the performance of the company's sales representatives. Each sales representative is solely responsible for one sales territory, and the manager decides that it is reasonable to measure the performance, y, of a sales representative by using the yearly sales of the company's product in the representative's sales territory. The manager feels that sales performance, y, substantially depends on five independent variables:

x_1 = number of months the representative has been employed by the company,

x_2 = sales of the company's product and competing products in the sales territory,

x_3 = dollar advertising expenditure in the territory,

x_4 = weighted average of the company's market share in the territory for the previous four years,

x_5 = change in the company's market share in the territory over the previous four years.

In Table 12.2, we present values of y and x_1 through x_5 for 25 randomly selected sales representatives. To understand the values of y and x_2 in the table, note that sales of the company's product or any competing product are measured in hundreds of units of the product sold. Therefore, for example, the first sales figure of 3,669.88 in Table 12.2 means that the first randomly selected sales representative sold 366,988 units of the company's product during the year.

Plots of y versus x_1 through x_5 are given beside Table 12.2. Since each plot has an approximate straight-line appearance, it is reasonable to relate y to x_1 through x_5 by using the regression model

$$y = \beta_0 + \beta_1 x_1 + \beta_2 x_2 + \beta_3 x_3 + \beta_4 x_4 + \beta_5 x_5 + \varepsilon.$$

TABLE 12.2 Sales Territory Performance Study Data 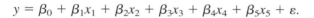 SalePerf

	Sales, y	Time with Company, x_1	Market Potential, x_2	Advertising, x_3	Market Share, x_4	Market Share Change, x_5
	3,669.88	43.10	74,065.11	4,582.88	2.51	0.34
	3,473.95	108.13	58,117.30	5,539.78	5.51	0.15
	2,295.10	13.82	21,118.49	2,950.38	10.91	−0.72
	4,675.56	186.18	68,521.27	2,243.07	8.27	0.17
	6,125.96	161.79	57,805.11	7,747.08	9.15	0.50
	2,134.94	8.94	37,806.94	402.44	5.51	0.15
	5,031.66	365.04	50,935.26	3,140.62	8.54	0.55
	3,367.45	220.32	35,602.08	2,086.16	7.07	−0.49
	6,519.45	127.64	46,176.77	8,846.25	12.54	1.24
	4,876.37	105.69	42,053.24	5,673.11	8.85	0.31
	2,468.27	57.72	36,829.71	2,761.76	5.38	0.37
	2,533.31	23.58	33,612.67	1,991.85	5.43	−0.65
	2,408.11	13.82	21,412.79	1,971.52	8.48	0.64
	2,337.38	13.82	20,416.87	1,737.38	7.80	1.01
	4,586.95	86.99	36,272.00	10,694.20	10.34	0.11
	2,729.24	165.85	23,093.26	8,618.61	5.15	0.04
	3,289.40	116.26	26,878.59	7,747.89	6.64	0.68
	2,800.78	42.28	39,571.96	4,565.81	5.45	0.66
	3,264.20	52.84	51,866.15	6,022.70	6.31	−0.10
	3,453.62	165.04	58,749.82	3,721.10	6.35	−0.03
	1,741.45	10.57	23,990.82	860.97	7.37	−1.63
	2,035.75	13.82	25,694.86	3,571.51	8.39	−0.43
	1,578.00	8.13	23,736.35	2,845.50	5.15	0.04
	4,167.44	58.54	34,314.29	5,060.11	12.88	0.22
	2,799.97	21.14	22,809.53	3,552.00	9.14	−0.74

The plots beside the table are labeled (top to bottom): Time, MktPoten, Adver, MktShare, Change — each showing Sales on the vertical axis.

Source: This data set is from a research study published in "An analytical approach for evaluation of sales territory performance," by David W. Cravens, Robert B. Woodruff, and Joseph C. Stamper, *Journal of Marketing*, January 1972, 31–37. We have updated the situation in our case study to be more modern.

Here, $\mu_{y|x_1, x_2, \ldots, x_5} = \beta_0 + \beta_1 x_1 + \beta_2 x_2 + \beta_3 x_3 + \beta_4 x_4 + \beta_5 x_5$ is the mean sales in all sales territories, where the values of the previously described five independent variables are x_1, x_2, x_3, x_4, and x_5. Furthermore, for example, the parameter β_3 equals the increase in mean sales that is associated with a \$1 increase in advertising expenditure (x_3) when the other four independent variables do not change. The main objective of the regression analysis is to help the sales manager evaluate sales performance by comparing actual performance to predicted performance. The manager has randomly selected the 25 representatives from all the representatives the company considers to be effective and wishes to use a regression model based on effective representatives to evaluate questionable representatives.

Exercises for Sections 12.1

CONCEPTS

For Exercises 12.1 through 12.5, consider the multiple regression model

$$y = \mu_{y|x_1, x_2, \ldots, x_k} + \varepsilon$$
$$= \beta_0 + \beta_1 x_1 + \beta_2 x_2 + \cdots + \beta_k x_k + \varepsilon.$$

12.1 What is y? What are $x_1, x_2, \ldots, x_k$?

12.2 Interpret $\mu_{y|x_1, x_2, \ldots, x_k}$.

12.3 What are $\beta_0, \beta_1, \beta_2, \ldots, \beta_k$?

12.4 What does the error term ε describe?

12.5 In your own words, interpret β_0, β_1, and β_2.

METHODS AND APPLICATIONS

12.6   THE REAL ESTATE SALES PRICE CASE
  ● RealEst2

A real estate agency collects the data in Table 12.3 concerning

  y = sales price of a house (in thousands of dollars),

  x_1 = home size (in hundreds of square feet),

  x_2 = rating (an overall "niceness rating" for the house expressed on a scale from 1 (worst) to 10 (best), provided by the real estate agency).

TABLE 12.3   **The Real Estate Sales Price Data**
  ● RealEst2

Sales Price, y	Home Size, x_1	Rating, x_2
180	23	5
98.1	11	2
173.1	20	9
136.5	17	3
141	15	8
165.9	21	4
193.5	24	7
127.8	13	6
163.5	19	7
172.5	25	2

Source: "Integrating judgement with a regression appraisal," by R. L. Andrews and J. T. Ferguson, *The Real Estate Appraiser and Analyst*, 52, no. 2 (1986). Reprinted by permission.

The agency wishes to develop a regression model that can be used to predict the sales prices of future houses it will list. Consider relating y to x_1 and x_2 by using the model

$$y = \mu_{y|x_1, x_2} + \varepsilon$$
$$= \beta_0 + \beta_1 x_1 + \beta_2 x_2 + \varepsilon.$$

a. Discuss why the data plots given beside Table 12.3 indicate that this model might be reasonable.

b. Interpret

$$\mu_{y|x_1=20, x_2=9} = \beta_0 + \beta_1(20) + \beta_2(9).$$

c. Interpret β_0, β_1, and β_2.

d. What factors are represented by the error term in this model? Give a specific example of these factors.

12.7   THE FRESH DETERGENT CASE   ● Fresh2

Enterprise Industries produces Fresh, a brand of liquid laundry detergent. In order to more effectively manage its inventory and make revenue projections, the company would like to better predict demand for Fresh. To develop a prediction model, the company has gathered data concerning demand for Fresh over the last 30 sales periods (each sales period is defined to be a four-week period). The demand data are presented in Table 12.4. Here, for each sales period,

  y = the demand for the large size bottle of Fresh (in hundreds of thousands of bottles) in the sales period,

  x_1 = the price (in dollars) of Fresh as offered by Enterprise Industries in the sales period,

  x_2 = the average industry price (in dollars) of competitors' similar detergents in the sales period,

  x_3 = Enterprise Industries' advertising expenditure (in hundreds of thousands of dollars) to promote Fresh in the sales period,

  $x_4 = x_2 - x_1$ = the "price difference" in the sales period.

Consider relating y to x_1, x_2, and x_3 by using the model

$$y = \beta_0 + \beta_1 x_1 + \beta_2 x_2 + \beta_3 x_3 + \varepsilon.$$

TABLE 12.4 Historical Data Concerning Demand for Fresh Detergent ● Fresh2

Sales Period	Price for Fresh, x_1	Average Industry Price, x_2	Price Difference, $x_4 = x_2 - x_1$	Advertising Expenditure for Fresh, x_3	Demand for Fresh, y	Sales Period	Price for Fresh, x_1	Average Industry Price, x_2	Price Difference, $x_4 = x_2 - x_1$	Advertising Expenditure for Fresh, x_3	Demand for Fresh, y
1	3.85	3.80	−0.05	5.50	7.38	16	3.80	4.10	0.30	6.80	8.87
2	3.75	4.00	0.25	6.75	8.51	17	3.70	4.20	0.50	7.10	9.26
3	3.70	4.30	0.60	7.25	9.52	18	3.80	4.30	0.50	7.00	9.00
4	3.70	3.70	0	5.50	7.50	19	3.70	4.10	0.40	6.80	8.75
5	3.60	3.85	0.25	7.00	9.33	20	3.80	3.75	−0.05	6.50	7.95
6	3.60	3.80	0.20	6.50	8.28	21	3.80	3.75	−0.05	6.25	7.65
7	3.60	3.75	0.15	6.75	8.75	22	3.75	3.65	−0.10	6.00	7.27
8	3.80	3.85	0.05	5.25	7.87	23	3.70	3.90	0.20	6.50	8.00
9	3.80	3.65	−0.15	5.25	7.10	24	3.55	3.65	0.10	7.00	8.50
10	3.85	4.00	0.15	6.00	8.00	25	3.60	4.10	0.50	6.80	8.75
11	3.90	4.10	0.20	6.50	7.89	26	3.65	4.25	0.60	6.80	9.21
12	3.90	4.00	0.10	6.25	8.15	27	3.70	3.65	−0.05	6.50	8.27
13	3.70	4.10	0.40	7.00	9.10	28	3.75	3.75	0	5.75	7.67
14	3.75	4.20	0.45	6.90	8.86	29	3.80	3.85	0.05	5.80	7.93
15	3.75	4.10	0.35	6.80	8.90	30	3.70	4.25	0.55	6.80	9.26

TABLE 12.5 Hospital Labour Needs Data ● HospLab

Hospital	Monthly X-Ray Exposures, x_1	Monthly Occupied Bed Days, x_2	Average Length of Stay, x_3	Monthly Labour Hours Required, y
1	2,463	472.92	4.45	566.52
2	2,048	1,339.75	6.92	696.82
3	3,940	620.25	4.28	1,033.15
4	6,505	568.33	3.90	1,603.62
5	5,723	1,497.60	5.50	1,611.37
6	11,520	1,365.83	4.60	1,613.27
7	5,779	1,687.00	5.62	1,854.17
8	5,969	1,639.92	5.15	2,160.55
9	8,461	2,872.33	6.18	2,305.58
10	20,106	3,655.08	6.15	3,503.93
11	13,313	2,912.00	5.88	3,571.89
12	10,771	3,921.00	4.88	3,741.40
13	15,543	3,865.67	5.50	4,026.52
14	34,703	12,446.33	10.78	11,732.17
15	39,204	14,098.40	7.05	15,414.94
16	86,533	15,524.00	6.35	18,854.45

Source: *Procedures and Analysis for Staffing Standards Development Regression Analysis Handbook* (San Diego, CA: Navy Manpower and Material Analysis Center, 1979).

a. Discuss why the data plots given under Table 12.4 indicate that this model might be reasonable.

b. Interpret

$\mu_{y|x_1 = 3.70, x_2 = 3.90, x_3 = 6.50}$
$= \beta_0 + \beta_1(3.70) + \beta_2(3.90) + \beta_3(6.50).$

c. Interpret $\beta_0, \beta_1, \beta_2, \beta_3$, and ε in the model.

d. Discuss why the data plots given under Table 12.4 indicate that it might be reasonable to use the alternative model

$y = \beta_0 + \beta_1 x_4 + \beta_2 x_3 + \varepsilon.$

12.8 THE HOSPITAL LABOUR NEEDS CASE
● HospLab

Table 12.5 presents data concerning the need for labour in 16 hospitals. Here

y = monthly labour hours required,

x_1 = monthly X-ray exposures,

x_2 = monthly occupied bed days (a hospital has one occupied bed day if one bed is occupied for an entire day),

x_3 = average length of patients' stay (in days).

The main objective of the regression analysis is to evaluate the performance of hospitals in terms of how many labour hours are used relative to how many labour hours are needed. Sixteen efficiently run hospitals are selected and a regression model based on efficiently run hospitals is created to evaluate the efficiency of questionable hospitals. Consider relating y to x_1, x_2, and x_3 by using the model

$$y = \beta_0 + \beta_1 x_1 + \beta_2 x_2 + \beta_3 x_3 + \varepsilon.$$

Discuss why the data plots given beside Table 12.5 indicate that this model might be reasonable. Interpret β_0, β_1, β_2, β_3, and ε in this model.

12.2 The Least Squares Estimates, and Point Estimation and Prediction

The regression parameters β_0, β_1, β_2, ..., β_k in the multiple regression model are unknown. Therefore, they must be estimated from data (observations of y, x_1, x_2, ..., x_k). To see how we might do this, let b_0, b_1, b_2, ..., b_k denote point estimates of the unknown parameters. Then, a point prediction of an observed value of the dependent variable

$$y = \beta_0 + \beta_1 x_1 + \beta_2 x_2 + \cdots + \beta_k x_k + \varepsilon$$

is

$$\hat{y} = b_0 + b_1 x_1 + b_2 x_2 + \cdots + b_k x_k,$$

which is called the **least squares prediction equation**. It is obtained by replacing β_0, β_1, and β_2 by their estimates b_0, b_1, and b_2. You will notice that the error term is not present in this equation. One of the assumptions in the regression model is that the expected value of the error term is 0. This was mentioned in Sections 11.3 and 11.4. More regression assumptions will be discussed in Section 12.3. Next, let y_i and $\hat{y}_i$ denote the observed and predicted values of the dependent variable for the ith observation, and define the **residual** for the ith observation to be $e_i = y_i - \hat{y}_i$. We then consider the **sum of squared residuals**

$$SSE = \sum_{i=1}^{n} (y_i - \hat{y}_i)^2.$$

Intuitively, if any particular values of b_0, b_1, b_2, ..., b_k are good point estimates, they will make (for $i = 1, 2, ..., n$) the predicted value $\hat{y}_i$ fairly close to the observed value y_i and thus will make the SSE fairly small. We define the **least squares point estimates** to be the values of b_0, b_1, b_2, ..., b_k that minimize the SSE.

It can be shown that a formula exists for computing the least squares point estimates of the parameters in the multiple regression model. This formula is written using a branch of mathematics called **matrix algebra** and is presented in Appendix F in the Online Learning Centre. In practice, the least squares point estimates can easily be computed using many standard statistical computer packages. In our discussion of multiple regression here, we will rely on MINITAB, Excel, and MegaStat to compute the needed estimates.

Example 12.2   The Sample Data in Table 12.1

Part 1: The least squares point estimates   Consider the model of the data in Table 12.1 (page 414):

$$y = \beta_0 + \beta_1 x_1 + \beta_2 x_2 + \varepsilon.$$

The MINITAB and Excel output in Figure 12.5 tells us that if we use the data in Table 12.1 to calculate the least squares point estimates of the parameters β_0, β_1, and β_2, we obtain $b_0 = 13.1087$, $b_1 = -0.09001$, and $b_2 = 0.08249$.

The point estimate $b_1 = -0.09001$ of β_1 says we estimate that y decreases (since b_1 is negative) by 0.09001 when x_1 increases by one and x_2 does not change. The point estimate $b_2 = 0.08249$ of β_2 says we estimate that y increases (since b_2 is positive) by 0.08249 when there is a one-unit increase in x_2 and x_1 does not change.

FIGURE 12.5   MINITAB and Excel Output of a Regression Analysis of the Data in Table 12.1 Using the Model $y = \beta_0 + \beta_1 x_1 + \beta_2 x_2 + \varepsilon$

(a) The MINITAB output

```
The regression equation is
Y = 13.1 - 0.0900 X1 + 0.0825 X2

Predictor          Coef        SE Coef  4           T  5          P  6
Constant        13.1087  1      0.8557         15.32        0.000
X1              -0.09001 2      0.01408        -6.39        0.001
X2               0.08249 3      0.02200         3.75        0.013

s = 0.367078  7     R-Sq = 97.4%  8      R-Sq(adj) = 96.3%  9

Analysis of Variance
Source           DF          SS          MS          F          P
Regression        2      24.875  10    12.438      92.30  13   0.000  14
Residual Error    5       0.674  11     0.135
Total             7      25.549  12

Values of Predictors for New Obs    Predicted Values for New Observations
New Obs X1 X2                       New Obs     Fit 15  SE Fit 16     95% CI 17          95% PI 18
     1 40.0  10.0                        1 10.333     0.170   (9.895, 10.771) (9.293, 11.374)
```

(b) The Excel output

Regression Statistics

Multiple R	0.9867
R Square	0.9736 [8]
Adjusted R Square	0.9631 [9]
Standard Error	0.3671 [7]
Observations	8

ANOVA

	df	SS	MS	F	Significance F
Regression	2	24.8750 [10]	12.4375	92.3031 [13]	0.0001 [14]
Residual	5	0.6737 [11]	0.1347		
Total	7	25.5488 [12]			

	Coefficients	Standard Error [4]	t Stat [5]	P-value [6]	Lower 95% [19]	Upper 95% [19]
Intercept	13.1087 [1]	0.8557	15.3193	2.15E-05	10.9091	15.3084
X1	-0.0900 [2]	0.0141	-6.3942	0.0014	-0.1262	-0.0538
X2	0.0825 [3]	0.0220	3.7493	0.0133	0.0259	0.1391

[1] b_0 [2] b_1 [3] b_2 [4] s_{b_j} = standard error of the estimate b_j [5] t statistics   [6] p values for t statistics   [7] s = standard error
[8] R^2 [9] Adjusted R^2 [10] Explained variation   [11] SSE = unexplained variation   [12] Total variation   [13] F(model) statistic
[14] p value for F(model)   [15] $\hat{y}$ = point prediction when x_1 = 40 and x_2 = 10   [16] $s_{\hat{y}}$ = standard error of the estimate $\hat{y}$
[17] 95% confidence interval when x_1 = 40 and x_2 = 10   [18] 95% prediction interval when x_1 = 40 and x_2 = 10   [19] 95% confidence interval for β_j

The equation

$$\hat{y} = b_0 + b_1 x_1 + b_2 x_2$$
$$= 13.1087 - 0.09001 x_1 + 0.08249 x_2$$

is the least squares prediction equation. This equation is given on the MINITAB output (labelled as the "regression equation"—note that b_0, b_1, and b_2 have been rounded to 13.1, −0.0900, and 0.0825). We can use this equation to compute a prediction for any observed value of y. For instance, a point prediction of $y_1 = 12.4$ (when $x_1 = 28.0$ and $x_2 = 18$) is

$$\hat{y}_1 = 13.1087 - 0.09001(28.0) + 0.08249(18)$$
$$= 12.0733.$$

This results in a residual equal to

$$e_1 = y_1 - \hat{y}_1 = 12.4 - 12.0733 = 0.3267.$$

TABLE 12.6 The Point Predictions and Residuals Using the Least Squares Point Estimates $b_0 = 13.1$, $b_1 = -0.0900$, and $b_2 = 0.0825$

x_1	x_2	y	$\hat{y} = b_0 + b_1x_1 + b_2x_2$ $= 13.1 - 0.0900x_1 + 0.0825x_2$	Residual, $e = y - \hat{y}$
28.0	18	12.4	12.0733	0.3267
28.0	14	11.7	11.7433	-0.0433
32.5	24	12.4	12.1632	0.2368
39.0	22	10.8	11.4131	-0.6131
45.9	8	9.4	9.6371	-0.2371
57.8	16	9.5	9.2259	0.2741
58.1	1	8.0	7.9614	0.0386
62.5	0	7.5	7.4829	0.0171

$$SSE = (0.3267)^2 + (-0.0433)^2 + \cdots + (0.0171)^2 = 0.674$$

Table 12.6 gives the point prediction obtained using the least squares prediction equation and the residual for each of the eight observed y values. In addition, this table tells us that the sum of squared residuals (*SSE*) equals 0.674.

The least squares prediction equation is the equation of a plane that we sometimes call the **least squares plane**. Figure 12.6 illustrates a portion of this plane—the portion that corresponds to the (x_1, x_2) combinations in the experimental region. Figure 12.6 also shows the residuals for each observation (here $n = 8$). These residuals are depicted as line segments drawn between the observed y values (the dots scattered around the least squares plane) and the predicted y values (the squares on the least squares plane). Because the least squares point estimates minimize the sum of squared residuals, we can interpret them as positioning the planar prediction equation in three-dimensional space so as to minimize the sum of squared distances between the observed and predicted y values. In this sense, we can say that the plane defined by the least squares point estimates is the best plane that can be positioned between the observed y values. The MINITAB output of the least squares plane is given in Figure 12.7.

Part 2: Estimating means and predicting individual values For combinations of values of x_1 and x_2 that are in the experimental region, the **least squares plane** (see Figure 12.6) is the estimate of the **plane of means** (see Figure 12.4 on page 416). This implies that the point on the least squares plane corresponding to x_1 and x_2,

$$\hat{y} = b_0 + b_1x_1 + b_2x_2$$
$$= 13.1087 - 0.09001x_1 + 0.08249x_2,$$

FIGURE 12.6 A Geometrical Interpretation of the Prediction Equation Relating $\hat{y}$ to x_1 and x_2

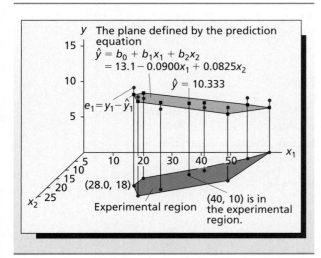

FIGURE 12.7 The MINITAB Output of the Least Squares Plane

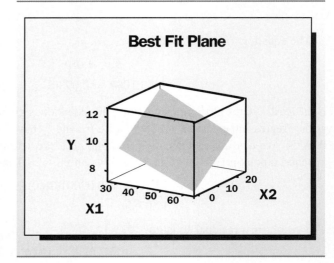

is the point estimate of $\mu_{y|x_1, x_2}$, the mean of all y values that could be observed at x_1 and x_2. In addition, because we predict the error term to be 0, $\hat{y}$ is also the point prediction of $y = \mu_{y|x_1, x_2} + \varepsilon$.

Generalizing the previous example, we obtain the following:

Point Estimation and Point Prediction in Multiple Regression

Let $b_0, b_1, b_2, \ldots, b_k$ be the least squares point estimates of the parameters $\beta_0, \beta_1, \beta_2, \ldots, \beta_k$ in the multiple regression model, and suppose that $x_{01}, x_{02}, \ldots, x_{0k}$ are specified values of the independent variables $x_1, x_2, \ldots, x_k$. If the combination of specified values is inside the experimental region, then

$$\hat{y} = b_0 + b_1 x_{01} + b_2 x_{02} + \cdots + b_k x_{0k}$$

is the **point estimate** of the **mean value of the dependent variable** when the values of the independent variables are $x_{01}, x_{02}, \ldots, x_{0k}$. In addition, $\hat{y}$ is the **point prediction** of an **individual value of the dependent variable** when the values of the independent variables are $x_{01}, x_{02}, \ldots, x_{0k}$. Again, you will notice that the error term is not included in the estimated multiple regression model due to the fact that the expected value of the error term is 0.

Example 12.3 The Sales Territory Performance Case

Figure 12.8 presents the MegaStat output of a regression analysis of the data in Table 12.2 using the model

$$y = \beta_0 + \beta_1 x_1 + \beta_2 x_2 + \beta_3 x_3 + \beta_4 x_4 + \beta_5 x_5 + \varepsilon.$$

On this output, x_1, x_2, x_3, x_4, and x_5 are denoted as Time, MktPoten, Adver, MktShare, and Change, respectively. The MegaStat output tells us that the least squares point estimates of the

FIGURE 12.8 **MegaStat Output of the Sales Territory Performance Data Using the Model $y = \beta_0 + \beta_1 x_1 + \beta_2 x_2 + \beta_3 x_3 + \beta_4 x_4 + \beta_5 x_5 + \varepsilon$**

Regression Analysis	R^2 0.915						
	Adjusted R^2 0.893 [7]	[6]		n 25		= significant at 0.05 level	
	R 0.957			k 5		= significant at 0.01 level	
	Std. Error 430.232 [8]			Dep. Var. **Sales**			

ANOVA table

Source	SS	df	MS	F	p-value
Regression	37,862,658.9002 [1]	5	7,572,531.7800	40.91 [4]	1.59E-09 [5]
Residual	3,516,890.0266 [2]	19	185,099.4751		
Total	41,379,548.9269 [3]	24			

Regression output

variables	coefficients [9]	std. error [10]	t(df=19) [11]	p-value [12]	confidence interval [17] 95% lower	95% upper
Intercept	-1,113.7879	419.8869	-2.653	0.0157	-1,992.6213	-234.9545
Time	3.6121	1.1817	3.057	0.0065	1.1388	6.0854
MktPoten	0.0421	0.0067	6.253	5.27E-06	0.0280	0.0562
Adver	0.1289	0.0370	3.479	0.0025	0.0513	0.2064
MktShare	256.9555	39.1361	6.566	2.76E-06	175.0428	338.8683
Change	324.5334	157.2831	2.063	0.0530	-4.6638	653.7307

Predicted values for: Sales

Predicted [13]	95% Confidence Interval [14] lower	upper	95% Prediction Interval [15] lower	upper	Leverage [16]
4,181.74333	3,884.90651	4,478.58015	3,233.59431	5,129.89235	0.109

[1] Explained variation	[2] SSE = unexplained variation	[3] Total variation	[4] F(model)	[5] p value for F(model)
[6] R^2	[7] Adjusted R^2	[8] s = standard error	[9] b_j = least squares estimate of β_j	[10] s_{b_j} = standard error of the estimate b_j
[11] t statistics for testing significance of independent variables		[12] p values for t statistics	[13] $\hat{y}$ = point prediction	
[14] 95% confidence interval	[15] 95% prediction interval	[16] distance value	[17] 95% confidence interval for β_j	

model parameters are $b_0 = -1,113.7879$, $b_1 = 3.6121$, $b_2 = 0.0421$, $b_3 = 0.1289$, $b_4 = 256.9555$, and $b_5 = 324.5334$. These estimates give the least squares prediction equation

$$\hat{y} = -1,113.7879 + 3.6121x_1 + 0.0421x_2 + 0.1289x_3 + 256.9555x_4 + 324.5334x_5.$$

Recalling that the sales values in Table 12.2 are measured in hundreds of units of the product sold, the point estimate $b_3 = 0.1289$ says we estimate that mean sales increase by 0.1289 hundreds of units—that is, by 12.89 units—for each dollar increase in advertising expenditure when the other four independent variables do not change. If the company sells each unit for $1.10, this implies that we estimate that mean sales revenue increases by ($1.10)(12.89) = $14.18 for each dollar increase in advertising expenditure when the other four independent variables do not change. The other β values in the model can be interpreted similarly.

    Consider a questionable sales representative for whom Time = 85.42, MktPoten = 35,182.73, Adver = 7,281.65, MktShare = 9.64, and Change = 0.28. The point prediction of the sales corresponding to this combination of values of the independent variables is

$$\hat{y} = -1,113.7879 + 3.6121(85.42) + 0.0421(35,182.73)$$
$$+ 0.1289(7,281.65) + 256.9555(9.64) + 324.5334(0.28)$$
$$= 4,181.74 \text{ (that is, 418,174 units),}$$

which is given on the MegaStat output. The actual sales for the questionable sales representative were 3,087.52. This sales figure is 1,094.22 less than the point prediction $\hat{y} = 4,181.74$. Later, when we study prediction intervals in multiple regression (see Section 12.6), we will be able to determine whether there is strong evidence that this sales figure is unusually low.

Exercises for Section 12.2

CONCEPTS

12.9   In the multiple regression model, what sum of squared deviations do the least squares point estimates minimize?

12.10   When using the multiple regression model, how do we obtain a point estimate of the mean value of the dependent variable and a point prediction of an individual value of the dependent variable?

METHODS AND APPLICATIONS

12.11 **THE REAL ESTATE SALES PRICE CASE**
     🔵 RealEst2

Figures 12.9 and 12.10 give the MINITAB and Excel output of a regression analysis of the real estate sales price data in Table 12.3 (page 418) using the model

$$y = \beta_0 + \beta_1 x_1 + \beta_2 x_2 + \varepsilon.$$

FIGURE 12.9   **MINITAB Output of a Regression Analysis of the Real Estate Sales Price Data Using the Model $y = \beta_0 + \beta_1 x_1 + \beta_2 x_2 + \varepsilon$**

```
The regression equation is
SalesPrice = 29.3 + 5.61 HomeSize + 3.83 Rating

Predictor     Coef   SE Coef      T      P
Constant    29.347     4.891    6.00  0.001
HomeSize    5.6128    0.2285   24.56  0.000
Rating      3.8344    0.4332    8.85  0.000

S = 3.24164   R-Sq = 99.0%   R-Sq(adj) = 98.7%

Analysis of Variance
Source          DF       SS      MS       F      P
Regression       2   7374.0  3687.0  350.87  0.000
Residual Error   7     73.6    10.5
Total            9   7447.5

Values of Predictors for New Obs    Predicted Values for New Observations
New Obs  HomeSize  Rating          New Obs    Fit   SE Fit       95% CI             95% PI
      1      20.0    8.00                1  172.28     1.57  (168.56, 175.99)  (163.76, 180.80)
```

FIGURE 12.10   Excel Output of a Regression Analysis of the Real Estate Sales Price Data Using the Model $y = \beta_0 + \beta_1 x_1 + \beta_2 x_2 + \varepsilon$

Regression Statistics

Multiple R	0.9950
R Square	0.9901
Adjusted R Square	0.9873
Standard Error	3.2416
Observations	10

ANOVA	df	SS	MS	F	Significance F
Regression	2	7,373.9516	3,686.9758	350.8665	9.58E-08
Residual	7	73.5574	10.5082		
Total	9	7,447.5090			

	Coefficients	Standard Error	t Stat	P-value	Lower 95%	Upper 95%
Intercept	29.3468	4.8914	5.9996	0.0005	17.7804	40.9132
Home Size (x1)	5.6128	0.2285	24.5615	4.73E-08	5.0724	6.1532
Rating (x2)	3.8344	0.4332	8.8514	4.75E-05	2.8101	4.8588

a. Using the MINITAB or Excel output, find (on the output) and report the values of b_0, b_1, and b_2, the least squares point estimates of β_0, β_1, and β_2. Interpret b_0, b_1, and b_2.

b. Calculate a point estimate of the mean sales price of all houses with 2,000 square feet (about 180 m²) and a rating of 8, and a point prediction of the sales price of an individual house with 2,000 square feet and a rating of 8. Find this point estimate (prediction), which is given at the bottom of the MINITAB output.

12.12 THE FRESH DETERGENT CASE ◆ Fresh2

Figure 12.11 gives the MegaStat output of a regression analysis of the Fresh detergent demand data in

Table 12.4 (page 419) using the model

$$y = \beta_0 + \beta_1 x_1 + \beta_2 x_2 + \beta_3 x_3 + \varepsilon.$$

a. Find (on the output) and report the values of b_0, b_1, b_2, and b_3, the least squares point estimates of β_0, β_1, β_2, and β_3. Interpret b_0, b_1, b_2, and b_3.

b. Consider the demand for Fresh detergent in a future sales period when Enterprise Industries' price for Fresh will be $x_1 = 3.70$, the average price of competitors' similar detergents will be $x_2 = 3.90$, and Enterprise Industries' advertising expenditure for Fresh will be $x_3 = 6.50$. The point prediction of this demand is given at the bottom of the MegaStat output.

FIGURE 12.11   MegaStat Output of a Regression Analysis of the Fresh Detergent Demand Data Using the Model $y = \beta_0 + \beta_1 x_1 + \beta_2 x_2 + \beta_3 x_3 + \varepsilon$

Regression Analysis

R²	0.894		
Adjusted R²	0.881	n	30
R	0.945	k	3
Std. Error	0.235	Dep. Var.	Demand (y)

ANOVA table

Source	SS	df	MS	F	p-value
Regression	12.0268	3	4.0089	72.80	8.88E-13
Residual	1.4318	26	0.0551		
Total	13.4586	29			

Regression output

variables	coefficients	std. error	t (df = 26)	p-value	95% lower	95% upper
Intercept	7.5891	2.4450	3.104	0.0046	2.5633	12.6149
Price (x1)	-2.3577	0.6379	-3.696	0.0010	-3.6690	-1.0464
IndPrice (x2)	1.6122	0.2954	5.459	1.01E-05	1.0051	2.2193
AdvExp (x3)	0.5012	0.1259	3.981	0.0005	0.2424	0.7599

Predicted values for: Demand (y)

Price (x1)	IndPrice (x2)	AdvExp (x3)	Predicted	95% Confidence Interval lower	upper	95% Prediction Interval lower	upper	Leverage
3.7	3.9	6.5	8.4107	8.3143	8.5070	7.9188	8.9025	0.040

FIGURE 12.12   Excel and MegaStat Output of a Regression Analysis of the Hospital Labour Needs Data Using the Model $y = \beta_0 + \beta_1 x_1 + \beta_2 x_2 + \beta_3 x_3 + \varepsilon$

(a) The Excel output

Regression Statistics

Multiple R	0.9981
R Square	0.9961
Adjusted R Square	0.9952
Standard Error	387.1598
Observations	16

ANOVA

	df	SS	MS	F	Significance F
Regression	3	462,327,889.4	154,109,296.5	1,028.1309	9.92E-15
Residual	12	1,798,712.2	149,892.7		
Total	15	464,126,601.6			

	Coefficients	Standard Error	t Stat	P-value	Lower 95%	Upper 95%
Intercept	1,946.8020	504.1819	3.8613	0.0023	848.2840	3,045.3201
XRay (x1)	0.0386	0.0130	2.9579	0.0120	0.0102	0.0670
BedDays (x2)	1.0394	0.0676	15.3857	2.91E-09	0.8922	1.1866
LengthStay (x3)	-413.7578	98.5983	-4.1964	0.0012	-628.5850	-198.9306

(b) Prediction using MegaStat

Predicted values for: LabourHours

				95% Confidence Interval		95% Prediction Interval		
XRay (x1)	BedDays (x2)	LengthStay (x3)	Predicted	lower	upper	lower	upper	Leverage
56,194	14,077.88	6.89	15,896.2473	15,378.0313	16,414.4632	14,906.2361	16,886.2584	0.3774

Report this point prediction and show how it was calculated.

c. Using the price for Fresh ($3.70), make a point prediction of the sales revenue from Fresh in the future sales period.

12.13   THE HOSPITAL LABOUR NEEDS CASE
● HospLab

Figure 12.12 gives the Excel and MegaStat output of a regression analysis of the hospital labour needs data in Table 12.5 (page 419) using the model

$$y = \beta_0 + \beta_1 x_1 + \beta_2 x_2 + \beta_3 x_3 + \varepsilon.$$

Note that the variables x_1, x_2, and x_3 are denoted as XRay, BedDays, and LengthStay on the output.

a. Find (on the output) and interpret b_0, b_1, b_2, and b_3, the least squares point estimates of β_0, β_1, β_2, and β_3.

b. Consider a questionable hospital for which XRay = 56,194, BedDays = 14,077.88, and

LengthStay = 6.89. A point prediction of the labour hours corresponding to this combination of values of the independent variables is given on the MegaStat output. Report this point prediction and show how it was calculated.

c. If the actual number of labour hours used by the questionable hospital was $y = 17,207.31$, how does this y value compare with the point prediction?

12.3 Model Assumptions and the Standard Error

Model assumptions   In order to perform hypothesis tests and set up various types of intervals when using the multiple regression model

$$y = \beta_0 + \beta_1 x_1 + \beta_2 x_2 + \cdots + \beta_k x_k + \varepsilon,$$

we need to make certain assumptions about the error term ε. At any given combination of values of $x_1, x_2, \ldots, x_k$, there is a population of error term values that could potentially occur. These error term values describe the different potential effects on y of all factors other than the combination of values of $x_1, x_2, \ldots, x_k$. Therefore, these error term values explain the variation in the

y values that could be observed at the combination of values of $x_1, x_2, \ldots, x_k$. We make the following four assumptions about the potential error term values:

Assumptions for the Multiple Regression Model

1 At any given combination of values of x_1, $x_2, \ldots, x_k$, the population of potential error term values has a mean equal to 0.

2 **Constant variance assumption:** At any given combination of values of $x_1, x_2, \ldots, x_k$, the population of potential error term values has a variance that does not depend on the combination of values of $x_1, x_2, \ldots, x_k$. That is, the different populations of potential error term values corresponding to different combinations of values of $x_1, x_2, \ldots, x_k$ have equal variances. We denote the constant variance as σ^2.

3 **Normality assumption:** At any given combination of values of $x_1, x_2, \ldots, x_k$, the population of potential error term values has a **normal distribution**.

4 **Independence assumption:** Any one value of the error term ε is **statistically independent** of any other value of ε. That is, the value of the error term ε corresponding to an observed value of y is statistically independent of the error term corresponding to any other observed value of y.

Taken together, the first three assumptions say that, at any given combination of values of x_1, $x_2, \ldots, x_k$, the population of potential error term values is normally distributed with mean 0 and a variance σ^2 that does not depend on the combination of values of $x_1, x_2, \ldots, x_k$. Because the potential error term values cause the variation in the potential y values, the first three assumptions imply that, at any given combination of values of $x_1, x_2, \ldots, x_k$, the population of y values that could be observed is normally distributed with mean $\beta_0 + \beta_1 x_1 + \beta_2 x_2 + \cdots + \beta_k x_k$ and a variance σ^2 that does not depend on the combination of values of $x_1, x_2, \ldots, x_k$. Furthermore, the independence assumption says that, when time series data are utilized in a regression study, there are no patterns in the error term values. In Section 12.13, we show how to check the validity of the regression assumptions. As in simple linear regression, only pronounced departures from the assumptions must be remedied.

The mean square error and the standard error   To present statistical inference formulas in later sections, we need to be able to compute point estimates of σ^2 and σ (the constant variance and standard deviation of the different error term populations). We show how to do this in the following box:

The Mean Square Error and the Standard Error

Suppose that the multiple regression model

$$y = \beta_0 + \beta_1 x_1 + \beta_2 x_2 + \cdots + \beta_k x_k + \varepsilon$$

utilizes k independent variables and thus has $(k + 1)$ parameters $\beta_0, \beta_1, \beta_2, \ldots, \beta_k$. Then, if the regression assumptions are satisfied, and if the SSE is the sum of squared residuals for the model:

1 A point estimate of σ^2 is the **mean square error**

$$s^2 = \frac{SSE}{n - (k + 1)}.$$

2 A point estimate of σ is the **standard error**

$$s = \sqrt{\frac{SSE}{n - (k + 1)}}.$$

In order to explain these point estimates, recall that σ^2 is the variance of the population of y values (for given values of $x_1, x_2, \ldots, x_k$) around the mean value $\mu_{y|x_1, x_2, \ldots, x_k}$. Since $\hat{y}$ is the point estimate of this mean, it seems natural to use $SSE = \Sigma(y_i - \hat{y}_i)^2$ to help construct a point estimate of σ^2. We divide the SSE by $n - (k + 1)$ because it can be proven that doing so makes the resulting s^2 an unbiased point estimate of σ^2. We call $n - (k + 1)$ the **number of degrees of freedom** associated with the SSE.

We will see in Section 12.7 that if a particular regression model gives a small standard error, then the model will give short prediction intervals and thus accurate predictions of individual y values. For example, Table 12.6 (page 422) shows that the SSE for the model in Table 12.1,

$$y = \beta_0 + \beta_1 x_1 + \beta_2 x_2 + \varepsilon,$$

is 0.674. Since this model utilizes $k = 2$ independent variables and thus has $k + 1 = 3$ parameters (β_0, β_1, and β_2), a point estimate of σ^2 is the mean square error

$$s^2 = \frac{SSE}{n - (k + 1)} = \frac{0.674}{8 - 3} = \frac{0.674}{5} = 0.1348,$$

and a point estimate of σ is the standard error $s = \sqrt{0.1348} = 0.3671$. Note that $SSE = 0.674$, $s^2 = 0.1348 \approx 0.135$, and $s = 0.3671$ are given on the MINITAB and Excel outputs in Figure 12.5 (page 421). Also note that the s of 0.3671 for the two independent variable model is less than the s of 0.6542 for the simple linear regression model that uses only the average x_1 value to predict y (see Example 11.6, pages 391 to 393).

As another example, the SSE for the sales territory performance model

$$y = \beta_0 + \beta_1 x_1 + \beta_2 x_2 + \beta_3 x_3 + \beta_4 x_4 + \beta_5 x_5 + \varepsilon$$

is 3,516,890.0266. Since this model utilizes $k = 5$ independent variables and thus has $k + 1 = 6$ parameters, a point estimate of σ^2 is the mean square error

$$s^2 = \frac{SSE}{n - (k + 1)} = \frac{3,516,890.0266}{25 - 6} = 185,099.4751,$$

and a point estimate of σ is the standard error $s = \sqrt{185,099.4751} = 430.2319$. Note that these values of the SSE, s^2, and s are given on the MegaStat output in Figure 12.8 (page 423).

12.4 R^2 and Adjusted R^2

The multiple coefficient of determination, R^2   In this section, we discuss several ways to assess the utility of a multiple regression model. We first discuss a quantity called the **multiple coefficient of determination**, which is denoted R^2. The formulas for R^2 and several other related quantities are given in the following box:

The Multiple Coefficient of Determination, R^2

For the multiple regression model:

1 **Total variation** $= \sum (y_i - \bar{y})^2$.

2 **Explained variation** $= \sum (\hat{y}_i - \bar{y})^2$.

3 **Unexplained variation** $= \sum (y_i - \hat{y}_i)^2$.

4 **Total variation = Explained variation + Unexplained variation.**

5 The **multiple coefficient of determination** is

$$R^2 = \frac{\text{Explained variation}}{\text{Total variation}}.$$

6 R^2 is the proportion of the total variation in the n observed values of the dependent variable that is explained by the overall regression model.

7 **Multiple correlation coefficient** $= R = \sqrt{R^2}$.

For example, consider the model

$$y = \beta_0 + \beta_1 x_1 + \beta_2 x_2 + \varepsilon$$

and the following MINITAB output from the data in Table 12.1:

```
S = 0.367078    R-Sq = 97.4%    R-Sq(adj) = 96.3%


Analysis of Variance
Source            DF      SS       MS      F       P
Regression         2    24.875   12.438  92.30   0.000
Residual Error     5     0.674    0.135
Total              7    25.549
```

This output tells us that the total variation (SS Total), explained variation (SS Regression), and unexplained variation (SS Residual Error) for the model are, respectively, 25.549, 24.875, and 0.674. The output also tells us that the multiple coefficient of determination is

$$R^2 = \frac{\text{Explained variation}}{\text{Total variation}} = \frac{24.875}{25.549} = 0.974 \ (97.4\% \text{ on the output}),$$

which implies that the multiple correlation coefficient is $R = \sqrt{0.974} = 0.9869$. The value of $R^2 = 0.974$ says that the two independent variable model explains 97.4 percent of the total variation in the eight observed y values. The quantities given on the MINITAB output are also given on the following Excel output.

Regression Statistics

Multiple R	0.9867
R Square	0.9736
Adjusted R Square	0.9631
Standard Error	0.3671
Observations	8

ANOVA	df	SS	MS	F	Significance F
Regression	2	24.8750	12.4375	92.3031	0.0001
Residual	5	0.6737	0.1347		
Total	7	25.5488			

As another example, consider the sales territory performance model

$$y = \beta_0 + \beta_1 x_1 + \beta_2 x_2 + \beta_3 x_3 + \beta_4 x_4 + \beta_5 x_5 + \varepsilon$$

and the following MegaStat output:

Regression Analysis

	R^2	0.915	n	25
Adjusted	R^2	0.893	k	5
	R	0.957	Dep. Var.	Sales
Std. Error		430.232		

ANOVA table

Source	SS	df	MS	F	p-value
Regression	37,862,658.9002	5	7,572,531.7800	40.91	1.59E-09
Residual	3,516,890.0266	19	185,099.4751		
Total	41,379,548.9269	24			

This output tells us that the total, explained, and unexplained variations for the model are, respectively, 41,379,548.9269, 37,862,658.9002, and 3,516,890.0266. The MegaStat output also tells us that R^2 equals 0.915.

Adjusted R^2   Even if the independent variables in a regression model are unrelated to the dependent variable, they will make R^2 somewhat greater than 0. To avoid overestimating the importance of the independent variables, many analysts recommend calculating an **adjusted** multiple coefficient of determination.

Adjusted R^2

The **adjusted multiple coefficient of determination (adjusted R^2)** is

$$\bar{R}^2 = \left(R^2 - \frac{k}{n-1}\right)\left(\frac{n-1}{n-(k+1)}\right),$$

where R^2 is the multiple coefficient of determination, n is the number of observations, and k is the number of independent variables in the model under consideration.

To understand this formula, note that it can be shown that subtracting $k/(n-1)$ from R^2 helps avoid overestimating the importance of the k independent variables. Furthermore, multiplying $[R^2 - (k/(n-1))]$ by $(n-1)/(n-(k+1))$ makes $\overline{R}^2$ equal to 1 when R^2 equals 1.

As an example, consider the model of Table 12.1:

$$y = \beta_0 + \beta_1 x_1 + \beta_2 x_2 + \varepsilon.$$

Since we have seen that $R^2 = 0.974$, it follows that

$$\overline{R}^2 = \left(R^2 - \frac{k}{n-1}\right)\left(\frac{n-1}{n-(k+1)}\right)$$

$$= \left(0.974 - \frac{2}{8-1}\right)\left(\frac{8-1}{8-(2+1)}\right)$$

$$= 0.963,$$

which is given on the MINITAB and Excel outputs. Similarly, in addition to telling us that $R^2 = 0.915$ for the five independent variable sales territory performance model, the MegaStat output tells us that $\overline{R}^2 = 0.893$ for this model.

If R^2 is less than $k/(n-1)$ (which can happen), then $\overline{R}^2$ will be negative. In this case, statistical software systems set $\overline{R}^2$ equal to 0. Historically, R^2 and $\overline{R}^2$ have been popular measures of model utility—possibly because they are unitless and between 0 and 1. In general, we want R^2 and $\overline{R}^2$ to be near 1. However, sometimes even if a regression model has an R^2 and an $\overline{R}^2$ that are near 1, the model may still not be able to predict accurately. We will discuss assessing a model's ability to predict accurately, as well as using R^2 and $\overline{R}^2$ to help choose a regression model, as we proceed through this chapter.

12.5 The Overall F Test

Another way to assess the utility of a regression model is to test the significance of the regression relationship between y and $x_1, x_2, \ldots, x_k$. For the multiple regression model, we test the null hypothesis $H_0: \beta_1 = \beta_2 = \cdots = \beta_k = 0$, which says that **none of the independent variables $x_1, x_2, \ldots, x_k$ is significantly related to y (the regression relationship is not significant)**, versus the alternative hypothesis H_a: at least one of $\beta_1, \beta_2, \ldots, \beta_k$ does not equal 0, which says that **at least one of the independent variables is significantly related to y (the regression relationship is significant)**. If we can reject H_0 at level of significance α, we say that **the multiple regression model is significant at level of significance α**. We carry out the test as follows:

An F Test for the Multiple Regression Model

Suppose that the regression assumptions hold and that the multiple regression model has $(k+1)$ parameters, and consider testing

$$H_0: \beta_1 = \beta_2 = \cdots = \beta_k = 0$$

versus

H_a: at least one of $\beta_1, \beta_2, \ldots, \beta_k$ does not equal 0.

We define the **overall F statistic** to be

$$F(\text{model}) = \frac{(\text{Explained variation})/k}{(\text{Unexplained variation})/[n-(k+1)]}.$$

Also define the p value related to $F(\text{model})$ to be the area under the curve of the F distribution (with k and $[n-(k+1)]$ degrees of freedom) to the right of $F(\text{model})$. Then, we can reject H_0 in favour of H_a at level of significance α if either of the following equivalent conditions holds:

1 $F(\text{model}) > F_\alpha$.

2 p value $< \alpha$.

Here the point F_α is based on k numerator and $n-(k+1)$ denominator degrees of freedom.

Condition 1 is intuitively reasonable because a large value of $F(\text{model})$ would be caused by an explained variation that is large relative to the unexplained variation. This would occur if at least one independent variable in the regression model significantly affects y, which would imply that H_0 is false and H_a is true. For example, consider the model

$$y = \beta_0 + \beta_1 x_1 + \beta_2 x_2 + \varepsilon$$

from Table 12.1 and the following MINITAB output:

```
Analysis of Variance
Source            DF      SS       MS       F       P
Regression         2   24.875   12.438   92.30   0.000
Residual Error     5    0.674    0.135
Total              7   25.549
```

This output tells us that the explained and unexplained variations for this model are, respectively, 24.875 and 0.674. It follows, since there are $k = 2$ independent variables, that

$$
\begin{aligned}
F(\text{model}) &= \frac{(\text{Explained variation})/k}{(\text{Unexplained variation})/[n - (k + 1)]} \\
&= \frac{24.875/2}{0.674/[8 - (2 + 1)]} = \frac{12.438}{0.135} \\
&= 92.30.
\end{aligned}
$$

Note that this overall F statistic is given on the MINITAB output and is also given on the following Excel output:

ANOVA	df	SS	MS	F	Significance F
Regression	2	24.8750	12.4375	92.3031	0.0001
Residual	5	0.6737	0.1347		
Total	7	25.5488			

The p value related to $F(\text{model})$ is the area to the right of 92.30 under the curve of the F distribution with $k = 2$ numerator and $n - (k + 1) = 8 - 3 = 5$ denominator degrees of freedom. Both the MINITAB and the Excel output say this p value is less than 0.001.

If we wish to test the significance of the regression model at level of significance $\alpha = 0.05$, we use the rejection point $F_{0.05}$ based on 2 numerator and 5 denominator degrees of freedom. Using Table A.6, we find that $F_{0.05} = 5.79$. Since $F(\text{model}) = 92.30 > F_{0.05} = 5.79$, we can reject H_0 in favour of H_a at level of significance 0.05. Alternatively, since the p value is smaller than 0.001, we can reject H_0 at level of significance 0.001. Therefore, we have extremely strong evidence that the model is significant. That is, we have extremely strong evidence that at least one of the independent variables x_1 and x_2 in the model is significantly related to y.

Similarly, consider the following MegaStat output:

ANOVA table					
Source	SS	df	MS	F	p-value
Regression	37,862,658.9002	5	7,572,531.7800	40.91	1.59E-09
Residual	3,516,890.0266	19	185,099.4751		
Total	41,379,548.9269	24			

This output tells us that $F(\text{model}) = 40.91$ for the five independent variable sales territory performance model. Furthermore, since the MegaStat output also tells us that the p value related to $F(\text{model})$ is less than 0.001, we have extremely strong evidence that at least one of the five independent variables in this model is significantly related to sales territory performance.

If the overall F test tells us that at least one independent variable in a regression model is significant, we next attempt to decide which independent variables are significant. In the next section, we discuss one way to do this.

Exercises for Sections 12.3, 12.4, and 12.5

FIGURE 12.13   Output for Exercises 12.17, 12.18, and 12.19

(a) MINITAB output for Exercise 12.17

S = 3.24164   R-Sq = 99.0%   R-Sq(adj) = 98.7%

Analysis of Variance

Source	DF	SS	MS	F	P
Regression	2	7374.0	3687.0	350.87	0.000
Residual Error	7	73.6	10.5		
Total	9	7447.5			

(b) MegaStat output for Exercise 12.18

Regression Analysis

R^2	0.894			
Adjusted R^2	0.881		n	30
R	0.945		k	3
Std. Error	0.235		Dep. Var.	**Demand (y)**

ANOVA table

Source	SS	df	MS	F	p-value
Regression	12.0268	3	4.0089	72.80	8.88E-13
Residual	1.4318	26	0.0551		
Total	13.4586	29			

(c) Excel output for Exercise 12.19

Regression Statistics

Multiple R	0.9981
R Square	0.9961
Adjusted R Square	0.9952
Standard Error	387.1598
Observations	16

ANOVA	df	SS	MS	F	Significance F
Regression	3	462,327,889.4	154,109,296.5	1,028.1309	9.92E-15
Residual	12	1,798,712.2	149,892.7		
Total	15	464,126,601.6			

CONCEPTS

12.14 What is estimated by the mean square error, and what is estimated by the standard error?

12.15 **a.** What do R^2 and $\bar{R}^2$ measure?
  b. How do R^2 and $\bar{R}^2$ differ?

12.16 What is the purpose of the overall F test?

METHODS AND APPLICATIONS

In Exercises 12.17 to 12.19, we give MINITAB, MegaStat, and Excel outputs of regression analyses of the data sets related to three case studies introduced in Section 12.1. The outputs are shown in Figure 12.13. In each exercise, we give the regression model and the number of observations, n, used to perform the regression analysis under consideration. Using the appropriate model, sample size n, and output:

  a. Report the SSE, s^2, and s as shown on the output. Calculate s^2 from the SSE and other numbers.

  b. Report the total variation, unexplained variation, and explained variation as shown on the output.

  c. Report R^2 and $\bar{R}^2$ as shown on the output. Interpret R^2 and $\bar{R}^2$. Show how $\bar{R}^2$ has been calculated from R^2 and other numbers.

d. Calculate the F(model) statistic by using the explained variation, the unexplained variation, and other relevant quantities. Find F(model) on the output to check your answer.

e. Use the F(model) statistic and the appropriate rejection point to test the significance of the linear regression model under consideration by setting α equal to 0.05.

f. Use the F(model) statistic and the appropriate rejection point to test the significance of the linear regression model under consideration by setting α equal to 0.01.

g. Find the p value related to F(model) on the output. Using the p value, test the significance of the linear regression model by setting $\alpha = 0.10, 0.05, 0.01,$ and 0.001. What do you conclude?

12.17 THE REAL ESTATE SALES PRICE CASE 📀 RealEst2

Model: $y = \beta_0 + \beta_1 x_1 + \beta_2 x_2 + \varepsilon$
Sample size: $n = 10$

12.18 THE FRESH DETERGENT CASE 📀 Fresh2

Model: $y = \beta_0 + \beta_1 x_1 + \beta_2 x_2 + \beta_3 x_3 + \varepsilon$
Sample size: $n = 30$

12.19 THE HOSPITAL LABOUR NEEDS CASE 📀 HospLab

Model: $y = \beta_0 + \beta_1 x_1 + \beta_2 x_2 + \beta_3 x_3 + \varepsilon$
Sample size: $n = 16$

12.6 Testing the Significance of an Independent Variable

Consider the multiple regression model

$$y = \beta_0 + \beta_1 x_1 + \beta_2 x_2 + \cdots + \beta_k x_k + \varepsilon.$$

In order to gain information about which independent variables significantly affect y, we can test the significance of a single independent variable. We arbitrarily refer to this variable as x_j and assume that it is multiplied by the parameter β_j. For example, if $j = 1$, we are testing the significance of x_1, which is multiplied by β_1; if $j = 2$, we are testing the significance of x_2, which is multiplied by β_2. To test the significance of x_j, we test the null hypothesis $H_0: \beta_j = 0$. We usually test H_0 versus the alternative hypothesis $H_a: \beta_j \neq 0$. **It is reasonable to conclude that x_j is significantly related to y in the regression model under consideration if H_0 can be rejected in favour of H_a at a small level of significance.** Here the phrase "in the regression model under consideration" is very important. This is because it can be shown that whether x_j is significantly related to y in a particular regression model can depend on what other independent variables are included in the model. This issue will be discussed in detail in Section 12.12.

Testing the significance of x_j in a multiple regression model is similar to testing the significance of the slope in the simple linear regression model (recall we test $H_0: \beta_1 = 0$ in simple regression). It can be proven that, if the regression assumptions hold, the population of all possible values of the least squares point estimate b_j is normally distributed with mean β_j and standard deviation σ_{b_j}. The point estimate of σ_{b_j} is called the **standard error of the estimate b_j** and is denoted s_{b_j}. The formula for s_{b_j} involves matrix algebra and is discussed in Appendix F in the Online Learning Centre. In our discussion here, we will rely on MINITAB, MegaStat, and Excel to compute s_{b_j}. It can be shown that, if the regression assumptions hold, the population of all possible values of

$$\frac{b_j - \beta_j}{s_{b_j}}$$

has a t distribution with $n - (k + 1)$ degrees of freedom. It follows that, if the null hypothesis $H_0: \beta_j = 0$ is true, the population of all possible values of the test statistic

$$t = \frac{b_j}{s_{b_j}}$$

has a t distribution with $n - (k + 1)$ degrees of freedom. Therefore, we can test the significance of x_j as follows:

Testing the Significance of the Independent Variable x_j

Define the test statistic

$$t = \frac{b_j}{s_{b_j}}$$

and suppose that the regression assumptions hold.

Then, we can test $H_0: \beta_j = 0$ versus a particular alternative hypothesis at significance level α by using the appropriate rejection point rule or, equivalently, the corresponding p value.

Alternative Hypothesis	Rejection Point Rule: Reject H_0 if	p Value (Reject H_0 if p Value $< \alpha$)
$H_a: \beta_j \neq 0$	$|t| > t_{\alpha/2}$	Twice the area under the t curve to the right of $|t|$
$H_a: \beta_j > 0$	$t > t_\alpha$	The area under the t curve to the right of t
$H_a: \beta_j < 0$	$t < -t_\alpha$	The area under the t curve to the left of t

Here $t_{\alpha/2}$, t_α, and all p values are based on $n - (k + 1)$ degrees of freedom.

As in testing $H_0: \beta_1 = 0$ in simple linear regression, we usually use the two-sided alternative hypothesis $H_a: \beta_j \neq 0$ unless we have theoretical reasons to believe that β_j has a particular (plus or minus) sign (referred to as a one-tailed prediction). Moreover, MINITAB, MegaStat, and Excel present the results for the two-sided test.

It is customary to test the significance of each and every independent variable in a regression model. Generally speaking,

1 If we can reject $H_0: \beta_j = 0$ at the 0.05 level of significance, we have strong evidence that the independent variable x_j is significantly related to y in the regression model.

2 If we can reject $H_0: \beta_j = 0$ at the 0.01 level of significance, we have very strong evidence that x_j is significantly related to y in the regression model.

3 The smaller the significance level α at which H_0 can be rejected, the stronger is the evidence that x_j is significantly related to y in the regression model.

Example 12.4   The Sales Territory Performance Case

Consider the sales territory performance model

$$y = \beta_0 + \beta_1 x_1 + \beta_2 x_2 + \beta_3 x_3 + \beta_4 x_4 + \beta_5 x_5 + \varepsilon.$$

Because the MegaStat output in Figure 12.14 tells us that the p values associated with Time, MktPoten, Adver, and MktShare are all less than 0.01, we have very strong evidence that these variables are significantly related to y and, thus, are important in this model. Since the p value associated with Change is 0.0530, we have close to strong evidence that this variable is also important.

FIGURE 12.14   MegaStat Output of t Statistics and p Values for the Sales Territory Performance Model

Regression output					confidence interval	
variables	coefficients	std. error	t (df=19)	p-value	95% lower	95% upper
Intercept	−1,113.7879	419.8869	−2.653	0.0157	−1,992.6213	−234.9545
Time	3.6121	1.1817	3.057	0.0065	1.1388	6.0854
MktPoten	0.0421	0.0067	6.253	5.27E-06	0.0280	0.0562
Adver	0.1289	0.0370	3.479	0.0025	0.0513	0.2064
MktShare	256.9555	39.1361	6.566	2.76E-06	175.0428	338.8683
Change	324.5334	157.2831	2.063	0.0530	−4.6638	653.7307

The following box demonstrates how to calculate a confidence interval for a regression parameter. In Section 12.7, confidence and prediction intervals are discussed.

A Confidence Interval for the Regression Parameter β_j

If the regression assumptions hold, a $100(1 - \alpha)$ percent confidence interval for β_j is

$$[b_j \pm t_{\alpha/2}s_{b_j}].$$

Here $t_{\alpha/2}$ is based on $n - (k + 1)$ degrees of freedom.

Exercises for Section 12.6

CONCEPTS

12.20 What do we conclude about x_j if we can reject $H_0: \beta_j = 0$ in favour of $H_a: \beta_j \neq 0$ by setting
  a. α equal to 0.05?
  b. α equal to 0.01?

12.21 Give an example of a practical application of the confidence interval for β_j.

METHODS AND APPLICATIONS

In Exercises 12.22 through 12.24, we refer to MINITAB, MegaStat, and Excel outputs of regression analyses of the data sets related to three case studies introduced in Section 12.1. The outputs are given in Figure 12.15. Using the appropriate output, do the following for **each parameter** β_j in the model under consideration:

  a. Find b_j, s_{b_j}, and the t statistic for testing $H_0: \beta_j = 0$ on the output, and report their values. Show how t was calculated by using b_j and s_{b_j}.
  b. Using the t statistic and appropriate rejection points, test $H_0: \beta_j = 0$ versus $H_a: \beta_j \neq 0$ by setting α equal to 0.05.

Which independent variables are significantly related to y in the model with $\alpha = 0.05$?
  c. Using the t statistic and appropriate rejection points, test $H_0: \beta_j = 0$ versus $H_a: \beta_j \neq 0$ by setting α equal to 0.01. Which independent variables are significantly related to y in the model with $\alpha = 0.01$?
  d. Find the p value for testing $H_0: \beta_j = 0$ versus $H_a: \beta_j \neq 0$ on the output. Using the p value, determine whether we can reject H_0 by setting α equal to 0.10, 0.05, 0.01, and 0.001. What do you conclude about the significance of the independent variables in the model?
  e. Calculate the 95 percent confidence interval for β_j. Discuss one practical application of this interval.
  f. Calculate the 99 percent confidence interval for β_j. Discuss one practical application of this interval.

12.22 THE REAL ESTATE SALES PRICE CASE
  ◆ RealEst2

Use the MINITAB output in Figure 12.15(a) to do parts a through f for each of β_0, β_1, and β_2.

FIGURE 12.15 *t* Statistics and *p* Values for Three Case Studies

(a) MINITAB output for the real estate sales price case (sample size: $n = 10$)

Predictor	Coef	SE Coef	T	P
Constant	29.347	4.891	6.00	0.001
Homesize	5.6128	0.2285	24.56	0.000
Rating	3.8344	0.4332	8.85	0.000

(b) MegaStat output for the Fresh detergent case (sample size: $n = 30$)

Regression output

variables	coefficients	std. error	t (df=26)	p-value	confidence interval 95% lower	95% upper
Intercept	7.5891	2.4450	3.104	0.0046	2.5633	12.6149
Price (x1)	−2.3577	0.6379	−3.696	0.0010	−3.6690	−1.0464
IndPrice (x2)	1.6122	0.2954	5.459	1.01E-05	1.0051	2.2193
AdvExp (x3)	0.5012	0.1259	3.981	0.0005	0.2424	0.7599

(c) Excel output for the hospital labour needs case (sample size: $n = 16$)

	Coefficients	Standard Error	t Stat	P-value	Lower 95%	Upper 95%
Intercept	1,946.8020	504.1819	3.8613	0.0023	848.2840	3,045.3201
XRay (x1)	0.0386	0.0130	2.9579	0.0120	0.0102	0.0670
BedDays (x2)	1.0394	0.0676	15.3857	2.91E-09	0.8922	1.1866
LengthStay (x3)	−413.7578	98.5983	−4.1964	0.0012	−628.5850	−198.9306

12.23   THE FRESH DETERGENT CASE

● Fresh2

Use the MegaStat output in Figure 12.15(b) to do parts a through f for each of β_0, β_1, β_2, and β_3.

12.24   THE HOSPITAL LABOUR NEEDS CASE
● HospLab

Use the Excel output in Figure 12.15(c) to do parts a through f for each of β_0, β_1, β_2, and β_3.

12.7 Confidence and Prediction Intervals

In this section, we show how to use the multiple regression model to find a **confidence interval for a mean value of y** and a **prediction interval for an individual value of y**. We first present an example of these intervals, and then we discuss the logic behind and formulas used to compute the intervals.

Example 12.5 The Sales Territory Performance Case

Consider a questionable sales representative for whom TIME = 85.42, MktPoten = 35,182.73, Adver = 7,281.65, MktShare = 9.64, and Change = 0.28. We have seen in Example 12.3 that the point prediction of the sales corresponding to this combination of values of the independent variables is

$$\hat{y} = -1{,}113.7879 + 3.6121(85.42) + 0.0421(35{,}182.73)$$
$$+ \ 0.1289(7{,}281.65) + 256.9555(9.64) + 324.5334(0.28)$$
$$= 4{,}181.74 \text{ (that is, 418,174 units).}$$

This point prediction is given at the bottom of the MegaStat output in Figure 12.8, which we repeat here:

Predicted values for: Sales

| | 95% Confidence Interval | | 95% Prediction Interval | | |
Predicted	lower	upper	lower	upper	Leverage
4,181.74333	3,884.90651	4,478.58015	3,233.59431	5,129.89235	0.109

In addition to giving $\hat{y} = 4{,}181.74$, the MegaStat output tells us that a 95 percent prediction interval for y is [3,233.59, 5,129.89]. Furthermore, the actual sales y for the questionable representative were 3,087.52. This actual sales figure is less than the point prediction $\hat{y} = 4{,}181.74$ and is less than the lower bound of the 95 percent prediction interval for y, [3,233.59, 5,129.89]. Therefore, we conclude that there is strong evidence that the actual performance of the questionable representative is less than predicted performance. We should investigate the reason for this. Perhaps the questionable representative needs special training.

BI

In general,

$$\hat{y} = b_0 + b_1 x_{01} + \cdots + b_k x_{0k}$$

is the **point estimate of the mean value of y** when the values of the independent variables are $x_{01}, x_{02}, \ldots, x_{0k}$. Calling this mean value $\mu_{y|x_{01}, x_{02}, \ldots, x_{0k}}$, it can be proven that, if the regression assumptions hold, the population of all possible values of $\hat{y}$ is normally distributed with mean $\mu_{y|x_{01}, x_{02}, \ldots, x_{0k}}$ and standard deviation

$$\sigma_{\hat{y}} = \sigma \sqrt{\text{Distance value.}}$$

The formula for the distance value involves matrix algebra and is given in Appendix F in the Online Learning Centre. We will soon see how to use MINITAB or MegaStat output to find the distance value. It can be shown that the farther the values $x_{01}, x_{02}, \ldots, x_{0k}$ are from the centre of the experimental region, the larger is the distance value. We regard the centre of the experimental region to be the point $(\bar{x}_1, \bar{x}_2, \ldots, \bar{x}_k)$, where $\bar{x}_1$ is the average of the observed x_1 values, $\bar{x}_2$ is the average of the observed x_2 values, and so forth. Since s is the point estimate of σ, the point estimate of $\sigma_{\hat{y}}$ is

$$s_{\hat{y}} = s\sqrt{\text{Distance value}},$$

which is called the **standard error of the estimate $\hat{y}$**. Using this standard error, we can form a confidence interval:

A Confidence Interval for a Mean Value of y

If the regression assumptions hold, a **100(1 − α) percent confidence interval for the mean value of y** when the values of the independent variables are $x_{01}, x_{02}, \ldots, x_{0k}$ is

$$[\hat{y} \pm t_{\alpha/2}s\sqrt{\text{Distance value}}].$$

Here $t_{\alpha/2}$ is based on $n - (k + 1)$ degrees of freedom.

To develop an interval for an individual value of y, we consider the prediction error $y - \hat{y}$. It can be proven that, if the regression assumptions hold, the population of all possible prediction errors is normally distributed with mean 0 and standard deviation

$$\sigma_{(y-\hat{y})} = \sigma\sqrt{1 + \text{Distance value}}.$$

The point estimate of $\sigma_{(y-\hat{y})}$ is

$$s_{(y-\hat{y})} = s\sqrt{1 + \text{Distance value}},$$

which is called the **standard error of the prediction error**. Using this standard error, we can form a prediction interval:

A Prediction Interval for an Individual Value of y

If the regression assumptions hold, a **100(1 − α) percent prediction interval for an individual value of y** when the values of the independent variables are $x_{01}, x_{02}, \ldots, x_{0k}$ is

$$[\hat{y} \pm t_{\alpha/2}s\sqrt{1 + \text{Distance value}}].$$

Here $t_{\alpha/2}$ is based on $n - (k + 1)$ degrees of freedom.

Recall that the farther the values $x_{01}, x_{02}, \ldots, x_{0k}$ are from the centre of the experimental region, the larger is the distance value. It follows that the farther the values $x_{01}, x_{02}, \ldots, x_{0k}$ are from the centre of the experimental region, the longer (less precise) are the confidence intervals and prediction intervals provided by a regression model.

MINITAB gives $s_{\hat{y}} = s\sqrt{\text{Distance value}}$ under the heading "SE Fit." Since the MINITAB output also gives s, the distance value can be found by calculating $(s_{\hat{y}}/s)^2$. For example, the MegaStat output in Example 12.5 tells us that $\hat{y} = 4{,}181.74$. This output also tells us that the distance value, which is given under the heading "Leverage" on the output, equals 0.109. Therefore, since s for the five-variable sales territory performance model equals 430.232, it follows that the 95 percent prediction interval given on the MegaStat output of Example 12.5 was calculated as follows:

$$[\hat{y} \pm t_{0.025}s\sqrt{1 + \text{Distance value}}]$$
$$= [4{,}181.74 \pm 2.093(430.232)\sqrt{1 + 0.109}]$$
$$= [3{,}233.59, 5{,}129.89].$$

Here $t_{0.025} = 2.093$ is based on $n - (k + 1) = 25 - 6 = 19$ degrees of freedom.

Exercises for Section 12.7

CONCEPTS

12.25 What does the distance value measure?

12.26 How do we obtain the distance value from MINITAB output and MegaStat output?

METHODS AND APPLICATIONS

12.27 **THE REAL ESTATE SALES PRICE CASE**

● RealEst2

The MINITAB output in Figure 12.16(a) relates to a house with 2,000 square feet (about 180 m²) and a rating of 8.

a. Report (as shown on the output) a point estimate of and a 95 percent confidence interval for the mean sales price of all houses with 2,000 square feet and a rating of 8.

b. Report (as shown on the output) a point prediction of and a 95 percent prediction interval for the actual sales price of an individual house with 2,000 square feet and a rating of 8.

c. Find 99 percent confidence and prediction intervals for the mean and actual sales prices referred to in parts a and b. Hint: $n = 10$ and $s = 3.24164$.

12.28 **THE FRESH DETERGENT CASE** ● Fresh2

Consider the demand for Fresh detergent in a future sales period when Enterprise Industries' price for Fresh will be $x_1 = 3.70$, the average price of competitors' similar detergents will be $x_2 = 3.90$, and Enterprise Industries' advertising expenditure for Fresh will be $x_3 = 6.50$. A 95 percent prediction interval for this demand is given on the MegaStat output in Figure 12.16(b).

a. Find and report the 95 percent prediction interval on the output. If Enterprise Industries plans to have in inventory the number of bottles implied by the upper limit of this interval, it can be very confident that it will have enough bottles to meet demand for Fresh in the future sales period. How many bottles is this? If we multiply the number of bottles implied by the lower limit of the prediction

interval by the price of Fresh ($3.70), we can be very confident that the resulting dollar amount will be the minimal revenue from Fresh in the future sales period. What is this dollar amount?

b. Calculate a 99 percent prediction interval for the demand for Fresh in the future sales period. Hint: $n = 30$.

c. Recall that the data plots given at the bottom of Table 12.4 (page 419) suggest that the model $y = \beta_0 + \beta_1 x_4 + \beta_2 x_3 + \varepsilon$ might appropriately relate demand for Fresh (y) to the price difference ($x_4 = x_2 - x_1$) and advertising expenditure (x_3). The 95 percent prediction interval given by this model for the demand for Fresh in the future sales period is [7.89034, 8.88523]. Is this interval shorter or longer than the interval of part a? What does this imply about which model might best predict y?

12.29 **THE HOSPITAL LABOUR NEEDS CASE**

● HospLab

Consider a questionable hospital for which XRay = 56,194, BedDays = 14,077.88, and LengthStay = 6.89. A 95 percent prediction interval for the labour hours corresponding to this combination of values of the independent variables is given on the MegaStat output in Figure 12.16(c). Find and report the prediction interval on the output. Then use this interval to determine if the actual number of labour hours used by the questionable hospital ($y = 17,207.31$) is unusually low or high.

FIGURE 12.16   MegaStat and MINITAB Output for Exercises 12.27, 12.28, and 12.29

(a) MINITAB output for Exercise 12.27

New Obs	Fit	SE Fit	95% CI	95% PI
1	172.28	1.57	(168.56, 175.99)	(163.76, 180.80)

(b) MegaStat output for Exercise 12.28

Predicted	95% Confidence Interval lower	upper	95% Prediction Interval lower	upper	Leverage
8.4107	8.3143	8.5070	7.9188	8.9025	0.040

(c) MegaStat output for Exercise 12.29

Predicted	95% Confidence Interval lower	upper	95% Prediction Interval lower	upper	Leverage
15,896.2473	15,378.0313	16,414.4632	14,906.2361	16,886.2584	0.3774

12.8 The Quadratic Regression Model (Optional)

One useful form of the multiple regression model is what we call the **quadratic regression model**. Assuming that we have obtained n observations—each consisting of an observed value of y and a corresponding value of x—the model is as follows:

The Quadratic Regression Model

The **quadratic regression model** relating y to x is

$$y = \beta_0 + \beta_1 x + \beta_2 x^2 + \varepsilon,$$

where

1 $\beta_0 + \beta_1 x + \beta_2 x^2$ is $\mu_{y|x}$, the mean value of the dependent variable y when the value of the independent variable is x.

2 β_0, β_1, and β_2 are (unknown) **regression parameters** relating the mean value of y to x.

3 ε is an error term that describes the effects on y of all factors other than x and x^2.

The quadratic equation $\mu_{y|x} = \beta_0 + \beta_1 x + \beta_2 x^2$ that relates $\mu_{y|x}$ to x is the equation of a **parabola**. Two parabolas are shown in Figure 12.17(a) and (b) and help to interpret the parameters β_0, β_1, and β_2. Here β_0 is the **y intercept** of the parabola (the value of $\mu_{y|x}$ when $x = 0$). Furthermore, β_1 is the **shift parameter** of the parabola: the value of β_1 shifts the parabola to the left or right. Specifically, increasing the value of β_1 shifts the parabola to the left. Lastly, β_2 is the **rate of curvature** of the parabola. If β_2 is greater than 0, the parabola opens upward (see Figure 12.17(a)). If β_2 is less than 0, the parabola opens downward

FIGURE **12.17**   The Mean Value of the Dependent Variable Changing in a Quadratic Fashion as x Increases ($\mu_{y|x} = \beta_0 + \beta_1 x + \beta_2 x^2$)

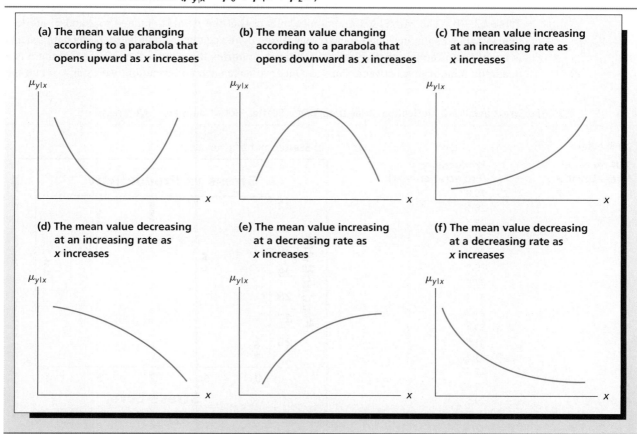

(a) The mean value changing according to a parabola that opens upward as x increases

(b) The mean value changing according to a parabola that opens downward as x increases

(c) The mean value increasing at an increasing rate as x increases

(d) The mean value decreasing at an increasing rate as x increases

(e) The mean value increasing at a decreasing rate as x increases

(f) The mean value decreasing at a decreasing rate as x increases (see Figure 12.17(b)). If a scatter plot of y versus x shows points scattered around a parabola, or a part of a parabola (some typical parts are shown in Figure 12.17(c), (d), (e), and (f)), then the quadratic regression model might appropriately relate y to x.

Example 12.6 The Stress and Work Motivation Case

Stress is typically a difficult psychological variable to measure. Although the word *stress* usually has negative connotations, some stress may actually be motivating in the workplace. Stress researchers have suggested that too little stress and too much stress result in lower work performance, but a moderate amount of stress is motivating and improves work performance (so the pattern/correlation would be nonlinear in nature). To test this hypothesis, the human resources (HR) department administers a stress questionnaire to 15 employees in which people rate their stress level on a 0 (no stress) to 4 (high stress) scale. Work performance was measured as the average number of projects completed by the employee per year, averaged over the last five years (in order to improve the reliability of the measure). Table 12.7(a) gives the results of the test. Here the dependent variable y is productivity (in projects per year) and the independent variable x is the self-reported stress level.

Table 12.7(b) gives a scatter plot of y versus x. Since the scatter plot has the appearance of a quadratic curve (that is, part of a parabola), it seems reasonable to relate y to x by using the quadratic model

$$y = \beta_0 + \beta_1 x + \beta_2 x^2 + \varepsilon.$$

Figure 12.18 gives the MINITAB output of a regression analysis of the data using this quadratic model. Here the squared term x^2 is denoted as UnitsSq on the output. The MINITAB output tells us that the least squares point estimates of the model parameters are $b_0 = 25.7152$, $b_1 = 4.9762$, and $b_2 = -1.01905$. These estimates give us the least squares prediction equation

$$\hat{y} = 25.7152 + 4.9762x - 1.01905x^2.$$

Intuitively, this is the equation of the best quadratic curve that can be fitted to the data plotted in Table 12.7(b). The MINITAB output also tells us that the p values related to x and x^2 are less than 0.001. This implies that we have very strong evidence that each of these model components is significant. The fact that x^2 seems significant confirms the graphical evidence that there is a quadratic relationship between y and x. Once we have such confirmation, we usually retain the

TABLE **12.7** The Stress and Work Motivation Study Data, and a Scatter Plot of the Data 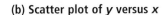 StressProd

(a) The data

Self-reported Stress Level, x	Productivity, y (Projects per Year)
0	25.8
0	26.1
0	25.4
1	29.6
1	29.2
1	29.8
2	32.0
2	31.4
2	31.7
3	31.7
3	31.5
3	31.2
4	29.4
4	29.0
4	29.5

(b) Scatter plot of y versus x

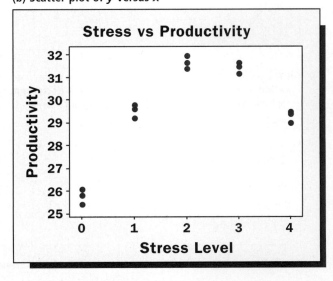

FIGURE **12.18**   **MINITAB Output of a Regression Analysis of the Stress and Motivation Data Using the Quadratic Model**

```
The regression equation is
Productivity = 25.7 + 4.98 Units - 1.02 UnitsSq

Predictor        Coef  SE Coef       T       P
Constant      25.7152   0.1554  165.43   0.000
Units          4.9762   0.1841   27.02   0.000
UnitsSq       -1.01905  0.04414  -23.09   0.000

S = 0.286079   R-Sq = 98.6%   R-Sq(adj) = 98.3%

Analysis of Variance
Source          DF       SS      MS       F       P
Regression       2   67.915  33.958  414.92   0.000
Residual Error  12    0.982   0.082
Total           14   68.897

Values of Predictors for New Obs   Predicted Values for New Observations
New Obs  Unit   UnitsSq            New Obs      Fit  SE Fit        95% CI                 95% PI
      1  2.44    5.9536                  1  31.7901  0.1111  (31.5481, 32.0322)  (31.1215, 32.4588)
```

linear term x in the model no matter what the size of its p value. The reason is that geometrical considerations indicate that it is best to use both x and x^2 to model a quadratic relationship.

The HR department wishes to find the value of x that results in the highest productivity score. Using calculus, it can be shown that the value $x = 2.44$ maximizes predicted productivity, suggesting that, in theory, productivity will be highest for an individual worker who scores between 2 and 3 on the stress scale. This will result in a predicted productivity score equal to

$$\hat{y} = 25.7152 + 4.9762(2.44) - 1.01905(2.44)^2$$
$$= 31.7901 \text{ average projects completed per year.}$$

Note that $\hat{y} = 31.7901$ is given at the bottom of the MINITAB output in Figure 12.18. In addition, the MINITAB output tells us that a 95 percent confidence interval for the mean productivity score that would be obtained by all of the employees is [31.5481, 32.0322]. The MINITAB output also tells us that a 95 percent prediction interval for the average number of projects completed by an individual employee is [31.1215, 32.4588].

We now consider a model that employs both a linear and a quadratic term for one independent variable and also employs another linear term for a second independent variable.

Example 12.7 The Fresh Detergent Case

Enterprise Industries produces Fresh, a brand of liquid laundry detergent. In order to more effectively manage its inventory and make revenue projections, the company would like to better predict demand for Fresh. To develop a prediction model, the company has gathered data concerning demand for Fresh over the last 30 sales periods (each sales period is defined to be a four-week period). The demand data are presented in Table 12.8. Here, for each sales period,

  y = the demand for the large size bottle of Fresh (in hundreds of thousands of bottles) in the sales period,

  x_1 = the price (in dollars) of Fresh as offered by Enterprise Industries in the sales period,

  x_2 = the average industry price (in dollars) of competitors' similar detergents in the sales period,

  x_3 = Enterprise Industries' advertising expenditure (in hundreds of thousands of dollars) to promote Fresh in the sales period,

  $x_4 = x_2 - x_1$ = the "price difference" in the sales period.

TABLE **12.8** Historical Data, Including Price Differences, Concerning Demand
for Fresh Detergent   ● Fresh2

Sales Period	Price for Fresh, x_1 (Dollars)	Average Industry Price, x_2 (Dollars)	Price Difference, $x_4 = x_2 - x_1$ (Dollars)	Advertising Expenditure for Fresh, x_3 (Hundreds of Thousands of Dollars)	Demand for Fresh, y (Hundreds of Thousands of Bottles)
1	3.85	3.80	−0.05	5.50	7.38
2	3.75	4.00	0.25	6.75	8.51
3	3.70	4.30	0.60	7.25	9.52
4	3.70	3.70	0	5.50	7.50
5	3.60	3.85	0.25	7.00	9.33
6	3.60	3.80	0.20	6.50	8.28
7	3.60	3.75	0.15	6.75	8.75
8	3.80	3.85	0.05	5.25	7.87
9	3.80	3.65	−0.15	5.25	7.10
10	3.85	4.00	0.15	6.00	8.00
11	3.90	4.10	0.20	6.50	7.89
12	3.90	4.00	0.10	6.25	8.15
13	3.70	4.10	0.40	7.00	9.10
14	3.75	4.20	0.45	6.90	8.86
15	3.75	4.10	0.35	6.80	8.90
16	3.80	4.10	0.30	6.80	8.87
17	3.70	4.20	0.50	7.10	9.26
18	3.80	4.30	0.50	7.00	9.00
19	3.70	4.10	0.40	6.80	8.75
20	3.80	3.75	−0.05	6.50	7.95
21	3.80	3.75	−0.05	6.25	7.65
22	3.75	3.65	−0.10	6.00	7.27
23	3.70	3.90	0.20	6.50	8.00
24	3.55	3.65	0.10	7.00	8.50
25	3.60	4.10	0.50	6.80	8.75
26	3.65	4.25	0.60	6.80	9.21
27	3.70	3.65	−0.05	6.50	8.27
28	3.75	3.75	0	5.75	7.67
29	3.80	3.85	0.05	5.80	7.93
30	3.70	4.25	0.55	6.80	9.26

To begin our analysis, suppose that Enterprise Industries believes on theoretical grounds that the single independent variable x_4 adequately describes the effects of x_1 and x_2 on y. That is, perhaps demand for Fresh depends more on how the price for Fresh compares to competitors' prices than it does on the absolute levels of the prices for Fresh and other competing detergents. This makes sense since most consumers must buy a certain amount of detergent no matter what the price is. We will examine the validity of using x_4 to predict y more fully in Exercise 12.33 on page 445. For now, we will build a prediction model utilizing x_3 and x_4.

Figure 12.19 presents scatter plots of y versus x_4 and y versus x_3. The plot in Figure 12.19(a) indicates that y tends to increase in a straight-line fashion as x_4 increases. This suggests that the simple linear model

$$y = \beta_0 + \beta_1 x_4 + \varepsilon$$

might appropriately relate y to x_4. The plot in Figure 12.19(b) indicates that y tends to increase in a curved fashion as x_3 increases. Since this curve appears to have the shape of Figure 12.17(c), this suggests that the quadratic model

$$y = \beta_0 + \beta_1 x_3 + \beta_2 x_3^2 + \varepsilon$$

might appropriately relate y to x_3.

FIGURE 12.19 Scatter Plots of the Fresh Demand Data

(a) Plot of *y* (Demand for Fresh Detergent) versus x_4 (Price Difference)

(b) Plot of *y* (Demand for Fresh Detergent) versus x_3 (Advertising Expenditure for Fresh)

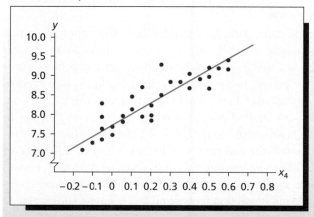
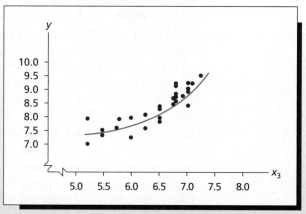

To construct a prediction model based on both x_3 and x_4, it seems reasonable to combine these two models to form the regression model

$$y = \beta_0 + \beta_1 x_4 + \beta_2 x_3 + \beta_3 x_3^2 + \varepsilon.$$

Here we have arbitrarily ordered the x_4, x_3, and x_3^2 terms in the combined model, and we have renumbered the subscripts on the β's appropriately. In the combined model,

$$\beta_0 + \beta_1 x_4 + \beta_2 x_3 + \beta_3 x_3^2$$

is the mean demand for Fresh when the price difference is x_4 and the advertising expenditure is x_3. The error term describes the effects on demand of all factors other than x_4 and x_3.

Figure 12.20(a) presents the Excel output of a regression analysis of the Fresh demand data using the combined model. The output tells us that the least squares point estimates of the model

FIGURE 12.20 Excel and MegaStat Output of a Regression Analysis of the Fresh Demand Data in Table 12.8 Using the Model $y = \beta_0 + \beta_1 x_4 + \beta_2 x_3 + \beta_3 x_3^2 + \varepsilon$

(a) The Excel output

Regression Statistics

Multiple R	0.9515
R Square	0.9054
Adjusted R Square	0.8945
Standard Error	0.2213
Observations	30

ANOVA	df	SS	MS	F	Significance F
Regression	3	12.1853	4.0618	82.9409	1.94E-13
Residual	26	1.2733	0.0490		
Total	29	13.4586			

	Coefficients	Standard Error	t Stat	P-value	Lower 95%	Upper 95%
Intercept	17.3244	5.6415	3.0709	0.0050	5.7282	28.9206
PriceDif (x4)	1.3070	0.3036	4.3048	0.0002	0.6829	1.9311
AdvExp (x3)	-3.6956	1.8503	-1.9973	0.0564	-7.4989	0.1077
x3Sq	0.3486	0.1512	2.3060	0.0293	0.0379	0.6594

(b) Prediction using MegaStat

Predicted values for: Y

	95% Confidence Interval		95% Prediction Interval		
Predicted	lower	upper	lower	upper	Leverage
8.29330	8.17378	8.41281	7.82298	8.76362	0.069

parameters are $b_0 = 17.3244$, $b_1 = 1.3070$, $b_2 = -3.6956$, and $b_3 = 0.3486$. The output also tells us that the p values related to x_4, x_3, and x_3^2 are 0.0002, 0.0564, and 0.0293. Therefore, we have strong evidence that each of the model components x_4 and x_3^2 is significant. Furthermore, although the p value related to x_3 is slightly greater than 0.05, we retain x_3 in the model because x_3^2 is significant.

In order to predict demand in a future sales period, Enterprise Industries must determine future values of x_3 and $x_4 = x_2 - x_1$. Of course, the company can set x_1 (its price for Fresh) and x_3 (its advertising expenditure). Also, it feels that by examining the prices of competitors' similar products immediately prior to a future period, it can very accurately predict x_2 (the average industry price for competitors' similar detergents). Furthermore, the company can react to any change in competitors' price to maintain any desired price difference $x_4 = x_2 - x_1$. This is an advantage of predicting on the basis of x_4 rather than on the basis of x_1 and x_2 (which the company cannot control). Therefore, suppose that the company will maintain a price difference of $0.20 (x_{04} = 0.20)$ and will spend $650,000 on advertising ($x_{03} = 6.50$) in a future sales period. Since this combination of price difference and advertising expenditure is in the experimental region defined by the data in Table 12.8, a point prediction of demand in the future sales period is

$$\hat{y} = 17.3244 + 1.3070x_{04} - 3.6956x_{03} + 0.3486x_{03}^2$$
$$= 17.3244 + 1.3070(0.20) - 3.6956(6.50) + 0.3486(6.50)^2$$
$$= 8.29330 \text{ (that is, 829,330 bottles).}$$

This quantity, in addition to being the point prediction of demand in a single sales period when the price difference is $0.20 and the advertising expenditure is $650,000, is also the point estimate of the mean of all possible demands when $x_4 = 0.20$ and $x_3 = 6.50$. Note that $\hat{y} = 8.29330$ is given on the MegaStat output of Figure 12.20(b). The output also gives a 95 percent confidence interval for mean demand when x_4 equals 0.20 and x_3 equals 6.50, which is [8.17378, 8.41281], and a 95 percent prediction interval for an individual demand when x_4 equals 0.20 and x_3 equals 6.50, which is [7.82298, 8.76362]. This latter interval says we are 95 percent confident that the actual demand in the future sales period will be between 782,298 bottles and 876,362 bottles. The upper limit of this interval can be used for inventory control. It says that if Enterprise Industries plans to have 876,362 bottles on hand to meet demand in the future sales period, then the company can be very confident that it will have enough bottles. The lower limit of the interval can be used to better understand Enterprise Industries' cash flow situation. It says the company can be very confident that it will sell at least 782,298 bottles in the future sales period. Therefore, for example, if the average competitors' price is $3.90 and thus Enterprise Industries' price is $3.70, the company can be very confident that its minimum revenue from the large size bottle of Fresh in the future period will be at least 782,298 × $3.70 = $2,894,502.60.

Exercises for Section 12.8

CONCEPTS

12.30 When does a scatter plot suggest the use of the quadratic regression model?

12.31 In the quadratic regression model, what are y, $(\beta_0 + \beta_1 x + \beta_2 x^2)$, and ε?

METHODS AND APPLICATIONS

12.32 **THE REAL ESTATE SALES PRICE CASE**
  ● RealEst2

Figure 12.21 presents the MINITAB output of a regression analysis of the real estate sales price data in Table 12.9 using the model

$$y = \beta_0 + \beta_1 x_1 + \beta_2 x_2 + \beta_3 x_2^2 + \varepsilon.$$

a. Discuss why the plots of y versus x_1 and y versus x_2 beside Table 12.9 indicate that this model might appropriately relate y to x_1 and x_2.

b. Do the p values for the independent variables in this model indicate that these independent variables are significant? Explain your answer.

c. Report and interpret a point prediction of and a 95 percent prediction interval for the sales price of an individual house with 2,000 square feet (about 180 m²) and a rating of 8 (see the bottom of the MINITAB output in Figure 12.21).

FIGURE **12.21**   **MINITAB Output of a Regression Analysis of the Real Estate Sales Price Data Using the Model** $y = \beta_0 + \beta_1 x_1 + \beta_2 x_2 + \beta_3 x_2^2 + \varepsilon$

```
The regression equation is
SalesPrice = 19.1 + 5.56 x1 + 9.22 x2 - 0.513 x2sq

Predictor      Coef   SE Coef      T      P
Constant     19.074     3.632   5.25  0.002
x1           5.5596    0.1255  44.29  0.000
x2            9.223     1.312   7.03  0.000
x2sq        -0.5129    0.1228  -4.18  0.006

S = 1.77128   R-Sq = 99.7%   R-Sq(adj) = 99.6%

Analysis of Variance
Source           DF       SS      MS      F       P
Regression        3   7428.7  2476.2  789.25  0.000
Residual Error    6     18.8     3.1
Total             9   7447.5


Values of Predictors for New Obs  Predicted Values for New Observations
New Obs    x1     x2   x2sq       New Obs    Fit  SE Fit         95% CI               95% PI
      1  20.0   8.00   64.0             1 171.222  0.895  (169.033, 173.411)  (166.367, 176.078)
```

TABLE **12.9**   **The Real Estate Sales Price Data**   ⬤ RealEst2

Sales Price, y	Home Size, x_1	Rating, x_2
180	23	5
98.1	11	2
173.1	20	9
136.5	17	3
141	15	8
165.9	21	4
193.5	24	7
127.8	13	6
163.5	19	7
172.5	25	2

Source: "Integrating judgement with a regression appraisal," by R. L. Andrews and J. T. Ferguson, *The Real Estate Appraiser and Analyst*, 52, no. 2 (1986). Reprinted by permission.

12.33   THE FRESH DETERGENT CASE   ⬤ Fresh2

Consider the demand for Fresh detergent in a future sales period when Enterprise Industries' price for Fresh will be $x_1 = 3.70$, the average price of competitors' similar detergents will be $x_2 = 3.90$, the price difference $x_4 = x_2 - x_1$ will be 0.20, and Enterprise Industries' advertising expenditure for Fresh will be $x_3 = 6.50$. We have seen in Example 12.7 that the 95 percent prediction interval for this demand given by the model

$$y = \beta_0 + \beta_1 x_4 + \beta_2 x_3 + \beta_3 x_3^2 + \varepsilon$$

is [7.82298, 8.76362]. The 95 percent prediction interval for this demand given by the model

$$y = \beta_0 + \beta_1 x_1 + \beta_2 x_2 + \beta_3 x_3 + \beta_4 x_3^2 + \varepsilon$$

is [7.84139, 8.79357]. Which interval is shorter? Based on this, which model seems better?

12.34 Pop-Canada is trying to decide on the right combination of two independent variables—x_1, caramel colour (0, 1, or 2 units), and x_2, maple syrup flavouring (0, 1, 2, or 3 units)—to improve the taste of its beverages. Taste tests were carried out using focus groups across Canada. The combinations of x_1 and x_2 used in the experiment, along with the corresponding values of y, are given in Table 12.10.   ⬤ PopCanada

a. Discuss why the data plots given beside Table 12.10 indicate that the model

$$y = \beta_0 + \beta_1 x_1 + \beta_2 x_1^2 + \beta_3 x_2 + \beta_4 x_2^2 + \varepsilon$$

might appropriately relate y to x_1 and x_2.

b. If we use MegaStat to analyze the data in Table 12.10 by using the model in part a, we obtain the output in Figure 12.22. Noting from Table 12.10 that the combination of one unit of caramel colour and two units of maple syrup seems to maximize rated taste, assume that Pop-Canada will use this combination to make its beverage. The estimation and prediction results at the bottom of the MegaStat output are for the combination $x_1 = 1$ and $x_2 = 2$.

(1) Use the computer output to find and report a point estimate of and a 95 percent confidence interval for the mean rated taste obtained by

TABLE **12.10** **Pop-Canada's Focus Group Results**   ● PopCanada

Rated Taste, y	Caramel Colour, x_1	Maple Syrup, x_2
27.4	0	0
28.0	0	0
28.6	0	0
29.6	1	0
30.6	1	0
28.6	2	0
29.8	2	0
32.0	0	1
33.0	0	1
33.3	1	1
34.5	1	1
32.3	0	2
33.5	0	2
34.4	1	2
35.0	1	2
35.6	1	2
33.3	2	2
34.0	2	2
34.7	2	2
33.4	1	3
32.0	2	3
33.0	2	3

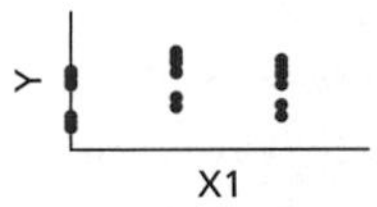

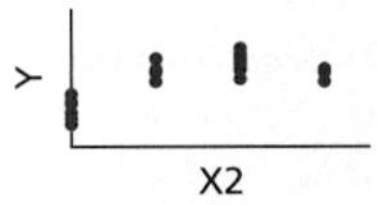

FIGURE **12.22**   **MegaStat Output of a Regression Analysis of the Pop-Canada Data Using the Model $y = \beta_0 + \beta_1 x_1 + \beta_2 x_1^2 + \beta_3 x_2 + \beta_4 x_2^2 + \varepsilon$**

Regression Analysis

R^2	0.947			
Adjusted R^2	0.935		n	22
R	0.973		k	4
Std. Error	0.631		Dep. Var.	**Y**

ANOVA table

Source	SS	df	MS	F	p-value
Regression	120.7137	4	30.1784	75.90	1.30E-10
Residual	6.7590	17	0.3976		
Total	127.4727	21			

Regression output					confidence interval	
variables	coefficients	std. error	t (df = 17)	p-value	95% lower	95% upper
Intercept	28.1589	0.2902	97.040	9.01E-25	27.5467	28.7711
X1	3.3133	0.5896	5.619	3.07E-05	2.0693	4.5573
X1SQ	−1.4111	0.2816	−5.012	0.0001	−2.0051	−0.8170
X2	5.2752	0.4129	12.776	3.83E-10	4.4041	6.1463
X2SQ	−1.3964	0.1509	−9.257	4.74E-08	−1.7146	−1.0781

Predicted values for: Y

	95% Confidence Interval		95% Prediction Interval		
Predicted	lower	upper	lower	upper	Leverage
35.0261	34.4997	35.5525	33.5954	36.4568	0.157

all samples of the beverage when it is made using one unit of caramel colour and two units of maple syrup.

(2) Use the computer output to find and report a point prediction of and a 95 percent prediction interval for the rated taste that would be obtained by an individual sample of the beverage when it is made using one unit of caramel colour and two units of maple syrup.

12.9 Interaction (Optional)

Multiple regression models often contain **interaction variables**. We form an interaction variable by multiplying two independent variables together. For instance, if a regression model includes the independent variables x_1 and x_2, then we can form the interaction variable x_1x_2. It is appropriate to employ an interaction variable if the relationship between the mean value of the dependent variable y and one of the independent variables is dependent on (that is, is different depending on) the value of the other independent variable. We explain the concept of interaction in the following example.

Example 12.8

Part 1: The data and data plots   Froid Frozen Foods has designed an experiment to study the effects of two types of advertising expenditures on sales of one of its lines of frozen foods. Twenty-five sales regions of equal sales potential were selected. Different combinations of x_1 = radio and television expenditures (measured in units of $1,000) and x_2 = print expenditures (measured in units of $1,000) were specified and randomly assigned to the sales regions. Table 12.11 shows the expenditure combinations along with the associated values of sales volume, measured in units of $10,000 and denoted y, for the sales regions during August of last year.

To help decide whether interaction exists between x_1 and x_2, we can plot the data in Table 12.11. To do this, we first plot y versus x_1. In constructing this plot, we make the plot character for each point the corresponding value of x_2 (x_2 = 1, 2, 3, 4, 5). The resulting plot (shown in Figure 12.23) is called a **plot of y versus x_1 for the different "levels" of x_2**. Looking at this plot, we see that the straight line relating y to x_1 when x_2 = 5 appears to have a smaller slope than does the line relating y to x_1 when x_2 = 1. That is, the rate of increase of the line corresponding to x_2 = 5 is less steep than the rate of increase of the line corresponding to x_2 = 1. Examining the entire data plot, we see that Figure 12.23 might suggest that the larger x_2 is, the smaller is the slope of the straight line relating y to x_1.

In Figure 12.24, we plot y versus x_2 for the different levels of x_1 (x_1 = 1, 2, 3, 4, 5). Here the plot character for each point is the corresponding value of x_1. We see that the straight line relating y to x_2 when x_1 = 5 appears to have a smaller slope than does the straight line relating y to x_2 when x_1 = 1. Looking at the entire data plot, we see that Figure 12.24 might suggest that the larger x_1 is, the smaller is the slope of the straight line relating y to x_2.

In summary, Figures 12.23 and 12.24 seem to imply that the more money spent on one type of advertising, the smaller is the slope of the straight line relating sales volume to the

TABLE 12.11   Froid Frozen Foods Sales Volume Data   ● Froid

Sales Region	Radio and Television Expenditures, x_1	Print Expenditures, x_2	Sales Volume, y	Sales Region	Radio and Television Expenditures, x_1	Print Expenditures, x_2	Sales Volume, y
1	1	1	3.27	14	3	4	17.99
2	1	2	8.38	15	3	5	19.85
3	1	3	11.28	16	4	1	9.46
4	1	4	14.50	17	4	2	12.61
5	1	5	19.63	18	4	3	15.50
6	2	1	5.84	19	4	4	17.68
7	2	2	10.01	20	4	5	21.02
8	2	3	12.46	21	5	1	12.23
9	2	4	16.67	22	5	2	13.58
10	2	5	19.83	23	5	3	16.77
11	3	1	8.51	24	5	4	20.56
12	3	2	10.14	25	5	5	21.05
13	3	3	14.75				

FIGURE **12.23**   Plot of y versus x_1 (Plot Character Is the Corresponding Value of x_2): The Larger x_2 Is, the Smaller Is the Slope of the Straight Line Relating y to x_1

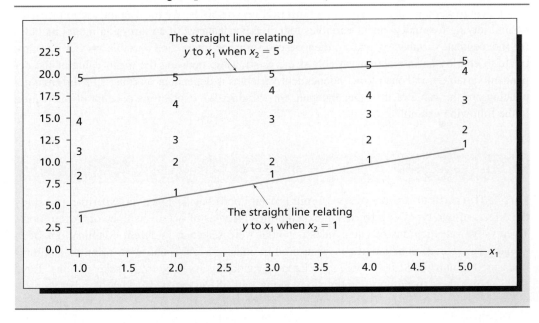

FIGURE **12.24**   Plot of y versus x_2 (Plot Character Is the Corresponding Value of x_1): The Larger x_1 Is, the Smaller Is the Slope of the Straight Line Relating y to x_2

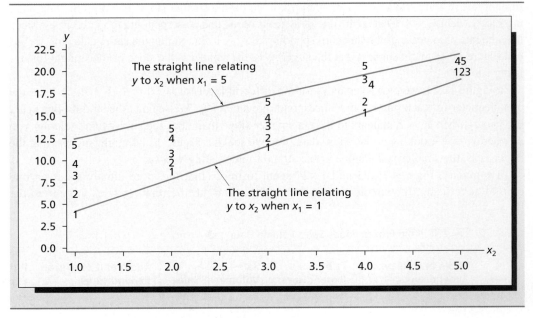

amount spent on the other type of advertising. This says that there is interaction between x_1 and x_2 because

1   The relationship between y and x_1 (the slope of the line relating y to x_1) is different for different values of x_2.

2   The relationship between y and x_2 (the slope of the line relating y to x_2) is different for different values of x_1.

Intuitively, interaction between x_1 and x_2 makes sense because as Froid Frozen Foods spends more money on one type of advertising, increases in spending on the other type of advertising might become less effective.

Part 2: Modelling the interaction between x_1 and x_2   The regression model

$$y = \beta_0 + \beta_1 x_1 + \beta_2 x_2 + \varepsilon$$

cannot describe the interaction between x_1 and x_2 because this model says that mean sales volume equals

$$\beta_0 + \beta_1 x_1 + \beta_2 x_2 = (\beta_0 + \beta_1 x_1) + \beta_2 x_2.$$

This implies that for any particular value of x_1, the slope of the straight line relating the mean value of y to x_2 will always be β_2. That is, no matter what the value of x_1 is, the slope of the line relating mean y to x_2 is always the same. This rules out the possibility of describing the relationships illustrated in Figure 12.24 by using the above model. The model also says that mean sales volume equals

$$\beta_0 + \beta_1 x_1 + \beta_2 x_2 = (\beta_0 + \beta_2 x_2) + \beta_1 x_1.$$

This implies that, no matter what the value of x_2 is, the slope of the line relating mean y to x_1 is always the same (here the slope equals β_1). This rules out the possibility of describing the relationships illustrated in Figure 12.23 by using the above model. In short, we say that the above model assumes **no interaction** between x_1 and x_2.

In order to model the interaction between x_1 and x_2, we can use the **cross-product term** or **interaction term** $x_1 x_2$. Therefore, we consider the model

$$y = \beta_0 + \beta_1 x_1 + \beta_2 x_2 + \beta_3 x_1 x_2 + \varepsilon.$$

This model says that mean sales volume equals

$$\beta_0 + \beta_1 x_1 + \beta_2 x_2 + \beta_3 x_1 x_2,$$

which can be rewritten as $(\beta_0 + \beta_1 x_1) + (\beta_2 + \beta_3 x_1) x_2$. **This implies that the slope of the line relating mean y to x_2, which is $(\beta_2 + \beta_3 x_1)$, will be different for different values of x_1.** This allows the **interaction model** to describe relationships such as those illustrated in Figure 12.24. Furthermore, for this model the mean sales volume

$$\beta_0 + \beta_1 x_1 + \beta_2 x_2 + \beta_3 x_1 x_2$$

can also be rewritten as $(\beta_0 + \beta_2 x_2) + (\beta_1 + \beta_3 x_2) x_1$. **This implies that the slope of the line relating mean y to x_1, which is $(\beta_1 + \beta_3 x_2)$, will be different for different values of x_2.** This allows the interaction model to describe relationships such as those illustrated in Figure 12.23. In short, we say that the model employing the term $x_1 x_2$ assumes that **interaction exists** between x_1 and x_2.

Part 3: Statistical inference   Figure 12.25 gives the MINITAB output of a regression analysis of the data in Table 12.11 by using the model

$$y = \beta_0 + \beta_1 x_1 + \beta_2 x_2 + \beta_3 x_1 x_2 + \varepsilon.$$

Note that $x_1 x_2$ is denoted as "Interaction" on the output. Since all of the p values related to the intercept and the independent variables are less than 0.01, we have very strong evidence that each of β_0, x_1, x_2, and $x_1 x_2$ is significant in the above model. In particular, the very small p value related to $x_1 x_2$ confirms that interaction exists between x_1 and x_2 as was originally suggested by the plots in Figures 12.23 and 12.24. (If there were little or no interaction between x_1 and x_2, the term $x_1 x_2$ would be insignificant since it would not help us to model the data.)

Next, suppose that Froid Frozen Foods will spend $2,000 on radio and television advertising ($x_1 = 2$) and $5,000 on print advertising ($x_2 = 5$) in a future month in a particular sales region. If there are no trend, seasonal, or other time-related influences affecting monthly sales volume, then it is reasonable to believe that the regression relationship between y and x_1 and x_2 that we have developed probably applies to the future month and particular sales region. It follows that

$$\hat{y} = -2.3497 + 2.3611(2) + 4.1831(5) - 0.3489(2)(5)$$
$$= 19.799 \text{ (that is, \$197,990)}$$

is a point estimate of mean sales volume when $2,000 is spent on radio and television advertising and $5,000 is spent on print advertising. In addition, $\hat{y}$ is a point prediction of the individual

FIGURE **12.25**   **MINITAB Output of a Regression Analysis of the Sales Volume Data in Table 12.11 by Using the Model** $y = \beta_0 + \beta_1 x_1 + \beta_2 x_2 + \beta_3 x_1 x_2 + \varepsilon$

```
The regression equation is
SalesVol = - 2.35 + 2.36 RadioTV + 4.18 Print - 0.349 Interaction

Predictor            Coef        SE Coef            T            P
Constant          -2.3497         0.6883        -3.41        0.003
RadioTV            2.3611         0.2075        11.38        0.000
Print              4.1831         0.2075        20.16        0.000
Interaction       -0.34890        0.06257       -5.58        0.000

S = 0.6257          R-Sq = 98.6%              R-Sq(adj) = 98.4%

Analysis of Variance
Source               DF            SS            MS            F            P
Regression            3         590.41        196.80        502.67        0.000
Residual Error       21           8.22          0.39
Total                24         598.63

Values of Predictors for New Obs        Predicted Values for New Observations
New Obs   RadioTV   Print   Interaction    New Obs     Fit   SE Fit      95% CI                95% PI
      1      2.00    5.00         10.0          1   19.799    0.265   (19.247, 20.351)    (18.385, 21.213)
```

sales volume that will be observed in the future month in the particular sales region. Besides giving $\hat{y} = 19.799$, the MINITAB output in Figure 12.25 tells us that the 95 percent confidence interval for mean sales volume is [19.247, 20.351] and that the 95 percent prediction interval for an individual sales volume is [18.385, 21.213]. This prediction interval says we are 95 percent confident that the individual sales volume in the future month in the particular sales region will be between \$183,850 and \$212,130. In Exercise 12.37 (on page 453), we will continue this example.

It is easy to construct data plots to check for interaction in the Froid Frozen Foods example because the company has carried out a designed experiment. In many regression problems, however, we do not carry out a designed experiment, and the data are "unstructured." In such a case, it may not be possible to construct the data plots needed to detect interaction between independent variables. For example, if we consider the Fresh demand data in Table 12.8, we might suspect that there is interaction between x_3 (advertising expenditure) and x_4 (the price difference). That is, we might suspect that the relationship between mean demand for Fresh and advertising expenditure is different for different levels of the price difference. For instance, increases in advertising expenditures might be more effective at some price differences than at others. To detect such interaction, we would like to construct plots of demand versus x_3 for different levels of x_4. However, examination of the Fresh demand data reveals that there are only a few observations at any one level of the price difference, and therefore the needed data plots cannot easily be made. In such a case, we can use t statistics and p values related to potential interaction terms to try to assess the importance of interaction. We illustrate this in the following example.

Example 12.9 The Fresh Detergent Case

Part 1: An interaction model and statistical inference   In Example 12.7, we considered the Fresh demand model

$$y = \beta_0 + \beta_1 x_4 + \beta_2 x_3 + \beta_3 x_3^2 + \varepsilon.$$

Since we might logically suspect that there is interaction between x_4 and x_3, we add the interaction term $x_4 x_3$ to this model and form the model

$$y = \beta_0 + \beta_1 x_4 + \beta_2 x_3 + \beta_3 x_3^2 + \beta_4 x_4 x_3 + \varepsilon.$$

Figure 12.26(a) presents the Excel output obtained by using this model to perform a regression analysis of the Fresh demand data. This output shows that each of the p values for testing the significance of the intercept and the independent variables is less than 0.05. Therefore, we have

FIGURE **12.26**   Excel and MegaStat Output of a Regression Analysis of the Fresh Demand Data by Using the Interaction Model $y = \beta_0 + \beta_1 x_4 + \beta_2 x_3 + \beta_3 x_3^2 + \beta_4 x_4 x_3 + \varepsilon$

(a) The Excel output

Regression Statistics

Multiple R	0.9596
R Square	0.9209
Adjusted R Square	0.9083
Standard Error	0.2063
Observations	30

ANOVA	df	SS	MS	F	Significance F
Regression	4	12.3942	3.0985	72.7771	2.11E-13
Residual	25	1.0644	0.0426		
Total	29	13.4586			

	Coefficients	Standard Error	t Stat	P-value	Lower 95%	Upper 95%
Intercept	29.1133	7.4832	3.8905	0.0007	13.7013	44.5252
PriceDif (x4)	11.1342	4.4459	2.5044	0.0192	1.9778	20.2906
AdvExp (x3)	−7.6080	2.4691	−3.0813	0.0050	−12.6932	−2.5228
x3sq	0.6712	0.2027	3.3115	0.0028	0.2538	1.0887
x4x3	−1.4777	0.6672	−2.2149	0.0361	−2.8518	−0.1037

(b) Prediction using MegaStat

Predicted values for: Y

Predicted	95% Confidence Interval		95% Prediction Interval		Leverage
	lower	upper	lower	upper	
8.32725	8.21121	8.44329	7.88673	8.76777	0.075

strong evidence that the intercept and each of x_4, x_3, x_3^2, and $x_4 x_3$ are significant. In particular, since the p value related to $x_4 x_3$ is 0.0361, we have strong evidence that the interaction variable $x_4 x_3$ is important. This confirms that the interaction between x_3 and x_4 that we suspected really does exist.

Suppose again that Enterprise Industries wishes to predict demand for Fresh in a future sales period when the price difference will be $0.20 ($x_4 = 0.20$) and when the advertising expenditure for Fresh will be $650,000 ($x_3 = 6.50$). Using the least squares point estimates in Figure 12.26, the needed point prediction is

$$\hat{y} = 29.1133 + 11.1342(0.20) - 7.6080(6.50) + 0.6712(6.50)^2$$
$$- 1.4777(0.20)(6.50)$$
$$= 8.327,25 \,(832,725 \text{ bottles}).$$

This point prediction is given on the MegaStat output of Figure 12.26(b), which also tells us that the 95 percent confidence interval for mean demand when x_4 equals 0.20 and x_3 equals 6.50 is [8.21121, 8.44329] and that the 95 percent prediction interval for an individual demand when x_4 equals 0.20 and x_3 equals 6.50 is [7.88673, 8.76777]. Notice that this prediction interval is shorter than the 95 percent prediction interval—[7.82298, 8.76362]—obtained using the model that omits the interaction term $x_4 x_3$ and predicts y on the basis of x_4, x_3, and x_3^2. This is another indication that it is useful to include the interaction variable $x_4 x_3$ in the model.

Part 2: The nature of interaction between x_3 and x_4   To understand the exact nature of the interaction between x_3 and x_4, consider the prediction equation

$$\hat{y} = 29.1133 + 11.1342 x_4 - 7.6080 x_3 + 0.6712 x_3^2 - 1.4777 x_4 x_3$$

obtained by using the Fresh demand interaction model. If we set x_4 equal to 0.10 and place this value of x_4 into the prediction equation, we obtain

$$\hat{y} = 29.1133 + 11.1342 x_4 - 7.6080 x_3 + 0.6712 x_3^2 - 1.4777 x_4 x_3$$
$$= 29.1133 + 11.1342(0.10) - 7.6080 x_3 + 0.6712 x_3^2 - 1.4777(0.10) x_3$$
$$= 30.2267 - 7.7558 x_3 + 0.6712 x_3^2.$$

FIGURE **12.27**   Interaction between x_4 and x_3 in the Fresh Detergent Case

(a) Calculating values of predicted demand when x_4 equals 0.10

x_3	$\hat{y} = 30.2267 - 7.7558x_3 + 0.6712x_3^2$
6.0	$\hat{y} = 30.2267 - 7.7558(6.0) + 0.6712(6.0)^2 = 7.86$
6.4	$\hat{y} = 30.2267 - 7.7558(6.4) + 0.6712(6.4)^2 = 8.08$
6.8	$\hat{y} = 30.2267 - 7.7558(6.8) + 0.6712(6.8)^2 = 8.52$

(b) Calculating values of predicted demand when x_4 equals 0.30

x_3	$\hat{y} = 32.4535 - 8.0513x_3 + 0.6712x_3^2$
6.0	$\hat{y} = 32.4535 - 8.0513(6.0) + 0.6712(6.0)^2 = 8.31$
6.4	$\hat{y} = 32.4535 - 8.0513(6.4) + 0.6712(6.4)^2 = 8.42$
6.8	$\hat{y} = 32.4535 - 8.0513(6.8) + 0.6712(6.8)^2 = 8.74$

(c) Illustrating the interaction

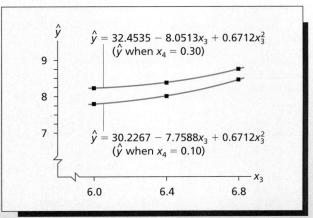

This quadratic equation shows us how predicted demand changes as advertising expenditure x_3 increases when the price difference is 0.10. Next we set x_4 equal to 0.30. If we place this value of x_4 into the Fresh prediction equation, we obtain

$$\hat{y} = 29.1133 + 11.1342x_4 - 7.6080x_3 + 0.6712x_3^2 - 1.4777x_4x_3$$
$$= 29.1133 + 11.1342(0.30) - 7.6080x_3 + 0.6712x_3^2 - 1.4777(0.30)x_3$$
$$= 32.4535 - 8.0513x_3 + 0.6712x_3^2.$$

This quadratic equation shows us how predicted demand changes as advertising expenditure x_3 increases when the price difference is 0.30.

In Figure 12.27(a) and (b), we calculate three points (predicted demands) on each of these quadratic curves. Figure 12.27(c) shows graphs of the two quadratic curves with the predicted demands plotted on these graphs. Comparing these graphs, we see that predicted demand is higher when x_4 equals 0.30 than when x_4 equals 0.10. This makes sense—predicted demand should be higher when Enterprise Industries has a larger price advantage. Furthermore, for each curve we see that predicted demand increases at an increasing rate as x_3 increases. However, the rate of increase in predicted demand is slower when x_4 equals 0.30 than when x_4 equals 0.10—this is the effect of the interaction between x_3 and x_4.

This type of interaction is logical because when the price difference is large (the price for Fresh is low relative to the average industry price), the mean demand for Fresh will be high (assuming the quality of Fresh is comparable to competing brands). Thus, with mean demand already high because many consumers are buying Fresh on the basis of price, there may be little opportunity for increased advertising expenditure to increase mean demand. However, when the price difference is smaller, there may be more potential consumers who are not buying Fresh who can be convinced to do so by increased advertising. Thus, when the price difference is smaller, increased advertising expenditure is more effective than it is when the price difference is larger.

It should be noted that this type of interaction between x_4 and x_3 was estimated from the observed Fresh demand data in Table 12.8. This is because we obtained the least squares point estimates using these data. We are not hypothesizing the existence of the interaction; the importance of the x_4x_3 term and the least squares point estimates tell us that this type of interaction exists. However, we can only hypothesize the reasons behind the interaction. We should also point out that this type of interaction can be assumed to exist only for values of x_4 and x_3 inside the experimental region. Examination of the Fresh demand data shows that Fresh was being sold at either a price advantage (when the price of Fresh is lower than the average industry price) or at a slight price disadvantage (when the price of Fresh is slightly higher than the average industry price). However, if Fresh were sometimes sold at a large price disadvantage, the type of interaction that exists between x_4 and x_3 might be different. In such a case, increases in advertising expenditure might be very ineffective because most consumers will not wish to buy a product with a much higher price.

A final comment is in order. If a p value indicates that an interaction term (say, x_1x_2) is important, then it is usual practice to retain the corresponding linear terms (x_1 and x_2) in the model no matter what the size of their p values. The reason is that doing so can be shown to give a model that will better describe the interaction between x_1 and x_2.

Exercises for Section 12.9

CONCEPTS

12.35 If a regression model utilizes the independent variables x_1 and x_2, how do we form an interaction variable involving x_1 and x_2?

12.36 What is meant when we say that interaction exists between two independent variables?

METHODS AND APPLICATIONS

12.37 Consider the Froid Frozen Foods sales volume model
● Froid

$$y = \beta_0 + \beta_1x_1 + \beta_2x_2 + \beta_3x_1x_2 + \varepsilon.$$

a. We have seen in Example 12.8 that $\beta_1 + \beta_3x_2$ is the slope of the line relating mean y to x_1 at a given value of x_2. This slope is the increase in mean sales volume (in units of $10,000) obtained by increasing radio and TV advertising by $1,000 when print advertising is x_2 thousand dollars. Using $b_1 = 2.3611$ and $b_3 = -0.3489$ from the MINITAB output in Figure 12.25 (page 450), a point estimate of the slope $\beta_1 + \beta_3x_2$ is $2.3611 - 0.3489x_2$. Calculate this point estimate for each of the values 1, 2, 3, 4, and 5 of x_2. Interpret the five point estimates.

b. We have seen in Example 12.8 that $\beta_2 + \beta_3x_1$ is the slope of the line relating mean y to x_2 at a given value of x_1. This slope is the increase in mean sales volume (in units of $10,000) obtained by increasing print advertising by $1,000 when radio and TV advertising is x_1 thousand dollars. Using $b_2 = 4.1831$ and $b_3 = -0.3489$ from the MINITAB output in Figure 12.25, a point estimate of the slope $\beta_2 + \beta_3x_1$ is $4.1831 - 0.3489x_1$. Calculate this point estimate for each of the values 1, 2, 3, 4, and 5 of x_1. Interpret the five point estimates.

c. By comparing the five point estimates calculated in part b with the five point estimates calculated in part a, discuss why it is reasonable to conclude that increasing print advertising expenditures is more effective than increasing radio and TV advertising expenditures.

12.38 THE REAL ESTATE SALES PRICE CASE
● RealEst2

We concluded in Exercise 12.32 (pages 444 and 445) that the model

$$y = \beta_0 + \beta_1x_1 + \beta_2x_2 + \beta_3x_2^2 + \varepsilon$$

might appropriately relate y to x_1 and x_2. To investigate whether interaction exists between x_1 and x_2, we

consider the model

$$y = \beta_0 + \beta_1x_1 + \beta_2x_2 + \beta_3x_2^2 + \beta_4x_1x_2 + \varepsilon.$$

Figure 12.28 presents the MINITAB output of a regression analysis of the real estate sales price data using this model.

a. Does the p value for x_1x_2 indicate that this interaction variable is important? Do the p values for the other independent variables in the model indicate that these variables are important? Explain your answer.

b. Report and interpret a point prediction of and a 95 percent prediction interval for the sales price of an individual house with 2,000 square feet (about 180 m^2) and a rating of 8 (see the bottom of the MINITAB output in Figure 12.28). Is the 95 percent prediction interval given by the model

$$y = \beta_0 + \beta_1x_1 + \beta_2x_2 + \beta_3x_2^2 + \beta_4x_1x_2 + \varepsilon$$

shorter than the 95 percent prediction interval given by the model

$$y = \beta_0 + \beta_1x_1 + \beta_2x_2 + \beta_3x_2^2 + \varepsilon$$

(see the MINITAB output in Figure 12.21 on page 445). If so, what does this mean?

12.39 THE REAL ESTATE SALES PRICE CASE ● RealEst2

In this exercise, we study the nature of the interaction between x_1, area, and x_2, rating.

a. Consider all houses with a rating of 2. In this case, the predicted sales price is (using the least squares point estimates in Figure 12.28)

$$\hat{y} = b_0 + b_1x_1 + b_2x_2 + b_3x_2^2 + b_4x_1x_2$$
$$= 27.438 + 5.0813x_1 + 7.2899(2) - 0.5311(2)^2$$
$$+ 0.11473x_1(2).$$

Calculate $\hat{y}$ when $x_1 = 13$ and 22. Plot $\hat{y}$ versus x_1 for $x_1 = 13$ and 22.

b. Consider all houses with a rating of 8. In this case, the predicted sales price is (using the least squares point estimates in Figure 12.28)

$$\hat{y} = b_0 + b_1x_1 + b_2x_2 + b_3x_2^2 + b_4x_1x_2$$
$$= 27.438 + 5.0813x_1 + 7.2899(8) - 0.5311(8)^2$$
$$+ 0.11473x_1(8).$$

Calculate $\hat{y}$ when $x_1 = 13$ and 22. Plot $\hat{y}$ versus x_1 for $x_1 = 13$ and 22.

c. By comparing the plots you made in parts a and b, discuss the nature of the interaction between x_1 and x_2.

FIGURE **12.28** MINITAB Output of a Regression Analysis of the Real Estate Sales Price Data Using the Model $y = \beta_0 + \beta_1 x_1 + \beta_2 x_2 + \beta_3 x_2^2 + \beta_4 x_1 x_2 + \varepsilon$

```
The regression equation is
SalesPrice = 27.4 + 5.08 x1 + 7.29 x2 - 0.531 x2sq + 0.115 x1x2

Predictor      Coef   SE Coef      T      P
Constant     27.438     3.059   8.97  0.000
x1            5.0813    0.1476  34.42  0.000
x2            7.2899    0.9089   8.02  0.000
x2sq         -0.53110   0.06978 -7.61  0.001
x1x2          0.11473   0.03103  3.70  0.014

S = 1.00404   R-Sq = 99.9%   R-Sq(adj) = 99.9%

Analysis of Variance
Source           DF       SS      MS       F       P
Regression        4   7442.5  1860.6 1845.66  0.000
Residual Error    5      5.0     1.0
Total             9   7447.5

Values of Predictors for New Obs   Predicted Values for New Observations
New Obs    x1    x2   x2sq  x1x2   New Obs     Fit  SE Fit       95% CI              95% PI
      1  20.0  8.00   64.0   160         1  171.751   0.527 (170.396, 173.105) (168.836, 174.665)
```

PART 3
Dummy
Variables and
Advanced
Statistical
Inferences
(Optional)

12.10 Using Dummy Variables to Model Qualitative Independent Variables (Optional)

While the levels (or values) of a quantitative independent variable are numerical, the levels of a **qualitative** independent variable are defined by describing them. For instance, the type of sales technique used by a door-to-door salesperson is a qualitative independent variable. Here we might define three different levels—high pressure, medium pressure, and low pressure.

We can model the effects of the different levels of a qualitative independent variable by using what we call **dummy variables** (also called **indicator variables**). Such variables are usually defined so that they take on two values—either 0 or 1. To see how we use dummy variables, we begin with an example.

Example 12.10

Part 1: The data and data plots Suppose that Electronics World, a chain of stores that sells audio and video equipment, has gathered the data in Table 12.12. These data concern store sales volume in July of last year (y, measured in thousands of dollars), the number of households in the store's area (x, measured in thousands), and the location of the store (on a suburban street or in a suburban shopping mall—a qualitative independent variable). Figure 12.29 gives a data plot of y versus x. Stores with a street location are plotted as solid dots, while stores with a mall location are plotted as asterisks. Notice that the line relating y to x for mall locations has a higher y intercept than does the line relating y to x for street locations.

Part 2: A dummy variable model In order to model the effects of the street and shopping mall locations, we define a dummy variable denoted D_M as follows:

$$D_M = \begin{cases} 1 & \text{if a store is in a mall location,} \\ 0 & \text{otherwise.} \end{cases}$$

Using this dummy variable, we consider the regression model

$$y = \beta_0 + \beta_1 x + \beta_2 D_M + \varepsilon.$$

TABLE **12.12** The Electronics World Sales Volume Data   ◐ Electronics1

Store	Number of Households, x	Location	Sales Volume, y
1	161	Street	157.27
2	99	Street	93.28
3	135	Street	136.81
4	120	Street	123.79
5	164	Street	153.51
6	221	Mall	241.74
7	179	Mall	201.54
8	204	Mall	206.71
9	214	Mall	229.78
10	101	Mall	135.22

FIGURE **12.29** Plot of the Sales Volume Data and a Geometrical Interpretation of the Model $y = \beta_0 + \beta_1 x + \beta_2 D_M + \varepsilon$

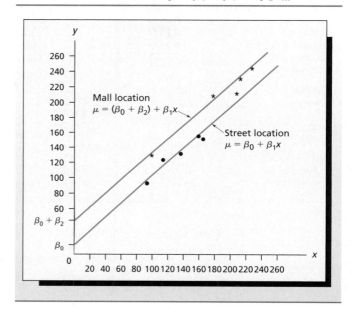

This model and the definition of D_M imply that

1 For a street location, mean sales volume equals

$$\beta_0 + \beta_1 x + \beta_2 D_M = \beta_0 + \beta_1 x + \beta_2(0)$$
$$= \beta_0 + \beta_1 x.$$

2 For a mall location, mean sales volume equals

$$\beta_0 + \beta_1 x + \beta_2 D_M = \beta_0 + \beta_1 x + \beta_2(1)$$
$$= (\beta_0 + \beta_2) + \beta_1 x.$$

Thus, the dummy variable allows us to model the situation illustrated in Figure 12.29. Here the lines relating mean sales volume to x for street and mall locations have different y intercepts—β_0 and $(\beta_0 + \beta_2)$—and the same slope, β_1. Note that β_2 is the difference between the mean monthly sales volume for stores in mall locations and the mean monthly sales volume for stores in street locations, when all these stores have the same number of households in their areas. That is, we can say that β_2 represents the effect on mean sales of a mall location compared to a street location. The Excel output in Figure 12.30 tells us that the least squares point estimate of β_2 is $b_2 = 29.2157$. This says that for any given number of households in a store's area, we estimate that the mean monthly sales volume in a mall location is \$29,215.70 greater than the mean monthly sales volume in a street location.

Part 3: A dummy variable model for comparing three locations   In addition to the data concerning street and mall locations in Table 12.12, Electronics World has also collected data concerning downtown locations. The complete data set is given in Table 12.13 and plotted in Figure 12.31. Here stores with a downtown location are plotted as open circles. A model describing these data is

$$y = \beta_0 + \beta_1 x + \beta_2 D_M + \beta_3 D_D + \varepsilon.$$

Here the dummy variable D_M is as previously defined and the dummy variable D_D is defined as follows:

$$D_D = \begin{cases} 1 & \text{if a store is in a downtown location,} \\ 0 & \text{otherwise.} \end{cases}$$

FIGURE 12.30   **Excel Output of a Regression Analysis of the Sales Volume Data Using the Model**
$$y = \beta_0 + \beta_1 x + \beta_2 D_M + \varepsilon$$

Regression Statistics

Multiple R	0.9913
R Square	0.9827
Adjusted R Square	0.9778
Standard Error	7.3288
Observations	10

ANOVA	df	SS	MS	F	Significance F
Regression	2	21,411.7977	10,705.8989	199.3216	6.75E-07
Residual	7	375.9817	53.7117		
Total	9	21,787.7795			

	Coefficients	Standard Error	t Stat	P-value	Lower 95%	Upper 95%
Intercept	17.3598	9.4470	1.8376	0.1087	−4.9788	39.6985
Households (x)	0.8510	0.0652	13.0439	3.63E-06	0.6968	1.0053
DummyMall	29.2157	5.5940	5.2227	0.0012	15.9881	42.4434

Then, we have the following:

1   For a street location, mean sales volume equals

$$\beta_0 + \beta_1 x + \beta_2 D_M + \beta_3 D_D = \beta_0 + \beta_1 x + \beta_2(0) + \beta_3(0)$$
$$= \beta_0 + \beta_1 x.$$

2   For a mall location, mean sales volume equals

$$\beta_0 + \beta_1 x + \beta_2 D_M + \beta_3 D_D = \beta_0 + \beta_1 x + \beta_2(1) + \beta_3(0)$$
$$= (\beta_0 + \beta_2) + \beta_1 x.$$

3   For a downtown location, mean sales volume equals

$$\beta_0 + \beta_1 x + \beta_2 D_M + \beta_3 D_D = \beta_0 + \beta_1 x + \beta_2(0) + \beta_3(1)$$
$$= (\beta_0 + \beta_3) + \beta_1 x.$$

TABLE 12.13   **The Complete Electronics World Sales Volume Data**

⬤ Electronics2

Store	Number of Households, x	Location	Sales Volume, y
1	161	Street	157.27
2	99	Street	93.28
3	135	Street	136.81
4	120	Street	123.79
5	164	Street	153.51
6	221	Mall	241.74
7	179	Mall	201.54
8	204	Mall	206.71
9	214	Mall	229.78
10	101	Mall	135.22
11	231	Downtown	224.71
12	206	Downtown	195.29
13	248	Downtown	242.16
14	107	Downtown	115.21
15	205	Downtown	197.82

FIGURE 12.31   **Plot of the Complete Electronics World Sales Volume Data and a Geometrical Interpretation of the Model**
$$y = \beta_0 + \beta_1 x + \beta_2 D_M + \beta_3 D_D + \varepsilon$$

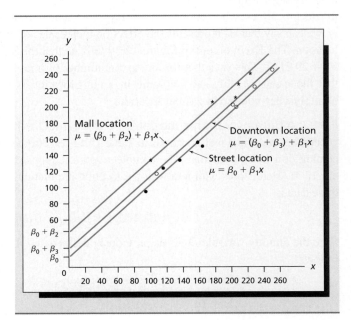

Thus, the dummy variables allow us to model the situation illustrated in Figure 12.31. Here the lines relating mean sales volume to x for street, mall, and downtown locations have different y-intercepts—β_0, $(\beta_0 + \beta_2)$, and $(\beta_0 + \beta_3)$—and the same slope, β_1. Note that β_2 represents the effect on mean sales of a mall location compared to a street location, and β_3 represents the effect on mean sales of a downtown location compared to a street location. Furthermore, the difference between β_2 and β_3, $\beta_2 - \beta_3$, represents the effect on mean sales of a mall location compared to a downtown location.

Part 4: Comparing the three locations   Figure 12.32 gives the MINITAB and Excel output of a regression analysis of the sales volume data using the dummy variable model. The output tells us that the least squares point estimate of β_2 is $b_2 = 28.374$. This says that for any given number of households in a store's area, we estimate that the mean monthly sales volume in a mall location is \$28,374 greater than the mean monthly sales volume in a street location. Furthermore, since the Excel output tells us that a 95 percent confidence interval for β_2 is [18.5545, 38.193], we are 95 percent confident that for any given number of households in a store's area, the mean monthly sales volume in a mall location is between \$18,554.50 and \$38,193 greater than the mean monthly sales volume in a street location. The MINITAB and Excel output also shows that the t statistic for testing $H_0: \beta_2 = 0$ versus $H_a: \beta_2 \neq 0$ equals 6.36 and that the related p value is less than 0.001. Therefore, we have very strong evidence that there is a difference between the mean monthly sales volumes in mall and street locations.

FIGURE **12.32**   **MINITAB and Excel Output of a Regression Analysis of the Sales Volume Data Using the Model**
$$y = \beta_0 + \beta_1 x + \beta_2 D_M + \beta_3 D_D + \varepsilon$$

(a) The MINITAB output

```
The regression equation is
Sales = 15.0 + 0.869 Households + 28.4 DMall + 6.86 DDowntown

Predictor       Coef   SE Coef        T       P
Constant      14.978     6.188     2.42   0.034
Households   0.86859   0.04049    21.45   0.000
DMall         28.374     4.461     6.36   0.000
DDowntown      6.864     4.770     1.44   0.178

S = 6.34941    R-Sq = 98.7%    R-Sq(adj) = 98.3%

Analysis of Variance
Source          DF       SS       MS       F       P
Regression       3    33269    11090   275.07   0.000
Residual Error  11      443       40
Total           14    33712
```

```
Values of Predictors for New Obs        Predicted Values for New Observations
New Obs  Households  DMall DDowntown    New Obs      Fit   SE Fit         95% CI            95% PI
      1         200      1         0          1   217.07     2.91  (210.65, 223.48)  (201.69, 232.45)
```

(b) The Excel output

Regression Statistics	
Multiple R	0.9934
R Square	0.9868
Adjusted R Square	0.9833
Standard Error	6.3494
Observations	15

ANOVA	df	SS	MS	F	Significance F
Regression	3	33,268.6953	11,089.5651	275.0729	1.27E-10
Residual	11	443.4650	40.3150		
Total	14	33,712.1603			

	Coefficients	Standard Error	t Stat	P-value	Lower 95%	Upper 95%
Intercept	14.9777	6.1884	2.4203	0.0340	1.3570	28.5984
Households (x)	0.8686	0.0405	21.4520	2.52E-10	0.7795	0.9577
DummyMall	28.3738	4.4613	6.3600	5.37E-05	18.5545	38.1930
DummyDtown	6.8638	4.7705	1.4388	0.1780	-3.6360	17.3635

We next note that the output in Figure 12.32 shows that the least squares point estimate of β_3 is $b_3 = 6.864$. Therefore, we estimate that for any given number of households in a store's area, the mean monthly sales volume in a downtown location is \$6,864 greater than the mean monthly sales volume in a street location. Furthermore, the Excel output shows that a 95 percent confidence interval for β_3 is $[-3.636, 17.3635]$. This says we are 95 percent confident that for any given number of households in a store's area, the mean monthly sales volume in a downtown location is between \$3,636 less than and \$17,363.50 greater than the mean monthly sales volume in a street location. The MINITAB and Excel output also show that the t statistic and p value for testing H_0: $\beta_3 = 0$ versus H_a: $\beta_3 \neq 0$ are, respectively, 1.44 and 0.178. Therefore, we do not have strong evidence that there is a difference between the mean monthly sales volumes in downtown and street locations.

Finally, note that, since $b_2 = 28.374$ and $b_3 = 6.864$, the point estimate of $\beta_2 - \beta_3$ is $b_2 - b_3 = 28.374 - 6.864 = 21.51$. Therefore, we estimate that mean monthly sales volume in a mall location is \$21,510 higher than mean monthly sales volume in a downtown location. Near the end of this section, we show how to compare the mall and downtown locations by using a confidence interval and a hypothesis test. We will find that there is very strong evidence that the mean monthly sales volume in a mall location is higher than the mean monthly sales volume in a downtown location. In summary, the mall location seems to give a higher mean monthly sales volume than either the street or the downtown location.

Part 5: Predicting a future sales volume   Suppose that Electronics World wishes to predict the sales volume in a future month for an individual store that has 200,000 households in its area and is located in a shopping mall. The point prediction of this sales volume is (since $D_M = 1$ and $D_D = 0$ when a store is in a shopping mall)

$$\hat{y} = b_0 + b_1(200) + b_2(1) + b_3(0)$$
$$= 14.978 + 0.8686(200) + 28.374(1)$$
$$= 217.07.$$

This point prediction is given at the bottom of the MINITAB output in Figure 12.32(a). The corresponding 95 percent prediction interval, which is $[201.69, 232.45]$, says we are 95 percent confident that the sales volume in a future sales period for an individual mall store that has 200,000 households in its area will be between \$201,690 and \$232,450.

Part 6: Interaction models   Consider the Electronics World data for street and mall locations given in Table 12.12 (page 455) and the model

$$y = \beta_0 + \beta_1 x + \beta_2 D_M + \beta_3 x D_M + \varepsilon.$$

This model uses the **cross-product**, or **interaction**, **term** xD_M and implies the following:

1   For a street location, mean sales volume equals (since $D_M = 0$)

$$\beta_0 + \beta_1 x + \beta_2(0) + \beta_3 x(0) = \beta_0 + \beta_1 x.$$

2   For a mall location, mean sales volume equals (since $D_M = 1$)

$$\beta_0 + \beta_1 x + \beta_2(1) + \beta_3 x(1) = (\beta_0 + \beta_2) + (\beta_1 + \beta_3)x.$$

As illustrated in Figure 12.33, if we use this model, then the straight lines relating mean sales volume to x for street and mall locations have **different y intercepts** and **different slopes**. Therefore, we say that this model assumes **interaction** between x and store location. Such a model is appropriate if the relationship between mean sales volume and x depends on (that is, is different for) the street and mall store locations. In general, **interaction** exists between two independent variables if the relationship between (for example, the slope of the line relating) the mean value of the dependent variable and one of the independent variables depends upon the value (or level) of the other independent variable. Figure 12.34 gives the MegaStat output of a regression analysis of the sales volume data using the interaction model. Here D_M and xD_M are labelled as DM and XDM, respectively, on the output. The MegaStat output tells us that the p value related to the significance of xD_M is 0.5886. This large p value tells us that the interaction term is not important. It follows that the no-interaction model on pages 454 and 455 seems best.

FIGURE **12.33**   **Geometrical Interpretation of the Sales Volume Model**
$$y = \beta_0 + \beta_1 x + \beta_2 D_M + \beta_3 x D_M + \varepsilon$$

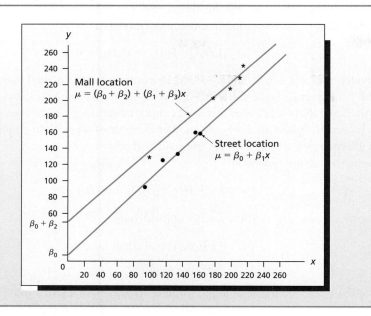

FIGURE **12.34**   **MegaStat Output Using the Interaction Model** $y = \beta_0 + \beta_1 x + \beta_2 DM + \beta_3 x DM + \varepsilon$

Regression Analysis

R²	0.984		
Adjusted R²	0.975	n	10
R	0.992	k	3
Std. Error	7.709	Dep. Var.	**Sales**

ANOVA table

Source	SS	df	MS	F	p-value
Regression	21,431.1861	3	7,143.7287	120.20	9.53E-06
Residual	356.5933	6	59.4322		
Total	21,787.7795	9			

Regression output

variables	coefficients	std. error	t (df = 6)	p-value	confidence interval 95% lower	95% upper
Intercept	7.9004	19.3142	0.409	0.6967	−39.3598	55.1607
X	0.9207	0.1399	6.579	0.0006	0.5783	1.2631
DM	42.7297	24.3812	1.753	0.1302	−16.9290	102.3885
XDM	−0.0917	0.1606	−0.571	0.5886	−0.4846	0.3012

Next consider the Electronics World data for street, mall, and downtown locations given in Table 12.13 (page 456). In modelling these data, if we believe that interaction exists between the number of households in a store's area and store location, we might consider using the model

$$y = \beta_0 + \beta_1 x + \beta_2 D_M + \beta_3 D_D + \beta_4 x D_M + \beta_5 x D_D + \varepsilon.$$

Similar to Figure 12.33, this model implies that the straight lines relating mean sales volume to x for the street, mall, and downtown locations have **different y intercepts** and **different slopes**. If we perform a regression analysis of the sales volume data using this interaction model, we find that the p values related to the significance of $x D_M$ and $x D_D$ are large: −0.5334 and 0.8132, respectively. Because these interaction terms are not significant, it seems best to employ the no-interaction model on pages 455 and 456.

In general, if we wish to model the effect of a qualitative independent variable with a levels, we use $a - 1$ dummy variables. The parameter multiplied by a particular dummy variable expresses the effect of the level represented by that dummy variable with respect to the effect of the level that is not represented by a dummy variable. For example, if we wish to compare the effects on sales, y, of four different types of advertising campaigns—television (T), radio (R), magazine (M), and mailed coupons (C)—we might employ the model

$$y = \beta_0 + \beta_1 D_T + \beta_2 D_R + \beta_3 D_M + \varepsilon.$$

Since this model does not use a dummy variable to represent the mailed coupon advertising campaign, the parameter β_1 is the difference between mean sales when a television advertising campaign is used and mean sales when a mailed coupon advertising campaign is used. The interpretations of β_2 and β_3 follow similarly. As another example, if we wish to employ a confidence interval and a hypothesis test to compare the mall and downtown locations in the Electronics World example, we can use the model

$$y = \beta_0 + \beta_1 x + \beta_2 D_S + \beta_3 D_M + \varepsilon.$$

Here the dummy variable D_M is as previously defined, and

$$D_S = \begin{cases} 1 & \text{if a store is in a street location,} \\ 0 & \text{otherwise.} \end{cases}$$

Since this model does not use a dummy variable to represent the downtown location, the parameter β_2 expresses the effect on mean sales of a street location compared to a downtown location, and the parameter β_3 expresses the effect on mean sales of a mall location compared to a downtown location.

The Excel output of the least squares point estimates of the parameters of this model is as follows:

	Coefficients	Standard Error	t Stat	P-value	Lower 95%	Upper 95%
Intercept	21.8415	8.5585	2.5520	0.0269	3.0044	40.6785
Households (x)	0.8686	0.0405	21.4520	2.52E-10	0.7795	0.9577
DummyStreet	−6.8638	4.7705	−1.4388	0.1780	−17.3635	3.6360
DummyMall	21.5100	4.0651	5.2914	0.0003	12.5628	30.4572

Since the least squares point estimate of β_3 is $b_3 = 21.51$, we estimate that for any given number of households in a store's area, the mean monthly sales volume in a mall location is \$21,510 higher than the mean monthly sales volume in a downtown location. The Excel output tells us that a 95 percent confidence interval for β_3 is [12.5628, 30.4572]. Therefore, we are 95 percent confident that for any given number of households in a store's area, the mean monthly sales volume in a mall location is between \$12,562.80 and \$30,457.20 greater than the mean monthly sales volume in a downtown location. The Excel output also shows that the t statistic and p value for testing $H_0: \beta_3 = 0$ versus $H_a: \beta_3 \neq 0$ in this model are, respectively, 5.2914 and 0.0003. Therefore, we have very strong evidence that there is a difference between the mean monthly sales volumes in mall and downtown locations.

In some situations, dummy variables represent the effects of unusual events or occurrences that may have an important effect on the dependent variable. For instance, suppose we wish to build a regression model relating quarterly sales of automobiles (y) to automobile prices (x_1), fuel prices (x_2), and personal income (x_3). If an autoworkers' strike occurred in a particular quarter that had a major effect on automobile sales, then we might define a dummy variable D_S to be equal to 1 if an autoworkers' strike occurs and 0 otherwise. The least squares point estimate of the regression parameter multiplied by D_S would estimate the effect of the strike on mean auto sales. Finally, dummy variables can be used to model the impact of regularly occurring **seasonal** influences on time series data—for example, the effect of the hot summer months on soft drink sales. This is discussed in Chapter 16.

Exercises for Section 12.10

CONCEPTS

12.40 What is a qualitative independent variable?

12.41 How do we use dummy variables to model the effects of a qualitative independent variable?

12.42 What does the parameter multiplied by a dummy variable express?

METHODS AND APPLICATIONS

12.43 Neter, Kutner, Nachtsheim, and Wasserman (1996) relate the speed, y, with which a particular insurance innovation is adopted to the size of the insurance firm, x, and the type of firm. The dependent variable y is measured by the number of months elapsed between the time the first firm adopted the innovation and the time the firm being considered adopted the innovation. The size of the firm, x, is measured by the total assets of the firm, and the type of firm—a qualitative independent variable—is either a mutual company or a stock company. The data in Table 12.14 are observed.

a. Discuss why the data plot below indicates that the model

$$y = \beta_0 + \beta_1 x + \beta_2 D_S + \varepsilon$$

might appropriately describe the observed data. Here D_S equals 1 if the firm is a stock company and 0 if the firm is a mutual company.

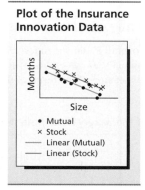

Plot of the Insurance Innovation Data

- Mutual
- × Stock
- — Linear (Mutual)
- — Linear (Stock)

b. The model of part a implies that the mean adoption time of an insurance innovation by mutual companies with asset size x equals

$$\beta_0 + \beta_1 x + \beta_2(0) = \beta_0 + \beta_1 x$$

and that the mean adoption time by stock companies with asset size x equals

$$\beta_0 + \beta_1 x + \beta_2(1) = \beta_0 + \beta_1 x + \beta_2.$$

The difference between these two means equals the model parameter β_2. In your own words, interpret the practical meaning of β_2.

c. Figure 12.35 presents the Excel output of a regression analysis of the insurance innovation data using the model of part a. Using the output, test H_0: $\beta_2 = 0$ versus H_a: $\beta_2 \neq 0$ by setting $\alpha = 0.05$ and 0.01. Interpret the practical meaning of the result of this test. Also use the computer output to find, report, and interpret a 95 percent confidence interval for β_2.

d. If we add the interaction term xD_S to the model of part a, we find that the p value related to this term is 0.9821. What does this imply?

12.44 THE SHELF DISPLAY CASE ● BakeSale

The Tastee Bakery Company supplies a bakery product to many supermarkets in a metropolitan area. The company wishes to study the effect of the height of the shelf display employed by the supermarkets on monthly sales, y (measured in cases of 10 units each), for this product. Shelf display height has three levels—bottom (B), middle (M), and top (T). For each shelf display height, six supermarkets of equal sales potential will be randomly selected, and each supermarket will display the product using its assigned shelf height for a month. At the end of the month, sales of the bakery product at the 18 participating stores will be recorded. When the experiment is carried out, the data in Table 12.15 are obtained. Here we assume that the set of sales amounts for each

TABLE **12.14** The Insurance Innovation Data ● InsInnov

Firm	Number of Months Elapsed, y	Size of Firm (Millions of Dollars), x	Type of Firm	Firm	Number of Months Elapsed, y	Size of Firm (Millions of Dollars), x	Type of Firm
1	17	151	Mutual	11	28	164	Stock
2	26	92	Mutual	12	15	272	Stock
3	21	175	Mutual	13	11	295	Stock
4	30	31	Mutual	14	38	68	Stock
5	22	104	Mutual	15	31	85	Stock
6	0	277	Mutual	16	21	224	Stock
7	12	210	Mutual	17	20	166	Stock
8	19	120	Mutual	18	13	305	Stock
9	4	290	Mutual	19	30	124	Stock
10	16	238	Mutual	20	14	246	Stock

FIGURE **12.35**   **Excel Output of a Regression Analysis of the Insurance Innovation Data Using the Model**
$y = \beta_0 + \beta_1 x + \beta_2 D_s + \varepsilon$

Regression Statistics

Multiple R	0.9461
R Square	0.8951
Adjusted R Square	0.8827
Standard Error	3.2211
Observations	20

ANOVA	df	SS	MS	F	Significance F
Regression	2	1,504.4133	752.2067	72.4971	4.77E-09
Residual	17	176.3867	10.3757		
Total	19	1,680.8			

	Coefficients	Standard Error	t Stat	P-value	Lower 95%	Upper 95%
Intercept	33.8741	1.8139	18.6751	9.15E-13	30.0472	37.7010
Size of Firm (x)	−0.1017	0.0089	−11.4430	2.07E-09	−0.1205	−0.0830
DummyStock	8.0555	1.4591	5.5208	3.74E-05	4.9770	11.1339

TABLE **12.15**   **Bakery Sales Study Data (Sales in Cases)**   ● BakeSale

	Shelf Display Height	
Bottom, B	Middle, M	Top, T
58.2	73.0	52.4
53.7	78.1	49.7
55.8	75.4	50.9
55.7	76.2	54.0
52.5	78.4	52.1
58.9	82.1	49.9

display height is a sample that has been randomly selected from the population of all sales amounts that could be obtained (at supermarkets of the given sales potential) when using that display height. To compare the population mean sales amounts μ_B, μ_M, and μ_T that would be obtained by using the bottom, middle, and top display heights, we use the following dummy variable regression model:

$$y = \beta_B + \beta_M D_M + \beta_T D_T + \varepsilon.$$

Here D_M equals 1 if a middle display height is used and 0 otherwise; D_T equals 1 if a top display height is used and 0 otherwise. Figure 12.36 presents the MINITAB output of a regression analysis of the bakery sales study data using this model.[1]

a. By using the definitions of the dummy variables, show that

$$\mu_B = \beta_B, \ \mu_M = \beta_B + \beta_M, \text{ and } \mu_T = \beta_B + \beta_T.$$

b. Use the overall F statistic to test H_0: $\beta_M = \beta_T = 0$ or, equivalently, H_0: $\mu_B = \mu_M = \mu_T$. Interpret the practical meaning of the result of this test.

FIGURE **12.36**   **MINITAB Output of a Dummy Variable Regression Analysis of the Bakery Sales Data in Table 12.15**

```
The regression equation is
Bakery Sales = 55.8 + 21.4 DMiddle - 4.30 DTop

Predictor     Coef   SE Coef      T      P
Constant    55.800    1.013   55.07  0.000
DMiddle     21.400    1.433   14.93  0.000
DTop        -4.300    1.433   -3.00  0.009

S = 2.48193   R-Sq = 96.1%   R-Sq(adj) = 95.6%

Analysis of Variance
Source             DF      SS      MS       F      P
Regression          2  2273.9  1136.9  184.57  0.000
Residual Error     15    92.4     6.2
Total              17  2366.3

Values of Predictors for New Obs    Predicted Values for New Observations
New Obs  DMiddle  DTop              New Obs    Fit  SE Fit       95% CI              95% PI
      1        1     0                    1  77.200   1.013  (75.040, 79.360)  (71.486, 82.914)
```

[1]In general, the regression approach of this exercise produces the same comparisons of several population means that are produced by **one-way analysis of variance** (see Section 10.2). In Appendix G in the Online Learning Centre, we discuss the regression approach to **two-way analysis of variance** (see Section 10.4).

c. Show that your results in part a imply that

$$\mu_M - \mu_B = \beta_M, \mu_T - \mu_B = \beta_T,$$
$$\text{and } \mu_M - \mu_T = \beta_M - \beta_T.$$

Then use the least squares point estimates of the model parameters to find a point estimate of each of the three differences in means. Also find a 95 percent confidence interval for and test the significance of each of the first two differences in means. Interpret your results.

d. Find a point estimate of mean sales when using a middle display height, a 95 percent confidence interval for mean sales when using a middle display height, and a 95 percent prediction interval for sales at an individual supermarket that employs a middle display height (see the bottom of the MINITAB output in Figure 12.36).

e. Consider the alternative model

$$y = \beta_T + \beta_B D_B + \beta_M D_M + \varepsilon.$$

Here D_B equals 1 if a bottom display height is used and 0 otherwise. The MINITAB output of the least squares point estimates of the parameters of this model is as follows:

```
Predictor    Coef    SE Coef      T       P
Constant    51.500    1.013    50.83   0.000
DBottom      4.300    1.433     3.00   0.009
DMiddle     25.700    1.433    17.94   0.000
```

Since β_M expresses the effect of the middle display height with respect to the effect of the top display height, β_M equals $\mu_M - \mu_T$. Use the MINITAB output to calculate a 95 percent confidence interval for and test the significance of $\mu_M - \mu_T$. Interpret your results.

12.45 THE FRESH DETERGENT CASE ● Fresh3

Recall from Exercise 12.7 (on pages 418 and 419) that Enterprise Industries has observed the historical data in Table 12.4 (page 419) concerning y (demand for Fresh liquid laundry detergent), x_1 (the price of Fresh), x_2 (the average industry price of competitors' similar detergents), and x_3 (Enterprise Industries' advertising expenditure for Fresh). To ultimately increase the demand for Fresh, Enterprise Industries' marketing department is comparing the effectiveness of three different advertising campaigns. These campaigns are denoted as campaigns A, B, and C. Campaign A consists entirely of television commercials, campaign B consists of a balanced mixture of television and radio commercials, and campaign C consists of a balanced mixture of television, radio, newspaper, and magazine ads. To conduct the study, Enterprise Industries has randomly selected one advertising campaign to be used in each of the 30 sales periods in Table 12.4. Although logic would indicate that each of campaigns A, B, and C should be used in 10 of the 30 sales periods, Enterprise Industries has made previous commitments to the advertising media involved in the study. As a

TABLE 12.16 Advertising Campaigns Used by Enterprise Industries ● Fresh3

Sales Period	Advertising Campaign	Sales Period	Advertising Campaign
1	B	16	B
2	B	17	B
3	B	18	A
4	A	19	B
5	C	20	B
6	A	21	C
7	C	22	A
8	C	23	A
9	B	24	A
10	C	25	A
11	A	26	B
12	C	27	C
13	C	28	B
14	A	29	C
15	B	30	C

result, campaigns A, B, and C were randomly assigned to, respectively, 9, 11, and 10 sales periods. Furthermore, advertising was done in only the first three weeks of each sales period, so that the carryover effect of the campaign used in a sales period to the next sales period would be minimized. Table 12.16 lists the campaigns used in the sales periods.

To compare the effectiveness of advertising campaigns A, B, and C, we define two dummy variables. Specifically, we define the dummy variable D_B to equal 1 if campaign B is used in a sales period and 0 otherwise. Furthermore, we define the dummy variable D_C to equal 1 if campaign C is used in a sales period and 0 otherwise. Figure 12.37 presents the MegaStat output of a regression analysis of the Fresh demand data by using the model

$$y = \beta_0 + \beta_1 x_1 + \beta_2 x_2 + \beta_3 x_3 + \beta_4 D_B + \beta_5 D_C + \varepsilon.$$

a. In this model, the parameter β_4 represents the effect on mean demand of advertising campaign B compared to advertising campaign A, and the parameter β_5 represents the effect on mean demand of advertising campaign C compared to advertising campaign A. Use the regression output to find and report a point estimate of each of the above effects and to test the significance of each of the above effects. Also find and report a 95 percent confidence interval for each of the above effects. Interpret your results.

b. The prediction results at the bottom of the MegaStat output correspond to a future period when the price of Fresh will be $x_1 = 3.70$, the competitor's average price of similar detergents will be $x_2 = 3.90$, the advertising expenditure for Fresh will be $x_3 = 6.50$, and advertising campaign C will be used. Show how $\hat{y} = 8.61621$ is calculated. Then find, report, and interpret a 95 percent confidence interval for mean demand and a 95 percent prediction interval for an individual demand

FIGURE 12.37   MegaStat Output of a Dummy Variable Regression Model Analysis of the Fresh Demand Data

Regression Analysis

R^2 0.960

Adjusted R^2 0.951   n 30

R 0.980   k 5

Std. Error 0.150   Dep. Var. **Demand**

ANOVA table

Source	SS	df	MS	F	p-value
Regression	12.9166	5	2.5833	114.39	6.24E-16
Residual	0.5420	24	0.0226		
Total	13.4586	29			

Regression output | | | | | **confidence interval** | |
variables	coefficients	std. error	t (df = 24)	p-value	95% lower	95% upper
Intercept	8.7154	1.5849	5.499	1.18E-05	5.4443	11.9866
X1	−2.7680	0.4144	−6.679	6.58E-07	−3.6234	−1.9127
X2	1.6667	0.1913	8.711	6.77E-09	1.2718	2.0616
X3	0.4927	0.0806	6.110	2.60E-06	0.3263	0.6592
DB	0.2695	0.0695	3.880	0.0007	0.1262	0.4128
DC	0.4396	0.0703	6.250	1.85E-06	0.2944	0.5847

Predicted values for: Demand

	95% Confidence Interval		95% Prediction Interval			
Predicted	**lower**	**upper**	**lower**	**upper**	**Leverage**	
8.61621	8.51380	8.71862	8.28958	8.94285	0.109	

when $x_1 = 3.70$, $x_2 = 3.90$, $x_3 = 6.50$, and campaign C is used.

c. Consider the alternative model

$$y = \beta_0 + \beta_1 x_1 + \beta_2 x_2 + \beta_3 x_3 + \beta_4 D_A + \beta_5 D_C + \varepsilon.$$

Here D_A equals 1 if advertising campaign A is used and 0 otherwise. Describe the effect represented by the regression parameter β_5.

d. The MegaStat output of the least squares point estimates of the parameters of the model of part c is as in Figure 12.38. Use the MegaStat output to test the significance of the effect represented by β_5 and find a 95 percent confidence interval for β_5. Interpret your results.

12.46   THE FRESH DETERGENT CASE   ◆ Fresh3

Figure 12.39 presents the MegaStat output of a regression analysis of the Fresh demand data using the model

$$y = \beta_0 + \beta_1 x_1 + \beta_2 x_2 + \beta_3 x_3 + \beta_4 D_B + \beta_5 D_C + \beta_6 x_3 D_B + \beta_7 x_3 D_C + \varepsilon,$$

where the dummy variables D_B and D_C are defined as in Exercise 12.45.

a. This model assumes that there is interaction between advertising expenditure, x_3, and type of advertising campaign. What do the p values related to the significance of the cross-product terms $x_3 D_B$ and $x_3 D_C$ say about the need for these interaction terms and about whether there is interaction between x_3 and type of advertising campaign?

b. The prediction results at the bottom of Figure 12.39 are for a future sales period in which $x_1 = 3.70$, $x_2 = 3.90$, $x_3 = 6.50$, and advertising campaign C will be used. Use the output to find and report a point prediction of and a 95 percent prediction interval for Fresh demand in such a sales period. Is the 95 percent prediction interval given by this model shorter or longer than the 95 percent prediction interval given by the model that utilizes D_B and D_C in Exercise 12.45? What are the implications of this comparison?

FIGURE 12.38   MegaStat Output for Exercise 12.45(d)

Regression output | | | | | **confidence interval** | |
variables	coefficients	std. error	t (df = 23)	p-value	95% lower	95% upper
Intercept	8.9849	1.5971	5.626	8.61E-06	5.6888	12.2811
X1	−2.7680	0.4144	−6.679	6.58E-07	−3.6234	−1.9127
X2	1.6667	0.1913	8.711	6.77E-09	1.2718	2.0616
X3	0.4927	0.0806	6.110	2.60E-06	0.3263	0.6592
DA	−0.2695	0.0695	−3.880	0.0007	−0.4128	−0.1262
DC	0.1701	0.0669	2.543	0.0179	0.0320	0.3081

FIGURE **12.39** **MegaStat Output of a Regression Analysis of the Fresh Demand Data Using the Model**
$$y = \beta_0 + \beta_1 x_1 + \beta_2 x_2 + \beta_3 x_3 + \beta_4 D_B + \beta_5 D_C + \beta_6 x_3 D_B + \beta_7 x_3 D_C + \varepsilon$$

Regression output variables	coefficients	std. error	t (df = 22)	p-value	confidence interval 95% lower	95% upper
Intercept	8.7619	1.7071	5.133	3.82E-05	5.2216	12.3021
X1	−2.7895	0.4339	−6.428	1.81E-06	−3.6894	−1.8895
X2	1.6365	0.2062	7.938	6.72E-08	1.2089	2.0641
X3	0.5160	0.1288	4.007	0.0006	0.2489	0.7831
DB	0.2539	0.8722	0.291	0.7737	−1.5550	2.0628
DC	0.8435	0.9739	0.866	0.3958	−1.1762	2.8631
X3DB	0.0030	0.1334	0.023	0.9822	−0.2736	0.2797
X3DC	−0.0629	0.1502	−0.419	0.6794	−0.3744	0.2486

Predicted values for: Demand						R² 0.960
	95% Confidence Interval		95% Prediction Interval			Adjusted R² 0.948
Predicted	lower	upper	lower	upper	Leverage	R 0.980
8.61178	8.50372	8.71984	8.27089	8.95266	0.112	Std. Error 0.156

12.11 The Partial *F* Test: Testing the Significance of a Portion of a Regression Model (Optional)

We now present a **partial *F* test** that allows us to test the significance of a set of independent variables in a regression model. That is, we can use this *F* test to test the significance of a **portion** of a regression model. For example, in the Electronics World situation, we employed the dummy variable model

$$y = \beta_0 + \beta_1 x + \beta_2 D_M + \beta_3 D_D + \varepsilon.$$

It might be useful to test the significance of the dummy variables D_M and D_D. We can do this by testing the null hypothesis

$$H_0: \beta_2 = \beta_3 = 0,$$

which says that neither dummy variable significantly affects *y*, versus the alternative hypothesis

$$H_a: \text{at least one of } \beta_2 \text{ and } \beta_3 \text{ does not equal } 0,$$

which says that at least one of the dummy variables significantly affects *y*. Because β_2 and β_3 represent the effects of the mall and downtown locations with respect to the street location, the null hypothesis says that the effects of the mall, downtown, and street locations on mean sales volume do not differ (insignificant dummy variables). The alternative hypothesis says that at least two locations have different effects on mean sales volume (at least one significant dummy variable).

In general, consider the regression model

$$y = \beta_0 + \beta_1 x_1 + \cdots + \beta_g x_g + \beta_{g+1} x_{g+1} + \cdots + \beta_k x_k + \varepsilon.$$

Suppose we wish to test the null hypothesis

$$H_0: \beta_{g+1} = \beta_{g+2} = \cdots = \beta_k = 0,$$

which says that none of the independent variables $x_{g+1}, x_{g+2}, \ldots, x_k$ affect *y*, versus the alternative hypothesis

$$H_a: \text{at least one of } \beta_{g+1}, \beta_{g+2}, \ldots, \beta_k \text{ does not equal } 0,$$

which says that at least one of the independent variables $x_{g+1}, x_{g+2}, \ldots, x_k$ affects *y*. If we can reject H_0 in favour of H_a by specifying a **small** probability of a Type I error, then it is reasonable to conclude that at least one of $x_{g+1}, x_{g+2}, \ldots, x_k$ **significantly** affects y. In this case, we should use t statistics and other techniques to determine which of $x_{g+1}, x_{g+2}, \ldots, x_k$ significantly affect y. To test H_0 versus H_a, consider the following two models:

$$\text{\textbf{Complete model:}} \quad y = \beta_0 + \beta_1 x_1 + \cdots + \beta_g x_g + \beta_{g+1} x_{g+1} + \cdots + \beta_k x_k + \varepsilon.$$

$$\text{\textbf{Reduced model:}} \quad y = \beta_0 + \beta_1 x_1 + \cdots + \beta_g x_g + \varepsilon.$$

Here the complete model is assumed to have k independent variables, the reduced model is the complete model under the assumption that H_0 is true, and $(k - g)$ denotes the number of regression parameters we have set equal to 0 in the statement of H_0.

To carry out this test, we calculate SSE_C, **the unexplained variation for the complete model**, and SSE_R, **the unexplained variation for the reduced model**. The appropriate test statistic is based on the difference

$$SSE_R - SSE_C,$$

which is called **the drop in the unexplained variation attributable to the independent variables $x_{g+1}, x_{g+2}, \ldots, x_k$.** In the following box, we give the formula for the test statistic and show how to carry out the test:

The Partial F Test: An F Test for a Portion of a Regression Model

Suppose that the regression assumptions hold and consider testing

$$H_0: \beta_{g+1} = \beta_{g+2} = \cdots = \beta_k = 0$$

versus

H_a: at least one of $\beta_{g+1}, \beta_{g+2}, \ldots, \beta_k$ does not equal 0.

We define the **partial F statistic** to be

$$F = \frac{(SSE_R - SSE_C)/(k - g)}{SSE_C/[n - (k + 1)]}.$$

Also define the p value related to F to be the area under the curve of the F distribution (with $k - g$ and $n - (k + 1)$ degrees of freedom) to the right of F. Then, we can reject H_0 in favour of H_a at level of significance α if either of the following equivalent conditions holds:

1    $F > F_\alpha$.

2   p value $< \alpha$.

Here the point F_α is based on $k - g$ numerator and $n - (k + 1)$ denominator degrees of freedom.

It can be shown that the "extra" independent variables $x_{g+1}, x_{g+2}, \ldots, x_k$ will always explain some of the variation in the observed y values and, therefore, will always make SSE_C somewhat smaller than SSE_R. Condition 1 says that we should reject H_0 if

$$F = \frac{(SSE_R - SSE_C)/(k - g)}{SSE_C/[n - (k + 1)]}$$

is large. This is reasonable because a large value of F would result from a large value of $(SSE_R - SSE_C)$, which would be obtained if at least one of the independent variables $x_{g+1}, x_{g+2}, \ldots, x_k$ makes SSE_C substantially smaller than SSE_R. This would suggest that H_0 is false and that H_a is true.

Before looking at an example, we should point out that testing the significance of a single independent variable by using a partial F test is equivalent[2] to carrying out this test by using the previously discussed t test (see Section 12.6).

---

[2] It can be shown that when we test $H_0: \beta_j = 0$ versus $H_a: \beta_j \neq 0$ using a partial F test,

$$F = t^2 \quad \text{and} \quad F_\alpha = (t_{\alpha/2})^2.$$

Here $t_{\alpha/2}$ is based on $n - (k + 1)$ degrees of freedom, and F_α is based on 1 numerator and $n - (k + 1)$ denominator degrees of freedom. Hence, the rejection conditions

$$|t| > t_{\alpha/2} \quad \text{and} \quad F > F_\alpha$$

are equivalent. It can also be shown that in this case the p value related to t equals the p value related to F.

FIGURE 12.40   MINITAB Output of a Correlation Matrix for the Sales Territory Performance Data

	Sales	Time	MktPoten	Adver	MktShare	Change	Accts	WkLoad
Time	0.623							
	0.001							
MktPoten	0.598	0.454						
	0.002	0.023						
Adver	0.596	0.249	0.174		Cell Contents: Pearson correlation			
	0.002	0.230	0.405		P-Value			
MktShare	0.484	0.106	−0.211	0.264				
	0.014	0.613	0.312	0.201				
Change	0.489	0.251	0.268	0.377	0.085			
	0.013	0.225	0.195	0.064	0.685			
Accts	0.754	0.758	0.479	0.200	0.403	0.327		
	0.000	0.000	0.016	0.338	0.046	0.110		
WkLoad	−0.117	−0.179	−0.259	−0.272	0.349	−0.288	−0.199	
	0.577	0.391	0.212	0.188	0.087	0.163	0.341	
Rating	0.402	0.101	0.359	0.411	−0.024	0.549	0.229	−0.277
	0.046	0.631	0.078	0.041	0.911	0.004	0.272	0.180

WKLOAD. However, the simple correlation coefficients between SALES and the other seven independent variables range from 0.402 to 0.754, with associated p values ranging from 0.046 to 0.000. This indicates the existence of potentially useful relationships between SALES and these seven independent variables.

While simple correlation coefficients (and scatter plots) give us a preliminary understanding of the data, they cannot be relied upon alone to tell us which independent variables are significantly related to the dependent variable. One reason for this is a condition called **multicollinearity**. Multicollinearity is said to exist among the independent variables in a regression situation if these independent variables are related to or dependent upon each other. One way to investigate multicollinearity is to examine the correlation matrix. To understand this, note that all of the simple correlation coefficients located in the first column of this matrix measure the **simple correlations between the independent variables**. For example, the simple correlation coefficient between ACCTS and TIME is 0.758, which says that the ACCTS values increase as the TIME values increase. Such a relationship makes sense because it is logical that the longer a sales representative has been with the company, the more accounts they handle. Statisticians often regard multicollinearity in a data set to be severe if at least one simple correlation coefficient between the independent variables is at least 0.9. Since the largest such simple correlation coefficient in Figure 12.40 is 0.758, this is not true for the sales territory performance data. Note, however, that even moderate multicollinearity can be a potential problem. This will be demonstrated later using the sales territory performance data.

Another way to measure multicollinearity is to use **variance inflation factors**. Consider a regression model relating a dependent variable y to a set of independent variables $x_1, \ldots, x_{j-1},$ $x_j, x_{j+1}, \ldots, x_k$. The variance inflation factor for the independent variable x_j in this set is denoted VIF_j and is defined by the equation

$$VIF_j = \frac{1}{1 - R_j^2},$$

where R_j^2 is the multiple coefficient of determination for the regression model that relates x_j to all the other independent variables $x_1, \ldots, x_{j-1}, x_{j+1}, \ldots, x_k$ in the set. For example, Figure 12.41 gives the MegaStat output of the t statistics, p values, and variance inflation factors for the sales territory performance model that relates y to all eight independent variables. The largest variance inflation factor is $VIF_6 = 5.639$. To calculate VIF_6, MegaStat first calculates the multiple coefficient of determination for the regression model that relates x_6 to x_1, $x_2, x_3, x_4, x_5, x_7,$ and x_8 to be $R_6^2 = 0.822673$. It then follows that

$$VIF_6 = \frac{1}{1 - R_6^2} = \frac{1}{1 - 0.822673} = 5.639.$$

FIGURE **12.41**   **MegaStat Output of the *t* Statistics, *p* Values, and Variance Inflation Factors for the Sales Territory Performance Model**

$$y = \beta_0 + \beta_1 x_1 + \beta_2 x_2 + \beta_3 x_3 + \beta_4 x_4 + \beta_5 x_5 + \beta_6 x_6 + \beta_7 x_7 + \beta_8 x_8 + \varepsilon$$

Regression output variables	coefficients	std. error	t (df = 16)	p-value	confidence interval 95% lower	95% upper	VIF
Intercept	−1,507.8137	778.6349	−1.936	0.0707	−3158.4457	142.8182	
Time	2.0096	1.9307	1.041	0.3134	−2.0832	6.1024	3.343
MktPoten	0.0372	0.0082	4.536	0.0003	0.0198	0.0546	1.978
Adver	0.1510	0.0471	3.205	0.0055	0.0511	0.2509	1.910
MktShare	199.0235	67.0279	2.969	0.0090	56.9307	341.1164	3.236
Change	290.8551	186.7820	1.557	0.1390	−105.1049	686.8152	1.602
Accts	5.5510	4.7755	1.162	0.2621	−4.5728	15.6747	5.639
WkLoad	19.7939	33.6767	0.588	0.5649	−51.5975	91.1853	1.818
Rating	8.1893	128.5056	0.064	0.9500	−264.2304	280.6090	1.809
							2.667 mean VIF

In general, if $R_j^2 = 0$, which says that x_j is not related to the other independent variables, then the variance inflation factor VIF_j equals 1. On the other hand, if $R_j^2 > 0$, which says that x_j is related to the other independent variables, then $(1 - R_j^2)$ is less than 1, making VIF_j greater than 1. Both the largest variance inflation factor among the independent variables and the mean $\overline{VIF}$ of the variance inflation factors for the independent variables indicate the severity of multicollinearity. Generally, the multicollinearity between independent variables is considered severe if

1   The largest variance inflation factor is greater than 10 (which means that the largest R_j^2 is greater than 0.9).

2   The mean $\overline{VIF}$ of the variance inflation factors is substantially greater than 1.

The largest variance inflation factor in Figure 12.41 is not greater than 10, and the average of the variance inflation factors, which is 2.667, would probably not be considered substantially greater than 1. Therefore, we would probably not consider the multicollinearity among the eight independent variables to be severe.

The reason that VIF_j is called the variance inflation factor is that it can be shown that, when VIF_j is greater than 1, the standard deviation σ_{b_j} of the population of all possible values of the least squares point estimate b_j is likely to be inflated beyond its value when $R_j^2 = 0$. If σ_{b_j} is greatly inflated, two slightly different samples of values of the dependent variable can yield two substantially different values of b_j. To intuitively understand why strong multicollinearity can significantly affect the least squares point estimates, consider the so-called picket fence display in the page margin. This figure depicts two independent variables (x_1 and x_2) exhibiting strong multicollinearity (note that as x_1 increases, x_2 increases). The heights of the pickets on the fence represent the y observations. If we assume that the model

The picket fence display

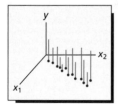

$$y = \beta_0 + \beta_1 x_1 + \beta_2 x_2 + \varepsilon$$

adequately describes these data, then calculating the least squares point estimates amounts to fitting a plane to the points on the top of the picket fence. Clearly, this plane would be quite unstable. That is, a slightly different height of one of the pickets (a slightly different y value) could cause the slant of the fitted plane (and the least squares point estimates that determine this slant) to radically change. It follows that, when strong multicollinearity exists, sampling variation can result in least squares point estimates that differ substantially from the true values of the regression parameters. In fact, some of the least squares point estimates may have a sign (positive or negative) that differs from the sign of the true value of the parameter (we will see an example of this in the exercises). Therefore, when strong multicollinearity exists, it is dangerous to individually interpret the least squares point estimates.

The most important problem caused by multicollinearity is that, even when multicollinearity is not severe, it can hinder our ability to use the t statistics and related p values to assess the importance of the independent variables. Recall that we can reject H_0: $\beta_j = 0$ in favour of H_a: $\beta_j \neq 0$ at level of significance α if and only if the absolute value of the corresponding t statistic is greater than $t_{\alpha/2}$ based on $n - (k + 1)$ degrees of freedom or, equivalently, if and only if the related p value is less than α. Thus, the larger (in absolute value) the t statistic is and the smaller the p value is, the stronger is the evidence that we should reject H_0: $\beta_j = 0$ and the stronger is the evidence that the independent variable x_j is significant. When multicollinearity exists, the sizes of the t statistic and of the related p value **measure the additional importance of the independent variable x_j over the combined importance of the other independent variables in the regression model**. Since two or more correlated independent variables contribute redundant information, multicollinearity often causes the t statistics obtained by relating a dependent variable to a set of correlated independent variables to be smaller (in absolute value) than the t statistics that would be obtained if separate regression analyses were run, where each separate regression analysis relates the dependent variable to a smaller set (for example, only one) of the correlated independent variables. Thus, multicollinearity can cause some of the correlated independent variables to appear less important—in terms of having small absolute t statistics and large p values—than they really are. Another way to understand this is to note that since multicollinearity inflates σ_{b_j}, it inflates the point estimate s_{b_j} of σ_{b_j}. Since $t = b_j/s_{b_j}$, an inflated value of s_{b_j} can (depending on the size of b_j) cause t to be small (and the related p value to be large). This would suggest that x_j is not significant even though x_j may really be important.

For example, Figure 12.41 tells us that when we perform a regression analysis of the sales territory performance data using a model that relates y to all eight independent variables, the p values related to TIME, MKTPOTEN, ADVER, MKTSHARE, CHANGE, ACCTS, WKLOAD, and RATING are, respectively, 0.3134, 0.0003, 0.0055, 0.0090, 0.1390, 0.2621, 0.5650, and 0.9500. By contrast, recall from Figure 12.8 (page 423) that when we perform a regression analysis of the sales territory performance data using a model that relates y to the first five independent variables, the p values related to TIME, MKTPOTEN, ADVER, MKTSHARE, and CHANGE are, respectively, 0.0065, 0.0001, 0.0025, 0.0001, and 0.0530. Note that TIME (p value = 0.0065) seems **highly significant** and CHANGE (p value = 0.0530) seems **somewhat significant** in the five independent variable model. However, when we consider the model that uses all eight independent variables, TIME (p value = 0.3134) seems **insignificant** and CHANGE (p value = 0.1390) seems **somewhat insignificant**. The reason that TIME and CHANGE seem more significant in the five independent variable model is that, since this model uses fewer variables, TIME and CHANGE contribute less overlapping information and thus have more additional importance in this model.

Comparing regression models on the basis of R^2, s, adjusted R^2, prediction interval length, and the C statistic

We have seen that when multicollinearity exists in a model, the p value associated with an independent variable in the model measures the additional importance of the variable over the combined importance of the other variables in the model. Therefore, it can be difficult to use the p values to determine which variables to retain in and which variables to remove from a model. The implication of this is that we need to evaluate more than the **additional importance** of each independent variable in a regression model. We also need to evaluate how well the independent variables **work together** to accurately describe, predict, and control the dependent variable. One way to do this is to determine if the **overall** model gives a high R^2 and $\overline{R}^2$, a small s, and short prediction intervals.

It can be proven that **adding any independent variable to a regression model, even an unimportant independent variable, will decrease the unexplained variation and will increase the explained variation**. Therefore, since the total variation $\Sigma(y_i - \overline{y})^2$ depends only on the observed y values and thus remains unchanged when we add an independent variable to a regression model, it follows that **adding any independent variable to a regression model will increase**

$$R^2 = \frac{\textbf{Explained variation}}{\textbf{Total variation}}.$$

This implies that R^2 cannot tell us (by decreasing) that adding an independent variable is undesirable. That is, although we wish to obtain a model with a large R^2, there are better criteria than R^2 that can be used to **compare** regression models.

One better criterion is the standard error

$$s = \sqrt{\frac{SSE}{n - (k + 1)}}.$$

When we add an independent variable to a regression model, the number of model parameters $(k + 1)$ increases by one, and thus the number of degrees of freedom $n - (k + 1)$ decreases by one. If the decrease in $n - (k + 1)$, which is used in the denominator to calculate s, is proportionally more than the decrease in the SSE (the unexplained variation) that is caused by adding the independent variable to the model, then s will increase. **If s increases, this tells us that we should not add the independent variable to the model.** To see one reason why, consider the formula for the prediction interval for y:

$$[\hat{y} \pm t_{\alpha/2}s\sqrt{1 + \text{Distance value}}].$$

Since **adding an independent variable** to a model decreases the number of degrees of freedom, adding the variable will increase the $t_{\alpha/2}$ point used to calculate the prediction interval. To understand this, look at any column of the t table in Table A.4 and scan from the bottom of the column to the top—you can see that the t points increase as the degrees of freedom decrease. It can also be shown that adding any independent variable to a regression model will not decrease (and usually increases) the distance value. Therefore, since adding an independent variable increases $t_{\alpha/2}$ and does not decrease the distance value, **if s increases, the length of the prediction interval for y will increase**. This means the model will predict less accurately and thus we should not add the independent variable.

On the other hand, if adding an independent variable to a regression model **decreases** s, the length of a prediction interval for y will decrease if and only if the decrease in s is enough to offset the increase in $t_{\alpha/2}$ and the (possible) increase in the distance value. Therefore, **an independent variable should not be included in a final regression model unless it reduces s enough to reduce the length of the desired prediction interval for y.** However, we must balance the length of the prediction interval or, in general, the "goodness" of any criterion, against the difficulty and expense of using the model. For instance, predicting y requires knowing the corresponding values of the independent variables. So we must decide whether including an independent variable reduces s and prediction interval lengths enough to offset the potential errors caused by possible inaccurate determination of values of the independent variables, or the possible expense of determining these values. If adding an independent variable provides prediction intervals that are only slightly shorter while making the model more difficult and/or more expensive to use, we might decide that including the variable is not desirable.

Since a key factor is the length of the prediction intervals provided by the model, one might wonder why we do not simply make direct comparisons of prediction interval lengths (without looking at s). It is useful to compare interval lengths, but these lengths depend on the distance value, which depends on how far the values of the independent variables we wish to predict for are from the centre of the experimental region. We often wish to compute prediction intervals for several different combinations of values of the independent variables (and thus for several different values of the distance value). Thus, we would compute prediction intervals with slightly different lengths. However, the standard error s is a constant factor with respect to the length of prediction intervals (as long as we are considering the same regression model). Thus, it is common practice to compare regression models on the basis of s (and s^2). Finally, note that it can be shown that the standard error s decreases if and only if $\bar{R}^2$ (adjusted R^2) increases. It follows that, if we are comparing regression models, the model that gives the smallest s gives the largest $\bar{R}^2$.

Example 12.12   The Sales Territory Performance Case

Figure 12.42 gives MINITAB and MegaStat output resulting from calculating R^2, $\bar{R}^2$, and s for **all possible regression models** based on all possible combinations of the eight independent variables in the sales territory performance situation (we will explain the values of C_p on the output

FIGURE 12.42   MINITAB and MegaStat Output of Some of the Best Sales Territory Performance Regression Models

(a) The MINITAB output of the two best models of each size

Vars	R-Sq	R-Sq(adj)	Mallows C-p	S	Time	MktPoten	Adver	MktShare	Change	Accts	WkLoad	Rating
1	56.8	55.0	67.6	881.09						X		
1	38.8	36.1	104.6	1049.3	X							
2	77.5	75.5	27.2	650.39			X			X		
2	74.6	72.3	33.1	691.10		X	X					
3	84.9	82.7	14.0	545.51		X	X	X				
3	82.8	80.3	18.4	582.64		X	X			X		
4	90.0	88.1	5.4	453.84		X	X	X		X		
4	89.6	87.5	6.4	463.95	X	X	X	X				
5	91.5	89.3	4.4	430.23	X	X	X	X	X			
5	91.2	88.9	5.0	436.75		X	X	X	X	X		
6	92.0	89.4	5.4	428.00	X	X	X	X	X	X		
6	91.6	88.9	6.1	438.20		X	X	X	X	X	X	
7	92.2	89.0	7.0	435.67	X	X	X	X	X	X	X	
7	92.0	88.8	7.3	440.30	X	X	X	X	X	X		X
8	92.2	88.3	9.0	449.03	X	X	X	X	X	X	X	X

(b) The MegaStat output of the best single model of each size

Nvar	Time	MktPoten	Adver	MktShare	Change	Accts	WkLoad	Rating	s	Adj R^2	R^2	Cp	p-value
1						0.0000			881.093	0.550	0.568	67.558	1.35E-05
2			0.0002			0.0000			650.392	0.755	0.775	27.156	7.45E-08
3		0.0000	0.0011	0.0000					545.515	0.827	0.849	13.995	8.43E-09
4		0.0001	0.0001	0.0011		0.0043			453.836	0.881	0.900	5.431	9.56E-10
5	0.0065	0.0000	0.0025	0.0000	0.0530				430.232	0.893	0.915	4.443	1.59E-09
6	0.1983	0.0001	0.0018	0.0004	0.0927	0.2881			428.004	0.894	0.920	5.354	6.14E-09
7	0.2868	0.0002	0.0027	0.0066	0.0897	0.2339	0.5501		435.674	0.890	0.922	7.004	3.21E-08
8	0.3134	0.0003	0.0055	0.0090	0.1390	0.2621	0.5649	0.9500	449.026	0.883	0.922	9.000	1.82E-07

(c) The MegaStat output of the best eight models

Nvar	Time	MktPoten	Adver	MktShare	Change	Accts	WkLoad	Rating	s	Adj R^2	R^2	Cp	p-value
6	0.1983	0.0001	0.0018	0.0004	0.0927	0.2881			428.004	0.894	0.920	5.354	6.14E-09
5	0.0065	0.0000	0.0025	0.0000	0.0530				430.232	0.893	0.915	4.443	1.59E-09
7	0.2868	0.0002	0.0027	0.0066	0.0897	0.2339	0.5501		435.674	0.890	0.922	7.004	3.21E-08
5		0.0001	0.0006	0.0006	0.1236	0.0089			436.746	0.889	0.912	4.975	2.10E-09
6		0.0002	0.0006	0.0098	0.1035	0.0070	0.3621		438.197	0.889	0.916	6.142	9.31E-09
7	0.2204	0.0002	0.0040	0.0006	0.1449	0.3194		0.9258	440.297	0.888	0.920	7.345	3.82E-08
6	0.0081	0.0000	0.0054	0.0000	0.1143			0.7692	440.936	0.887	0.915	6.357	1.04E-08
6	0.0083	0.0000	0.0044	0.0000	0.0629			0.9474	441.966	0.887	0.915	6.438	1.08E-08

after we complete this example). The MINITAB output gives the two best models of each size in terms of s and $\overline{R}^2$—the two best one-variable models, the two best two-variable models, the two best three-variable models, and so on. The first MegaStat output gives the best single model of each size, and the second MegaStat output gives the eight best models of any size, in terms of s and $\overline{R}^2$. The MegaStat output also gives the p values for the variables in each model. Examining the output, we see that the three models with the smallest values of s and largest values of $\overline{R}^2$ are

1   The six-variable model that contains

TIME, MKTPOTEN, ADVER, MKTSHARE, CHANGE, ACCTS

and has $s = 428.004$ and $\overline{R}^2 = 89.4$; we refer to this model as Model 1.

2   The five-variable model that contains

TIME, MKTPOTEN, ADVER, MKTSHARE, CHANGE

and has $s = 430.232$ and $\overline{R}^2 = 89.3$; we refer to this model as Model 2.

3   The seven-variable model that contains

TIME, MKTPOTEN, ADVER, MKTSHARE, CHANGE, ACCTS, WKLOAD

and has $s = 435.674$ and $\overline{R}^2 = 89.0$; we refer to this model as Model 3.

To see that s can increase when we add an independent variable to a regression model, note that s increases from 428.004 to 435.674 when we add WKLOAD to Model 1 to form Model 3. In this case, although it can be verified that adding WKLOAD decreases the unexplained variation from 3,297,279.3342 to 3,226,756.2751, this decrease is enough to offset the change in the denominator of

$$s^2 = \frac{SSE}{n - (k + 1)},$$

which decreases from $25 - 7 = 18$ to $25 - 8 = 17$. To see that prediction interval lengths might increase even though s decreases, consider adding ACCTS to Model 2 to form Model 1. This decreases s from 430.232 to 428.004. However, consider a questionable sales representative for whom TIME = 85.42, MKTPOTEN = 35,182.73, ADVER = 7,281.65, MKTSHARE = 9.64, CHANGE = 0.28, and ACCTS = 120.61. The 95 percent prediction interval given by Model 2 for sales corresponding to this combination of values of the independent variables is [3,233.59, 5,129.89] and has length $5,129.89 - 3,233.59 = 1,896.3$. The 95 percent prediction interval given by Model 1 for such sales is [3,193.86, 5,093.14] and has length $5,093.14 - 3,193.86 = 1,899.28$. In other words, the slight decrease in s accomplished by adding ACCTS to Model 2 to form Model 1 is not enough to offset the increases in $t_{\alpha/2}$ and the distance value (which can be shown to increase from 0.109 to 0.115), and thus the length of the prediction interval given by Model 1 increases. In addition, the extra independent variable ACCTS in Model 1 has a p value of 0.2881. Therefore, we conclude that Model 2 is better than Model 1 and is, in fact, the "best" sales territory performance model (using only linear terms).

Another quantity that can be used for comparing regression models is called the **C statistic** (also often called the **C_p statistic**). To show how to calculate the C statistic, suppose that we wish to choose an appropriate set of independent variables from p potential independent variables. We first calculate the mean square error, which we denote as s_p^2, for the model using all p potential independent variables. Then, if the SSE is the unexplained variation for another particular model that has k independent variables, it follows that the C statistic for this model is

$$C = \frac{SSE}{s_p^2} - [n - 2(k + 1)].$$

For example, consider the sales territory performance case. It can be verified that the mean square error for the model using all $p = 8$ independent variables is 201,621.21 and that the SSE for the model using the first $k = 5$ independent variables (Model 2 in the previous example) is 3,516,812.7933. It follows that the C statistic for this latter model is

$$C = \frac{3,516,812.7933}{201,621.21} - [25 - 2(5 + 1)] = 4.4.$$

Because the C statistic for a given model is a function of the model's SSE, and because we want the SSE to be small, **we want C to be small**. Although adding an unimportant independent variable to a regression model will decrease the SSE, adding such a variable can increase C. This can happen when the decrease in the SSE caused by the addition of the extra independent variable is not enough to offset the decrease in $n - 2(k + 1)$ caused by the addition of the extra independent variable (which increases k by 1). It should be noted that although adding an unimportant independent variable to a regression model can increase both s^2 and C, there is no exact relationship between s^2 and C.

While we want C to be small, it can be shown from the theory behind the C statistic that **we also wish to find a model for which the C statistic roughly equals $k + 1$**, the number of parameters in the model. **If a model has a C statistic substantially greater than $k + 1$, it can be shown that this model has substantial bias and is undesirable.** Thus, although we want to find a model for which C is as small as possible, if C for such a model is substantially greater than $k + 1$, we may prefer to choose a different model for which C is slightly larger and more nearly equal to the number of parameters in that (different) model. **If a particular model has a small value of C and C for this model is less than $k + 1$, then the model should be considered desirable.** Finally, it should be noted that for the model that includes all p potential independent variables (and thus utilizes $p + 1$ parameters), it can be shown that $C = p + 1$.

If we examine Figure 12.42, we see that Model 2 of the previous example has the smallest C statistic. The C statistic for this model equals 4.4. Since $C = 4.4$ is less than $k + 1 = 6$, the model is not biased. Therefore, this model should be considered best with respect to the C statistic.

Stepwise regression and backward elimination   In some situations, it is useful to employ an **iterative model selection procedure**, where at each step a single independent variable is added to or deleted from a regression model, and a new regression model is evaluated. We discuss here two such procedures—**stepwise regression** and **backward elimination**.

There are slight variations in the way different computer packages carry out **stepwise regression**. Assuming that y is the dependent variable and $x_1, x_2, \ldots, x_p$ are the p potential independent variables, we explain how most of the computer packages perform stepwise regression. Stepwise regression uses t statistics (and related p values) to determine the significance of the independent variables in various regression models. In this context, we say that **the t statistic indicates that the independent variable x_j is significant at the α level if and only if the related p value is less than α.** Then, stepwise regression is carried out as follows.

Choice of α_{entry} and α_{stay}   Before beginning the stepwise procedure, we choose a value of α_{entry}, which we call **the probability of a Type I error related to entering an independent variable into the regression model.** We also choose a value of α_{stay}, which we call **the probability of a Type I error related to retaining an independent variable that was previously entered into the model.** Although there are many considerations in choosing these values, it is common practice to set both α_{entry} and α_{stay} equal to 0.05 or 0.10.

Step 1: The stepwise procedure considers the p possible one independent variable regression models of the form

$$y = \beta_0 + \beta_1 x_j + \varepsilon.$$

Each different model includes a different potential independent variable. For each model, the t statistic (and p value) related to testing $H_0: \beta_1 = 0$ versus $H_a: \beta_1 \neq 0$ is calculated. Denoting the independent variable giving the largest absolute value of the t statistic (and the smallest p value) by the symbol $x_{[1]}$, we consider the model

$$y = \beta_0 + \beta_1 x_{[1]} + \varepsilon.$$

If the t statistic does not indicate that $x_{[1]}$ is significant at the α_{entry} level, then the stepwise procedure terminates by concluding that none of the independent variables are significant at the α_{entry} level. If the t statistic indicates that the independent variable $x_{[1]}$ is significant at the α_{entry} level, then $x_{[1]}$ is retained for use in Step 2.

Step 2: The stepwise procedure considers the $p - 1$ possible two independent variable regression models of the form

$$y = \beta_0 + \beta_1 x_{[1]} + \beta_2 x_j + \varepsilon.$$

Each different model includes $x_{[1]}$, the independent variable chosen in Step 1, and a different potential independent variable chosen from the remaining $p - 1$ independent variables that were not chosen in Step 1. For each model, the t statistic (and p value) related to testing $H_0: \beta_2 = 0$ versus $H_a: \beta_2 \neq 0$ is calculated. Denoting the independent variable giving the largest absolute value of the t statistic (and the smallest p value) by the symbol $x_{[2]}$, we consider the model

$$y = \beta_0 + \beta_1 x_{[1]} + \beta_2 x_{[2]} + \varepsilon.$$

If the t statistic indicates that $x_{[2]}$ is significant at the α_{entry} level, then $x_{[2]}$ is retained in this model, and the stepwise procedure checks to see whether $x_{[1]}$ should be allowed to stay in the model. This check should be made because multicollinearity will probably cause the t statistic related to the importance of $x_{[1]}$ to change when $x_{[2]}$ is added to the model. If the t statistic does not indicate that $x_{[1]}$ is significant at the α_{stay} level, then the stepwise procedure returns to the beginning of Step 2. Starting with a new one independent variable model that uses the new significant independent variable $x_{[2]}$, the stepwise procedure attempts to find a new two independent variable model

$$y = \beta_0 + \beta_1 x_{[2]} + \beta_2 x_j + \varepsilon.$$

If the t statistic indicates that $x_{[1]}$ is significant at the α_{stay} level in the model

$$y = \beta_0 + \beta_1 x_{[1]} + \beta_2 x_{[2]} + \varepsilon,$$

then both the independent variables $x_{[1]}$ and $x_{[2]}$ are retained for use in further steps.

Further steps   The stepwise procedure continues by adding independent variables one at a time to the model. At each step, an independent variable is added to the model if it has the largest (in absolute value) t statistic of the independent variables not in the model and if its t statistic indicates that it is significant at the α_{entry} level. After adding an independent variable, the stepwise procedure checks all the independent variables already included in the model and removes an independent variable if it has the smallest (in absolute value) t statistic of the independent variables already included in the model and if its t statistic indicates that it is not significant at the α_{stay} level. This removal procedure is sequentially continued, and only after the necessary removals are made does the stepwise procedure attempt to add another independent variable to the model. The stepwise procedure terminates when all the independent variables not in the model are insignificant at the α_{entry} level or when the variable to be added to the model is the one just removed from it.

For example, again consider the sales territory performance data. We let x_1, x_2, x_3, x_4, x_5, x_6, x_7, and x_8 be the eight potential independent variables employed in the stepwise procedure. Figure 12.43(a) gives the MINITAB output of the stepwise regression employing these independent variables where both α_{entry} and α_{stay} have been set equal to 0.10. The stepwise procedure

1   Adds ACCTS (x_6) on the first step.
2   Adds ADVER (x_3) and retains ACCTS on the second step.
3   Adds MKTPOTEN (x_2) and retains ACCTS and ADVER on the third step.
4   Adds MKTSHARE (x_4) and retains ACCTS, ADVER, and MKTPOTEN on the fourth step.

The procedure terminates after step 4 when no more independent variables can be added. Therefore, the stepwise procedure arrives at the model that utilizes x_2, x_3, x_4, and x_6.

To carry out **backward elimination**, we perform a regression analysis by using a regression model containing all the p potential independent variables. Then the independent variable with the smallest (in absolute value) t statistic is chosen. If the t statistic indicates that this independent variable is significant at the α_{stay} level (α_{stay} is chosen prior to the beginning of the procedure), then the procedure terminates by choosing the regression model containing all p independent variables. If this independent variable is not significant at the α_{stay} level, then it is removed from the model, and a regression analysis is performed by using a regression model containing all the remaining independent variables. The procedure continues by removing independent variables one at a time from the model. At each step, an independent variable is removed from the model if it has the smallest (in absolute value) t statistic of the independent variables remaining in the model and if it is not significant at the α_{stay} level. The procedure terminates when no independent variable remaining in the model can be removed. Backward elimination is generally considered a reasonable procedure, especially for analysts who like to start with all possible independent variables in the model so that they will not miss anything important.

To illustrate backward elimination, we first note that choosing the independent variable that has the smallest (in absolute value) t statistic in a model is equivalent to choosing the independent variable that has the largest p value in the model. With this in mind, Figure 12.43(b) gives the MINITAB output of a backward elimination of the sales territory performance data. Here the

FIGURE 12.43   The MINITAB Output of Stepwise Regression and Backward Elimination for the Sales Territory Performance Problem

(a) Stepwise regression ($\alpha_{entry} = \alpha_{stay} = 0.10$)

Alpha-to-Enter: 0.1 Alpha-to-Remove: 0.1
Response is Sales on 8 predictors, with N = 25

Step	1	2	3	4
Constant	709.32	50.30	-327.23	-1441.94
Accts	21.7	19.0	15.6	9.2
T-Value	5.50	6.41	5.19	3.22
P-Value	0.000	0.000	0.000	0.004
Adver		0.227	0.216	0.175
T-Value		4.50	4.77	4.74
P-Value		0.000	0.000	0.000
MktPoten			0.0219	0.0382
T-Value			2.53	4.79
P-Value			0.019	0.000
MktShare				190
T-Value				3.82
P-Value				0.001
S	881	650	583	454
R-Sq	56.85	77.51	82.77	90.04
R-Sq(adj)	54.97	75.47	80.31	88.05
Mallows C-p	67.6	27.2	18.4	5.4

(b) Backward elimination ($\alpha_{stay} = 0.05$)

Backward elimination. Alpha-to-Remove: 0.05
Response is Sales on 8 predictors, with N = 25

Step	1	2	3	4	5
Constant	-1508	-1486	-1165	-1114	-1312
Time	2.0	2.0	2.3	3.6	3.8
T-Value	1.04	1.10	1.34	3.06	3.01
P-Value	0.313	0.287	0.198	0.006	0.007
MktPoten	0.0372	0.0373	0.0383	0.0421	0.0444
T-Value	4.54	4.75	5.07	6.25	6.20
P-Value	0.000	0.000	0.000	0.000	0.000
Adver	0.151	0.152	0.141	0.129	0.152
T-Value	3.21	3.51	3.66	3.48	4.01
P-Value	0.006	0.003	0.002	0.003	0.001
MktShare	199	198	222	257	259
T-Value	2.97	3.09	4.38	6.57	6.15
P-Value	0.009	0.007	0.000	0.000	0.000
Change	291	296	285	325	
T-Value	1.56	1.80	1.78	2.06	
P-Value	0.139	0.090	0.093	0.053	
Accts	5.6	5.6	4.4		
T-Value	1.16	1.23	1.09		
P-Value	0.262	0.234	0.288		
WkLoad	20	20			
T-Value	0.59	0.61			
P-Value	0.565	0.550			
Rating	8				
T-Value	0.06				
P-Value	0.950				
S	449	436	428	430	464
R-Sq	92.20	92.20	92.03	91.50	89.60
R-Sq(adj)	88.31	88.99	89.38	89.26	87.52
Mallows C-p	9.0	7.0	5.4	4.4	6.4

backward elimination uses $\alpha_{stay} = 0.05$, begins with the model using all eight independent variables, and removes (in order) RATING (x_8), then WKLOAD (x_7), then ACCTS (x_6), and finally CHANGE (x_5). The procedure terminates when no independent variable remaining can be removed—that is, when no independent variable has a related p value greater than $\alpha_{stay} = 0.05$—and arrives at a model that uses TIME (x_1), MKTPOTEN (x_2), ADVER (x_3), and MKTSHARE (x_4). This model has an s of 464 and an $\overline{R}^2$ of 0.8752 and is inferior to the model arrived at by stepwise regression, which has an s of 454 and an $\overline{R}^2$ of 0.8805 (see Figure 12.43(a)). However, the backward elimination process allows us to find a model that is better than either of these. If we look at the model considered by backward elimination after RATING (x_8), WKLOAD (x_7), and ACCTS (x_6) have been removed, we have the model using x_1, x_2, x_3, x_4, and x_5. This model has an s of 430 and an $\overline{R}^2$ of 0.8926, and in Example 12.12 we reasoned that this model is perhaps the best sales territory performance model. Interestingly, this is the model that backward elimination would arrive at if we were to set α_{stay} equal to 0.10 rather than 0.05—note that this model has no p values greater than 0.10.

The sales territory performance example brings home two important points. First, the models obtained by backward elimination and stepwise regression depend on the choices of α_{entry} and α_{stay} (whichever is appropriate). Second, it is best not to think of these methods as "automatic model-building procedures." Rather, they should be regarded as processes that allow us to find and evaluate a variety of model choices.

Exercises for Section 12.12

CONCEPTS

12.52 What is multicollinearity? What problems can be caused by multicollinearity?

12.53 Discuss how we compare regression models.

METHODS AND APPLICATIONS

12.54   THE HOSPITAL LABOUR NEEDS CASE
   ● HospLab2

Table 12.5 (page 419) presents data concerning the need for labour in 16 hospitals. This table gives values of the dependent variable Hours (monthly labour hours) and of the independent variables Xray (monthly X-ray exposures), BedDays (monthly occupied bed days—a hospital has one occupied bed day if one bed is occupied for an entire day), and Length (average

length of patients' stay, in days). The data in Table 12.5 are part of a larger data set. The complete data set consists of two additional independent variables—Load (average daily patient load) and Pop (eligible population in the area, in thousands)—values of which are given in Table 12.18. Figure 12.44 gives MINITAB and MegaStat output of multicollinearity analysis and model building for the complete hospital labour needs data set.

a. Find the three largest simple correlation coefficients between the independent variables in Figure 12.44(a). Also find the three largest variance inflation factors in Figure 12.44(b).

b. Based on your answers to part a, which independent variables are most strongly involved in multicollinearity?

FIGURE 12.44   MINITAB and MegaStat Output of Multicollinearity Analysis and Model Building for the Hospital Labour Needs Data

(a) The MegaStat output of a correlation matrix

	Load	Xray	BedDays	Pop	Length	Hours
Load	1.0000					
Xray	0.9051	1.0000				
BedDays	0.9999	0.9048	1.0000			
Pop	0.9353	0.9124	0.9328	1.0000		
Length	0.6610	0.4243	0.6609	0.4515	1.0000	
Hours	0.9886	0.9425	0.9889	0.9465	0.5603	1.0000

16 sample size

±0.497 critical value 0.05 (two-tail)
±0.623 critical value 0.01 (two-tail)

(b) The MINITAB output of the variance inflation factors

Predictor	Coef	SE Coef	T	P	VIF
Constant	2270.4	670.8	3.38	0.007	
Load	-9.30	60.81	-0.15	0.882	9334.5
XRay	0.04112	0.01368	3.01	0.013	8.1
BedDays	1.413	1.925	0.73	0.480	8684.2
Pop	-3.223	4.474	-0.72	0.488	23.0
Length	-467.9	131.6	-3.55	0.005	4.2

(c) The MegaStat output of the best single model of each size

Nvar	Load	Xray	BedDays	Pop	Length	s	Adj R²	R²	Cp	p-value
1			0.0000			856.707	0.976	0.978	52.313	5.51E-13
2			0.0000		0.0001	489.126	0.992	0.993	9.467	7.41E-15
3		0.0120	0.0000		0.0012	387.160	0.995	0.996	3.258	9.92E-15
4		0.0091	0.0000	0.2690	0.0013	381.555	0.995	0.997	4.023	1.86E-13
5	0.8815	0.0132	0.4799	0.4878	0.0052	399.712	0.995	0.997	6.000	5.65E-12

(d) The MegaStat output of the best five models

Nvar	Load	Xray	BedDays	Pop	Length	s	Adj R²	R²	Cp	p-value
4		0.0091	0.0000	0.2690	0.0013	381.555	0.995	0.997	4.023	1.86E-13
3		0.0120	0.0000		0.0012	387.160	0.995	0.996	3.258	9.92E-15
4	0.3981	0.0121	0.1381		0.0018	390.876	0.995	0.996	4.519	2.43E-13
4	0.0000	0.0097		0.1398	0.0011	391.236	0.995	0.996	4.538	2.45E-13
5	0.8815	0.0132	0.4799	0.4878	0.0052	399.712	0.995	0.997	6.000	5.65E-12

TABLE **12.18** Patient Load and Population for Exercise 12.54

Load	Pop
15.57	18.0
44.02	9.5
20.42	12.8
18.74	36.7
49.20	35.7
44.92	24.0
55.48	43.3
59.28	46.7
94.39	78.7
128.02	180.5
96.00	60.9
131.42	103.7
127.21	126.8
409.20	169.4
463.70	331.4
510.22	371.6

c. Do any least squares point estimates have a sign (positive or negative) that is different from what we would intuitively expect—another indication of multicollinearity?

d. The p value associated with $F(\text{model})$ for the model in Figure 12.44(b) is less than 0.0001. In general, if the p value associated with $F(\text{model})$ is much smaller than any of the p values associated with the independent variables, this is another indication of multicollinearity. Is this true in this situation?

e. Figure 12.44(c) and (d) indicates that the two best hospital labour needs models are the model using Xray, BedDays, Pop, and Length, which we will call Model 1, and the model using Xray, BedDays, and Length, which we will call Model 2. Which model gives the smallest value of s and the largest value of $\overline{R}^2$? Which model gives the smallest value of C? Consider a questionable hospital for which Xray = 56,194, BedDays = 14,077.88, Pop = 329.7, and Length = 6.89. The 95 percent prediction intervals given by Models 1 and 2 for labour hours corresponding to this combination of values of the independent variables are, respectively, [14,888.43, 16,861.30] and [14,906.24, 16,886.26]. Which model gives the shorter prediction interval?

f. Consider Figure 12.45. Which model is chosen by both stepwise regression and backward elimination? Overall, which model seems best?

12.55 Market Planning, a marketing research firm, has obtained the prescription sales data in Table 12.19 for $n = 20$ independent pharmacies.[3] In this table, y is the average weekly prescription sales over the past year (in units of $1,000), x_1 is the floor space (in square feet), x_2 is the percentage of floor space allocated to the prescription department, x_3 is the number of parking spaces available to the store, x_4 is the weekly per capita income for the surrounding community (in units of $100), and x_5 is a **dummy variable** that equals 1 if the pharmacy is located in a shopping centre and 0 otherwise. Use the MegaStat output in Figure 12.46 to discuss why the model using FloorSpace and Presc.Pct might be the best model describing prescription sales. The least squares point estimates of the parameters of this model can be calculated to be $b_0 = 48.2909$, $b_1 = -0.003842$, and $b_2 = -0.5819$. Discuss what b_1 and b_2 say about obtaining high prescription sales. ● PreSales

FIGURE **12.45** MINITAB Output of a Stepwise Regression and a Backward Elimination of the Hospital Labour Needs Data

(a) Stepwise regression ($\alpha_{\text{entry}} = \alpha_{\text{stay}} = 0.10$)

Step	1	2	3
Constant	-70.23	2741.24	1946.80
BedDays	1.101	1.223	1.039
T-Value	24.87	36.30	15.39
P-Value	0.000	0.000	0.000
Length		-572	-414
T-Value		-5.47	-4.20
P-Value		0.000	0.001
XRay			0.039
T-Value			2.96
P-Value			0.012
S	857	489	387
R-Sq	97.79	99.33	99.61

(b) Backward elimination ($\alpha_{\text{stay}} = 0.05$)

Step	1	2	3
Constant	2270	2311	1947
Load	-9		
T-Value	-0.15		
P-Value	0.882		
XRay	0.041	0.041	0.039
T-Value	3.01	3.16	2.96
P-Value	0.013	0.009	0.012
BedDays	1.413	1.119	1.039
T-Value	0.73	11.74	15.39
P-Value	0.480	0.000	0.000
Pop	-3.2	-3.7	
T-Value	-0.72	-1.16	
P-Value	0.488	0.269	
Length	-468	-477	-414
T-Value	-3.55	-4.28	-4.20
P-Value	0.005	0.001	0.001
S		400	382	387
R-Sq	99.66	99.65	99.61

[3]This problem is taken from an example in *An Introduction to Statistical Methods and Data Analysis*, 2nd ed. by L. Ott, (Boston: PWS-KENT Publishing Company, 1987). Used with permission.

TABLE **12.19** Prescription Sales Data   ● PreSales

Pharmacy	Sales, y	Floor Space, x_1	Prescription Percentage, x_2	Parking, x_3	Income, x_4	Shopping Centre, x_5
1	22	4,900	9	40	18	1
2	19	5,800	10	50	20	1
3	24	5,000	11	55	17	1
4	28	4,400	12	30	19	0
5	18	3,850	13	42	10	0
6	21	5,300	15	20	22	1
7	29	4,100	20	25	8	0
8	15	4,700	22	60	15	1
9	12	5,600	24	45	16	1
10	14	4,900	27	82	14	1
11	18	3,700	28	56	12	0
12	19	3,800	31	38	8	0
13	15	2,400	36	35	6	0
14	22	1,800	37	28	4	0
15	13	3,100	40	43	6	0
16	16	2,300	41	20	5	0
17	8	4,400	42	46	7	1
18	6	3,300	42	15	4	0
19	7	2,900	45	30	9	1
20	17	2,400	46	16	3	0

Source: From *An Introduction to Statistical Methods and Data Analysis,* by 2nd ed L. Ott,. Copyright © 1984. Reprinted with permission of Brooks/Cole, an imprint of the Wadsworth Group, a division of Thomson Learning. Fax 800-730-2215.

FIGURE **12.46**   **The MegaStat Output of the Single Best Model of Each Size for the Prescription Sales Data**

Nvar	FloorSpace	Presc.Pct	Parking	Income	ShopCntr?	s	Adj R^2	R^2	Cp	p-value
1		0.0014				4.835	0.408	0.439	10.171	0.0014
2	0.0035	0.0000				3.842	0.626	0.666	1.606	0.0001
3	0.1523	0.0002			0.2716	3.809	0.633	0.691	2.436	0.0002
4	0.1997	0.0003	0.5371		0.3424	3.883	0.618	0.699	4.062	0.0008
5	0.2095	0.0087	0.5819	0.8066	0.3564	4.010	0.593	0.700	6.000	0.0025

12.13 Residual Analysis in Multiple Regression (Optional)

In Section 11.10, we showed how to use residual analysis to check the regression assumptions for a simple linear regression model. In multiple regression, we proceed similarly. Specifically, for a multiple regression model we plot the residuals given by the model against (1) values of each independent variable, (2) values of the predicted value of the dependent variable, and (3) the time order in which the data have been observed (if the regression data are time series data). A fanning-out pattern on a residual plot indicates an increasing error variance; a funneling-in pattern indicates a decreasing error variance. Both violate the constant variance assumption. A curved pattern on a residual plot indicates that the functional form of the regression model is incorrect. If the regression data are time series data, a cyclical pattern on the residual plot versus time suggests positive autocorrelation, while an alternating pattern suggests negative autocorrelation. Both violate the independence assumption. On the other hand, if all residual plots have (at least approximately) a horizontal band appearance, then it is reasonable to believe that the constant variance, correct functional form, and independence assumptions approximately hold. To check the normality assumption, we can construct a histogram, stem-and-leaf display, and normal plot of the residuals. The histogram and stem-and-leaf display should look bell-shaped and symmetric about 0; the normal plot should have a straight-line appearance.

To illustrate these ideas, consider the sales territory performance data in Table 12.2 (page 417). Figure 12.8 (page 423) gives the MegaStat output of a regression analysis of these data using the model

$$y = \beta_0 + \beta_1 x_1 + \beta_2 x_2 + \beta_3 x_3 + \beta_4 x_4 + \beta_5 x_5 + \varepsilon.$$

The least squares point estimates on the output give the prediction equation

$$\hat{y} = -1{,}113.7879 + 3.6121 x_1 + 0.0421 x_2 + 0.1289 x_3 + 256.9555 x_4 + 324.5334 x_5.$$

Using this prediction equation, we can calculate the predicted sales values and residuals given on the MegaStat output of Figure 12.47. For example, observation 10 on this output corresponds to a sales representative for whom $x_1 = 105.69$, $x_2 = 42{,}053.24$, $x_3 = 5{,}673.11$, $x_4 = 8.85$, and $x_5 = 0.31$. If we insert these values into the prediction equation, we obtain a predicted sales value of $\hat{y}_{10} = 4{,}143.597$. Since the actual sales for the sales representative are $y_{10} = 4{,}876.370$, the residual e_{10} equals the difference between $y_{10} = 4{,}876.370$ and $\hat{y}_{10} = 4{,}143.597$, which is 732.773. The normal plot of the residuals in Figure 12.48(a) has a straight-line appearance. The plot of the residuals versus predicted sales in Figure 12.48(b) has a horizontal band appearance, as do the plots of the residuals versus the independent variables (the plot versus x_3, advertising, is shown in Figure 12.48(c)). We conclude that the regression assumptions approximately hold for the sales territory performance model (note that because the data are cross-sectional, a residual plot versus time is not appropriate).

FIGURE **12.47**   MegaStat Output of the Sales Territory Performance Model Residuals

Observation	Sales	Predicted	Residual
1	3,669.880	3,504.990	164.890
2	3,473.950	3,901.180	−427.230
3	2,295.100	2,774.866	−479.766
4	4,675.560	4,911.872	−236.312
5	6,125.960	5,415.196	710.764
6	2,134.940	2,026.090	108.850
7	5,031.660	5,126.127	−94.467
8	3,367.450	3,106.925	260.525
9	6,519.450	6,055.297	464.153
10	4,876.370	4,143.597	732.773
11	2,468.270	2,503.165	−34.895
12	2,533.310	1,827.065	706.245
13	2,408.110	2,478.083	−69.973
14	2,337.380	2,351.344	−13.964
15	4,586.950	4,797.688	−210.738
16	2,729.240	2,904.099	−174.859
17	3,289.400	3,362.660	−73.260
18	2,800.780	2,907.376	−106.596
19	3,264.200	3,625.026	−360.826
20	3,453.620	4,056.443	−602.823
21	1,741.450	1,409.835	331.615
22	2,035.750	2,494.101	−458.351
23	1,578.000	1,617.561	−39.561
24	4,167.440	4,574.903	−407.463
25	2,799.970	2,488.700	311.270

FIGURE **12.48**   MegaStat Residual Plots for the Sales Territory Performance Model

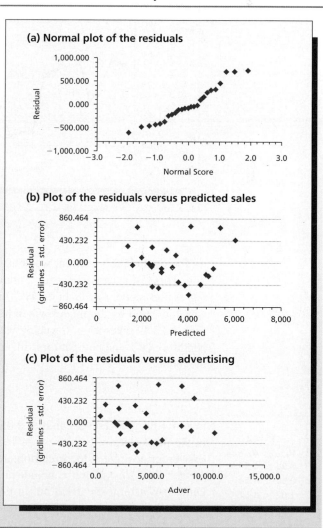

(a) Normal plot of the residuals

(b) Plot of the residuals versus predicted sales

(c) Plot of the residuals versus advertising

FIGURE 12.49   Folio Bookstore Sales and Advertising Data, and Residual Analysis

(a) The data and the MegaStat output of the residuals from a simple linear regression relating
Folio's sales to Folio's advertising expenditure   ● BookSales

Observation	Adver	Compadv	Sales	Predicted	Residual
1	18	10	22	18.7	3.3
2	20	10	27	23.0	4.0
3	20	15	23	23.0	−0.0
4	25	15	31	33.9	−2.9
5	28	15	45	40.4	4.6
6	29	20	47	42.6	4.4
7	29	20	45	42.6	2.4
8	28	25	42	40.4	1.6
9	30	35	37	44.7	−7.7
10	31	35	39	46.9	−7.9
11	34	35	45	53.4	−8.4
12	35	30	52	55.6	−3.6
13	36	30	57	57.8	−0.8
14	38	25	62	62.1	−0.1
15	41	20	73	68.6	4.4
16	45	20	84	77.3	6.7

Durbin-Watson = 0.65

(b) MegaStat output of a plot of the residuals versus time

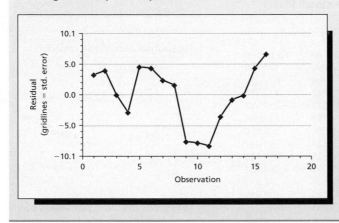

To conclude this section, we consider the **Durbin–Watson test** for first-order autocorrelation. This test is carried out for a multiple regression model exactly as it is for a simple linear regression model (see Section 11.10), except that we consider k, the number of independent variables used by the model, when looking up the critical values $d_{L,\alpha}$ and $d_{U,\alpha}$. For example, Figure 12.49 gives $n = 16$ weekly values of Folio Bookstore sales (y), Folio's advertising expenditure (x_1), and competitors' advertising expenditure (x_2). The Durbin–Watson statistic for the model

$$y = \beta_0 + \beta_1 x_1 + \beta_2 x_2 + \varepsilon$$

k = 2		
n	$d_{L,.05}$	$d_{U,.05}$
15	0.95	1.54
16	0.98	1.54
17	1.02	1.54
18	1.05	1.53

is $d = 1.63$. If we set α equal to 0.05, then we use Table A.10—a portion of which is shown in the page margin. Because $n = 16$ and $k = 2$, the appropriate critical values for a test for first-order positive autocorrelation are $d_{L,0.05} = 0.98$ and $d_{U,0.05} = 1.54$. Because $d = 1.63$ is greater than $d_{U,0.05}$, we conclude that there is no first-order positive autocorrelation. The Durbin–Watson test carried out in Figure 12.49 indicates that this autocorrelation does exist for the model relating y to x_1. Therefore, adding x_2 to this model seems to have removed the autocorrelation.

Exercises for Section 12.13

CONCEPTS

12.56 Discuss how we use the residuals to check the regression assumptions for a multiple regression model.

12.57 Discuss how we carry out the Durbin–Watson test for a multiple regression model.

METHODS AND APPLICATIONS

12.58 THE HOSPITAL LABOUR NEEDS CASE   ● HospLab

Consider the hospital labour needs data in Table 12.5 (page 419). Figure 12.50 gives residual plots that are obtained when we perform a regression analysis of these data by using the model

$$y = \beta_0 + \beta_1 x_1 + \beta_2 x_2 + \beta_3 x_3 + \varepsilon.$$

a. Interpret the normal plot of the residuals.

b. Interpret the residual plots versus predicted labour hours, BedDays (x_2), and Length (x_3). Note: The first two of these plots, as well as the plot versus Xray (x_1) (not shown), indicate that there are 3 hospitals that are substantially larger than the other 13 hospitals. We will discuss the potential **influence** of these three large hospitals in Section 12.14.

12.59 THE FRESH DETERGENT CASE   ● Fresh2

Recall that Table 12.4 (page 419) gives values for $n = 30$ sales periods of demand for Fresh liquid laundry detergent (y), price difference (x_4), and advertising expenditure (x_3).

a. Figure 12.51(a) gives the residual plot versus x_3 that is obtained when the regression model relating

y to x_4 and x_3 is used to analyze the Fresh detergent data. Discuss why the residual plot indicates that we should add x_3^2 to the model.

b. Figure 12.51(b) gives the residual plot versus time and the Durbin–Watson statistic that are obtained when the regression model relating y to x_4, x_3, and x_3^2 is used to analyze the Fresh detergent data. Test for positive autocorrelation by setting α equal to 0.05.

12.60 THE QHIC CASE   ● QHIC

Consider the quadratic regression model describing the QHIC data. Figure 12.52 shows that the residual plot versus x for this model fans out, indicating that the error term ε tends to become larger as x increases. To remedy this violation of the constant variance assumption, we divide all terms in the quadratic model by x. This gives the transformed model

$$\frac{y}{x} = \beta_0\left(\frac{1}{x}\right) + \beta_1 + \beta_2 x + \frac{\varepsilon}{x}.$$

Figure 12.53(a) and (b) gives a regression output and a residual plot versus x for this model.

a. Does the residual plot indicate that the constant variance assumption holds for the transformed model?

b. Consider a home worth \$220,000. We let μ_0 represent the mean yearly upkeep expenditure for all homes worth \$220,000, and we let y_0 represent the yearly upkeep expenditure for an individual home worth \$220,000. The bottom of the MINITAB output

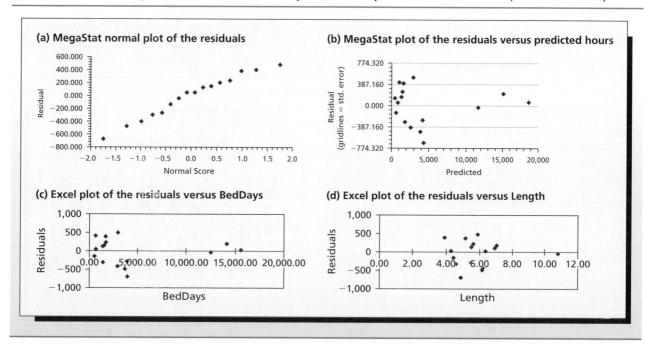

FIGURE 12.50   **MegaStat and Excel Residual Analysis for the Hospital Labour Needs Model (for Exercise 12.58)**

FIGURE 12.51   MegaStat and MINITAB Output for Exercise 12.59

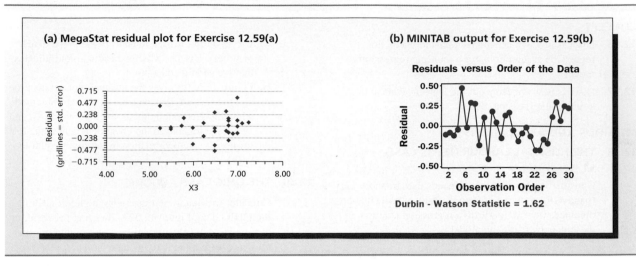

(a) MegaStat residual plot for Exercise 12.59(a)

(b) MINITAB output for Exercise 12.59(b)

FIGURE 12.52   MINITAB Plot of the Quadratic QHIC
Model Residuals Versus *x*

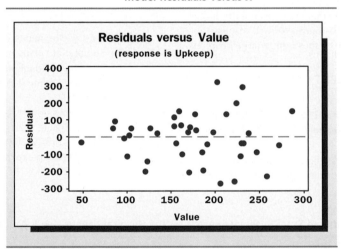

FIGURE 12.53   MINITAB Output for Exercise 12.60

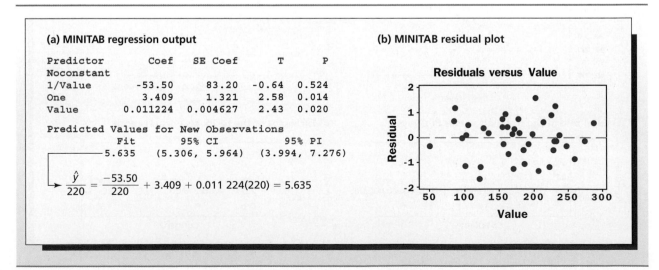

(a) MINITAB regression output

Predictor	Coef	SE Coef	T	P
Noconstant				
1/Value	-53.50	83.20	-0.64	0.524
One	3.409	1.321	2.58	0.014
Value	0.011224	0.004627	2.43	0.020

Predicted Values for New Observations
Fit   95% CI   95% PI
5.635   (5.306, 5.964)   (3.994, 7.276)

$$\frac{\hat{y}}{220} = \frac{-53.50}{220} + 3.409 + 0.011\,224(220) = 5.635$$

(b) MINITAB residual plot

in Figure 12.53(a) tells us that $\hat{y}/220 = 5.635$ is a point estimate of $\mu_0/220$ and a point prediction of $y_0/220$. Multiply this result by 220 to obtain $\hat{y}$. Multiply the ends of the confidence interval and prediction interval shown on the MINITAB output by 220. This will give a 95 percent confidence interval for μ_0 and a 95 percent prediction interval for y_0.

12.14 Diagnostics for Detecting Outlying and Influential Observations (Optional)

Introduction   An observation that is well separated from the rest of the data is called an **outlier**. An observation that would cause some important aspect of the regression analysis (for example, the least squares point estimates or the standard error s) to substantially change if it were removed from the data set is called **influential**. An observation may be an outlier with respect to its y value and/or its x values, but an outlier may or may not be influential. We illustrate these ideas by considering Figure 12.54, which is a hypothetical plot of the values of a dependent variable y against an independent variable x. Observation 1 in this figure is outlying with respect to its y value. However, it is not outlying with respect to its x value, since its x value is near the middle of the other x values. Moreover, observation 1 may not be influential because there are several observations with similar x values and nonoutlying y values, which will keep the least squares point estimates from being excessively influenced by observation 1. Observation 2 in Figure 12.54 is outlying with respect to its x value, but since its y value is consistent with the regression relationship displayed by the nonoutlying observations, it is probably not influential. Observation 3, however, is probably influential, because it is outlying with respect to its x value and because its y value is not consistent with the regression relationship displayed by the other observations.

In addition to using data plots (such as Figure 12.54), we can use more sophisticated procedures to detect outlying and influential observations. These procedures are particularly important when we are performing a multiple regression analysis and thus simple data plots are unlikely to tell us what we need to know. To illustrate, we consider the data in Table 12.20, which concern the need for labour in 17 hospitals. Specifically, this table gives values of the dependent variable Hours (y, monthly labour hours required) and of the independent variables Xray (x_1, monthly

FIGURE 12.54   **Data Plot Illustrating Outlying and Influential Observations**

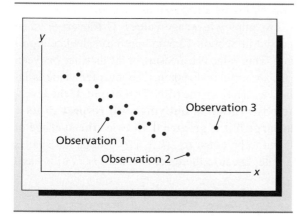

TABLE 12.20   **Hospital Labour Needs Data**   ● HospLab3

Hospital	Hours, y	Xray, x_1	BedDays, x_2	Length, x_3
1	566.52	2,463	472.92	4.45
2	696.82	2,048	1,339.75	6.92
3	1,033.15	3,940	620.25	4.28
4	1,603.62	6,505	568.33	3.90
5	1,611.37	5,723	1,497.60	5.50
6	1,613.27	11,520	1,365.83	4.60
7	1,854.17	5,779	1,687.00	5.62
8	2,160.55	5,969	1,639.92	5.15
9	2,305.58	8,461	2,872.33	6.18
10	3,503.93	20,106	3,655.08	6.15
11	3,571.89	13,313	2,912.00	5.88
12	3,741.40	10,771	3,921.00	4.88
13	4,026.52	15,543	3,865.67	5.50
14	10,343.81	36,194	7,684.10	7.00
15	11,732.17	34,703	12,446.33	10.78
16	15,414.94	39,204	14,098.40	7.05
17	18,854.45	86,533	15,524.00	6.35

Source: *Procedures and Analysis for Staffing Standards Development: Regression Analysis Handbook* (San Diego, CA: Navy Manpower and Material Analysis Center, 1979).

FIGURE 12.55   The MegaStat and MINITAB Output of Outlying and Influential Observation Diagnostics for Model I

(a) MegaStat Output   **(b) MINITAB Output**

Observation	Hours	Predicted	Residual	Leverage	Studentized Residual	Studentized Deleted Residual	Cook's D	TRES1	HI1	COOK1
1	566.520	688.409	−121.889	0.121	−0.211	−0.203	0.002	−0.2035	0.120749	0.00153
2	696.820	721.848	−25.028	0.226	−0.046	−0.044	0.000	−0.04447	0.226128	0.00016
3	1,033.150	965.393	67.757	0.130	0.118	0.114	0.001	0.11356	0.129664	0.00052
4	1,603.620	1,172.464	431.156	0.159	0.765	0.752	0.028	0.75174	0.158762	0.02759
5	1,611.370	1,526.780	84.590	0.085	0.144	0.138	0.000	0.1383	0.084914	0.00048
6	1,613.270	1,993.869	−380.599	0.112	−0.657	−0.642	0.014	−0.64194	0.112011	0.01361
7	1,854.170	1,676.558	177.612	0.084	0.302	0.291	0.002	0.29105	0.084078	0.00209
8	2,160.550	1,791.405	369.145	0.083	0.627	0.612	0.009	0.61176	0.083005	0.0089
9	2,305.580	2,798.761	−493.181	0.085	−0.838	−0.828	0.016	−0.82827	0.084596	0.01624
10	3,503.930	4,191.333	−687.403	0.120	−1.192	−1.214	0.049	−1.21359	0.120262	0.04857
11	3,571.890	3,190.957	380.933	0.077	0.645	0.630	0.009	0.62993	0.077335	0.00872
12	3,741.400	4,364.502	−623.102	0.177	−1.117	−1.129	0.067	−1.129	0.177058	0.06714
13	4,026.520	4,364.229	−337.709	0.064	−0.568	−0.553	0.006	−0.55255	0.064498	0.00556
14	10,343.810	8,713.307	1,630.503	0.146	2.871	4.558	0.353	4.55845	0.146451	0.35349
15	11,732.170	12,080.864	−348.694	0.682	−1.005	−1.006	0.541	−1.00588	0.681763	0.5414
16	15,414.940	15,133.026	281.914	0.785	0.990	0.989	0.897	0.98925	0.78548	0.89729
17	18,854.450	19,260.453	−406.003	0.863	-1.786	−1.975	5.033	−1.97506	0.863247	5.03294

X-ray exposures), BedDays (x_2, monthly occupied bed days—a hospital has one occupied bed day if one bed is occupied for an entire day), and Length (x_3, average length of patients' stay, in days). When we perform a regression analysis of these data using the model

$$y = \beta_0 + \beta_1 x_1 + \beta_2 x_2 + \beta_3 x_3 + \varepsilon,$$

we find that the least squares point estimates of the model parameters and their associated p values (given in parentheses) are $b_0 = 1{,}523.3892$ (0.0749), $b_1 = 0.0530$ (0.0205), $b_2 = 0.9785$ (<0.0001), and $b_3 = -320.9508$ (0.0563). In addition, Figure 12.55 gives the MegaStat and MINITAB output of outlying and influential observation diagnostics for the model, which we will sometimes refer to as Model I. The main objective of the regression analysis is to evaluate the performance of hospitals in terms of how many labour hours are used relative to how many labour hours are needed. Seventeen hospitals were selected from hospitals that were thought to be efficiently run. A regression model based on efficiently run hospitals can then be used to evaluate the efficiency of questionable hospitals.

Leverage values   To interpret the diagnostics in Figure 12.55, we first identify outliers with respect to their x values. One way to do this is to employ **leverage values**. The leverage value for an observation is the **distance value** discussed in Section 12.6 and used to calculate a prediction interval for the y value of the observation. This value is a measure of the distance between the observation's x values and the centre of the experimental region. The leverage value is labelled as "Leverage" on the MegaStat output and as "HI1" on the MINITAB output. **If the leverage value for an observation is large, the observation is outlying with respect to its x values. A leverage value is considered to be large if it is greater than twice the average of all of the leverage values,** which can be shown to be equal to $2(k + 1)/n$ (MegaStat shades such a leverage value in dark blue). For example, because there are $n = 17$ observations and the model

$$y = \beta_0 + \beta_1 x_1 + \beta_2 x_2 + \beta_3 x_3 + \varepsilon$$

utilizes $k = 3$ independent variables, twice the average leverage value is $2(k + 1)/n = 2(3 + 1)/17 = 0.4706$. Looking at Figure 12.55, we see that the leverage values for hospitals 15, 16, and 17 are, respectively, 0.682, 0.785, and 0.863. Because these leverage values are greater than 0.4706, we conclude that **hospitals 15, 16, and 17 are outliers with respect to their x values**. This is because x_1 (monthly X-ray exposures) and x_2 (monthly occupied bed days) are substantially larger for hospitals 15, 16, and 17 than for hospitals 1 through 14. In other words, hospitals 15, 16, and 17 are substantially larger hospitals than hospitals 1 through 14.

Residuals and studentized residuals   To identify outliers with respect to their y values, we can use residuals. Any residual that is substantially different from the others is suspect. For example, hospital 14's values of Xray, BedDays, and Length are 36,194, 7,684.1, and 7. Using the least squares point estimates for Model I, it follows that the point prediction of labour hours for hospital 14 is

$$\hat{y}_{14} = 1,523.3892 + 0.0530(36,194) + 0.9785(7,684.1) - 320.9508(7)$$
$$= 8,713,307,$$

Because the actual number of labour hours for hospital 14 is $y_{14} = 10,343.810$, the residual e_{14} for hospital 14 is the difference between $y_{14} = 10,343.810$ and $\hat{y}_{14} = 8,713.307$, which is 1,630.503. Figure 12.55 shows the residuals for all 17 hospitals. Since $e_{14} = 1,630.503$ is much larger than the other residuals, it seems that the number of labour hours for hospital 14 is much larger than that predicted by the regression model. To obtain a somewhat more precise idea about whether an observation is an outlier with respect to its y value, we can calculate the **studentized residual** for the observation. The studentized residual for an observation is the observation's residual divided by the residual's standard error.[4] As a very rough rule of thumb, if the studentized residual for an observation is greater than 2 in absolute value, we have some evidence that the observation is an outlier with respect to its y value. For example, because Figure 12.55 tells us that the studentized residual (see "Studentized Residual" on the MegaStat output) for hospital 14 is 2.871, we have some evidence that hospital 14 is an outlier with respect to its y value.[5]

Deleted residuals and studentized deleted residuals   Many statisticians feel that an excellent way to identify an outlier with respect to its y value is to use the **deleted, or PRESS, residual**. To calculate the deleted residual for observation i, we subtract from y_i the point prediction $\hat{y}_{(i)}$ computed using least squares point estimates based on all n observations except for observation i. We do this because, if observation i is an outlier with respect to its y value, using this observation to compute the usual least squares point estimates might "draw" the usual point prediction $\hat{y}_i$ toward y_i and thus cause the resulting usual residual to be small. This would falsely imply that observation i is not an outlier with respect to its y value. For example, consider using observation 3 in Figure 12.54 (page 485) to determine the least squares line. Doing this might draw the least squares line toward observation 3, causing the point prediction $\hat{y}_3$ given by the line to be near y_3 and thus the usual residual $y_3 - \hat{y}_3$ to be small. This would falsely imply that observation 3 is not an outlier with respect to its y value. To illustrate more precisely the concept of the deleted residual, recall that hospital 14's values of Xray, BedDays, and Length are 36,194, 7,684.1, and 7. Furthermore, let $b_0^{(14)}$, $b_1^{(14)}$, $b_2^{(14)}$, and $b_3^{(14)}$ denote the least squares point estimates of β_0, β_1, β_2, and β_3 that are calculated by using all 17 observations in Table 12.20 except for observation 14. Then, it can be shown that the point prediction of y_{14} using these least squares point estimates,

$$\hat{y}_{(14)} = b_0^{(14)} + b_1^{(14)}(36,194) + b_2^{(14)}(7,684.1) + b_3^{(14)}(7),$$

equals 8,433.43. It follows that the deleted residual for hospital 14 is the difference between $y_{14} = 10,343.810$ and $\hat{y}_{(14)} = 8,433.43$, which is 1,910.38. Standard statistical software packages calculate the deleted residual for each observation and divide this residual by its standard error to form the **studentized deleted residual**. The studentized deleted residual is labelled as "Studentized Deleted Residual" on the MegaStat output and as "TRES1" on the MINITAB output. Examining Figure 12.55, we see that the studentized deleted residual for hospital 14 is 4.558.

To evaluate the studentized deleted residual for an observation, we compare this quantity with two t distribution points—$t_{0.025}$ and $t_{0.005}$—based on $n - k - 2$ degrees of freedom. Specifically, if the studentized deleted residual is greater in absolute value than $t_{0.025}$ (and thus is shaded in light blue on the MegaStat output), then there is **some evidence** that the observation is an outlier with respect to its y value. If the studentized deleted residual is greater in absolute value than $t_{0.005}$ (and thus is shaded in dark blue on the MegaStat output), then there is **strong evidence** that the observation is an outlier with respect to its y value. The data analysis experience of the

---

[4]The formula for the residual's standard error, as well as the formulas for the other outlying and influential observation diagnostics discussed in this section, will be given in an optional technical note at the end of this section.

[5]Both MegaStat and MINITAB give all of the diagnostics discussed in this section.

authors leads us to suggest that one should not be overly concerned that an observation is an outlier with respect to its y value unless the studentized deleted residual is greater in absolute value than $t_{0.005}$. For the hospital labour needs model, $n - k - 2 = 17 - 3 - 2 = 12$, and therefore $t_{0.025} = 2.179$ and $t_{0.005} = 3.055$. The studentized deleted residual for hospital 14, which equals 4.558, is greater in absolute value than both $t_{0.025} = 2.179$ and $t_{0.005} = 3.055$. Therefore, we should be very concerned that **hospital 14 is an outlier with respect to its y value**.

Cook's distance measure   One way to determine if an observation is influential is to calculate **Cook's distance measure**, which we sometimes refer to as **Cook's D**, or simply D. Cook's D is labelled as "Cook's D" on the MegaStat output and as "Cook1" on the MINITAB output (see Figure 12.55). It can be shown that, if Cook's D for observation i is large, the least squares point estimates calculated by using all n observations differ substantially (**as a group**) from the least squares point estimates calculated by using all n observations except for observation i. This would say that observation i is influential. To determine whether D is large, we compare D with two F distribution points—$F_{0.80}$, the 20th percentile of the F distribution, and $F_{0.50}$, the 50th percentile of the F distribution—based on $(k + 1)$ numerator and $[n - (k + 1)]$ denominator degrees of freedom. If D is less than $F_{0.80}$, the observation should not be considered influential. If D is greater than $F_{0.50}$ (and thus is shaded in dark blue on the MegaStat output), the observation should be considered influential. If D is between $F_{0.80}$ and $F_{0.50}$ (and thus is shaded in light blue on the MegaStat output), then the nearer D is to $F_{0.50}$, the greater is the influence of the observation. Examining Figure 12.55, we see that for observation 17 Cook's D is 5.033 and is the largest value of Cook's D on the output. This value of Cook's D is greater than $F_{0.05} = 3.18$, which is based on $k + 1 = 4$ numerator and $n - (k + 1) = 17 - 4 = 13$ denominator degrees of freedom. Since $F_{0.05}$ is itself greater than $F_{0.50}$, Cook's D for observation 17 is greater than $F_{0.50}$, which says that **removing hospital 17 from the data set would substantially change (as a group) the least squares point estimates** of the parameters β_0, β_1, β_2, and β_3. Therefore, hospital 17 is **influential**, as is hospital 16—note that the values of Cook's D for both hospitals are shaded in dark blue on the MegaStat output.

In general, if we decide (by using Cook's D) that removing observation i from the data set would substantially change (as a group) the least squares point estimates, we might wish to determine whether the point estimate of a particular parameter β_j would change substantially. We might also wish to determine if the point prediction of y_i would change substantially. We discuss in the supplementary exercises how to make such determinations.

What to do about outlying and influential observations   To illustrate how we deal with outlying and influential observations, we summarize what we have learned in the hospital labour needs case:

1   Hospitals 15, 16, and 17, outliers with respect to their x values, are larger than the other hospitals. Hospitals 16 and 17 are influential in that removing either from the data set would substantially change (as a group) the least squares point estimates of the parameters β_0, β_1, β_2, and β_3.

2   Hospital 14 is an outlier with respect to its y value. Furthermore, hospital 14 is influential in that, because its residual ($e_{14} = 1{,}630.5$) is large, the sum of squared residuals and thus the standard error s (which equals 614.779) are larger than they would be if hospital 14 were removed from the data set.

We recommend first dealing with outliers with respect to their y values, because they affect the overall fit of the model. Often when we decide what to do with such outliers, other problems become much less important or disappear. In general, we should first check to see if the y value in question was recorded correctly. If it was recorded incorrectly, it should be corrected and the regression should be rerun. If it cannot be corrected, we should consider discarding the corresponding observation and rerunning the regression. We will assume that the labour hours for hospital 14 ($y_{14} = 10{,}343.8$) were recorded correctly.

A technical note (optional)   Suppose we perform a regression analysis of n observations by using a regression model that utilizes k independent variables. Let SSE and s denote the unexplained variation and the standard error for the regression model. Also, let h_i and $e_i = y_i - \hat{y}_i$

denote the leverage value and the usual residual for observation i. Then, the standard error of the residual e_i can be proven to equal $s\sqrt{1 - h_i}$. This implies that the **studentized residual** for observation i equals $e_i/(s\sqrt{1 - h_i})$. Furthermore, let $d_i = y_i - \hat{y}_{(i)}$ denote the **deleted residual** for observation i, and let s_{d_i} denote the standard error of d_i. Then, it can be shown that the **deleted residual** d_i and the **studentized deleted residual** d_i/s_{d_i} can be calculated by using the equations

$$d_i = \frac{e_i}{1 - h_i} \quad \text{and} \quad \frac{d_i}{s_{d_i}} = e_i \left[\frac{n - k - 2}{SSE(1 - h_i) - e_i^2} \right]^{1/2}.$$

Finally, if D_i denotes the value of Cook's D statistic for observation i, it can be proven that

$$D_i = \frac{e_i^2}{(k + 1)s^2} \left[\frac{h_i}{(1 - h_i)^2} \right].$$

Exercises for Section 12.14

CONCEPTS

12.61 What do leverage values identify? What do studentized deleted residuals identify?

12.62 What does Cook's distance measure identify?

METHODS AND APPLICATIONS

Figure 12.56(a) presents the output of the regression model of the hospital labour data with hospital 14 (a possible outlier) removed. Figure 12.56(c) represents the original regression

FIGURE 12.56 MegaStat Outlying and Influential Observation Diagnostics and Residual Plots

(a) Model I diagnostics without hospital 14

Obs	Residual	Leverage	Studentized Residual	Studentized Deleted Residual	Cook's D
1	−125.624	0.121	−0.346	−0.333	0.004
2	141.691	0.235	0.418	0.404	0.013
3	60.555	0.130	0.168	0.161	0.001
4	428.812	0.159	1.208	1.234	0.069
5	162.866	0.087	0.440	0.425	0.005
6	−294.287	0.114	−0.808	−0.795	0.021
7	256.296	0.086	0.692	0.677	0.011
8	409.814	0.084	1.106	1.117	0.028
9	−396.076	0.088	−1.071	−1.078	0.028
10	−472.953	0.135	−1.313	−1.359	0.067
11	517.698	0.083	1.397	1.461	0.044
12	−677.234	0.178	−1.929	−2.224	0.202
13	−262.164	0.066	−0.701	−0.685	0.009
14	−29.679	0.714	−0.143	−0.137	0.013
15	218.990	0.787	1.225	1.254	1.384
16	61.298	0.933	0.613	0.597	1.317

(b) Model II diagnostics

Obs	Residual	Leverage	Studentized Residual	Studentized Deleted Residual	Cook's D
1	−461.012	0.155	−1.379	−1.439	0.070
2	77.456	0.229	0.242	0.233	0.003
3	−254.577	0.161	−0.764	−0.750	0.022
4	68.769	0.198	0.211	0.202	0.002
5	77.192	0.085	0.222	0.213	0.001
6	−485.910	0.115	−1.420	−1.490	0.053
7	220.635	0.085	0.634	0.617	0.007
8	351.558	0.083	1.009	1.010	0.018
9	−144.646	0.121	−0.424	−0.409	0.005
10	−134.015	0.212	−0.415	−0.400	0.009
11	727.155	0.113	2.122	2.571	0.115
12	−204.698	0.230	−0.641	−0.624	0.025
13	162.093	0.140	0.480	0.464	0.007
14	266.801	0.706	1.352	1.406	0.877
15	−373.625	0.682	−1.821	−2.049	1.422
16	183.743	0.788	1.098	1.108	0.898
17	−76.920	0.896	−0.655	−0.639	0.738

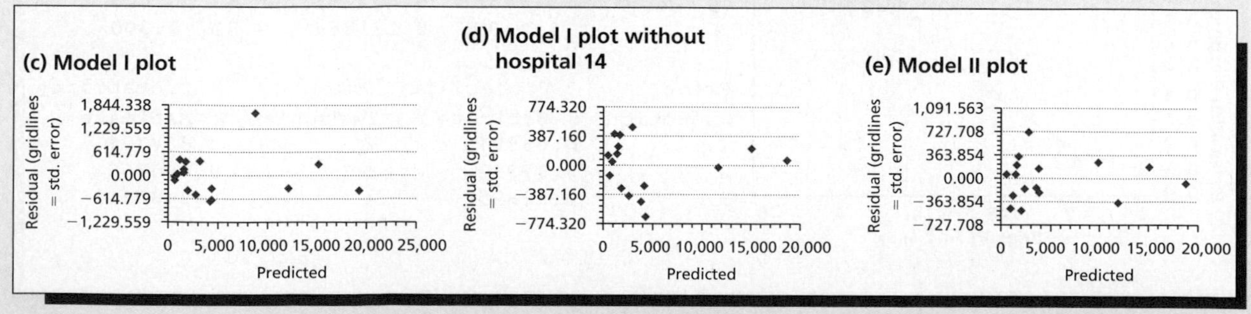

(c) Model I plot

(d) Model I plot without hospital 14

(e) Model II plot

model and Figure 12.56(d) represents the model plot without hospital 14.

12.63 Use Figure 12.56(a) to explain why Model I without hospital 14 has made the original hospital 17 considerably less influential and the original hospital 16 only slightly more influential.

12.64 Use Figure 12.56(b) and (e) to explain why Model II has made hospital 17 considerably less influential, hospital 15 slightly more influential, and hospital 14 no longer an outlier with respect to its y value.

12.15 Logistic Regression (Optional)

Logistic regression is used when the outcome (y variable) is dichotomous (two options). Some examples of dichotomous outcomes are living or dying after a medical treatment, voting for a particular candidate or not, hiring an individual or not, and buying a product or not.

Suppose that in a study of the effectiveness of offering a price reduction on a given product, 300 households with similar incomes were selected. A coupon offering a price reduction, x, on the product, as well as advertising material for the product, was sent to each household. The coupons offered different price reductions ($10, $20, $30, $40, $50, and $60), and 50 homes were assigned at random to each price reduction. The following table summarizes the number, y, and proportion, $\hat{p}$, of households redeeming coupons for each price reduction, x (expressed in units of $10):   ● PrcRed

x	1	2	3	4	5	6
y	4	7	20	35	44	46
$\hat{p}$	0.08	0.14	0.40	0.70	0.88	0.92

On the left side of Figure 12.57, we plot the $\hat{p}$ values versus the x values and draw a hypothetical curve through the plotted points. A theoretical curve with the shape of the curve in Figure 12.57 is the **logistic curve**

$$p(x) = \frac{e^{(\beta_0 + \beta_1 x)}}{1 + e^{(\beta_0 + \beta_1 x)}},$$

where $p(x)$ denotes the probability that a household receiving a coupon with a price reduction of x will redeem the coupon. The MINITAB output in Figure 12.57 tells us that the point estimates of β_0 and β_1 are $b_0 = -3.7456$ and $b_1 = 1.1109$. (The point estimates in logistic regression are usually obtained by an advanced statistical procedure called **maximum likelihood estimation**.) Using these estimates, it follows that, for example

$$\hat{p}(5) = \frac{e^{(-3.7456 + 1.1109(5))}}{1 + e^{(-3.7456 + 1.1109(5))}} = \frac{6.1037}{1 + 6.1037} = 0.8593.$$

FIGURE 12.57   **MINITAB Output of a Logistic Regression of the Price Reduction Data**

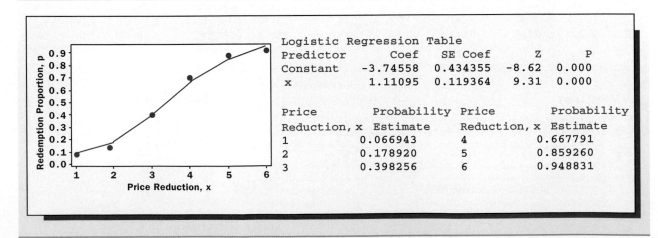

That is, $\hat{p}(5) = 0.8593$ is the point estimate of the probability that a household receiving a coupon with a price reduction of \$50 will redeem the coupon. The MINITAB output in Figure 12.57 gives the values of $\hat{p}(x)$ for $x = 1, 2, 3, 4, 5,$ and 6.

The **general logistic regression model** relates the probability that an event (such as redeeming a coupon) will occur to k independent variables $x_1, x_2, \ldots, x_k$. This general model is

$$p(x_1, x_2, \ldots, x_k) = \frac{e^{(\beta_0 + \beta_1 x_1 + \beta_2 x_2 + \cdots + \beta_k x_k)}}{1 + e^{(\beta_0 + \beta_1 x_1 + \beta_2 x_2 + \cdots + \beta_k x_k)}},$$

where $p(x_1, x_2, \ldots, x_k)$ is the probability that the event will occur when the values of the independent variables are $x_1, x_2, \ldots, x_k$. In order to estimate $\beta_0, \beta_1, \beta_2, \ldots, \beta_k$, we obtain n observations, with each observation consisting of observed values of $x_1, x_2, \ldots, x_k$ and of a dependent variable y. Here y is a **dummy variable** that equals 1 if the event has occurred and 0 otherwise.

For example, suppose that the personnel director of a firm has developed two tests to help determine whether potential employees would perform successfully in a particular position. To help estimate the usefulness of the tests, the director gives both tests to 43 employees that currently hold the position. Table 12.21 gives the scores of each employee on both tests and indicates whether the employee is currently performing successfully or unsuccessfully in the position. If the employee is performing successfully, we set the dummy variable Group equal to 1; if the employee is performing unsuccessfully, we set Group equal to 0. Let x_1 and x_2 denote the scores of a potential employee on tests 1 and 2, and let $p(x_1, x_2)$ denote the probability that a potential employee with scores x_1 and x_2 will perform successfully in the position. We can estimate the relationship between $p(x_1, x_2)$ and x_1 and x_2 by using the logistic regression model

$$p(x_1, x_2) = \frac{e^{(\beta_0 + \beta_1 x_1 + \beta_2 x_2)}}{1 + e^{(\beta_0 + \beta_1 x_1 + \beta_2 x_2)}}.$$

The MINITAB output in Figure 12.58 tells us that the point estimates of $\beta_0, \beta_1,$ and β_2 are $b_0 = -56.17$, $b_1 = 0.4833$, and $b_2 = 0.1652$. Consider, therefore, a potential employee who

TABLE **12.21**   **The Performance Data**   ● PerfTest

Group	Test 1	Test 2	Group	Test 1	Test 2
1	96	85	1	87	82
1	96	88	0	93	74
1	91	81	0	90	84
1	95	78	0	91	81
1	92	85	0	91	78
1	93	87	0	88	78
1	98	84	0	86	86
1	92	82	0	79	81
1	97	89	0	83	84
1	95	96	0	79	77
1	99	93	0	88	75
1	89	90	0	81	85
1	94	90	0	85	83
1	92	94	0	82	72
1	94	84	0	82	81
1	90	92	0	81	77
1	91	70	0	86	76
1	90	81	0	81	84
1	86	81	0	85	78
1	90	76	0	83	77
1	91	79	0	81	71
1	88	83			

Source: *Applied Regression Analysis for Business and Economics,* 2nd ed., by T. Dielman. Copyright © 1996. Reprinted with permission of Brooks/Cole, an imprint of the Wadsworth Group, a division of Thomson Learning. Fax 800-730-2215.

FIGURE **12.58**   **MINITAB Output of a Logistic Regression of the Performance Data**

```
Response Information

Variable  Value  Count
Group     1        23    (Event)
          0        20
          Total    43
Logistic Regression Table
                                               Odds     95% CI
Predictor      Coef    SE Coef     Z      P    Ratio  Lower  Upper
Constant   -56.1704   17.4516   -3.22  0.001
Test 1       0.483314  0.157779   3.06  0.002   1.62   1.19   2.21
Test 2       0.165218  0.102070   1.62  0.106   1.18   0.97   1.44

Log-Likelihood = -13.959
Test that all slopes are zero: G = 31.483, DF = 2, P-Value = 0.000
```

scores a 93 on test 1 and an 84 on test 2. It follows that a point estimate of the probability that the potential employee will perform successfully in the position is

$$\hat{p}(93, 84) = \frac{e^{(-56.17 + 0.4833(93) + 0.1652(84))}}{1 + e^{(-56.17 + 0.4833(93) + 0.1652(84))}} = \frac{14.206506}{15.206506} = 0.9342.$$

If we **classify** a potential employee into group 1 ("will perform successfully"), as opposed to group 2 ("will not perform successfully"), if and only if $\hat{p}(x_1, x_2)$ is greater than 0.5, this potential employee is classified into group 1.

To further analyze the logistic regression output, we consider several hypothesis tests that are based on the chi-square distribution. We first consider testing H_0: $\beta_1 = \beta_2 = 0$ versus H_a: at least one of β_1 or β_2 does not equal 0. The p value for this test is the area under the chi-square curve with $k = 2$ degrees of freedom to the right of the test statistic value $G = 31.483$. Although the calculation of G is not demonstrated in this book, the MINITAB output gives the value of G and the related p value, which is less than 0.001. This p value implies that we have extremely strong evidence that at least one of β_1 and β_2 does not equal zero. The p value for testing H_0: $\beta_1 = 0$ versus H_a: $\beta_1 \neq 0$ is the area under the chi-square curve with one degree of freedom to the right of the square of $z = (b_1/s_{b_1}) = (0.4833/0.1578) = 3.06$. The MINITAB output tells us that this p value is 0.002, which implies that we have very strong evidence that the score on test 1 is related to the probability of a potential employee's success. The p value for testing H_0: $\beta_2 = 0$ versus H_a: $\beta_2 \neq 0$ is the area under the chi-square curve with one degree of freedom to the right of the square of $z = (b_2/s_{b_2}) = (0.1652/0.1021) = 1.62$. The MINITAB output tells us that this p value is 0.106, which implies that we do not have strong evidence that the score on test 2 is related to the probability of a potential employee's success. In Exercise 12.67, we will consider a logistic regression model that uses only the score on test 1 to estimate the probability of a potential employee's success.

The **odds** of success for a potential employee is defined to be the probability of success divided by the probability of failure for the employee. That is,

$$\text{odds} = \frac{p(x_1, x_2)}{1 - p(x_1, x_2)}.$$

For the potential employee who scores a 93 on test 1 and an 84 on test 2, we estimate that the odds of success are $0.9342/(1 - 0.9342) = 14.22$. That is, we estimate that the odds of success for the potential employee are about 14 to 1. It can be shown that $e^{b_1} = e^{0.4833} = 1.62$ is a point estimate of the **odds ratio for x_1**, which is the proportional change in the odds (for any potential employee) that is associated with an increase of one in x_1 when x_2 stays constant. This point estimate of the odds ratio for x_1 is shown on the MINITAB output and says that, for every one-point increase in the score on test 1 when the score on test 2 stays constant, we estimate that a potential employee's odds of success increase by 62 percent. Furthermore, the 95 percent confidence interval for the odds ratio for x_1—[1.19, 2.21]—does not contain 1. Therefore, as with the (equivalent) chi-square test of H_0: $\beta_1 = 0$, we conclude that there is strong evidence that the score on test 1 is related to the probability of success for a potential employee. Similarly, it can be shown that $e^{b_2} = e^{0.1652} = 1.18$ is a point estimate of the **odds ratio for x_2**, which is the proportional change in the odds (for any potential employee) that is associated with an increase of one in x_2 when x_1

stays constant. This point estimate of the odds ratio for x_2 is shown on the MINITAB output and says that, for every one-point increase in the score on test 2 when the score on test 1 stays constant, we estimate that a potential employee's odds of success increases by 18 percent. However, the 95 percent confidence interval for the odds ratio for x_2—[0.97, 1.44]—contains 1. Therefore, as with the equivalent chi-square test of $H_0: \beta_2 = 0$, we cannot conclude that there is strong evidence that the score on test 2 is related to the probability of success for a potential employee.

To conclude this section, consider the general logistic regression model

$$p(x_1, x_2, \ldots, x_k) = \frac{e^{(\beta_0 + \beta_1 x_1 + \beta_2 x_2 + \cdots + \beta_k x_k)}}{1 + e^{(\beta_0 + \beta_1 x_1 + \beta_2 x_2 + \cdots + \beta_k x_k)}},$$

where $p(x_1, x_2, \ldots, x_k)$ is the probability that the event under consideration will occur when the values of the independent variables are $x_1, x_2, \ldots, x_k$. The **odds** of the event occurring is defined to be $p(x_1, x_2, \ldots, x_k)/(1 - p(x_1, x_2, \ldots, x_k))$, which is the probability that the event will occur divided by the probability that the event will not occur. It can be shown that the odds equals $e^{(\beta_0 + \beta_1 x_1 + \beta_2 x_2 + \cdots + \beta_k x_k)}$. The natural logarithm of the odds is $(\beta_0 + \beta_1 x_1 + \beta_2 x_2 + \cdots + \beta_k x_k)$, which is called the **logit**. If $b_0, b_1, b_2, \ldots, b_k$ are the point estimates of $\beta_0, \beta_1, \beta_2, \ldots, \beta_k$, the point estimate of the logit, denoted $\widehat{\ell g}$, is $(b_0 + b_1 x_1 + b_2 x_2 + \cdots + b_k x_k)$. It follows that the point estimate of the probability that the event will occur is

$$\hat{p}(x_1, x_2, \ldots, x_k) = \frac{e^{\widehat{\ell g}}}{1 + e^{\widehat{\ell g}}} = \frac{e^{(b_0 + b_1 x_1 + b_2 x_2 + \cdots + b_k x_k)}}{1 + e^{(b_0 + b_1 x_1 + b_2 x_2 + \cdots + b_k x_k)}}.$$

Finally, consider an arbitrary independent variable x_j. It can be shown that e^{b_j} is the point estimate of the **odds ratio for x_j**, which is the proportional change in the odds that is associated with a one-unit increase in x_j when the other independent variables stay constant.

Exercises for Section 12.15

CONCEPTS

12.65 What two values does the dependent variable equal in logistic regression? What do these values represent?

12.66 What is the odds? What is the odds ratio?

METHODS AND APPLICATIONS

12.67 If we use the logistic regression model

$$p(x_1) = \frac{e^{(\beta_0 + \beta_1 x_1)}}{1 + e^{(\beta_0 + \beta_1 x_1)}}$$

to analyze the performance data in Table 12.21, we find that the point estimates of the model parameters

and their associated p values (given in parentheses) are $b_0 = -43.37$ (0.001) and $b_1 = 0.4897$ (0.001). Find a point estimate of the probability of success for a potential employee who scores a 93 on test 1. Using $b_1 = 0.4897$, find a point estimate of the odds ratio for x_1. Interpret this point estimate.

12.68 Mendenhall and Sincich (1993) present data that can be used to investigate allegations of sex discrimination in the hiring practices of a particular firm. These data are as in Table 12.22. ● Sex

TABLE **12.22** Data for Exercise 12.68

Hiring Status, y	Education, x_1 (Years)	Experience, x_2 (Years)	Sex, x_3	Hiring Status, y	Education, x_1 (Years)	Experience, x_2 (Years)	Sex, x_3
0	6	2	0	1	4	5	1
0	4	0	1	0	6	4	0
1	6	6	1	0	8	0	1
1	6	3	1	1	6	1	1
0	4	1	0	0	4	7	0
1	8	3	0	0	4	1	1
0	4	2	1	0	4	5	0
0	4	4	0	0	6	0	1
0	6	1	0	1	8	5	1
1	8	10	0	0	4	9	0
0	4	2	1	0	8	1	0
0	8	5	0	0	6	1	1
0	4	2	0	1	4	10	1
0	6	7	0	1	6	12	0

In this table, y is a dummy variable that equals 1 if a potential employee was hired and 0 otherwise, x_1 is the number of years of education of the potential employee, x_2 is the number of years of experience of the potential employee, and x_3 is a dummy variable that equals 1 if the potential employee was a male and 0 if the potential employee was a female. If we use the logistic regression model

$$p(x_1, x_2, x_3) = \frac{e^{(\beta_0 + \beta_1 x_1 + \beta_2 x_2 + \beta_3 x_3)}}{1 + e^{(\beta_0 + \beta_1 x_1 + \beta_2 x_2 + \beta_3 x_3)}}$$

to analyze these data, we find that the point estimates of the model parameters and their associated p values (given in parentheses) are $b_0 = -14.2483$ (0.0191),

$b_1 = 1.1549$ (0.0552), $b_2 = 0.9098$ (0.0341), and $b_3 = 5.6037$ (0.0313).

a. Consider a potential employee with 4 years of education and 5 years of experience. Find a point estimate of the probability that the potential employee will be hired if the potential employee is a male, and find a point estimate of the probability that the potential employee will be hired if the potential employee is a female.

b. Using $b_3 = 5.6037$, find a point estimate of the odds ratio for x_3. Interpret this odds ratio. Using the p value describing the importance of x_3, can we conclude that there is strong evidence that the sex of the applicant is related to the probability that a potential employee will be hired?

CHAPTER SUMMARY

This chapter has discussed **multiple regression analysis**. We began by considering the **multiple regression model**. We next discussed the **least squares point estimates** of the model parameters, the assumptions behind the model, and some ways to judge **overall model utility**—the **standard error**, the **multiple coefficient of determination**, the **adjusted multiple coefficient of determination**, and the **overall F test**. Then we considered testing the significance of a single independent variable in a multiple regression model, calculating a **confidence interval** for the mean value of the dependent variable, and calculating a **prediction interval** for an individual value of the dependent variable. We continued this chapter by discussing using **squared terms** to model **quadratic** relationships, using **cross-product terms** to model **interaction**, and using **dummy variables** to model **qualitative** independent variables. We then

considered how to use the **partial F test** to evaluate a portion of a regression model. We next discussed **multicollinearity**, which can adversely affect the ability of the t statistics and associated p values to assess the importance of the independent variables in a regression model. For this reason, we need to determine if the overall model gives a **high R^2**, a **small s**, a **high adjusted R^2**, **short prediction intervals**, and a **small C**. We considered how to compare regression models on the basis of these criteria, and we also showed how to use **stepwise regression** and **backward elimination** to help select a regression model. We concluded this chapter by showing (1) how to use residual analysis to check the regression assumptions for multiple regression models, (2) how to use various diagnostics to detect **outlying** and **influential** observations, and (3) how to use **logistic regression** to estimate the probability that an event will occur.

Glossary of Terms

dummy variable: A variable that takes on the value 0 or 1 and is used to describe the effects of the different levels of a qualitative independent variable in a regression model. (page 454)

experimental region: The range of the previously observed combinations of values of the independent variables. (page 415)

influential observation: An observation that causes the least squares point estimates (or other aspects of the regression analysis) to be substantially different from what they would be if the observation were removed from the data. (page 485)

interaction: The situation in which the relationship between the mean value of the dependent variable and an independent

variable is dependent on the value of another independent variable. (page 447)

multicollinearity: The situation in which the independent variables used in a regression analysis are related to each other. (page 469)

multiple regression model: An equation that describes the relationship between a dependent variable and more than one independent variable. (page 414)

outlier: An observation that is well separated from the rest of the data with respect to its y value and/or its x values. (page 485)

IMPORTANT FORMULAS AND TESTS

The multiple regression model: page 417

The least squares point estimates: page 420

Point estimate of a mean value of y: page 423

Point prediction of an individual value of y: page 423

Mean square error: page 427

Standard error: page 427

Total variation: page 428

Explained variation: page 428

Unexplained variation: page 428

Multiple coefficient of determination: page 428

Multiple correlation coefficient: page 428

Adjusted multiple coefficient of determination: page 429

An F test for the linear regression model: page 430

Sampling distribution of b_j: page 433

Testing the significance of an independent variable: page 434

Confidence interval for β_j: page 435

Sampling distribution of $\hat{y}$ (and the distance value): page 436

Confidence interval for a mean value of y: page 437

Prediction interval for an individual value of y: page 437

The quadratic regression model: page 439

The partial F test: page 466

Variance inflation factor: page 469

C statistic: page 474

The Durbin–Watson test: page 482

Leverage value: page 486

Studentized residual: pages 487, 489

Deleted (PRESS) residual: pages 487, 489

The studentized deleted residual: pages 487, 489

Cook's distance measure: pages 488, 489

The logistic regression model: page 491

Odds: page 492

SUPPLEMENTARY EXERCISES

12.69 In a September 1982 article in *Business Economics*, Allmon related y = Crest toothpaste sales in a given year (in thousands of dollars) to x_1 = Crest advertising budget in the year (in thousands of dollars), x_2 = ratio of Crest's advertising budget to Colgate's advertising budget in the year, and x_3 = U.S. personal disposable income in the year (in billions of dollars). The data analyzed are given in Table 12.23. When we perform a regression analysis of these data using the model

$$y = \beta_0 + \beta_1 x_1 + \beta_2 x_2 + \beta_3 x_3 + \varepsilon,$$

we find that the least squares point estimates of the model parameters and their associated p values (given in parentheses) are $b_0 = 30,626$ (0.156), $b_1 = 3.893$ (0.094), $b_2 = -29,607$ (0.245), and $b_3 = 86.52$ (<0.001). Suppose it was estimated at the end of 1979 that in 1980 the advertising budget for Crest would be 28,000, the ratio of Crest's advertising budget to Colgate's advertising budget would be 1.56, and the U.S. personal disposable income would be 1,821.7. Using the model, we would obtain a point prediction of about 251,057, thus giving us the 95 percent prediction interval [221,986, 280,128] for Crest sales in 1980. Show how the point prediction was calculated. ● Crest

12.70 The trend in home building in recent years has been to emphasize open spaces and great rooms, rather than smaller living rooms and family rooms. A builder of speculative homes (Oxford Homes) in

London, Ontario, had been building such homes, but these homes had been taking many months to sell and selling for substantially less than the asking price. In order to determine what types of homes would attract residents of the community, the builder contacted a statistician. The statistician went to a local real estate agency and obtained the data in Table 12.24. This table presents the sales price y, square footage x_1, number of rooms x_2, number of bedrooms x_3, and age x_4 for each of 63 single-family residences recently sold in the community. When we perform a regression analysis of these data using the model

$$y = \beta_0 + \beta_1 x_1 + \beta_2 x_2 + \beta_3 x_3 + \beta_4 x_4 + \varepsilon,$$

we find that the least squares point estimates of the model parameters and their associated p values (given in parentheses) are $b_0 = 10.3676$ (0.3710), $b_1 = 0.0500$ (<0.001), $b_2 = 6.3218$ (0.0152), $b_3 = -11.1032$ (0.0635), and $b_4 = -0.4319$ (0.0002). Discuss why the estimates $b_2 = 6.3218$ and $b_3 = -11.1032$ suggest that it might be more profitable when building a house with specified square footage (1) to include both a (smaller) living room and family room rather than a (larger) great room and (2) to not increase the number of bedrooms (at the cost of another type of room) that would normally be included in a house with specified square footage. ● OxHome

TABLE 12.23 Crest Toothpaste Sales Data ● Crest

Year	Crest Sales, y	Crest Budget, x_1	Ratio, x_2	U.S. Personal Disposable Income, x_3	
1967	105,000	16,300	1.25	547.9	
1968	105,000	15,800	1.34	593.4	
1969	121,600	16,000	1.22	638.9	
1970	113,750	14,200	1.00	695.3	
1971	113,750	15,000	1.15	751.8	
1972	128,925	14,000	1.13	810.3	
1973	142,500	15,400	1.05	914.5	
1974	126,000	18,250	1.27	998.3	
1975	162,000	17,300	1.07	1,096.1	
1976	191,625	23,000	1.17	1,194.4	
1977	189,000	19,300	1.07	1,311.5	
1978	210,000	23,056	1.54	1,462.9	
1979	224,250	26,000	1.59	1,641.7	

TABLE **12.24**　Measurements Taken on 63 Single-Family Residences　◉ OxHome

Residence	Sales Price, y (× $1,000)	Square Feet, x_1	Rooms, x_2	Bedrooms, x_3	Age, x_4	Residence	Sales Price, y (× $1,000)	Square Feet, x_1	Rooms, x_2	Bedrooms, x_3	Age, x_4
1	53.5	1,008	5	2	35	33	63.0	1,053	5	2	24
2	49.0	1,290	6	3	36	34	60.0	1,728	6	3	26
3	50.5	860	8	2	36	35	34.0	416	3	1	42
4	49.9	912	5	3	41	36	52.0	1,040	5	2	9
5	52.0	1,204	6	3	40	37	75.0	1,496	6	3	30
6	55.0	1,204	5	3	10	38	93.0	1,936	8	4	39
7	80.5	1,764	8	4	64	39	60.0	1,904	7	4	32
8	86.0	1,600	7	3	19	40	73.0	1,080	5	2	24
9	69.0	1,255	5	3	16	41	71.0	1,768	8	4	74
10	149.0	3,600	10	5	17	42	83.0	1,503	6	3	14
11	46.0	864	5	3	37	43	90.0	1,736	7	3	16
12	38.0	720	4	2	41	44	83.0	1,695	6	3	12
13	49.5	1,008	6	3	35	45	115.0	2,186	8	4	12
14	105.0	1,950	8	3	52	46	50.0	888	5	2	34
15	152.5	2,086	7	3	12	47	55.2	1,120	6	3	29
16	85.0	2,011	9	4	76	48	61.0	1,400	5	3	33
17	60.0	1,465	6	3	102	49	147.0	2,165	7	3	2
18	58.5	1,232	5	2	69	50	210.0	2,353	8	4	15
19	101.0	1,736	7	3	67	51	60.0	1,536	6	3	36
20	79.4	1,296	6	3	11	52	100.0	1,972	8	3	37
21	125.0	1,996	7	3	9	53	44.5	1,120	5	3	27
22	87.9	1,874	5	2	14	54	55.0	1,664	7	3	79
23	80.0	1,580	5	3	11	55	53.4	925	5	3	20
24	94.0	1,920	5	3	14	56	65.0	1,288	5	3	2
25	74.0	1,430	9	3	16	57	73.0	1,400	5	3	2
26	69.0	1,486	6	3	27	58	40.0	1,376	6	3	103
27	63.0	1,008	5	2	35	59	141.0	2,038	12	4	62
28	67.5	1,282	5	3	20	60	68.0	1,572	6	3	29
29	35.0	1,134	5	2	74	61	139.0	1,545	6	3	9
30	142.5	2,400	9	4	15	62	140.0	1,993	6	3	4
31	92.2	1,701	5	3	15	63	55.0	1,130	5	2	21
32	56.0	1,020	6	3	16						

Note: Based on the statistical results, the builder realized that there are many families with children in London and that the parents in such families would rather have one living area for the children (the family room) and a separate living area for themselves (the living room). The builder started modifying the open-space homes accordingly and greatly increased profits.

12.71 Recall from Exercise 11.74 (page 411) that Erb, Harvey, and Viskanta studied the relationship between credit rating and investment risk for 40 countries. In a more recent article (*Journal of Portfolio Management*, Spring 1996), these authors studied the volatility of a country's stock market returns by considering the standard deviation of these returns. They used the model　◉ InvRisk2

$$y = \beta_0 + \beta_1 x_1 + \beta_2 x_2 + \beta_3 x_1 x_2 + \varepsilon$$

to relate y, the standard deviation of a country's stock returns, to x_1, the country's credit rating, and x_2, a dummy variable that equals 1 if the country is a developing country and 0 if the country is an emerging country. When regression analysis is used to fit this

model to the data in Table 12.25, we find that the least squares point estimates of the model parameters and their associated p values (given in parentheses) are $b_0 = 56.9171$ (<0.001), $b_1 = -0.5574$ (<0.001), $b_2 = -18.2934$ (0.0026), and $b_3 = 0.3537$ (<0.001). Using the least squares point estimates, show that the equation $\hat{y} = 56.9171 - 0.5574x_1$ estimates the relationship between stock market return volatility and credit rating for emerging countries, and that the equation $\hat{y} = 38.6237 - 0.2037x_1$ estimates the relationship between stock market return volatility and credit rating for developing countries. Then use these equations to discuss the nature of the interaction between x_1 and x_2.

12.72 MODEL BUILDING WITH SQUARED AND INTERACTION TERMS

Recall from Example 12.12 (pages 472 to 474) that we concluded that perhaps the best sales territory performance model using only linear terms is the model using TIME, MKTPOTEN, ADVER, MKTSHARE, and CHANGE. For this model, $s = 430.23$ and $\overline{R}^2 = 0.893$.

TABLE **12.25** The Stock Market Return Volatility Data ● InvRisk2

Country	Standard Deviation of Return, y	Credit Rating, x_1	Developing or Emerging	Country	Standard Deviation of Return, y	Credit Rating, x_1	Developing or Emerging
Afghanistan	55.7	8.3	E	New Zealand	24.3	69.4	D
Australia	23.9	71.2	D	Nigeria	46.2	15.8	E
China	27.2	57.0	E	Oman	28.6	51.8	D
Cuba	55.0	8.7	E	Panama	38.6	26.4	E
Germany	20.3	90.9	D	Spain	23.4	73.7	D
France	20.6	89.1	D	Sudan	60.5	6.0	E
India	30.3	46.1	E	Taiwan	22.2	79.9	D
Belgium	22.3	79.2	D	Norway	21.4	84.6	D
Canada	22.1	80.3	D	Sweden	23.3	74.1	D
Ethiopia	47.9	14.1	E	Togo	45.1	17.0	E
Haiti	54.9	8.8	E	Ukraine	46.3	15.7	E
Japan	20.2	91.6	D	United Kingdom	20.8	87.8	D
Libya	36.7	30.0	E	United States	20.3	90.7	D
Malaysia	24.3	69.1	E	Vietnam	36.9	29.5	E
Mexico	31.8	41.8	E	Zimbabwe	36.2	31.0	E

Source: "Expected returns and volatility in 135 countries." by C. B. Erb, C. R. Harvey, and T. E. Viskanta, *Journal of Portfolio Management*, Vol. 22, no. 3, Spring 1996, pp. 54–55 (Exhibit 6). This copyrighted material is reprinted with permission from the *Journal of Portfolio Management*, a publication of Institutional Investor, Inc., 488 Madison Ave., New York, NY 10022.

To decide which squared and pairwise interaction terms should be added to this model, we consider all possible squares and pairwise interactions of the five linear independent variables in this model. So that we can better understand the MINITAB output to follow, the MINITAB notation for these squares and pairwise interactions is as in Figure 12.59(a).

Consider having MINITAB evaluate all possible models involving these squared and pairwise interaction terms, where the five linear terms TIME, MKTPOTEN, ADVER, MKTSHARE, and CHANGE are included in each possible model. If we have MINITAB do this and find the best single model of each size, we obtain the output in Figure 12.59(b).

FIGURE **12.59** MINITAB Notation and Output for Exercise 12.72

(a) MINITAB notation for Exercise 12.72

SQT	=	TIME*TIME		TC	=	TIME*CHANGE
SQMP	=	MKTPOTEN*MKTPOTEN		MPA	=	MKTPOTEN*ADVER
SQA	=	ADVER*ADVER		MPMS	=	MKTPOTEN*MKTSHARE
SQMS	=	MKTSHARE*MKTSHARE		MPC	=	MKTPOTEN*CHANGE
SQC	=	CHANGE*CHANGE		AMS	=	ADVER*MKTSHARE
TMP	=	TIME*MKTPOTEN		AC	=	ADVER*CHANGE
TA	=	TIME*ADVER		MSC	=	MKTSHARE*CHANGE
TMS	=	TIME*MKTSHARE				

(b) MINITAB output for Exercise 12.72

```
The following variables are included in all models: Time MktPoten Adver MktShare Change
                                              S   S                                 M
                                              S Q S Q S T       T       M P M A     M
                                Mallows       Q M Q M Q M T M T P M P M A M S
Vars  R-Sq  R-Sq(adj)   C-p       S    T P A S C P A S C A S C S C C
   1  94.2      92.2   43.2   365.87                    X
   2  95.8      94.1   29.7   318.19  X                 X
   3  96.5      94.7   25.8   301.61  X                 X   X
   4  97.0      95.3   22.5   285.54  X             X X       X
   5  97.5      95.7   20.3   272.05  X             X X       X     X
   6  98.1      96.5   16.4   244.00  X     X       X X       X           X
   7  98.7      97.4   13.0   210.70  X X           X X       X       X X
   8  99.0      97.8   12.3   193.95  X X       X   X X       X       X X
   9  99.2      98.0   12.7   185.45  X X     X     X X       X       X X X
  10  99.3      98.2   13.3   175.70  X X     X     X X       X X X X X
  11  99.4      98.2   14.6   177.09  X X     X   X X X       X X X X X
  12  99.5      98.2   15.8   174.60  X X     X   X X X X     X X X X X
  13  99.5      98.1   17.5   183.22  X X X     X X X X X     X X X X X
  14  99.6      97.9   19.1   189.77  X X     X X X X X X X X X X X X
  15  99.6      97.4   21.0   210.78  X X X X X X X X X X X X X X X X
```

The model using 12 squared and pairwise interaction terms has the smallest s. However, if we want a somewhat simpler model, note that s does not increase substantially until we move from a model with seven squared and pairwise interaction terms to a model with six such terms. It can also be verified that the model with seven squared and pairwise interaction terms is the largest model for which all of the independent variables have p values less than 0.05. Therefore, we might consider this model to have an optimal mix of a small s and simplicity. Identify s and $\overline{R}^2$ for this model. How do the s and $\overline{R}^2$ you identified compare with the s and $\overline{R}^2$ for the model using only the linear terms TIME, MKTPOTEN, ADVER, MKTSHARE, and CHANGE?

12.73 THE FRESH DETERGENT CASE   ● Fresh3

Recall from Exercise 12.45 (pages 463 and 464) that Enterprise Industries has advertised Fresh liquid laundry detergent by using three different advertising campaigns—advertising campaign A (television commercials), advertising campaign B (a balanced mixture of television and radio commercials), and advertising campaign C (a balanced mixture of television, radio, newspaper, and magazine ads). To compare the effectiveness of these advertising campaigns, consider the model

$$y = \beta_0 + \beta_1 x_4 + \beta_2 x_3 + \beta_3 x_3^2 + \beta_4 x_4 x_3$$
$$+ \beta_5 D_B + \beta_6 D_C + \varepsilon.$$

Here, y is demand for Fresh, x_4 is the price difference, x_3 is Enterprise Industries' advertising expenditure for Fresh, D_B equals 1 if advertising campaign B is used in a sales period and 0 otherwise, and D_C equals 1 if advertising campaign C is used in a sales period and 0 otherwise. If we use this model to perform a regression analysis of the data in Tables 12.4 and 12.16, we obtain the partial MegaStat output in Figure 12.60(a).

a. In the above model, the parameter β_5 represents the effect on mean demand of advertising campaign B compared to advertising campaign A, and the parameter β_6 represents the effect on mean demand of advertising campaign C compared to advertising campaign A. Use the regression output to find a point estimate of and to test the significance of each of the above effects. Also find a 95 percent confidence interval for each of the above effects. Interpret your results.

b. Consider the alternative model

$$y = \beta_0 + \beta_1 x_4 + \beta_2 x_3 + \beta_3 x_3^2 + \beta_4 x_4 x_3$$
$$+ \beta_5 D_A + \beta_6 D_C + \varepsilon.$$

Here D_A equals 1 if advertising campaign A is used and 0 otherwise. The MegaStat output of the least squares point estimates of the parameters of this model is as in Figure 12.60(b). Noting that β_6 represents the effect on mean demand of advertising campaign C compared to advertising campaign B, find a point estimate of and a 95 percent confidence interval for this effect. Also test the significance of this effect. Interpret your results.

c. Consider the alternative model

$$y = \beta_0 + \beta_1 x_4 + \beta_2 x_3 + \beta_3 x_3^2 + \beta_4 x_4 x_3 + \beta_5 D_A$$
$$+ \beta_6 D_C + \beta_7 x_3 D_B + \beta_8 x_3 D_C + \varepsilon.$$

The MegaStat output of the least squares point estimates of the parameters of this model is as in Figure 12.60(c).

Let $\mu_{[d,a,A]}$, $\mu_{[d,a,B]}$, and $\mu_{[d,a,C]}$ denote the mean demands for Fresh when the price difference is d, the advertising expenditure is a, and we use advertising campaigns A, B, and C, respectively. The model of this part implies that

$$\mu_{[d,a,A]} = \beta_0 + \beta_1 d + \beta_2 a + \beta_3 a^2 + \beta_4 da$$
$$+ \beta_5(0) + \beta_6(0) + \beta_7 a(0) + \beta_8 a(0),$$

$$\mu_{[d,a,B]} = \beta_0 + \beta_1 d + \beta_2 a + \beta_3 a^2 + \beta_4 da$$
$$+ \beta_5(1) + \beta_6(0) + \beta_7 a(1) + \beta_8 a(0),$$

$$\mu_{[d,a,C]} = \beta_0 + \beta_1 d + \beta_2 a + \beta_3 a^2 + \beta_4 da$$
$$+ \beta_5(0) + \beta_6(1) + \beta_7 a(0) + \beta_8 a(1).$$

Using these equations, verify that $\mu_{[d,a,C]} - \mu_{[d,a,A]}$ equals $\beta_6 + \beta_8 a$. Then, using the least squares point estimates, show that a point estimate of $\mu_{[d,a,C]} - \mu_{[d,a,A]}$ equals 0.3266 when $a = 6.2$ and equals 0.4080 when $a = 6.6$. Also verify that $\mu_{[d,a,C]} - \mu_{[d,a,B]}$ equals $\beta_6 - \beta_5 + \beta_8 a - \beta_7 a$. Using the least squares point estimates, show that a point estimate of $\mu_{[d,a,C]} - \mu_{[d,a,B]}$ equals 0.14266 when $a = 6.2$ and 0.18118 when $a = 6.6$. Discuss why these results imply that the larger advertising expenditure a is, the larger is the improvement in mean sales obtained by using advertising campaign C rather than advertising campaign A or B.

d. The prediction results given at the bottom of the MegaStat outputs in Figure 11.60(a) and (c) correspond to a future period when the price difference will be $x_4 = 0.20$, the advertising expenditure will be $x_3 = 6.50$, and campaign C will be used. Which model—the first model or the third model of this exercise—gives the shortest 95 percent prediction interval for Fresh demand? Using all of the results in this exercise, discuss why there might be a small amount of interaction between advertising expenditure and advertising campaign.

12.74 THE DIFFERENCE IN ESTIMATE OF β_j STATISTIC

Consider the difference between the least squares point estimate b_j of β_j, computed using all n observations, and the least squares point estimate $b_j^{(i)}$ of β_j, computed using all n observations except for observation i. SAS (an advanced software system) calculates this difference for each observation and divides the difference by its standard error to form the **difference in estimate of β_j statistic**. If the absolute value of this statistic is greater than 2 (a sometimes used critical value for this statistic), then removing observation i from the data set would substantially change the least squares point estimate of β_j. For example, consider the hospital labour needs model of Section 12.14 that uses all 17 observations to relate y to x_1, x_2, and x_3. Also consider

FIGURE **12.60**   MegaStat Output for Exercise 12.73

(a) Partial MegaStat output for Exercise 12.73

Regression output

variables	coefficients	std. error	t (df = 23)	p-value	confidence interval 95% lower	95% upper
Intercept	25.6127	4.7938	5.343	2.00E-05	15.6960	35.5294
X4	9.0587	3.0317	2.988	0.0066	2.7871	15.3302
X3	6.5377	1.5014	−4.134	0.0004	−9.8090	−3.2664
X3SQ	0.5844	0.1299	4.500	0.0002	0.3158	0.8531
X43	−1.1565	0.4557	−2.538	0.0184	−2.0992	−0.2137
DB	0.2137	0.0622	3.438	0.0022	0.0851	0.3423
DC	0.3818	0.0613	6.233	2.33E-06	0.2551	0.5085

Predicted values for: Y

	95% Confidence Interval		95% Prediction Interval			
Predicted	lower	upper	lower	upper	Leverage	
8.50068	8.40370	8.59765	8.21322	8.78813	0.128	

R^2 0.971
Adjusted R^2 0.963
R 0.985
Std. Error 0.131

(b) MegaStat output of least squares point estimates for Exercise 12.73(b)

Regression output

variables	coefficients	std. error	t (df = 23)	p-value	confidence interval 95% lower	95% upper
Intercept	25.8264	4.7946	5.387	1.80E-05	15.9081	35.7447
X4	9.0587	3.0317	2.988	0.0066	2.7871	15.3302
X3	−6.5377	1.5814	−4.134	0.0004	−9.8090	−3.2664
X3SQ	0.5844	0.1299	4.500	0.0002	0.3158	0.8531
X43	−1.1565	0.4557	−2.538	0.0184	−2.0992	−0.2137
DA	−0.2137	0.0622	−3.438	0.0022	−0.3423	−0.0851
DC	0.1681	0.0637	2.638	0.0147	0.0363	0.2999

(c) MegaStat output of least squares point estimates for Exercise 12.73(c)

Regression output

variables	coefficients	std. error	t (df = 21)	p-value	confidence interval 95% lower	95% upper	
Intercept	28.6873	5.1285	5.594	1.50E-05	18.0221	39.3526	R^2 0.974
X4	10.8253	3.2988	3.282	0.0036	3.9651	17.6855	Adjusted R^2 0.964
X3	−7.4115	1.6617	−4.460	0.0002	−10.8671	−3.9558	R 0.987
X3SQ	0.6458	0.1346	4.798	0.0001	0.3659	0.9257	Std. Error 0.129
X43	−1.4156	0.4929	−2.872	0.0091	−2.4406	−0.3907	
DB	−0.4807	0.7309	−0.658	0.5179	−2.0007	1.0393	n 30
DC	−0.9351	0.8357	−1.119	0.2758	−2.6731	0.8029	k 8
X3DB	0.1072	0.1117	0.960	0.3480	−0.1251	0.3395	Dep. Var. Y
X3DC	0.2035	0.1288	1.580	0.1291	−0.0644	0.4714	

Predicted values for: Y

	95% Confidence Interval		95% Prediction Interval		
Predicted	lower	upper	lower	upper	Leverage
8.51183	8.41229	8.61136	8.22486	8.79879	0.137

the columns labelled "Dfbetas" in Figure 12.61. Notice that there are four such columns—one for each model parameter—which are labelled INTERCEP, X1, X2, and X3. Each of these columns contains the difference in estimate of β_j statistic related to the column's parameter label for each observation. We see that for observation 17, "INTERCEP Dfbetas" (= 0.0294), "X2 Dfbetas" (= 1.2688), and "X3 Dfbetas" (= 0.3155) are all less than 2 in absolute value. This says that the least squares point estimates of β_0, β_2, and β_3 probably would not change substantially if hospital 17 were removed from the data set. However, for observation 17, "X1 Dfbetas" (= −3.0114) is greater than 2 in absolute value. What does this say?

Note: If we remove hospital 14 from the data set or use a dummy variable to model the inefficiency of large hospitals (see Section 12.14), then hospital 17

becomes much less influential with respect to the difference in estimate of β_j statistic.

Note: For further information about estimating the β_j statistic, see Bowerman and O'Connell (1990). MINITAB and MegaStat do not give this statistic.

12.75   **THE DIFFERENCE IN FITS STATISTIC**

Consider the difference between the point prediction $\hat{y}_i$ of y_i computed using least squares point estimates based on all n observations and the point prediction $\hat{y}_{(i)}$ of y_i computed using least squares point estimates based on all n observations except for observation i. Some statistical software packages calculate this difference for each observation and divide the difference by its standard error to form the **difference in fits statistic**. If the absolute value of this statistic is greater than 2 (a sometimes used critical value for this statistic), then removing

FIGURE **12.61**   Difference in Estimate of β_j Statistics

Obs	INTERCEP Dfbetas	X1 Dfbetas	X2 Dfbetas	X3 Dfbetas
1	-0.0477	0.0157	-0.0083	0.0309
2	0.0138	-0.0050	0.0119	-0.0183
3	0.0307	-0.0084	0.0060	-0.0216
4	0.2416	-0.0217	0.0251	-0.1821
5	0.0035	0.0014	-0.0099	0.0074
6	-0.0881	-0.0703	0.0724	0.0401
7	0.0045	-0.0008	-0.0180	0.0179
8	0.0764	-0.0319	0.0063	-0.0314
9	0.0309	0.0243	0.0304	-0.0873
10	0.1787	-0.2924	0.3163	-0.2544
11	-0.0265	0.0560	-0.0792	0.0680
12	-0.4387	0.3549	-0.3782	0.3864
13	-0.0671	0.0230	-0.0243	0.0390
14	-0.8544	1.1389	-0.9198	0.9620
15	0.9616	0.1324	-0.0133	-0.9561
16	0.9880	-1.4289	1.7339	-1.1029
17	0.0294	-3.0114	1.2688	0.3155

observation i from the data set would substantially change the point prediction of y_i. For example, consider the hospital labour needs model of Section 12.14 that uses all 17 observations to relate y to x_1, x_2, and x_3. Also consider the MINITAB output of the column labelled "Dffits" below. This column contains the difference in fits statistic for each observation. The value of this statistic for observation 17 is -4.9623. What does this say?

Note: If we remove hospital 14 from the data set or use a dummy variable to model the inefficiency of large hospitals (see Section 12.14), then hospital 17 becomes much less influential with respect to the difference in fits statistic.

Note: The formula for the difference in fits statistic for observation i is found by multiplying the formula for the studentized deleted residual for observation i by $[h_i/(1 - h_i)]^{1/2}$. Here h_i is the leverage value for observation i.

Difference in Fits Statistics

Hosp	Dffits
1	-0.07541
2	-0.02404
3	0.04383
4	0.32657
5	0.04213
6	-0.22799
7	0.08818
8	0.18406
9	-0.25179
10	-0.44871
11	0.18237
12	-0.52368
13	-0.14509
14	1.88820
15	-1.47227
16	1.89295
17	-4.96226

12.76   DISCRIMINATE ANALYSIS   ⊙ PerfTest

Consider the performance data in Table 12.21 (page 491). In Section 12.15, we used logistic regression to classify a potential employee into group 1 ("will perform successfully") or group 0 ("will not perform successfully"). Another way to make the classification is to use **discriminant analysis**. For example, Figure 12.62 presents the MINITAB output of a discriminant analysis of the performance data. This figure gives a **discriminant equation for group 0** and a **discriminant equation for group 1**. Denoting these equations as $\hat{y}_{(0)}$ and $\hat{y}_{(1)}$, the MINITAB output tells us that

$$\hat{y}_{(0)} = -298.27 + 5.20x_1 + 1.97x_2 \text{ and}$$
$$\hat{y}_{(1)} = -351.65 + 5.68x_1 + 2.10x_2.$$

A prospective employee is classified into group 1 if and only if $\hat{y}_{(1)}$ is greater than $\hat{y}_{(0)}$. For example, consider a prospective employee who scores a 93 on test 1 and an 84 on test 2. For this prospective employee, $\hat{y}_{(0)} = 350.81$ and $\hat{y}_{(1)} = 352.99$. Since $\hat{y}_{(1)}$ is greater than $\hat{y}_{(0)}$, the prospective employee is classified into group 1. Calculate $\hat{y}_{(0)}$ and $\hat{y}_{(1)}$ for a prospective employee who scores an 85 on test 1 and an 82 on test 2. Then classify this employee into group 0 or group 1. Interpret your classification.

FIGURE **12.62**   MINITAB Output of a Discriminant Analysis of the Performance Data

Linear Discriminant Function for Groups		
	0	1
Constant	-298.27	-351.65
Test 1	5.20	5.68
Test 2	1.97	2.10

Note: Discriminant analysis is a **multivariate statistical technique**. In Appendix H in the Online Learning Centre, we discuss three other multivariate techniques—factor analysis, cluster analysis, and multidimensional scaling.

12.77 INTERNET EXERCISE

Statistics Canada (http://www.statcan.ca) is conducting an ongoing study of Canadian Internet use. In the study description (http://www.statcan.ca/Daily/English/060815/d060815b.htm), click on the link "Definitions, data sources and methods: survey number 4432" near the bottom of the page. Read the section dealing with error detection and explain how multiple regression techniques could be used to help detect possible outliers.

CHAPTER 13

Nonparametric Methods

LEARNING OBJECTIVES

After reading this chapter, you should be able to

- identify when a researcher would use a nonparametric method versus a parametric method

- identify and understand the different conditions required in order to compute a Wilcoxon rank sum test versus a Wilcoxon signed ranks test as well as be able to conduct the appropriate test properly

- understand when to use the Kruskal–Wallis *H* test and be able to conduct the test properly

- understand the difference between Spearman's rank correlation coefficient and Pearson's correlation coefficient

- compute Spearman's rank correlation coefficient and test the value for significance

CHAPTER OUTLINE

Recall from Chapter 2 that the manufacturer of a DVD recorder has randomly selected a sample of 20 purchasers who have owned the recorder for one year. Each purchaser in the sample is asked to rank their satisfaction with the recorder along the following 10-point scale:

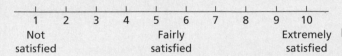

| 1 | 2 | 3 | 4 | 5 | 6 | 7 | 8 | 9 | 10 |

Not satisfied   Fairly satisfied   Extremely satisfied

The stem-and-leaf display below gives the 20 ratings obtained:

```
 1   0
 2
 3   0
 4
 5   00
 6
 7   0
 8   000000
 9   00000
10   0000
```

Let μ denote the mean rating that would be given by all purchasers who have owned the DVD recorder for one

year, and suppose we wish to show that μ exceeds 7. To do this, we will test $H_0: \mu \le 7$ versus $H_a: \mu > 7$. The mean and the standard deviation of the sample of 20 ratings are $\bar{x} = 7.7$ and $s = 2.4301$, and the test statistic t is

$$t = \frac{\bar{x} - 7}{s/\sqrt{n}} = \frac{7.7 - 7}{2.4301/\sqrt{20}} = 1.2882.$$

Because $t = 1.2882$ is less than $t_{0.10} = 1.328$ (based on 19 degrees of freedom), we cannot reject $H_0: \mu \le 7$ by setting α equal to 0.10. That is, the t test does not provide even mildly strong evidence that μ exceeds 7. But how appropriate is the t test in this situation? The t test is, in fact, not appropriate for two reasons:

1. The t test assumes that, when the sample size n is small (less than 30), the sampled population is normally distributed (or, at least, mound-shaped and not highly skewed to the right or left). The stem-and-leaf display of the ratings indicates the population of all DVD recorder ratings might be highly skewed to the left (negatively skewed).

2. The rating of 1 in the stem-and-leaf display is an extreme **outlier** (see Figure 2.28 on page 59). This outlier, along with the other small ratings of 3, 5, and 5 in

the tail of the stem-and-leaf display, affects both the sample mean and the sample standard deviation. First, the sample mean of 7.7 is "pulled down" by the low ratings and thus is smaller than the sample median, which is 8. Although there is not much difference here between the mean and the median, the outlier and overall skewness indicate that the median might be a better measure of central tendency. More important, however, is the fact that the low ratings inflate the sample standard deviation s. As a result, although the sample mean of 7.7 is greater than 7, the inflated s of 2.4301 makes the denominator of the t statistic large enough to cause us to not reject $H_0: \mu \leq 7$. Intuitively, therefore, even if the population mean DVD recorder rating really does exceed 7, the t test is not **powerful enough** to tell us that this is true.

In addition, some statisticians would consider the t test to be inappropriate for a third reason. The variable DVD recorder rating is an **ordinal variable**. Recall from Section 1.4 that an ordinal variable is a **qualitative variable** with a meaningful **ordering**, or **ranking**, of the categories. In general, when the measurements of an ordinal variable are numerical, statisticians debate whether the ordinal variable is "somewhat quantitative." Statisticians who argue that a DVD recorder rating is not somewhat quantitative would reason, for instance, that the difference between 10 (extremely satisfied) and 6 (fairly satisfied) may not be the same as the difference between 5 (fairly satisfied) and 1 (not satisfied), or may not satisfy the conditions of an **interval scale**. In other words, although each difference is four rating points, the two differences may not be the same qualitatively. Other statisticians would argue that as soon as respondents see equally spaced numbers (even though the numbers are described by words), their responses are influenced enough to make the ordinal variable somewhat quantitative. In general, the choice of words associated with the numbers probably substantially affects whether an ordinal variable may be considered somewhat quantitative. However, in practice, numerical ordinal ratings are often analyzed as though they are quantitative. For example, although a teacher's effectiveness rating given by a student is considered to be an ordinal variable with the possible measurements 4 (excellent), 3 (good), 2 (average), 1 (poor), and 0 (unsatisfactory), a teacher's effectiveness **average** is calculated. Furthermore, some statisticians would argue that when there are "fairly many" numerical ordinal ratings (for example, the 10 ratings in the DVD recorder example), it is even more reasonable to consider the ratings somewhat quantitative and thus to analyze means and variances. However, for statisticians who feel that numerical ordinal ratings should never be considered quantitative, analyzing the means and standard deviations of these ratings—and thus performing t tests—would always be considered inappropriate.

In general, consider the one-sample t test (see Section 8.5), the two independent sample t tests and the paired difference t test (see Chapter 9), and the one-way analysis of variance (ANOVA) F test (see Section 10.2). All of these procedures assume that the sampled populations are normally distributed (or mound-shaped and not highly skewed to the right or left (positively or negatively skewed)). When this assumption is not satisfied, we can use techniques that do not require assumptions about the shapes of the probability distributions of the sampled populations. These techniques are often called **nonparametric methods**, and we discuss several of these methods in this chapter. Specifically, we consider four nonparametric tests that can be used in place of the previously mentioned t and F tests. These four nonparametric tests are the **sign test**, the **Wilcoxon rank sum test**, the **Wilcoxon signed ranks test**, and the **Kruskal–Wallis H test**. These tests require no assumptions about the shapes of the sampled populations. In addition, these nonparametric tests are usually better than the t and F tests at correctly finding statistically significant differences in the presence of outliers and extreme skewness. Therefore, we say that the nonparametric tests can be **more powerful** than the t and F tests. For example, we will find in Section 13.1 that, although the t test does not allow us to conclude that the population **mean** DVD recorder rating exceeds 7, the nonparametric sign test does allow us to conclude that the population **median** DVD recorder rating exceeds 7.

Each nonparametric test discussed in this chapter theoretically assumes that each sampled population under consideration is described by a continuous probability distribution. However, in most situations, each nonparametric technique is slightly **statistically conservative** if the sampled population is described by a discrete probability distribution. This means, for example, that a nonparametric hypothesis test has a slightly smaller chance of falsely rejecting the null hypothesis than the specified α value would seem to indicate if the sampled population is described by a discrete probability distribution. Furthermore, since each nonparametric technique is based essentially on **ranking** the observed sample values, and not on the exact sizes of the sample values, it can be used to analyze any type of data that can be ranked. This includes ordinal data (for example, teaching effectiveness ratings and DVD recorder ratings) as well as quantitative data.

To conclude this introduction, we note that t and F tests are more powerful (better at correctly finding statistically significant differences) than nonparametric tests when the sampled populations are normally distributed (or mound-shaped and not highly skewed to the right or left (positively or negatively skewed)). In addition, nonparametric tests are largely limited to simple settings. For example, a nonparametric measure of correlation between two variables—**Spearman's rank correlation coefficient**—is discussed at the end of this chapter. However, nonparametric tests do not extend easily to multiple regression and complex experimental designs. This is one reason that we have stressed t and F procedures in this book. These procedures can be extended to more advanced statistical methods.

13.1 The Sign Test: A Hypothesis Test about the Median

If a population is highly skewed to the right or left (positively or negatively skewed), then the population median might be a better measure of central tendency than the population mean. Furthermore, if the sample size is small and the population is highly skewed or clearly not mound-shaped, then the t test for the population mean that we presented in Section 8.5 might not be valid. For these reasons, when we have taken a small sample and if it is possible that the sampled population might be far from being normally distributed, it is sometimes useful to use a hypothesis test about the population median. This test, called the **sign test**, is valid for any sample size and population shape. To illustrate the sign test, we consider the following example.

Example 13.1

The leading digital music player is advertised to have a median lifetime (or time to failure) of 6,000 hours of continuous play. The developer of a new digital music player wishes to show that the median lifetime of the new player exceeds 6,000 hours of continuous play. To this end, the developer randomly selects 20 new players and tests them in continuous play until each fails. Figure 13.1(a) presents the 20 lifetimes obtained (expressed in hours and arranged in increasing order), and Figure 13.1(b) shows a stem-and-leaf display of these lifetimes. The stem-and-leaf display and the three low lifetimes of 5, 947, and 2,142 suggest that the population of all lifetimes might be highly skewed to the left (i.e., negatively skewed). In addition, the sample size is small. Therefore, it might be reasonable to use the sign test.

In order to show that the population median lifetime, M_d, of the new digital music player exceeds 6,000 (hours), recall that this median divides the population of ordered lifetimes into two equal parts. It follows that, if more than half of the individual population lifetimes exceed 6,000, the population median, M_d, exceeds 6,000. Let p denote the proportion of the individual population lifetimes that exceed 6,000. Then, we can reject $H_0: M_d = 6,000$ in favour of $H_a: M_d > 6,000$ if we can reject $H_0: p = 0.5$ in favour of $H_a: p > 0.5$. Let x denote the total number of lifetimes that exceed 6,000 in a random sample of 20 lifetimes. If $H_0: p = 0.5$ is true, then x is a binomial random variable where $n = 20$ and $p = 0.5$. This says that if $H_0: p = 0.5$ is true, then we would expect $\mu_x = np = 20(0.5) = 10$ of the 20 lifetimes to exceed 6,000. Considering the 20 lifetimes we have actually observed, we note that 15 of these 20 lifetimes exceed 6,000. The p value for testing $H_0: p = 0.5$ versus $H_a: p > 0.5$ is the probability, computed assuming that $H_0: p = 0.5$

FIGURE 13.1 The Digital Music Player Lifetime Data and Associated Statistical Analyses

(a) The digital music player lifetime data ● DigMus

5	947	2,142	4,867	5,840	6,085	6,238	6,411	6,507	6,687
6,827	6,985	7,082	7,176	7,285	7,410	7,563	7,668	7,724	7,846

(c) MINITAB output of the sign test of $H_0: M_d = 6,000$ versus $H_a: M_d > 6,000$

```
Sign test of median = 6000 versus > 6000
              N   Below   Equal   Above        P   Median
LifeTime   20       5       0      15   0.0207     6757
```

(d) MegaStat output of the sign test of $H_0: M_d = 6,000$ versus $H_a: M_d > 6,000$

Sign Test

6,000 hypothesized value	5 below	binomial
6,757 median Life Time	0 equal	0.0207 p-value (one-tailed, upper)
20 n	15 above	

(b) A stem-and-leaf display

```
0   005
0   947
1
1
2   142
2
3
3
4
4   867
5
5   840
6   085 238 411
6   507 687 827 985
7   082 176 285 410
7   563 668 724 846
```

is true, of observing a sample result that is as large as or larger than the sample result we have actually observed. The p value is calculated as follows:

$$p \text{ value} = P(x \geq 15) = \sum_{x=15}^{20} \frac{20!}{x!\,(20-x)!}\,(0.5)^x(0.5)^{20-x}.$$

Using the binomial distribution table in Table A.1, we find that

$$p \text{ value} = P(x \geq 15)$$
$$= P(x = 15) + P(x = 16) + P(x = 17) + P(x = 18)$$
$$+ P(x = 19) + P(x = 20)$$
$$= 0.0148 + 0.0046 + 0.0011 + 0.0002 + 0.0000 + 0.0000$$
$$= 0.0207.$$

This says that if H_0: $p = 0.5$ is true, then the probability that at least 15 out of 20 lifetimes would exceed 6,000 is only 0.0207. Therefore, we have strong evidence against H_0: $p = 0.5$ and in favour of H_a: $p > 0.5$. That is, we have strong evidence that H_0: $M_d = 6{,}000$ is false and H_a: $M_d > 6{,}000$ is true. This implies that it is reasonable to conclude that the median lifetime of the new digital music player exceeds the advertised median lifetime of the market's leading digital music player. Figure 13.1(c) and (d) presents the MINITAB and MegaStat output of the sign test of H_0: $M_d = 6{,}000$ versus H_a: $M_d > 6{,}000$. In addition, the output tells us that a point estimate of the population median lifetime is the sample median of 6,757 hours.

We summarize how to carry out the sign test in the following box:

The Sign Test for a Population Median

Suppose we have randomly selected a sample of size n from a population, and suppose we wish to test the null hypothesis H_0: $M_d = M_0$ versus one of H_a: $M_d < M_0$, H_a: $M_d > M_0$, and H_a: $M_d \neq M_0$, where M_d denotes the population median. Define the test statistic S as follows:

1 If the alternative is H_a: $M_d < M_0$, then $S =$ the number of sample measurements less than M_0.

2 If the alternative is H_a: $M_d > M_0$, then $S =$ the number of sample measurements greater than M_0.

3 If the alternative is H_a: $M_d \neq M_0$, then $S =$ the larger of S_1 and S_2, where S_1 is the number of sample measurements less than M_0 and S_2 is the number of sample measurements greater than M_0.

Furthermore, define x to be a binomial variable with parameters n and $p = 0.5$. Then, we can test H_0: $M_d = M_0$ versus a particular alternative hypothesis at level of significance α by using the appropriate p value.

Alternative Hypothesis	p Value (reject H_0 if p value $< \alpha$)
H_a: $M_d > M_0$	The probability that x is greater than or equal to S
H_a: $M_d < M_0$	The probability that x is greater than or equal to S
H_a: $M_d \neq M_0$	Twice the probability that x is greater than or equal to S

Here we can use Table A.1 to find the p value.

We next point out that, when we take a large sample, we can use the normal approximation to the binomial distribution to implement the sign test. Here, when the null hypothesis H_0: $M_d = M_0$ (or H_0: $p = 0.5$) is true, the binomial variable x is approximately normally distributed with mean $np = n(0.5) = 0.5n$ and standard deviation $\sqrt{np(1-p)} = \sqrt{n(0.5)(1-0.5)} = 0.5\sqrt{n}$. The test is based on the test statistic

$$z = \frac{(S - 0.5) - 0.5n}{0.5\sqrt{n}},$$

where S is as defined in the previous box and where we subtract 0.5 from S as a correction for continuity. This motivates the following test:

The Large Sample Sign Test for a Population Median

Suppose we have taken a large sample (for this test, $n \geq 10$ will suffice). Define S as in the previous box, and define the test statistic

$$z = \frac{(S - 0.5) - 0.5n}{0.5\sqrt{n}}.$$

We can test $H_0: M_d = M_0$ versus a particular alternative hypothesis at level of significance α by using the appropriate rejection point rule or, equivalently, the corresponding p value.

Alternative Hypothesis	Rejection Point Rule: Reject H_0 if	p Value (Reject H_0 if p Value $< \alpha$)
$H_a: M_d > M_0$	$z > z_\alpha$	The area under the standard normal curve to the right of z
$H_a: M_d < M_0$	$z > z_\alpha$	The area under the standard normal curve to the right of z
$H_a: M_d \neq M_0$	$z > z_{\alpha/2}$	Twice the area under the standard normal curve to the right of z

Example 13.2

Consider Example 13.1. Because the sample size $n = 20$ is greater than 10, we can use the large sample sign test to test $H_0: M_d = 6{,}000$ versus $H_a: M_d > 6{,}000$. Because $S = 15$ is the number of digital music player lifetimes that exceed $M_0 = 6{,}000$, the test statistic z is

$$z = \frac{(S - 0.5) - 0.5n}{0.5\sqrt{n}} = \frac{(15 - 0.5) - 0.5(20)}{0.5\sqrt{20}} = 2.01.$$

The p value for the test is the area under the standard normal curve to the right of $z = 2.01$, which is $0.5 - 0.4778 = 0.0222$. Because this p value is less than 0.05, we have strong evidence that $H_a: M_d > 6{,}000$ is true. Also note that the large sample, approximate p value of 0.0222 given by the normal distribution is fairly close to the exact p value of 0.0207 given by the binomial distribution (see Figure 13.1(c)).

To conclude this section, we consider the DVD recorder rating example discussed in the chapter introduction, and we let M_d denote the median rating that would be given by all purchasers who have owned the DVD recorder for one year. Below we present the MINITAB output of the sign test of $H_0: M_d = 7.5$ versus $H_a: M_d > 7.5$:

```
Sign test of median = 7.500 versus > 7.500
              N    Below   Equal   Above        P    Median
DVD Rating    20       5       0      15   0.0207     8.000
```

Because the p value of 0.0207 is less than 0.05, we have strong evidence that the population median rating exceeds 7.5. Furthermore, note that the sign test has reached this conclusion by showing that **more than 50 percent** of all DVD recorder ratings exceed 7.5. It follows, since a rating exceeding 7.5 is the same as a rating being at least 8 (because of the discrete nature of the ratings), that we have strong evidence that the population median rating is at least 8.

Exercises for Section 13.1

CONCEPTS

13.1 What is a nonparametric test? Why would such a test be particularly useful when we must take a small sample?

13.2 When we perform the sign test, we use the sample data to compute a p value. What probability distribution is used to compute the p value? Explain.

FIGURE **13.2** **MINITAB Output for Exercise 13.4**

```
Sign test of median = 3.500 versus > 3.500
          N   Below   Equal   Above        P   Median
Ratio     7       0       0       7   0.0078    6.000
```

METHODS AND APPLICATIONS

13.3 Consider the following sample of five chemical yields:
● ChemYield

$$801 \quad 814 \quad 784 \quad 836 \quad 820$$

    a. Use this sample to test H_0: $M_d = 800$ versus H_a: $M_d \neq 800$ by setting $\alpha = 0.01$.

    b. Use this sample to test H_0: $M_d = 750$ versus H_a: $M_d > 750$ by setting $\alpha = 0.05$.

13.4 Consider the following sample of seven bad debt ratios:
● BadDebt

$$7\% \quad 4\% \quad 6\% \quad 7\% \quad 5\% \quad 4\% \quad 9\%$$

Use this sample and the MINITAB output in Figure 13.2 to test the null hypothesis that the median bad debt ratio equals 3.5 percent versus the alternative hypothesis that the median bad debt ratio exceeds 3.5 percent by setting α equal to 0.05.

13.5 A local newspaper randomly selects 20 patrons of the Springwood Restaurant on a given Saturday night and has each patron rate the quality of their meal as 5 (excellent), 4 (good), 3 (average), 2 (poor), or 1 (unsatisfactory). When the results are summarized, it is found that there are sixteen ratings of 5, three ratings of 4, and one rating of 3. Let M_d denote the population median rating that would be given by all possible patrons of the restaurant on the Saturday night.

    a. Test H_0: $M_d = 4.5$ versus H_a: $M_d > 4.5$ by setting $\alpha = 0.05$.

    b. Reason that your conclusion in part a implies that we have very strong evidence that the median rating that would be given by all possible patrons is 5.

13.6 Suppose that a particular type of plant has a median growing height of 20 cm in a specified time period when the best plant food currently on the market is used as directed. A developer of a new plant food wishes to show that the new plant food increases the median growing height. If a stem-and-leaf display indicates that the population of all growing heights using the new plant food is markedly nonnormal, it would be appropriate to use the sign test to test H_0: $M_d = 20$ versus H_a: $M_d > 20$. Here M_d denotes the population median growing height when the new plant food is used. Suppose that 13 out of 15 sample plants grown using the new plant food reach a height of more than 20 cm. Test H_0: $M_d = 20$ versus H_a: $M_d > 20$ by using the large sample sign test.

13.7 A common application of the sign test deals with analyzing consumer preferences. For instance, suppose that a blind taste test is administered to nine randomly selected convenience store customers. Each participant is asked to express a preference for either Coke or Pepsi after tasting unidentified samples of each soft drink. The sample results are expressed by recording a $+1$ for each consumer who prefers Coke and a -1 for each consumer who prefers Pepsi. Note that sometimes, rather than recording either a $+1$ or a -1, we simply record the sign $+$ or $-$, hence the name "sign test." A 0 is recorded if a consumer is unable to rank the two brands, and these observations are eliminated from the analysis.

    The null hypothesis in this application says that there is no difference in preferences for Coke and Pepsi. If this null hypothesis is true, then the number of $+1$ values in the population of all preferences should equal the number of -1 values, which implies that the median preference $M_d = 0$ (and that the proportion p of $+1$ values equals 0.5). The alternative hypothesis says that there is a significant difference in preferences (or that there is a significant difference in the number of $+1$ values and -1 values in the population of all preferences). This implies that the median preference does not equal 0 (and that the proportion p of $+1$ values does not equal 0.5). ● CokePep

    a. Table 13.1 gives the results of the taste test administered to the nine randomly selected consumers.

TABLE **13.1** Results of a Taste Test of Coke versus Pepsi ● CokePep

Customer	Preference (Coke or Pepsi)	Value (Sign)
1	Coke	+1
2	Pepsi	−1
3	Pepsi	−1
4	Coke	+1
5	Coke	+1
6	Pepsi	−1
7	Coke	+1
8	Coke	+1
9	Pepsi	−1

Sign Test				
	0 hypothesized value	4 below		binomial
9 n	1 median Value (sign)	0 equal	1.0000	p-value (two-tailed)
		5 above		

If we consider testing $H_0: M_d = 0$ versus $H_a: M_d \neq 0$, where M_d is the median of the ($+1$ and -1) preference rankings, determine the values of S_1, S_2, and S for the sign test needed to test H_0 versus H_a. Identify the value of S on the MegaStat output.

b. Use the value of S to find the p value for testing H_0: $M_d = 0$ versus $H_a: M_d \neq 0$. Then use the p value to test H_0 versus H_a by setting α equal to 0.10, 0.05, 0.01, and 0.001. How much evidence is there of a difference in the preferences for Coke and Pepsi? What do you conclude?

13.2 The Wilcoxon Rank Sum Test

We can use t tests for comparing two population means in an independent samples experiment. If the sampled populations are far from normally distributed and the sample sizes are small, these tests are not valid. In such a case, a nonparametric method should be used to compare the populations.

We have seen that the mean of a population measures the **central tendency**, or **location**, of the probability distribution describing the population. Thus, for instance, if a t test provides strong evidence that μ_1 is greater than μ_2, we might conclude that the probability distribution of population 1 is **shifted to the right** of the probability distribution of population 2. The nonparametric test for comparing the locations of two populations is not (necessarily) a test about the difference between population means. Rather, it is a more general test to detect whether the probability distribution of population 1 is shifted to the right (or left) of the probability distribution of population 2.[1] Furthermore, **the nonparametric test is valid for any shapes that might describe the sampled populations**.

In this section, we present the **Wilcoxon rank sum test** (also called the **Mann–Whitney test**), which is used to compare the locations of two populations when **independent samples** are selected. To perform this test, we first combine all of the observations in both samples into a single set, and we rank these observations from smallest to largest, with the smallest observation receiving rank 1, the next smallest observation receiving rank 2, and so forth. The sum of the ranks of the observations in each sample is then calculated. If the probability distributions of the two populations are identical, we would expect the sum of the ranks for sample 1 to roughly equal the sum of the ranks for sample 2. However, if, for example, the sum of the ranks for sample 1 is substantially larger than the sum of the ranks for sample 2, this would suggest that the probability distribution of population 1 is shifted to the right of the probability distribution of population 2, and vice versa. We explain how to carry out the Wilcoxon rank sum test in the following box:

The Wilcoxon Rank Sum Test

Let D_1 and D_2 denote the probability distributions of populations 1 and 2, and assume that we randomly select independent samples of sizes n_1 and n_2 from populations 1 and 2. Rank the $n_1 + n_2$ observations in the two samples from the smallest (rank 1) to the largest (rank $n_1 + n_2$). Here, if two or more observations are equal, we assign to each "tied" observation a rank equal to the average of the consecutive ranks that would otherwise be assigned to the tied observations. Let T_1 denote the sum of the ranks of the observations in sample 1, and let T_2 denote the sum of the ranks of the observations in sample 2. Furthermore, define the **test statistic T** to be T_1 if $n_1 \leq n_2$ and T_2 if $n_1 > n_2$. Then, we can test

H_0: D_1 and D_2 are identical probability distributions

versus a particular alternative hypothesis at level of significance α by using the appropriate rejection point rule.

Alternative Hypothesis	Rejection Point Rule: Reject H_0 if
H_a: D_1 is shifted to the right of D_2	$T \geq T_U$ if $n_1 \leq n_2$ $T \leq T_L$ if $n_1 > n_2$
H_a: D_1 is shifted to the left of D_2	$T \leq T_L$ if $n_1 \leq n_2$ $T \geq T_U$ if $n_1 > n_2$
H_a: D_1 is shifted to the right or left of D_2	$T \leq T_L$ or $T \geq T_U$

The first two alternative hypotheses above are **one-sided**, while the third alternative hypothesis is **two-sided**. Values of the rejection points T_U and T_L are given in Table A.15 for values of n_1 and n_2 from 3 to 10.

---

[1]To be precise, we say that the probability distribution of population 1 is shifted to the right (left) of the probability distribution of population 2 if there is more than a 50 percent chance that a randomly selected observation from population 1 will be greater than (less than) a randomly selected observation from population 2.

TABLE 13.2 A Portion of the Wilcoxon Rank Sum Table Rejection Points for $\alpha = 0.05$ (One-Sided); $\alpha = 0.10$ (Two-Sided)

n_2 \ n_1	3 T_L	3 T_U	4 T_L	4 T_U	5 T_I	5 T_U	6 T_L	6 T_U	7 T_L	7 T_U	8 T_L	8 T_U	9 T_L	9 T_U	10 T_L	10 T_U
3	6	15	7	17	7	20	8	22	9	24	9	27	10	29	11	31
4	7	17	12	24	13	27	14	30	15	33	16	36	17	39	18	42
5	7	20	13	27	19	36	20	40	22	43	24	46	25	50	26	54
6	8	22	14	30	20	40	28	50	30	54	32	58	33	63	35	67
7	9	24	15	33	22	43	30	54	39	66	41	71	43	76	46	80
8	9	27	16	36	24	46	32	58	41	71	52	84	54	90	57	95
9	10	29	17	39	25	50	33	63	43	76	54	90	66	105	69	111
10	11	31	18	42	26	54	35	67	46	80	57	95	69	111	83	127

$\alpha = 0.05$ one-sided; $\alpha = 0.10$ two-sided

Table 13.2 repeats a portion of Table A.15. This table gives the rejection point (T_U or T_L) for testing a one-sided alternative hypothesis at level of significance $\alpha = 0.05$ and also gives the rejection points (T_U and T_L) for testing a two-sided alternative hypothesis at level of significance $\alpha = 0.10$. The rejection points are tabulated according to n_1 and n_2, the sizes of the samples taken from populations 1 and 2, respectively. For instance, as shown in Table 13.2, if we have taken a sample of size $n_1 = 10$ from population 1, and if we have taken a sample of size $n_2 = 7$ from population 2, then for a one-sided test with $\alpha = 0.05$, we use $T_U = 80$ or $T_L = 46$. Similarly, if $n_1 = 10$ and $n_2 = 7$, we use $T_U = 80$ and $T_L = 46$ for a two-sided test with $\alpha = 0.10$.

Example 13.3

The Railway Association of Canada (see http://www.railcan.ca) reports that passenger trains travel at an average speed of 160 km/h and freight trains at 105 km/h. One complaint that many city commuters have about the train system is that the flow of traffic is interrupted by trains passing through the city on level crossings. Wait times were assessed within a city for those waiting at passenger rail crossovers (10 measures taken) versus freight crossovers (7 measures taken). The resulting wait times (in seconds) are given in Figure 13.3. The box plots indicate that the population of all possible wait times for the two populations of train types (passenger and freight) might be skewed to the right. A Wilcoxon rank sum test will be conducted on the data.

Because passenger trains travel at 55 km/h faster than freight trains in Canada, it was predicted that wait times would be shorter for passenger train crossings than freight train crossings. Therefore, the null hypothesis is

H_0: the crossing wait times will be the same for passenger and freight trains

versus the alternative hypothesis of

H_a: the wait times will be shorter for passenger trains than for freight trains.

To perform the test, rank the $n_1 + n_2 = 10 + 7 = 17$ wait times in the two samples as shown in Figure 13.3(a). Note that, since there are two wait times of 145 seconds that are tied as the sixth and seventh wait times, these values are each assigned the average rank of 6.5. The sum of the ranks in wait times for the passenger trains is $T_1 = 72.5$, and for freight trains it is $T_2 = 80.5$. Because $n_1 = 10$ is greater than $n_2 = 7$, the summary box states that the test statistic is $T_2 = 80.5$ and that H_0 can be rejected in favour of H_a at the 0.05 significance level if T is greater than or equal to T_U. Because $T_2 = 80.5$ is greater than $T_U = 80$ (see Table 13.2), we can conclude at the 0.05 level of significance that the passenger wait times are shifted to the left, and are therefore "systematically less than" the wait times for freight trains. This might result because passenger trains travel faster than freight trains. Of course it might also result from freight trains being longer than passenger trains, but that is for another study!

FIGURE **13.3**   **Analysis of Passenger and Freight Level Crossing Times**   ● Crossing

(a) Wait times (in seconds)

Passenger		Freight		Box Plots of Passenger and Freight Times
Time	Rank	Time	Rank	
48	1	109	4	
97	2	145	6.5	
103	3	196	10	
117	5	273	13	
145	6.5	289	14	
151	8	417	16	
179	9	505	17	
220	11		$T_2 = 80.5$	
257	12			
294	15			
	$T_1 = 72.5$			

(b) MINITAB output of the Wilcoxon rank sum test for the wait times

```
Passenger  N = 10    Median = 148.0
Freight    N =  7    Median = 273.0
Point estimate for ETA1-ETA2 is -98.0
95.5 Percent CI for ETA1-ETA2 is (-248.0,7.9)
W = 72.5
Test of ETA1 = ETA2 vs ETA1 < ETA2 is significant at 0.0486
The test is significant at 0.0485 (adjusted for ties)
```

Figure 13.3(b) presents the MINITAB output of the Wilcoxon rank sum test for the wait times. In general, MINITAB gives T_1, the sum of the ranks of the observations in sample 1, as the test statistic, which MINITAB denotes as W. If, as in the present example, n_1 is greater than n_2 and thus the correct test statistic is T_2, **we can obtain T_2 by subtracting T_1 from**

$$(n_1 + n_2)(n_1 + n_2 + 1)/2.$$

This last quantity can be proven to equal the sum of the ranks of the $(n_1 + n_2)$ observations in both samples. In the present example, this quantity equals

$$(10 + 7)(10 + 7 + 1)/2 = (17)(18)/2 = 153.$$

Therefore, because the MINITAB output tells us that $T_1 = 72.5$, the correct test statistic T_2 is $(153 - 72.5) = 80.5$. In addition to giving T_1, MINITAB gives two p values related to the hypothesis test. The first p value—0.0486—is calculated assuming that there are no ties. Since there is a tie, the second p value—0.0485—is adjusted accordingly and is more correct (although there is little difference in this situation).

In general, the Wilcoxon rank sum test tests the equality of the population medians if the distributions of the sampled populations have the same shapes and equal variances. MINITAB tells us that under these assumptions, a point estimate of the difference in the population medians is −98.0 (seconds), and a 95.5 percent confidence interval for the difference in the population medians is [−248.0, 7.9]. Note that the point estimate of the difference in the population medians, which is −98.0, is not equal to the difference in the sample medians, which is 148.0 − 273.0 = −125.0. In the present example, the box plots in Figure 13.3 indicate that the variances of the two populations are not equal. In fact, in most situations it is a bit too much to ask that the sampled populations have exactly the same shapes and equal variances (although we will see in Exercise 13.12 that this might be approximately true in some situations).

As another example, suppose that on a given Saturday night a local newspaper randomly selects 20 patrons from each of two restaurants and has each patron rate the quality of their meal as 5 (excellent), 4 (good), 3 (average), 2 (poor), or 1 (unsatisfactory). The following results are obtained:

Rating	Restaurant 1 Patrons	Restaurant 2 Patrons	Total Patrons	Ranks Involved	Average Rank	Restaurant 1 Rank Sum	Restaurant 2 Rank Sum
5	15	5	20	21–40	30.5	(15)(30.5) = 457.5	(5)(30.5) = 152.5
4	4	11	15	6–20	13	(4)(13) = 52	(11)(13) = 143
3	1	2	3	3, 4, 5	4	(1)(4) = 4	(2)(4) = 8
2	0	1	1	2	2	(0)(2) = 0	(1)(2) = 2
1	0	1	1	1	1	(0)(1) = 0	(1)(1) = 1
						$T_1 = 513.5$	$T_2 = 306.5$

Suppose that we wish to test

H_0: the probability distributions of all possible Saturday night meal ratings for restaurants 1 and 2 are identical

versus

H_a: the probability distribution of all possible Saturday night meal ratings for restaurant 1 is shifted to the right or left of the probability distribution of all possible Saturday night meal ratings for restaurant 2.

Because there are only five numerical ordinal ratings, there are many ties. The above table shows how we determine the sum of the ranks for each sample. Because $n_1 = 20$ and $n_2 = 20$, we cannot obtain rejection points by using Table A.15 (which gives rejection points for sample sizes up to $n_1 = 10$ and $n_2 = 10$). However, we can use a large sample, normal approximation, which is valid if both n_1 and n_2 are at least 10. The normal approximation involves making two modifications. First, we replace the test statistic T in the previously given summary box by a standardized value of the test statistic. This standardized value, denoted z, is calculated by subtracting the mean $\mu_T = n_i(n_1 + n_2 + 1)/2$ from the test statistic T and then dividing the resulting difference by the standard deviation $\sigma_T = \sqrt{n_1 n_2(n_1 + n_2 + 1)/12}$. Here n_i in the expression for μ_T equals n_1 if the test statistic T is T_1 and n_2 if T is T_2. Second, when testing a one-sided alternative hypothesis, we replace the rejection points T_U and T_L by the normal points z_α and $-z_\alpha$. When testing a two-sided alternative hypothesis, we replace T_U and T_L by $z_{\alpha/2}$ and $-z_{\alpha/2}$. For the current example, $n_1 = n_2$, and thus the test statistic T is $T_1 = 513.5$. Furthermore,

$$\mu_T = \frac{n_1(n_1 + n_2 + 1)}{2} = \frac{20(20 + 20 + 1)}{2} = 410,$$

$$\sigma_T = \sqrt{\frac{n_1 n_2(n_1 + n_2 + 1)}{12}} = \sqrt{\frac{20(20)(41)}{12}} = 36.968455,$$

and

$$z = \frac{T - \mu_T}{\sigma_T} = \frac{513.5 - 410}{36.968455} = 2.7997.$$

Because we are testing a "shifted right or left" (that is, a two-sided) alternative hypothesis, the summary box tells us that we reject the null hypothesis if $T \leq T_L$ or $T \geq T_U$. Stated in terms of standardized values, we reject the null hypothesis if $z < -z_{\alpha/2}$ or $z > z_{\alpha/2}$ (here we use strict inequalities to be consistent with other normal distribution rejection point conditions). If we set $\alpha = 0.01$, we use the rejection points $-z_{0.005} = -2.575$ and $z_{0.005} = 2.575$. Because $z = 2.7997$ is greater than $z_{0.005} = 2.575$, we reject the null hypothesis at the 0.01 level of significance. Therefore, we have very strong evidence that there is a systematic difference between the Saturday night meal ratings at restaurants 1 and 2. Looking at the original data, we would estimate that Saturday night meal ratings are higher at restaurant 1.

We will conclude this section with a final comment. When there are ties, an adjusted formula for σ_T takes the ties into account. If (as in the restaurant example) we ignore the formula, the results we obtain are statistically conservative. Therefore, if we rejected the null hypothesis by using the unadjusted formula, we would reject the null hypothesis by using the adjusted formula.

Exercises for Section 13.2

CONCEPTS

13.8 Explain the circumstances in which we use the Wilcoxon rank sum test.

13.9 Identify the parametric test corresponding to the Wilcoxon rank sum test. What assumption is needed for the validity of this parametric test (and not needed for the Wilcoxon rank sum test)?

METHODS AND APPLICATIONS

13.10 A loan officer at a bank wishes to compare the mortgage rates charged at banks with the mortgage rates of brokers. Two independent random samples of bank mortgage rates and broker mortgage rates are obtained with the results in Figure 13.4(a).

Because both samples are small, the bank officer is uncertain about the shape of the distributions of bank and broker mortgage rates. Therefore, the Wilcoxon rank sum test will be used to compare the two types of mortgage rates.   ● MortRate

a. Let D_1 be the distribution of bank mortgage rates and let D_2 be the distribution of broker mortgage

rates. Carry out the Wilcoxon rank sum test to determine whether D_1 and D_2 are identical versus the alternative that D_1 is shifted to the right or left of D_2. Use $\alpha = 0.05$.

b. Carry out the Wilcoxon rank sum test to determine whether D_1 is shifted to the right of D_2. Use $\alpha = 0.025$. What do you conclude?

13.11 A company collected employee absenteeism data (in hours per year) at two of its manufacturing plants. The data were obtained by randomly selecting a sample from all of the employees at the first plant, and by randomly selecting another independent sample from all of the employees at the second plant. For each randomly selected employee, absenteeism records were used to determine the exact number of hours the employee had been absent during the past year. The results in Figure 13.4(b) were obtained.   ● Absent

Use a Wilcoxon rank sum test and the MINITAB output in Figure 13.4(c) to determine whether absenteeism is different at the two plants. Use $\alpha = 0.05$.

FIGURE 13.4   Data and Output for Exercises 13.10, 13.11, and 13.13

(a) Mortgage rates for Exercise 13.10

Bank Rates:	11.25	10.50	11.50	11.00	10.00	9.75	11.50	10.25
Broker Rates:	9.25	10.25	8.75	11.00	9.50	9.00	9.10	8.50

(b) Absenteeism results for Exercise 13.11

Plant 1:	10	131	53	37	59	29	45	26	39	36
Plant 2:	21	46	33	31	49	33	39	19	12	35

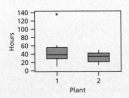

(c) MINITAB output of absenteeism results for Exercise 13.11

```
             N   Median
Plant 1   10    38.00
Plant 2   10    33.00
Point estimate for ETA1-ETA2 is 7.00
95.5 Percent CI for ETA1-ETA2 is (-6.99,24.01)
W = 120.5
Test of ETA1 = ETA2 vs ETA1 not = ETA2 is significant at 0.2568
The test is significant at 0.2565 (adjusted for ties)
```

(d) Illness data for Exercise 13.13

Response	Females	Males	Total
5	2	1	3
4	23	5	28
3	50	22	72
2	108	57	165
1	13	22	35

Sex	N	Sum of Scores
Female	196	31996.5
Male	107	14059.5

$T = 14059.5$ $z = -3.33353$
Test significant at 0.0009

Source: "Consumers' perceptions nand concerns about safety and healthfulness of food served at fairs and festivals," by H. C. Boo, M. S. thesis, Purdue University, 1997.

13.12 Kevin travels frequently to Winnipeg, Manitoba, from London, Ontario. He uses either ExecuAir or EconoAir. He realizes that flight delays are inevitable but would prefer to give his business to the airline with the best on-time arrival record. The number of minutes that his flight arrived late for the last seven trips is given below. Negative numbers mean that the flight was early.

ExecuAir: 2, −1, 4, −5, 3, 7, −2
EconoAir: −3, 6, 8, 9, 10 −7, 5

Is there evidence to suggest that ExecuAir is superior to EconoAir in terms of its on-time arrival record? Use the Wilcoxon rank sum test and test at $\alpha = 0.05$.

13.13 Moore (2000) reports on a study by Boo (1997), who asked 303 randomly selected people at fairs:

> How often do you think people become sick because of food they consume prepared at outdoor fairs and festivals?

The possible responses were 5 (always), 4 (often), 3 (more often than not), 2 (once in a while), and 1 (very rarely). The data in Figure 13.4(d) were obtained.

The computer output at the right of the data presents the results of a Wilcoxon rank sum test that attempts to determine if men and women systematically differ in their responses. Here the normal approximation has been used to calculate the p value of 0.0009. What do you conclude?

13.3 The Wilcoxon Signed Ranks Test

We can use a t test to compare two population means in a paired difference experiment. If the sample size is small and the population of paired differences is far from normally distributed, this test is not valid and we should use a nonparametric test. In this section, we present the **Wilcoxon signed ranks test**, which is a nonparametric test for comparing two populations when a **paired difference experiment** has been carried out.

The Wilcoxon Signed Ranks Test

Let D_1 and D_2 denote the probability distributions of populations 1 and 2, and assume that we have randomly selected n matched pairs of observations from populations 1 and 2. Calculate the paired differences of the n matched pairs by subtracting each paired population 2 observation from the corresponding population 1 observation, and rank the absolute values of the n paired differences from the smallest (rank 1) to the largest (rank n). Here paired differences equal to 0 are eliminated, and the number n of paired differences is reduced accordingly. Furthermore, if two or more absolute paired differences are equal, we assign to each "tied" absolute paired difference a rank equal to the average of the consecutive ranks that would otherwise be assigned to the tied absolute paired differences. Let

$T^- =$ the sum of the ranks associated with the negative paired differences

and

$T^+ =$ the sum of the ranks associated with the positive paired differences.

We can test

H_0: D_1 and D_2 are identical probability distributions

versus a particular alternative hypothesis at level of significance α by using the appropriate test statistic and the corresponding rejection point rule.

Alternative Hypothesis	Test Statistic	Rejection Point Rule: Reject H_0 if
H_a: D_1 is shifted to the right of D_2	T^-	$T^- \leq T_0$
H_a: D_1 is shifted to the left of D_2	T^+	$T^+ \leq T_0$
H_a: D_1 is shifted to the right or left of D_2	$T =$ the smaller of T^- and T^+	$T \leq T_0$

The first two alternative hypotheses above are **one-sided**, while the third alternative hypothesis is **two-sided**. Values of the rejection point T_0 are given in Table A.16 for values of n from 5 to 50.

Table 13.3 repeats a portion of Table A.16. This table gives the rejection point T_0 for testing one-sided and two-sided alternative hypotheses at several different values of α. The rejection points are tabulated according to n, the number of paired differences. For instance, Table 13.3 shows that, if we are analyzing 10 paired differences, the rejection point for testing a one-sided alternative hypothesis at the 0.01 level of significance is equal to $T_0 = 5$. This table also shows that we would use the rejection point $T_0 = 5$ for testing a two-sided alternative hypothesis at level of significance $\alpha = 0.02$.

TABLE 13.3   A Portion of the Wilcoxon Signed Ranks Table

One-Sided	Two-Sided	$n = 5$	$n = 6$	$n = 7$	$n = 8$	$n = 9$	$n = 10$
$\alpha = 0.05$	$\alpha = 0.10$	1	2	4	6	8	11
$\alpha = 0.025$	$\alpha = 0.05$		1	2	4	6	8
$\alpha = 0.01$	$\alpha = 0.02$			0	2	3	5
$\alpha = 0.005$	$\alpha = 0.01$				0	2	3
		$n = 11$	$n = 12$	$n = 13$	$n = 14$	$n = 15$	$n = 16$
$\alpha = 0.05$	$\alpha = 0.10$	14	17	21	26	30	36
$\alpha = 0.025$	$\alpha = 0.05$	11	14	17	21	25	30
$\alpha = 0.01$	$\alpha = 0.02$	7	10	13	16	20	24
$\alpha = 0.005$	$\alpha = 0.01$	5	7	10	13	16	19

Example 13.4 The Repair Cost Comparison Case

Consider the automobile repair cost data given in Figure 13.5(a). If we fear that the population of all possible paired differences of repair cost estimates at garages 1 and 2 may be far from normally distributed, we can perform the Wilcoxon signed ranks test. Here we test

H_0: the probability distributions of the populations of all possible repair cost estimates at garages 1 and 2 are identical

versus

H_a: the probability distribution of repair cost estimates at garage 1 is shifted to the left of the probability distribution of repair cost estimates at garage 2.

To perform this test, we find the absolute value of each paired difference, and we assign ranks to the absolute differences (see Figure 13.5(a)). Because of the form of the alternative hypothesis (see the preceding summary box), we use the test statistic

T^+ = the sum of the ranks associated with the positive paired differences.

FIGURE 13.5   Analysis of Repair Cost Estimates at Two Garages

(a) Sample of $n = 7$ Paired Differences of the Repair Cost Estimates at Garages 1 and 2   ● Repair
(Cost Estimates in Hundreds of Dollars)

Sample of $n = 7$ Damaged Cars	Repair Cost Estimates at Garage 1	Repair Cost Estimates at Garage 2	Sample of $n = 7$ Paired Differences	Absolute Paired Differences	Ranks
Car 1	$ 7.1	$ 7.9	$d_1 = -0.8$	0.8	4
Car 2	9.0	10.1	$d_2 = -1.1$	1.1	5
Car 3	11.0	12.2	$d_3 = -1.2$	1.2	6
Car 4	8.9	8.8	$d_4 = 0.1$	0.1	1
Car 5	9.9	10.4	$d_5 = -0.5$	0.5	2
Car 6	9.1	9.8	$d_6 = -0.7$	0.7	3
Car 7	10.3	11.7	$d_7 = -1.4$	1.4	7

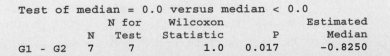

(b) MINITAB output of the Wilcoxon signed ranks test

```
Test of median = 0.0 versus median < 0.0
              N for   Wilcoxon            Estimated
          N   Test    Statistic     P      Median
G1 - G2   7     7          1.0   0.017    -0.8250
```

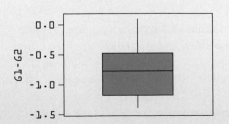

Because 0.1 is the only positive paired difference, and because the rank associated with this difference equals 1, we find that $T^+ = 1$. The alternative hypothesis is one-sided, and we are analyzing $n = 7$ paired differences. Therefore, Table 13.3 tells us that we can test H_0 versus H_a at the 0.05, 0.025, and 0.01 levels of significance by setting the rejection point T_0 equal to 4, 2, and 0, respectively. The rejection point condition is $T^+ \leq T_0$. It follows that, since $T^+ = 1$ is less than or equal to 4 and 2, but is not less than or equal to 0, we can reject H_0 in favour of H_a at the 0.05 and 0.025 levels of significance, but not at the 0.01 level of significance. Therefore, we have strong evidence that the probability distribution of repair cost estimates at garage 1 is shifted to the left of the probability distribution of repair cost estimates at garage 2. That is, the repair cost estimates at garage 1 seem to be systematically lower than the repair cost estimates at garage 2. Figure 13.5(b) presents the MINITAB output of the Wilcoxon signed ranks test for this repair cost comparison. In general, MINITAB gives T^+ as the "Wilcoxon statistic," even if T^- is the appropriate test statistic. It can be shown that **T^- can be obtained by subtracting T^+ from $n(n + 1)/2$**, where n is the total number of paired differences being analyzed.

Notice that in Example 13.4 the nonparametric Wilcoxon signed ranks test would not allow us to reject H_0 in favour of H_a at the 0.01 level of significance. On the other hand, a **parametric** paired difference t test would allow us to reject H_0: $\mu_1 - \mu_2 = 0$ in favour of H_a: $\mu_1 - \mu_2 < 0$ at the 0.01 level of significance (see Example 9.10). In general, **a parametric test is often more powerful** than the analogous nonparametric test. That is, the parametric test often allows us to reject H_0 at smaller values of α. Therefore, if the assumptions for the parametric test are satisfied—for example, if, when we are using small samples, the sampled populations are approximately normally distributed—it is preferable to use the parametric test. **The advantage of nonparametric tests is that they can be used without assuming that the sampled populations have the shapes of any particular probability distributions.** As an example, this can be important when reporting statistical conclusions if the guidelines specify that, when reporting statistical conclusions, the validity of the assumptions behind the statistical methods used must be fully justified. If, for instance, there are insufficient data to justify the assumption that the sampled populations are approximately normally distributed, then we must use a nonparametric method to make conclusions.

Finally, if the sample size n is at least 25, we can use a large sample approximation of the Wilcoxon signed ranks test. This is done by making two modifications. First, we replace the test statistic (T^- or T^+) by a standardized value of the test statistic. This standardized value is calculated by subtracting the mean $n(n + 1)/4$ from the test statistic (T^- or T^+) and then dividing the resulting difference by the standard deviation $\sqrt{n(n + 1)(2n + 1)/24}$. Second, when testing a one-sided alternative hypothesis, we replace the rejection point T_0 by the normal point $-z_\alpha$. When testing a two-sided alternative hypothesis, we replace T_0 by $-z_{\alpha/2}$.

Exercises for Section 13.3

CONCEPTS

13.14 Explain the circumstances in which we use the Wilcoxon signed ranks test.

13.15 Identify the parametric test corresponding to the Wilcoxon signed ranks test. What assumption is needed for the validity of the parametric test (and not needed for the Wilcoxon signed ranks test)?

METHODS AND APPLICATIONS

13.16 A consumer advocacy group is concerned about the ability of tax preparation firms to correctly prepare complex returns. To test the performance of tax preparers in two different tax preparation firms—Quick Tax and Discount Tax—the group designed a tax case for a family with a gross annual income of $150,000 involving several thorny tax issues. In a "tax-off" competition, the advocacy group randomly selected independent samples of 10 preparers from each firm and asked each preparer to compute the tax liability for the test case. The preparers' returns were collected, and the group computed the difference between each preparer's computed tax and the actual tax that should have been computed. The data in Table 13.4 consist of the resulting two sets of tax computation errors, one for preparers from Quick Tax and the other for preparers from Discount Tax. Fully interpret the MINITAB output in Table 13.4

TABLE **13.4** Tax Computation Errors and MINITAB Output for Exercise 13.7

Quick Tax Errors	Discount Tax Errors	Difference
857	156	701
920	200	720
1,090	202	888
1,594	390	1,204
1,820	526	1,294
1,943	749	1,194
1,987	911	1,076
2,008	920	1,088
2,083	2,145	−62
2,439	2,602	−163

```
Test of median = 0.0 versus median not = 0.0
       N   N for Test   Wilcoxon Statistic      P   Estimated Median
Q-D   10           10                 52.0   0.014              898.0
```

of a Wilcoxon signed ranks test analysis of these data. ● TaxErr

13.17 Table 13.5 lists the number of people who immigrated to Canada for the years (Y) 2004 and 2005 as published by Citizenship and Immigration Canada. Enter the data into Excel and conduct the Wilcoxon–Mann/Whitney test (using MegaStat). Based on the output, would you suggest that there has been a significant change in the pattern of immigration from the 10 countries listed? Explain your answer.

13.18 A human resources director wishes to assess the benefits of sending a company's managers to an innovative management course. Twelve of the company's managers are randomly selected to attend the course, and a psychologist interviews each participating manager before and after taking the course. Based on these interviews, the psychologist rates the manager's leadership ability on a 1-to-100 scale. The pretest and posttest leadership scores for each of the 12 managers are given in Table 13.6. ● Leader

a. Let D_1 be the distribution of leadership scores before taking the course, and let D_2 be the distribution of leadership scores after taking the course. Carry out the Wilcoxon signed ranks test to test whether D_1 and D_2 are identical (that is, the course has no effect on leadership scores) versus the alternative that D_2 is shifted to the right or left of D_1 (that is, the course affects leadership scores). Use $\alpha = 0.05$.

b. Carry out the Wilcoxon signed ranks test to determine whether D_2 is shifted to the right of D_1. Use $\alpha = 0.05$. What do you conclude?

13.19 In a study examining the difference in attitudes between preexposure and postexposure to an advertisement, 10 people were tested. The data obtained and related MegaStat output are shown in Table 13.7. Use the Wilcoxon signed ranks test and the MegaStat output to determine whether the distributions of preexposure and postexposure attitude scores are different. Use $\alpha = 0.05$. ● AdStudy

TABLE **13.5** Immigration by Top 10 Source Countries into Canada (Number of People) ● Immigration

	Y2004	Y2005
China	36,429	42,291
India	25,576	33,146
Philippines	13,303	17,525
Pakistan	12,795	13,576
United States	7,507	9,262
Colombia	4,438	6,031
United Kingdom	6,062	5,865
South Korea	5,337	5,819
Iran	6,063	5,502
France	5,028	5,430

Y = Year

Source: http://www.cic.gc.ca/english/resources/statistics/facts2005/permanent/12.asp.

TABLE **13.6** Pretest and Posttest Leadership Scores ● Leader

Manager	Pretest Score	Posttest Score	Difference
1	35	54	−19
2	27	43	−16
3	51	53	−2
4	38	50	−12
5	32	42	−10
6	44	58	−14
7	33	35	−2
8	26	39	−13
9	40	47	−7
10	50	48	2
11	36	41	−5
12	31	37	−6

TABLE 13.7   **Preexposure and Postexposure Attitude Scores for an Advertising Study**   ◯ AdStudy

Subject	Preexposure Attitudes (A_1)	Postexposure Attitudes (A_2)	Attitude Change (d_i)
1	50	53	3
2	25	27	2
3	30	38	8
4	50	55	5
5	60	61	1
6	80	85	5
7	45	45	0
8	30	31	1
9	65	72	7
10	70	78	8

Wilcoxon Signed Rank Test

variables: Pre. Attitudes(A1) - Post. Attitudes(A2)

0	sum of positive ranks
45	sum of negative ranks
9	n
22.50	expected value
7.89	standard deviation
−2.85	z, corrected for ties
0.0043	p-value (two-tailed)

Source: *Essentials of Marketing Research*, by W. R. Dillon, T. J. Madden, and N. H. Firtle (Burr Ridge, IL: Richard D. Irwin, 1993), p. 435. Copyright © 1993. Reprinted by permission of McGraw-Hill Companies, Inc.

13.4 Comparing Several Populations Using the Kruskal–Wallis *H* Test

If we fear that the normality and/or equal variances assumptions for one-way ANOVA do not hold, we can use a nonparametric approach to compare several populations. One such approach is the **Kruskal–Wallis *H* test**, which compares the locations of three or more populations by using independent random samples and a completely randomized experimental design.

In general, suppose we wish to use the Kruskal–Wallis *H* test to compare the locations of *p* populations by using *p* independent samples of observations randomly selected from these populations. We first rank all of the observations in the *p* samples from smallest to largest. If n_i denotes the number of observations in the *i*th sample, we are ranking a total of $n = (n_1 + n_2 + \cdots + n_p)$ observations. Furthermore, we assign tied observations the average of the consecutive ranks that would otherwise be assigned to the tied observations. Next we calculate the sum of the ranks of the observations in each sample. Letting T_i denote the rank sum for the *i*th sample, we obtain the rank sums $T_1, T_2, \ldots, T_p$. For example, suppose that a company wants to decrease the culture shock experienced by managers who work on a project in a foreign country for a year. Three types of enculturation training methods are assessed using the experimental method, and learning of the new culture is tested using a standard test. Training type *A* uses information about the new culture only (books, videotapes, etc.). Training type *B* is interactive and includes behavioural modelling with an instructor from the new culture. Training type *C* is the control group, which receives no information or behavioural modelling. Fifteen managers in total are tested with five each being randomly assigned to one of the three training types. The resulting data are presented in Table 13.8, in which higher scores represent greater learning about

TABLE 13.8   **The Training Type Results and Rank Sums**   ◯ TrainingType

Training Type A	Training Type B	Training Type C
34.0 (3.5)	35.3 (9)	33.3 (2)
35.0 (8)	36.5 (13)	34.0 (3.5)
34.3 (5)	36.4 (12)	34.7 (6)
35.5 (10)	37.0 (14)	33.0 (1)
35.8 (11)	37.6 (15)	34.9 (7)
$T_1 = 37.5$	$T_2 = 63$	$T_3 = 19.5$

the new culture on the standard test (rank values are given in brackets). If we sum the ranks in each sample, we find that $T_1 = 37.5$, $T_2 = 63$, and $T_3 = 19.5$. Note that, although the box plots in Table 13.8 do not indicate any serious violations of the normality or equal variances assumptions, the samples are quite small, and thus we cannot be sure that these assumptions approximately hold. Therefore, it is reasonable to compare training types A, B, and C by using the Kruskal–Wallis H test.

The Kruskal–Wallis H Test

Consider testing the null hypothesis H_0 that the p populations under consideration are identical versus the alternative hypothesis H_a that at least two populations differ in location (that is, are shifted either to the left or to the right of one another). We can reject H_0 in favour of H_a at level of significance α if the **Kruskal–Wallis H statistic**

$$H = \frac{12}{n(n+1)} \sum_{i=1}^{p} \frac{T_i^2}{n_i} - 3(n+1)$$

is greater than the χ_α^2 point based on $p-1$ degrees of freedom. Here, for this test to be valid, there should be five or more observations in each sample. Furthermore, the number of ties should be small relative to the total number of observations. Values of χ_α^2 are given in Table A.17.

In this training type case, $\chi_{0.05}^2$ based on $p - 1 = 2$ degrees of freedom is 5.99147 (see Table A.17). Furthermore, since $n = n_1 + n_2 + n_3 = 15$, the Kruskal–Wallis H statistic is

$$H = \frac{12}{15(15+1)}\left[\frac{(37.5)^2}{5} + \frac{(63)^2}{5} + \frac{(19.5)^2}{5}\right] - 3(15+1)$$

$$= \frac{12}{240}\left[\frac{1,406.25}{5} + \frac{3,969}{5} + \frac{380.25}{5}\right] - 48 = 9.555.$$

Because $H = 9.555 > \chi_{0.05}^2 = 5.99147$, we can reject H_0 at the 0.05 level of significance. Therefore, we have strong evidence that at least two of the three populations of test scores differ in location. Figure 13.6 presents the MINITAB output of the Kruskal–Wallis H test in this training type case.

To conclude this section, we note that, if the Kruskal–Wallis H test leads us to conclude that the p populations differ in location, there are various procedures for comparing pairs of populations. A simple procedure is to use the Wilcoxon rank sum test to compare pairs of populations. For example, if we use this test to make separate, **two-sided** comparisons of (1) training types A and B, (2) training types A and C, and (3) training types B and C, and if we set α equal to 0.05 for each comparison, we find that the test scores given by training type B differ systematically from the scores given by training types A and C. Examining the scores in Table 13.8, we would estimate that training type B results in the highest test scores. One problem, however, with using the Wilcoxon rank sum test to make pairwise comparisons is that it is difficult to know how to set α for each comparison. Therefore, some practitioners prefer to make **simultaneous** pairwise comparisons (such as given by the Tukey simultaneous confidence intervals discussed in Chapter 10). Gibbons (1985) discusses a nonparametric approach for making simultaneous pairwise comparisons.

F I G U R E 13.6   **MINITAB Output of the Kruskal–Wallis H Test in the Training Method Experiment**

```
Kruskal-Wallis Test on Training
Type      N     Median     Ave Rank          Z
A         5      35.00          7.5      -0.31
B         5      36.50         12.6       2.82
C         5      34.00          3.9      -2.51
Overall  15                     8.0

H = 9.56    DF = 2    P = 0.008
H = 9.57    DF = 2    P = 0.008   (adjusted for ties)
```

Exercises for Section 13.4

CONCEPTS

13.20 Explain the circumstances in which we use the Kruskal–Wallis *H* test.

13.21 Identify the parametric test corresponding to the Kruskal–Wallis *H* test.

13.22 What are the assumptions needed for the validity of the parametric test identified in Exercise 13.21 that are not needed for the Kruskal–Wallis *H* test?

METHODS AND APPLICATIONS

In each of Exercises 13.23 through 13.26, use the given independent samples to perform the Kruskal–Wallis *H* test of the null hypothesis H_0 that the corresponding populations are identical versus the alternative hypothesis H_a that at least two populations differ in location. Note that we previously analyzed each of these data sets using the one-way ANOVA *F* test in Chapter 10.

13.23 Use the Kruskal–Wallis *H* test to compare display panels *A*, *B*, and *C* using the data in Table 13.9. Use $\alpha = 0.05$. ● Display3

13.24 Use the Kruskal–Wallis *H* test to compare bottle designs *A*, *B*, and *C* using the data in Table 13.10. Use $\alpha = 0.01$. ● BottleDes

13.25 Use the Kruskal–Wallis *H* test and the MINITAB output in Figure 13.7 to compare the bottom (*B*), middle (*M*), and top (*T*) display heights using the data in Table 13.11. Use $\alpha = 0.05$. Then repeat the analysis if the first sales value for the middle display height is found to be incorrect and must be removed from the data set. ● BakeSale

13.26 Use the Kruskal–Wallis *H* test to compare golf ball brands Alpha, Best, Century, and Divot using the data in Table 13.12. Use $\alpha = 0.01$ and the MegaStat output to the right of Table 13.12. ● GolfBall

TABLE 13.9 Display Panel Study Data (Time, in Seconds, Required to Stabilize Air Traffic Emergency Condition)
● Display3

Display Panel		
A	*B*	*C*
21	24	40
27	21	36
24	18	35
26	19	32
25	20	37

TABLE 13.10 Bottle Design Study Data (Sales during a 24-Hour Period)
● BottleDes

Bottle Design		
A	*B*	*C*
16	33	23
18	31	27
19	37	21
17	29	28
13	34	25

FIGURE 13.7 MINITAB Output of the Kruskal–Wallis *H* Test for the Bakery Sales Data

```
Kruskal-Wallis Test on Bakery Sales

Display   N   Median   Ave Rank      Z
Bottom    6   55.75         9.2   -0.19
Middle    6   77.15        15.5    3.37
Top       6   51.50         3.8   -3.18
Overall  18                 9.5
H = 14.36    DF = 2    P = 0.001
```

TABLE 13.11 Bakery Sales Study Data (Sales in Cases) ● BakeSale

	Shelf Display Height	
Bottom (*B*)	Middle (*M*)	Top (*T*)
58.2	73.0	52.4
53.7	78.1	49.7
55.8	75.4	50.9
55.7	76.2	54.0
52.5	78.4	52.1
58.9	82.1	49.9

TABLE 13.12 Golf Ball Durability Test Results ● GolfBall

Brand			
Alpha	Best	Century	Divot
281	270	218	364
220	334	244	302
274	307	225	325
242	290	273	337
251	331	249	355

Kruskal–Wallis Test

Median	n	Avg. Rank		
251.00	5	6.80	Alpha	13.834 H
307.00	5	13.40	Best	3 d.f.
244.00	5	4.80	Century	0.0031 p-value
337.00	5	17.00	Divot	
277.50	20		Total	

13.27 A statistics professor at a local university believes that the amount of time that students spend studying depends on the term the student is studying in. Fall, winter, and spring terms were considered. Students were randomly selected during three different times of year during a one-year period and asked to estimate the number of hours spent studying per week. Here are the students' estimates:

Fall: 5, 2, 6, 9, 4, 7, 5, 3
Winter: 9, 7, 12, 11, 8, 10, 6, 11, 5, 9
Spring: 6, 9, 5, 8, 8, 5, 3, 4, 7

Conduct a Kruskal–Wallis test at the $\alpha = 0.05$ level of significance. Based on the results of the hypothesis test, is there evidence to suggest that the average study times are not all the same, that is, that the amount of time studying differs throughout the school year?

13.5 Spearman's Rank Correlation Coefficient

In Chapter 11, we showed how to test the significance of a population correlation coefficient. This test is based on the assumption that the population of all possible combinations of values of x and y has a bivariate normal probability distribution. If we fear that this assumption is badly violated, we can use a nonparametric approach. One such approach is **Spearman's rank correlation coefficient**,[2] which is denoted r_s.

To illustrate, suppose that Electronics World, a chain of stores that sells audio and video equipment, has gathered the data in Table 13.13. The company wishes to study the relationship between store sales volume in July of last year (y, measured in thousands of dollars) and the number of households in the store's area (x, measured in thousands). Spearman's rank correlation coefficient is found by first ranking the values of x and y separately (ties are treated by averaging the tied ranks). To calculate r_s, we use the formula

$$r = \frac{\Sigma xy - \dfrac{\Sigma x \Sigma y}{n}}{\sqrt{\left(\Sigma x^2 - \dfrac{(\Sigma x)^2}{n_1}\right)\left(\Sigma y^2 - \dfrac{(\Sigma y^2)}{n_2}\right)}}$$

TABLE **13.13**   Electronics World Sales Volume Data and Ranks for 15 Stores ❍ Electronics

Store	Number of Households, x	Sales Volume, y	x Rank	y Rank	Difference, d	d^2
1	161	157.27	6	7	−1	1
2	99	93.28	1	1	0	0
3	135	136.81	5	5	0	0
4	120	123.79	4	3	1	1
5	164	153.51	7	6	1	1
6	221	241.74	13	14	−1	1
7	179	201.54	8	10	−2	4
8	204	206.71	9	11	−2	4
9	214	229.78	12	13	−1	1
10	101	135.22	2	4	−2	4
11	231	224.71	14	12	2	4
12	206	195.29	11	8	3	9
13	248	242.16	15	15	0	0
14	107	115.21	3	2	1	1
15	205	197.82	10	9	1	1
						$\Sigma d_i^2 = 32$

[2]Charles Spearman was the advisor of Karl Pearson, who developed the correlation coefficient described in Chapter 11.

for r and replace the x and y values in that formula by their ranks. If there are no ties in the ranks, this formula can be calculated by the simple equation

$$r_s = 1 - \frac{6\Sigma d_i^2}{n(n^2 - 1)},$$

where d_i is the difference between the x rank and the y rank for the ith observation (if there are few ties in the ranks, this formula is approximately valid). To deal with a tie, sum the tied ranks and divide the sum by the number of ties to create an "average" rank value to assign to the tied cases. For example, Table 13.13 gives the ranks of x and y, the difference between the ranks, and the squared difference for each of the $n = 15$ stores in the Electronics World example. Because the sum of the squared differences is 32, we calculate r_s to be

$$r_s = 1 - \frac{6(32)}{15(225 - 1)} = 0.9429.$$

Equivalently, if we have MINITAB (1) find the ranks of the x (household) values (which we call the *HRanks*) and the ranks of the y (sales) values (which we call the *SRanks*) and (2) use the formula for r to calculate the correlation coefficient between the *HRanks* and *SRanks*, we obtain the following output:

```
Pearson correlation of HRank and SRank = 0.943
```

This large positive value of r_s says that there is a strong positive rank correlation between the numbers of households and sales volumes in the sample.

In general, let ρ_s denote the **population rank correlation coefficient**—the rank correlation coefficient for the population of all possible (x, y) values. We can test the significance of ρ_s by using **Spearman's rank correlation test**.

Spearman's Rank Correlation Test

Let r_s denote Spearman's rank correlation coefficient. Then, we can test $H_0: \rho_s = 0$ versus a particular alternative hypothesis at level of significance α by using the appropriate rejection point rule.

Alternative Hypothesis	Rejection Point Rule: Reject H_0 if
$H_a: \rho_s > 0$	$r_s > r_\alpha$
$H_a: \rho_s < 0$	$r_s < -r_\alpha$
$H_a: \rho_s \neq 0$	$|r_s| > r_{\alpha/2}$

Table A.18 gives values of the rejection points r_α, $-r_\alpha$, and $r_{\alpha/2}$ for values of n from 5 to 30. Note that for this test to be valid, the number of ties encountered in ranking the observations should be small relative to the number of observations.

A portion of Table A.18 is reproduced here as Table 13.14. To illustrate using this table, suppose in the Electronics World example that we wish to test $H_0: \rho_s = 0$ versus $H_a: \rho_s > 0$ by setting $\alpha = 0.05$. Because there are $n = 15$ stores, Table 13.14 tells us that we use the rejection point $r_{0.05} = 0.441$. Because $r_s = 0.9429$ is greater than this rejection point, we can reject $H_0: \rho_s = 0$ in favour of $H_a: \rho_s > 0$ by setting $\alpha = 0.05$. Therefore, we have strong evidence that in July of last year the sales volume of an Electronics World store was positively correlated with the number of households in the store's area.

To illustrate testing a two-sided alternative hypothesis, consider Table 13.15. This table presents the rankings of $n = 12$ midsize cars given by two automobile magazines. Here each magazine has ranked the cars from 1 (best) to 12 (worst) on the basis of overall ride. Because the two magazines sometimes have differing views, we cannot theorize about whether their rankings would be positively or negatively correlated. Therefore, we will test $H_0: \rho_s = 0$ versus $H_a: \rho_s \neq 0$. The summary box tells us that to perform this test at level of significance α, we use the rejection point $r_{\alpha/2}$. To look up $r_{\alpha/2}$ in Table A.18 (or Table 13.14), we replace the symbol α by the

| TABLE 13.14 | Critical Values for Spearman's Rank Correlation Coefficient |

n	$\alpha = 0.05$	$\alpha = 0.025$	$\alpha = 0.01$	$\alpha = 0.005$
10	0.564	0.648	0.745	0.794
11	0.523	0.623	0.736	0.818
12	0.497	0.591	0.703	0.780
13	0.475	0.566	0.673	0.745
14	0.457	0.545	0.646	0.716
15	0.441	0.525	0.623	0.689
16	0.425	0.507	0.601	0.666
17	0.412	0.490	0.582	0.645
18	0.399	0.476	0.564	0.625
19	0.388	0.462	0.549	0.608
20	0.377	0.450	0.534	0.591

TABLE 13.15   Rankings of 12 Midsize Cars by Two Automobile Magazines ● CarRank

Car	Magazine 1 Ranking	Magazine 2 Ranking
1	5	7
2	1	1
3	4	5
4	7	4
5	6	6
6	8	10
7	9	8
8	12	11
9	2	3
10	3	2
11	10	12
12	11	9

symbol $\alpha/2$. For example, consider setting $\alpha = 0.05$. Then, since $\alpha/2 = 0.025$, we look in Table 13.14 for the value 0.025. Because there are $n = 12$ cars, we find that $r_{0.025} = 0.591$. Spearman's rank correlation coefficient for the car-ranking data can be calculated to be 0.8951. Because $r_s = 0.8951$ is greater than $r_{0.025} = 0.591$, we reject H_0 at the 0.05 level of significance. Therefore, we conclude that the midsize car ride rankings given by the two magazines are correlated. Furthermore, because $r_s = 0.8951$, we estimate that these rankings are positively correlated.

   To conclude this section, we make two comments. First, the car-ranking example illustrates that Spearman's rank correlation coefficient and test can be used when the raw measurements of the x and/or y variables are themselves **ranks**. Ranks are measurements of an ordinal variable, and Spearman's nonparametric approach applies to ordinal variables. Second, it can be shown that if the sample size n is at least 10, then we can carry out an approximation to Spearman's rank correlation test by replacing r_s by the t statistic

$$t = \frac{r_s\sqrt{n-2}}{\sqrt{1 - r_s^2}}$$

and by replacing the rejection points r_α, $-r_\alpha$, and $r_{\alpha/2}$ by the t points t_α, $-t_\alpha$, and $t_{\alpha/2}$ (with $n - 2$ degrees of freedom). Table A.18 gives r_α points for sample sizes up to $n = 30$. However, if the sample size exceeds 30, we can use the z points z_α, $-z_\alpha$, and $z_{\alpha/2}$ in place of the corresponding t points.

Exercises for Section 13.5

CONCEPTS

13.28 Explain the circumstances in which we use Spearman's rank correlation coefficient.

13.29 Write the formula that we use to compute Spearman's rank correlation coefficient in each case.
   a. There are no (or few) ties in the ranks of the x and y values.
   b. There are many ties in the ranks of the x and y values.

METHODS AND APPLICATIONS

13.30 A sales manager ranks 10 people at the end of their training on the basis of their sales potential. A year later, the number of units sold by each person is determined. The data and MegaStat output in Table 13.16(a) are

obtained. Note that the manager's ranking of 1 is "best."
   ● SalesRank
   a. Find r_s on the MegaStat output and use Table 13.14 to find the critical value for testing $H_0: \rho_s = 0$ versus $H_a: \rho_s \neq 0$ at the 0.05 level of significance. Do we reject H_0?
   b. The MegaStat output gives approximate critical values for $\alpha = 0.05$ and $\alpha = 0.01$. Do these approximate critical values, which are based on the t distribution, differ by much from the exact critical values in Table 13.14 (recall that $n = 10$)?

13.31 Use the MINITAB output below Table 13.16(b) to find r_s, and then test $H_0: \rho_s = 0$ versus $H_a: \rho_s > 0$ for the service time data in Table 13.16(b). ● CopyServ

TABLE 13.16 Data and MegaStat and MINITAB Output for Exercises 13.30 and 13.31

(a) Training data and MegaStat output for Exercise 13.30

Person	1	2	3	4	5	6	7	8	9	10
Manager's Ranking, x	7	4	2	6	1	10	3	5	9	8
Units Sold, y	770	630	820	580	720	440	690	810	560	470

	MgrRank, x	UnitSold, y
MgrRank, x	1.000	
UnitSold, y	−0.721	1.000

10 sample size

±0.632 critical value 0.05 (two-tail)
±0.765 critical value 0.01 (two-tail)

(b) Service time data and MINITAB output for Exercise 13.31

Copiers Serviced, x	4	2	5	7	1	3	4	5	2	4	6
Minutes Required, y	109	58	138	189	37	82	103	134	68	112	154

Pearson correlation of CRank and MRank = 0.986

CHAPTER SUMMARY

The validity of many of the inference procedures presented in this book requires that various assumptions be met. Often, for instance, a normality assumption is required. In this chapter, we have learned that, when the needed assumptions are not met, we must employ a **nonparametric method**. Such a method does not require any assumptions about the shape(s) of the distribution(s) of the sampled population(s).

We first presented the **sign test**, which is a hypothesis test about a population median. This test is useful when we have taken a sample from a population that may not be normally distributed. We next presented two nonparametric tests for comparing the locations of two populations. The first such test, the **Wilcoxon rank sum test**, is appropriate when an **independent samples experiment** has been carried out. The second, the

Wilcoxon signed ranks test, is appropriate when a **paired difference experiment** has been carried out. Both of these tests can be used without assuming that the sampled populations have the shapes of any particular probability distributions. We then discussed the **Kruskal–Wallis H test**, which is a nonparametric test for comparing the locations of several populations by using independent samples. This test, which employs the chi-square distribution, can be used when the normality and/or equal variances assumptions for one-way ANOVA do not hold. Finally, we presented a nonparametric approach for testing the significance of a population correlation coefficient. Here we saw how to compute **Spearman's rank correlation coefficient**, and we discussed how to use this quantity to test the significance of the population correlation coefficient.

GLOSSARY OF TERMS

Kruskal–Wallis H test: A nonparametric test for comparing the locations of three or more populations by using independent random samples. (page 518)

nonparametric test: A hypothesis test that requires no assumptions about the distribution(s) of the sampled population(s). (page 503)

sign test: A hypothesis test about a population median that requires no assumptions about the sampled population. (page 504)

Spearman's rank correlation coefficient: A correlation coefficient computed using the ranks of the observed values of two variables, x and y. (page 520)

Wilcoxon rank sum test: A nonparametric test for comparing the locations of two populations when an independent samples experiment has been carried out. (page 508)

Wilcoxon signed ranks test: A nonparametric test for comparing the locations of two populations when a paired difference experiment has been carried out. (page 513)

IMPORTANT FORMULAS AND TESTS

Sign test for a population median: page 505
Large sample sign test: page 506
Wilcoxon rank sum test: page 508
Wilcoxon rank sum test (large sample approximation): page 511
Wilcoxon signed ranks test: page 513

Wilcoxon signed ranks test (large sample approximation): page 515
Kruskal–Wallis H statistic: page 518
Kruskal–Wallis H test: page 518
Spearman's rank correlation coefficient: page 520
Spearman's rank correlation test: page 521

SUPPLEMENTARY EXERCISES

13.32 Again consider the price comparison situation in which weekly expenses were compared at two chains—Miller's and Albert's (see Exercise 9.64). Recall that independent random samples at the two chains yielded the following weekly expenses:
● ShopExp

Miller's

$119.25	$121.32	$122.34	$120.14	$122.19
$123.71	$121.72	$122.42	$123.63	$122.44

Albert's

$111.99	$114.88	$115.11	$117.02	$116.89
$116.62	$115.38	$114.40	$113.91	$111.87

Because the sample sizes are small, there might be reason to doubt that the populations of expenses at the two chains are normally distributed. Therefore, use a Wilcoxon rank sum test to determine whether expenses at Miller's and Albert's differ. Use $\alpha = 0.05$.

13.33 A drug company wishes to compare the effects of three different drugs (X, Y, and Z) that are being developed to reduce cholesterol levels. Each drug is administered to six patients at the recommended dosage for six months. At the end of this period, the reduction in cholesterol level is recorded for each patient. The results are given in Table 13.17. Assuming that the three samples are independent, use a nonparametric test to see whether the effects of the three drugs differ. Use $\alpha = 0.05$. ● CholRed

13.34 Table 13.18 lists the monthly receipts for restaurants, caterers, and taverns by province for July 2007 in millions of dollars. Also listed in Table 13.18 is the population of each province in July 2007, in thousands. Enter the data into Excel and compute both the

TABLE 13.17 Reduction of Cholesterol Levels Using Three Drugs
● CholRed

	Drug	
X	**Y**	**Z**
22	40	15
31	35	9
19	47	14
27	41	11
25	39	21
18	33	5

Pearson correlation coefficient (from Chapter 11) and the Spearman rank correlation coefficient. How do the two values differ? Which statistic do you feel is most appropriate and why? ● Receipts

13.35 During 2007, a company implemented a number of policies aimed at reducing the ages of its customers' accounts. In order to assess the effectiveness of these measures, the company randomly selects 10 customer accounts. The average age of each account is determined for each of the years 2006 and 2007. These data are given in Table 13.19. Use a nonparametric technique to attempt to show that average account ages have decreased from 2006 to 2007. Use $\alpha = 0.05$. ● AcctAge

13.36 The following data represent the total number of people employed and the total revenue (in thousands of dollars) of the Canadian film and video distribution and videocassette wholesaling industry for the years 2000 to 2005. Compute the Spearman rank correlation coefficient for these two variables. What does

TABLE 13.18 Monthly Receipts for Restaurants, Caterers, and Taverns, and Population Values by Province for July 2007

Province	Receipts ($1,000,000s)	Population (1,000s)[a]
Newfoundland and Labrador	40	514
Prince Edward Island	16	138
Nova Scotia	88	936
New Brunswick	65	751
Québec	754	7,598
Ontario	1,418	12,565
Manitoba	90	1,174
Saskatchewan	89	990
Alberta	430	3,281
British Columbia	599	4,260
Yukon	3	31
Northwest Territories	7	43
Nunavut	0	30

[a]Preliminary postcensal estimates.

Source: http://www40.statcan.ca/l01/cst01/econ92.htm, http://www.statcan.ca/Daily/English/070927/d070927a.htm.

TABLE 13.19 Average Account Ages in 2006 and 2007 for 10 Randomly Selected Accounts ● AcctAge

Account	Average Age of Account in 2006 (Days)	Average Age of Account in 2007 (Days)
1	35	27
2	24	19
3	47	40
4	28	30
5	41	33
6	33	25
7	35	31
8	51	29
9	18	15
10	28	21

the resulting value tell you about the relationship between the number of employees and total revenue? ● CanFilm

Year	Employed	Revenue ($1,000s)
2000/01	3,592	2,813,116
2001/02	3,900	3,036,646
2002/03	4,033	3,278,386
2003/04	3,972	3,437,629
2004/05	4,152	359,617

Source: http://www4U.statcan.ca/l01/cst01/arts15.htm.

13.37 A loan officer wishes to compare the interest rates being charged for 48-month fixed-rate auto loans and 48-month variable-rate auto loans. Two independent, random samples of auto loan rates are selected. A sample of eight 48-month fixed-rate auto loans had the following loan rates: ● AutoLoan

10.29%   9.75%   9.50%   9.99%   9.75%
9.99%   11.40%   10.00%

A sample of five 48-month variable-rate auto loans had loan rates as follows:

9.59%   8.75%   8.99%   8.50%   9.00%

Perform a nonparametric test to determine whether loan rates for 48-month fixed-rate auto loans differ from loan rates for 48-month variable-rate auto loans. Use $\alpha = 0.05$. Explain your conclusion.

13.38 A large bank wishes to limit the median debt-to-equity ratio for its portfolio of commercial loans to 1.5. The bank randomly selects 15 of its commercial loan accounts. Audits result in the following debt-to-equity ratios: ● DebtEq

1.31	1.05	1.45	1.21	1.19
1.78	1.37	1.41	1.22	1.11
1.46	1.33	1.29	1.32	1.65

Can it be concluded that the median debt-to-equity ratio is less than 1.5 at the 0.05 level of significance? Explain.

13.39 INTERNET EXERCISE

Go to the Web site http://lib.stat.cmu.edu/DASL/Datafiles/Heliumfootball.html. Carry out the Wilcoxon signed ranks test to determine whether the distributions of the distances for air-filled and helium-filled footballs are different. Use $\alpha = 0.05$.

CHAPTER **14**

Chi-Square Tests

LEARNING OBJECTIVES

After reading this chapter, you should be able to

- conduct a chi-square goodness of fit test
- describe the type of data used in a chi-square goodness of fit test
- compute the degrees of freedom and examine the significance of the chi-square test statistic
- explain how a chi-square goodness of fit test can be used to examine the relationship between two variables
- conduct a chi-square goodness of fit test between two variables
- explain how graphs may be used to demonstrate the relationship between variables

CHAPTER OUTLINE

14.1 Chi-Square Goodness of Fit Tests

14.2 A Chi-Square Test for Independence

In this chapter, we present two useful hypothesis tests based on the **chi-square distribution**. First, we consider the **chi-square goodness of fit test**. This test evaluates whether data falling into several categories do so with a hypothesized set of probabilities. Second, we discuss the **chi-square test for independence**. Here data are classified on two dimensions and are summarized in a **contingency table**. The test for independence then evaluates whether the cross-classified variables are independent of each other. If we conclude that the variables are not independent, then we have established that the variables in question are related, and we must then investigate the nature of the relationship.

14.1 Chi-Square Goodness of Fit Tests

Multinomial probabilities   Sometimes we collect count data in order to study how the counts are distributed among several **categories** or **cells**. As an example, we might study consumer preferences for four different brands of a product. To do this, we select a random sample of consumers, and we ask each survey participant to indicate a brand preference. We then count the number of consumers who prefer each of the four brands. Here we have four categories (brands), and we study the distribution of the counts in each category in order to see which brands are preferred.

CHAPTER 13

We often use categorical data to carry out a statistical inference. For instance, suppose that a major wholesaler in London, Ontario, carries four different brands of microwave ovens. Historically, consumer behaviour in London has resulted in the market shares shown in Table 14.1. The wholesaler plans to begin doing business in a new territory—Edmonton, Alberta. To study whether its policies for stocking the four brands of ovens in London can also be used in Edmonton, the wholesaler compares consumer preferences for the four ovens in Edmonton with the historical market shares observed in London. A random sample of 400 consumers in Edmonton gives the preferences shown in Table 14.2.

TABLE 14.1   **Market Shares for Four Microwave Oven Brands in London, Ontario**   ● MicroWav

Brand	Market Share
1	20%
2	35%
3	30%
4	15%

TABLE 14.2   **Brand Preferences for Four Microwave Ovens in Edmonton, Alberta**   ● MicroWav

Brand	Observed Frequency (Number of Consumers Sampled Who Prefer the Brand)
1	102
2	121
3	120
4	57

To compare consumer preferences in London and Edmonton, we must consider a **multinomial experiment**. This is similar to the binomial experiment. However, a binomial experiment concerns count data that can be classified into two categories, while a multinomial experiment concerns count data that are classified into more than two categories. Specifically, the assumptions for the multinomial experiment are as follows:

The Multinomial Experiment

1   We perform an experiment in which we carry out n identical trials and in which there are k possible outcomes on each trial.

2   The probabilities of the k outcomes are denoted $p_1, p_2, \ldots, p_k$, where $p_1 + p_2 + \cdots + p_k = 1$. These probabilities stay the same from trial to trial.

3   The trials in the experiment are independent.

4   The results of the experiment are observed frequencies (counts) of the number of trials that result in each of the k possible outcomes. The frequencies are denoted $f_1, f_2, \ldots, f_k$. That is, f_1 is the number of trials resulting in the first possible outcome, f_2 is the number of trials resulting in the second possible outcome, and so forth.

Notice that the scenario that defines a multinomial experiment is similar to that which defines a binomial experiment. In fact, a binomial experiment is simply a multinomial experiment in which k equals 2 (there are two possible outcomes on each trial).

In general, the probabilities $p_1, p_2, \ldots, p_k$ are unknown, and we estimate their values. Or, we compare estimates of these probabilities with a set of specified values. We now look at such an example.

Example 14.1 The Microwave Oven Preference Case

Suppose the microwave oven wholesaler wishes to compare consumer preferences in Edmonton with the historical market shares in London. If the consumer preferences in Edmonton are substantially different, the wholesaler will consider changing its policies for stocking the ovens. Here we will define

p_1 = the proportion of Edmonton consumers who prefer brand 1,
p_2 = the proportion of Edmonton consumers who prefer brand 2,
p_3 = the proportion of Edmonton consumers who prefer brand 3,
p_4 = the proportion of Edmonton consumers who prefer brand 4.

Remembering that the historical market shares for brands 1, 2, 3, and 4 in London are 20 percent, 35 percent, 30 percent, and 15 percent, we test the null hypothesis

$$H_0: p_1 = 0.20, \quad p_2 = 0.35, \quad p_3 = 0.30, \quad \text{and} \quad p_4 = 0.15,$$

which says that consumer preferences in Edmonton are consistent with the historical market shares in London. We test H_0 versus

$$H_a: \text{the previously stated null hypothesis is not true.}$$

To test H_0, we must compare the observed frequencies given in Table 14.2 with the **expected frequencies** for the brands calculated on the assumption that H_0 is true. For instance, if H_0 is true, we would expect $400(0.20) = 80$ of the 400 Edmonton consumers surveyed to prefer brand 1. Denoting this expected frequency for brand 1 as E_1, the expected frequencies for brands 2, 3, and 4 when H_0 is true are $E_2 = 400(0.35) = 140$, $E_3 = 400(0.30) = 120$, and $E_4 = 400(0.15) = 60$. Recalling that Table 14.2 gives the observed frequency for each brand, we have $f_1 = 102$, $f_2 = 121, f_3 = 120$, and $f_4 = 57$. We now compare the observed and expected frequencies by computing a **chi-square statistic** as follows:

$$\chi^2 = \sum_{i=1}^{k=4} \frac{(f_i - E_i)^2}{E_i}$$

$$= \frac{(102 - 80)^2}{80} + \frac{(121 - 140)^2}{140} + \frac{(120 - 120)^2}{120} + \frac{(57 - 60)^2}{60}$$

$$= \frac{484}{80} + \frac{361}{140} + \frac{0}{120} + \frac{9}{60} = 8.7786.$$

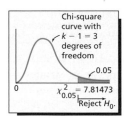

Chi-square curve with $k - 1 = 3$ degrees of freedom

0.05

$\chi^2_{0.05} = 7.81473$

Reject H_0.

Clearly, the more the observed frequencies differ from the expected frequencies, the larger χ^2 will be and the more doubt will be cast on the null hypothesis. If the chi-square statistic is large enough (beyond a rejection point), then we reject H_0.

To find an appropriate rejection point, it can be shown that, when the null hypothesis is true, the sampling distribution of χ^2 is approximately a χ^2 distribution with $k - 1 = 4 - 1 = 3$ degrees of freedom. If we wish to test H_0 at the 0.05 level of significance, we reject H_0 if and only if

$$\chi^2_{\text{obtained}} > \chi^2_{0.05}.$$

Because Table A.17 tells us that the $\chi^2_{0.05}$ point corresponding to $k - 1 = 3$ degrees of freedom equals 7.81473, we find that

$$\chi^2_{\text{obtained}} = 8.7786 > \chi^2_{0.05} = 7.81473,$$

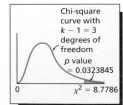

Chi-square curve with $k - 1 = 3$ degrees of freedom

p value = 0.0323845

0

$\chi^2 = 8.7786$

and we reject H_0 at the 0.05 level of significance. Alternatively, the p value for this hypothesis test is the area under the curve of the chi-square distribution with 3 degrees of freedom to the right of $\chi^2 = 8.7786$. This p value can be calculated to be 0.0323845. Because this p value is less than 0.05, we can reject H_0 at the 0.05 level of significance. Although there is no single MINITAB dialogue box that produces a chi-square goodness of fit test, Figure 14.1 shows the output of a MINITAB session that computes the chi-square statistic and its related p value for the oven wholesaler problem.

FIGURE **14.1** **Output of a MINITAB Session That Computes the Chi-Square Statistic and Its Related *p* Value for the Oven Wholesaler Example**

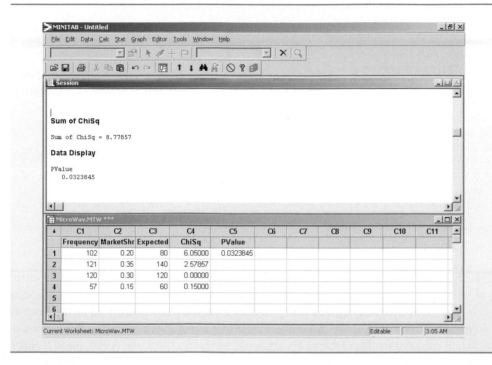

We conclude that consumer preferences in Edmonton for the four brands of ovens are not consistent with the historical market shares in London. Based on this conclusion, the wholesaler should consider changing its stocking policies for microwave ovens when it enters the Edmonton market. To study how to change its policies, the wholesaler might compute a 95 percent confidence interval for, say, the proportion of consumers in Edmonton who prefer brand 2. Because $\hat{p}_2 = 121/400 = 0.3025$, this interval is (see Section 7.4, page 219)

$$\left[\hat{p}_2 \pm z_{0.025}\sqrt{\frac{\hat{p}_2(1-\hat{p}_2)}{n}}\right] = \left[0.3025 \pm 1.96\sqrt{\frac{0.3025(1-0.3025)}{400}}\right]$$

$$= [0.2575, 0.3475].$$

Because this entire interval is below 0.35, it suggests that (1) the market share for brand 2 ovens in Edmonton will be smaller than the 35 percent market share that this brand commands in London, and (2) fewer brand 2 ovens (on a percentage basis) should be stocked in Edmonton. For brand 1, the interval is found to be [0.2125, 0.2977], which is greater then the historic 0.20, suggesting market shares may be larger for brand 1. The confidence interval for brand 3 is [0.2551, 0.3449], which contains the historic 0.30, suggesting the same level of interest. For brand 4, the interval is [0.1082, 0.1768], which contains the historic 0.15, suggesting, as is the case for brand 3, the same level of interest in Edmonton as in London.

In the following box, we give a general chi-square goodness of fit test for multinomial probabilities:

A Goodness of Fit Test for Multinomial Probabilities

Consider a **multinomial experiment** in which each of n randomly selected items is classified into one of k groups. We let

f_i = the number of items classified into group i (that is, the ith observed frequency),

$E_i = np_i$

= the expected number of items that would be classified into group i if p_i is the probability of a randomly selected item being classified into group i (that is, the ith expected frequency).

If we wish to test

H_0: the values of the multinomial probabilities are $p_1, p_2, \ldots, p_k$—that is, the probability of a randomly selected item being classified into group 1 is p_1, the probability of a randomly selected item being classified into group 2 is p_2, and so forth,

versus

H_a: at least one of the multinomial probabilities is not equal to the value stated in H_0,

we define the **chi-square goodness of fit statistic** to be

$$\chi^2 = \sum_{i=1}^{k} \frac{(f_i - E_i)^2}{E_i}.$$

Also, we define the p value related to χ^2 to be the area under the curve of the chi-square distribution with $k - 1$ degrees of freedom to the right of χ^2.

Then, we can reject H_0 in favour of H_a at level of significance α if either of the following equivalent conditions holds:

1   $\chi^2 > \chi^2_\alpha$.

2   p value $< \alpha$.

Here the χ^2_α point is based on $k - 1$ degrees of freedom.

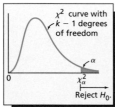

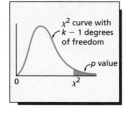

This test is based on the fact that it can be shown that, when H_0 is true, the sampling distribution of χ^2 is approximately a chi-square distribution with $k - 1$ degrees of freedom if the sample size n is large. **It is generally agreed that n should be considered large if all of the "expected cell frequencies" (E_i values) are at least 5.** Furthermore, research implies that this condition on the E_i values can be somewhat relaxed. For example, Moore and McCabe (1993) indicate that **it is reasonable to use the chi-square approximation if the number of groups (k) exceeds 4, the average of the E_i values is at least 5, and the smallest E_i value is at least 1.** Notice that in Example 14.1 all of the E_i values are much larger than 5. Therefore, the chi-square test is valid.

A special version of the chi-square goodness of fit test for multinomial probabilities is called a **test for homogeneity**. This involves testing the null hypothesis that all of the multinomial probabilities are equal. For instance, in the microwave oven situation, we would test

$$H_0: p_1 = p_2 = p_3 = p_4 = 0.25,$$

which would say that no single brand of microwave oven is preferred to any of the other brands (equal preferences). If this null hypothesis is rejected in favour of

$$H_a: \text{at least one of } p_1, p_2, p_3, \text{ and } p_4 \text{ exceeds } 0.25,$$

we would conclude that there is a preference for one or more of the brands. Here each of the expected cell frequencies equals $0.25(400) = 100$. Remembering that the observed cell frequencies are $f_1 = 102, f_2 = 121, f_3 = 120$, and $f_4 = 57$, the chi-square statistic is

$$\chi^2 = \sum_{i=1}^{4} \frac{(f_i - E_i)^2}{E_i}$$

$$= \frac{(102 - 100)^2}{100} + \frac{(121 - 100)^2}{100} + \frac{(120 - 100)^2}{100} + \frac{(57 - 100)^2}{100}$$

$$= 0.04 + 4.41 + 4 + 18.49 = 26.94.$$

Because $\chi^2 = 26.94$ is greater than $\chi^2_{0.05} = 7.81473$ (see the section of Table A.17 in the margin with $k - 1 = 4 - 1 = 3$ degrees of freedom), we reject H_0 at level of significance 0.05. We conclude that preferences for the four brands are not equal and that at least one brand is preferred to the others.

Normal distributions   We have seen that many statistical methods are based on the assumption that a random sample has been selected from a normally distributed population. We can check the validity of the normality assumption by using frequency distributions, stem-and-leaf displays, histograms, and normal plots. Another approach is to use a chi-square goodness of fit test to check the normality assumption.

A Chi-Square Table: Values of χ^2_α

df	$\chi^2_{0.10}$	$\chi^2_{0.05}$
1	2.70554	3.84146
2	4.60517	5.99147
3	6.25139	7.81473
4	7.77944	9.48773
5	9.23635	11.0705
6	10.6446	12.5916
7	12.0170	14.0671
8	13.3616	15.5073
9	14.6837	16.9190
10	15.9871	18.3070
11	17.2750	19.6751
12	18.5494	21.0261
13	19.8119	22.3621

TABLE **14.3** A Sample of 49 Test Scores ● TestScores

30.8	30.9	32.0	32.3	32.6
31.7	30.4	31.4	32.7	31.4
30.1	32.5	30.8	31.2	31.8
31.6	30.3	32.8	30.6	31.9
32.1	31.3	32.0	31.7	32.8
33.3	32.1	31.5	31.4	31.5
31.3	32.5	32.4	32.2	31.6
31.0	31.8	31.0	31.5	30.6
32.0	30.4	29.8	31.7	32.2
32.4	30.5	31.1	30.6	

FIGURE **14.2** MINITAB and MegaStat Outputs of a Stem-and-Leaf
Display of the 49 Test Scores

(a) The MINITAB Output

```
Stem-and-Leaf Display: Scores

Stem-and-leaf of Scores   N = 49
Leaf Unit = 0.10

   1    29  8
   5    30  1344
  12    30  5666889
  21    31  001233444
 (11)   31  55566777889
  17    32  0001122344
   7    32  556788
   1    33  3
```

(b) The MegaStat Output

Stem and Leaf plot for Scores

stem unit = 1
leaf unit = 0.1

Frequency	Stem	Leaf
1	29	8
4	30	1344
7	30	5666889
9	31	001233444
11	31	55566777889
10	32	0001122344
6	32	556788
1	33	3
49		

Consider the sample of 49 test scores given in Table 14.3. The stem-and-leaf display of these scores (in Figure 14.2) is symmetrical and bell-shaped. This suggests that the sample of test scores has been randomly selected from a normally distributed population. In this example, we use a chi-square goodness of fit test to check the normality of the scores.

To perform this test, we first divide the number line into intervals (or categories). One way to do this is to use the class boundaries typical of a histogram. Table 14.4 gives these intervals and also gives observed frequencies (counts of the number of scores in each interval). The chi-square test is done by comparing these observed frequencies with the expected frequencies in the right-most column of Table 14.4. To explain how the expected frequencies are calculated, we first use the sample mean $\bar{x} = 31.55$ and the sample standard deviation $s = 0.8$ of the 49 scores as point estimates of the population mean μ and population standard deviation σ. Then, for example, consider

TABLE **14.4** Observed and Expected Cell Frequencies for a Chi-Square Goodness of Fit
Test for Testing the Normality of the 49 Test Scores in Table 14.3 ● TestScores

Interval	Observed Frequency (f_i)	p_i If the Population of Scores Is Normally Distributed	Expected Frequency, $E_i = np_i = 49p_i$
Less than 30.35	3	$p_1 = P(\text{score} < 30.35) = 0.0668$	$E_1 = 49(0.0668) = 3.2732$
[30.35, 30.95]	9	$p_2 = P(30.35 < \text{score} < 30.95) = 0.1598$	$E_2 = 49(0.1598) = 7.8302$
[30.95, 31.55]	12	$p_3 = P(30.95 < \text{score} < 31.55) = 0.2734$	$E_3 = 49(0.2734) = 13.3966$
[31.55, 32.15]	13	$p_4 = P(31.55 < \text{score} < 32.15) = 0.2734$	$E_4 = 49(0.2734) = 13.3966$
[32.15, 32.75]	9	$p_5 = P(32.15 < \text{score} < 32.75) = 0.1598$	$E_5 = 49(0.1598) = 7.8302$
Greater than 32.75	3	$p_6 = P(\text{score} > 32.75) = 0.0668$	$E_6 = 49(0.0668) = 3.2732$

p_1, the probability that a randomly selected score will be in the first interval (less than 30.35) in Table 14.4 if the population of all scores is normally distributed. We estimate p_1 to be

$$p_1 = P(\text{score} < 30.35) = P\left(z < \frac{30.35 - 31.55}{0.8}\right)$$

$$= P(z < -1.5) = 0.5 - 0.4332 = 0.0668.$$

So, if the scores are normally distributed, then we would expect that 6.68 percent of the 49 observations would fall in that interval. Therefore, it follows that $E_1 = 49p_1 = 49(0.0668) = 3.2732$ is the expected frequency for the first interval under the normality assumption. Next, if we consider p_2, the probability that a randomly selected score will be in the second interval in Table 14.4 if the population of all scores is normally distributed, we estimate p_2 to be

$$p_2 = P(30.35 < \text{score} < 30.95) = P\left(\frac{30.35 - 31.55}{0.8} < z < \frac{30.95 - 31.55}{0.8}\right)$$

$$= P(-1.5 < z < -0.75) = 0.4332 - 0.2734 = 0.1598.$$

It follows that $E_2 = 49p_2 = 49(0.1598) = 7.8302$ is the expected frequency for the second interval under the normality assumption. The other expected frequencies are computed similarly. In general, p_i is the probability that a randomly selected score will be in interval i if the population of all possible scores is normally distributed with mean 31.55 and standard deviation 0.8, and E_i is the expected number of the 49 scores that would be in interval i if the population of all possible scores has this normal distribution.

It seems reasonable to reject the null hypothesis

H_0: the population of all scores is normally distributed

in favour of the alternative hypothesis

H_a: the population of all scores is not normally distributed

if the observed frequencies in Table 14.4 differ substantially from the corresponding expected frequencies. We compare the observed frequencies with the expected frequencies under the normality assumption by computing the chi-square statistic

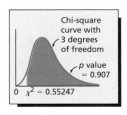

$$\chi^2 = \sum_{i=1}^{6} \frac{(f_i - E_i)^2}{E_i}$$

$$= \frac{(3 - 3.2732)^2}{3.2732} + \frac{(9 - 7.8302)^2}{7.8302} + \frac{(12 - 13.3966)^2}{13.3966}$$

$$+ \frac{(13 - 13.3966)^2}{13.3966} + \frac{(9 - 7.8302)^2}{7.8302} + \frac{(3 - 3.2732)^2}{3.2732}$$

$$= 0.55247.$$

Because we have estimated $m = 2$ parameters (μ and σ) in computing the expected frequencies (E_i values), it can be shown that the sampling distribution of χ^2 is approximately a chi-square distribution with $k - 1 - m = 6 - 1 - 2 = 3$ degrees of freedom. Therefore, we can reject H_0 at level of significance α if

$$\chi^2 > \chi^2_\alpha,$$

where the χ^2_α point is based on $k - 1 - m = 6 - 1 - 2 = 3$ degrees of freedom. If we wish to test H_0 at the 0.05 level of significance, Table A.17 tells us that $\chi^2_{0.05} = 7.81473$. Therefore, because

$$\chi^2 = 0.55247 < \chi^2_{0.05} = 7.81473,$$

we cannot reject H_0 at the 0.05 level of significance, and we cannot reject the hypothesis that the population of all scores is normally distributed. Therefore, for practical purposes it is probably reasonable to assume that the population of all test scores is approximately normally distributed and that inferences based on this assumption are valid. Finally, the p value for this test, which is the area under the chi-square curve with 3 degrees of freedom to the right of $\chi^2 = 0.55247$, can be shown to equal 0.907. Because this p value is large (much greater than 0.05), we have little evidence to support rejecting the null hypothesis (normality).

Note that although some of the expected cell frequencies in Table 14.4 are not at least 5, the number of classes (groups) is 6 (which exceeds 4), the average of the expected cell frequencies is at least 5, and the smallest expected cell frequency is at least 1. Therefore, it is probably reasonable to consider the result of this chi-square test valid. If we choose to base the chi-square test on the more restrictive assumption that all of the expected cell frequencies are at least 5, then we can combine adjacent cell frequencies as follows:

Original f_i Values	Original p_i Values	Original E_i Values	Combined E_i Values	Combined p_i Values	Combined f_i Values
3	0.0668	3.2732	11.1034	0.2266	12
9	0.1598	7.8302			
12	0.2734	13.3966	13.3966	0.2734	12
13	0.2734	13.3966	13.3966	0.2734	13
9	0.1598	7.8302	11.1034	0.2266	12
3	0.0668	3.2732			

When we use these combined cell frequencies, the chi-square approximation is based on $k - 1 - m = 4 - 1 - 2 = 1$ degree of freedom. We find that $\chi^2 = 0.30214$ and p value $= 0.582545$. Because this p value is much greater than 0.05, we cannot reject the hypothesis of normality at the 0.05 level of significance.

In the test score example, we based the intervals employed in the chi-square goodness of fit test on the class boundaries typical of a histogram. Another way to establish intervals for such a test is to compute the sample mean $\bar{x}$ and the sample standard deviation s and to use intervals based on the empirical rule as follows:

Interval 1: less than $\bar{x} - 2s$.

Interval 2: $\bar{x} - 2s < \bar{x} - s$.

Interval 3: $\bar{x} - s < \bar{x}$.

Interval 4: $\bar{x} < \bar{x} + s$.

Interval 5: $\bar{x} + s < \bar{x} + 2s$.

Interval 6: greater than $\bar{x} + 2s$.

However, care must be taken to ensure that each of the expected frequencies is large enough (using the previously discussed criteria).

No matter how the intervals are established, we use $\bar{x}$ as an estimate of the population mean μ and s as an estimate of the population standard deviation σ when we calculate the expected frequencies (E_i values). Because we are estimating $m = 2$ population parameters, the rejection point χ^2_α is based on $k - 1 - m = k - 1 - 2 = k - 3$ degrees of freedom, where k is the number of intervals employed.

In the following box, we summarize how to carry out this chi-square test:

A Goodness of Fit Test for a Normal Distribution

1   We will test the following null and alternative hypotheses:

H_0: the population has a normal distribution,

H_a: the population does not have a normal distribution.

2   Select a random sample of size n and compute the sample mean $\bar{x}$ and sample standard deviation s.

3   Define k intervals for the test. Two reasonable ways to do this are to use the classes of a histogram of the data and to use intervals based on the empirical rule.

4   Record the observed frequency (f_i) for each interval.

5   Calculate the expected frequency (E_i) for each interval under the normality assumption. Do

this by computing the probability that a normal variable with mean $\bar{x}$ and standard deviation s is within the interval and by multiplying this probability by n. Make sure that each expected frequency is large enough. If necessary, combine intervals to make the expected frequencies large enough.

6   Calculate the chi-square statistic

$$\chi^2 = \sum_{i=1}^{k} \frac{(f_i - E_i)^2}{E_i},$$

and define the p value for the test to be the area under the curve of the chi-square distribution with $k - 3$ degrees of freedom to the right of χ^2.

7   Reject H_0 in favour of H_a at level of significance α if either of the following equivalent conditions holds:

a. $\chi^2 > \chi^2_\alpha$.   **b.** p value $< \alpha$.

Here the χ^2_α point is based on $k - 3$ degrees of freedom.

While chi-square goodness of fit tests are often used to verify that it is reasonable to assume that a random sample has been selected from a normally distributed population, such tests can also check other distribution forms. For instance, we might verify that it is reasonable to assume that a random sample has been selected from a Poisson distribution. In general, **the number of degrees of freedom for the chi-square goodness of fit test will equal $k - 1 - m$**, where k is the number of intervals or categories employed in the test and m is the number of population parameters that must be estimated to calculate the needed expected frequencies.

Exercises for Section 14.1

CONCEPTS

14.1   Describe the characteristics that define a multinomial experiment.

14.2   Give the conditions that the expected cell frequencies must meet in order to validly carry out a chi-square goodness of fit test.

14.3   Explain the purpose of a goodness of fit test.

14.4   When performing a chi-square goodness of fit test, why does a large value of the chi-square statistic provide evidence that H_0 should be rejected?

14.5   State two ways to obtain intervals for a goodness of fit test of normality.

METHODS AND APPLICATIONS

14.6   The proportions of yearly sales across a province in Canada for five popular fruits (apples, oranges, bananas, peaches, and grapefruit, in terms of units sold to each person per year) were found to be 36 percent, 26 percent, 21 percent, 9 percent, and 8 percent, respectively. Suppose that a new survey of 1,000 shoppers in a city within that province was conducted and the following purchase frequencies were found:

Apples	Oranges	Bananas	Peaches	Grapefruit
391	202	275	53	79

a. Show that it is appropriate to carry out a chi-square test using these data.
b. Test to determine whether the city market shares differ from those of the province. Use $\alpha = 0.05$.

14.7   Last rating period, the percentages of viewers watching several channels in a certain time period in a major TV market were as follows: TVRate

Station 1 (News)	Station 2 (News)	Station 3 (Sitcom)	Station 4 (News)	Others
15%	19%	22%	16%	28%

Suppose that in the current rating period, a survey of 2,000 viewers gives the following frequencies:

Station 1 (News)	Station 2 (News)	Station 3 (Sitcom)	Station 4 (News)	Others
182	536	354	151	777

a. Show that it is appropriate to carry out a chi-square test using these data.
b. Test to determine whether the viewing shares in the current rating period differ from those in the last rating period at the 0.10 level of significance. What do you conclude?

14.8   In the *Journal of Marketing Research* (November 1996), Gupta studied the extent to which the purchase behaviour of **scanner panels** is representative of overall brand preferences. A scanner panel is a sample of households whose purchase data are recorded when a magnetic identification card is presented at a store checkout. Table 14.5 gives peanut butter purchase data collected by the ACNielsen Company using a panel of 2,500 households in Sioux Falls, South Dakota. The data were collected over 102 weeks. The table also gives the market shares obtained by recording all peanut butter purchases at the same stores during the same period.   ◐ ScanPan

TABLE **14.5** Peanut Butter Purchase Data

Brand	Size	Number of Purchases by Household Panel	Market Shares
Jif	18 oz.	3,165	20.10%
Jif	20	1,892	10.10
Jif	40	726	5.42
Peter Pan	10	4,079	16.01
Skippy	18	6,206	28.56
Skippy	28	1,627	12.33
Skippy	40	1,420	7.48
Total		19,115	

Goodness of Fit Test

obs	expected	O − E	(O − E)²/E	% of chisq
3,165	2,842.115	677.115	119.331	13.56
1,892	1,930.615	−38.615	0.772	0.09
726	1,036.033	−310.033	92.777	10.54
4,079	3,060.312	1,018.689	339.092	38.52
6,206	5,459.244	746.756	102.147	11.60
1,627	2,356.880	−729.880	226.029	25.68
1,420	1,429.802	−9.802	0.067	0.01
19,115	19,115.000	0.000	880.216	100.00

880.22 chisquare   6 df   7.10E-187   p-value

Source: Reprinted with permission from *The Journal of Marketing Research*, published by the American Marketing Association. "Do household scanner data provide representative inferences from brand choices? A comparison with store data," by S. Gupta et al., *The Journal of Marketing Research*, Vol. 33, p. 393 (Table 6).

a. Show that it is appropriate to carry out a chi-square test.

b. Test to determine whether the purchase behaviour of the panel of 2,500 households is consistent with the purchase behaviour of the population of all peanut butter purchasers. Assume here that purchase decisions by panel members are reasonably independent, and set $\alpha = 0.05$.

14.9 The purchase frequencies for six different brands of digital cameras are observed at an electronics store over one month: DigCam

Brand	Purchase Frequency
Canon	131
Hewlett-Packard	273
Kodak	119
Olympus	301
Sanyo	176
Sony	200

a. Carry out a test of homogeneity for these data with $\alpha = 0.025$.

b. Interpret the results of your test.

14.10 A wholesaler has recently developed a computerized sales invoicing system. Prior to implementing this system, a manual system was used. The distribution of the number of errors per invoice for the manual system is as follows: Invoice2

Errors per Invoice	0	1	2	3	More Than 3
Percentage of Invoices	87%	8%	3%	1%	1%

After implementation of the computerized system, a random sample of 500 invoices gives the following error distribution:

Errors per Invoice	0	1	2	3	More Than 3
Number of Invoices	479	10	8	2	1

a. Show that it is appropriate to carry out a chi-square test using these data.

b. Use the Excel output in Figure 14.3 to determine whether the error percentages for the computerized system differ from those for the manual system at the 0.05 level of significance. What do you conclude?

14.11 Consider the sample of 65 payment times given in Table 14.6. Use these data to carry out a chi-square goodness of fit test to test whether the population of all payment times is normally

FIGURE **14.3**   **Excel Output for Exercise 14.10**

```
     pi      Ei      fi    (f-E)^2/E
    0.87    435     479     4.4506
    0.08    40      10     22.5000
    0.03    15       8      3.2667
    0.01     5       2      1.8000
    0.01     5       1      3.2000
                  Chi-     35.21724   p-value 0.0000001096
                 Square
```

TABLE **14.6** A Sample of Payment Times (in Days) for 65 Randomly Selected Invoices   ● PayTime

22	29	16	15	18	17	12	13	17	16	15
19	17	10	21	15	14	17	18	12	20	14
16	15	16	20	22	14	25	19	23	15	19
18	23	22	16	16	19	13	18	24	24	26
13	18	17	15	24	15	17	14	18	17	21
16	21	25	19	20	27	16	17	16	21	

distributed by doing the following:
● PayTime

a. It can be shown that $\bar{x} = 18.1077$ and that $s = 3.9612$ for the payment time data. Use these values to compute the intervals

   (1) Less than $\bar{x} - 2s$.
   (2) $\bar{x} - 2s < \bar{x} - s$.
   (3) $\bar{x} - s < \bar{x}$.
   (4) $\bar{x} < \bar{x} + s$.
   (5) $\bar{x} + s < \bar{x} + 2s$.
   (6) Greater than $\bar{x} + 2s$.

b. Assuming that the population of all payment times is normally distributed, find the probability that a randomly selected payment time will be contained in each of the intervals in part a. Use these probabilities to compute the expected frequency under the normality assumption for each interval.

c. Verify that the average of the expected frequencies is at least 5 and that the smallest expected frequency is at least 1. What does this tell us?

d. Formulate the null and alternative hypotheses for the chi-square test of normality.

e. For each interval in part a, find the observed frequency. Then calculate the chi-square statistic needed for the chi-square test of normality.

f. Use the chi-square statistic to test normality at the 0.05 level of significance. What do you conclude?

14.12 Consider the sample of 60 bottle design ratings given in Table 14.7. Use these data to carry out a chi-square goodness of fit test to determine whether the population of all bottle design ratings is normally distributed. Use $\alpha = 0.05$, and note that $\bar{x} = 30.35$ and $s = 3.1073$ for the 60 bottle design ratings.
● Design

14.13 Table 14.8 gives a frequency distribution describing the number of errors found in thirty 1,000-word typing tests. Suppose that we wish to determine whether the number of errors can be described by a Poisson distribution with mean $\mu = 4.5$. Using the Poisson probability tables, copy and complete the table. Then perform an appropriate chi-square goodness of fit test at the 0.05 level of significance. What do you conclude about whether the number of errors can be described by a Poisson distribution with $\mu = 4.5$? Explain.   ● TestErr

TABLE **14.7** A Sample of Bottle Design Ratings (Composite Scores for a Systematic Sample of 60 Shoppers)   ● Design

34	33	33	29	26	33	28	25	32	33
32	25	27	33	22	27	32	33	32	29
24	30	20	34	31	32	30	35	33	31
32	28	30	31	31	33	29	27	34	31
31	28	33	31	32	28	26	29	32	34
32	30	34	32	30	30	32	31	29	33

TABLE **14.8** Frequency Distribution of Errors for Exercise 14.13

Number of Errors	Observed Frequency	Probability Assuming Errors Are Poisson Distributed with $\mu = 4.5$	Expected Frequency
0–1	6		
2–3	5		
4–5	7		
6–7	8		
8 or more	4		

14.2 A Chi-Square Test for Independence

One way to study the relationship between two variables is to classify multinomial count data on two scales (or dimensions) by setting up a **contingency table**.

Example 14.2 The Client Satisfaction Case

A financial institution sells three kinds of investment products—a stock fund, a bond fund, and a tax-deferred annuity. The company is examining whether customer satisfaction depends on the type of investment product purchased. To do this, 100 clients are randomly selected from the population of clients who have purchased shares in exactly one of the funds. The company records the fund type purchased by these clients and asks each sampled client to rate their level of satisfaction with the fund as high, medium, or low. Table 14.9 gives the survey results.

We can look at the data in Table 14.9 in an organized way by constructing a **contingency table** (also called a **two-way cross-classification table**). Such a table classifies the data on two dimensions—type of fund and degree of client satisfaction. Figure 14.4 gives MegaStat and

TABLE 14.9 Results of a Customer Satisfaction Survey Given to 100 Randomly Selected Clients Who Invest in One of Three Fund Types—a Bond Fund, a Stock Fund, or a Tax-Deferred Annuity ● Invest

Client	Fund Type	Level of Satisfaction	Client	Fund Type	Level of Satisfaction	Client	Fund Type	Level of Satisfaction
1	BOND	HIGH	35	STOCK	HIGH	69	BOND	MED
2	STOCK	HIGH	36	BOND	MED	70	TAXDEF	MED
3	TAXDEF	MED	37	TAXDEF	MED	71	TAXDEF	MED
4	TAXDEF	MED	38	TAXDEF	LOW	72	BOND	HIGH
5	STOCK	LOW	39	STOCK	HIGH	73	TAXDEF	MED
6	STOCK	HIGH	40	TAXDEF	MED	74	TAXDEF	LOW
7	STOCK	HIGH	41	BOND	HIGH	75	STOCK	HIGH
8	BOND	MED	42	BOND	HIGH	76	BOND	HIGH
9	TAXDEF	LOW	43	BOND	LOW	77	TAXDEF	LOW
10	TAXDEF	LOW	44	TAXDEF	LOW	78	BOND	MED
11	STOCK	MED	45	STOCK	HIGH	79	STOCK	HIGH
12	BOND	LOW	46	BOND	HIGH	80	STOCK	HIGH
13	STOCK	HIGH	47	BOND	MED	81	BOND	MED
14	TAXDEF	MED	48	STOCK	HIGH	82	TAXDEF	MED
15	TAXDEF	MED	49	TAXDEF	MED	83	BOND	HIGH
16	TAXDEF	LOW	50	TAXDEF	MED	84	STOCK	MED
17	STOCK	HIGH	51	STOCK	HIGH	85	STOCK	HIGH
18	BOND	HIGH	52	TAXDEF	MED	86	BOND	MED
19	BOND	MED	53	STOCK	HIGH	87	TAXDEF	MED
20	TAXDEF	MED	54	TAXDEF	MED	88	TAXDEF	LOW
21	TAXDEF	MED	55	STOCK	LOW	89	STOCK	HIGH
22	BOND	HIGH	56	BOND	HIGH	90	TAXDEF	MED
23	TAXDEF	MED	57	STOCK	HIGH	91	BOND	HIGH
24	TAXDEF	LOW	58	BOND	MED	92	TAXDEF	HIGH
25	STOCK	HIGH	59	TAXDEF	LOW	93	TAXDEF	LOW
26	BOND	HIGH	60	TAXDEF	LOW	94	TAXDEF	LOW
27	TAXDEF	LOW	61	STOCK	MED	95	STOCK	HIGH
28	BOND	MED	62	BOND	LOW	96	BOND	HIGH
29	STOCK	HIGH	63	STOCK	HIGH	97	BOND	MED
30	STOCK	HIGH	64	TAXDEF	MED	98	STOCK	HIGH
31	BOND	MED	65	TAXDEF	MED	99	TAXDEF	MED
32	TAXDEF	MED	66	TAXDEF	LOW	100	TAXDEF	MED
33	BOND	HIGH	67	STOCK	HIGH			
34	STOCK	MED	68	BOND	HIGH			

FIGURE 14.4 MegaStat and MINITAB Output of a Contingency Table of Fund Type versus Level of Client Satisfaction (See the Survey Results in Table 14.9) Invest

(a) The MegaStat output

Cross-tabulation

Fund Type		HIGH	MED	LOW	Total
		Satisfaction Rating			
BOND	Observed	15	12	3	30
	% of row	50.0%	40.0%	10.0%	100.5%
	% of column	37.5%	30.0%	15.0%	30.0%
	% of total	15.0%	12.0%	3.0%	30.0%
STOCK	Observed	24	4	2	30
	% of row	80.0%	13.3%	6.7%	100.0%
	% of column	60.0%	10.0%	10.0%	30.0%
	% of total	24.0%	4.0%	2.0%	30.0%
TAXDEF	Observed	1	24	15	40
	% of row	2.5%	60.0%	37.5%	100.0%
	% of column	2.5%	60.0%	75.0%	40.0%
	% of total	1.0%	24.0%	15.0%	40.0%
Total	Observed	40	40	20	100
	% of row	40.0%	40.0%	20.0%	100.0%
	% of column	100.0%	100.0%	100.0%	100.0%
	% of total	40.0%	40.0%	20.0%	100.0%

46.44[a] chi-square
4 df
2.00E-09[b] p-value

(b) The MINITAB output

Rows: FundType Columns: SatRating

	High	Med	Low	All
Bond	15	12	3	30
	50.00	40.00	10.00	100.00
	37.50	30.00	15.00	30.00
	12	12	6	30
Stock	24	4	2	30
	80.00	13.33	6.67	100.00
	60.00	10.00	10.00	30.00
	12	12	6	30
TaxDef	1	24	15	40
	2.50	60.00	37.50	100.00
	2.50	60.00	75.00	40.00
	16	16	8	40
All	40	40	20	100
	40.00	40.00	20.00	100.00
	100.00	100.00	100.00	100.00
	40	40	20	100

Pearson Chi-Square = 46.438, DF = 4
P-Value = 0.000

Cell Contents: Count
% of Row
% of Column
Expected count

[a]Chi-square statistic.
[b]p value for chi-square.

MINITAB output of a contingency table of fund type versus level of satisfaction. This table consists of a row for each fund type and a column for each level of satisfaction. Together, the rows and columns form a "cell" for each fund type–satisfaction level combination. That is, there is a cell for each **contingency** with respect to fund type and satisfaction level. Both the MegaStat and MINITAB output give a **cell frequency** for each cell, which is the top number given in the cell. This is a count (observed frequency) of the number of surveyed clients with the cell's fund type–satisfaction level combination. For instance, 15 of the surveyed clients invest in the bond fund and report high satisfaction, while 24 of the surveyed clients invest in the tax-deferred annuity and report medium satisfaction. In addition to the cell frequencies, each output also gives the following:

Row totals (at the far right of each table): These are counts of the numbers of clients who invest in each fund type. These row totals tell us that

1 30 clients invest in the bond fund.
2 30 clients invest in the stock fund.
3 40 clients invest in the tax-deferred annuity.

Column totals (at the bottom of each table): These are counts of the numbers of clients who report high, medium, and low satisfaction. These column totals tell us that

1 40 clients report high satisfaction.
2 40 clients report medium satisfaction.
3 20 clients report low satisfaction.

Overall total (the bottom right entry in each table): This tells us that a total of 100 clients were surveyed.

Besides the row and column totals, both outputs give **row and total percentages** (directly below the row and column totals). For example, 30.00 percent of the surveyed clients invest in the bond fund, and 20.00 percent of the surveyed clients report low satisfaction. Furthermore, in addition to a cell frequency, the MegaStat output gives a **row percentage**, a **column percentage**, and a **cell percentage** for each cell (these are below the cell frequency in each cell). For instance, looking at the bond fund–high satisfaction cell, we see that the 15 clients in this cell make up 50.0 percent of the 30 clients who invest in the bond fund, and they make up 37.5 percent of the 40 clients who report high satisfaction. In addition, these 15 clients make up 15.0 percent of the 100 clients surveyed. The MINITAB output gives a row percentage and a column percentage, but not a cell percentage, for each cell. The last number that appears in each cell of the MINITAB output is the estimated cell frequency (explained later in this section).

Looking at the contingency tables, it appears that the level of client satisfaction may be related to the fund type. We see that higher satisfaction ratings seem to be reported by stock and bond fund investors, while holders of tax-deferred annuities report lower satisfaction ratings. To carry out a formal statistical test, we can test the null hypothesis

$$H_0: \text{fund type and level of client satisfaction are independent}$$

versus

$$H_a: \text{fund type and level of client satisfaction are dependent.}$$

In order to perform this test, we compare the counts (or **observed cell frequencies**) in the contingency table with the counts that would appear in the contingency table if we assumed that fund type and level of satisfaction were independent. Because these latter counts are computed by assuming independence, we call them the **expected cell frequencies under the independence assumption**. We illustrate how to calculate these expected cell frequencies by considering the cell corresponding to the bond fund and high client satisfaction. We first use the data in the contingency table to compute an estimate of the probability that a randomly selected client invests in the bond fund. Denoting this probability as p_B, we estimate p_B by dividing the row total for the bond fund by the total number of clients surveyed. That is, denoting the row total for the bond fund as r_B and letting n denote the total number of clients surveyed, the estimate of p_B is $r_B/n = 30/100 = 0.3$. Next we compute an estimate of the probability that a randomly selected client will report high satisfaction. Denoting this probability as p_H, we estimate p_H by dividing the column total for high satisfaction by the total number of clients surveyed. That is, denoting the column total for high satisfaction as c_H, the estimate of p_H is $c_H/n = 40/100 = 0.4$. Next, assuming that investing in the bond fund and reporting high satisfaction are **independent**, we compute an estimate of the probability that a randomly selected client invests in the bond fund and reports high satisfaction. Denoting this probability as p_{BH}, we can compute its estimate by recalling from Section 3.4 that if two events A and B are statistically independent, then $P(A \cap B)$ equals $P(A)P(B)$. It follows that, if we assume that investing in the bond fund and reporting high satisfaction are independent, we can compute an estimate of p_{BH} by multiplying the estimate of p_B by the estimate of p_H. That is, the estimate of p_{BH} is $(r_B/n)(c_H/n) = (0.3)(0.4) = 0.12$. Finally, we compute an estimate of the expected cell frequency under the independence assumption. Denoting the expected cell frequency as E_{BH}, the estimate of E_{BH} is

$$\hat{E}_{BH} = n\left(\frac{r_B}{n}\right)\left(\frac{c_H}{n}\right) = 100(0.3)(0.4) = 12.$$

This estimated expected cell frequency is given in the MINITAB output of Figure 14.4(b) as the last number under the observed cell frequency for the bond fund–high satisfaction cell.

Noting that the expression for $\hat{E}_{BH}$ can be written as

$$\hat{E}_{BH} = n\left(\frac{r_B}{n}\right)\left(\frac{c_H}{n}\right) = \frac{r_B c_H}{n},$$

we can generalize to obtain a formula for the estimated expected cell frequency for any cell in the contingency table. Letting $\hat{E}_{ij}$ denote the estimated expected cell frequency corresponding to row i and column j in the contingency table, we see that

$$\hat{E}_{ij} = \frac{r_i c_j}{n},$$

where r_i is the row total for row i and c_j is the column total for column j. For example, for the fund type–satisfaction level contingency table, we obtain

$$\hat{E}_{SL} = \frac{r_S c_L}{n} = \frac{30(20)}{100} = \frac{600}{100} = 6$$

and

$$\hat{E}_{TM} = \frac{r_T c_M}{n} = \frac{40(40)}{100} = \frac{1,600}{100} = 16.$$

Intuitively, these estimated expected cell frequencies tell us what the contingency table looks like if fund type and level of client satisfaction are independent.

To test the null hypothesis of independence, we will compute a chi-square statistic that compares the observed cell frequencies with the estimated expected cell frequencies calculated assuming independence. Letting f_{ij} denote the observed cell frequency for cell ij, we compute

$$\chi^2 = \sum_{\text{all cells}} \frac{(f_{ij} - \hat{E}_{ij})^2}{\hat{E}_{ij}}$$

$$= \frac{(f_{BH} - \hat{E}_{BH})^2}{\hat{E}_{BH}} + \frac{(f_{BM} - \hat{E}_{BM})^2}{\hat{E}_{BM}} + \cdots + \frac{(f_{TL} - \hat{E}_{TL})^2}{\hat{E}_{TL}}$$

$$= \frac{(15 - 12)^2}{12} + \frac{(12 - 12)^2}{12} + \frac{(3 - 6)^2}{6} + \frac{(24 - 12)^2}{12} + \frac{(4 - 12)^2}{12}$$

$$+ \frac{(2 - 6)^2}{6} + \frac{(1 - 16)^2}{16} + \frac{(24 - 16)^2}{16} + \frac{(15 - 8)^2}{8}$$

$$= 46.4375.$$

If the value of the chi-square statistic is large, this indicates that the observed cell frequencies differ substantially from the expected cell frequencies calculated by assuming independence. Therefore, the larger the value of chi-square, the more doubt is cast on the null hypothesis of independence.

To find an appropriate rejection point, we let r denote the number of rows in the contingency table and c denote the number of columns. Then, it can be shown that, when the null hypothesis of independence is true, the sampling distribution of χ^2 is approximately a χ^2 distribution with $(r - 1)(c - 1) = (3 - 1)(3 - 1) = 4$ degrees of freedom. If we test H_0 at the 0.05 level of significance, we reject H_0 if and only if

$$\chi^2 > \chi^2_{0.05}.$$

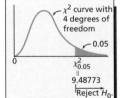

Because Table A.17 tells us that the $\chi^2_{0.05}$ point corresponding to $(r - 1)(c - 1) = 4$ degrees of freedom equals 9.48773, we have

$$\chi^2 = 46.4375 > \chi^2_{0.05} = 9.48773,$$

and we reject H_0 at the 0.05 level of significance. We conclude that fund type and level of client satisfaction are not independent.

In the following box, we summarize how to carry out a chi-square test for independence:

A Chi-Square Test for Independence

Suppose that each of n randomly selected elements is classified on two dimensions, and suppose that the result of the two-way classification is a **contingency table with r rows and c columns**. Let

f_{ij} = the cell frequency corresponding to row i and column j of the contingency table

(that is, the number of elements classified in row i and column j),

r_i = the row total for row i in the contingency table,

c_j = the column total for column j in the contingency table,

$$\hat{E}_{ij} = \frac{r_i c_j}{n}$$

= the estimated expected number of elements that would be classified in row i and column j of the contingency table if the two classifications are statistically independent.

If we wish to test

H_0: the two classifications are statistically independent

versus

H_a: the two classifications are statistically dependent,

we define the test statistic

$$\chi^2 = \sum_{\text{all cells}} \frac{(f_{ij} - \hat{E}_{ij})^2}{\hat{E}_{ij}}.$$

Also, we define the p value related to χ^2 to be the area under the curve of the chi-square distribution with $(r - 1)(c - 1)$ degrees of freedom to the right of χ^2.

Then, we can reject H_0 in favour of H_a at level of significance α if either of the following equivalent conditions holds:

1   $\chi^2 > \chi^2_\alpha$.

2   p value $< \alpha$.

Here the χ^2_α point is based on $(r - 1)(c - 1)$ degrees of freedom.

This test is based on the fact that it can be shown that, when the null hypothesis of independence is true, the sampling distribution of χ^2 is approximately a chi-square distribution with $(r - 1)(c - 1)$ degrees of freedom if the sample size n is large. **It is generally agreed that n should be considered large if all of the estimated expected cell frequencies ($\hat{E}_{ij}$ values) are at least 5.** Moore and McCabe (1993) indicate that **it is reasonable to use the chi-square approximation if the number of cells (rc) exceeds 4, the average of the $\hat{E}_{ij}$ values is at least 5, and the smallest $\hat{E}_{ij}$ value is at least 1.** Notice that in Figure 14.4(b) all of the estimated expected cell frequencies are greater than 5.

Again consider the MegaStat and MINITAB outputs of Figure 14.4, which give the contingency table of fund type versus level of client satisfaction. Both outputs give the chi-square statistic ($= 46.438$) for testing the null hypothesis of independence, as well as the related p value. We see that this p value is less than 0.001. It follows that we can reject

H_0: fund type and level of client satisfaction are independent

at the 0.05 level of significance because the p value is less than 0.05.

In order to study the nature of the dependency between the classifications in a contingency table, it is often useful to plot the row and/or column percentages. As an example, Figure 14.5

FIGURE **14.5**   Plots of Row Percentages versus Investment Type for the Contingency Table in Figure 14.4(a)

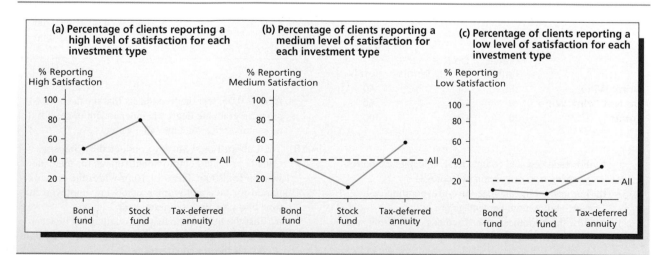

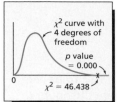

gives plots of the row percentages in the contingency table of Figure 14.4(a). For instance, the column in this contingency table corresponding to a high level of satisfaction tells us that 40.00 percent of the surveyed clients report a high level of satisfaction. If fund type and level of satisfaction really were independent, then we would expect roughly 40 percent of the clients in each of the three categories—bond fund participants, stock fund participants, and tax-deferred annuity holders—to report a high level of satisfaction. That is, we would expect the row percentages in the high satisfaction column to be roughly 40 percent in each row. However, Figure 14.5(a) gives a plot of the percentages of clients reporting a high level of satisfaction for each investment type (that is, the figure plots the three row percentages in the high satisfaction column). We see that these percentages vary considerably. Noting that the dashed line in the figure is the 40 percent reporting a high level of satisfaction for the overall group, we see that the percentage of stock fund participants reporting high satisfaction is 80 percent. This is far above the 40 percent we would expect if independence existed. On the other hand, the percentage of tax-deferred annuity holders reporting high satisfaction is only 2.5 percent— way below the expected 40 percent if independence existed. In a similar fashion, Figure 14.5(b) and (c) plots the row percentages for the medium and low satisfaction columns in the contingency table. These plots indicate that stock fund participants report medium and low levels of satisfaction less frequently than the overall group of clients, and that tax-deferred annuity participants report medium and low levels of satisfaction more frequently than the overall group of clients. Note that the chi-square test for independence can be used to test the equality of several population proportions.

Exercises for Section 14.2

CONCEPTS

14.14 What is the purpose behind summarizing data in the form of a two-way contingency table?

14.15 When performing a chi-square test for independence, how are the "cell frequencies under the independence assumption" calculated? Why are these frequencies calculated?

METHODS AND APPLICATIONS

14.16 A marketing research firm wishes to study the relationship between wine consumption and whether a person likes to watch professional tennis on television. One hundred randomly selected people are asked whether they drink wine and whether they watch tennis. The following results are obtained:
  ◔ WineCons

	Watch Tennis	Do Not Watch Tennis	Totals
Drink Wine	16	24	40
Do Not Drink Wine	4	56	60
Totals	20	80	100

  a. For each row and column total, calculate the corresponding row or column percentage.
  b. For each cell, calculate the corresponding cell, row, and column percentages.
  c. Test the hypothesis that whether people drink wine is independent of whether people watch tennis. Set $\alpha = 0.05$.

  d. Given the results of the chi-square test, does it make sense to advertise wine during a televised tennis match (assuming that the ratings for the tennis match are high enough)? Explain.

14.17 A random sample of Canadian university undergraduate students were given a questionnaire in order to learn whether or not they would consider seeking a graduate degree. Male and female students were questioned and their responses were as follows:

Pursue a Graduate Degree	Male	Female	Total
Yes	79	121	200
No	86	114	200
Total	165	235	400

  At $\alpha = 0.05$, test the hypothesis that the decision to pursue a graduate degree is independent of sex for these university students. ◔ Degree

14.18 The Labour Force Survey conducted by Statistics Canada provided employment figures for men and women for 2006. Table 14.10 provides the values reported for men and women who were employed full-time and part-time separately. ◔ Labour
  a. Test the hypothesis that the relationship between sex and employment status is independent by computing the chi-square value.

TABLE **14.10** **Employment by Sex Statistics for Canadians in 2006** ● Labour

			Sex		
			Male	**Female**	**Total**
Employ	**Full-time**	Count	6,972	5,157	12,129
		Expected count	6,475.8	5,653.2	12,129.0
		Percent within employ	57.5%	42.5%	100.0%
		Percent within sex	93.5%	79.2%	86.9%
		Percent of total	49.9%	36.9%	86.9%
	Part-time	Count	483	1351	1,834
		Expected count	979.2	854.8	1,834.0
		Percent within employ	26.3%	73.7%	100.0%
		Percent within sex	6.5%	20.8%	13.1%
		Percent of total	3.5%	9.7%	13.1%
Total		Count	7,455	6,508	13,963
		Expected count	7,455.0	6,508.0	13,963.0
		Percent within employ	53.4%	46.6%	100.0%
		Percent within sex	100.0%	100.0%	100.0%
		Percent of total	53.4%	46.6%	100.0%

Source: Adapted from the Statistics Canada CANSIM database, http://cansim2.statcan.ca, table number 282–0002, September 8, 2006.

b. Looking at the percentage values in Table 14.10, what conclusions can you draw for men versus women in terms of patterns of employment?

14.19 In the book *Essentials of Marketing Research*, Dillon, Madden, and Firtle discuss the relationship between delivery time and computer-assisted ordering. A sample of 40 firms shows that 16 use computer-assisted ordering, while 24 do not. Furthermore, past data are used to categorize each firm's delivery times as below the industry average, equal to the industry average, or above the industry average. The results obtained are given in Table 14.11.

a. Test the hypothesis that delivery time performance is independent of whether computer-assisted ordering is used. What do you conclude by setting $\alpha = 0.05$? ● DelTime

b. Verify that a chi-square test is appropriate.

c. Is there a difference between delivery-time performance between firms using computer-assisted ordering and those not using computer-assisted ordering?

d. Carry out graphical analysis to investigate the relationship between delivery-time performance and computer-assisted ordering. Describe the relationship.

14.20 A television station wishes to study the relationship between viewership of its 11 P.M. news program and viewer age (18 years or less, 19 to 35, 36 to 54, 55 or older). A sample of 250 television viewers in each age group is randomly selected, and the number who watch the station's 11 P.M. news is found for each sample. The results are given in Table 14.12. ● TVView

a. Let $p_1, p_2, p_3,$ and p_4 be the proportions of all viewers in each age group who watch the station's

TABLE **14.11** **A Contingency Table Relating Delivery Time and Computer-Assisted Ordering** ● DelTime

Computer-Assisted Ordering	Below Industry Average	Delivery Time Equal to Industry Average	Above Industry Average	Row Total
No	4	12	8	24
Yes	10	4	2	16
Column Total	14	16	10	40

TABLE **14.12** **A Summary of the Results of a TV Viewership Study** ● TVView

Watch 11 P.M. News?	Age Group 18 or Less	19 to 35	36 to 54	55 or Older	Total
Yes	37	48	56	73	214
No	213	202	194	177	786
Total	250	250	250	250	1,000

11 P.M. news. If these proportions are equal, then whether a viewer watches the station's 11 P.M. news is independent of the viewer's age group. Therefore, we can test the null hypothesis H_0 that $p_1, p_2, p_3,$ and p_4 are equal by carrying out a chi-square test for independence. Perform this test by setting $\alpha = 0.05$.

b. Compute a 95 percent confidence interval for the difference between p_1 and p_4.

CHAPTER SUMMARY

In this chapter, we presented two hypothesis tests that employ the **chi-square distribution**. In Section 14.1, we discussed a **chi-square goodness of fit test**. Here we considered a situation in which we study how count data are distributed among various categories. In particular, we considered a **multinomial experiment** in which randomly selected items are classified into several groups, and we saw how to perform a goodness of fit test for the multinomial probabilities associated with these groups. We also explained how to perform a goodness of fit test for normality. In Section 14.2, we presented a **chi-square test for independence**. Here we classify count data on two dimensions, and we summarize the cross-classification in the form of a **contingency table**. We use the cross-classified data to test whether the two classifications are **statistically independent**, which is really a way to see whether the classifications are related. We also learned that we can use graphical analysis to investigate the nature of the relationship between the classifications.

GLOSSARY OF TERMS

chi-square test for independence: A test to determine whether two classifications are independent. (pages 540–541)
contingency table: A table that summarizes data that have been classified on two dimensions or scales. (page 537)
goodness of fit test for multinomial probabilities: A test to determine whether multinomial probabilities are equal to a specific set of values. (page 527)

goodness of fit test for normality: A test to determine if a sample has been randomly selected from a normally distributed population. (page 531)
homogeneity (test for): A test of the null hypothesis that all multinomial probabilities are equal. (page 530)
multinomial experiment: An experiment that concerns count data that are classified into more than two categories. (page 527)

IMPORTANT FORMULAS AND TESTS

A goodness of fit test for multinomial probabilities: pages 529–530
A goodness of fit test for a normal distribution: pages 533–534

A test for homogeneity: page 530
A chi-square test for independence: pages 540–541

SUPPLEMENTARY EXERCISES

14.21 Leonard has just handed in his statistics midterm exam. It was a multiple choice exam with 50 questions. He is curious, and a little worried, about the distribution of his responses. On a scrap piece of paper, he recorded the number of As, Bs, Cs, and Ds he selected. The results are as follows:
● Exam

A	B	C	D
10	14	17	9

a. At $\alpha = 0.05$, carry out a test of homogeneity for this data.
b. Leonard believes that the answers to any multiple choice test should be distributed evenly. Is this true in his case?

14.22 An occupant traffic study was carried out to aid in the remodelling of a large building on a university campus. The building has five entrances, and the choice of entrance was recorded for a random sample of 300 people entering the building. The results obtained are given in the following table: ● EntrPref

Entrance				
I	II	III	IV	V
30	91	97	40	42

Test the null hypothesis that the five entrances are equally used by setting α equal to 0.05. Find a 95 percent confidence interval for the proportion of all people who use Entrance III.

14.23 In a 1993 article in *Accounting and Business Research*, Meier, Alam, and Pearson studied auditor lobbying on several proposed U.S. accounting standards that affect banks and savings and loan associations. As part of this study, the authors investigated auditors' positions regarding proposed changes in accounting standards that would increase client firms' reported earnings. It was hypothesized that auditors would favour such proposed changes

TABLE 14.13 Auditor and Client Positions Regarding Earnings-Increasing Changes in Accounting Standards ● AuditPos

(a) Auditor Positions

	Large Firms	Small Firms	Total
In Favour	13	130	143
Opposed	10	24	34
Total	23	154	177

(b) Client Positions

	Large Firms	Small Firms	Total
In Favour	12	120	132
Opposed	11	34	45
Total	23	154	177

Source: "Auditor lobbying for accounting standards: The case of banks and savings and loan associations," by Heidi Hylton Meier, Pervaiz Alam, and Michael A. Pearson, *Accounting and Business Research*, 23, no. 92 (1993), pp. 477–487.

because their clients' managers would receive higher compensation (salary, bonuses, and so on) when client earnings were reported to be higher. Table 14.13 summarizes auditor and client positions (in favour or opposed) regarding proposed changes in accounting standards that would increase client firms' reported earnings. Here the auditor and client positions are cross-classified versus the size of the client firm.

● AuditPos

a. Test to determine whether auditor positions regarding earnings-increasing changes in accounting standards depend on the size of the client firm. Use $\alpha = 0.05$.

b. Test to determine whether client positions regarding earnings-increasing changes in accounting standards depend on the size of the client firm. Use $\alpha = 0.05$.

c. Carry out a graphical analysis to investigate a possible relationship between (1) auditor positions and the size of the client firm and (2) client positions and the size of the client firm.

d. Does the relationship between position and the size of the client firm seem to be similar for both auditors and clients? Explain.

14.24 In the book *Business Research Methods* (5th ed.), Cooper and Emory discuss a market researcher for an automaker who is studying consumer preferences for styling features of larger sedans. Buyers, who were classified as first-time buyers or repeat buyers, were asked to express their preference for one of two types of styling—European styling or Japanese styling. Of 40 first-time buyers, 8 preferred European styling and 32 preferred Japanese styling. Of 60 repeat buyers, 40 preferred European styling and 20 preferred Japanese styling.

a. Set up a contingency table for these data.

b. Test the hypothesis that buyer status (repeat versus first-time) and styling preference are independent at the 0.05 level of significance. What do you conclude?

c. Carry out a graphical analysis to investigate the nature of any relationship between buyer status and styling preference. Describe the relationship.

14.25 Again consider the situation of Exercise 14.23. Table 14.14 summarizes auditor positions regarding proposed changes in accounting standards that would decrease client firms' reported earnings. Determine whether the relationship between auditor position and the size of the client firm is the same for earnings-decreasing changes in accounting standards as it is for earnings-increasing changes in accounting standards. Justify your answer using both a statistical test and a graphical analysis. ● AuditPos2

14.26 The manager of a chain of three discount drug stores wishes to investigate the level of discount coupon redemption at its stores. All three stores have the same sales volume. Therefore, the manager will randomly sample 200 customers at each store with regard to coupon usage. The survey results are given in Table 14.15. Test the hypothesis that redemption level and location are independent with $\alpha = 0.01$. Use the MINITAB output in Figure 14.6. ● Coupon

TABLE 14.14 Auditor Positions Regarding Earnings-Decreasing Changes in Accounting Standards ● AuditPos2

	Large Firms	Small Firms	Total
In Favour	27	152	179
Opposed	29	154	183
Total	56	306	362

Source: "Auditor lobbying for accounting standards: The case of banks and savings and loan associations," by Heidi Hylton Meier, Pervaiz Alam, and Michael A. Pearson, *Accounting and Business Research*, 23, no. 92 (1993), pp. 477–487.

TABLE 14.15 Results of the Coupon Redemption Study ● Coupon

Coupon Redemption Level	Store Location Midtown	North Side	South Side	Total
High	69	97	52	218
Medium	101	93	76	270
Low	30	10	72	112
Total	200	200	200	600

FIGURE **14.6**   **MINITAB Output of a Chi-Square Test for Independence in the Coupon Redemption Study**

```
Expected counts are below observed counts

         Midtown   North   South   Total
High        69       97      52     218
          72.67    72.67   72.67

Medium     101       93      76     270
          90.00    90.00   90.00

Low         30       10      72     112
          37.33    37.33   37.33

Total      200      200     200     600

Chi-Sq = 71.476, DF = 4, P-Value = 0.000
```

14.27   THE VIDEO GAME SATISFACTION RATING CASE

Consider the sample of 65 customer satisfaction ratings given in Table 14.16. Carry out a chi-square goodness of fit test of normality for the population of all customer satisfaction ratings. Recall that we previously calculated $\bar{x} = 42.95$ and $s = 2.6424$ for the 65 ratings.
● VideoGame

TABLE **14.16**   **A Sample of 65 Customer Satisfaction Ratings**   ● VideoGame

39	46	42	40	45	44	44	44	45
45	44	46	46	46	41	46	46	
38	40	40	41	43	38	48	39	
42	39	47	43	47	43	44	41	
42	40	44	39	43	36	41	44	
41	42	43	43	41	44	45	42	
38	45	45	46	40	44	44	47	
42	44	45	45	43	45	44	43	

14.28   In Major League Baseball, the World Series is held every year (barring any strikes) to determine a World champion. Here is a summary of the results of the World Series played from the years 1903 to 2005:
● WorldSeries

Result (Best of 7)	4-0	4-1	4-2	4-3
Frequency	19	21	22	35

Test at $\alpha = 0.05$ whether or not these data are compatible with the model that each World Series game is an independent trial with $p = P(\text{American League wins})$ $= P(\text{National League wins}) = 0.5$. This is a tricky question. You need to consider two scenarios. That is, the National League or the American League could win the World Series in each case (in four games, five games, six games, or seven games). In order to determine the probability that a series will be won in n games, remember that a team will have to win three games in $n - 1$ games and then win its fourth game in the nth game.

14.29   At a local casino, a dice game is played such that the shooter bets on the number of sixes they will roll with three dice. The payout is proportional to the number of sixes actually rolled. A player has been rolling the dice for a few hours. The observed frequencies for the number of sixes rolled are as follows: ● Dice

Number of Sixes Rolled	0	1	2	3
Frequency	45	40	14	1

The casino has become quite suspicious of this person, and they have hired you to analyze the data. Conduct the appropriate chi-square goodness of fit test to see whether or not something out of the ordinary is occurring with this player. That is, check to see whether or not this player is using fair dice. Run the test using $\alpha = 0.05$. What do you conclude?

14.30   A random sample of police records was obtained and the following table shows the number of crimes committed in a midsized Canadian city for each day of the week: ● Crimes

Day	Number of Crimes
Sunday	79
Monday	68
Tuesday	54
Wednesday	69
Thursday	81
Friday	97
Saturday	118

Use a chi-square goodness of fit test to determine whether or not the number of crimes committed in this city is uniformly distributed over a seven-day week. Test this hypothesis at $\alpha = 0.05$.

14.31   The leading or first digit of legitimate records, such as invoices or expense claims, tends to follow a distribution that is referred to as Benford's law. The distribution is given as follows: ● Benfords

Leading Digit	Probability
1	0.301
2	0.176
3	0.125
4	0.097
5	0.079
6	0.067
7	0.058
8	0.051
9	0.046

Suppose that you suspect that your purchasing manager, who does not know about this law, is faking invoices and redirecting money to their own account. You investigate by taking a random sample of 81 invoices to an auditor. Here are the observed counts for the leading digits on these invoices:

Leading Digit	1	2	3	4	5	6	7	8	9
Observed Frequency	11	11	6	9	7	11	11	4	11

Is there evidence to suggest that these invoices have been faked? Conduct a chi-square goodness of fit test at $\alpha = 0.05$ to test whether or not these invoices follow Benford's law.

14.32 INTERNET EXERCISE

There are many different types of lotteries in Canada, but a popular one is Lotto 6/49. The player chooses six numbers from a list of numbers ranging from 1 to 49. In order to win the jackpot, players must match all six of their selected numbers with the six numbers drawn. A player may also win a prize for as few as two matched numbers (plus the bonus number).

Go to the Web site http://www.lottolore.com/l649stat.html to obtain draw statistics for all Lotto 6/49 draws from June 12, 1982, to the most recent draw. Perform a chi-square goodness of fit test to determine whether or not the numbers forming the winning combination come up with equal probability, that is, with probability 6/49 in this case. Use a p value to run this test and test at the 0.05 level of significance. You will have to use linear interpolation here as the chi-square table does not have a row for $df = 48$. Ignore the statistics involving the bonus numbers for this exercise, and just use the data in the regular column.

Hint: It would be best to use a spreadsheet to conduct this test. Cut and paste the data from the Web site into Excel or some other spreadsheet program and modify them so that you only have the numbers you need (just the regularly drawn numbers), and then set up the chi-square test statistic calculation and run the test.

Note: We have simplified this example. In order to calculate a more accurate p value, you would have to run computer simulations. The real model is more complex than the one described above. The above chi-square test does not account for the fact that the balls are drawn without replacement.

www.mcgrawhill.ca/olc/bowerman

CHAPTER **15**

Decision Theory

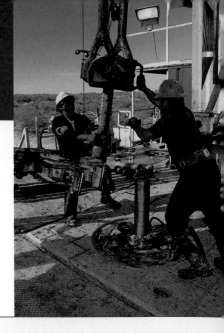

LEARNING OBJECTIVES

After reading this chapter, you should be able to

- understand the various states of nature when making a decision
- identify alternatives
- calculate the payoffs for each alternative
- understand the differences in making decisions in the three degrees of uncertainty—certainty, uncertainty, and risk
- know when to use the maximin criterion and the maximax criterion
- use the expected monetary value criterion
- construct a decision tree
- use posterior analysis to determine the best alternative for each of several sampling results
- carry out preposterior analysis to assess the value of sample information and calculate the expected value of this information
- identify a risk seeker, a risk averter, and a risk neutral based on the shape of the utility curve
- understand the meaning of utility and when and how it is used to make decisions

CHAPTER OUTLINE

15.1 Introduction to Decision Theory

15.2 Decision Making Using Posterior Probabilities

15.3 Introduction to Utility Theory

15.4 Decision Making Using Utility Theory

Every day, businesses and the people who run them face a myriad of decisions. For instance, a manufacturer might need to decide where to locate a new factory and might also need to decide how large the new facility should be. Or an investor might decide where to invest money from among several possible investment choices. In this chapter, we study some probabilistic methods that can help a decision maker to make intelligent decisions. In Section 15.1, we formally introduce **decision theory**. We discuss the elements of a decision problem, and we present strategies for making decisions when we face various levels of uncertainty. We also show how to construct a **decision tree**, which is a diagram that can help us analyze a decision problem, and we show how the concept of **expected value** can help us make decisions. In Section 15.2, we show how to use **sample information** to help us make decisions, and we demonstrate how to assess the worth of sample information in order to decide whether the sample information should be obtained. In Section 15.3, we introduce **utility theory**, and in Section 15.4, we explain how utility theory can be used to help make decisions.

Many of this chapter's concepts are presented in the context of the following case:

The Oil-Drilling Case. An oil company uses decision theory to help it decide whether to drill for oil on a particular site. The company can perform a seismic experiment at the site to obtain information about the site's potential, and the company uses decision theory to decide whether to drill based on the various possible survey results. In addition, decision theory is employed to determine whether the seismic experiment should be carried out.

15.1 Introduction to Decision Theory

Suppose that a real estate developer is proposing to develop a condominium complex on an exclusive parcel of lakefront property. The developer wishes to choose between three possible options: building a large complex, building a medium-sized complex, and building a small complex. The profitability of each option depends on the level of demand for condominium units after the complex has been built. For simplicity, the developer considers only two possible levels of demand: high and low; the developer must choose whether to build a large, medium, or small complex based on their beliefs about whether demand for condominium units will be high or low.

The real estate developer's situation requires a decision. **Decision theory** is a general approach that helps decision makers make intelligent choices. A decision theory problem typically involves the following elements:

1   **States of nature:** A set of potential future conditions that affect the results of the decision. For instance, the level of demand (high or low) for condominium units will affect profits after the developer chooses to build a large, medium, or small complex. Thus, we have two states of nature: high demand and low demand.

2   **Alternatives:** Several alternative actions for the decision maker to choose from. For example, the real estate developer can choose between building a large, a medium, and a small condominium complex. Therefore, the developer has three alternatives: large, medium, and small.

3   **Payoffs:** A payoff for each alternative under each potential state of nature. The payoffs are often summarized in a **payoff table**. For instance, Table 15.1 gives a payoff table for the condominium complex situation. This table gives the profit[1] for each alternative under the different states of nature. For example, the payoff table tells us that, if the developer builds a large complex and demand for units turns out to be high, a profit of $22 million will be realized. However, if the developer builds a large complex and demand for units turns out to be low, a loss of $11 million will be suffered.

Once the states of nature have been identified, the alternatives have been listed, and the payoffs have been determined, we evaluate the alternatives by using a **decision criterion**. How this is done depends on the **degree of uncertainty** associated with the states of nature. Here there are three possibilities:

1   **Certainty:** We know for certain which state of nature will actually occur.

2   **Uncertainty:** We have no information about the likelihoods of the various states of nature.

3   **Risk:** The likelihood (probability) of each state of nature can be estimated.

Decision making under certainty   In the unlikely event that we know for certain which state of nature will actually occur, we simply choose the alternative that gives the best payoff for

---

[1]Here profits are really present values representing current dollar values of expected future income minus costs.

TABLE **15.1**   A Payoff Table for the Condominium Complex Situation

	States of Nature	
Alternatives	Low Demand	High Demand
Small Complex	$8 million	$8 million
Medium Complex	$5 million	$15 million
Large Complex	−$11 million	$22 million

that state of nature. For instance, in the condominium complex situation, if we know that demand for units will be high, then the payoff table (see Table 15.1) tells us that the best alternative is to build a large complex and that this choice will yield a profit of $22 million. On the other hand, if we know that demand for units will be low, then the payoff table tells us that the best alternative is to build a small complex and that this choice will yield a profit of $8 million.

Of course, we rarely (if ever) know for certain which state of nature will actually occur. However, analyzing the payoff table in this way often provides insight into the nature of the problem. For instance, examining the payoff table tells us that, if we know that demand for units will be low, building either a small complex or a medium complex will be far superior to building a large complex (which would yield an $11 million loss).

Decision making under uncertainty   This is the exact opposite of certainty. Here we have no information about how likely the different states of nature are. That is, we have no idea how to assign probabilities to the different states of nature.

In such a case, several approaches are possible; we will discuss two commonly used methods. The first is called the **maximin criterion**.

Maximin: Find the worst possible payoff for each alternative, and then choose the alternative that yields the maximum worst possible payoff (or the best worst-case scenario).

For instance, to apply the maximin criterion to the condominium complex situation, we proceed as follows (see Table 15.1):

1   If a small complex is built, the worst possible payoff is $8 million.

2   If a medium complex is built, the worst possible payoff is $5 million.

3   If a large complex is built, the worst possible payoff is −$11 million.

Because the maximum of these worst possible payoffs is $8 million, the developer should choose to build a small complex.

The maximin criterion is a **pessimistic approach** because it considers the worst possible payoff for each alternative. When an alternative is chosen using the maximin criterion, the actual payoff obtained may be higher than the maximum worst possible payoff. However, using the maximin criterion assures a **guaranteed minimum** payoff.

A second approach is called the **maximax criterion**.

Maximax: Find the best possible payoff for each alternative, and then choose the alternative that yields the maximum best possible payoff.

To apply the maximax criterion to the condominium complex situation, we proceed as follows (see Table 15.1):

1   If a small complex is built, the best possible payoff is $8 million.

2   If a medium complex is built, the best possible payoff is $15 million.

3   If a large complex is built, the best possible payoff is $22 million.

Because the maximum of these best possible payoffs is $22 million, the developer should choose to build a large complex.

The maximax criterion is an **optimistic approach** because we always choose the alternative that yields the highest possible payoff. This is a "go for broke" strategy, and the actual payoff obtained may be far less than the highest possible payoff. For example, in the condominium complex situation, if a large complex is built and demand for units turns out to be low, an $11 million loss will be suffered (instead of a $22 million profit).

Decision making under risk   In this case, we can estimate the probability of occurrence for each state of nature. Thus, we have a situation in which we have more information about the states of nature than in the case of uncertainty and less information than in the case of certainty. Here a commonly used approach is to use the **expected monetary value criterion**. This involves computing the expected monetary payoff for each alternative and choosing the alternative with the largest expected payoff.

The expected value criterion can be employed by using **prior probabilities**. As an example, suppose that in the condominium complex situation the developer assigns prior probabilities of 0.7 and 0.3 to high and low demands, respectively. We find the expected monetary value for each alternative by multiplying the probability of occurrence for each state of nature by the payoff associated with the state of nature and by summing these products. Referring to the payoff table in Table 15.1, the expected monetary values are as follows:

Small complex: Expected value = 0.3($8 million) + 0.7($8 million) = $8 million.

Medium complex: Expected value = 0.3($5 million) + 0.7($15 million) = $12 million.

Large complex: Expected value = 0.3(−$11 million) + 0.7($22 million) = $12.1 million.

Choosing the alternative with the highest expected monetary value, the developer would choose to build a large complex.

Remember that the expected payoff is not necessarily equal to the actual payoff that will be realized. Rather, the expected payoff is the long-run average payoff that would be realized if many identical decisions were made. For instance, the expected monetary payoff of $12.1 million for a large complex is the average payoff that would be obtained if many large condominium complexes were built. Thus, the expected monetary value criterion is best used when many similar decisions will be made.

Using a decision tree   It is often convenient to depict the alternatives, states of nature, payoffs, and probabilities (in the case of risk) in the form of a **decision tree** or **tree diagram**. The diagram is made up of **nodes** and **branches**. We use square nodes to denote decision points and circular nodes to denote chance events. The branches emanating from a decision point represent alternatives, and the branches emanating from a circular node represent the possible states of nature. Figure 15.1 presents a decision tree for the condominium complex situation (in the case of risk as described previously). Notice that the payoffs are shown at the rightmost end of each branch and that the probabilities associated with the various states of nature are given in parentheses corresponding to each branch emanating from a chance node. The expected monetary values for the alternatives are shown below the chance nodes. The double slashes placed through the small complex and medium complex branches indicate that these alternatives would not be chosen (because of their lower expected payoffs) and that the large complex alternative would be selected.

A decision tree is particularly useful when a problem involves a sequence of decisions. For instance, in the condominium complex situation, if demand turns out to be small, it might be possible to improve payoffs by selling the condominiums at lower prices. Figure 15.2 shows a decision tree in which, after a decision to build a small, medium, or large condominium complex is made, the developer can choose to either keep the same prices or charge lower prices for condominium units. In order to analyze the decision tree, we start with the last (rightmost) decision to be made. For each decision, we choose the alternative that gives the highest payoff. For instance, if the developer builds a large complex and demand turns out to be low, the developer should lower prices (as indicated by the double slash through the alternative of same prices). If decisions are followed by chance events, we choose the alternative that gives the highest expected monetary value. For example, again looking at Figure 15.2, we see that a medium complex should now be built because of its highest expected monetary value (0.3($12 million) + 0.7($15 million) = $14.1 million). This is indicated by the double slashes drawn through the small and large complex alternatives. Looking at the entire decision tree in Figure 15.2, we see that the developer should build a medium complex and should sell condominium units at lower prices if demand turns out to be low.

FIGURE **15.1**   A Decision Tree for the Condominium Complex Situation

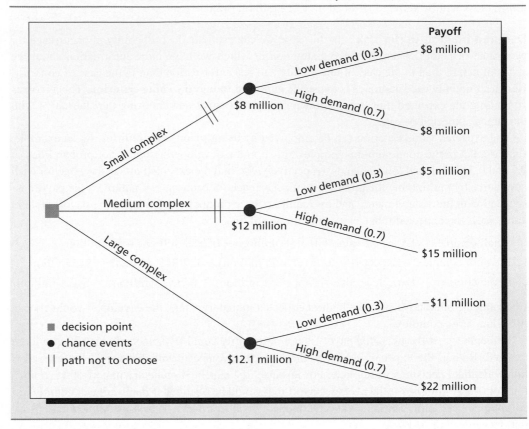

Payoff

Small complex — $8 million
Low demand (0.3) — $8 million
High demand (0.7) — $8 million

Medium complex — $12 million
Low demand (0.3) — $5 million
High demand (0.7) — $15 million

Large complex — $12.1 million
Low demand (0.3) — −$11 million
High demand (0.7) — $22 million

■ decision point
● chance events
|| path not to choose

FIGURE **15.2**   A Decision Tree with Sequential Decisions

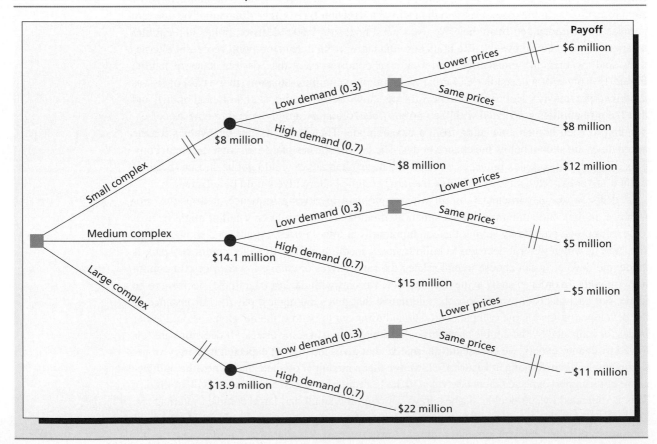

Payoff

Small complex
$8 million
Low demand (0.3)
Lower prices — $6 million
Same prices — $8 million
High demand (0.7) — $8 million

Medium complex
$14.1 million
Low demand (0.3)
Lower prices — $12 million
Same prices — $5 million
High demand (0.7) — $15 million

Large complex
$13.9 million
Low demand (0.3)
Lower prices — −$5 million
Same prices — −$11 million
High demand (0.7) — $22 million

Sometimes it is possible to determine exactly which state of nature will occur in the future. For example, in the condominium complex situation, the level of demand for units might depend on whether a new resort casino is built in the area. While the developer may have prior probabilities concerning whether the casino will be built, it might be feasible to postpone a decision about the size of the condominium complex until a final decision about the resort casino has been made.

If we can find out exactly which state of nature will occur, we say we have obtained **perfect information**. There is usually a cost involved in obtaining this information (if it can be obtained at all). For instance, we might have to acquire an option on the lakefront property on which the condominium complex is to be built in order to postpone a decision about the size of the complex. Or perfect information might be acquired by conducting some sort of research that must be paid for. A question that arises here is whether it is worth the cost to obtain perfect information. We can answer this question by computing the **expected value of perfect information**, which we denote as the **EVPI**. The EVPI is defined as follows:

EVPI = Expected payoff under certainty − Expected payoff under risk.

For instance, in the condominium complex situation depicted in the decision tree of Figure 15.1, we found that the expected payoff under risk is $12.1 million (which is the expected payoff associated with building a large complex). To find the expected payoff under certainty, we find the highest payoff under each state of nature. Referring to Table 15.1, we see that if demand is low, the highest payoff is $8 million (when we build a small complex), and if demand is high, the highest payoff is $22 million (when we build a large complex). Because the prior probabilities of high and low demand are, respectively, 0.7 and 0.3, the expected payoff under certainty is 0.7($22 million) + 0.3($8 million) = $17.8 million. Therefore, the expected value of perfect information is $17.8 million − $12.1 million = $5.7 million. This is the maximum amount of money that the developer should be willing to pay to obtain perfect information. That is, the land option should be purchased if it costs $5.7 million or less. Then, if the casino is not built (and demand is low), a small condominium complex should be built; if the casino is built (and demand is high), a large condominium complex should be built. On the other hand, if the land option costs more than $5.7 million, the developer should choose the alternative with the highest expected payoff (which would mean building a large complex—see Figure 15.1).

Finally, another approach to dealing with risk involves assigning what we call **utilities** to monetary values. These utilities reflect the decision maker's attitude toward risk: that is, does the decision maker avoid risk or are they a risk taker? Here the decision maker chooses the alternative that **maximizes expected utility**. The reader interested in this approach is referred to Section 15.3.

Exercises for Section 15.1

CONCEPTS

15.1 Explain the differences between decision making under certainty, decision making under uncertainty, and decision making under risk.

15.2 Explain how to use the
a. Maximin criterion.
b. Maximax criterion.
c. Expected monetary value criterion.

15.3 Explain how to find the expected value of perfect information.

METHODS AND APPLICATIONS

Exercises 15.4 through 15.9 refer to an example in the book *Production/Operations Management* by Stevenson. The example involves a capacity-planning problem in which a company must choose to build a small, medium, or large production facility. The payoff obtained will depend on whether future demand is low, moderate, or high, and the payoffs are as given in the following table: ● CapPlan

Alternatives	Possible Future Demand		
	Low	Moderate	High
Small Facility	$10[a]	$10	$10
Medium Facility	7	12	12
Large Facility	−4	2	16

[a]Present value in $ millions.

Source: *Production/Operations Management*, 5th ed., by W. J. Stevenson (Burr Ridge, IL: Richard D. Irwin, 1996), p. 73.

15.4 Find the best alternative (and the resulting payoff) in the given payoff table if it is known with certainty that demand will be
a. Low. **b.** Medium. **c.** High.

15.5 Given the payoff table, find the alternative that would be chosen using the maximin criterion.

15.6 Given the payoff table, find the alternative that would be chosen using the maximax criterion.

15.7 Suppose that the company assigns prior probabilities of 0.3, 0.5, and 0.2 to low, moderate, and high demands, respectively.

    a. Find the expected monetary value for each alternative (small, medium, and large).

    b. What is the best alternative if we use the expected monetary value criterion?

15.8 Construct a decision tree for the information in the payoff table assuming that the prior probabilities of low, moderate, and high demands are, respectively, 0.3, 0.5, and 0.2.

15.9 For the information in the payoff table, find

    a. The expected payoff under certainty.

    b. The expected value of perfect information, EVPI.

15.10 Figure 15.3 gives a decision tree presented in the book *Production/Operations Management* by Stevenson. Use this tree diagram to do the following:

    a. Find the expected monetary value for each of the alternatives (subcontract, expand, and build).

    b. Determine the alternative that should be selected in order to maximize the expected monetary value.

15.11 A firm wishes to choose the location for a new factory. Profits obtained will depend on whether a new railroad spur is constructed to serve the town in which the new factory will be located. The payoff table on the next page summarizes the relevant information. ● FactLoc

FIGURE 15.3   Decision Tree for Exercise 15.13

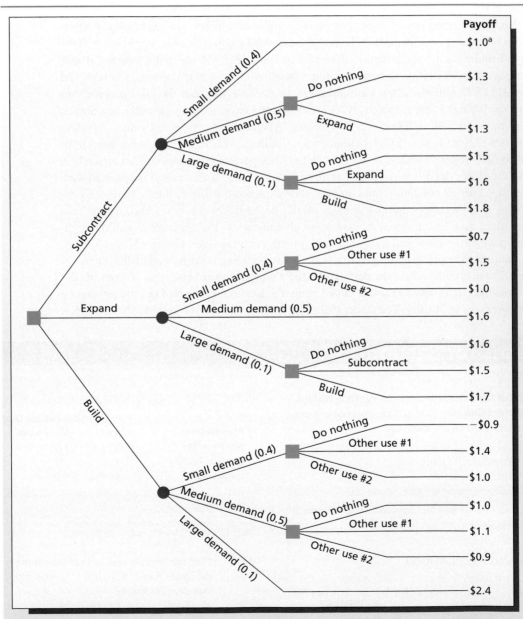

ªNet present value in millions.

Source: Reprinted with permission from *Production/Operations Management*, 6th ed., by W. J. Stevenson, p. 228. Copyright © 1999 by The McGraw-Hill Companies, Inc.

Alternatives	New Railroad Spur Built	No New Railroad Spur
Location A	$1[a]	$14
Location B	2	10
Location C	4	6

[a]Profits in $ millions.

Determine the location that should be chosen if the firm uses

a. The maximin criterion.

b. The maximax criterion.

15.12 Refer to the information given in Exercise 15.11. Use the probabilities of 0.60 for a new railroad spur and 0.40 for no new railroad spur. FactLoc

a. Compute the expected monetary value for each location.

b. Find the location that should be selected using the expected monetary value criterion.

c. Compute the EVPI, expected value of perfect information.

15.13 Construct a decision tree for the information given in Exercises 15.11 and 15.12. FactLoc

15.2 Decision Making Using Posterior Probabilities

We have seen that the expected monetary value criterion tells us to choose the alternative with the highest expected payoff. In Section 15.1, we computed expected payoffs by using prior probabilities. When we use the expected monetary value criterion to choose the best alternative based on expected values computed using prior probabilities, we call this **prior decision analysis**. Often, however, sample information can be obtained to help us make decisions. In such a case, we compute expected values by using **posterior probabilities**, and we call the analysis **posterior decision analysis**. In the following example, we demonstrate how to carry out posterior analysis.

Example 15.1 The Oil-Drilling Case

An oil company needs to decide whether to drill for oil on a particular site, and the company has assigned prior probabilities to the states of nature $S_1 \equiv$ no oil, $S_2 \equiv$ some oil, and $S_3 \equiv$ much oil of 0.7, 0.2, and 0.1, respectively. Figure 15.4 gives a decision tree and payoff table for a **prior analysis** of the oil-drilling situation. Here, using the prior probabilities, the expected monetary value associated with drilling is

$$0.7(-\$700,000) + 0.2(\$500,000) + 0.1(\$2,000,000) = -\$190,000,$$

while the expected monetary value associated with not drilling is

$$0.7(0) + 0.2(0) + 0.1(0) = 0.$$

Therefore, prior analysis tells us that the oil company should not drill.

FIGURE **15.4**   A Decision Tree and Payoff Table for a Prior Analysis of the Oil-Drilling Case

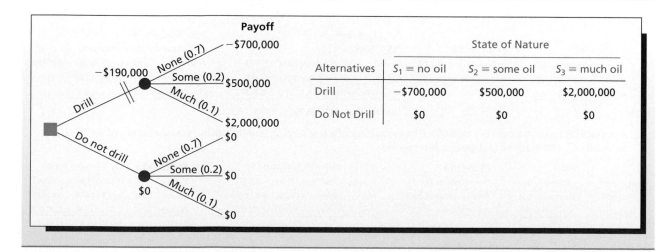

The oil company can obtain more information about the drilling site by performing a seismic experiment with three possible readings: low, medium, and high. The accuracy of the seismic experiment is expressed by the conditional probabilities in Figure 15.5(a), and we have used these conditional probabilities to update the prior probabilities of no oil, some oil, and much oil to posterior probabilities in the probability revision tables in Figure 15.5(b), (c), and (d). For instance, in Figure 15.5(b), we found that

$$P(\text{none}\,|\,\text{high}) = 0.21875, \qquad P(\text{some}\,|\,\text{high}) = 0.03125, \quad \text{and} \qquad P(\text{much}\,|\,\text{high}) = 0.75.$$

FIGURE **15.5**   A Tree Diagram and Probability Revision Tables in the Oil-Drilling Example

(a) A tree diagram illustrating the prior and conditional probabilities

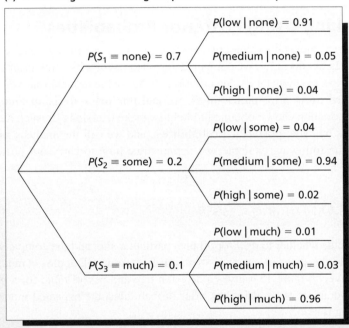

(b) A probability revision table for calculating the probability of a high reading and the posterior probabilities of no oil (S_1), some oil (S_2), and much oil (S_3) given a high reading

S_j	$P(S_j)$	$P(\text{high}\,|\,S_j)$	$P(S_j \cap \text{high}) = P(S_j)P(\text{high}\,|\,S_j)$	$P(S_j\,|\,\text{high}) = P(S_j \cap \text{high})/P(\text{high})$
$S_1 \equiv$ none	$P(\text{none}) = 0.7$	$P(\text{high}\,|\,\text{none}) = 0.04$	$P(\text{none} \cap \text{high}) = 0.7(0.04) = 0.028$	$P(\text{none}\,|\,\text{high}) = 0.028/0.128 = 0.21875$
$S_2 \equiv$ some	$P(\text{some}) = 0.2$	$P(\text{high}\,|\,\text{some}) = 0.02$	$P(\text{some} \cap \text{high}) = 0.2(0.02) = 0.004$	$P(\text{some}\,|\,\text{high}) = 0.004/0.128 = 0.03125$
$S_3 \equiv$ much	$P(\text{much}) = 0.1$	$P(\text{high}\,|\,\text{much}) = 0.96$	$P(\text{much} \cap \text{high}) = 0.1(0.96) = 0.096$	$P(\text{much}\,|\,\text{high}) = 0.096/0.128 = 0.75$
Total	1		$P(\text{high}) = 0.028 + 0.004 + 0.096 = 0.128$	1

(c) A probability revision table for calculating the probability of a medium reading and the posterior probabilities of no oil (S_1), some oil (S_2), and much oil (S_3) given a medium reading

S_j	$P(S_j)$	$P(\text{medium}\,|\,S_j)$	$P(S_j \cap \text{medium}) =$ $P(S_j)P(\text{medium}\,|\,S_j)$	$P(S_j\,|\,\text{medium}) =$ $P(S_j \cap \text{medium})/P(\text{medium})$
$S_1 \equiv$ none	$P(\text{none}) = 0.7$	$P(\text{medium}\,|\,\text{none}) = 0.05$	$P(\text{none} \cap \text{medium}) = 0.7(0.05) = 0.035$	$P(\text{none}\,|\,\text{medium}) = 0.035/0.226 = 0.15487$
$S_2 \equiv$ some	$P(\text{some}) = 0.2$	$P(\text{medium}\,|\,\text{some}) = 0.94$	$P(\text{some} \cap \text{medium}) = 0.2(0.94) = 0.188$	$P(\text{some}\,|\,\text{medium}) = 0.188/0.226 = 0.83186$
$S_3 \equiv$ much	$P(\text{much}) = 0.1$	$P(\text{medium}\,|\,\text{much}) = 0.03$	$P(\text{much} \cap \text{medium}) = 0.1(0.03) = 0.003$	$P(\text{much}\,|\,\text{medium}) = 0.003/0.226 = 0.01327$
Total	1		$P(\text{medium}) = 0.035 + 0.188 + 0.003 = 0.226$	1

(d) A probability revision table for calculating the probability of a low reading and the posterior probabilities of no oil (S_1), some oil (S_2), and much oil (S_3) given a low reading

S_j	$P(S_j)$	$P(\text{low}\,|\,S_j)$	$P(S_j \cap \text{low}) = P(S_j)P(\text{low}\,|\,S_j)$	$P(S_j\,|\,\text{low}) = P(S_j \cap \text{low})/P(\text{low})$
$S_1 \equiv$ none	$P(\text{none}) = 0.7$	$P(\text{low}\,|\,\text{none}) = 0.91$	$P(\text{none} \cap \text{low}) = 0.7(0.91) = 0.637$	$P(\text{none}\,|\,\text{low}) = 0.637/0.646 = 0.98607$
$S_2 \equiv$ some	$P(\text{some}) = 0.2$	$P(\text{low}\,|\,\text{some}) = 0.04$	$P(\text{some} \cap \text{low}) = 0.2(0.04) = 0.008$	$P(\text{some}\,|\,\text{low}) = 0.008/0.646 = 0.01238$
$S_3 \equiv$ much	$P(\text{much}) = 0.1$	$P(\text{low}\,|\,\text{much}) = 0.01$	$P(\text{much} \cap \text{low}) = 0.1(0.01) = 0.001$	$P(\text{much}\,|\,\text{low}) = 0.001/0.646 = 0.00155$
Total	1		$P(\text{low}) = 0.637 + 0.008 + 0.001 = 0.646$	1

The tree diagram in (a) shows:

$P(S_1 \equiv \text{none}) = 0.7$
 - $P(\text{low}\,|\,\text{none}) = 0.91$
 - $P(\text{medium}\,|\,\text{none}) = 0.05$
 - $P(\text{high}\,|\,\text{none}) = 0.04$

$P(S_2 \equiv \text{some}) = 0.2$
 - $P(\text{low}\,|\,\text{some}) = 0.04$
 - $P(\text{medium}\,|\,\text{some}) = 0.94$
 - $P(\text{high}\,|\,\text{some}) = 0.02$

$P(S_3 \equiv \text{much}) = 0.1$
 - $P(\text{low}\,|\,\text{much}) = 0.01$
 - $P(\text{medium}\,|\,\text{much}) = 0.03$
 - $P(\text{high}\,|\,\text{much}) = 0.96$

We also used the conditional probabilities in Figure 15.5(a) to compute $P(\text{high}) = 0.128$, $P(\text{medium}) = 0.226$, and $P(\text{low}) = 0.646$, the probabilities of a high, a medium, and a low reading, respectively.

Figure 15.6 presents a decision tree for a **posterior analysis** of the oil-drilling problem. The leftmost decision node represents the decision of whether to conduct the seismic experiment.

FIGURE 15.6   A Decision Tree for a Posterior Analysis of the Oil-Drilling Case

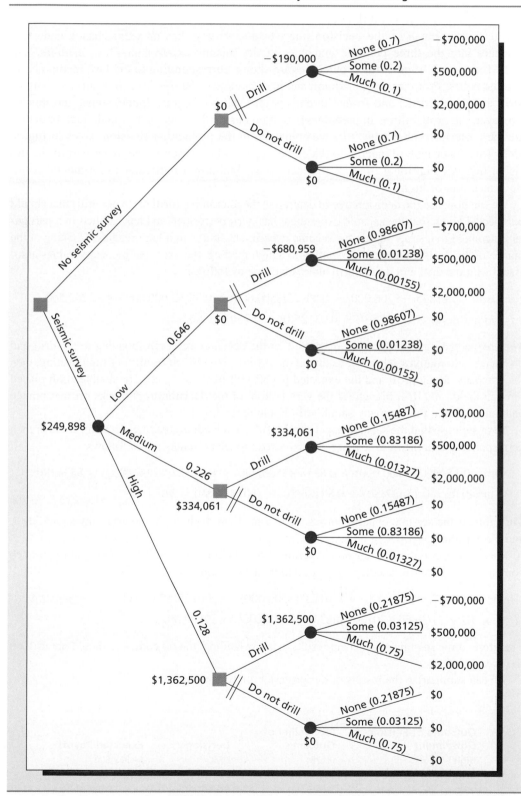

The upper branch (no seismic survey) contains a second decision node representing the alternatives in our decision problem (that is, drill or do not drill). At the ends of the drill and do not drill branches we have chance nodes that branch into the three states of nature—no oil (none), some oil (some), and much oil (much). The appropriate payoff is placed at the rightmost end of each branch, and since this uppermost branch corresponds to no seismic survey, the probabilities in parentheses for the states of nature are the prior probabilities. The expected payoff associated with drilling (which we found to be −$190,000) is shown at the chance node for the drill branch, and the expected payoff associated with not drilling (which we found to be $0) is shown at the chance node for the do not drill branch.

The lower branch of the decision tree (seismic survey) has an extra chance node that branches into the three possible outcomes of the seismic experiment—low, medium, and high. The probabilities of these outcomes are shown corresponding to the low, medium, and high branches. From the low, medium, and high branches, the tree branches into alternatives (drill and do not drill) and from alternatives into states of nature (none, some, and much). However, the probabilities in parentheses written beside the none, some, and much branches are the posterior probabilities that we computed in the probability revision tables in Figure 15.5. This is because advancing to the end of a particular branch in the lower part of the decision tree is conditional; that is, it depends on obtaining a particular experimental result (low, medium, or high).

We can now use the decision tree to determine the alternative (drill or do not drill) that should be selected given that the seismic experiment has been performed and has resulted in a particular outcome. First, suppose that the seismic experiment results in a high reading. Looking at the branch of the decision tree corresponding to a high reading, the expected monetary values associated with the drill and do not drill alternatives are as follows:

Drill: $0.21875(-\$700,000) + 0.03125(\$500,000) + 0.75(\$2,000,000) = \$1,362,500.$

Do not drill: $0.21875(0) + 0.03125(0) + 0.75(0) = \$0.$

These expected monetary values are placed on the decision tree corresponding to the drill and do not drill alternatives. They tell us that, if the seismic experiment results in a high reading, then the company should drill and the expected payoff will be $1,362,500. The double slash placed through the do not drill branch (at the very bottom of the decision tree) blocks off that branch and indicates that the company should drill if a high reading is obtained.

Next suppose that the seismic experiment results in a medium reading. Looking at the branch corresponding to a medium reading, the expected monetary values are as follows:

Drill: $0.15487(-\$700,000) + 0.83186(\$500,000) + 0.01327(\$2,000,000) = \$334,061.$

Do not drill: $0.15487(\$0) + 0.83186(\$0) + 0.01327(\$0) = \$0.$

Therefore, if the seismic experiment results in a medium reading, the oil company should drill, and the expected payoff will be $334,061.

Finally, suppose that the seismic experiment results in a low reading. Looking at the branch corresponding to a low reading, the expected monetary values are as follows:

Drill: $0.98607(-\$700,000) + 0.01238(\$500,000) + 0.00155(\$2,000,000) = -\$680,959.$

Do not drill: $0.98607(\$0) + 0.01238(\$0) + 0.00155(\$0) = \$0.$

Therefore, if the seismic experiment results in a low reading, the oil company should not drill on the site.

We can summarize the results of our posterior analysis as follows:

Outcome of Seismic Experiment	Probability of Outcome	Decision	Expected Payoff
High	0.128	Drill	$1,362,500
Medium	0.226	Drill	$334,061
Low	0.646	Do not drill	$0

If we carry out the seismic experiment, we now know what action should be taken for each possible outcome (low, medium, or high). However, there is a cost involved when we conduct the seismic experiment. If, for instance, it costs $100,000 to perform the seismic experiment, we need to investigate whether it is worth it to perform the experiment. This will depend on the expected worth of the information provided by the experiment. Naturally, we must decide whether the experiment is worth it **before** our posterior analysis is actually done. Therefore, when we assess the worth of the sample information, we say that we are performing a **preposterior analysis**.

In order to assess the worth of the sample information, we compute the **expected payoff of sampling**. To calculate this result, we find the expected payoff and the probability of each sample outcome (that is, at each possible outcome of the seismic experiment). Looking at the decision tree in Figure 15.6, we find the following:

Experimental Outcome	Expected Payoff	Probability
Low	$0	0.646
Medium	$334,061	0.226
High	$1,362,500	0.128

Therefore, the **expected payoff of sampling**, which is denoted **EPS**, is

$$EPS = 0.646(\$0) + 0.226(\$334,061) + 0.128(\$1,362,500) = \$249,898.$$

To find the worth of the sample information, we compare the expected payoff of sampling to the **expected payoff of no sampling**, which is denoted **EPNS**. The EPNS is the expected payoff of the alternative that we would choose by using the expected monetary value criterion with the prior probabilities. Recalling that we summarized our prior analysis in the tree diagram of Figure 15.4, we found that (based on the prior probabilities) we should choose not to drill and that the expected payoff of this action is $0. Therefore, EPNS = $0.

We compare the EPS and the EPNS by computing the **expected value of sample information**, which is denoted **EVSI** and is defined to be the expected payoff of sampling minus the expected payoff of no sampling. Therefore,

$$EVSI = EPS - EPNS = \$249,898 - \$0 = \$249,898.$$

The EVSI is the expected gain from conducting the seismic experiment, and the oil company should pay no more than this amount to carry out the seismic experiment. If the experiment costs $100,000, then it is worth the expense to conduct the experiment. Moreover, the difference between the EVSI and the cost of sampling is called the **expected net gain of sampling**, which is denoted **ENGS**. Here

$$ENGS = EVSI - \$100,000 = \$249,898 - \$100,000 = \$149,898.$$

As long as the ENGS is greater than $0, it is worth it to carry out the seismic experiment. That is, the oil company should carry out the seismic experiment before it chooses whether or not to drill. Then, as discussed earlier, our posterior analysis says that if the experiment gives a medium or high reading, the oil company should drill, and if the experiment gives a low reading, the oil company should not drill.

Exercises for Section 15.2

CONCEPTS

15.14 Explain what is meant by each of the following and describe the purpose of each:
  a. Prior analysis.
  b. Posterior analysis.
  c. Preposterior analysis.

15.15 Define and interpret each of the following:
  a. Expected payoff of sampling, EPS.
  b. Expected payoff of no sampling, EPNS.

  c. Expected value of sample information, EVSI.
  d. Expected net gain of sampling, ENGS.

METHODS AND APPLICATIONS

Exercises 15.16 through 15.21 refer to the following situation.

In the book *Making Hard Decisions: An Introduction to Decision Analysis* (2nd ed.), Clemen presents an example in which an investor wishes to choose between investing money in (1) a high-risk stock, (2) a low-risk stock, and (3) a savings account. The payoffs received from the two stocks will depend on the behaviour of the stock market—that is, whether the market goes up, stays the same, or goes down over the investment period. In addition, in order to obtain more information about the market behaviour that might be anticipated during the investment period, the investor can hire an economist as a consultant to predict the future market behaviour. The results of the consultation will be one of the following three possibilities: (1) economist says "up," (2) economist says "flat" (the same), and (3) economist says "down." The conditional probabilities that express the ability of the economist to accurately forecast market behaviour are given in the following table:

Economist's Prediction	True Market State		
	Up	Flat	Down
Up	0.80	0.15	0.20
Flat	0.10	0.70	0.20
Down	0.10	0.15	0.60 🌐 InvDec

For instance, using this table we see that P(economist says "up" | market up) = 0.80. Figure 15.7 gives an incomplete decision tree for the investor's situation. Notice that this decision tree gives all relevant payoffs and also gives the prior probabilities of up, flat, and down, which are, respectively, 0.5, 0.3, and 0.2. Using the information provided here, and any needed information on the decision tree of Figure 15.7, do the following:

15.16 Identify and list each of the following for the investor's decision problem:
  a. The investor's alternative actions.
  b. The states of nature.
  c. The possible results of sampling (that is, of information gathering).

15.17 Write out the payoff table for the investor's decision problem.

15.18 Carry out a prior analysis of the investor's decision problem. That is, determine the investment choice that should be made and find the expected monetary value of that choice assuming that the investor does not consult the economist about future stock market behaviour.

15.19 Set up probability revision tables to
  a. Find the probability that the economist says "up" and find the posterior probabilities of market up, market flat, and market down given that the economist says "up."
  b. Find the probability that the economist says "flat" and find the posterior probabilities of market up, market flat, and market down given that the economist says "flat."
  c. Find the probability that the economist says "down" and find the posterior probabilities of market up, market flat, and market down given that the economist says "down."
  d. Reproduce the decision tree of Figure 15.7 and insert the probabilities you found in parts a, b, and c in their appropriate locations.

15.20 Carry out a posterior analysis of the investor's decision problem. That is, determine the investment choice that should be made and find the expected monetary value of that choice assuming
  a. The economist says "up."
  b. The economist says "flat."
  c. The economist says "down."

15.21 Carry out a preposterior analysis of the investor's decision problem by finding
  a. The expected monetary value associated with consulting the economist; that is, find the EPS.
  b. The expected monetary value associated with not consulting the economist; that is, find the EPNS.
  c. The expected value of sample information, EVSI.
  d. The maximum amount the investor should be willing to pay for the economist's consulting advice.

Exercises 15.22 through 15.28 refer to the following situation.

A firm designs and manufactures automatic electronic control devices that are installed at customers' plant sites. The control devices are shipped by truck to customers' sites. While in transit, the devices sometimes get out of alignment. More specifically, a device has a prior probability of 0.10 of getting out of alignment during shipment. When a control device is delivered to the customer's plant site, the customer can install the device. If the customer installs the device, and if the device is in alignment, the manufacturer of the control device will realize a profit of $15,000. If the customer installs the device, and if the device is out of alignment, the manufacturer must dismantle, realign, and reinstall the device for the customer. This procedure costs $3,000, and therefore the manufacturer will realize a profit of $12,000. As an alternative to customer installation, the manufacturer can send two engineers to the customer's plant site to check the alignment of the control device, to realign the device if necessary before installation, and to supervise the installation. Because it is less costly to realign the device before it is installed, sending the engineers costs $500. Therefore, if the engineers are sent to assist with the installation, the manufacturer realizes a profit of $14,500 (this is true whether or not the engineers must realign the device at the site).

Before a control device is installed, a piece of test equipment can be used by the customer to check the device's alignment. The test equipment has two readings, "in" or "out" of alignment. Given that the control device is in alignment, there is a 0.8 probability that the test equipment will read "in." Given that the control device is out of alignment, there is a 0.9 probability that the test equipment will read "out."

15.22 Identify and list each of the following for the control device situation:
  a. The firm's alternative actions.
  b. The states of nature.
  c. The possible results of sampling (that is, of information gathering).

15.23 Write out the payoff table for the control device situation.

15.24 Construct a decision tree for a prior analysis of the control device situation. Then determine whether the

FIGURE **15.7**   **An Incomplete Decision Tree for the Investor's Decision Problem of Exercises 15.16 through 15.21**

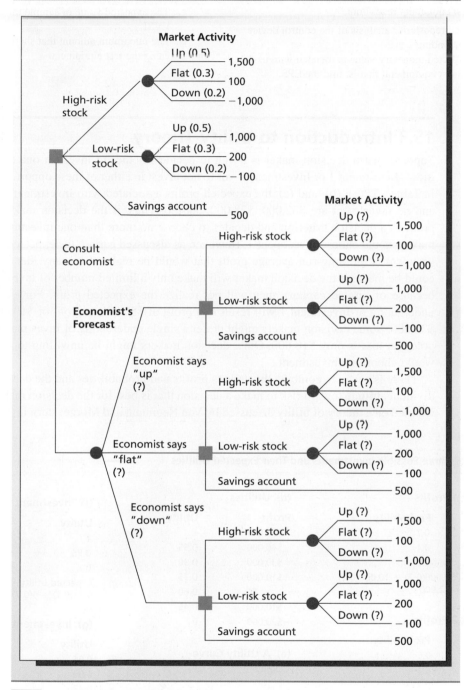

engineers should be sent, assuming that the piece of test equipment is not employed to check the device's alignment. Also find the expected monetary value associated with the best alternative action.

15.25 Set up probability revision tables to do the following:
  a. Find the probability that the test equipment reads "in" and find the posterior probabilities of in alignment and out of alignment given that the test equipment reads "in."

  b. Find the probability that the test equipment reads "out" and find the posterior probabilities of in alignment and out of alignment given that the test equipment reads "out."

15.26 Construct a decision tree for a posterior and a preposterior analysis of the control device situation.

15.27 Carry out a posterior analysis of the control device problem. That is, decide whether the engineers should be sent, and find the expected monetary value

associated with either sending or not sending (depending on which is best) the engineers assuming
   a. The test equipment reads "in."
   b. The test equipment reads "out."

15.28 Carry out a preposterior analysis of the control device problem by finding
   a. The expected monetary value associated with using the test equipment; that is, find the EPS.

   b. The expected monetary value associated with not using the test equipment; that is, find the EPNS.
   c. The expected value of sample information, EVSI.
   d. The maximum amount that should be paid for using the test equipment.

15.3 Introduction to Utility Theory

Suppose that a decision maker is trying to decide whether to invest in one of two opportunities—Investment 1 or Investment 2—or to not invest in either of these opportunities. As shown in Table 15.2(a), (b), and (c), the expected profits associated with Investment 1, Investment 2, and no investment are $32,000, $28,000, and $0. Thus, if the decision maker uses expected profit as a decision criterion and decides to choose no more than one investment, the decision maker should choose Investment 1. However, as discussed earlier, the expected profit for an investment is the long-run average profit that would be realized if many identical investments could be made. If the decision maker will make only a limited number of investments (perhaps because of limited capital), they will not realize the expected profit. For example, a single undertaking of Investment 1 will result in a profit of $50,000, a profit of $10,000, or a loss of $20,000. Some decision makers might prefer a single undertaking of Investment 2, because the potential loss is only $10,000. Other decision makers might be unwilling to risk $10,000 and would choose no investment.

There is a way to combine the various profits and probabilities and the decision maker's individual attitude toward risk to make a decision that is best for the decision maker. The method is based on a theory of utility discussed by Von Neumann and Morgenstern in *Theory of Games*

TABLE **15.2**   Three Possible Investments and Their Expected Utilities

(a) Investment 1 Profits

Profit	Probability
$50,000	0.7
$10,000	0.1
−$20,000	0.2

Expected profit = 50,000(0.7) + 10,000(0.1) + (−20,000)(0.2) = 32,000

(b) Investment 2 Profits

Profit	Probability
$40,000	0.6
$30,000	0.2
−$10,000	0.2

Expected profit = 40,000(0.6) + 30,000(0.2) + (−10,000)(0.2) = 28,000

(c) No Investment Profit

Profit	Probability
$0	1

Expected profit = 0(1) = 0

(d) Utilities

Profit	Utility
$50,000	1
$40,000	0.95
$30,000	0.90
$10,000	0.75
$0	0.60
−$10,000	0.45
−$20,000	0

(e) A Utility Curve

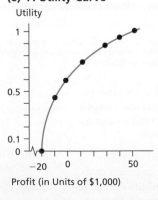

Profit (in Units of $1,000)

(f) Investment 1 Utilities

Utility	Probability
1	0.7
0.75	0.1
0	0.2

Expected utility = 1(0.7) + 0.75(0.1) + 0(0.2) = 0.775

(g) Investment 2 Utilities

Utility	Probability
0.95	0.6
0.90	0.2
0.45	0.2

Expected utility = 0.95(0.6) + 0.90(0.2) + 0.45(0.2) = 0.84

(h) No Investment Utility

Utility	Probability
0.60	1

Expected utility = 0.60(1) = 0.60

and Economic Behavior. This theory says that if a decision maker agrees with certain assumptions about rational behaviour, then the decision maker should replace the profits in the various investments by **utilities** and choose the investment that gives the **highest expected utility**. To find the utility of a particular profit, we first arrange the profits from largest to smallest. The utility of the largest profit is 1 and the utility of the smallest profit is 0. The utility of any particular intermediate profit is the probability, call it u, such that the decision maker is **indifferent** between (1) getting the particular intermediate profit with certainty and (2) playing a lottery (or game) in which the probability is u of getting the highest profit and the probability is $1 - u$ of getting the smallest profit. Table 15.2(d) arranges the profits in Table 15.2(a), (b), and (c) in increasing order and gives a specific decision maker's utility for each profit. The utility of 0.95 for $40,000 means that the decision maker is indifferent between (1) getting $40,000 with certainty and (2) playing a lottery in which the probability is 0.95 of getting $50,000 and the probability is 0.05 of losing $20,000. The utilities for the other profits are interpreted similarly. Table 15.2(f), (g), and (h) shows the investments with profits replaced by utilities. Because Investment 2 has the highest expected utility, the decision maker should choose Investment 2.

Table 15.2(e) shows a plot of the specific decision maker's utilities versus the profits. The curve connecting the plot points is the **utility curve** for the decision maker. This curve is an example of a **risk averter's curve**. In general, a risk averter's curve portrays a rapid increase in utility for initial amounts of money followed by a gradual levelling off for larger amounts of money. This curve is appropriate for many individuals or businesses because the marginal value of each additional dollar is not as great once a large amount of money has been earned. A risk averter's curve is shown in the page margin, as are a **risk seeker's curve** and a **risk neutral's curve**. The risk seeker's curve represents an individual who is willing to take large risks to have the opportunity to make large profits. The risk neutral's curve represents an individual for whom each additional dollar has the same value. It can be shown that this individual should choose the investment with the highest expected profit.

A risk averter's curve:

A risk seeker's curve:

A risk neutral's curve:

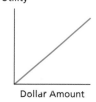

Exercises for Section 15.3

CONCEPTS

15.29 What is a utility?

15.30 What is a risk averter? a risk seeker? a risk neutral?

METHODS AND APPLICATIONS

15.31 Suppose that a decision maker has the opportunity to invest in an oil-drilling operation that has a 0.3 chance of yielding a profit of $1,000,000, a 0.4 chance of yielding a profit of $400,000, and a 0.3 chance of yielding a profit of −$100,000. Also suppose that the decision maker's utilities for $400,000 and $0 are 0.9 and 0.7. Explain the meanings of these utilities.

15.32 Judy is wondering whether or not to purchase real estate. The value of the house she buys at the end of one year will depend on the state of the market. She estimates that for each $200,000 she invests, the possible value of the real estate at year's end is as follows:

Value at Year's End	Capital Gain	Probability
$280,000	$80,000	0.30
$250,000	$50,000	0.40
$210,000	$10,000	0.10
$150,000	−$50,000	0.20

Her utility values for the above capital gains are 0.9, 0.7, 0.3, and 0, respectively. Calculate Judy's expected utility.

15.4 Decision Making Using Utility Theory

In the face of uncertainty, one should maximize one's **expected utility**, rather than money, in order to make decisions. In the last section, we learned about the utility function. This is a function that describes a person's level of satisfaction or happiness. If we convert each dollar value or payoff into utility values, we can proceed as we did in the last section and choose the option that yields the highest expected utility. Making decisions based on a person's utility function takes into account that person's risk tolerance. In the last section, we looked at three possible investments and their expected utilities. Consider another investment example.

Example 15.2 To Buy Stocks or Not To Buy Stocks?

Ken is deciding whether to invest $10,000 in the stock market or deposit the money into a GIC that will pay him 14 percent per year (we know that this rate is very high, but we will assume for the purpose of this example that it is possible). Kenny is knowledgeable when it comes to the stock market and has done some research. Based on previous market activity in the past 100 years, he estimates that there is a 60 percent chance that the market will be bullish next year, and hence give him a return of 30 percent; a 20 percent chance that the market will be steady, and offer a return of 5 percent; and a 20 percent chance that the market will be bearish, in which case he will lose 10 percent.

We will determine his best investment decision in two ways: first by maximizing expected monetary value and then by maximizing expected utility.

Here is the decision tree with monetary payoffs:

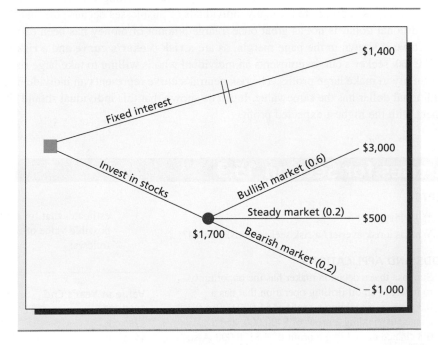

In order to make a decision based on expected utility, we need to convert the dollar values to utility values. This is somewhat arbitrary, and the numbers will vary from person to person, but here is one possibility for Ken:

	Payoff	Utility	Probability
Bullish Market	$3,000	1.00	0.6
Fixed Interest	$1,400	0.80	1.0
Steady Market	$500	0.60	0.2
Bearish Market	−$1,000	0	0.2

Remember that the best scenario is assigned a utility value of 1 and the worst scenario is assigned a value of 0. The other two options are assigned values based on personal feelings.

Here's the decision tree with the utility values in place:

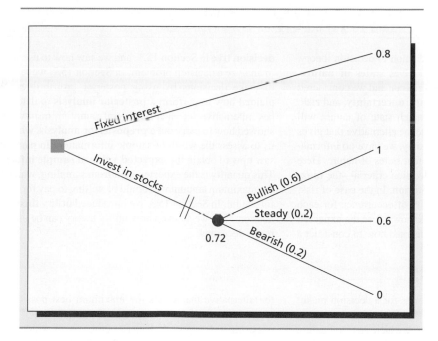

We see that our decision changes when the criteria for making decisions changes. Why is this? Our decision changed to the more conservative option of the fixed interest investment when maximizing utility because now we are accounting for Ken's risk tolerance. Money is not all that matters here. Peace of mind seems to be the deciding factor when using expected utility.

Exercises for Section 15.4

CONCEPTS

15.33 If a person is risk averse, in which interval will the greatest change in utility lie: $0 to $500,000, $500,000 to $1,000,000, or $1,000,000 to $1,500,000?

15.34 If a person is a risk seeker, in which interval will the greatest change in utility lie: $0 to $500,000, $500,000 to $1,000,000, or $1,000,000 to $1,500,000?

METHODS AND APPLICATIONS

15.35 Consider Exercise 15.31. Find the expected utility of the oil-drilling operation. Find the expected utility of not investing. What should the decision maker do if they wish to maximize expected utility?

15.36 Judy is wondering whether or not to borrow $200,000 in order to invest in the real estate market. Assume that she has saved enough money to cover the closing costs of the sale. Once she sells her house, she must pay off the amount of the loan plus 12 percent interest. She can receive a tax credit for a portion of the interest paid. Specifically, she can write off $1 in taxes for every $2 in interest she pays, so that only half the interest is an expense to her. If the real estate rises in value, the increase in value will be a tax-free capital gain, but no profit is guaranteed due to the interest costs. She estimates that for each $200,000 she invests, the possible value of the real estate at year's end is as follows:

Value at Year's End	Capital Gain	Probability
$280,000	$80,000	0.30
$250,000	$50,000	0.40
$210,000	$10,000	0.10
$150,000	−$50,000	0.20

Selected utility values for Judy are given in the table below:

Net Gain (in $1,000s)	Utility[a]
$200	1.00
150	0.96
100	0.89
50	0.80
0	0.62
−50	0.37
−100	0

[a]If intermediate utility values are needed, use linear interpolation.

a. Is Judy a risk seeker, a risk averter, or a risk neutral? Graph her utility curve to answer that question.

b. Should Judy borrow $200,000 or not? Choose the option that maximizes her expected utility.

CHAPTER SUMMARY

We began this chapter with an introduction to decision theory. We saw that a decision problem involves **states of nature**, **alternatives**, **payoffs**, and **decision criteria**, and we considered three degrees of uncertainty—**certainty**, **uncertainty**, and **risk**. In the case of certainty, we know which state of nature will actually occur. Here we simply choose the alternative that gives the best payoff. In the case of uncertainty, we have no information about the likelihood of the different states of nature. Here we discussed two commonly used decision criteria—the **maximin criterion** and the **maximax criterion**. In the case of risk, we are able to estimate the probability of occurrence for each state of nature. In this case, we learned how to use the **expected monetary value criterion**. We also learned how to construct a decision tree in Section 15.1, and we saw how to use such a tree to analyze a decision problem. In Section 15.2, we learned how to make decisions by using posterior probabilities. We explained how to perform a **posterior analysis** to determine the best alternative for each of several sampling results. Then we showed how to carry out a **preposterior analysis**, which allows us to assess the worth of sample information. In particular, we saw how to obtain the **expected value of sample information**. This quantity is the expected gain from sampling, which tells us the maximum amount we should be willing to pay for sample information. In Section 15.3, we introduced **utility theory**, and in Section 15.4, we showed how utility theory can be used to help make decisions.

GLOSSARY OF TERMS

alternatives: Several alternative actions for a decision maker to choose from. (page 549)

certainty: When we know for certain which state of nature will actually occur. (page 549)

decision criterion: A rule used to make a decision. (page 549)

decision theory: An approach that helps decision makers to make intelligent choices. (page 549)

decision tree: A diagram consisting of nodes and branches that depicts the information for a decision problem. (page 551)

expected monetary value criterion: A decision criterion in which one computes the expected monetary payoff for each alternative and then chooses the alternative yielding the largest expected payoff. (page 551)

expected net gain of sampling: The difference between the expected value of sample information and the cost of sampling. If this quantity is positive, it is worth it to perform sampling. (page 559)

expected value of perfect information: The difference between the expected payoff under certainty and the expected payoff under risk. (page 553)

expected value of sample information: The difference between the expected payoff of sampling and the expected payoff of no sampling. This measures the expected gain from sampling. (page 559)

maximax criterion: A decision criterion in which one finds the best possible payoff for each alternative and then chooses the alternative that yields the maximum best possible payoff. (page 550)

maximin criterion: A decision criterion in which one finds the worst possible payoff for each alternative and then chooses the alternative that yields the maximum worst possible payoff. (page 550)

payoff table: A tabular summary of the payoffs in a decision problem. (page 549)

perfect information: Information that tells us exactly which state of nature will occur. (page 553)

posterior decision analysis: Using a decision criterion based on posterior probabilities to choose the best alternative in a decision problem. (page 555)

preposterior analysis: When we assess the worth of sample information before performing a posterior decision analysis. (page 559)

prior decision analysis: Using a decision criterion based on prior probabilities to choose the best alternative in a decision problem. (page 555)

risk: When the likelihood (probability) of each state of nature can be estimated. (page 549)

states of nature: A set of potential future conditions that will affect the results of a decision. (page 549)

uncertainty: When we have no information about the likelihoods of the various states of nature. (page 549)

utility: A measure of monetary value based on an individual's attitude toward risk. (page 563)

IMPORTANT FORMULAS

Maximin criterion: page 550

Maximax criterion: page 550

Expected monetary value criterion: page 551

Decision tree: page 551

Expected value of perfect information: page 553

Expected payoff of sampling: page 559

Expected payoff of no sampling: page 559

Expected value of sample information: page 559

Expected net gain of sampling: page 559

Expected utility: page 563

SUPPLEMENTARY EXERCISES

15.37 In the book *Making Hard Decisions: An Introduction to Decision Analysis*, Clemen presents a decision tree for a research and development decision (note that payoffs are given in millions of dollars, which is denoted by M). Based on this decision tree (shown in Figure 15.8), answer the following:

FIGURE **15.8**   **A Decision Tree for a Research and Development Decision**

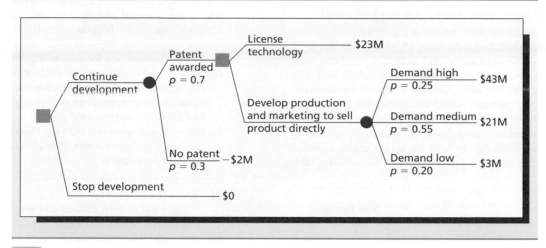

a. Should development of the research project be continued or stopped? Justify your answer by using relevant calculations, and explain your reasoning.

b. If development is continued and if a patent is awarded, should the new technology be licensed, or should the company develop production and marketing to sell the product directly? Justify your answer by using relevant calculations, and explain your reasoning.

15.38 On any given day, the probability that a river is polluted by a carbon tetrachloride spill is 0.10. Each day, a test is conducted to determine whether the river is polluted by carbon tetrachloride. This test has proven correct 80 percent of the time. Suppose that on a particular day the test indicates carbon tetrachloride pollution. What is the probability that such pollution actually exists?

15.39 In the book *Production/Operations Management*, Stevenson presents a decision tree concerning a firm's decision about the size of a production facility. This decision tree is given in Figure 15.9 (payoffs are given in millions of dollars). Use the decision tree to determine which alternative (build small or build

FIGURE **15.9**   **A Decision Tree for a Production Facility Decision**

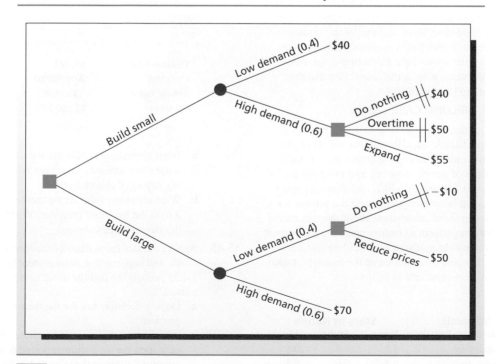

large) should be chosen in order to maximize the expected monetary payoff. What is the expected monetary payoff associated with the best alternative?

15.40 Consider the decision tree in Figure 15.9 and the situation described in Exercise 15.39. Suppose that a marketing research study can be done to obtain more information about whether demand will be high or low. The marketing research study will result in one of two outcomes: favourable (indicating that demand will be high) or unfavourable (indicating that demand will be low). The accuracy of marketing research studies like the one to be carried out can be expressed by the conditional probabilities in the following table:

Study Outcome	True Demand	
	High	**Low**
Favourable	0.9	0.2
Unfavourable	0.1	0.8

For instance, P(favourable | high) = 0.9 and P(unfavourable | low) = 0.8. Given the prior probabilities and payoffs in Figure 15.9, do the following:
a. Carry out a posterior analysis. Find the best alternative (build small or build large) for each possible study result (favourable or unfavourable), and find the associated expected payoffs.
b. Carry out a preposterior analysis. Determine the maximum amount that should be paid for the marketing research study.

15.41 A marketing major will interview for an internship with a major consumer products manufacturer/distributor. Before the interview, the marketing major feels that the chances of being offered an internship are 40 percent. Suppose that of the students who have been offered internships with this company, 90 percent had good interviews, and that of the students who have not been offered internships, 50 percent had good interviews. If the marketing major has a good interview, what is the probability that they will be offered an internship?

15.42 THE OIL-DRILLING CASE ● DrillTst

Again consider the oil-drilling case that was described in Example 15.1. Recall that the oil company wishes to decide whether to drill and that the prior probabilities of no oil, some oil, and much oil are P(none) = 0.7, P(some) = 0.2, and P(much) = 0.1. Suppose that, instead of performing the seismic survey to obtain more information about the site, the oil company can perform a cheaper magnetic experiment with two possible results: a high reading and a low reading. The past performance of the magnetic experiment can be summarized as follows:

Magnetic Experiment Result	State of Nature		
	None	**Some**	**Much**
Low Reading	0.8	0.4	0.1
High Reading	0.2	0.6	0.9

Here, for example, P(low | none) = 0.8 and P(high | some) = 0.6. Recalling that the payoffs associated with no oil, some oil, and much oil are −$700,000, $500,000, and $2,000,000, respectively, do the following:
a. Draw a decision tree for this decision problem.
b. Carry out a posterior analysis. Find the best alternative (drill or do not drill) for each possible result of the magnetic experiment (low or high), and find the associated expected payoffs.
c. Carry out a preposterior analysis. Determine the maximum amount that should be paid for the magnetic experiment.

15.43 Suppose that you are given the following two options:
(i) Toss a fair die once:
   • If you roll an even number, you get $1,500,000.
   • If you roll an odd number, you get $0.
(ii) Take $500,000 for certain.
a. Before you perform any calculations, make a choice. If you polled members of your class randomly, do you think that everyone would choose the same option? Why or why not?
b. Now determine the optimal decision using
   (1) Expected monetary value.
   (2) Expected utility.
   Do the results in part b agree with any reasons you came up with in part a?

15.44 In an exercise in the book *Production/Operations Management*, Stevenson considers a theme park whose lease is about to expire. The theme park's management wishes to decide whether to renew its lease for another 10 years or relocate near the site of a new motel complex. The town planning board is debating whether to approve the motel complex. A consultant estimates the payoffs of the theme park's alternatives under each state of nature, as shown in the following payoff table:

Theme Park Options	Motel Approved	Motel Rejected
Renew Lease	$500,000	$4,000,000
Relocate	$5,000,000	$100,000

a. What alternative should the theme park choose if it uses the maximax criterion? What is the resulting payoff of this choice?
b. What alternative should the theme park choose if it uses the maximin criterion? What is the resulting payoff of this choice?

15.45 Again consider the situation described in Exercise 15.44, and suppose that management believes there is a 0.35 probability that the motel complex will be approved.
a. Draw a decision tree for the theme park's decision problem.
b. Which alternative should be chosen if the theme park uses the maximum expected monetary value criterion? What is the expected monetary payoff for this choice?

c. Suppose that management is offered the option of a temporary lease while the planning board decides whether to approve the motel complex.

If the lease costs $100,000, should the theme park's management sign the lease? Justify your answer.

15.46 INTERNET EXERCISE

Doughnut businesses always seem to be thriving, but as was the case when the American chain Krispy Kreme came to Canada, some doughnut franchises fail (see http://www.cbc.ca/money/story/2005/09/07/krispykreme_20050907.html?ref=rss). Deciding to open a doughnut franchise comes with some risk. Go to the Tim Horton's Web site (http://www.timhortons.com/en/join/franchise_ca.html) and examine the factors associated with opening a franchise. In addition to the cost of the licence and the franchise cost, the interested party is also required to finance a building (and possible property). Create a decision tree to

assess the possible payoffs and losses involved in opening a doughnut franchise

CHAPTER 16

Time Series Forecasting

LEARNING OBJECTIVES

After reading this chapter, you should be able to

- define when a time series represents a trend, a seasonal pattern, or a cyclical pattern, or is irregular

- describe how you would use a time series regression model to assess if a trend is present in a data set

- demonstrate when you would use multiplicative decomposition methods versus exponential smoothing

- explain how forecast predictions can be assessed using the mean absolute deviation and the mean squared deviation methods

- describe how the Canadian Consumer Price Index is computed and what information it provides

CHAPTER OUTLINE

16.1 Time Series Components and Models

16.2 Time Series Regression: Basic Models

16.3 Time Series Regression: More Advanced Models (Optional)

16.4 Multiplicative Decomposition

16.5 Exponential Smoothing

16.6 Forecast Error Comparisons

16.7 Index Numbers

Demand for some products changes over time. For example, Canadians tend to be in the market for lawnmowers more in the summer than in the winter, whereas the opposite pattern exists for snow blowers. How suppliers meet these changing demands is the focus of this chapter, which deals with **time series** analyses, or collecting observations on a variable of interest in **time order**. In this chapter, we discuss developing

and using **univariate time series models**, which forecast future values of a time series **solely on the basis of past values of the time series**. Often univariate time series models forecast future time series values by extrapolating the **trend** and/or **seasonal patterns** exhibited by the past values of the time series. To illustrate these ideas, we consider several cases in this chapter, including the following:

The DVD Player Sales Case. By extrapolating an upward trend in past sales of the X-12 DVD player, Smith's Department Stores forecasts future sales of this product. The forecasts help the department store chain to better implement its inventory and financial policies.

The Traveller's Rest Case. By extrapolating an upward trend and the seasonal behaviour of its past hotel room occupancies, Traveller's Rest forecasts future hotel room occupancies. The forecasts help the hotel chain to more effectively hire help and acquire supplies.

16.1 Time Series Components and Models

In order to identify patterns in time series data, it is often convenient to think of such data as consisting of several components: **trend**, **cycle**, **seasonal variations**, and **irregular fluctuations**. **Trend** refers to the upward or downward movement that characterizes a time series over time. Thus, trend reflects the long-run growth or decline in the time series. Trend movements can represent a variety of factors. For example, long-run movements in the sales of a particular industry might be determined by changes in consumer tastes, increases in total population, and increases in per capita income. **Cycle** refers to recurring up-and-down movements around trend levels. These fluctuations can last from 2 to 10 years or even longer measured from peak to peak or trough to trough. One of the common cyclical fluctuations found in time series data is the **business cycle**, which is represented by fluctuations in the time series caused by recurrent periods of prosperity and recession. **Seasonal variations** are periodic patterns in a time series that complete themselves within a calendar year or less and then are repeated on a regular basis. Often seasonal variations occur yearly. For example, soft drink sales and hotel room occupancies are annually higher in the summer months, while department store sales are annually higher during the winter holiday season. Seasonal variations can also last less than one year. For example, daily restaurant patronage might exhibit within-week seasonal variation, with daily patronage higher on Fridays and Saturdays. **Irregular fluctuations** are erratic time series movements that follow no recognizable or regular pattern. Such movements represent what is "left over" in a time series after trend, cycle, and seasonal variations have been accounted for.

Time series that exhibit trend, seasonal, and cyclical components are illustrated in Figure 16.1. In Figure 16.1(a), a time series of sales observations that has an essentially straight-line or linear trend is plotted. Figure 16.1(b) portrays a time series of sales observations that contains a seasonal pattern that repeats annually, with higher sales in the winter months. Figure 16.1(c) exhibits a time series of agricultural yields that is cyclical, repeating a cycle about once every 10 years.

Time series models attempt to identify significant patterns in the components of a time series. Then, assuming that these patterns will continue into the future, time series models extrapolate these patterns to forecast future time series values. In Section 16.2 and optional Section 16.3, we discuss forecasting by **time series regression models**, and in Section 16.4 we discuss forecasting by using an intuitive method called **multiplicative decomposition**. Both of these approaches assume that the time series components remain essentially constant over time. If the time series components might be changing slowly over time, it is appropriate to forecast by using **exponential smoothing**. This approach is discussed in Section 16.5. If the time series components might be changing fairly quickly over time, it is appropriate to forecast by using the **Box–Jenkins methodology**. This advanced approach is discussed in Appendix I.

FIGURE **16.1** Time Series Exhibiting Trend, Seasonal, and Cyclical Components

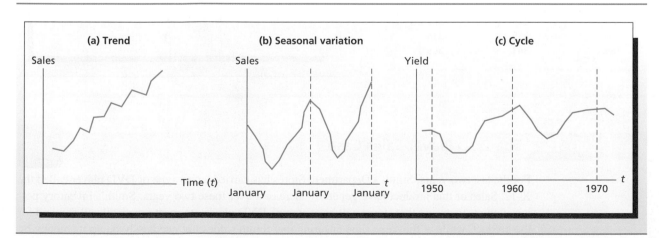

16.2 Time Series Regression: Basic Models

Modelling trend components   We begin this section with two examples.

Example 16.1 The Cod Catch Case

The Coast City Seafood Company owns a fleet of fishing trawlers and operates a fish-processing plant. In order to forecast its minimum and maximum possible revenues from cod sales and plan the operations of its fish-processing plant, the company wants to make both point forecasts and prediction interval forecasts of its monthly cod catch (measured in tonnes). The company has recorded monthly cod catch for the previous two years (years 1 and 2). The cod history is given in Table 16.1. A runs plot (or time series plot) shows that the cod catches appear to randomly fluctuate around a constant average level (see the plot in Figure 16.2). Because the company subjectively believes that this data pattern will continue in the future, it seems reasonable to use the **no trend** regression model

$$y_t = \beta_0 + \varepsilon_t$$

to forecast cod catch in future months. It can be shown that for the no trend regression model the least squares point estimate b_0 of β_0 is $\bar{y}$, the average of the n observed time series values. Because the average $\bar{y}$ of the $n = 24$ observed cod catches is 351.29, it follows that $\hat{y}_t = b_0 = 351.29$ is the point prediction of the cod catch (y_t) in any future month. Furthermore, it can be shown that a $100(1 - \alpha)$ percent prediction interval for any future y_t value described by the no trend model is $[\hat{y}_t \pm t_{\alpha/2}s\sqrt{1 + (1/n)}]$. Here s is the sample standard deviation of the n observed time series values, and $t_{\alpha/2}$ is based on $n - 1$ degrees of freedom. For example, because s can be calculated to be 33.82 for the $n = 24$ cod catches, and because $t_{0.025}$ based on $n - 1 = 23$ degrees of freedom is 2.069, it follows that a 95 percent prediction interval for the cod catch in any future month is $[351.29 \pm 2.069(33.82)\sqrt{1 + (1/24)}]$, or $[279.92, 422.66]$.

TABLE 16.1 **Cod Catch (in Tonnes)**
🌐 CodCatch

Month	Year 1	Year 2
Jan.	362	276
Feb.	381	334
Mar.	317	394
Apr.	297	334
May	399	384
Jun.	402	314
Jul.	375	344
Aug.	349	337
Sep.	386	345
Oct.	328	362
Nov.	389	314
Dec.	343	365

FIGURE 16.2   **Plot of Cod Catch versus Time**

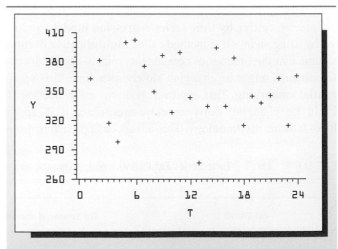

Example 16.2 The DVD Player Sales Case

For the last two years, Smith's Department Stores has carried a new type of DVD player called the X-12. Sales of this product have generally increased over these two years. Smith's inventory policy attempts to ensure that stores will have enough DVD players to meet practically all demand for the product, while at the same time ensuring that Smith's does not needlessly tie up its money by ordering more DVD players than can be sold. In order to implement this inventory policy in future months, Smith's requires both point predictions and prediction intervals for total monthly demand.

The monthly demand data for the last two years are given in Table 16.2. A runs plot of the demand data is shown in Figure 16.3. The demands appear to randomly fluctuate around an average level that increases over time in a linear fashion. Furthermore, Smith's believes that this trend will continue for at least the next year. Thus, it is reasonable to use the **linear trend** regression model

$$y_t = \beta_0 + \beta_1 t + \varepsilon_t$$

to forecast sales in future months. Notice that this model is just a simple linear regression model in which the time period t plays the role of the independent variable. The least squares point estimates of β_0 and β_1 can be calculated to be $b_0 = 198.028986$ and $b_1 = 8.074348$. Therefore, for example, point forecasts of product demand in January and February of year 3 (time periods 25 and 26) are, respectively,

$$\hat{y}_{25} = 198.028986 + 8.074348(25) = 399.9 \quad \text{and}$$
$$\hat{y}_{26} = 198.028986 + 8.074348(26) = 408.0$$

Note that the Excel output under Table 16.2 gives these point forecasts. In addition, it can be shown using either the formulas for simple linear regression or a computer software package that a 95 percent prediction interval for demand in time period 25 is [328.6, 471.2] and that a 95 percent prediction interval for demand in time period 26 is [336.0, 479.9]. These prediction intervals can help Smith's implement its inventory policy. For instance, if Smith's stocks 471 DVD players in January of year 3, we can be reasonably sure that monthly demand will be met.

TABLE **16.2**   DVD Player Sales Data
   DVDSale

Month	Year 1	Year 2
Jan.	197	296
Feb.	211	276
Mar.	203	305
Apr.	247	308
May	239	356
Jun.	269	393
Jul.	308	363
Aug.	262	386
Sep.	258	443
Oct.	256	308
Nov.	261	358
Dec.	288	384

FIGURE **16.3**   Plot of DVD Player Sales versus Time

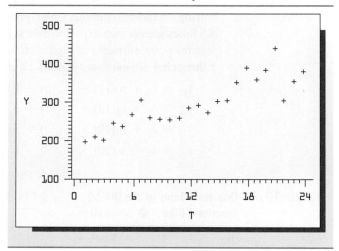

A	B	C	D
358	23		
384	24		
399.8877	25	USING	TREND
407.962	26		

Example 16.1 illustrates that the intercept β_0 can be used to model a lack of trend over time, and Example 16.2 illustrates that the expression $(\beta_0 + \beta_1 t)$ can model a linear trend over time. In addition, as will be illustrated in the exercises, the expression $(\beta_0 + \beta_1 t + \beta_2 t^2)$ can model a quadratic trend over time.

Modelling seasonal components   We next consider how to forecast time series described by trend and seasonal components.

Example 16.3 The Bike Sales Case

Table 16.3 presents quarterly sales of the TRK-50 mountain bike for the previous four years at a bicycle shop in Switzerland. The MINITAB plot in Figure 16.4 shows that the bike sales exhibit a linear trend and a strong seasonal pattern, with bike sales being higher in the spring and summer quarters than in the winter and fall quarters. If we let y_t denote the number of TRK-50 mountain bikes sold in time period t at the Swiss bike shop, then a regression model describing y_t is

$$y_t = \beta_0 + \beta_1 t + \beta_{Q2}Q_2 + \beta_{Q3}Q_3 + \beta_{Q4}Q_4 + \varepsilon_t.$$

Here the expression $(\beta_0 + \beta_1 t)$ models the linear trend evident in Figure 16.4. Q_2, Q_3, and Q_4 are dummy variables defined for quarters 2, 3, and 4. Specifically, Q_2 equals 1 if quarterly bike sales were observed in quarter 2 (spring) and 0 otherwise, Q_3 equals 1 if quarterly bike sales were observed in quarter 3 (summer) and 0 otherwise, and Q_4 equals 1 if quarterly bike sales were observed in quarter 4 (fall) and 0 otherwise. Note that we have not defined a dummy variable for quarter 1 (winter). It follows that the regression parameters β_{Q2}, β_{Q3}, and β_{Q4} compare quarters 2, 3, and 4 with quarter 1. Intuitively, for example, β_{Q4} is the difference, excluding trend, between the level of the time series (y_t) in quarter 4 (fall) and the level of the time series in quarter 1 (winter). A positive β_{Q4} would imply that, excluding trend, bike sales in the fall can be expected to be higher than bike sales in the winter. A negative β_{Q4} would imply that, excluding trend, bike sales in the fall can be expected to be lower than bike sales in the winter.

Figure 16.5 gives the MINITAB output of a regression analysis of the quarterly bike sales by using the dummy variable model. The MINITAB output tells us that the linear trend and the seasonal dummy variables are significant (every t statistic has a related p value less than 0.01). Also notice that the least squares point estimates of β_{Q2}, β_{Q3}, and β_{Q4} are, respectively, $b_{Q2} = 21$, $b_{Q3} = 33.5$, and $b_{Q4} = 4.5$. It follows that, excluding trend, expected bike sales in quarter 2 (spring), quarter 3 (summer), and quarter 4 (fall) are estimated to be, respectively, 21, 33.5, and 4.5 bikes greater than expected bike sales in quarter 1 (winter). Furthermore, using all of the least squares point estimates in Figure 16.5, we can compute point forecasts of bike sales in quarters 1 through 4 of next year (periods 17 through 20) as follows:

$$\hat{y}_{17} = b_0 + b_1(17) + b_{Q2}(0) + b_{Q3}(0) + b_{Q4}(0) = 8.75 + 0.5(17) = 17.250,$$
$$\hat{y}_{18} = b_0 + b_1(18) + b_{Q2}(1) + b_{Q3}(0) + b_{Q4}(0) = 8.75 + 0.5(18) + 21 = 38.750,$$
$$\hat{y}_{19} = b_0 + b_1(19) + b_{Q2}(0) + b_{Q3}(1) + b_{Q4}(0) = 8.75 + 0.5(19) + 33.5 = 51.750,$$
$$\hat{y}_{20} = b_0 + b_1(20) + b_{Q2}(0) + b_{Q3}(0) + b_{Q4}(1) = 8.75 + 0.5(20) + 4.5 = 23.250.$$

TABLE **16.3**　Quarterly Sales of the TRK-50 Mountain Bike　🌐 BikeSales

Year	Quarter	t	Sales, y_t
1	1 (Winter)	1	10
	2 (Spring)	2	31
	3 (Summer)	3	43
	4 (Fall)	4	16
2	1	5	11
	2	6	33
	3	7	45
	4	8	17
3	1	9	13
	2	10	34
	3	11	48
	4	12	19
4	1	13	15
	2	14	37
	3	15	51
	4	16	21

FIGURE **16.4**　MINITAB Plot of TRK-50 Bike Sales

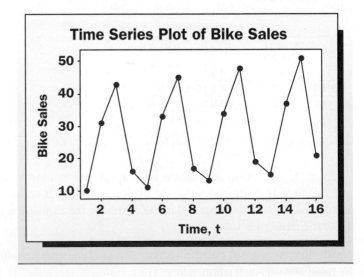

FIGURE **16.5**   **MINITAB Output of an Analysis of the Quarterly Bike Sales by Using Dummy Variable Regression**

```
The regression equation is
BikeSales = 8.75 + 0.500 Time + 21.0 Q2 + 33.5 Q3 + 4.50 Q4


Predictor      Coef    SE Coef       T       P
Constant     8.7500     0.4281   20.44   0.000
Time        0.50000    0.03769   13.27   0.000
Q2          21.0000     0.4782   43.91   0.000
Q3          33.5000     0.4827   69.41   0.000
Q4           4.5000     0.4900    9.18   0.000

S = 0.674200   R-Sq = 99.8%   R-Sq(adj) = 99.8%

Values of Predictors for New Obs   Predicted Values for New Observations
New Obs  Time    Q2   Q3   Q4      New Obs    Fit   SE Fit      95% CI            95% PI
      1  17.0     0    0    0            1  17.250   0.506  (16.137, 18.363)  (15.395, 19.105)
      2  18.0     1    0    0            2  38.750   0.506  (37.637, 39.863)  (36.895, 40.605)
      3  19.0     0    1    0            3  51.750   0.506  (50.637, 52.863)  (49.895, 53.605)
      4  20.0     0    0    1            4  23.250   0.506  (22.137, 24.363)  (21.395, 25.105)
```

These point forecasts are given at the bottom of the MINITAB output, as are 95 percent prediction intervals for y_{17}, y_{18}, y_{19}, and y_{20}. The upper limits of these prediction intervals suggest that the bicycle shop can be reasonably sure that it will meet demand for the TRK-50 mountain bike if the numbers of bikes it stocks in quarters 1 through 4 are, respectively, 19, 41, 54, and 25 bikes.

We next consider Table 16.4, which presents a time series of hotel room occupancies observed by Traveller's Rest, a corporation that operates four hotels. The analysts in the operating division of the corporation were asked to develop a model that could be used to obtain short-term forecasts (up to one year) of the number of occupied rooms in the hotels. These forecasts were needed by various personnel to assist in hiring additional help during the summer months, ordering materials that have long delivery lead times, budgeting of local advertising expenditures, and so on. The available historical data consisted of the number of occupied rooms during each day for the previous 14 years. Because it was desired to obtain monthly forecasts, these data were reduced to monthly averages by dividing each monthly total by the number of days in the month. The monthly room averages for the previous 14 years are the time series values given in Table 16.4. A runs plot of these values in Figure 16.6 shows that the monthly room averages follow a strong trend and have a seasonal pattern with one major and several minor peaks during the year. Note that the major peak each year occurs during the high summer travel months of June, July, and August.

Although the quarterly bike sales and monthly hotel room averages both exhibit seasonal variation, they exhibit different kinds of seasonal variation. The quarterly bike sales plotted in Figure 16.4 exhibit **constant seasonal variation**. In general, constant seasonal variation is seasonal variation where the magnitude of the seasonal swing does not depend on the level of the time series. On the other hand, **increasing seasonal variation** is seasonal variation where the magnitude of the seasonal swing increases as the level of the time series increases. Figure 16.6 shows that the monthly hotel room averages exhibit increasing seasonal variation. We have illustrated in the bike sales case that we can use **dummy variables** to model constant seasonal variation. The number of dummy variables that we use is, in general, the number of seasons minus 1. For example, if we model quarterly data, we use three dummy variables (as in the bike sales case). If we model monthly data, we use 11 dummy variables (this will be illustrated in optional Section 16.3). If a time series exhibits increasing seasonal variation, one approach is to first use a **fractional power transformation** (see Section 11.10) that produces a transformed time series exhibiting constant seasonal variation. Then, as will be shown in Section 16.3, we use dummy variables to model the constant seasonal variation. A second approach to modelling increasing seasonal variation is to use a **multiplicative model** and a technique called **multiplicative decomposition**. This approach, which is intuitive, is discussed in Section 16.4.

TABLE 16.4   **Monthly Hotel Room Averages**   ● TravRest

t	y_t	t	y_t	t	y_t	t	y_t	t	y_t	t	y_t	t	y_t	t	y_t
1	501	22	587	43	785	64	657	85	645	106	759	127	1,067	148	827
2	488	23	497	44	830	65	680	86	602	107	643	128	1,038	149	788
3	504	24	558	45	645	66	759	87	601	108	728	129	812	150	937
4	578	25	555	46	643	67	878	88	709	109	691	130	790	151	1,076
5	545	26	523	47	551	68	881	89	706	110	649	131	692	152	1,125
6	632	27	532	48	606	69	705	90	817	111	656	132	782	153	840
7	728	28	623	49	585	70	684	91	930	112	735	133	758	154	864
8	725	29	598	50	553	71	577	92	983	113	748	134	709	155	717
9	585	30	683	51	576	72	656	93	745	114	837	135	715	156	813
10	542	31	774	52	665	73	645	94	735	115	995	136	788	157	811
11	480	32	780	53	656	74	593	95	620	116	1,040	137	794	158	732
12	530	33	609	54	720	75	617	96	698	117	809	138	893	159	745
13	518	34	604	55	826	76	686	97	665	118	793	139	1,046	160	844
14	489	35	531	56	838	77	679	98	626	119	692	140	1,075	161	833
15	528	36	592	57	652	78	773	99	649	120	763	141	812	162	935
16	599	37	578	58	661	79	906	100	740	121	723	142	822	163	1,110
17	572	38	543	59	584	80	934	101	729	122	655	143	714	164	1,124
18	659	39	565	60	644	81	713	102	824	123	658	144	802	165	868
19	739	40	648	61	623	82	710	103	937	124	761	145	748	166	860
20	758	41	615	62	553	83	600	104	994	125	768	146	731	167	762
21	602	42	697	63	599	84	676	105	781	126	885	147	748	168	877

FIGURE 16.6   **Plot of the Monthly Hotel Room Averages versus Time**

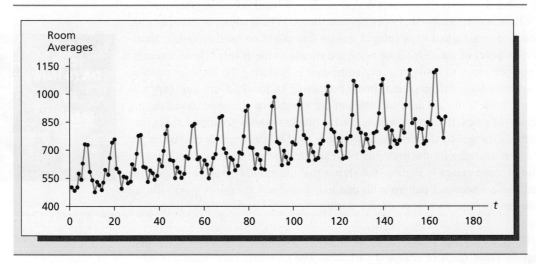

Exercises for Section 16.2

CONCEPTS

16.1 Discuss how we model no trend and a linear trend.

16.2 Discuss the difference between constant seasonal variation and increasing seasonal variation.

16.3 Discuss how we use dummy variables to model constant seasonal variation.

METHODS AND APPLICATIONS

16.4 CANADIAN TIRE SALES

Table 16.5 provides the consolidated quarterly results from Canadian Tire's *2006 Second Quarter Report to Shareholders*.

In this report, Canadian Tire states that they "experience stronger revenues and earnings in the second and fourth quarters of each year because of the seasonal nature" of their merchandise.

a. Plot the values and determine if you agree with their statement from the data provided.

b. Demonstrate that a linear regression model would not be the best fit to the data.

TABLE 16.5 Net Earnings (in $ millions) for Canadian Tire ● CanTire

Year	Quarter	Time	Earnings
2004	3	1	69.4
2004	4	2	100.4
2005	1	3	35.3
2005	2	4	92.2
2005	3	5	84.4
2005	4	6	118.2
2006	1	7	47.6
2006	2	8	103.3

Source: http://media.corporate-ir.net/media_files/TOR/ctc.ca/reports/Q206Report.pdf.

16.5 THE WATCH SALES CASE ● WatchSale

The past 20 monthly sales figures for a new type of watch sold at Lambert's Discount Stores are given in Table 16.6.

a. Plot the watch sales values versus time and discuss why the plot indicates that the model

$$y_t = \beta_0 + \beta_1 t + \varepsilon_t$$

might appropriately describe these values.

b. The least squares point estimates of β_0 and β_1 can be calculated to be $b_0 = 290.089474$ and $b_1 = 8.667669$. Use b_0 and b_1 to show that a point forecast of watch sales in period 21 is $\hat{y}_{21} = 472.1$ (see the Excel output in Table 16.6). Use the formulas of simple linear regression analysis or a computer software package to show that a 95 percent prediction interval for watch sales in period 21 is [421.5, 522.7].

TABLE 16.6 Watch Sales Values ● WatchSale

Month	Sales	Month	Sales
1	298	11	356
2	302	12	371
3	301	13	399
4	351	14	392
5	336	15	425
6	361	16	411
7	407	17	455
8	351	18	457
9	357	19	465
10	346	20	481

A	B	C	D
465	19		
481	20		
472.1105	21	USING	TREND

16.6 THE AIR CONDITIONER SALES CASE ● ACSales

Quarterly sales of the Bargain 8000-BTU Air Conditioner at the Bargain Department Stores chain over the past three years are as given in Table 16.7.

a. Plot sales versus time and discuss why the plot indicates that the model

$$y_t = \beta_0 + \beta_1 t + \beta_2 t^2 + \beta_{Q2} Q_2 + \beta_{Q3} Q_3 + \beta_{Q4} Q_4 + \varepsilon_t$$

might appropriately describe the sales values. In this model, Q_2, Q_3, and Q_4 are appropriately defined dummy variables for quarters 2, 3, and 4.

To the right of Table 16.7 is the MINITAB output of a regression analysis of the air conditioner sales data using this model.

b. Define the dummy variables Q_2, Q_3, and Q_4. Then use the MINITAB output to find, report, and interpret the least squares point estimates of β_{Q2}, β_{Q3}, and β_{Q4}.

c. At the bottom of the MINITAB output are point and prediction interval forecasts of air conditioner sales in the four quarters of year 4. Find and report these forecasts and show how they were calculated.

TABLE 16.7 Air Conditioner Sales ● ACSales

Year	Quarter	Sales
1	1	2,915
	2	8,032
	3	10,411
	4	2,427
2	1	4,381
	2	9,138
	3	11,386
	4	3,382
3	1	5,105
	2	9,894
	3	12,300
	4	4,013

```
The regression equation is
Sales = 2625 + 383 T - 11.4 TSq + 4630 Q2 + 6739 Q3 - 1565 Q4

Predictor      Coef    SE Coef       T      P
Constant     2624.5      100.4   26.15  0.000     S = 92.4244
T            382.82      34.03   11.25  0.000     R-Sq = 100.0%
TSq         -11.354       2.541   -4.47  0.004     R-Sq(adj)= 99.9%
Q2          4629.74      76.08   60.86  0.000
Q3          6738.85      77.38   87.09  0.000
Q4         -1565.32      79.34  -19.73  0.000

Time     Fit   SE Fit        95% CI              95% PI
  13   5682.4    112.6  ( 5406.9,  5957.9)  ( 5325.9,  6038.8)
  14  10388.4    142.8  (10039.0, 10737.8)  ( 9972.2, 10804.6)
  15  12551.0    177.2  (12117.4, 12984.7)  (12061.9, 13040.2)
  16   4277.7    213.9  ( 3754.4,  4801.1)  ( 3707.6,  4847.8)
```

16.3 Time Series Regression: More Advanced Models (Optional)

Example 16.4 The Traveller's Rest Case

Consider taking the square roots, quartic roots, and natural logarithms of the monthly hotel room averages in Table 16.4. If we do this and plot the resulting three sets of transformed values versus time, we find that the quartic root transformation best equalizes the seasonal variation. Figure 16.7 presents a plot of the quartic roots of the monthly hotel room averages versus time. Letting y_t denote the hotel room average observed in time period t, it follows that a regression model describing the quartic root of y_t is

$$y_t^{0.25} = \beta_0 + \beta_1 t + \beta_{M1}M_1 + \beta_{M2}M_2 + \cdots + \beta_{M11}M_{11} + \varepsilon_t.$$

The expression $(\beta_0 + \beta_1 t)$ models the linear trend evident in Figure 16.7. Furthermore, M_1, $M_2, \ldots, M_{11}$ are dummy variables defined for January (month 1) through November (month 11). For example, M_1 equals 1 if a monthly room average was observed in January, and 0 otherwise; M_2 equals 1 if a monthly room average was observed in February, and 0 otherwise. Note that we have not defined a dummy variable for December (month 12). It follows that the regression parameters $\beta_{M1}, \beta_{M2}, \ldots, \beta_{M11}$ compare January through November with December. Intuitively, for example, β_{M1} is the difference, excluding trend, between the level of the time series $(y_t^{0.25})$ in January and the level of the time series in December. A positive β_{M1} would imply that, excluding trend, the value of the time series in January can be expected to be greater than the value in December. A negative β_{M1} would imply that, excluding trend, the value of the time series in January can be expected to be smaller than the value in December.

Figure 16.8 gives relevant portions of the MegaStat output of a regression analysis of the hotel room data using the quartic root dummy variable model. The MegaStat output tells us that the linear trend and the seasonal dummy variables are significant (every t statistic has a related p value less than 0.05). In addition, although not shown on the output, $R^2 = 0.988$. Now consider time period 169, which is January of next year and which therefore implies that $M_1 = 1$ and that all the other dummy variables equal 0. Using the least squares point estimates in Figure 16.8, we compute a point forecast of $y_{169}^{0.25}$ to be

$$b_0 + b_1(169) + b_{M1}(1) = 4.807318 + 0.003515(169) + (-0.052467)(1)$$
$$= 5.3489.$$

FIGURE **16.7**   Plot of the Quartic Roots of the Monthly Hotel Room Averages versus Time

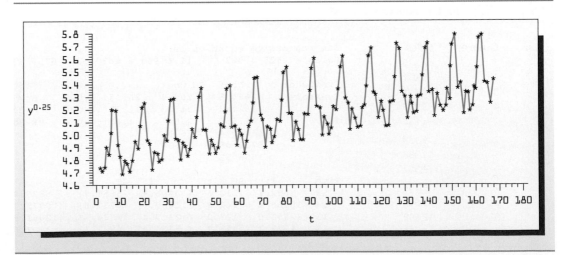

FIGURE **16.8**   **MegaStat Output of an Analysis of the Quartic Roots of the Room Averages Using Dummy Variable Regression (TFY2 = $y_t^{0.25}$)**

Regression output variables	coefficients	std. error	t (df = 155)	p-value	confidence interval 95% lower	95% upper
Intercept	4.807318	0.00846255	568.070	4.06E-259	4.7906	4.8240
t	0.003515	0.00004449	79.009	3.95E-127	0.0034	0.0036
M1	−0.052467	0.01055475	−4.971	1.75E-06	−0.0733	−0.0316
M2	−0.140790	0.01055278	−13.342	1.59E-27	−0.1616	−0.1199
M3	−0.107103	0.01055100	−10.151	7.02E-19	−0.1279	−0.0863
M4	0.049882	0.01054940	4.728	5.05E-06	0.0290	0.0707
M5	0.025417	0.01054800	2.410	0.0171	0.0046	0.0463
M6	0.190170	0.01054678	18.031	6.85E-40	0.1693	0.2110
M7	0.382455	0.01054575	36.266	1.28E-77	0.3616	0.4033
M8	0.413370	0.01054490	39.201	2.41E-82	0.3925	0.4342
M9	0.071417	0.01054424	6.773	2.47E-10	0.0506	0.0922
M10	0.050641	0.01054377	4.803	3.66E-06	0.0298	0.0715
M11	−0.141943	0.01054349	−13.463	7.47E-28	−0.1628	−0.1211

Durbin-Watson = 1.26

Predicted values for: TFY2

t	Predicted	95% Confidence Intervals lower	upper	95% Prediction Intervals lower	upper	Leverage
169	5.3489	5.3322	5.3656	5.2913	5.4065	0.092
170	5.2641	5.2474	5.2808	5.2065	5.3217	0.092
171	5.3013	5.2846	5.3180	5.2437	5.3589	0.092
172	5.4618	5.4451	5.4785	5.4042	5.5194	0.092
173	5.4409	5.4241	5.4576	5.3833	5.4984	0.092
174	5.6091	5.5924	5.6258	5.5515	5.6667	0.092
175	5.8049	5.7882	5.8216	5.7473	5.8625	0.092
176	5.8394	5.8226	5.8561	5.7818	5.8969	0.092
177	5.5009	5.4842	5.5176	5.4433	5.5585	0.092
178	5.4837	5.4669	5.5004	5.4261	5.5412	0.092
179	5.2946	5.2779	5.3113	5.2370	5.3522	0.092
180	5.4400	5.4233	5.4568	5.3825	5.4976	0.092

Note that this point forecast is given in Figure 16.8 (see time period 169). It follows that a point forecast of y_{169} is

$$(5.3489)^4 = 818.57.$$

Furthermore, the MegaStat output shows that a 95 percent prediction interval for $y_{169}^{0.25}$ is [5.2913, 5.4065]. It follows that a 95 percent prediction interval for y_{169} is

$$[(5.2913)^4, (5.4065)^4] = [783.88, 854.41].$$

This interval says that Traveller's Rest can be 95 percent confident that the monthly hotel room average in period 169 will be no less than 783.88 rooms per day and no more than 854.41 rooms per day. Lastly, note that the MegaStat output also gives point forecasts of and 95 percent prediction intervals for the quartic roots of the hotel room averages in February through December of next year (time periods 170 through 180).

The validity of the regression methods just illustrated requires that the independence assumption be satisfied. However, when time series data are analyzed, this assumption is often violated. It is quite common for the time-ordered error terms to exhibit **positive** or **negative autocorrelation**. In Section 11.10, we discussed positive and negative autocorrelation, and we saw that we can use residual plots to check for these kinds of autocorrelation.

One type of positive or negative autocorrelation is called **first-order autocorrelation**. It says that ε_t, the error term in time period t, is related to ε_{t-1}, the error term in time period $t-1$, by the equation

$$\varepsilon_t = \phi \varepsilon_{t-1} + a_t.$$

Here we assume that ϕ (phi) is the correlation coefficient that measures the relationship between error terms separated by one time period, and a_t is an error term (often called a **random shock**) that satisfies the usual regression assumptions. To check for positive or negative first-order auto-correlation, we can use the **Durbin–Watson statistic d**, which was discussed in Section 11.10. For example, it can be verified that this statistic shows no evidence of positive or negative first-order autocorrelation in the error terms of the DVD player sales model or in the error terms of the bike sales model. However, note from the MegaStat output in Figure 16.8 that the Durbin–Watson statistic for the dummy variable regression model describing the quartic roots of the hotel room averages is $d = 1.26$. Because the dummy variable regression model uses $k = 12$ independent variables, and because Tables A.10, A.11, and A.12 do not give the **Durbin–Watson critical points** corresponding to $k = 12$, we cannot test for autocorrelation using these tables. However, it can be shown that $d = 1.26$ is quite small and indicates **positive autocorrelation** in the error terms. One approach to dealing with first-order autocorrelation in the error terms is to predict future values of the error terms by using the model $\varepsilon_t = \phi \varepsilon_{t-1} + a_t$. Of course the error term ε_t could be related to more than just the previous error term ε_{t-1}. It could be related to any number of previous error terms. The **autoregressive error term model of order q**,

$$\varepsilon_t = \phi_1 \varepsilon_{t-1} + \phi_2 \varepsilon_{t-2} + \cdots + \phi_q \varepsilon_{t-q} + a_t,$$

relates ε_t, the error term in time period t, to the previous error terms $\varepsilon_{t-1}, \varepsilon_{t-2}, \ldots, \varepsilon_{t-q}$. Here $\phi_1, \phi_2, \ldots, \phi_q$ are unknown parameters, and a_t is an error term (random shock) with mean 0 that satisfies the regression assumptions. The **Box–Jenkins methodology** can be used to systematically identify an autoregressive error term model that relates ε_t to an appropriate number of past error terms. More generally, the Box–Jenkins methodology can be employed to predict future time series values (y_t) by using a procedure that combines the autoregressive error term model of order q with the model

$$y_t = \beta_0 + \beta_1 y_{t-1} + \beta_2 y_{t-2} + \cdots + \beta_p y_{t-p} + \varepsilon_t.$$

This latter model, which is called the **autoregressive observation model of order p**, expresses the observation y_t in terms of the previous observations $y_{t-1}, y_{t-2}, \ldots, y_{t-p}$ and an error term ε_t. The Box–Jenkins methodology, which is discussed in Appendix I, identifies which previous observations and which previous error terms describe y_t.

Although sophisticated techniques such as the Box–Jenkins methodology can be quite useful, studies show that the regression techniques discussed in Section 16.2 and in this section often provide accurate forecasts, even if we ignore the autocorrelation in the error terms. In fact, whenever we observe time series data, we should determine whether trend and/or seasonal effects exist. For example, the Fresh demand data in Table 16.8 are time series data observed over 30 consecutive four-week sales periods. Although we can predict demand for Fresh detergent on the basis of price difference and advertising expenditure, this demand could also be affected by a linear or quadratic trend over time and/or by seasonal effects (for example, more laundry detergent might be sold in summer sales periods when children are home from school; see Figure 16.9(a) and (b)). If we try using trend equations and dummy variables to search for trend and seasonal effects, we find that these effects do not exist in the Fresh demand data. However, in the supplementary exercises (see Exercise 16.38), we present a situation where we use trend equations and seasonal dummy variables, as well as **causal variables** such as price difference and advertising expenditure, to predict demand for a fishing lure.

Sales Period	Price for Fresh, x_1 (Dollars)	Average Industry Price, x_2 (Dollars)	Price Difference, $x_4 = x_2 - x_1$ (Dollars)	Advertising Expenditure for Fresh, x_3 (Hundreds of Thousands of Dollars)	Demand for Fresh, y (Hundreds of Thousands of Bottles)
1	3.85	3.80	−0.05	5.50	7.38
2	3.75	4.00	0.25	6.75	8.51
3	3.70	4.30	0.60	7.25	9.52
4	3.70	3.70	0	5.50	7.50
5	3.60	3.85	0.25	7.00	9.33
6	3.60	3.80	0.20	6.50	8.28
7	3.60	3.75	0.15	6.75	8.75
8	3.80	3.85	0.05	5.25	7.87
9	3.80	3.65	−0.15	5.25	7.10
10	3.85	4.00	0.15	6.00	8.00
11	3.90	4.10	0.20	6.50	7.89
12	3.90	4.00	0.10	6.25	8.15
13	3.70	4.10	0.40	7.00	9.10
14	3.75	4.20	0.45	6.90	8.86
15	3.75	4.10	0.35	6.80	8.90
16	3.80	4.10	0.30	6.80	8.87
17	3.70	4.20	0.50	7.10	9.26
18	3.80	4.30	0.50	7.00	9.00
19	3.70	4.10	0.40	6.80	8.75
20	3.80	3.75	−0.05	6.50	7.95
21	3.80	3.75	−0.05	6.25	7.65
22	3.75	3.65	−0.10	6.00	7.27
23	3.70	3.90	0.20	6.50	8.00
24	3.55	3.65	0.10	7.00	8.50
25	3.60	4.10	0.50	6.80	8.75
26	3.65	4.25	0.60	6.80	9.21
27	3.70	3.65	−0.05	6.50	8.27
28	3.75	3.75	0	5.75	7.67
29	3.80	3.85	0.05	5.80	7.93
30	3.70	4.25	0.55	6.80	9.26

FIGURE 16.9 Scatter Plots of the Fresh Demand Data

(a) Plot of y (Demand for Fresh Detergent) versus x_4 (Price Difference)

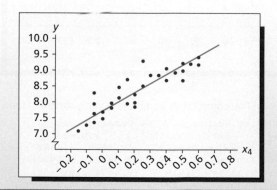

(b) Plot of y (Demand for Fresh Detergent) versus x_3 (Advertising Expenditure for Fresh)

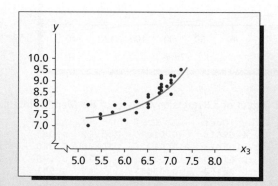

Exercises for Section 16.3

CONCEPTS

16.7 What transformations can be used to transform a time series exhibiting increasing seasonal variation into a time series exhibiting constant seasonal variation?

16.8 What is the purpose of an autoregressive error term model?

METHODS AND APPLICATIONS

16.9 Table 16.9 gives the monthly international passenger totals over the last 11 years for an airline company. A plot of these passenger totals reveals an upward trend with increasing seasonal variation, and the natural logarithmic transformation is found to best equalize the seasonal variation (see Figure 16.10(a)

and (b)). Figure 16.10(c) gives the MINITAB output of a regression analysis of the monthly international passenger totals by using the model

$$\ln y_t = \beta_0 + \beta_1 t + \beta_{M1}M_1 + \beta_{M2}M_2 + \cdots + \beta_{M11}M_{11} + \varepsilon_t.$$

Here $M_1, M_2, \ldots, M_{11}$ are appropriately defined dummy variables for January (month 1) through

TABLE **16.9**	Monthly International Passenger Totals (Thousands of Passengers)	● AirPass

Year	Jan.	Feb.	Mar.	Apr.	May	Jun.	Jul.	Aug.	Sep.	Oct.	Nov.	Dec.
1	112	118	132	129	121	135	148	148	136	119	104	118
2	115	126	141	135	125	149	170	170	158	133	114	140
3	145	150	178	163	172	178	199	199	184	162	146	166
4	171	180	193	181	183	218	230	242	209	191	172	194
5	196	196	236	235	229	243	264	272	237	211	180	201
6	204	188	235	227	234	264	302	293	259	229	203	229
7	242	233	267	269	270	315	364	347	312	274	237	278
8	284	277	317	313	318	374	413	405	355	306	271	306
9	315	301	356	348	355	422	465	467	404	347	305	336
10	340	318	362	348	363	435	491	505	404	359	310	337
11	360	342	406	396	420	472	548	559	463	407	362	405

Source: *FAA Statistical Handbook of Civil Aviation* (several annual issues). These data were originally presented by Box and Jenkins (1976). We have updated the situation in this exercise to be more modern.

FIGURE **16.10**	Analysis of the Monthly International Passenger Totals

(a) Plot of the passenger totals

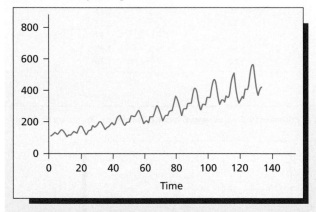

(b) Plot of the natural logarithms of the passenger totals

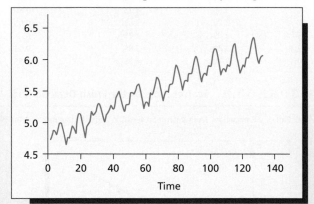

(c) MINITAB Output of a Regression Analysis of the Monthly International Passenger Totals Using the Dummy Variable Model

```
Predictor      Coef     SE Coef        T       P     Predicted Values for New Observations
Constant    4.69618     0.01973   238.02   0.000     Time     Fit    SE Fit        95% PI
Time      0.0103075   0.0001316    78.30   0.000      133  6.08610   0.01973   (5.96593, 6.20627)
Jan         0.01903     0.02451     0.78   0.439      134  6.07888   0.01973   (5.95871, 6.19905)
Feb         0.00150     0.02451     0.06   0.951      135  6.22564   0.01973   (6.10547, 6.34581)
Mar         0.13795     0.02450     5.63   0.000      136  6.19383   0.01973   (6.07366, 6.31400)
Apr         0.09583     0.02449     3.91   0.000      137  6.20008   0.01973   (6.07991, 6.32025)
May         0.09178     0.02449     3.75   0.000      138  6.33292   0.01973   (6.21276, 6.45309)
Jun         0.21432     0.02448     8.75   0.000      139  6.44360   0.01973   (6.32343, 6.56377)
Jul         0.31469     0.02448    12.85   0.000      140  6.44682   0.01973   (6.32665, 6.56699)
Aug         0.30759     0.02448    12.57   0.000      141  6.31605   0.01973   (6.19588, 6.43622)
Sep         0.16652     0.02448     6.80   0.000      142  6.18515   0.01973   (6.06498, 6.30531)
Oct         0.02531     0.02447     1.03   0.303      143  6.05455   0.01973   (5.93438, 6.17472)
Nov        -0.11559     0.02447    -4.72   0.000      144  6.18045   0.01973   (6.06028, 6.30062)

S = 0.0573917    R-Sq = 98.3%    R-Sq(adj) = 98.1%    Durbin-Watson statistic = 0.420944
```

November (month 11). Let y_{133} denote the international passenger totals in month 133 (January of next year). The MINITAB output tells us that a point forecast of and a 95 percent prediction interval for ln y_{133} are, respectively, 6.08610 and [5.96593, 6.20627]. Using the least squares point estimates on the MINITAB output, show how the point forecast

was calculated. Then, by calculating $e^{6.08610}$ and $[e^{5.96593}, e^{6.20627}]$, find a point forecast of and a 95 percent prediction interval for y_{133}.	● AirPass

16.10	Use the Durbin–Watson statistic given at the bottom of the MINITAB output in Figure 16.10(c) to test for positive autocorrelation.

16.4 Multiplicative Decomposition

When a time series exhibits increasing (or decreasing) seasonal variation, we can use the **multiplicative decomposition method** to decompose the time series into its **trend**, **seasonal**, **cyclical**, and **irregular** components. This is illustrated in the following example.

Example 16.5 The Tasty Cola Case

The Discount Cola Shop owns and operates 10 soft drink stores and sells Tasty Cola, a soft drink introduced just three years ago and gaining in popularity. Discount Cola orders Tasty Cola from the regional distributor. To better implement its inventory policy, Discount Cola needs to forecast monthly Tasty Cola sales (in hundreds of cases).

Discount Cola has recorded monthly Tasty Cola sales for the previous three years. This time series is given in Table 16.10 and plotted in Figure 16.11. Notice that, in addition to having a linear trend, the Tasty Cola sales time series possesses seasonal variation, with sales of the soft drink greatest in the summer and early fall months and lowest in the winter months. Because, furthermore, the seasonal variation seems to be increasing, we will see as we progress through this example that it might be reasonable to conclude that y_t, the sales of Tasty Cola in period t, is described by the **multiplicative model**

$$y_t = TR_t \times SN_t \times CL_t \times IR_t.$$

TABLE **16.10** **Monthly Sales of Tasty Cola (in Hundreds of Cases)**

⬤ TastyCola

Year	Month	t	Sales, y_t	Year	Month	t	Sales, y_t
1	1 (Jan.)	1	189	2	7	19	831
	2 (Feb.)	2	229		8	20	960
	3 (Mar.)	3	249		9	21	1,152
	4 (Apr.)	4	289		10	22	759
	5 (May)	5	260		11	23	607
	6 (Jun.)	6	431		12	24	371
	7 (Jul.)	7	660	3	1	25	298
	8 (Aug.)	8	777		2	26	378
	9 (Sep.)	9	915		3	27	373
	10 (Oct.)	10	613		4	28	443
	11 (Nov.)	11	485		5	29	374
	12 (Dec.)	12	277		6	30	660
2	1	13	244		7	31	1,004
	2	14	296		8	32	1,153
	3	15	319		9	33	1,388
	4	16	370		10	34	904
	5	17	313		11	35	715
	6	18	556		12	36	441

FIGURE **16.11** **Monthly Sales of Tasty Cola (in Hundreds of Cases)**

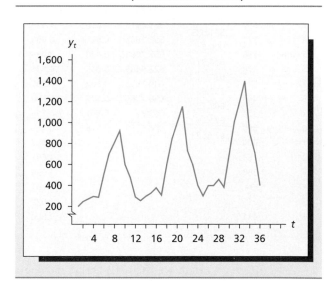

Here TR_t, SN_t, CL_t, and IR_t represent the trend, seasonal, cyclical, and irregular components, respectively, of the time series in time period t.

Table 16.11 summarizes the calculations needed to find estimates—denoted tr_t, sn_t, cl_t, and ir_t—of TR_t, SN_t, CL_t, and IR_t. As shown in the table, we begin by calculating **moving averages** and **centred moving averages**. The purpose behind computing these averages is to eliminate seasonal variations and irregular fluctuations from the data. The first moving average of the first 12 Tasty Cola sales values is

$$\frac{189 + 229 + 249 + 289 + 260 + 431 + 660 + 777 + 915 + 613 + 485 + 277}{12}$$

$$= 447.833.$$

TABLE 16.11   Tasty Cola Sales and the Multiplicative Decomposition Method   ● TastyCola

t, Time Period	y_t, Tasty Cola Sales	First Step, 12-Period Moving Average	$tr_t \times cl_t$, Centred Moving Average	$sn_t \times ir_t$, $\dfrac{y_t}{tr_t \times cl_t}$	sn_t, Table 16.12	d_t, $\dfrac{y_t}{sn_t}$	tr_t, 380.163 +9.489t	$tr_t \times sn_t$, Multiply tr_t by sn_t	$cl_t \times ir_t$, $\dfrac{y_t}{tr_t \times sn_t}$	cl_t, 3-Period Moving Average	ir_t, $\dfrac{y_t}{tr_t \times sn_t \times cl_t}$
1 (Jan.)	189				0.493	383.37	389.652	192.10	0.9839		
2	229				0.596	384.23	399.141	237.89	0.9626	0.9902	0.9721
3	249				0.595	418.49	408.630	243.13	1.0241	1.0010	1.0231
4	289				0.680	425	418.119	284.32	1.0165	1.0396	0.9778
5	260				0.564	460.99	427.608	241.17	1.0781	1.0315	1.0452
6	431	447.833			0.986	437.12	437.097	430.98	1.0000	1.0285	0.9723
7	660	452.417	450.125	1.466	1.467	449.9	446.586	655.14	1.0074	1.0046	1.0028
8	777	458	455.2085	1.707	1.693	458.95	456.075	772.13	1.0063	1.0004	1.0059
9	915	463.833	460.9165	1.985	1.990	459.79	465.564	926.47	0.9876	0.9937	0.9939
10	613	470.583	467.208	1.312	1.307	469.01	475.053	620.89	0.9873	0.9825	1.0049
11	485	475	472.7915	1.026	1.029	471.33	489.542	498.59	0.9727	0.9648	1.0082
12	277	485.417	480.2085	0.577	0.600	461.67	494.031	296.42	0.9345	0.9634	0.9700
13 (Jan.)	244	499.667	492.542	0.495	0.493	494.97	503.520	248.24	0.9829	0.9618	1.0219
14	296	514.917	507.292	0.583	0.596	496.64	513.009	305.75	0.9681	0.9924	0.9755
15	319	534.667	524.792	0.608	0.595	536.13	522.498	310.89	1.0261	1.0057	1.0203
16	370	546.833	540.75	0.684	0.680	544.12	531.987	361.75	1.0228	1.0246	0.9982
17	313	557	551.9165	0.567	0.564	554.97	541.476	305.39	1.0249	1.0237	1.0012
18	556	564.833	560.9165	0.991	0.986	563.89	550.965	543.25	1.0235	1.0197	1.0037
19	831	569.333	567.083	1.465	1.467	566.46	560.454	822.19	1.0107	1.0097	1.0010
20	960	576.167	572.75	1.676	1.693	567.04	569.943	964.91	0.9949	1.0016	0.9933
21	1,152	580.667	578.417	1.992	1.990	578.89	579.432	1,153.07	0.9991	0.9934	1.0057
22	759	586.75	583.7085	1.300	1.307	580.72	588.921	769.72	0.9861	0.9903	0.9958
23	607	591.833	589.2915	1.030	1.029	589.89	598.410	615.76	0.9858	0.9964	0.9894
24	371	600.5	596.1665	0.622	0.600	618.33	607.899	364.74	1.0172	0.9940	1.0233
25 (Jan.)	298	614.917	607.7085	0.490	0.493	604.46	617.388	304.37	0.9791	1.0027	0.9765
26	378	631	622.9585	0.607	0.596	634.23	626.877	373.62	1.0117	0.9920	1.0199
27	373	650.667	640.8335	0.582	0.595	626.89	636.366	378.64	0.9851	1.0018	0.9833
28	443	662.75	656.7085	0.675	0.680	651.47	645.855	439.18	1.0087	1.0030	1.0057
29	374	671.75	667.25	0.561	0.564	663.12	655.344	369.61	1.0119	1.0091	1.0028
30	660	677.583	674.6665	0.978	0.986	669.37	664.833	655.53	1.0068	1.0112	0.9956
31	1,004				1.467	684.39	674.322	989.23	1.0149	1.0059	1.0089
32	1,153				1.693	681.04	683.811	1,157.69	0.9959	1.0053	0.9906
33	1,388				1.990	697.49	693.300	1,379.67	1.0060	0.9954	1.0106
34	904				1.307	691.66	702.789	918.55	0.9842	0.9886	0.9955
35	715				1.029	694.85	712.278	732.93	0.9755	0.9927	0.9827
36	441				0.600	735	721.707	433.06	1.0183		

Here we use a 12-period moving average because the Tasty Cola time series data are monthly (12 time periods or "seasons" per year). If the data were quarterly, we would compute a four-period moving average. The second moving average is obtained by dropping the first sales value (y_1) from and including the next sales value (y_{13}) in the average. Thus, we obtain

$$\frac{229 + 249 + 289 + 260 + 431 + 660 + 777 + 915 + 613 + 485 + 277 + 244}{12}$$

$$= 452.417.$$

The third moving average is obtained by dropping y_2 from and including y_{14} in the average. We obtain

$$\frac{249 + 289 + 260 + 431 + 660 + 777 + 915 + 613 + 485 + 277 + 244 + 296}{12} = 458.$$

Successive moving averages are computed similarly until we include y_{36} in the last moving average. Note that we use the term *moving average* here because, as we calculate these averages, we move along by dropping the most remote observation in the previous average and by including the "next" observation in the new average.

The first moving average corresponds to a time that is midway between periods 6 and 7, the second moving average corresponds to a time that is midway between periods 7 and 8, and so forth. In order to obtain averages corresponding to time periods in the original Tasty Cola time series, we calculate **centred moving averages**. The centred moving averages are 2-period moving averages of the previously computed 12-period moving averages. Thus, the first centred moving average is

$$\frac{447.833 + 452.417}{2} = 450.125.$$

The second centred moving average is

$$\frac{452.417 + 458}{2} = 455.2085.$$

Successive centred moving averages are calculated similarly. The 12-period moving averages and centred moving averages for the Tasty Cola sales time series are given in Table 16.11.

If the original moving averages had been computed using an odd number of time series values, the centring procedure would not have been necessary. For example, if we had three seasons per year, we would compute three-period moving averages. Then, the first moving average would correspond to period 2, the second moving average would correspond to period 3, and so on. However, most seasonal time series are quarterly, monthly, or weekly, so the centring procedure is necessary.

The centred moving average in time period t is considered to equal $tr_t \times cl_t$, the estimate of $TR_t \times CL_t$, because the averaging procedure is assumed to have removed seasonal variations (note that each moving average is computed using exactly one observation from each season) and (short-term) irregular fluctuations. The (longer-term) trend effects and cyclical effects—that is, $tr_t \times cl_t$—remain.

Because the model

$$y_t = TR_t \times SN_t \times CL_t \times IR_t$$

implies that

$$SN_t \times IR_t = \frac{y_t}{TR_t \times CL_t},$$

it follows that the estimate $sn_t \times ir_t$ of $SN_t \times IR_t$ is

$$sn_t \times ir_t = \frac{y_t}{tr_t \times cl_t}.$$

Noting that the values of $sn_t \times ir_t$ are calculated in Table 16.11, we can find sn_t by grouping the values of $sn_t \times ir_t$ by months and calculating an average, $\overline{sn}_t$, for each month. These monthly averages are given for the Tasty Cola data in Table 16.12. The monthly averages are then normalized so that they sum to the number of time periods in a year. Denoting the number of time periods in a year by L (for instance, $L = 4$ for quarterly data and $L = 12$ for monthly data), we accomplish the normalization by multiplying each value of $\overline{sn}_t$ by the quantity

$$\frac{L}{\Sigma \, \overline{sn}_t} = \frac{12}{0.4925 + 0.595 + \cdots + 0.5995}$$

$$= \frac{12}{11.9895} = 1.0008758.$$

This normalization process results in the estimate $sn_t = 1.0008758(\overline{sn}_t)$, which is the estimate of SN_t. These calculations are summarized in Table 16.12.

Having calculated the values of sn_t and placed them in Table 16.11, we next define the **deseasonalized observation** in time period t to be

$$d_t = \frac{y_t}{sn_t}.$$

TABLE **16.12**   Estimation of the Seasonal
                   Factors   ● TastyCola

		$sn_t \times ir_t = y_t /$ $(tr_t \times cl_t)$		$\overline{sn}_t$	$sn_t =$ $1.0008758(\overline{sn}_t)$
		Year 1	Year 2		
1	Jan.	0.495	0.490	0.4925	0.493
2	Feb.	0.583	0.607	0.595	0.596
3	Mar.	0.608	0.582	0.595	0.595
4	Apr.	0.684	0.675	0.6795	0.680
5	May	0.567	0.561	0.564	0.564
6	Jun.	0.991	0.978	0.9845	0.986
7	Jul.	1.466	1.465	1.4655	1.467
8	Aug.	1.707	1.676	1.6915	1.693
9	Sep.	1.985	1.992	1.9885	1.990
10	Oct.	1.312	1.300	1.306	1.307
11	Nov.	1.026	1.030	1.028	1.029
12	Dec.	0.577	0.622	0.5995	0.600

FIGURE **16.12**   Plot of Tasty Cola Sales and
                    Deseasonalized Sales

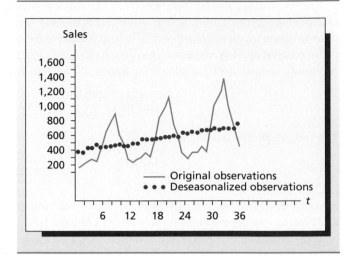

Deseasonalized observations are computed to better estimate the trend component TR_t. Dividing y_t by the estimated seasonal factor removes the seasonality from the data and allows us to better understand the nature of the trend. The deseasonalized observations are calculated in Table 16.11 plotted in Figure 16.12. Since the deseasonalized observations have a straight-line appearance, it seems reasonable to assume a linear trend

$$TR_t = \beta_0 + \beta_1 t.$$

We estimate TR_t by fitting a straight line to the deseasonalized observations. That is, we compute the least squares point estimates of the parameters in the simple linear regression model relating the dependent variable d_t to the independent variable t:

$$d_t = \beta_0 + \beta_1 t + \varepsilon_t.$$

We obtain $b_0 = 380.163$ and $b_1 = 9.489$. It follows that the estimate of TR_t is

$$tr_t = b_0 + b_1 t = 380.163 + 9.489t.$$

The values of tr_t are calculated in Table 16.11. Note that, for example, although $y_{22} = 759$ (the Tasty Cola sales in period 22 (October of year 2)) is larger than $tr_{22} = 588.921$ (the estimated trend in period 22), $d_{22} = 580.72$ is smaller than $tr_{22} = 588.921$. This implies that, on a deseasonalized basis, Tasty Cola sales were slightly down in October of year 2. This might have been caused by a slightly colder October than usual.

Thus far, we have found estimates sn_t and tr_t of SN_t and TR_t. Because the model

$$y_t = TR_t \times SN_t \times CL_t \times IR_t$$

implies that

$$CL_t \times IR_t = \frac{y_t}{TR_t \times SN_t},$$

it follows that the estimate of $CL_t \times IR_t$ is

$$cl_t \times ir_t = \frac{y_t}{tr_t \times sn_t}.$$

Moreover, experience has shown that, when considering either monthly or quarterly data, we can average out ir_t and thus calculate the estimate cl_t of CL_t by computing a three-period moving average of the $cl_t \times ir_t$ values.

Finally, we calculate the estimate ir_t of IR_t by using the equation

$$ir_t = \frac{cl_t \times ir_t}{cl_t} = \frac{y_t}{tr_t \times sn_t \times cl_t}.$$

The calculations of the values cl_t and ir_t for the Tasty Cola data are summarized in Table 16.11. Because there are only three years of data, and because most of the values of cl_t are near 1, we cannot discern a well-defined cycle. Furthermore, examining the values of ir_t, we cannot detect a pattern in the estimates of the irregular factors.

Traditionally, the estimates tr_t, sn_t, cl_t, and ir_t obtained by using the multiplicative decomposition method are used to describe the time series. However, we can also use these estimates to forecast future values of the time series. If there is no pattern in the irregular component, we predict IR_t to equal 1. Therefore, the point forecast of y_t is

$$\hat{y}_t = tr_t \times sn_t \times cl_t$$

if a well-defined cycle exists and can be predicted. The point forecast is

$$\hat{y}_t = tr_t \times sn_t$$

if a well-defined cycle does not exist or if CL_t cannot be predicted, as in the Tasty Cola example. Because values of $tr_t \times sn_t$ have been calculated in column 9 of Table 16.11, these values are the point forecasts of the $n = 36$ historical Tasty Cola sales values. Furthermore, we present in Table 16.13 point forecasts of future Tasty Cola sales in the 12 months of year 4. Recalling that the estimated trend equation is $tr_t = 380.163 + 9.489t$ and that the estimated seasonal factor for August is 1.693 (see Table 16.12), it follows, for example, that the point forecast of Tasty Cola sales in period 44 (August of year 4) is

$$\hat{y}_{44} = tr_{44} \times sn_{44}$$
$$= (380.163 + 9.489(44))(1.693)$$
$$= 797.699(1.693)$$
$$= 1350.50.$$

Although there is no theoretically correct prediction interval for y_t, a **fairly accurate approximate $100(1 - \alpha)$ percent prediction interval for y_t** is obtained by computing an interval that is centred at $\hat{y}_t$ and has a length equal to the length of the $100(1 - \alpha)$ percent prediction interval for the **deseasonalized observation d_t**. Here the interval for d_t is obtained by using the model

$$d_t = TR_t + \varepsilon_t$$
$$= \beta_0 + \beta_1 t + \varepsilon_t.$$

For instance, using MINITAB to predict d_t on the basis of this model, we find that a 95 percent prediction interval for d_{44} is [769.959, 825.439]. Because this interval has a length equal to $825.439 - 769.959 = 55.48$, it follows that an approximate 95 percent prediction interval for y_{44} is

$$\left[\hat{y}_{44} \pm \frac{55.48}{2}\right] = [1350.50 \pm 27.74]$$
$$= [1322.76, 1378.24].$$

TABLE **16.13**   **Forecasts of Future Values of Tasty Cola Sales Calculated Using the Multiplicative Decomposition Method**   ◑ TastyCola

t	sn_t	$tr_t = 380.163 + 9.489t$	Point Prediction, $\hat{y}_t = tr_t \times sn_t$	Approximate 95% Prediction Interval	y_t
37	0.493	731.273	360.52	[333.72, 387.32]	352
38	0.596	740.762	441.48	[414.56, 468.40]	445
39	0.595	750.252	446.40	[419.36, 473.44]	453
40	0.680	759.741	516.62	[489.45, 543.79]	541
41	0.564	769.231	433.85	[406.55, 461.15]	457
42	0.986	778.720	767.82	[740.38, 795.26]	762
43	1.467	788.209	1,156.30	[1,128.71, 1,183.89]	1,194
44	1.693	797.699	1,350.50	[1,322.76, 1,378.24]	1,361
45	1.990	807.188	1,606.30	[1,578.41, 1,634.19]	1,615
46	1.307	816.678	1,067.40	[1,039.35, 1,095.45]	1,059
47	1.029	826.167	850.12	[821.90, 878.34]	824
48	0.600	835.657	501.39	[473, 529.78]	495

FIGURE **16.13**   **A Plot of the Observed and Forecast Tasty Cola Sales Values**

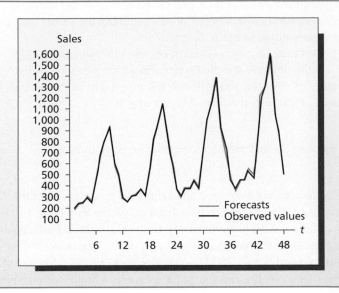

In Table 16.13, we give the approximate 95 percent prediction intervals (calculated by the above method) for Tasty Cola sales in the 12 months of year 4.

Next suppose we actually observe Tasty Cola sales in year 4, and these sales are as given in Table 16.13. In Figure 16.13, we plot the observed and forecast sales for all 48 sales periods. In practice, the comparison of the observed and forecast sales in years 1 through 3 would be used by the analyst to determine whether the forecasting equation adequately fits the historical data. An adequate fit (as indicated by Figure 16.13, for example) might prompt an analyst to use this equation to calculate forecasts for future time periods. One reason that the Tasty Cola forecasting equation

$$\hat{y}_t = tr_t \times sn_t$$
$$= (380.163 + 9.489t)sn_t$$

provides reasonable forecasts is that this equation multiplies tr_t by sn_t. Therefore, as the average level of the time series (determined by the trend) increases, the seasonal swing of the time series increases, which is consistent with the data plots in Figures 16.11 and 16.13. For example, note from Table 16.12 that the estimated seasonal factor for August is 1.693. The forecasting equation yields a prediction of Tasty Cola sales in August of year 1 equal to

$$\hat{y}_8 = [380.163 + 9.489(8)]1.693$$
$$= (456.075)(1.693)$$
$$= 772.13.$$

This implies a seasonal swing of $772.13 - 456.075 = 316.055$ (hundreds of cases) above 456.075, the estimated trend level. The forecasting equation yields a prediction of Tasty Cola sales in August of year 2 equal to

$$\hat{y}_{20} = [380.163 + 9.489(20)]1.693$$
$$= (569.943)(1.693)$$
$$= 964.91,$$

which implies an increased seasonal swing of $964.91 - 569.943 = 394.967$ (hundreds of cases) above 569.943, the estimated trend level. In general, then, the forecasting equation is appropriate for forecasting a time series with a seasonal swing that is proportional to the average level of the time series as determined by the trend—that is, a time series exhibiting increasing seasonal variation.

MINITAB carries out a modified version of the multiplicative decomposition method discussed in this section, but it is possible that MINITAB's modified version makes some conceptual errors that can result in biased estimates of the time series components. MegaStat estimates the seasonal factors and the trend line exactly as described in this section. MegaStat does not estimate the cyclical and irregular components, however, because it is often reasonable to make forecasts by using estimates of the seasonal factors and trend line.

Exercises for Section 16.4

CONCEPTS

16.11 Explain how the multiplicative decomposition model estimates seasonal factors.

16.12 Explain how the multiplicative decomposition method estimates the trend effect.

16.13 Discuss how the multiplicative decomposition method makes point forecasts of future time series values.

METHODS AND APPLICATIONS

Exercises 16.14 through 16.18 are based on the following situation: International Machinery produces a tractor and wishes to use **quarterly** tractor sales data observed in the last four years to predict quarterly tractor sales next year. The MegaStat output in Figure 16.14 gives the tractor sales data and the estimates of the seasonal factors and trend line for the data. ● IntMach

FIGURE **16.14** MegaStat Output of Tractor Sales Data for Exercises 16.14 through 16.18

t	Year	Quarter	Sales, y	Centred Moving Average	Ratio to Centred Moving Average	Seasonal Indexes	Sales, y, Deseasonalized
1	1	1	293			1.191	245.9
2	1	2	392			1.521	257.7
3	1	3	221	275.125	0.803	0.804	275.0
4	1	4	147	302.000	0.487	0.484	303.9
5	2	1	388	325.250	1.193	1.191	325.7
6	2	2	512	338.125	1.514	1.521	336.6
7	2	3	287	354.125	0.810	0.804	357.1
8	2	4	184	381.500	0.482	0.484	380.4
9	3	1	479	405.000	1.183	1.191	402.0
10	3	2	640	417.375	1.533	1.521	420.7
11	3	3	347	435.000	0.798	0.804	431.8
12	3	4	223	462.125	0.483	0.484	461.0
13	4	1	581	484.375	1.199	1.191	487.7
14	4	2	755	497.625	1.517	1.521	496.3
15	4	3	410			0.804	510.2
16	4	4	266			0.484	549.9

$y = 19.95x + 220.54$
$R^2 = 0.9965$

— Sales, y
— Deseasonalized
— Linear (Deseasonalized)

Calculation of Seasonal Indexes

	1	2	3	4	
1			0.803	0.487	
2	1.193	1.514	0.810	0.482	
3	1.183	1.533	0.798	0.483	
4	1.199	1.517			
mean:	1.192	1.522	0.804	0.484	4.001
adjusted:	1.191	1.521	0.804	0.484	4.000

16.14 Find and identify the four seasonal factors for quarters 1, 2, 3, and 4.

16.15 What type of trend is indicated by the plot of the deseasonalized data?

16.16 What is the equation of the estimated trend that has been calculated using the deseasonalized data?

16.17 Compute a point forecast of tractor sales (based on trend and seasonal factors) for each of the quarters next year.

16.18 Compute an approximate 95 percent prediction interval forecast of tractor sales for each of the quarters next year. Use the fact that the half-lengths of 95 percent prediction intervals for the deseasonalized sales values in the four quarters of next year are 14, 14.4, 14.6, and 15.

16.19 If we use the multiplicative decomposition method to analyze the quarterly bicycle sales data given in

Table 16.3 (page 574), we find that the quarterly seasonal factors are 0.46, 1.22, 1.68, and 0.64. Furthermore, if we use a statistical software package to fit a straight line to the deseasonalized sales values, we find that the estimate of the trend is ● BikeSales

$$tr_t = 22.61 + 0.59t.$$

In addition, we find that the half-lengths of 95 percent prediction intervals for the deseasonalized sales values in the four quarters of the next year are 2.80, 2.85, 2.92, and 2.98.

a. Calculate point predictions of bicycle sales in the four quarters of the next year.

b. Calculate approximate 95 percent prediction intervals for bicycle sales in the four quarters of the next year.

16.5 Exponential Smoothing

In ongoing forecasting systems, forecasts of future time series values are made each period for succeeding periods. At the end of each period, the estimates of the time series parameters and the forecasting equation need to be updated to account for the most recent observation. This updating accounts for possible changes in the parameters that may occur over time. In addition, such changes may imply that unequal weights should be applied to the time series observations when the estimates of the parameters are updated.

Simple exponential smoothing   We begin by assuming that a time series is appropriately described by the no trend equation

$$y_t = \beta_0 + \varepsilon_t.$$

When the parameter β_0 remains constant over time, we have seen that it is reasonable to forecast future values of y_t by using regression analysis (see Example 16.1). In such a case, the least squares point estimate of β_0 is

$$b_0 = \bar{y} = \text{the average of the observed time series values.}$$

When we compute the point estimate b_0, we are **equally weighting** each of the previously observed time series values $y_1, y_2, \ldots, y_n$.

When the value of the parameter β_0 is slowly changing over time, the equal weighting scheme may not be appropriate. Instead, it may be desirable to weight recent observations more heavily than remote observations. **Simple exponential smoothing** is a forecasting method that applies unequal weights to the time series observations. This unequal weighting is accomplished by using a **smoothing constant** that determines how much weight is attached to each observation. The most recent observation is given the most weight. More distantly past observations are given successively smaller weights. The procedure allows the forecaster to update the estimate of β_0 so that changes in the value of this parameter can be detected and incorporated into the forecasting equation. We illustrate simple exponential smoothing in the following example.

Example 16.6 The Cod Catch Case

Consider the cod catch data of Example 16.1, which are given in Table 16.1 (page 572). The plot of these data (in Figure 16.2 on page 572) suggests that the no trend model

$$y_t = \beta_0 + \varepsilon_t$$

may appropriately describe the cod catch series. The parameter β_0 could also be slowly changing over time.

We begin the simple exponential smoothing procedure by calculating an initial estimate of the average level β_0 of the series. This estimate is denoted S_0 and is computed by averaging the first six time series values. We obtain

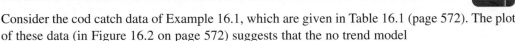

$$S_0 = \frac{\sum_{t=1}^{6} y_t}{6} = \frac{362 + 381 + \cdots + 402}{6} = 359.67.$$

Note that, because simple exponential smoothing attempts to track changes over time in the average level β_0 by using newly observed values to update the estimates of β_0, we use only six of the $n = 24$ time series observations to calculate the initial estimate of β_0. If we do this, then 18 observations remain to tell us how β_0 may be changing over time. Experience has shown that, in general, it is reasonable to calculate initial estimates in exponential smoothing procedures by using half of the historical data. However, it can be shown that, in simple exponential smoothing, using six observations is reasonable (it would not, however, be reasonable to use a very small number of observations because doing so might make the initial estimate so different from the true value of β_0 that the exponential smoothing procedure would be adversely affected).

Next assume that at the end of time period $T-1$ we have an estimate S_{T-1} of β_0. Then, assuming that in time period T we obtain a new observation y_T, we can update S_{T-1} to S_T, which is an estimate made in period T of β_0. We compute the updated estimate by using the **smoothing equation**

$$S_T = \alpha y_T + (1 - \alpha)S_{T-1}.$$

Here α is a smoothing constant between 0 and 1. The updating equation says that S_T, the estimate made in time period T of β_0, equals a fraction α (for example, 0.1) of the newly observed time series observation y_T plus a fraction $(1 - \alpha)$ (for example, 0.9) of S_{T-1}, the estimate made in time period $T-1$ of β_0. The more the average level of the process is changing, the more a newly observed time series value should influence our estimate, and thus the larger the smoothing constant α should be set. In the following, we use historical data to determine an appropriate value of α.

We will now begin with the initial estimate $S_0 = 359.67$ and update this initial estimate by applying the smoothing equation to the 24 observed cod catches. To do this, we arbitrarily set α equal to 0.02, and to judge the appropriateness of this choice of α we calculate **one-period-ahead** forecasts of the historical cod catches as we carry out the smoothing procedure. Because the initial estimate of β_0 is $S_0 = 359.67$, it follows that 360 is the rounded forecast made at time 0 for y_1, the value of the time series in period 1. Because we see from Table 16.14 that $y_1 = 362$, we have a forecast error of $362 - 360 = 2$. Using $y_1 = 362$, we can update S_0 to S_1, an estimate made in period 1 of the average level of the time series, by using the equation

$$S_1 = \alpha y_1 + (1 - \alpha)S_0$$
$$= 0.02(362) + 0.98(359.67) = 359.72.$$

Because this implies that 360 is the rounded forecast made in period 1 for y_2, and because we see from Table 16.14 that $y_2 = 381$, we have a forecast error of $381 - 360 = 21$. Using $y_2 = 381$, we can update S_1 to S_2, an estimate made in period 2 of β_0, by using the equation

$$S_2 = \alpha y_2 + (1 - \alpha)S_1$$
$$= 0.02(381) + 0.98(359.72) = 360.14.$$

TABLE **16.14** One-Period-Ahead Forecasting of the Historical Cod Catch Time Series Using Simple Exponential Smoothing with $\alpha = 0.02$ ⬥ CodCatch

Year	Month	Actual Cod Catch, y_T	Smoothed Estimate, S_T ($S_0 = 359.67$)	Forecast Made Last Period	Forecast Error	Squared Forecast Error
1	Jan.	362	359.72	360	2	4
	Feb.	381	360.14	360	21	441
	Mar.	317	359.28	360	−43	1,849
	Apr.	297	358.03	359	−62	3,844
	May	399	358.85	358	41	1,681
	Jun.	402	359.71	359	43	1,849
	Jul.	375	360.02	360	15	225
	Aug.	349	359.80	360	−11	121
	Sep.	386	360.32	360	26	676
	Oct.	328	359.68	360	−32	1,024
	Nov.	389	360.26	360	29	841
	Dec.	343	359.92	360	−17	289
2	Jan.	276	358.24	360	−84	7,056
	Feb.	334	357.75	358	−24	576
	Mar.	394	358.48	358	36	1,296
	Apr.	334	357.99	358	−24	576
	May	384	358.51	358	26	676
	Jun.	314	357.62	359	−45	2,025
	Jul.	344	357.35	358	−14	196
	Aug.	337	356.94	357	−20	400
	Sep.	345	356.70	357	−12	144
	Oct.	362	356.81	357	5	25
	Nov.	314	355.95	357	−43	1,849
	Dec.	365	356.13	356	9	81

This implies that 360 is the rounded forecast made in period 2 for y_3. We see from Table 16.14 that $y_3 = 317$, resulting in a forecast error of $317 - 360 = -43$. This procedure is continued through the entire 24 periods of historical data. The results are summarized in Table 16.14. Using the results in this table, we find that, for $\alpha = 0.02$, the sum of squared forecast errors is 27,744. To find a "good" value of α, we evaluate the sum of squared forecast errors for values of α ranging from 0.02 to 0.30 in increments of 0.02 (in most exponential smoothing applications, the value of the smoothing constant used is between 0.01 and 0.30). When we do this, we find that $\alpha = 0.02$ minimizes the sum of squared forecast errors. Since this minimizing value of α is small, it appears to be best to apply small weights to new observations, which tells us that the level of the time series is not changing very much.

In general, simple exponential smoothing is carried out as follows:

Simple Exponential Smoothing

1   Suppose that the time series $y_1, \ldots, y_n$ is described by the equation

$$y_t = \beta_0 + \varepsilon_t,$$

where the average level β_0 of the process may be slowly changing over time. Then, the estimate S_T of β_0 made in time period T is given by the **smoothing equation**

$$S_T = \alpha y_T + (1 - \alpha)S_{T-1},$$

where α is a smoothing constant between 0 and 1 and S_{T-1} is the estimate of β_0 made in time period $T - 1$.

2   A point forecast made in time period T for any future value of the time series is S_T.

3   If we observe y_{T+1} in time period $T + 1$, we can update S_T to S_{T+1} by using the equation

$$S_{T+1} = \alpha y_{T+1} + (1 - \alpha)S_T,$$

and a point forecast made in time period $T + 1$ for any future value of the time series is S_{T+1}.

Example 16.7 The Cod Catch Case

In Example 16.6, we saw that $\alpha = 0.02$ is a "good" value of the smoothing constant when forecasting the 24 observed cod catches in Table 16.14. Therefore, we will use simple exponential smoothing with $\alpha = 0.02$ to forecast future monthly cod catches. From Table 16.14, we see that $S_{24} = 356.13$ is the estimate made in month 24 of the average level β_0 of the monthly cod catches. It follows that the point forecast made in month 24 of any future monthly cod catch is 356.13 tonnes of cod. Now, assuming that we observe a cod catch in January of year 3 of $y_{25} = 384$, we can update S_{24} to S_{25} by using the equation

$$S_{25} = \alpha y_{25} + (1 - \alpha)S_{24}$$
$$= 0.02(384) + 0.98(356.13)$$
$$= 356.69.$$

This implies that the point forecast made in month 25 of any future monthly cod catch is 356.69 tonnes of cod.

By using the smoothing equation

$$S_T = \alpha y_T + (1 - \alpha)S_{T-1},$$

it can be shown that S_T, the estimate made in time period T of the average level β_0 of the time series, can be expressed as

$$S_T = \alpha y_T + \alpha(1 - \alpha)y_{T-1} + \alpha(1 - \alpha)^2 y_{T-2}$$
$$+ \cdots + \alpha(1 - \alpha)^{T-1}y_1 + (1 - \alpha)^T S_0.$$

The coefficients measuring the contributions of the observations $y_T, y_{T-1}, y_{T-2}, \ldots, y_1$—that is, $\alpha, \alpha(1-\alpha), \alpha(1-\alpha)^2, \ldots, \alpha(1-\alpha)^{T-1}$—decrease **exponentially** with time. For this reason, we refer to this procedure as simple exponential smoothing.

Because the coefficients measuring the contributions of $y_T, y_{T-1}, y_{T-2}, \ldots, y_1$ are decreasing exponentially, the most recent observation y_T makes the largest contribution to the current estimate of β_0. Older observations make smaller and smaller contributions to this estimate. Thus, remote observations are **dampened out** of the current estimate of β_0 as time advances. The rate at which remote observations are dampened out depends on the smoothing constant α. For values of α near 1, remote observations are dampened out quickly. For example, if $\alpha = 0.9$, we obtain coefficients 0.9, 0.09, 0.009, 0.0009, ... For values of α near 0, remote observations are dampened out more slowly (if $\alpha = 0.1$, we obtain coefficients 0.1, 0.09, 0.081, 0.0729, ...). The choice of a smoothing constant α is usually made by simulated forecasting of a historical data set, as illustrated in Example 16.6.

Computer software packages can be used to implement exponential smoothing. These packages choose the smoothing constant (or constants) in different ways and also compute approximate prediction intervals in different ways. Optimally, the user should carefully investigate how the computer software package implements exponential smoothing. At a minimum, the user should not trust the forecasts given by the software package if they seem illogical.

Figure 16.15 gives the MINITAB output of using simple exponential smoothing to forecast in month 24 the cod catches in future months. Note that MINITAB has selected the smoothing

FIGURE **16.15** MINITAB Output of Using Simple Exponential Smoothing to Forecast the Cod Catches

(a) The graphical forecasts

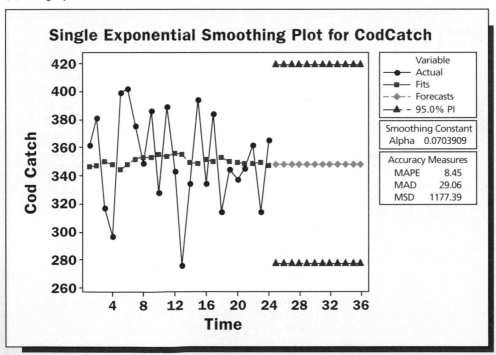

(b) The numerical forecasts of the cod catch in month 25 (and any other future month)

```
            Forecasts
            Period  Forecast    Lower     Upper
            25       348.168   276.976   419.360
```

constant $\alpha = 0.0703909$ and tells us that the point forecast and the 95 percent prediction interval forecast of the cod catch in any future month are, respectively, 348.168 and [276.976, 419.360]. Looking at Figure 16.15(a), these forecasts seem intuitively reasonable. A MegaStat output of simple exponential smoothing for the cod catch data is given in Appendix 16.3 at the Online Learning Centre.

Holt–Winters' models   Various extensions of simple exponential smoothing can be used to forecast time series that are described by models different from the model

$$y_t = \beta_0 + \varepsilon_t.$$

For example, **Holt–Winters' double exponential smoothing** can forecast time series that are described by the linear trend model

$$y_t = \beta_0 + \beta_1 t + \varepsilon_t.$$

Here we assume that β_0 and β_1 (and thus the linear trend) may be changing slowly over time. To implement Holt–Winters' double exponential smoothing, we find initial estimates of β_0 and β_1 and then use updating equations to track changes in these estimates. The updating equation for the estimate of β_0 uses a smoothing constant that MINITAB calls **alpha**, and the updating equation for the estimate of β_1 uses a smoothing constant that MINITAB calls **gamma** (see Appendix D for the updating equations). Furthermore, we show in Figure 16.16 the MINITAB output of using double exponential smoothing in month 24 to forecast the sales of the X-12 DVD player

FIGURE **16.16**   **MINITAB Output of Using Double Exponential Smoothing to Forecast DVD Player Sales**

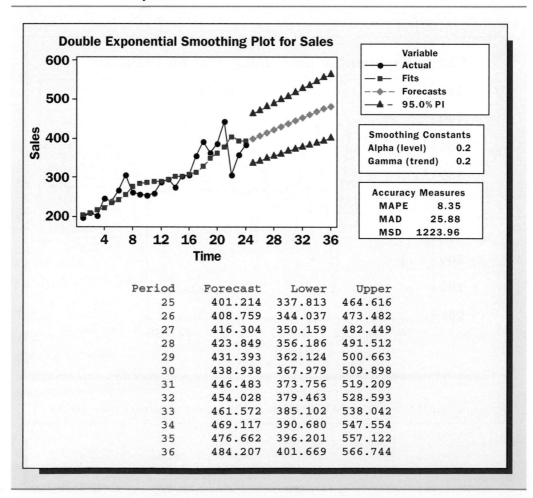

Period	Forecast	Lower	Upper
25	401.214	337.813	464.616
26	408.759	344.037	473.482
27	416.304	350.159	482.449
28	423.849	356.186	491.512
29	431.393	362.124	500.663
30	438.938	367.979	509.898
31	446.483	373.756	519.209
32	454.028	379.463	528.593
33	461.572	385.102	538.042
34	469.117	390.680	547.554
35	476.662	396.201	557.122
36	484.207	401.669	566.744

in months 25 through 36. Here MINITAB used its **default option** of choosing each of the smoothing constants alpha and gamma equal to 0.2. The resulting point and 95 percent prediction interval forecasts seem intuitively reasonable. Generally speaking, choosing alpha and gamma equal to 0.2 gives reasonable results, but (as an option) MINITAB will also choose its own values of alpha and gamma.

As another example, the **multiplicative Winters' method** can be used to forecast time series that are described by the model

$$y_t = (\beta_0 + \beta_1 t) \times SN_t + \varepsilon_t.$$

Here we assume that β_0 and β_1 (and thus the linear trend) and SN_t (which represents the seasonal pattern) may be changing slowly over time. To implement the multiplicative Winters' method, we find initial estimates of β_0, β_1, and the seasonal factors and then use updating equations to track changes in these estimates. The updating equations for the estimates of β_0, β_1, and the seasonal factors use smoothing constants that MINITAB calls **alpha**, **gamma**, and **delta** (see Appendix D for these updating equations). Furthermore, we present in Figure 16.17 the MINITAB output of using Winters' method in month 36 to forecast the sales of Tasty Cola in months 37 through 48. Here MINITAB used its default option of choosing each of the smoothing constants alpha, gamma, and delta to be 0.2. The resulting point forecasts seem intuitively reasonable, but the 95 percent prediction intervals seem very wide. These wide prediction intervals result from a combination of a short historical series (36 sales values) and MINITAB obtaining inaccurate initial estimates of the model parameters. When the historical series is long (for example, see Exercise 16.27), MINITAB usually obtains reasonable prediction intervals.

FIGURE **16.17**   MINITAB Output of Using Winters' Method to Forecast Tasty Cola Sales

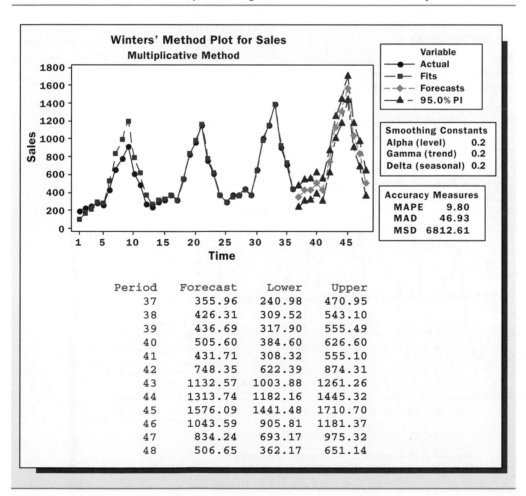

Period	Forecast	Lower	Upper
37	355.96	240.98	470.95
38	426.31	309.52	543.10
39	436.69	317.90	555.49
40	505.60	384.60	626.60
41	431.71	308.32	555.10
42	748.35	622.39	874.31
43	1132.57	1003.88	1261.26
44	1313.74	1182.16	1445.32
45	1576.09	1441.48	1710.70
46	1043.59	905.81	1181.37
47	834.24	693.17	975.32
48	506.65	362.17	651.14

Finally, note that MINITAB will not choose its own values of alpha, gamma, and delta. However, the user can simply experiment with different combinations of values of these smoothing constants until a combination is found that produces adequate results.

Exercises for Section 16.5

CONCEPTS

16.20 In general, when it is appropriate to use exponential smoothing?

16.21 What is the purpose of the smoothing constant in exponential smoothing?

16.22 What are the differences between the types of time series forecast by simple exponential smoothing, double exponential smoothing, and Winters' method?

METHODS AND APPLICATIONS

16.23 THE COD CATCH CASE ● CodCatch

Consider Table 16.14 (page 591). Verify that S_3, an estimate made in period 3 of β_0, is 359.28. Also verify that the one-period-ahead forecast error for period 4 is -62, as shown in Table 16.14.

16.24 THE COD CATCH CASE ● CodCatch

Consider Example 16.7 (page 592). Suppose that we observe a cod catch in February of year 3 of $y_{26} =$ 328. Update $S_{25} = 356.69$ to S_{26}, a point forecast made in month 26 of any future monthly cod catch. Use $\alpha = 0.02$ as in Example 16.7.

16.25 THE LUMBER PRODUCTION CASE
● LumberProd

Figure 16.18 gives the MINITAB output of using simple exponential smoothing to forecast yearly lumber

production. Here MINITAB has estimated the smoothing constant alpha to be 0.0361553. Use the MINITAB output to find and report the point prediction of and the 95 percent prediction interval for the total lumber production in a future year.

16.26 THE WATCH SALES CASE ● WatchSale

Figure 16.19 gives the MINITAB output of using double exponential smoothing in month 20 to forecast watch sales in months 21 through 26. Here we have used MINITAB's default option that sets each of the smoothing constants alpha and gamma equal to 0.2. Find and report the point prediction of and a 95 percent prediction interval for watch sales in month 21.

16.27 THE TRAVELLER'S REST CASE ● TravRest

Figure 16.20 gives the MINITAB output of using Winters' method in month 168 to forecast the monthly hotel room averages in months 169 through 180. Here we have used MINITAB's default option that sets each of the smoothing constants alpha, gamma, and delta equal to 0.2. Use the MINITAB output to find and report the point prediction of and a 95 percent prediction interval for the monthly hotel room average in period 169.

FIGURE **16.18**   MINITAB Output of Using Simple Exponential Smoothing to Forecast Lumber Production

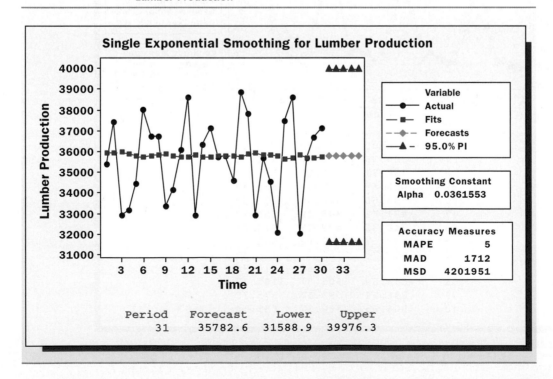

Period	Forecast	Lower	Upper
31	35782.6	31588.9	39976.3

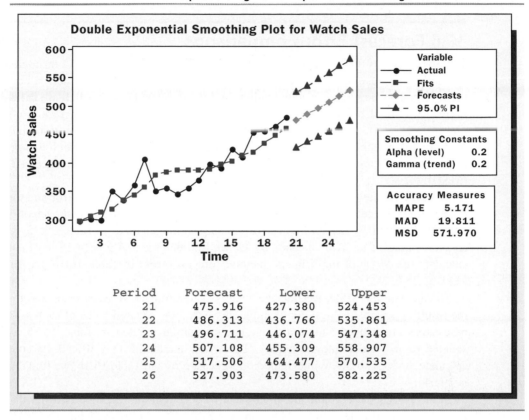

Double Exponential Smoothing Plot for Watch Sales

Period	Forecast	Lower	Upper
21	475.916	427.380	524.453
22	486.313	436.766	535.861
23	496.711	446.074	547.348
24	507.108	455.309	558.907
25	517.506	464.477	570.535
26	527.903	473.580	582.225

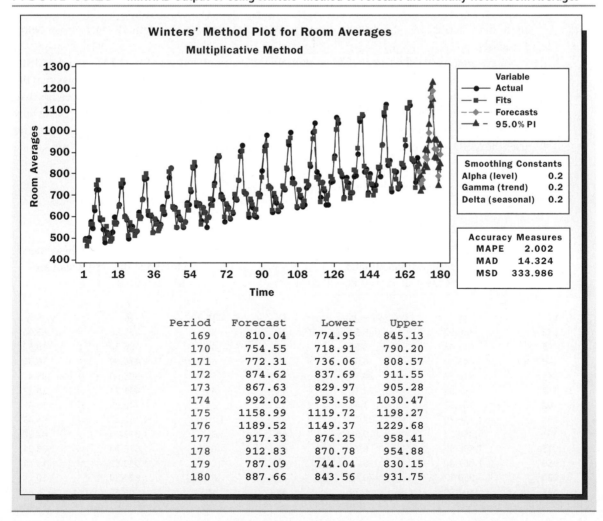

Winters' Method Plot for Room Averages
Multiplicative Method

Period	Forecast	Lower	Upper
169	810.04	774.95	845.13
170	754.55	718.91	790.20
171	772.31	736.06	808.57
172	874.62	837.69	911.55
173	867.63	829.97	905.28
174	992.02	953.58	1030.47
175	1158.99	1119.72	1198.27
176	1189.52	1149.37	1229.68
177	917.33	876.25	958.41
178	912.83	870.78	954.88
179	787.09	744.04	830.15
180	887.66	843.56	931.75

16.6 Forecast Error Comparisons

Table 16.15 gives the actual values of Tasty Cola sales (y_t) in periods 37 through 48 and the multiplicative decomposition method point forecasts ($\hat{y}_t$) of these actual values. Consider the **differences** between the actual values and the point forecasts, which are called **forecast errors** and are also given in Table 16.15. We can use these forecast errors to compare the point forecasts given by the multiplicative decomposition method with the point forecasts given by other techniques, such as Winters' method. Two criteria by which to compare forecasting methods are the **mean absolute deviation (MAD)** and the **mean squared deviation (MSD)**.

To calculate the MAD, we find the absolute value of each forecast error and then average the resulting absolute values. For example, if we find the absolute value of each of the 12 forecast errors given by the multiplicative decomposition method in Table 16.15, sum the 12 absolute values, and divide the sum by 12, we find that the MAD is 14.15. By contrast, if we calculate the MAD of the Winters' method forecast errors in Table 16.16, we find that the MAD is 25.6.

To calculate the MSD, we find the squared value of each forecast error and then average the resulting squared values. For example, if we find the squared value of each of the 12 forecast errors given by the multiplicative decomposition method in Table 16.15, sum the 12 squared values, and divide the sum by 12, we find that the MSD is 307.80. By contrast, if we calculate the MSD of the Winters' method forecast errors in Table 16.16, we find that the MSD is 892.44.

In the Tasty Cola example, the multiplicative decomposition method is better than Winters' method with respect to both the MAD and the MSD. This probably indicates that the time series components describing Tasty Cola sales are not changing, which is what the multiplicative decomposition method (and time series regression methods) assumes. If the components of a time series are slowly changing, exponential smoothing methods may give better forecasts.

In general, we want a forecasting method that gives small values of the MAD and the MSD. Note, however, that the MSD is the average of the **squared forecast errors**. It follows that the MSD, unlike the MAD, penalizes a forecasting method much more for large forecast errors than for small forecast errors. Therefore, the forecasting method that gives the smallest MSD may not be the forecasting method that gives the smallest MAD. Furthermore, the forecaster who uses the MSD to choose a forecasting method would prefer several smaller forecast errors to one large error.

TABLE 16.15	Forecast Errors Given by the Multiplicative Decomposition Method in the Tasty Cola Case ● TastyCola		
t	y_t	$\hat{y}_t$	$y_t - \hat{y}_t$
37	352	360.52	−8.52
38	445	441.48	3.52
39	453	446.40	6.6
40	541	516.62	24.38
41	457	433.85	23.15
42	762	767.82	−5.82
43	1,194	1,156.30	37.7
44	1,361	1,350.50	10.5
45	1,615	1,606.30	8.7
46	1,059	1,067.40	−8.4
47	824	850.12	−26.12
48	495	501.39	−6.39

TABLE 16.16	Forecast Errors Given by Winters' Method in the Tasty Cola Case ● TastyCola		
t	y_t	$\hat{y}_t$	$y_t - \hat{y}_t$
37	352	355.96	−3.96
38	445	426.31	18.69
39	453	436.69	16.31
40	541	505.60	35.4
41	457	431.71	25.29
42	762	748.35	13.65
43	1,194	1,132.57	61.43
44	1,361	1,313.74	47.26
45	1,615	1,576.09	38.91
46	1,059	1,043.59	15.41
47	824	834.24	−10.24
48	495	506.65	−11.65

Exercises for Section 16.6

CONCEPTS

16.28 What is the MAD? What is the MSD? How do we use these quantities?

16.29 Why does the MSD penalize a forecasting method much more for large forecast errors than for small forecast errors?

METHODS AND APPLICATIONS

Exercises 16.30 and 16.31 compare two forecasting methods— method *A* and method *B*. Suppose that method *A* gives the point forecasts 57, 61, and 70 of three future time series values. Method *B* gives the point forecasts 59, 65, and 73 of these three future values. The three future values turn out to be 60, 64, and 67.

16.30 Calculate the MAD and the MSD for method *A*. Calculate the MAD and the MSD for method *B*.

16.31 Which method—method *A* or method *B*—gives the smallest MAD? the smallest MSD?

16.7 Index Numbers

We often wish to compare a value of a time series relative to another value of the time series. For example, Statistics Canada reported in October 2006 that an 18.7 percent drop in gasoline prices decreased "the All-items Consumer Price Index (CPI) from 2.1% in August to 0.7% in September," but that when energy was excluded, "the index increased from 1.5% to 1.8% during the same period" (http://www.statcan.ca/Daily/English/061020/d061020a.htm). In order to make such comparisons, we must describe the time series. We have seen (in Section 16.4) that time series decomposition can be employed to describe a time series. Another way to describe time-related data is to use **index numbers**.

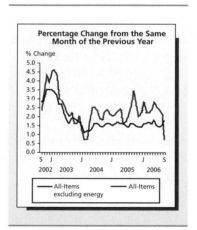

Source: http://www.statcan.ca/Daily/English/061020/c061020a.gif, http://www.statcan.ca/Daily/English/061020/c061020b.gif.

When we compare time series values to the same previous value, we say that the previous value is in the **base time period**, and successive comparisons of time series values to the value in the base period form a sequence of **index numbers**. More formally, a **simple index number** (or **simple index**) is defined as follows:

A **simple index** is obtained by dividing the current value of a time series by the value of the time series in the base time period and by multiplying this ratio by 100. That is, if y_t denotes the current value and y_0 denotes the value in the base time period, then the **simple index number** is

$$\frac{y_t}{y_0} \times 100.$$

The time series values used to construct an index are often **quantities** or **prices**. In Canada, the CPI was originally tabulated by the Department of Labour in the early 1990s. The monthly CPI is compiled by Statistics Canada and represents the retail price of 600 goods and services considered to be "a representative shopping basket" that encompasses an average household's costs, such as food, clothing, and housing. Each item in the basket is weighted based on the purchasing patterns of consumers, and the sum is computed. As explained by the Bank of Canada (see http://www.bankofcanada.ca/en/backgrounders/bg-i4.html), purchasing food typically costs more

FIGURE 16.21   Bank of Canada Inflation Calculator

How to use the Calculator
Enter any dollar amount, and the years you wish to compare, then click the CALCULATE button.

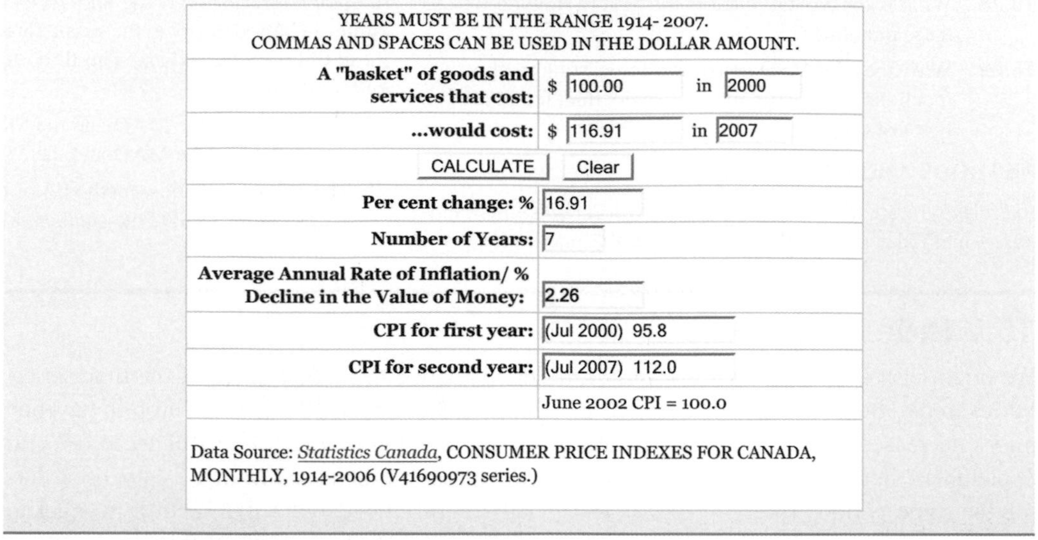

YEARS MUST BE IN THE RANGE 1914- 2007.
COMMAS AND SPACES CAN BE USED IN THE DOLLAR AMOUNT.

A "basket" of goods and services that cost:	$ 100.00	in 2000
...would cost:	$ 116.91	in 2007
CALCULATE Clear		
Per cent change: %	16.91	
Number of Years:	7	
Average Annual Rate of Inflation/ % Decline in the Value of Money:	2.26	
CPI for first year:	(Jul 2000) 95.8	
CPI for second year:	(Jul 2007) 112.0	
	June 2002 CPI = 100.0	

Data Source: _Statistics Canada_, CONSUMER PRICE INDEXES FOR CANADA, MONTHLY, 1914-2006 (V41690973 series.)

Source: http://www.bankofcanada.ca/en/rates/inflation_calc.html.

than buying clothing, so an increase in food prices has a greater weight or impact on the consumer. The CPI is then used for cost-of-living adjustments and represents a measure of inflation.

In Canada, the CPI is computed against a base year of 1992 (and the base year is always set to $100; previously the base year was 1986). The Bank of Canada has an online "Inflation Calculator" (see Figure 16.21), which uses CPI indexes from 1914. For example, a $100 bag of groceries and services in 1914 would be equivalent to $1,898.31 in 2007 with an average annual inflation rate of 3.22 percent (over 93 years). For a shorter time interval, $100 in 2000 would be equivalent to $116.91 in 2007 with the average inflation rate of 2.26 percent over these years.

Because the CPI deals with prices, and these values are quantities, the time series of index values can also be called a **quantity index**. In addition, because the CPI represents the total sum of expenditures, it is also referred to as an **aggregate price index**, computed as follows:

An **aggregate price index** is

$$\left(\frac{\Sigma p_t}{\Sigma p_0} \right) \times 100,$$

where Σp_t is the sum of the prices in the current time period and Σp_0 is the sum of the prices in the base year.

In addition, as mentioned above, Statistics Canada weights the items in the CPI calculations based on the relative importance of the items. For example, weights given by Statistics Canada for CPI items are listed in Table 16.17. In this table, the sum of the weights is 100. As can be seen in Table 16.17, shelter has a greater weight than food, which in turn has over three times the weight of clothing and footwear. This weighting means that the CPI could also be referred to as a **weighted aggregate price index**.

Two versions of this kind of index are commonly used. The first version is called a **Laspeyres index**. Here the quantities that are specified for the base year are also employed for all succeeding time periods. In general, we have the following:

A **Laspeyres index** is

$$\frac{\Sigma p_t q_0}{\Sigma p_0 q_0} \times 100,$$

where p_0 represents a base period price, q_0 represents a base period quantity, and p_t represents a current period price.

TABLE **16.17** Relative Importance Weights for the
Canadian CPI for July 2007 ◐ CPIWeights

Item	Relative Importance
All-items	100.00
Food	17.04
Shelter	26.62
Household operations and furnishings	11.10
Clothing and footwear	5.36
Transportation	19.88
Health and personal care	4.73
Recreation, education, and reading	12.20
Alcoholic beverages and tobacco products	3.07

Source: http://www.statcan.ca/english/freepub/62-001-XIE/62-001-XIE2007007.pdf.

Because the Laspeyres index employs the base period quantities in all succeeding time periods, this index allows for ready comparison of prices for identical quantities of goods purchased. Such an index is useful as long as the base quantities provide a reasonable representation of consumption patterns in succeeding time periods. However, sometimes purchasing patterns can change drastically as consumer preferences change or as dramatic price changes occur. If consumption patterns in the current period are very different from the quantities specified in the base period, then a Laspeyres index can be misleading because it relates to quantities of goods that few people would purchase.

A second version of the weighted aggregate price index is called a **Paasche index**. Here we update the quantities so that they reflect consumption patterns in the current time period.

A **Paasche index** is

$$\frac{\sum p_t q_t}{\sum p_0 q_t} \times 100,$$

where p_0 represents a base period price, p_t represents a current period price, and q_t represents a current period quantity.

Because the Paasche index uses quantities from the current period, it reflects current buying habits. However, the Paasche index requires quantity data for each year, which can be difficult to obtain. Furthermore, although each period is compared to the base period, it is difficult to compare the index at other points in time. This is because different quantities are used in different periods, and thus changes in the index are affected by changes in both prices and quantities.

Exercises for Section 16.7

CONCEPTS

16.32 Explain the difference between a simple index and an aggregate index.

16.33 Explain the difference between a Laspeyres index and a Paasche index.

METHODS AND APPLICATIONS

16.34 Following are the statistics for new motor vehicle sales in Canada between 2002 and 2006 as reported by Statistics Canada: ◐ MotorSales

Year	2002	2003	2004	2005	2006
Sales (1000s)	1733	1626	1575	1630	1666

Source: http://www.statcan.ca/english/freepub/63-007-XIE/63-007-XIE2007006.pdf.

a. By using the year 2002 as the base year, construct a simple index for the new motor vehicle sales data.

b. Interpret the index in each of the years 2004 and 2006.

c. Plot the values and assess the overall pattern.

16.35 In the following table, we present the average prices of three precious metals—gold, silver, and platinum—for the years 1988 through 1996: ● Metals

Year	Gold Price ($US/Fine Oz.)	Silver Price ($US/Fine Oz.)	Platinum Price ($US/Troy Oz.)
1988	438	6.53	523
1989	383	5.50	507
1990	385	4.82	467
1991	363	4.04	371
1992	345	3.94	360
1993	361	4.30	374
1994	385	5.29	411
1995	368	5.15	425
1996	390	5.30	410

Source: Through 1994, U.S. Bureau of Mines; thereafter, U.S. Geological Survey, *Minerals Yearbook* and *Mineral Commodities Summaries*, as presented in *Statistical Abstract of the United States*, 1997, p. 701.

a. By using the year 1988 as the base year, construct a simple index for each of gold, silver, and platinum.

b. Using the three indexes you constructed in part a, describe price trends for gold, silver, and platinum from 1988 to 1996.

c. By using the year 1988 as the base year, construct an aggregate price index for these precious metals. Using the aggregate price index, describe trends for precious metals prices from 1988 to 1996.

d. By using the year 1990 as the base year, construct an aggregate price index for these precious metals.

16.36 In the following table, we present prices for three commonly used products—bread, fruits, and beverages for the years 2000 through 2006 ● CPIWeights

Year	Bread ($ per loaf)	Fruits ($ per kg)	Beverages ($ per L)
2000	$1.22	$1.71	$0.66
2001	$1.20	$1.64	$0.67
2002	$1.19	$1.74	$0.68
2003	$1.17	$2.04	$0.69
2004	$1.17	$1.85	$0.69
2005	$1.21	$1.55	$0.69
2006	$1.29	$2.25	$0.69

a. Consider a large family that consumes 1,850 loaves of bread, 150 kg of fruits, and 1,700 L of beverages every year. Construct the Laspeyres index for these food products using 2000 as the base year. Then describe how food prices have changed for this family over this period.

b. Consider a large family with the following food consumption pattern from 2000 to 2006.

Year	Bread (loaves)	Fruits (kg)	Beverages (L)
2000	2,200	150	1,500
2001	2,100	150	1,600
2002	2,000	150	1,700
2003	1,950	150	1,800
2004	1,950	150	2,000
2005	1,900	150	2,100
2006	1,750	150	2,250

Construct the Paasche index for these food products using 2000 as the base year. How does the Paasche index compare to the Laspeyres index you constructed in part a?

CHAPTER SUMMARY

In this chapter, we have discussed using **univariate time series** models to forecast future time series values. We began by seeing that it can be useful to think of a time series as consisting of **trend**, **seasonal**, **cyclical**, and **irregular components**. If these components remain **constant** over time, then it is appropriate to describe and forecast the time series by using a **time series regression model**. We discussed using such models to describe **no trend**, a **linear trend**, a **quadratic trend**, and **constant seasonal variation** (by utilizing dummy variables). We also considered various transformations that transform **increasing seasonal variation** into constant seasonal variation, and we saw that we can use the Durbin–Watson test to check for **first-order autocorrelation**. As an alternative to using a transformation and dummy variables to model increasing seasonal variation, we can use the **multiplicative decomposition method**. We discussed this intuitive method and saw how to calculate approximate prediction intervals when using it. We then turned to a consideration of **exponential smoothing**, which is appropriate to use if the components of a time series may be **changing slowly** over time. Specifically, we discussed **simple exponential smoothing, Holt–Winters' double exponential smoothing**, and the **multiplicative Winters' method**. We next considered how to compare forecasting methods by using the **mean absolute deviation (MAD)** and the **mean squared deviation (MSD)**. We concluded this chapter by showing how to use **index numbers** to describe time-related data.

GLOSSARY OF TERMS

cyclical variation: Recurring up-and-down movements of a time series around trend levels that last more than one calendar year (often 2 to 10 years) from peak to peak or trough to trough. (page 571)

deseasonalized time series: A time series that has had the effect of seasonal variation removed. (pages 585–586)

exponential smoothing: A forecasting method that weights recent observations more heavily than remote observations. (page 571)

index number: A number that compares a value of a time series relative to another value of the time series. (page 599)

irregular component: What is "left over" in a time series after trend, cycle, and seasonal variations have been accounted for. (page 571)

moving averages: Averages of successive groups of time series observations. (page 583)

seasonal variation: Periodic patterns in a time series that repeat themselves within a calendar year and are then repeated yearly. (page 571)

smoothing constant: A number that determines how much weight is attached to each observation when using exponential smoothing. (page 590)

time series: A set of observations that has been collected in time order. (page 570)

trend: The long-run upward or downward movement that characterizes a time series over a period of time. (page 571)

univariate time series model: A model that predicts future values of a time series solely on the basis of past values of the time series. (page 570)

IMPORTANT FORMULAS AND TESTS

No trend: page 572
Linear trend: page 573
Quadratic trend: page 574
Modelling constant seasonal variation by using dummy variables: pages 574–575
The multiplicative decomposition method: pages 583–589
Simple exponential smoothing: pages 590–594
Double exponential smoothing: page 594

Winters' method: page 595
Mean absolute deviation (MAD): page 598
Mean squared deviation (MSD): page 598
Simple index: page 599
Aggregate price index: page 600
Laspeyres index: page 600
Paasche index: page 601

SUPPLEMENTARY EXERCISES

16.37 The Workplace Safety Insurance Board of Ontario (http://www.wsib.on.ca) compiles statistics of workplace accidents and deaths. In Table 16.18 are the percentages of deaths that took place on the job of the total number of work-related fatalities claimed in Ontario from 1988 to 2005. The linear regression curve is shown in Figure 16.22. ● WSIB

   a. Would you state that the percentages of deaths on the job have decreased significantly?

b. Enter the raw data into a statistical package and forecast the predicted values for the next five years. How would you assess the accuracy of these predicted numbers?

16.38 Alluring Tackle, a manufacturer of fishing equipment, makes the Bass Grabber, a type of fishing lure. The company would like to develop a prediction model that can be used to obtain point forecasts and prediction interval forecasts of the sales of the Bass

TABLE 16.18 Percentage of Fatalities Claimed That Represent Death on the Job
● WSIB

Year	Percentage of Deaths	Year	Percentage of Deaths
1988	44	1997	25
1989	43	1998	29
1990	38	1999	26
1991	40	2000	27
1992	32	2001	30
1993	27	2002	23
1994	25	2003	26
1995	26	2004	22
1996	31	2005	18

Source: http://www.wsib.on.ca/wsib/wsibsite.nsf/Public/AnnualReports.

FIGURE 16.22 Percentage of Fatalities Claimed That Represent Death on the Job

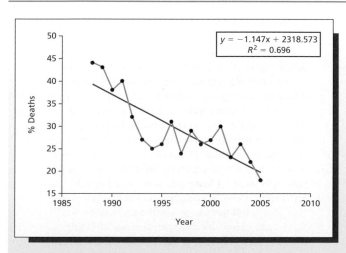

$y = -1.147x + 2318.573$
$R^2 = 0.696$

TABLE **16.19**   Sales of the Bass Grabber (in Tens of Thousands of Lures)   ● BassGrab

Period, t	Sales, y_t	Price, x_1	Average Industry Price, x_2	Advertising Expenditure, x_3
1	4.797	3.85	3.80	5.50
2	6.297	3.75	4.00	6.75
3	8.010	3.70	4.30	7.25
4	7.800	3.70	3.70	5.50
5	9.690	3.60	3.85	7.00
6	10.871	3.60	3.80	6.50
7	12.425	3.60	3.75	6.75
8	10.310	3.80	3.85	5.25
9	8.307	3.80	3.65	5.25
10	8.960	3.85	4.00	6.00
11	7.969	3.90	4.10	6.50
12	6.276	3.90	4.00	6.25
13	4.580	3.70	4.10	7.00
14	5.759	3.75	4.20	6.90
15	6.586	3.75	4.10	6.80
16	8.199	3.80	4.10	6.80
17	9.630	3.70	4.20	7.10
18	9.810	3.80	4.30	7.00
19	11.913	3.70	4.10	6.80
20	12.879	3.80	3.75	6.50
21	12.065	3.80	3.75	6.25
22	10.530	3.75	3.65	6.00
23	9.845	3.70	3.90	6.50
24	9.524	3.55	3.65	7.00
25	7.354	3.60	4.10	6.80
26	4.697	3.65	4.25	6.80
27	6.052	3.70	3.65	6.50
28	6.416	3.75	3.75	5.75
29	8.253	3.80	3.85	5.80
30	10.057	3.70	4.25	6.80

Grabber. The sales (in tens of thousands of lures) of the Bass Grabber in sales period t, where each sales period is defined to last four weeks, are denoted by the symbol y_t and are believed to be partially determined by one or more of the independent variables x_1 = the price in period t of the Bass Grabber as offered by Alluring Tackle (in dollars), x_2 = the average industry price in period t of competitors' similar lures (in dollars), and x_3 = the advertising expenditure in period t of Alluring Tackle to promote the Bass Grabber (in tens of thousands of dollars). The data in Table 16.19 have been observed over the past 30 sales periods, and a plot of these data indicates that sales of the Bass Grabber have been increasing in a linear fashion over time and have been seasonal, with sales of the lure being largest in the spring and summer, when most recreational fishing takes place. Alluring Tackle believes that this pattern will continue in the future. Hence, remembering that each year consists of 13 four-week seasons, a possible regression model for predicting y_t would relate y_t to x_1, x_2, x_3, t, and the seasonal dummy variables S_2, $S_3, \ldots, S_{13}$. Here, for example, S_2 equals 1 if sales period t is the second four-week season, and 0 otherwise. As another example, S_{13} equals 1 if sales period

t is the 13th four-week season, and 0 otherwise. If we calculate the least squares point estimates of the parameters of the model, we obtain the following prediction equation (the t statistic for the importance of each independent variable is given in parentheses under the independent variable):   ● BassGrab

$$\hat{y}_t = 0.1776 + 0.4071x_1 - 0.7837x_2 + 0.9934x_3 + 0.0435t$$
$$\phantom{\hat{y}_t =} (0.05)\quad (0.42)\quad (-1.51)\quad (4.89)\quad (6.49)$$
$$+\ 0.7800S_2 + 2.373S_3 + 3.488S_4 + 3.805S_5$$
$$ (3.16)\qquad (9.28)\qquad (12.88)\quad (13.01)$$
$$+\ 5.673S_6 + 6.738S_7 + 6.097S_8 + 4.301S_9$$
$$ (19.41)\quad (23.23)\quad (21.47)\quad (14.80)$$
$$+\ 3.856S_{10} + 2.621S_{11} + 0.9969S_{12} - 1.467S_{13}.$$
$$ (13.89)\qquad (9.24)\qquad (3.50)\qquad (-4.70)$$

a. For sales period 31, which is the fifth season of the year, x_1 will be 3.80, x_2 will be 3.90, and x_3 will be 6.80. Using these values, it can be shown that a point prediction and a 95 percent prediction interval for sales of the Bass Grabber are, respectively, 10.578 and [9.683, 11.473]. Using the given prediction equation, verify that the point prediction is 10.578.

b. Some *t* statistics indicate that some of the independent variables might not be important. Using the regression techniques of Chapter 12, try

to find a better model for predicting sales of the Bass Grabber.

16.39 INTERNET EXERCISE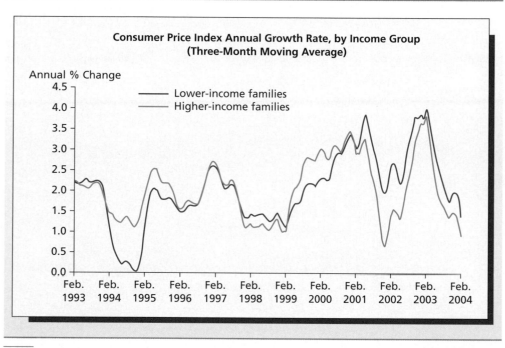

a. Below is a graph depicting the Consumer Price Index Annual Growth Rate by Income Group for Canada from 1993 to 2004. Examine the graph carefully and explain

   (1) When the CPI growth rate was different for lower- versus higher-income families.

   (2) When growth was the highest and when growth was the lowest.

b. Using a search engine of your choice, determine what happened economically in Canada during the periods of higher and lower growth rates and try to determine why, for some of these periods, income level had an effect.

Source: Statistics Canada, Catalogue no. 11-621-MIE2005030, http://www41.statcan.ca/3956/img/extra/ceb3956_004_7_e.gif.

Appendix **A**

Statistical Tables

TABLE A.1   A Binomial Probability Table:
             Binomial Probabilities (*n* between 2 and 6)

n = 2   *p*

x↓	.05	.10	.15	.20	.25	.30	.35	.40	.45	.50	
0	.9025	.8100	.7225	.6400	.5625	.4900	.4225	.3600	.3025	.2500	2
1	.0950	.1800	.2550	.3200	.3750	.4200	.4550	.4800	.4950	.5000	1
2	.0025	.0100	.0225	.0400	.0625	.0900	.1225	.1600	.2025	.2500	0
	.95	.90	.85	.80	.75	.70	.65	.60	.55	.50	x↑

n = 3   *p*

x↓	.05	.10	.15	.20	.25	.30	.35	.40	.45	.50	
0	.8574	.7290	.6141	.5120	.4219	.3430	.2746	.2160	.1664	.1250	3
1	.1354	.2430	.3251	.3840	.4219	.4410	.4436	.4320	.4084	.3750	2
2	.0071	.0270	.0574	.0960	.1406	.1890	.2389	.2880	.3341	.3750	1
3	.0001	.0010	.0034	.0080	.0156	.0270	.0429	.0640	.0911	.1250	0
	.95	.90	.85	.80	.75	.70	.65	.60	.55	.50	x↑

n = 4   *p*

x↓	.05	.10	.15	.20	.25	.30	.35	.40	.45	.50	
0	.8145	.6561	.5220	.4096	.3164	.2401	.1785	.1296	.0915	.0625	4
1	.1715	.2916	.3685	.4096	.4219	.4116	.3845	.3456	.2995	.2500	3
2	.0135	.0486	.0975	.1536	.2109	.2646	.3105	.3456	.3675	.3750	2
3	.0005	.0036	.0115	.0256	.0469	.0756	.1115	.1536	.2005	.2500	1
4	.0000	.0001	.0005	.0016	.0039	.0081	.0150	.0256	.0410	.0625	0
	.95	.90	.85	.80	.75	.70	.65	.60	.55	.50	x↑

n = 5   *p*

x↓	.05	.10	.15	.20	.25	.30	.35	.40	.45	.50	
0	.7738	.5905	.4437	.3277	.2373	.1681	.1160	.0778	.0503	.0313	5
1	.2036	.3281	.3915	.4096	.3955	.3602	.3124	.2592	.2059	.1563	4
2	.0214	.0729	.1382	.2048	.2637	.3087	.3364	.3456	.3369	.3125	3
3	.0011	.0081	.0244	.0512	.0879	.1323	.1811	.2304	.2757	.3125	2
4	.0000	.0005	.0022	.0064	.0146	.0284	.0488	.0768	.1128	.1563	1
5	.0000	.0000	.0001	.0003	.0010	.0024	.0053	.0102	.0185	.0313	0
	.95	.90	.85	.80	.75	.70	.65	.60	.55	.50	x↑

n = 6   *p*

x↓	.05	.10	.15	.20	.25	.30	.35	.40	.45	.50	
0	.7351	.5314	.3771	.2621	.1780	.1176	.0754	.0467	.0277	.0156	6
1	.2321	.3543	.3993	.3932	.3560	.3025	.2437	.1866	.1359	.0938	5
2	.0305	.0984	.1762	.2458	.2966	.3241	.3280	.3110	.2780	.2344	4
3	.0021	.0146	.0415	.0819	.1318	.1852	.2355	.2765	.3032	.3125	3
4	.0001	.0012	.0055	.0154	.0330	.0595	.0951	.1382	.1861	.2344	2
5	.0000	.0001	.0004	.0015	.0044	.0102	.0205	.0369	.0609	.0938	1
6	.0000	.0000	.0000	.0001	.0002	.0007	.0018	.0041	.0083	.0156	0
	.95	.90	.85	.80	.75	.70	.65	.60	.55	.50	x↑

(table continued)

TABLE **A.1**   *(continued)*
Binomial Probabilities (*n* between 7 and 10)

n = 7   *p*

x↓	.05	.10	.15	.20	.25	.30	.35	.40	.45	.50	
0	.6983	.4783	.3206	.2097	.1335	.0824	.0490	.0280	.0152	.0078	7
1	.2573	.3720	.3960	.3670	.3115	.2471	.1848	.1306	.0872	.0547	6
2	.0406	.1240	.2097	.2753	.3115	.3177	.2985	.2613	.2140	.1641	5
3	.0036	.0230	.0617	.1147	.1730	.2269	.2679	.2903	.2918	.2734	4
4	.0002	.0026	.0109	.0287	.0577	.0972	.1442	.1935	.2388	.2734	3
5	.0000	.0002	.0012	.0043	.0115	.0250	.0466	.0774	.1172	.1641	2
6	.0000	.0000	.0001	.0004	.0013	.0036	.0084	.0172	.0320	.0547	1
7	.0000	.0000	.0000	.0000	.0001	.0002	.0006	.0016	.0037	.0078	0
	.95	.90	.85	.80	.75	.70	.65	.60	.55	.50	x↑

n = 8   *p*

x↓	.05	.10	.15	.20	.25	.30	.35	.40	.45	.50	
0	.6634	.4305	.2725	.1678	.1001	.0576	.0319	.0168	.0084	.0039	8
1	.2793	.3826	.3847	.3355	.2670	.1977	.1373	.0896	.0548	.0313	7
2	.0515	.1488	.2376	.2936	.3115	.2965	.2587	.2090	.1569	.1094	6
3	.0054	.0331	.0839	.1468	.2076	.2541	.2786	.2787	.2568	.2188	5
4	.0004	.0046	.0185	.0459	.0865	.1361	.1875	.2322	.2627	.2734	4
5	.0000	.0004	.0026	.0092	.0231	.0467	.0808	.1239	.1719	.2188	3
6	.0000	.0000	.0002	.0011	.0038	.0100	.0217	.0413	.0703	.1094	2
7	.0000	.0000	.0000	.0001	.0004	.0012	.0033	.0079	.0164	.0313	1
8	.0000	.0000	.0000	.0000	.0000	.0001	.0002	.0007	.0017	.0039	0
	.95	.90	.85	.80	.75	.70	.65	.60	.55	.50	x↑

n = 9   *p*

x↓	.05	.10	.15	.20	.25	.30	.35	.40	.45	.50	
0	.6302	.3874	.2316	.1342	.0751	.0404	.0207	.0101	.0046	.0020	9
1	.2985	.3874	.3679	.3020	.2253	.1556	.1004	.0605	.0339	.0176	8
2	.0629	.1722	.2597	.3020	.3003	.2668	.2162	.1612	.1110	.0703	7
3	.0077	.0446	.1069	.1762	.2336	.2668	.2716	.2508	.2119	.1641	6
4	.0006	.0074	.0283	.0661	.1168	.1715	.2194	.2508	.2600	.2461	5
5	.0000	.0008	.0050	.0165	.0389	.0735	.1181	.1672	.2128	.2461	4
6	.0000	.0001	.0006	.0028	.0087	.0210	.0424	.0743	.1160	.1641	3
7	.0000	.0000	.0000	.0003	.0012	.0039	.0098	.0212	.0407	.0703	2
8	.0000	.0000	.0000	.0000	.0001	.0004	.0013	.0035	.0083	.0176	1
9	.0000	.0000	.0000	.0000	.0000	.0000	.0001	.0003	.0008	.0020	0
	.95	.90	.85	.80	.75	.70	.65	.60	.55	.50	x↑

n = 10   *p*

x↓	.05	.10	.15	.20	.25	.30	.35	.40	.45	.50	
0	.5987	.3487	.1969	.1074	.0563	.0282	.0135	.0060	.0025	.0010	10
1	.3151	.3874	.3474	.2684	.1877	.1211	.0725	.0403	.0207	.0098	9
2	.0746	.1937	.2759	.3020	.2816	.2335	.1757	.1209	.0763	.0439	8
3	.0105	.0574	.1298	.2013	.2503	.2668	.2522	.2150	.1665	.1172	7
4	.0010	.0112	.0401	.0881	.1460	.2001	.2377	.2508	.2384	.2051	6
5	.0001	.0015	.0085	.0264	.0584	.1029	.1536	.2007	.2340	.2461	5
6	.0000	.0001	.0012	.0055	.0162	.0368	.0689	.1115	.1596	.2051	4
7	.0000	.0000	.0001	.0008	.0031	.0090	.0212	.0425	.0746	.1172	3
8	.0000	.0000	.0000	.0001	.0004	.0014	.0043	.0106	.0229	.0439	2
9	.0000	.0000	.0000	.0000	.0000	.0001	.0005	.0016	.0042	.0098	1
10	.0000	.0000	.0000	.0000	.0000	.0000	.0000	.0001	.0003	.0010	0
	.95	.90	.85	.80	.75	.70	.65	.60	.55	.50	x↑

TABLE **A.1** *(continued)*
Binomial Probabilities (*n* equal to 12, 14, and 15)

n = 12   *p*

x↓	.05	.10	.15	.20	.25	.30	.35	.40	.45	.50	
0	.5404	.2824	.1422	.0687	.0317	.0130	.0057	.0022	.0008	.0002	12
1	.3413	.3766	.3012	.2062	.1267	.0712	.0368	.0174	.0075	.0029	11
2	.0988	.2301	.2924	.2835	.2323	.1678	.1088	.0639	.0339	.0161	10
3	.0173	.0852	.1720	.2362	.2581	.2397	.1954	.1419	.0923	.0537	9
4	.0021	.0213	.0683	.1329	.1936	.2311	.2367	.2128	.1700	.1208	8
5	.0002	.0038	.0193	.0532	.1032	.1585	.2039	.2270	.2225	.1934	7
6	.0000	.0005	.0040	.0155	.0401	.0792	.1281	.1766	.2124	.2256	6
7	.0000	.0000	.0006	.0033	.0115	.0291	.0591	.1009	.1489	.1934	5
8	.0000	.0000	.0001	.0005	.0024	.0078	.0199	.0420	.0762	.1208	4
9	.0000	.0000	.0000	.0001	.0004	.0015	.0048	.0125	.0277	.0537	3
10	.0000	.0000	.0000	.0000	.0000	.0002	.0008	.0025	.0068	.0161	2
11	.0000	.0000	.0000	.0000	.0000	.0000	.0001	.0003	.0010	.0029	1
12	.0000	.0000	.0000	.0000	.0000	.0000	.0000	.0000	.0001	.0002	0
	.95	.90	.85	.80	.75	.70	.65	.60	.55	.50	*x*↑

n = 14   *p*

x↓	.05	.10	.15	.20	.25	.30	.35	.40	.45	.50	
0	.4877	.2288	.1028	.0440	.0178	.0068	.0024	.0008	.0002	.0001	14
1	.3593	.3559	.2539	.1539	.0832	.0407	.0181	.0073	.0027	.0009	13
2	.1229	.2570	.2912	.2501	.1802	.1134	.0634	.0317	.0141	.0056	12
3	.0259	.1142	.2056	.2501	.2402	.1943	.1366	.0845	.0462	.0222	11
4	.0037	.0349	.0998	.1720	.2202	.2290	.2022	.1549	.1040	.0611	10
5	.0004	.0078	.0352	.0860	.1468	.1963	.2178	.2066	.1701	.1222	9
6	.0000	.0013	.0093	.0322	.0734	.1262	.1759	.2066	.2088	.1833	8
7	.0000	.0002	.0019	.0092	.0280	.0618	.1082	.1574	.1952	.2095	7
8	.0000	.0000	.0003	.0020	.0082	.0232	.0510	.0918	.1398	.1833	6
9	.0000	.0000	.0000	.0003	.0018	.0066	.0183	.0408	.0762	.1222	5
10	.0000	.0000	.0000	.0000	.0003	.0014	.0049	.0136	.0312	.0611	4
11	.0000	.0000	.0000	.0000	.0000	.0002	.0010	.0033	.0093	.0222	3
12	.0000	.0000	.0000	.0000	.0000	.0000	.0001	.0005	.0019	.0056	2
13	.0000	.0000	.0000	.0000	.0000	.0000	.0000	.0001	.0002	.0009	1
14	.0000	.0000	.0000	.0000	.0000	.0000	.0000	.0000	.0000	.0001	0
	.95	.90	.85	.80	.75	.70	.65	.60	.55	.50	*x*↑

n = 15   *p*

x↓	.05	.10	.15	.20	.25	.30	.35	.40	.45	.50	
0	.4633	.2059	.0874	.0352	.0134	.0047	.0016	.0005	.0001	.0000	15
1	.3658	.3432	.2312	.1319	.0668	.0305	.0126	.0047	.0016	.0005	14
2	.1348	.2669	.2856	.2309	.1559	.0916	.0476	.0219	.0090	.0032	13
3	.0307	.1285	.2184	.2501	.2252	.1700	.1110	.0634	.0318	.0139	12
4	.0049	.0428	.1156	.1876	.2252	.2186	.1792	.1268	.0780	.0417	11
5	.0006	.0105	.0449	.1032	.1651	.2061	.2123	.1859	.1404	.0916	10
6	.0000	.0019	.0132	.0430	.0917	.1472	.1906	.2066	.1914	.1527	9
7	.0000	.0003	.0030	.0138	.0393	.0811	.1319	.1771	.2013	.1964	8
8	.0000	.0000	.0005	.0035	.0131	.0348	.0710	.1181	.1647	.1964	7
9	.0000	.0000	.0001	.0007	.0034	.0116	.0298	.0612	.1048	.1527	6
10	.0000	.0000	.0000	.0001	.0007	.0030	.0096	.0245	.0515	.0916	5
11	.0000	.0000	.0000	.0000	.0001	.0006	.0024	.0074	.0191	.0417	4
12	.0000	.0000	.0000	.0000	.0000	.0001	.0004	.0016	.0052	.0139	3
13	.0000	.0000	.0000	.0000	.0000	.0000	.0001	.0003	.0010	.0032	2
14	.0000	.0000	.0000	.0000	.0000	.0000	.0000	.0000	.0001	.0005	1
15	.0000	.0000	.0000	.0000	.0000	.0000	.0000	.0000	.0000	.0000	0
	.95	.90	.85	.80	.75	.70	.65	.60	.55	.50	*x*↑

(table continued)

TABLE **A.1** *(continued)*
Binomial Probabilities (*n* equal to 16 and 18)

n = 16   *p*

x↓	.05	.10	.15	.20	.25	.30	.35	.40	.45	.50	
0	.4401	.1853	.0743	.0281	.0100	.0033	.0010	.0003	.0001	.0000	16
1	.3706	.3294	.2097	.1126	.0535	.0228	.0087	.0030	.0009	.0002	15
2	.1463	.2745	.2775	.2111	.1336	.0732	.0353	.0150	.0056	.0018	14
3	.0359	.1423	.2285	.2463	.2079	.1465	.0888	.0468	.0215	.0085	13
4	.0061	.0514	.1311	.2001	.2252	.2040	.1553	.1014	.0572	.0278	12
5	.0008	.0137	.0555	.1201	.1802	.2099	.2008	.1623	.1123	.0667	11
6	.0001	.0028	.0180	.0550	.1101	.1649	.1982	.1983	.1684	.1222	10
7	.0000	.0004	.0045	.0197	.0524	.1010	.1524	.1889	.1969	.1746	9
8	.0000	.0001	.0009	.0055	.0197	.0487	.0923	.1417	.1812	.1964	8
9	.0000	.0000	.0001	.0012	.0058	.0185	.0442	.0840	.1318	.1746	7
10	.0000	.0000	.0000	.0002	.0014	.0056	.0167	.0392	.0755	.1222	6
11	.0000	.0000	.0000	.0000	.0002	.0013	.0049	.0142	.0337	.0667	5
12	.0000	.0000	.0000	.0000	.0000	.0002	.0011	.0040	.0115	.0278	4
13	.0000	.0000	.0000	.0000	.0000	.0000	.0002	.0008	.0029	.0085	3
14	.0000	.0000	.0000	.0000	.0000	.0000	.0000	.0001	.0005	.0018	2
15	.0000	.0000	.0000	.0000	.0000	.0000	.0000	.0000	.0001	.0002	1
	.95	.90	.85	.80	.75	.70	.65	.60	.55	.50	*x*↑

n = 18   *p*

x↓	.05	.10	.15	.20	.25	.30	.35	.40	.45	.50	
0	.3972	.1501	.0536	.0180	.0056	.0016	.0004	.0001	.0000	.0000	18
1	.3763	.3002	.1704	.0811	.0338	.0126	.0042	.0012	.0003	.0001	17
2	.1683	.2835	.2556	.1723	.0958	.0458	.0190	.0069	.0022	.0006	16
3	.0473	.1680	.2406	.2297	.1704	.1046	.0547	.0246	.0095	.0031	15
4	.0093	.0700	.1592	.2153	.2130	.1681	.1104	.0614	.0291	.0117	14
5	.0014	.0218	.0787	.1507	.1988	.2017	.1664	.1146	.0666	.0327	13
6	.0002	.0052	.0301	.0816	.1436	.1873	.1941	.1655	.1181	.0708	12
7	.0000	.0010	.0091	.0350	.0820	.1376	.1792	.1892	.1657	.1214	11
8	.0000	.0002	.0022	.0120	.0376	.0811	.1327	.1734	.1864	.1669	10
9	.0000	.0000	.0004	.0033	.0139	.0386	.0794	.1284	.1694	.1855	9
10	.0000	.0000	.0001	.0008	.0042	.0149	.0385	.0771	.1248	.1669	8
11	.0000	.0000	.0000	.0001	.0010	.0046	.0151	.0374	.0742	.1214	7
12	.0000	.0000	.0000	.0000	.0002	.0012	.0047	.0145	.0354	.0708	6
13	.0000	.0000	.0000	.0000	.0000	.0002	.0012	.0045	.0134	.0327	5
14	.0000	.0000	.0000	.0000	.0000	.0000	.0002	.0011	.0039	.0117	4
15	.0000	.0000	.0000	.0000	.0000	.0000	.0000	.0002	.0009	.0031	3
16	.0000	.0000	.0000	.0000	.0000	.0000	.0000	.0000	.0001	.0006	2
17	.0000	.0000	.0000	.0000	.0000	.0000	.0000	.0000	.0000	.0001	1
	.95	.90	.85	.80	.75	.70	.65	.60	.55	.50	*x*↑

TABLE A.1   *(concluded)*
Binomial Probabilities (*n* equal to 20)

n = 20						p					
x↓	.05	.10	.15	.20	.25	.30	.35	.40	.45	.50	
0	.3585	.1216	.0388	.0115	.0032	.0008	.0002	.0000	.0000	.0000	20
1	.3774	.2702	.1368	.0576	.0211	.0068	.0020	.0005	.0001	.0000	19
2	.1887	.2852	.2293	.1369	.0669	.0278	.0100	.0031	.0008	.0002	18
3	.0596	.1901	.2428	.2054	.1339	.0716	.0323	.0123	.0040	.0011	17
4	.0133	.0898	.1821	.2182	.1897	.1304	.0738	.0350	.0139	.0046	16
5	.0022	.0319	.1028	.1746	.2023	.1789	.1272	.0746	.0365	.0148	15
6	.0003	.0089	.0454	.1091	.1686	.1916	.1712	.1244	.0746	.0370	14
7	.0000	.0020	.0160	.0545	.1124	.1643	.1844	.1659	.1221	.0739	13
8	.0000	.0004	.0046	.0222	.0609	.1144	.1614	.1797	.1623	.1201	12
9	.0000	.0001	.0011	.0074	.0271	.0654	.1158	.1597	.1771	.1602	11
10	.0000	.0000	.0002	.0020	.0099	.0308	.0686	.1171	.1593	.1762	10
11	.0000	.0000	.0000	.0005	.0030	.0120	.0336	.0710	.1185	.1602	9
12	.0000	.0000	.0000	.0001	.0008	.0039	.0136	.0355	.0727	.1201	8
13	.0000	.0000	.0000	.0000	.0002	.0010	.0045	.0146	.0366	.0739	7
14	.0000	.0000	.0000	.0000	.0000	.0002	.0012	.0049	.0150	.0370	6
15	.0000	.0000	.0000	.0000	.0000	.0000	.0003	.0013	.0049	.0148	5
16	.0000	.0000	.0000	.0000	.0000	.0000	.0000	.0003	.0013	.0046	4
17	.0000	.0000	.0000	.0000	.0000	.0000	.0000	.0000	.0002	.0011	3
18	.0000	.0000	.0000	.0000	.0000	.0000	.0000	.0000	.0000	.0002	2
	.95	.90	.85	.80	.75	.70	.65	.60	.55	.50	x↑

Source: Computed by D. K. Hildebrand. Found in D. K. Hildebrand and L. Ott, *Statistical Thinking for Managers*, 3rd ed. (Boston, MA: PWS-KENT Publishing Company, 1991).

TABLE A.2   A Poisson Probability Table
Poisson Probabilities (*μ* between .1 and 2.0)

x	.1	.2	.3	.4	.5	.6	.7	.8	.9	1.0
0	.9048	.8187	.7408	.6703	.6065	.5488	.4966	.4493	.4066	.3679
1	.0905	.1637	.2222	.2681	.3033	.3293	.3476	.3595	.3659	.3679
2	.0045	.0164	.0333	.0536	.0758	.0988	.1217	.1438	.1647	.1839
3	.0002	.0011	.0033	.0072	.0126	.0198	.0284	.0383	.0494	.0613
4	.0000	.0001	.0003	.0007	.0016	.0030	.0050	.0077	.0111	.0153
5	.0000	.0000	.0000	.0001	.0002	.0004	.0007	.0012	.0020	.0031
6	.0000	.0000	.0000	.0000	.0000	.0000	.0001	.0002	.0003	.0005

x	1.1	1.2	1.3	1.4	1.5	1.6	1.7	1.8	1.9	2.0
0	.3329	.3012	.2725	.2466	.2231	.2019	.1827	.1653	.1496	.1353
1	.3662	.3614	.3543	.3452	.3347	.3230	.3106	.2975	.2842	.2707
2	.2014	.2169	.2303	.2417	.2510	.2584	.2640	.2678	.2700	.2707
3	.0738	.0867	.0998	.1128	.1255	.1378	.1496	.1607	.1710	.1804
4	.0203	.0260	.0324	.0395	.0471	.0551	.0636	.0723	.0812	.0902
5	.0045	.0062	.0084	.0111	.0141	.0176	.0216	.0260	.0309	.0361
6	.0008	.0012	.0018	.0026	.0035	.0047	.0061	.0078	.0098	.0120
7	.0001	.0002	.0003	.0005	.0008	.0011	.0015	.0020	.0027	.0034
8	.0000	.0000	.0001	.0001	.0001	.0002	.0003	.0005	.0006	.0009

(table continued)

TABLE A.2   *(continued)*
Poisson Probabilities (μ between 2.1 and 5.0)

μ

x	2.1	2.2	2.3	2.4	2.5	2.6	2.7	2.8	2.9	3.0
0	.1225	.1108	.1003	.0907	.0821	.0743	.0672	.0608	.0550	.0498
1	.2572	.2438	.2306	.2177	.2052	.1931	.1815	.1703	.1596	.1494
2	.2700	.2681	.2652	.2613	.2565	.2510	.2450	.2384	.2314	.2240
3	.1890	.1966	.2033	.2090	.2138	.2176	.2205	.2225	.2237	.2240
4	.0992	.1082	.1169	.1254	.1336	.1414	.1488	.1557	.1622	.1680
5	.0417	.0476	.0538	.0602	.0668	.0735	.0804	.0872	.0940	.1008
6	.0146	.0174	.0206	.0241	.0278	.0319	.0362	.0407	.0455	.0504
7	.0044	.0055	.0068	.0083	.0099	.0118	.0139	.0163	.0188	.0216
8	.0011	.0015	.0019	.0025	.0031	.0038	.0047	.0057	.0068	.0081
9	.0003	.0004	.0005	.0007	.0009	.0011	.0014	.0018	.0022	.0027
10	.0001	.0001	.0001	.0002	.0002	.0003	.0004	.0005	.0006	.0008
11	.0000	.0000	.0000	.0000	.0000	.0001	.0001	.0001	.0002	.0002

μ

x	3.1	3.2	3.3	3.4	3.5	3.6	3.7	3.8	3.9	4.0
0	.0450	.0408	.0369	.0334	.0302	.0273	.0247	.0224	.0202	.0183
1	.1397	.1304	.1217	.1135	.1057	.0984	.0915	.0850	.0789	.0733
2	.2165	.2087	.2008	.1929	.1850	.1771	.1692	.1615	.1539	.1465
3	.2237	.2226	.2209	.2186	.2158	.2125	.2087	.2046	.2001	.1954
4	.1733	.1781	.1823	.1858	.1888	.1912	.1931	.1944	.1951	.1954
5	.1075	.1140	.1203	.1264	.1322	.1377	.1429	.1477	.1522	.1563
6	.0555	.0608	.0662	.0716	.0771	.0826	.0881	.0936	.0989	.1042
7	.0246	.0278	.0312	.0348	.0385	.0425	.0466	.0508	.0551	.0595
8	.0095	.0111	.0129	.0148	.0169	.0191	.0215	.0241	.0269	.0298
9	.0033	.0040	.0047	.0056	.0066	.0076	.0089	.0102	.0116	.0132
10	.0010	.0013	.0016	.0019	.0023	.0028	.0033	.0039	.0045	.0053
11	.0003	.0004	.0005	.0006	.0007	.0009	.0011	.0013	.0016	.0019
12	.0001	.0001	.0001	.0002	.0002	.0003	.0003	.0004	.0005	.0006
13	.0000	.0000	.0000	.0000	.0001	.0001	.0001	.0001	.0002	.0002

μ

x	4.1	4.2	4.3	4.4	4.5	4.6	4.7	4.8	4.9	5.0
0	.0166	.0150	.0136	.0123	.0111	.0101	.0091	.0082	.0074	.0067
1	.0679	.0630	.0583	.0540	.0500	.0462	.0427	.0395	.0365	.0337
2	.1393	.1323	.1254	.1188	.1125	.1063	.1005	.0948	.0894	.0842
3	.1904	.1852	.1798	.1743	.1687	.1631	.1574	.1517	.1460	.1404
4	.1951	.1944	.1933	.1917	.1898	.1875	.1849	.1820	.1789	.1755
5	.1600	.1633	.1662	.1687	.1708	.1725	.1738	.1747	.1753	.1755
6	.1093	.1143	.1191	.1237	.1281	.1323	.1362	.1398	.1432	.1462
7	.0640	.0686	.0732	.0778	.0824	.0869	.0914	.0959	.1002	.1044
8	.0328	.0360	.0393	.0428	.0463	.0500	.0537	.0575	.0614	.0653
9	.0150	.0168	.0188	.0209	.0232	.0255	.0281	.0307	.0334	.0363
10	.0061	.0071	.0081	.0092	.0104	.0118	.0132	.0147	.0164	.0181
11	.0023	.0027	.0032	.0037	.0043	.0049	.0056	.0064	.0073	.0082
12	.0008	.0009	.0011	.0013	.0016	.0019	.0022	.0026	.0030	.0034
13	.0002	.0003	.0004	.0005	.0006	.0007	.0008	.0009	.0011	.0013
14	.0001	.0001	.0001	.0001	.0002	.0002	.0003	.0003	.0004	.0005
15	.0000	.0000	.0000	.0000	.0001	.0001	.0001	.0001	.0001	.0002

TABLE A.2   *(concluded)*
Poisson Probabilities (μ between 5.5 and 20.0)

μ

x	5.5	6.0	6.5	7.0	7.5	8.0	8.5	9.0	9.5	10.0
0	.0041	.0025	.0015	.0009	.0006	.0003	.0002	.0001	.0001	.0000
1	.0225	.0149	.0098	.0064	.0041	.0027	.0017	.0011	.0007	.0005
2	.0618	.0446	.0318	.0223	.0156	.0107	.0074	.0050	.0034	.0023
3	.1133	.0892	.0688	.0521	.0389	.0286	.0208	.0150	.0107	.0076
4	.1558	.1339	.1118	.0912	.0729	.0573	.0443	.0337	.0254	.0189
5	.1714	.1606	.1454	.1277	.1094	.0916	.0752	.0607	.0483	.0378
6	.1571	.1606	.1575	.1490	.1367	.1221	.1066	.0911	.0764	.0631
7	.1234	.1377	.1462	.1490	.1465	.1396	.1294	.1171	.1037	.0901
8	.0849	.1033	.1188	.1304	.1373	.1396	.1375	.1318	.1232	.1126
9	.0519	.0688	.0858	.1014	.1144	.1241	.1299	.1318	.1300	.1251
10	.0285	.0413	.0558	.0710	.0858	.0993	.1104	.1186	.1235	.1251
11	.0143	.0225	.0330	.0452	.0585	.0722	.0853	.0970	.1067	.1137
12	.0065	.0113	.0179	.0263	.0366	.0481	.0604	.0728	.0844	.0948
13	.0028	.0052	.0089	.0142	.0211	.0296	.0395	.0504	.0617	.0729
14	.0011	.0022	.0041	.0071	.0113	.0169	.0240	.0324	.0419	.0521
15	.0004	.0009	.0018	.0033	.0057	.0090	.0136	.0194	.0265	.0347
16	.0001	.0003	.0007	.0014	.0026	.0045	.0072	.0109	.0157	.0217
17	.0000	.0001	.0003	.0006	.0012	.0021	.0036	.0058	.0088	.0128
18	.0000	.0000	.0001	.0002	.0005	.0009	.0017	.0029	.0046	.0071
19	.0000	.0000	.0000	.0001	.0002	.0004	.0008	.0014	.0023	.0037
20	.0000	.0000	.0000	.0000	.0001	.0002	.0003	.0006	.0011	.0019
21	.0000	.0000	.0000	.0000	.0000	.0001	.0001	.0003	.0005	.0009
22	.0000	.0000	.0000	.0000	.0000	.0000	.0001	.0001	.0002	.0004
23	.0000	.0000	.0000	.0000	.0000	.0000	.0000	.0000	.0001	.0002

μ

x	11.0	12.0	13.0	14.0	15.0	16.0	17.0	18.0	19.0	20.0
0	.0000	.0000	.0000	.0000	.0000	.0000	.0000	.0000	.0000	.0000
1	.0002	.0001	.0000	.0000	.0000	.0000	.0000	.0000	.0000	.0000
2	.0010	.0004	.0002	.0001	.0000	.0000	.0000	.0000	.0000	.0000
3	.0037	.0018	.0008	.0004	.0002	.0001	.0000	.0000	.0000	.0000
4	.0102	.0053	.0027	.0013	.0006	.0003	.0001	.0001	.0000	.0000
5	.0224	.0127	.0070	.0037	.0019	.0010	.0005	.0002	.0001	.0001
6	.0411	.0255	.0152	.0087	.0048	.0026	.0014	.0007	.0004	.0002
7	.0646	.0437	.0281	.0174	.0104	.0060	.0034	.0019	.0010	.0005
8	.0888	.0655	.0457	.0304	.0194	.0120	.0072	.0042	.0024	.0013
9	.1085	.0874	.0661	.0473	.0324	.0213	.0135	.0083	.0050	.0029
10	.1194	.1048	.0859	.0663	.0486	.0341	.0230	.0150	.0095	.0058
11	.1194	.1144	.1015	.0844	.0663	.0496	.0355	.0245	.0164	.0106
12	.1094	.1144	.1099	.0984	.0829	.0661	.0504	.0368	.0259	.0176
13	.0926	.1056	.1099	.1060	.0956	.0814	.0658	.0509	.0378	.0271
14	.0728	.0905	.1021	.1060	.1024	.0930	.0800	.0655	.0514	.0387
15	.0534	.0724	.0885	.0989	.1024	.0992	.0906	.0786	.0650	.0516
16	.0367	.0543	.0719	.0866	.0960	.0992	.0963	.0884	.0772	.0646
17	.0237	.0383	.0550	.0713	.0847	.0934	.0963	.0936	.0863	.0760
18	.0145	.0255	.0397	.0554	.0706	.0830	.0909	.0936	.0911	.0844
19	.0084	.0161	.0272	.0409	.0557	.0699	.0814	.0887	.0911	.0888
20	.0046	.0097	.0177	.0286	.0418	.0559	.0692	.0798	.0866	.0888
21	.0024	.0055	.0109	.0191	.0299	.0426	.0560	.0684	.0783	.0846
22	.0012	.0030	.0065	.0121	.0204	.0310	.0433	.0560	.0676	.0769
23	.0006	.0016	.0037	.0074	.0133	.0216	.0320	.0438	.0559	.0669
24	.0003	.0008	.0020	.0043	.0083	.0144	.0226	.0328	.0442	.0557
25	.0001	.0004	.0010	.0024	.0050	.0092	.0154	.0237	.0336	.0446
26	.0000	.0002	.0005	.0013	.0029	.0057	.0101	.0164	.0246	.0343
27	.0000	.0001	.0002	.0007	.0016	.0034	.0063	.0109	.0173	.0254
28	.0000	.0000	.0001	.0003	.0009	.0019	.0038	.0070	.0117	.0181
29	.0000	.0000	.0001	.0002	.0004	.0011	.0023	.0044	.0077	.0125
30	.0000	.0000	.0000	.0001	.0002	.0006	.0013	.0026	.0049	.0083
31	.0000	.0000	.0000	.0000	.0001	.0003	.0007	.0015	.0030	.0054
32	.0000	.0000	.0000	.0000	.0001	.0001	.0004	.0009	.0018	.0034
33	.0000	.0000	.0000	.0000	.0000	.0001	.0002	.0005	.0010	.0020

Source: Computed by D. K. Hildebrand. Found in D. K. Hildebrand and L. Ott, *Statistical Thinking for Managers,* 3rd ed. (Boston, MA: PWS-KENT Publishing Company, 1991).

TABLE A.3   **A Table of Areas under the Standard Normal Curve**

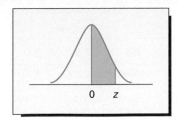

z	.00	.01	.02	.03	.04	.05	.06	.07	.08	.09
0.0	.0000	.0040	.0080	.0120	.0160	.0199	.0239	.0279	.0319	.0359
0.1	.0398	.0438	.0478	.0517	.0557	.0596	.0636	.0675	.0714	.0753
0.2	.0793	.0832	.0871	.0910	.0948	.0987	.1026	.1064	.1103	.1141
0.3	.1179	.1217	.1255	.1293	.1331	.1368	.1406	.1443	.1480	.1517
0.4	.1554	.1591	.1628	.1664	.1700	.1736	.1772	.1808	.1844	.1879
0.5	.1915	.1950	.1985	.2019	.2054	.2088	.2123	.2157	.2190	.2224
0.6	.2257	.2291	.2324	.2357	.2389	.2422	.2454	.2486	.2517	.2549
0.7	.2580	.2611	.2642	.2673	.2704	.2734	.2764	.2794	.2823	.2852
0.8	.2881	.2910	.2939	.2967	.2995	.3023	.3051	.3078	.3106	.3133
0.9	.3159	.3186	.3212	.3238	.3264	.3289	.3315	.3340	.3365	.3389
1.0	.3413	.3438	.3461	.3485	.3508	.3531	.3554	.3577	.3599	.3621
1.1	.3643	.3665	.3686	.3708	.3729	.3749	.3770	.3790	.3810	.3830
1.2	.3849	.3869	.3888	.3907	.3925	.3944	.3962	.3980	.3997	.4015
1.3	.4032	.4049	.4066	.4082	.4099	.4115	.4131	.4147	.4162	.4177
1.4	.4192	.4207	.4222	.4236	.4251	.4265	.4279	.4292	.4306	.4319
1.5	.4332	.4345	.4357	.4370	.4382	.4394	.4406	.4418	.4429	.4441
1.6	.4452	.4463	.4474	.4484	.4495	.4505	.4515	.4525	.4535	.4545
1.7	.4554	.4564	.4573	.4582	.4591	.4599	.4608	.4616	.4625	.4633
1.8	.4641	.4649	.4656	.4664	.4671	.4678	.4686	.4693	.4699	.4706
1.9	.4713	.4719	.4726	.4732	.4738	.4744	.4750	.4756	.4761	.4767
2.0	.4772	.4778	.4783	.4788	.4793	.4798	.4803	.4808	.4812	.4817
2.1	.4821	.4826	.4830	.4834	.4838	.4842	.4846	.4850	.4854	.4857
2.2	.4861	.4864	.4868	.4871	.4875	.4878	.4881	.4884	.4887	.4890
2.3	.4893	.4896	.4898	.4901	.4904	.4906	.4909	.4911	.4913	.4916
2.4	.4918	.4920	.4922	.4925	.4927	.4929	.4931	.4932	.4934	.4936
2.5	.4938	.4940	.4941	.4943	.4945	.4946	.4948	.4949	.4951	.4952
2.6	.4953	.4955	.4956	.4957	.4959	.4960	.4961	.4962	.4963	.4964
2.7	.4965	.4966	.4967	.4968	.4969	.4970	.4971	.4972	.4973	.4974
2.8	.4974	.4975	.4976	.4977	.4977	.4978	.4979	.4979	.4980	.4981
2.9	.4981	.4982	.4982	.4983	.4984	.4984	.4985	.4985	.4986	.4986
3.0	.4987	.4987	.4987	.4988	.4988	.4989	.4989	.4989	.4990	.4990

Source: A. Hald, *Statistical Tables and Formulas* (New York: Wiley, 1952), abridged from Table 1. Reproduced by permission of the publisher.

TABLE A.4   A *t* Table: Values of t_α for *df* = 1 through 48

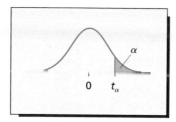

df	$t_{.100}$	$t_{.05}$	$t_{.025}$	$t_{.01}$	$t_{.005}$	$t_{.001}$	$t_{.0005}$
1	3.078	6.314	12.706	31.821	63.657	318.309	636.619
2	1.886	2.920	4.303	6.965	9.925	22.327	31.599
3	1.638	2.353	3.182	4.541	5.841	10.215	12.924
4	1.533	2.132	2.776	3.747	4.604	7.173	8.610
5	1.476	2.015	2.571	3.365	4.032	5.893	6.869
6	1.440	1.943	2.447	3.143	3.707	5.208	5.959
7	1.415	1.895	2.365	2.998	3.499	4.785	5.408
8	1.397	1.860	2.306	2.896	3.355	4.501	5.041
9	1.383	1.833	2.262	2.821	3.250	4.297	4.781
10	1.372	1.812	2.228	2.764	3.169	4.144	4.587
11	1.363	1.796	2.201	2.718	3.106	4.025	4.437
12	1.356	1.782	2.179	2.681	3.055	3.930	4.318
13	1.350	1.771	2.160	2.650	3.012	3.852	4.221
14	1.345	1.761	2.145	2.624	2.977	3.787	4.140
15	1.341	1.753	2.131	2.602	2.947	3.733	4.073
16	1.337	1.746	2.120	2.583	2.921	3.686	4.015
17	1.333	1.740	2.110	2.567	2.898	3.646	3.965
18	1.330	1.734	2.101	2.552	2.878	3.610	3.922
19	1.328	1.729	2.093	2.539	2.861	3.579	3.883
20	1.325	1.725	2.086	2.528	2.845	3.552	3.850
21	1.323	1.721	2.080	2.518	2.831	3.527	3.819
22	1.321	1.717	2.074	2.508	2.819	3.505	3.792
23	1.319	1.714	2.069	2.500	2.807	3.485	3.768
24	1.318	1.711	2.064	2.492	2.797	3.467	3.745
25	1.316	1.708	2.060	2.485	2.787	3.450	3.725
26	1.315	1.706	2.056	2.479	2.779	3.435	3.707
27	1.314	1.703	2.052	2.473	2.771	3.421	3.690
28	1.313	1.701	2.048	2.467	2.763	3.408	3.674
29	1.311	1.699	2.045	2.462	2.756	3.396	3.659
30	1.310	1.697	2.042	2.457	2.750	3.385	3.646
31	1.309	1.696	2.040	2.453	2.744	3.375	3.633
32	1.309	1.694	2.037	2.449	2.738	3.365	3.622
33	1.308	1.692	2.035	2.445	2.733	3.356	3.611
34	1.307	1.691	2.032	2.441	2.728	3.348	3.601
35	1.306	1.690	2.030	2.438	2.724	3.340	3.591
36	1.306	1.688	2.028	2.434	2.719	3.333	3.582
37	1.305	1.687	2.026	2.431	2.715	3.326	3.574
38	1.304	1.686	2.024	2.429	2.712	3.319	3.566
39	1.304	1.685	2.023	2.426	2.708	3.313	3.558
40	1.303	1.684	2.021	2.423	2.704	3.307	3.551
41	1.303	1.683	2.020	2.421	2.701	3.301	3.544
42	1.302	1.682	2.018	2.418	2.698	3.296	3.538
43	1.302	1.681	2.017	2.416	2.695	3.291	3.532
44	1.301	1.680	2.015	2.414	2.692	3.286	3.526
45	1.301	1.679	2.014	2.412	2.690	3.281	3.520
46	1.300	1.679	2.013	2.410	2.687	3.277	3.515
47	1.300	1.678	2.012	2.408	2.685	3.273	3.510
48	1.299	1.677	2.011	2.407	2.682	3.269	3.505

(table continued)

TABLE A.4 *(concluded)*   A *t* Table: Values of t_α for *df* = 49 through 100, 120, and ∞

df	$t_{.100}$	$t_{.05}$	$t_{.025}$	$t_{.01}$	$t_{.005}$	$t_{.001}$	$t_{.0005}$
49	1.299	1.677	2.010	2.405	2.680*	3.265	3.500
50	1.299	1.676	2.009	2.403	2.678	3.261	3.496
51	1.298	1.675	2.008	2.402	2.676	3.258	3.492
52	1.298	1.675	2.007	2.400	2.674	3.255	3.488
53	1.298	1.674	2.006	2.399	2.672	3.251	3.484
54	1.297	1.674	2.005	2.397	2.670	3.248	3.480
55	1.297	1.673	2.004	2.396	2.668	3.245	3.476
56	1.297	1.673	2.003	2.395	2.667	3.242	3.473
57	1.297	1.672	2.002	2.394	2.665	3.239	3.470
58	1.296	1.672	2.002	2.392	2.663	3.237	3.466
59	1.296	1.671	2.001	2.391	2.662	3.234	3.463
60	1.296	1.671	2.000	2.390	2.660	3.232	3.460
61	1.296	1.670	2.000	2.389	2.659	3.229	3.457
62	1.295	1.670	1.999	2.388	2.657	3.227	3.454
63	1.295	1.669	1.998	2.387	2.656	3.225	3.452
64	1.295	1.669	1.998	2.386	2.655	3.223	3.449
65	1.295	1.669	1.997	2.385	2.654	3.220	3.447
66	1.295	1.668	1.997	2.384	2.652	3.218	3.444
67	1.294	1.668	1.996	2.383	2.651	3.216	3.442
68	1.294	1.668	1.995	2.382	2.650	3.214	3.439
69	1.294	1.667	1.995	2.382	2.649	3.213	3.437
70	1.294	1.667	1.994	2.381	2.648	3.211	3.435
71	1.294	1.667	1.994	2.380	2.647	3.209	3.433
72	1.293	1.666	1.993	2.379	2.646	3.207	3.431
73	1.293	1.666	1.993	2.379	2.645	3.206	3.429
74	1.293	1.666	1.993	2.378	2.644	3.204	3.427
75	1.293	1.665	1.992	2.377	2.643	3.202	3.425
76	1.293	1.665	1.992	2.376	2.642	3.201	3.423
77	1.293	1.665	1.991	2.376	2.641	3.199	3.421
78	1.292	1.665	1.991	2.375	2.640	3.198	3.420
79	1.292	1.664	1.990	2.374	2.640	3.197	3.418
80	1.292	1.664	1.990	2.374	2.639	3.195	3.416
81	1.292	1.664	1.990	2.373	2.638	3.194	3.415
82	1.292	1.664	1.989	2.373	2.637	3.193	3.413
83	1.292	1.663	1.989	2.372	2.636	3.191	3.412
84	1.292	1.663	1.989	2.372	2.636	3.190	3.410
85	1.292	1.663	1.988	2.371	2.635	3.189	3.409
86	1.291	1.663	1.988	2.370	2.634	3.188	3.407
87	1.291	1.663	1.988	2.370	2.634	3.187	3.406
88	1.291	1.662	1.987	2.369	2.633	3.185	3.405
89	1.291	1.662	1.987	2.369	2.632	3.184	3.403
90	1.291	1.662	1.987	2.368	2.632	3.183	3.402
91	1.291	1.662	1.986	2.368	2.631	3.182	3.401
92	1.291	1.662	1.986	2.368	2.630	3.181	3.399
93	1.291	1.661	1.986	2.367	2.630	3.180	3.398
94	1.291	1.661	1.986	2.367	2.629	3.179	3.397
95	1.291	1.661	1.985	2.366	2.629	3.178	3.396
96	1.290	1.661	1.985	2.366	2.628	3.177	3.395
97	1.290	1.661	1.985	2.365	2.627	3.176	3.394
98	1.290	1.661	1.984	2.365	2.627	3.175	3.393
99	1.290	1.660	1.984	2.365	2.626	3.175	3.392
100	1.290	1.660	1.984	2.364	2.626	3.174	3.390
120	1.289	1.658	1.980	2.358	2.617	3.160	3.373
∞	1.282	1.645	1.960	2.326	2.576	3.090	3.291

Source: Provided by J. B. Orris using Excel.

TABLE A.5 An *F* Table: Values of $F_{.10}$

Numerator Degrees of Freedom (df_1)

df_2 \ df_1	1	2	3	4	5	6	7	8	9	10	12	15	20	24	30	40	60	120	∞
1	39.86	49.50	53.59	55.83	57.24	58.20	58.91	59.44	59.86	60.19	60.71	61.22	61.74	62.00	62.26	62.53	62.79	63.06	63.33
2	8.53	9.00	9.16	9.24	9.29	9.33	9.35	9.37	9.38	9.39	9.41	9.42	9.44	9.45	9.46	9.47	9.47	9.48	9.49
3	5.54	5.46	5.39	5.34	5.31	5.28	5.27	5.25	5.24	5.23	5.22	5.20	5.18	5.18	5.17	5.16	5.15	5.14	5.13
4	4.54	4.32	4.19	4.11	4.05	4.01	3.98	3.95	3.94	3.92	3.90	3.87	3.84	3.83	3.82	3.80	3.79	3.78	3.76
5	4.06	3.78	3.62	3.52	3.45	3.40	3.37	3.34	3.32	3.30	3.27	3.24	3.21	3.19	3.17	3.16	3.14	3.12	3.10
6	3.78	3.46	3.29	3.18	3.11	3.05	3.01	2.98	2.96	2.94	2.90	2.87	2.84	2.82	2.80	2.78	2.76	2.74	2.72
7	3.59	3.26	3.07	2.96	2.88	2.83	2.78	2.75	2.72	2.70	2.67	2.63	2.59	2.58	2.56	2.54	2.51	2.49	2.47
8	3.46	3.11	2.92	2.81	2.73	2.67	2.62	2.59	2.56	2.54	2.50	2.46	2.42	2.40	2.38	2.36	2.34	2.32	2.29
9	3.36	3.01	2.81	2.69	2.61	2.55	2.51	2.47	2.44	2.42	2.38	2.34	2.30	2.28	2.25	2.23	2.21	2.18	2.16
10	3.29	2.92	2.73	2.61	2.52	2.46	2.41	2.38	2.35	2.32	2.28	2.24	2.20	2.18	2.16	2.13	2.11	2.08	2.06
11	3.23	2.86	2.66	2.54	2.45	2.39	2.34	2.30	2.27	2.25	2.21	2.17	2.12	2.10	2.08	2.05	2.03	2.00	1.97
12	3.18	2.81	2.61	2.48	2.39	2.33	2.28	2.24	2.21	2.19	2.15	2.10	2.06	2.04	2.01	1.99	1.96	1.93	1.90
13	3.14	2.76	2.56	2.43	2.35	2.28	2.23	2.20	2.16	2.14	2.10	2.05	2.01	1.98	1.96	1.93	1.90	1.88	1.85
14	3.10	2.73	2.52	2.39	2.31	2.24	2.19	2.15	2.12	2.10	2.05	2.01	1.96	1.94	1.91	1.89	1.86	1.83	1.80
15	3.07	2.70	2.49	2.36	2.27	2.21	2.16	2.12	2.09	2.06	2.02	1.97	1.92	1.90	1.87	1.85	1.82	1.79	1.76
16	3.05	2.67	2.46	2.33	2.24	2.18	2.13	2.09	2.06	2.03	1.99	1.94	1.89	1.87	1.84	1.81	1.78	1.75	1.72
17	3.03	2.64	2.44	2.31	2.22	2.15	2.10	2.06	2.03	2.00	1.96	1.91	1.86	1.84	1.81	1.78	1.75	1.72	1.69
18	3.01	2.62	2.42	2.29	2.20	2.13	2.08	2.04	2.00	1.98	1.93	1.89	1.84	1.81	1.78	1.75	1.72	1.69	1.66
19	2.99	2.61	2.40	2.27	2.18	2.11	2.06	2.02	1.98	1.96	1.91	1.86	1.81	1.79	1.76	1.73	1.70	1.67	1.63
20	2.97	2.59	2.38	2.25	2.16	2.09	2.04	2.00	1.96	1.94	1.89	1.84	1.79	1.77	1.74	1.71	1.68	1.64	1.61
21	2.96	2.57	2.36	2.23	2.14	2.08	2.02	1.98	1.95	1.92	1.87	1.83	1.78	1.75	1.72	1.69	1.66	1.62	1.59
22	2.95	2.56	2.35	2.22	2.13	2.06	2.01	1.97	1.93	1.90	1.86	1.81	1.76	1.73	1.70	1.67	1.64	1.60	1.57
23	2.94	2.55	2.34	2.21	2.11	2.05	1.99	1.95	1.92	1.89	1.84	1.80	1.74	1.72	1.69	1.66	1.62	1.59	1.55
24	2.93	2.54	2.33	2.19	2.10	2.04	1.98	1.94	1.91	1.88	1.83	1.78	1.73	1.70	1.67	1.64	1.61	1.57	1.53
25	2.92	2.53	2.32	2.18	2.09	2.02	1.97	1.93	1.89	1.87	1.82	1.77	1.72	1.69	1.66	1.63	1.59	1.56	1.52
26	2.91	2.52	2.31	2.17	2.08	2.01	1.96	1.92	1.88	1.86	1.81	1.76	1.71	1.68	1.65	1.61	1.58	1.54	1.50
27	2.90	2.51	2.30	2.17	2.07	2.00	1.95	1.91	1.87	1.85	1.80	1.75	1.70	1.67	1.64	1.60	1.57	1.53	1.49
28	2.89	2.50	2.29	2.16	2.06	2.00	1.94	1.90	1.87	1.84	1.79	1.74	1.69	1.66	1.63	1.59	1.56	1.52	1.48
29	2.89	2.50	2.28	2.15	2.06	1.99	1.93	1.89	1.86	1.83	1.78	1.73	1.68	1.65	1.62	1.58	1.55	1.51	1.47
30	2.88	2.49	2.28	2.14	2.05	1.98	1.93	1.88	1.85	1.82	1.77	1.72	1.67	1.64	1.61	1.57	1.54	1.50	1.46
40	2.84	2.44	2.23	2.09	2.00	1.93	1.87	1.83	1.79	1.76	1.71	1.66	1.61	1.57	1.54	1.51	1.47	1.42	1.38
60	2.79	2.39	2.18	2.04	1.95	1.87	1.82	1.77	1.74	1.71	1.66	1.60	1.54	1.51	1.48	1.44	1.40	1.35	1.29
120	2.75	2.35	2.13	1.99	1.90	1.82	1.77	1.72	1.68	1.65	1.60	1.55	1.48	1.45	1.41	1.37	1.32	1.26	1.19
∞	2.71	2.30	2.08	1.94	1.85	1.77	1.72	1.67	1.63	1.60	1.55	1.49	1.42	1.38	1.34	1.30	1.24	1.17	1.00

Denominator Degrees of Freedom (df_2)

TABLE A.6   An *F* Table: Values of *F*.05

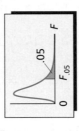

df_2 / df_1	1	2	3	4	5	6	7	8	9	10	12	15	20	24	30	40	60	120	∞
1	161.4	199.5	215.7	224.6	230.2	234.0	236.8	238.9	240.5	241.9	243.9	245.9	248.0	249.1	250.1	251.1	252.2	253.3	254.3
2	18.51	19.00	19.16	19.25	19.30	19.33	19.35	19.37	19.38	19.40	19.41	19.43	19.45	19.45	19.46	19.47	19.48	19.49	19.50
3	10.13	9.55	9.28	9.12	9.01	8.94	8.89	8.85	8.81	8.79	8.74	8.70	8.66	8.64	8.62	8.59	8.57	8.55	8.53
4	7.71	6.94	6.59	6.39	6.26	6.16	6.09	6.04	6.00	5.96	5.91	5.86	5.80	5.77	5.75	5.72	5.69	5.66	5.63
5	6.61	5.79	5.41	5.19	5.05	4.95	4.88	4.82	4.77	4.74	4.68	4.62	4.56	4.53	4.50	4.46	4.43	4.40	4.36
6	5.99	5.14	4.76	4.53	4.39	4.28	4.21	4.15	4.10	4.06	4.00	3.94	3.87	3.84	3.81	3.77	3.74	3.70	3.67
7	5.59	4.74	4.35	4.12	3.97	3.87	3.79	3.73	3.68	3.64	3.57	3.51	3.44	3.41	3.38	3.34	3.30	3.27	3.23
8	5.32	4.46	4.07	3.84	3.69	3.58	3.50	3.44	3.39	3.35	3.28	3.22	3.15	3.12	3.08	3.04	3.01	2.97	2.93
9	5.12	4.26	3.86	3.63	3.48	3.37	3.29	3.23	3.18	3.14	3.07	3.01	2.94	2.90	2.86	2.83	2.79	2.75	2.71
10	4.96	4.10	3.71	3.48	3.33	3.22	3.14	3.07	3.02	2.98	2.91	2.85	2.77	2.74	2.70	2.66	2.62	2.58	2.54
11	4.84	3.98	3.59	3.36	3.20	3.09	3.01	2.95	2.90	2.85	2.79	2.72	2.65	2.61	2.57	2.53	2.49	2.45	2.40
12	4.75	3.89	3.49	3.26	3.11	3.00	2.91	2.85	2.80	2.75	2.69	2.62	2.54	2.51	2.47	2.43	2.38	2.34	2.30
13	4.67	3.81	3.41	3.18	3.03	2.92	2.83	2.77	2.71	2.67	2.60	2.53	2.46	2.42	2.38	2.34	2.30	2.25	2.21
14	4.60	3.74	3.34	3.11	2.96	2.85	2.76	2.70	2.65	2.60	2.53	2.46	2.39	2.35	2.31	2.27	2.22	2.18	2.13
15	4.54	3.68	3.29	3.06	2.90	2.79	2.71	2.64	2.59	2.54	2.48	2.40	2.33	2.29	2.25	2.20	2.16	2.11	2.07
16	4.49	3.63	3.24	3.01	2.85	2.74	2.66	2.59	2.54	2.49	2.42	2.35	2.28	2.24	2.19	2.15	2.11	2.06	2.01
17	4.45	3.59	3.20	2.96	2.81	2.70	2.61	2.55	2.49	2.45	2.38	2.31	2.23	2.19	2.15	2.10	2.06	2.01	1.96
18	4.41	3.55	3.16	2.93	2.77	2.66	2.58	2.51	2.46	2.41	2.34	2.27	2.19	2.15	2.11	2.06	2.02	1.97	1.92
19	4.38	3.52	3.13	2.90	2.74	2.63	2.54	2.48	2.42	2.38	2.31	2.23	2.16	2.11	2.07	2.03	1.98	1.93	1.88
20	4.35	3.49	3.10	2.87	2.71	2.60	2.51	2.45	2.39	2.35	2.28	2.20	2.12	2.08	2.04	1.99	1.95	1.90	1.84
21	4.32	3.47	3.07	2.84	2.68	2.57	2.49	2.42	2.37	2.32	2.25	2.18	2.10	2.05	2.01	1.96	1.92	1.87	1.81
22	4.30	3.44	3.05	2.82	2.66	2.55	2.46	2.40	2.34	2.30	2.23	2.15	2.07	2.03	1.98	1.94	1.89	1.84	1.78
23	4.28	3.42	3.03	2.80	2.64	2.53	2.44	2.37	2.32	2.27	2.20	2.13	2.05	2.01	1.96	1.91	1.86	1.81	1.76
24	4.26	3.40	3.01	2.78	2.62	2.51	2.42	2.36	2.30	2.25	2.18	2.11	2.03	1.98	1.94	1.89	1.84	1.79	1.73
25	4.24	3.39	2.99	2.76	2.60	2.49	2.40	2.34	2.28	2.24	2.16	2.09	2.01	1.96	1.92	1.87	1.82	1.77	1.71
26	4.23	3.37	2.98	2.74	2.59	2.47	2.39	2.32	2.27	2.22	2.15	2.07	1.99	1.95	1.90	1.85	1.80	1.75	1.69
27	4.21	3.35	2.96	2.73	2.57	2.46	2.37	2.31	2.25	2.20	2.13	2.06	1.97	1.93	1.88	1.84	1.79	1.73	1.67
28	4.20	3.34	2.95	2.71	2.56	2.45	2.36	2.29	2.24	2.19	2.12	2.04	1.96	1.91	1.87	1.82	1.77	1.71	1.65
29	4.18	3.33	2.93	2.70	2.55	2.43	2.35	2.28	2.22	2.18	2.10	2.03	1.94	1.90	1.85	1.81	1.75	1.70	1.64
30	4.17	3.32	2.92	2.69	2.53	2.42	2.33	2.27	2.21	2.16	2.09	2.01	1.93	1.89	1.84	1.79	1.74	1.68	1.62
40	4.08	3.23	2.84	2.61	2.45	2.34	2.25	2.18	2.12	2.08	2.00	1.92	1.84	1.79	1.74	1.69	1.64	1.58	1.51
60	4.00	3.15	2.76	2.53	2.37	2.25	2.17	2.10	2.04	1.99	1.92	1.84	1.75	1.70	1.65	1.59	1.53	1.47	1.39
120	3.92	3.07	2.68	2.45	2.29	2.17	2.09	2.02	1.96	1.91	1.83	1.75	1.66	1.61	1.55	1.50	1.43	1.35	1.25
∞	3.84	3.00	2.60	2.37	2.21	2.10	2.01	1.94	1.88	1.83	1.75	1.67	1.57	1.52	1.46	1.39	1.32	1.22	1.00

Numerator Degrees of Freedom (df_1)

Denominator Degrees of Freedom (df_2)

Source: M. Merrington and C. M. Thompson, "Tables of Percentage Points of the Inverted Beta (*F*)-Distribution," *Biometrika* 33 (1943), pp. 73–88. Reproduced by permission of the Biometrika Trustees.

TABLE A.7 An F Table: Values of $F_{.025}$

df_1 / df_2	1	2	3	4	5	6	7	8	9	10	12	15	20	24	30	40	60	120	∞
1	647.8	799.5	864.2	899.6	921.8	937.1	948.2	956.7	963.3	968.6	976.7	984.9	993.1	997.2	1,001	1,006	1,010	1,014	1,018
2	38.51	39.00	39.17	39.25	39.30	39.33	39.36	39.37	39.39	39.40	39.41	39.43	39.45	39.46	39.46	39.47	39.48	39.49	39.50
3	17.44	16.04	15.44	15.10	14.88	14.73	14.62	14.54	14.47	14.42	14.34	14.25	14.17	14.12	14.08	14.04	13.99	13.95	13.90
4	12.22	10.65	9.98	9.60	9.36	9.20	9.07	8.98	8.90	8.84	8.75	8.66	8.56	8.51	8.46	8.41	8.36	8.31	8.26
5	10.01	8.43	7.76	7.39	7.15	6.98	6.85	6.76	6.68	6.62	6.52	6.43	6.33	6.28	6.23	6.18	6.12	6.07	6.02
6	8.81	7.26	6.60	6.23	5.99	5.82	5.70	5.60	5.52	5.46	5.37	5.27	5.17	5.12	5.07	5.01	4.96	4.90	4.85
7	8.07	6.54	5.89	5.52	5.29	5.12	4.99	4.90	4.82	4.76	4.67	4.57	4.47	4.42	4.36	4.31	4.25	4.20	4.14
8	7.57	6.06	5.42	5.05	4.82	4.65	4.53	4.43	4.36	4.30	4.20	4.10	4.00	3.95	3.89	3.84	3.78	3.73	3.67
9	7.21	5.71	5.08	4.72	4.48	4.32	4.20	4.10	4.03	3.96	3.87	3.77	3.67	3.61	3.56	3.51	3.45	3.39	3.33
10	6.94	5.46	4.83	4.47	4.24	4.07	3.95	3.85	3.78	3.72	3.62	3.52	3.42	3.37	3.31	3.26	3.20	3.14	3.08
11	6.72	5.26	4.63	4.28	4.04	3.88	3.76	3.66	3.59	3.53	3.43	3.33	3.23	3.17	3.12	3.06	3.00	2.94	2.88
12	6.55	5.10	4.47	4.12	3.89	3.73	3.61	3.51	3.44	3.37	3.28	3.18	3.07	3.02	2.96	2.91	2.85	2.79	2.72
13	6.41	4.97	4.35	4.00	3.77	3.60	3.48	3.39	3.31	3.25	3.15	3.05	2.95	2.89	2.84	2.78	2.72	2.66	2.60
14	6.30	4.86	4.24	3.89	3.66	3.50	3.38	3.29	3.21	3.15	3.05	2.95	2.84	2.79	2.73	2.67	2.61	2.55	2.49
15	6.20	4.77	4.15	3.80	3.58	3.41	3.29	3.20	3.12	3.06	2.96	2.86	2.76	2.70	2.64	2.59	2.52	2.46	2.40
16	6.12	4.69	4.08	3.73	3.50	3.34	3.22	3.12	3.05	2.99	2.89	2.79	2.68	2.63	2.57	2.51	2.45	2.38	2.32
17	6.04	4.62	4.01	3.66	3.44	3.28	3.16	3.06	2.98	2.92	2.82	2.72	2.62	2.56	2.50	2.44	2.38	2.32	2.25
18	5.98	4.56	3.95	3.61	3.38	3.22	3.10	3.01	2.93	2.87	2.77	2.67	2.56	2.50	2.44	2.38	2.32	2.26	2.19
19	5.92	4.51	3.90	3.56	3.33	3.17	3.05	2.96	2.88	2.82	2.72	2.62	2.51	2.45	2.39	2.33	2.27	2.20	2.13
20	5.87	4.46	3.86	3.51	3.29	3.13	3.01	2.91	2.84	2.77	2.68	2.57	2.46	2.41	2.35	2.29	2.22	2.16	2.09
21	5.83	4.42	3.82	3.48	3.25	3.09	2.97	2.87	2.80	2.73	2.64	2.53	2.42	2.37	2.31	2.25	2.18	2.11	2.04
22	5.79	4.38	3.78	3.44	3.22	3.05	2.93	2.84	2.76	2.70	2.60	2.50	2.39	2.33	2.27	2.21	2.14	2.08	2.00
23	5.75	4.35	3.75	3.41	3.18	3.02	2.90	2.81	2.73	2.67	2.57	2.47	2.36	2.30	2.24	2.18	2.11	2.04	1.97
24	5.72	4.32	3.72	3.38	3.15	2.99	2.87	2.78	2.70	2.64	2.54	2.44	2.33	2.27	2.21	2.15	2.08	2.01	1.94
25	5.69	4.29	3.69	3.35	3.13	2.97	2.85	2.75	2.68	2.61	2.51	2.41	2.30	2.24	2.18	2.12	2.05	1.98	1.91
26	5.66	4.27	3.67	3.33	3.10	2.94	2.82	2.73	2.65	2.59	2.49	2.39	2.28	2.22	2.16	2.09	2.03	1.95	1.88
27	5.63	4.24	3.65	3.31	3.08	2.92	2.80	2.71	2.63	2.57	2.47	2.36	2.25	2.19	2.13	2.07	2.00	1.93	1.85
28	5.61	4.22	3.63	3.29	3.06	2.90	2.78	2.69	2.61	2.55	2.45	2.34	2.23	2.17	2.11	2.05	1.98	1.91	1.83
29	5.59	4.20	3.61	3.27	3.04	2.88	2.76	2.67	2.59	2.53	2.43	2.32	2.21	2.15	2.09	2.03	1.96	1.89	1.81
30	5.57	4.18	3.59	3.25	3.03	2.87	2.75	2.65	2.57	2.51	2.41	2.31	2.20	2.14	2.07	2.01	1.94	1.87	1.79
40	5.42	4.05	3.46	3.13	2.90	2.74	2.62	2.53	2.45	2.39	2.29	2.18	2.07	2.01	1.94	1.88	1.80	1.72	1.64
60	5.29	3.93	3.34	3.01	2.79	2.63	2.51	2.41	2.33	2.27	2.17	2.06	1.94	1.88	1.82	1.74	1.67	1.58	1.48
120	5.15	3.80	3.23	2.89	2.67	2.52	2.39	2.30	2.22	2.16	2.05	1.94	1.82	1.76	1.69	1.61	1.53	1.43	1.31
∞	5.02	3.69	3.12	2.79	2.57	2.41	2.29	2.19	2.11	2.05	1.94	1.83	1.71	1.64	1.57	1.48	1.39	1.27	1.00

Numerator Degrees of Freedom (df_1)

Denominator Degrees of Freedom (df_2)

Source: M. Merrington and C. M. Thompson, "Tables of Percentage Points of the Inverted Beta (F)-Distribution," *Biometrika* 33 (1943), pp. 73–88. Reproduced by permission of the Biometrika Trustees.

TABLE A.8   An *F* Table: Values of $F_{.01}$

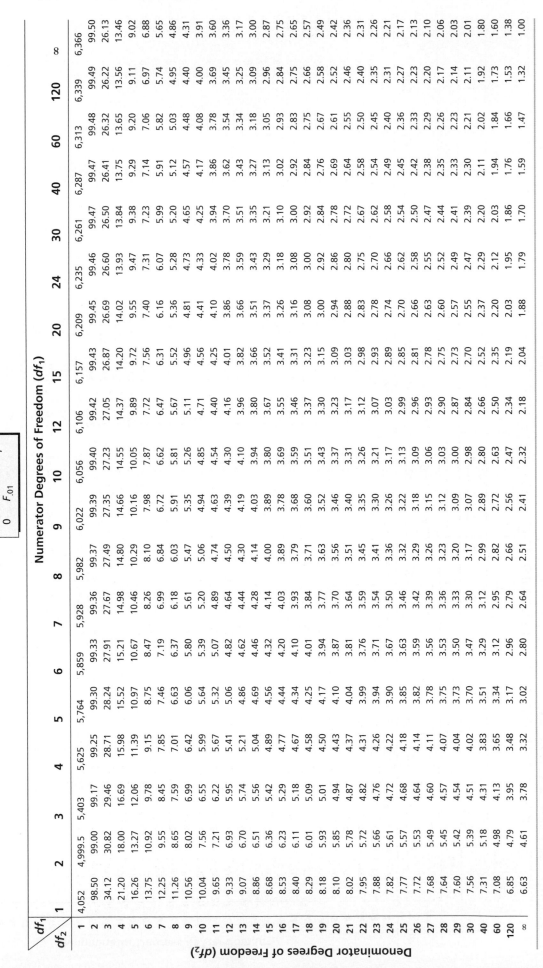

Numerator Degrees of Freedom (df_1)

df_2 \ df_1	1	2	3	4	5	6	7	8	9	10	12	15	20	24	30	40	60	120	∞
1	4,052	4,999.5	5,403	5,625	5,764	5,859	5,928	5,982	6,022	6,056	6,106	6,157	6,209	6,235	6,261	6,287	6,313	6,339	6,366
2	98.50	99.00	99.17	99.25	99.30	99.33	99.36	99.37	99.39	99.40	99.42	99.43	99.45	99.46	99.47	99.47	99.48	99.49	99.50
3	34.12	30.82	29.46	28.71	28.24	27.91	27.67	27.49	27.35	27.23	27.05	26.87	26.69	26.60	26.50	26.41	26.32	26.22	26.13
4	21.20	18.00	16.69	15.98	15.52	15.21	14.98	14.80	14.66	14.55	14.37	14.20	14.02	13.93	13.84	13.75	13.65	13.56	13.46
5	16.26	13.27	12.06	11.39	10.97	10.67	10.46	10.29	10.16	10.05	9.89	9.72	9.55	9.47	9.38	9.29	9.20	9.11	9.02
6	13.75	10.92	9.78	9.15	8.75	8.47	8.26	8.10	7.98	7.87	7.72	7.56	7.40	7.31	7.23	7.14	7.06	6.97	6.88
7	12.25	9.55	8.45	7.85	7.46	7.19	6.99	6.84	6.72	6.62	6.47	6.31	6.16	6.07	5.99	5.91	5.82	5.74	5.65
8	11.26	8.65	7.59	7.01	6.63	6.37	6.18	6.03	5.91	5.81	5.67	5.52	5.36	5.28	5.20	5.12	5.03	4.95	4.86
9	10.56	8.02	6.99	6.42	6.06	5.80	5.61	5.47	5.35	5.26	5.11	4.96	4.81	4.73	4.65	4.57	4.48	4.40	4.31
10	10.04	7.56	6.55	5.99	5.64	5.39	5.20	5.06	4.94	4.85	4.71	4.56	4.41	4.33	4.25	4.17	4.08	4.00	3.91
11	9.65	7.21	6.22	5.67	5.32	5.07	4.89	4.74	4.63	4.54	4.40	4.25	4.10	4.02	3.94	3.86	3.78	3.69	3.60
12	9.33	6.93	5.95	5.41	5.06	4.82	4.64	4.50	4.39	4.30	4.16	4.01	3.86	3.78	3.70	3.62	3.54	3.45	3.36
13	9.07	6.70	5.74	5.21	4.86	4.62	4.44	4.30	4.19	4.10	3.96	3.82	3.66	3.59	3.51	3.43	3.34	3.25	3.17
14	8.86	6.51	5.56	5.04	4.69	4.46	4.28	4.14	4.03	3.94	3.80	3.66	3.51	3.43	3.35	3.27	3.18	3.09	3.00
15	8.68	6.36	5.42	4.89	4.56	4.32	4.14	4.00	3.89	3.80	3.67	3.52	3.37	3.29	3.21	3.13	3.05	2.96	2.87
16	8.53	6.23	5.29	4.77	4.44	4.20	4.03	3.89	3.78	3.69	3.55	3.41	3.26	3.18	3.10	3.02	2.93	2.84	2.75
17	8.40	6.11	5.18	4.67	4.34	4.10	3.93	3.79	3.68	3.59	3.46	3.31	3.16	3.08	3.00	2.92	2.83	2.75	2.65
18	8.29	6.01	5.09	4.58	4.25	4.01	3.84	3.71	3.60	3.51	3.37	3.23	3.08	3.00	2.92	2.84	2.75	2.66	2.57
19	8.18	5.93	5.01	4.50	4.17	3.94	3.77	3.63	3.52	3.43	3.30	3.15	3.00	2.92	2.84	2.76	2.67	2.58	2.49
20	8.10	5.85	4.94	4.43	4.10	3.87	3.70	3.56	3.46	3.37	3.23	3.09	2.94	2.86	2.78	2.69	2.61	2.52	2.42
21	8.02	5.78	4.87	4.37	4.04	3.81	3.64	3.51	3.40	3.31	3.17	3.03	2.88	2.80	2.72	2.64	2.55	2.46	2.36
22	7.95	5.72	4.82	4.31	3.99	3.76	3.59	3.45	3.35	3.26	3.12	2.98	2.83	2.75	2.67	2.58	2.50	2.40	2.31
23	7.88	5.66	4.76	4.26	3.94	3.71	3.54	3.41	3.30	3.21	3.07	2.93	2.78	2.70	2.62	2.54	2.45	2.35	2.26
24	7.82	5.61	4.72	4.22	3.90	3.67	3.50	3.36	3.26	3.17	3.03	2.89	2.74	2.66	2.58	2.49	2.40	2.31	2.21
25	7.77	5.57	4.68	4.18	3.85	3.63	3.46	3.32	3.22	3.13	2.99	2.85	2.70	2.62	2.54	2.45	2.36	2.27	2.17
26	7.72	5.53	4.64	4.14	3.82	3.59	3.42	3.29	3.18	3.09	2.96	2.81	2.66	2.58	2.50	2.42	2.33	2.23	2.13
27	7.68	5.49	4.60	4.11	3.78	3.56	3.39	3.26	3.15	3.06	2.93	2.78	2.63	2.55	2.47	2.38	2.29	2.20	2.10
28	7.64	5.45	4.57	4.07	3.75	3.53	3.36	3.23	3.12	3.03	2.90	2.75	2.60	2.52	2.44	2.35	2.26	2.17	2.06
29	7.60	5.42	4.54	4.04	3.73	3.50	3.33	3.20	3.09	3.00	2.87	2.73	2.57	2.49	2.41	2.33	2.23	2.14	2.03
30	7.56	5.39	4.51	4.02	3.70	3.47	3.30	3.17	3.07	2.98	2.84	2.70	2.55	2.47	2.39	2.30	2.21	2.11	2.01
40	7.31	5.18	4.31	3.83	3.51	3.29	3.12	2.99	2.89	2.80	2.66	2.52	2.37	2.29	2.20	2.11	2.02	1.92	1.80
60	7.08	4.98	4.13	3.65	3.34	3.12	2.95	2.82	2.72	2.63	2.50	2.35	2.20	2.12	2.03	1.94	1.84	1.73	1.60
120	6.85	4.79	3.95	3.48	3.17	2.96	2.79	2.66	2.56	2.47	2.34	2.19	2.03	1.95	1.86	1.76	1.66	1.53	1.38
∞	6.63	4.61	3.78	3.32	3.02	2.80	2.64	2.51	2.41	2.32	2.18	2.04	1.88	1.79	1.70	1.59	1.47	1.32	1.00

Denominator Degrees of Freedom (df_2)

Source: M. Merrington and C. M. Thompson, "Tables of Percentage Points of the Inverted Beta (F)-Distribution," *Biometrika* 33 (1943), pp. 73–88. Reproduced by permission of the Biometrika Trustees.

TABLE A.9 Percentage Points of the Studentized Range
(Note: *r* is the "first value" and *v* is the "second value" referred to in Chapter 10.)

Entry is $q_{.10}$

v \ r	2	3	4	5	6	7	8	9	10	11	12	13	14	15	16	17	18	19	20
1	8.93	13.4	16.4	18.5	20.2	21.5	22.6	23.6	24.5	25.2	25.9	26.5	27.1	27.6	28.1	28.5	29.0	29.3	29.7
2	4.13	5.73	6.77	7.54	8.14	8.63	9.05	9.41	9.72	10.0	10.3	10.5	10.7	10.9	11.1	11.2	11.4	11.5	11.7
3	3.33	4.47	5.20	5.74	6.16	6.51	6.81	7.06	7.29	7.49	7.67	7.83	7.98	8.12	8.25	8.37	8.48	8.58	8.68
4	3.01	3.98	4.59	5.03	5.39	5.68	5.93	6.14	6.33	6.49	6.65	6.78	6.91	7.02	7.13	7.23	7.33	7.41	7.50
5	2.85	3.72	4.26	4.66	4.98	5.24	5.46	5.65	5.82	5.97	6.10	6.22	6.34	6.44	6.54	6.63	6.71	6.79	6.86
6	2.75	3.56	4.07	4.44	4.73	4.97	5.17	5.34	5.50	5.64	5.76	5.87	5.98	6.07	6.16	6.25	6.32	6.40	6.47
7	2.68	3.45	3.93	4.28	4.55	4.78	4.97	5.14	5.28	5.41	5.53	5.64	5.74	5.83	5.91	5.99	6.06	6.13	6.19
8	2.63	3.37	3.83	4.17	4.43	4.65	4.83	4.99	5.13	5.25	5.36	5.46	5.56	5.64	5.72	5.80	5.87	5.93	6.00
9	2.59	3.32	3.76	4.08	4.34	4.54	4.72	4.87	5.01	5.13	5.23	5.33	5.42	5.51	5.58	5.66	5.72	5.79	5.85
10	2.56	3.27	3.70	4.02	4.26	4.47	4.64	4.78	4.91	5.03	5.13	5.23	5.32	5.40	5.47	5.54	5.61	5.67	5.73
11	2.54	3.23	3.66	3.96	4.20	4.40	4.57	4.71	4.84	4.95	5.05	5.15	5.23	5.31	5.38	5.45	5.51	5.57	5.63
12	2.52	3.20	3.62	3.92	4.16	4.35	4.51	4.65	4.78	4.89	4.99	5.08	5.16	5.24	5.31	5.37	5.44	5.49	5.55
13	2.50	3.18	3.59	3.88	4.12	4.30	4.46	4.60	4.72	4.83	4.93	5.02	5.10	5.18	5.25	5.31	5.37	5.43	5.48
14	2.49	3.16	3.56	3.85	4.08	4.27	4.42	4.56	4.68	4.79	4.88	4.97	5.05	5.12	5.19	5.26	5.32	5.37	5.43
15	2.48	3.14	3.54	3.83	4.05	4.23	4.39	4.52	4.64	4.75	4.84	4.93	5.01	5.08	5.15	5.21	5.27	5.32	5.38
16	2.47	3.12	3.52	3.80	4.03	4.21	4.36	4.49	4.61	4.71	4.81	4.89	4.97	5.04	5.11	5.17	5.23	5.28	5.33
17	2.46	3.11	3.50	3.78	4.00	4.18	4.33	4.46	4.58	4.68	4.77	4.86	4.93	5.01	5.07	5.13	5.19	5.24	5.30
18	2.45	3.10	3.49	3.77	3.98	4.16	4.31	4.44	4.55	4.65	4.75	4.83	4.90	4.98	5.04	5.10	5.16	5.21	5.26
19	2.45	3.09	3.47	3.75	3.97	4.14	4.29	4.42	4.53	4.63	4.72	4.80	4.88	4.95	5.01	5.07	5.13	5.18	5.23
20	2.44	3.08	3.46	3.74	3.95	4.12	4.27	4.40	4.51	4.61	4.70	4.78	4.85	4.92	4.99	5.05	5.10	5.16	5.20
24	2.42	3.05	3.42	3.69	3.90	4.07	4.21	4.34	4.44	4.54	4.63	4.71	4.78	4.85	4.91	4.97	5.02	5.07	5.12
30	2.40	3.02	3.39	3.65	3.85	4.02	4.16	4.28	4.38	4.47	4.56	4.64	4.71	4.77	4.83	4.89	4.94	4.99	5.03
40	2.38	2.99	3.35	3.60	3.80	3.96	4.10	4.21	4.32	4.41	4.49	4.56	4.63	4.69	4.75	4.81	4.86	4.90	4.95
60	2.36	2.96	3.31	3.56	3.75	3.91	4.04	4.16	4.25	4.34	4.42	4.49	4.56	4.62	4.67	4.73	4.78	4.82	4.86
120	2.34	2.93	3.28	3.52	3.71	3.86	3.99	4.10	4.19	4.28	4.35	4.42	4.48	4.54	4.60	4.65	4.69	4.74	4.78
∞	2.33	2.90	3.24	3.48	3.66	3.81	3.93	4.04	4.13	4.21	4.28	4.35	4.41	4.47	4.52	4.57	4.61	4.65	4.69

(table continued)

TABLE A.9 *(continued)*

Entry is $q_{.05}$

v	2	3	4	5	6	7	8	9	10	11	12	13	14	15	16	17	18	19	20
1	18.0	27.0	32.8	37.1	40.4	43.1	45.4	47.4	49.1	50.6	52.0	53.2	54.3	55.4	56.3	57.2	58.0	58.8	59.6
2	6.08	8.33	9.80	10.9	11.7	12.4	13.0	13.5	14.0	14.4	14.7	15.1	15.4	15.7	15.9	16.1	16.4	16.6	16.8
3	4.50	5.91	6.82	7.50	8.04	8.48	8.85	9.18	9.46	9.72	9.95	10.2	10.3	10.5	10.7	10.8	11.0	11.1	11.2
4	3.93	5.04	5.76	6.29	6.71	7.05	7.35	7.60	7.83	8.03	8.21	8.37	8.52	8.66	8.79	8.91	9.03	9.13	9.23
5	3.64	4.60	5.22	5.67	6.03	6.33	6.58	6.80	6.99	7.17	7.32	7.47	7.60	7.72	7.83	7.93	8.03	8.12	8.21
6	3.46	4.34	4.90	5.30	5.63	5.90	6.12	6.32	6.49	6.65	6.79	6.92	7.03	7.14	7.24	7.34	7.43	7.51	7.59
7	3.34	4.16	4.68	5.06	5.36	5.61	5.82	6.00	6.16	6.30	6.43	6.55	6.66	6.76	6.85	6.94	7.02	7.10	7.17
8	3.26	4.04	4.53	4.89	5.17	5.40	5.60	5.77	5.92	6.05	6.18	6.29	6.39	6.48	6.57	6.65	6.73	6.80	6.87
9	3.20	3.95	4.41	4.76	5.02	5.24	5.43	5.59	5.74	5.87	5.98	6.09	6.19	6.28	6.36	6.44	6.51	6.58	6.64
10	3.15	3.88	4.33	4.65	4.91	5.12	5.30	5.46	5.60	5.72	5.83	5.93	6.03	6.11	6.19	6.27	6.34	6.40	6.47
11	3.11	3.82	4.26	4.57	4.82	5.03	5.20	5.35	5.49	5.61	5.71	5.81	5.90	5.98	6.06	6.13	6.20	6.27	6.33
12	3.08	3.77	4.20	4.51	4.75	4.95	5.12	5.27	5.39	5.51	5.61	5.71	5.80	5.88	5.95	6.02	6.09	6.15	6.21
13	3.06	3.73	4.15	4.45	4.69	4.88	5.05	5.19	5.32	5.43	5.53	5.63	5.71	5.79	5.86	5.93	5.99	6.05	6.11
14	3.03	3.70	4.11	4.41	4.64	4.83	4.99	5.13	5.25	5.36	5.46	5.55	5.64	5.71	5.79	5.85	5.91	5.97	6.03
15	3.01	3.67	4.08	4.37	4.59	4.78	4.94	5.08	5.20	5.31	5.40	5.49	5.57	5.65	5.72	5.78	5.85	5.90	5.96
16	3.00	3.65	4.05	4.33	4.56	4.74	4.90	5.03	5.15	5.26	5.35	5.44	5.52	5.59	5.66	5.73	5.79	5.84	5.90
17	2.98	3.63	4.02	4.30	4.52	4.70	4.86	4.99	5.11	5.21	5.31	5.39	5.47	5.54	5.61	5.67	5.73	5.79	5.84
18	2.97	3.61	4.00	4.28	4.49	4.67	4.82	4.96	5.07	5.17	5.27	5.35	5.43	5.50	5.57	5.63	5.69	5.74	5.79
19	2.96	3.59	3.98	4.25	4.47	4.65	4.79	4.92	5.04	5.14	5.23	5.31	5.39	5.46	5.53	5.59	5.65	5.70	5.75
20	2.95	3.58	3.96	4.23	4.45	4.62	4.77	4.90	5.01	5.11	5.20	5.28	5.36	5.43	5.49	5.55	5.61	5.66	5.71
24	2.92	3.53	3.90	4.17	4.37	4.54	4.68	4.81	4.92	5.01	5.10	5.18	5.25	5.32	5.38	5.44	5.49	5.55	5.59
30	2.89	3.49	3.85	4.10	4.30	4.46	4.60	4.72	4.82	4.92	5.00	5.08	5.15	5.21	5.27	5.33	5.38	5.43	5.47
40	2.86	3.44	3.79	4.04	4.23	4.39	4.52	4.63	4.73	4.82	4.90	4.98	5.04	5.11	5.16	5.22	5.27	5.31	5.36
60	2.83	3.40	3.74	3.98	4.16	4.31	4.44	4.55	4.65	4.73	4.81	4.88	4.94	5.00	5.06	5.11	5.15	5.20	5.24
120	2.80	3.36	3.68	3.92	4.10	4.24	4.36	4.47	4.56	4.64	4.71	4.78	4.84	4.90	4.95	5.00	5.04	5.09	5.13
∞	2.77	3.31	3.63	3.86	4.03	4.17	4.29	4.39	4.47	4.55	4.62	4.68	4.74	4.80	4.85	4.89	4.93	4.97	5.01

r

TABLE A.9 (concluded)

Entry is $q_{.01}$

v	\multicolumn{19}{c}{r}
	2	3	4	5	6	7	8	9	10	11	12	13	14	15	16	17	18	19	20
1	90.0	135	164	186	202	216	227	237	246	253	260	266	272	277	282	286	290	294	298
2	14.0	19.0	22.3	24.7	26.6	28.2	29.5	30.7	31.7	32.6	33.4	34.1	34.8	35.4	36.0	36.5	37.0	37.5	37.9
3	8.26	10.6	12.2	13.3	14.2	15.0	15.6	16.2	16.7	17.1	17.5	17.9	18.2	18.5	18.8	19.1	19.3	19.5	19.8
4	6.51	8.12	9.17	9.96	10.6	11.1	11.5	11.9	12.3	12.6	12.8	13.1	13.3	13.5	13.7	13.9	14.1	14.2	14.4
5	5.70	6.97	7.80	8.42	8.91	9.32	9.67	9.97	10.2	10.5	10.7	10.9	11.1	11.2	11.4	11.6	11.7	11.8	11.9
6	5.24	6.33	7.03	7.56	7.97	8.32	8.61	8.87	9.10	9.30	9.49	9.65	9.81	9.95	10.1	10.2	10.3	10.4	10.5
7	4.95	5.92	6.54	7.01	7.37	7.68	7.94	8.17	8.37	8.55	8.71	8.86	9.00	9.12	9.24	9.35	9.46	9.55	9.65
8	4.74	5.63	6.20	6.63	6.96	7.24	7.47	7.68	7.87	8.03	8.18	8.31	8.44	8.55	8.66	8.76	8.85	8.94	9.03
9	4.60	5.43	5.96	6.35	6.66	6.91	7.13	7.32	7.49	7.65	7.78	7.91	8.03	8.13	8.23	8.32	8.41	8.49	8.57
10	4.48	5.27	5.77	6.14	6.43	6.67	6.87	7.05	7.21	7.36	7.48	7.60	7.71	7.81	7.91	7.99	8.07	8.15	8.22
11	4.39	5.14	5.62	5.97	6.25	6.48	6.67	6.84	6.99	7.13	7.25	7.36	7.46	7.56	7.65	7.73	7.8	7.88	7.95
12	4.32	5.04	5.50	5.84	6.10	6.32	6.51	6.67	6.81	6.94	7.06	7.17	7.26	7.36	7.44	7.52	7.59	7.66	7.73
13	4.26	4.96	5.40	5.73	5.98	6.19	6.37	6.53	6.67	6.79	6.90	7.01	7.10	7.19	7.27	7.34	7.42	7.48	7.55
14	4.21	4.89	5.32	5.63	5.88	6.08	6.26	6.41	6.54	6.66	6.77	6.87	6.96	7.05	7.12	7.20	7.27	7.33	7.39
15	4.17	4.83	5.25	5.56	5.80	5.99	6.16	6.31	6.44	6.55	6.66	6.76	6.84	6.93	7.00	7.07	7.14	7.20	7.26
16	4.13	4.78	5.19	5.49	5.72	5.92	6.08	6.22	6.35	6.46	6.56	6.66	6.74	6.82	6.90	6.97	7.03	7.09	7.15
17	4.10	4.74	5.14	5.43	5.66	5.85	6.01	6.15	6.27	6.38	6.48	6.57	6.66	6.73	6.80	6.87	6.94	7.00	7.05
18	4.07	4.70	5.09	5.38	5.60	5.79	5.94	6.08	6.20	6.31	6.41	6.50	6.58	6.65	6.72	6.79	6.85	6.91	6.96
19	4.05	4.67	5.05	5.33	5.55	5.73	5.89	6.02	6.14	6.25	6.34	6.43	6.51	6.58	6.65	6.72	6.78	6.84	6.89
20	4.02	4.64	5.02	5.29	5.51	5.69	5.84	5.97	6.09	6.19	6.29	6.37	6.45	6.52	6.59	6.65	6.71	6.76	6.82
24	3.96	4.54	4.91	5.17	5.37	5.54	5.69	5.81	5.92	6.02	6.11	6.19	6.26	6.33	6.39	6.45	6.51	6.56	6.61
30	3.89	4.45	4.80	5.05	5.24	5.40	5.54	5.65	5.76	5.85	5.93	6.01	6.08	6.14	6.20	6.26	6.31	6.36	6.41
40	3.82	4.37	4.70	4.93	5.11	5.27	5.39	5.50	5.60	5.69	5.77	5.84	5.90	5.96	6.02	6.07	6.12	6.17	6.21
60	3.76	4.28	4.60	4.82	4.99	5.13	5.25	5.36	5.45	5.53	5.60	5.67	5.73	5.79	5.84	5.89	5.93	5.98	6.02
120	3.70	4.20	4.50	4.71	4.87	5.01	5.12	5.21	5.30	5.38	5.44	5.51	5.56	5.61	5.66	5.71	5.75	5.79	5.83
∞	3.64	4.12	4.40	4.60	4.76	4.88	4.99	5.08	5.16	5.23	5.29	5.35	5.40	5.45	5.49	5.54	5.57	5.61	5.65

Source: *The Analysis of Variance*, pp. 414–16, by Henry Scheffe, ©1959 by John Wiley & Sons, Inc. Reprinted by permission of John Wiley & Sons, Inc.

TABLE A.10   Critical Values for the Durbin–Watson *d* Statistic ($\alpha = .05$)

	k = 1		k = 2		k = 3		k = 4		k = 5	
n	$d_{L,.05}$	$d_{U,.05}$	$d_{L,.05}$	$d_{U,.05}$	$d_{L,.05}$	$d_{U,.05}$	$d_{L,.05}$	$d_{U,.05}$	$d_{L,.05}$	$d_{U,.05}$
15	1.08	1.36	0.95	1.54	0.82	1.75	0.69	1.97	0.56	2.21
16	1.10	1.37	0.98	1.54	0.86	1.73	0.74	1.93	0.62	2.15
17	1.13	1.38	1.02	1.54	0.90	1.71	0.78	1.90	0.67	2.10
18	1.16	1.39	1.05	1.53	0.93	1.69	0.82	1.87	0.71	2.06
19	1.18	1.40	1.08	1.53	0.97	1.68	0.86	1.85	0.75	2.02
20	1.20	1.41	1.10	1.54	1.00	1.68	0.90	1.83	0.79	1.99
21	1.22	1.42	1.13	1.54	1.03	1.67	0.93	1.81	0.83	1.96
22	1.24	1.43	1.15	1.54	1.05	1.66	0.96	1.80	0.86	1.94
23	1.26	1.44	1.17	1.54	1.08	1.66	0.99	1.79	0.90	1.92
24	1.27	1.45	1.19	1.55	1.10	1.66	1.01	1.78	0.93	1.90
25	1.29	1.45	1.21	1.55	1.12	1.66	1.04	1.77	0.95	1.89
26	1.30	1.46	1.22	1.55	1.14	1.65	1.06	1.76	0.98	1.88
27	1.32	1.47	1.24	1.56	1.16	1.65	1.08	1.76	1.01	1.86
28	1.33	1.48	1.26	1.56	1.18	1.65	1.10	1.75	1.03	1.85
29	1.34	1.48	1.27	1.56	1.20	1.65	1.12	1.74	1.05	1.84
30	1.35	1.49	1.28	1.57	1.21	1.65	1.14	1.74	1.07	1.83
31	1.36	1.50	1.30	1.57	1.23	1.65	1.16	1.74	1.09	1.83
32	1.37	1.50	1.31	1.57	1.24	1.65	1.18	1.73	1.11	1.82
33	1.38	1.51	1.32	1.58	1.26	1.65	1.19	1.73	1.13	1.81
34	1.39	1.51	1.33	1.58	1.27	1.65	1.21	1.73	1.15	1.81
35	1.40	1.52	1.34	1.58	1.28	1.65	1.22	1.73	1.16	1.80
36	1.41	1.52	1.35	1.59	1.29	1.65	1.24	1.73	1.18	1.80
37	1.42	1.53	1.36	1.59	1.31	1.66	1.25	1.72	1.19	1.80
38	1.43	1.54	1.37	1.59	1.32	1.66	1.26	1.72	1.21	1.79
39	1.43	1.54	1.38	1.60	1.33	1.66	1.27	1.72	1.22	1.79
40	1.44	1.54	1.39	1.60	1.34	1.66	1.29	1.72	1.23	1.79
45	1.48	1.57	1.43	1.62	1.38	1.67	1.34	1.72	1.29	1.78
50	1.50	1.59	1.46	1.63	1.42	1.67	1.38	1.72	1.34	1.77
55	1.53	1.60	1.49	1.64	1.45	1.68	1.41	1.72	1.38	1.77
60	1.55	1.62	1.51	1.65	1.48	1.69	1.44	1.73	1.41	1.77
65	1.57	1.63	1.54	1.66	1.50	1.70	1.47	1.73	1.44	1.77
70	1.58	1.64	1.55	1.67	1.52	1.70	1.49	1.74	1.46	1.77
75	1.60	1.65	1.57	1.68	1.54	1.71	1.51	1.74	1.49	1.77
80	1.61	1.66	1.59	1.69	1.56	1.72	1.53	1.74	1.51	1.77
85	1.62	1.67	1.60	1.70	1.57	1.72	1.55	1.75	1.52	1.77
90	1.63	1.68	1.61	1.70	1.59	1.73	1.57	1.75	1.54	1.78
95	1.64	1.69	1.62	1.71	1.60	1.73	1.58	1.75	1.56	1.78
100	1.65	1.69	1.63	1.72	1.61	1.74	1.59	1.76	1.57	1.78

TABLE A.11   Critical Values for the Durbin–Watson *d* Statistic ($\alpha = .025$)

	k = 1		k = 2		k = 3		k = 4		k = 5	
n	$d_{L,.025}$	$d_{U,.025}$	$d_{L,.025}$	$d_{U,.025}$	$d_{L,.025}$	$d_{U,.025}$	$d_{L,.025}$	$d_{U,.025}$	$d_{L,.025}$	$d_{U,.025}$
15	0.95	1.23	0.83	1.40	0.71	1.61	0.59	1.84	0.48	2.09
16	0.98	1.24	0.86	1.40	0.75	1.59	0.64	1.80	0.53	2.03
17	1.01	1.25	0.90	1.40	0.79	1.58	0.68	1.77	0.57	1.98
18	1.03	1.26	0.93	1.40	0.82	1.56	0.72	1.74	0.62	1.93
19	1.06	1.28	0.96	1.41	0.86	1.55	0.76	1.72	0.66	1.90
20	1.08	1.28	0.99	1.41	0.89	1.55	0.79	1.70	0.70	1.87
21	1.10	1.30	1.01	1.41	0.92	1.54	0.83	1.69	0.73	1.84
22	1.12	1.31	1.04	1.42	0.95	1.54	0.86	1.68	0.77	1.82
23	1.14	1.32	1.06	1.42	0.97	1.54	0.89	1.67	0.80	1.80
24	1.16	1.33	1.08	1.43	1.00	1.54	0.91	1.66	0.83	1.79
25	1.18	1.34	1.10	1.43	1.02	1.54	0.94	1.65	0.86	1.77
26	1.19	1.35	1.12	1.44	1.04	1.54	0.96	1.65	0.88	1.76
27	1.21	1.36	1.13	1.44	1.06	1.54	0.99	1.64	0.91	1.75
28	1.22	1.37	1.15	1.45	1.08	1.54	1.01	1.64	0.93	1.74
29	1.24	1.38	1.17	1.45	1.10	1.54	1.03	1.63	0.96	1.73
30	1.25	1.38	1.18	1.46	1.12	1.54	1.05	1.63	0.98	1.73
31	1.26	1.39	1.20	1.47	1.13	1.55	1.07	1.63	1.00	1.72
32	1.27	1.40	1.21	1.47	1.15	1.55	1.08	1.63	1.02	1.71
33	1.28	1.41	1.22	1.48	1.16	1.55	1.10	1.63	1.04	1.71
34	1.29	1.41	1.24	1.48	1.17	1.55	1.12	1.63	1.06	1.70
35	1.30	1.42	1.25	1.48	1.19	1.55	1.13	1.63	1.07	1.70
36	1.31	1.43	1.26	1.49	1.20	1.56	1.15	1.63	1.09	1.70
37	1.32	1.43	1.27	1.49	1.21	1.56	1.16	1.62	1.10	1.70
38	1.33	1.44	1.28	1.50	1.23	1.56	1.17	1.62	1.12	1.70
39	1.34	1.44	1.29	1.50	1.24	1.56	1.19	1.63	1.13	1.69
40	1.35	1.45	1.30	1.51	1.25	1.57	1.20	1.63	1.15	1.69
45	1.39	1.48	1.34	1.53	1.30	1.58	1.25	1.63	1.21	1.69
50	1.42	1.50	1.38	1.54	1.34	1.59	1.30	1.64	1.26	1.69
55	1.45	1.52	1.41	1.56	1.37	1.60	1.33	1.64	1.30	1.69
60	1.47	1.54	1.44	1.57	1.40	1.61	1.37	1.65	1.33	1.69
65	1.49	1.55	1.46	1.59	1.43	1.62	1.40	1.66	1.36	1.69
70	1.51	1.57	1.48	1.60	1.45	1.63	1.42	1.66	1.39	1.70
75	1.53	1.58	1.50	1.61	1.47	1.64	1.45	1.67	1.42	1.70
80	1.54	1.59	1.52	1.62	1.49	1.65	1.47	1.67	1.44	1.70
85	1.56	1.60	1.53	1.63	1.51	1.65	1.49	1.68	1.46	1.71
90	1.57	1.61	1.55	1.64	1.53	1.66	1.50	1.69	1.48	1.71
95	1.58	1.62	1.56	1.65	1.54	1.67	1.52	1.69	1.50	1.71
100	1.59	1.63	1.57	1.65	1.55	1.67	1.53	1.70	1.51	1.72

TABLE A.12   Critical Values for the Durbin–Watson d Statistic ($\alpha = .01$)

	$k = 1$		$k = 2$		$k = 3$		$k = 4$		$k = 5$	
n	$d_{L,.01}$	$d_{U,.01}$	$d_{L,.01}$	$d_{U,.01}$	$d_{L,.01}$	$d_{U,.01}$	$d_{L,.01}$	$d_{U,.01}$	$d_{L,.01}$	$d_{U,.01}$
15	0.81	1.07	0.70	1.25	0.59	1.46	0.49	1.70	0.39	1.96
16	0.84	1.09	0.74	1.25	0.63	1.44	0.53	1.66	0.44	1.90
17	0.87	1.10	0.77	1.25	0.67	1.43	0.57	1.63	0.48	1.85
18	0.90	1.12	0.80	1.26	0.71	1.42	0.61	1.60	0.52	1.80
19	0.93	1.13	0.83	1.26	0.74	1.41	0.65	1.58	0.56	1.77
20	0.95	1.15	0.86	1.27	0.77	1.41	0.68	1.57	0.60	1.74
21	0.97	1.16	0.89	1.27	0.80	1.41	0.72	1.55	0.63	1.71
22	1.00	1.17	0.91	1.28	0.83	1.40	0.75	1.54	0.66	1.69
23	1.02	1.19	0.94	1.29	0.86	1.40	0.77	1.53	0.70	1.67
24	1.04	1.20	0.96	1.30	0.88	1.41	0.80	1.53	0.72	1.66
25	1.05	1.21	0.98	1.30	0.90	1.41	0.83	1.52	0.75	1.65
26	1.07	1.22	1.00	1.31	0.93	1.41	0.85	1.52	0.78	1.64
27	1.09	1.23	1.02	1.32	0.95	1.41	0.88	1.51	0.81	1.63
28	1.10	1.24	1.04	1.32	0.97	1.41	0.90	1.51	0.83	1.62
29	1.12	1.25	1.05	1.33	0.99	1.42	0.92	1.51	0.85	1.61
30	1.13	1.26	1.07	1.34	1.01	1.42	0.94	1.51	0.88	1.61
31	1.15	1.27	1.08	1.34	1.02	1.42	0.96	1.51	0.90	1.60
32	1.16	1.28	1.10	1.35	1.04	1.43	0.98	1.51	0.92	1.60
33	1.17	1.29	1.11	1.36	1.05	1.43	1.00	1.51	0.94	1.59
34	1.18	1.30	1.13	1.36	1.07	1.43	1.01	1.51	0.95	1.59
35	1.19	1.31	1.14	1.37	1.08	1.44	1.03	1.51	0.97	1.59
36	1.21	1.32	1.15	1.38	1.10	1.44	1.04	1.51	0.99	1.59
37	1.22	1.32	1.16	1.38	1.11	1.45	1.06	1.51	1.00	1.59
38	1.23	1.33	1.18	1.39	1.12	1.45	1.07	1.52	1.02	1.58
39	1.24	1.34	1.19	1.39	1.14	1.45	1.09	1.52	1.03	1.58
40	1.25	1.34	1.20	1.40	1.15	1.46	1.10	1.52	1.05	1.58
45	1.29	1.38	1.24	1.42	1.20	1.48	1.16	1.53	1.11	1.58
50	1.32	1.40	1.28	1.45	1.24	1.49	1.20	1.54	1.16	1.59
55	1.36	1.43	1.32	1.47	1.28	1.51	1.25	1.55	1.21	1.59
60	1.38	1.45	1.35	1.48	1.32	1.52	1.28	1.56	1.25	1.60
65	1.41	1.47	1.38	1.50	1.35	1.53	1.31	1.57	1.28	1.61
70	1.43	1.49	1.40	1.52	1.37	1.55	1.34	1.58	1.31	1.61
75	1.45	1.50	1.42	1.53	1.39	1.56	1.37	1.59	1.34	1.62
80	1.47	1.52	1.44	1.54	1.42	1.57	1.39	1.60	1.36	1.62
85	1.48	1.53	1.46	1.55	1.43	1.58	1.41	1.60	1.39	1.63
90	1.50	1.54	1.47	1.56	1.45	1.59	1.43	1.61	1.41	1.64
95	1.51	1.55	1.49	1.57	1.47	1.60	1.45	1.62	1.42	1.64
100	1.52	1.56	1.50	1.58	1.48	1.60	1.46	1.63	1.44	1.65

Source: J. Durbin and G. S. Watson, "Testing for Serial Correlation in Least Squares Regression, II," *Biometrika* 30 (1951), pp. 159–78. Reproduced by permission of the Biometrika Trustees.

TABLE A.13   A Wilcoxon Rank Sum Table: Values of T_L and T_U

(a) $\alpha = .025$ One-Sided; $\alpha = .05$ Two-Sided

n_1 n_2	3		4		5		6		7		8		9		10	
	T_L	T_U	T_L	T_U	T_L	T_U	T_L	T_U	T_L	T_U	T_L	T_U	T_L	T_U	T_L	T_U
3	5	16	6	18	6	21	7	23	7	26	8	28	8	31	9	33
4	6	18	11	25	12	28	12	32	13	35	14	38	15	41	16	44
5	6	21	12	28	18	37	19	41	20	45	21	49	22	53	24	56
6	7	23	12	32	19	41	26	52	28	56	29	61	31	65	32	70
7	7	26	13	35	20	45	28	56	37	68	39	73	41	78	43	83
8	8	28	14	38	21	49	29	61	39	73	49	87	51	93	54	98
9	8	31	15	41	22	53	31	65	41	78	51	93	63	108	66	114
10	9	33	16	44	24	56	32	70	43	83	54	98	66	114	79	131

(b) $\alpha = .05$ One-Sided; $\alpha = .10$ Two-Sided

n_1 n_2	3		4		5		6		7		8		9		10	
	T_L	T_U	T_L	T_U	T_L	T_U	T_L	T_U	T_L	T_U	T_L	T_U	T_L	T_U	T_L	T_U
3	6	15	7	17	7	20	8	22	9	24	9	27	10	29	11	31
4	7	17	12	24	13	27	14	30	15	33	16	36	17	39	18	42
5	7	20	13	27	19	36	20	40	22	43	24	46	25	50	26	54
6	8	22	14	30	20	40	28	50	30	54	32	58	33	63	35	67
7	9	24	15	33	22	43	30	54	39	66	41	71	43	76	46	80
8	9	27	16	36	24	46	32	58	41	71	52	84	54	90	57	95
9	10	29	17	39	25	50	33	63	43	76	54	90	66	105	69	111
10	11	31	18	42	26	54	35	67	46	80	57	95	69	111	83	127

Source: F. Wilcoxon and R. A. Wilcox, "Some Rapid Approximate Statistical Procedures" (New York: American Cyanamid Company, 1964), pp. 20–23. Reproduced with the permission of American Cyanamid Company.

TABLE **A.14**   **A Wilcoxon Signed Ranks Table: Values of T_0**

One-Sided	Two-Sided	$n = 5$	$n = 6$	$n = 7$	$n = 8$	$n = 9$	$n = 10$
$\alpha = .05$	$\alpha = .10$	1	2	4	6	8	11
$\alpha = .025$	$\alpha = .05$		1	2	4	6	8
$\alpha = .01$	$\alpha = .02$			0	2	3	5
$\alpha = .005$	$\alpha = .01$				0	2	3
		$n = 11$	$n = 12$	$n = 13$	$n = 14$	$n = 15$	$n = 16$
$\alpha = .05$	$\alpha = .10$	14	17	21	26	30	36
$\alpha = .025$	$\alpha = .05$	11	14	17	21	25	30
$\alpha = .01$	$\alpha = .02$	7	10	13	16	20	24
$\alpha = .005$	$\alpha = .01$	5	7	10	13	16	19
		$n = 17$	$n = 18$	$n = 19$	$n = 20$	$n = 21$	$n = 22$
$\alpha = .05$	$\alpha = .10$	41	47	54	60	68	75
$\alpha = .025$	$\alpha = .05$	35	40	46	52	59	66
$\alpha = .01$	$\alpha = .02$	28	33	38	43	49	56
$\alpha = .005$	$\alpha = .01$	23	28	32	37	43	49
		$n = 23$	$n = 24$	$n = 25$	$n = 26$	$n = 27$	$n = 28$
$\alpha = .05$	$\alpha = .10$	83	92	101	110	120	130
$\alpha = .025$	$\alpha = .05$	73	81	90	98	107	117
$\alpha = .01$	$\alpha = .02$	62	69	77	85	93	102
$\alpha = .005$	$\alpha = .01$	55	61	68	76	84	92
		$n = 29$	$n = 30$	$n = 31$	$n = 32$	$n = 33$	$n = 34$
$\alpha = .05$	$\alpha = .10$	141	152	163	175	188	201
$\alpha = .025$	$\alpha = .05$	127	137	148	159	171	183
$\alpha = .01$	$\alpha = .02$	111	120	130	141	151	162
$\alpha = .005$	$\alpha = .01$	100	109	118	128	138	149
		$n = 35$	$n = 36$	$n = 37$	$n = 38$	$n = 39$	
$\alpha = .05$	$\alpha = .10$	214	228	242	256	271	
$\alpha = .025$	$\alpha = .05$	195	208	222	235	250	
$\alpha = .01$	$\alpha = .02$	174	186	198	211	224	
$\alpha = .005$	$\alpha = .01$	160	171	183	195	208	
		$n = 40$	$n = 41$	$n = 42$	$n = 43$	$n = 44$	$n = 45$
$\alpha = .05$	$\alpha = .10$	287	303	319	336	353	371
$\alpha = .025$	$\alpha = .05$	264	279	295	311	327	344
$\alpha = .01$	$\alpha = .02$	238	252	267	281	297	313
$\alpha = .005$	$\alpha = .01$	221	234	248	262	277	292
		$n = 46$	$n = 47$	$n = 48$	$n = 49$	$n = 50$	
$\alpha = .05$	$\alpha = .10$	389	408	427	446	466	
$\alpha = .025$	$\alpha = .05$	361	379	397	415	434	
$\alpha = .01$	$\alpha = .02$	329	345	362	380	398	
$\alpha = .005$	$\alpha = .01$	307	323	339	356	373	

Source: F. Wilcoxon and R. A. Wilcox, "Some Rapid Approximate Statistical Procedures" (New York: American Cyanamid Company, 1964), p. 28. Reproduced with the permission of American Cyanamid Company.

TABLE A.15   A Chi-Square Table: Values of χ_α^2

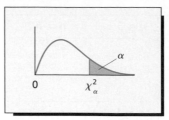

df	$\chi_{.995}^2$	$\chi_{.99}^2$	$\chi_{.975}^2$	$\chi_{.95}^2$	$\chi_{.90}^2$
1	.0000393	.0001571	.0009821	.0039321	.0157908
2	.0100251	.0201007	.0506356	.102587	.210720
3	.0717212	.114832	.215795	.341846	.584375
4	.206990	.297110	.484419	.710721	.063623
5	.411740	.554300	.831211	1.145476	1.61031
6	.675727	.872085	1.237347	1.63539	2.20413
7	.989265	1.239043	1.68987	2.16735	2.83311
8	1.344419	1.646482	2.17973	2.73264	3.48954
9	1.734926	2.087912	2.70039	3.32511	4.16816
10	2.15585	2.55821	3.24697	3.94030	4.86518
11	2.60321	3.05347	3.81575	4.57481	5.57779
12	3.07382	3.57056	4.40379	5.22603	6.30380
13	3.56503	4.10691	5.00874	5.89186	7.04150
14	4.07468	4.66043	5.62872	6.57063	7.78953
15	4.60094	5.22935	6.26214	7.26094	8.54675
16	5.14224	5.81221	6.90766	7.96164	9.31223
17	5.69724	6.40776	7.56418	8.67176	10.0852
18	6.26481	7.01491	8.23075	9.39046	10.8649
19	6.84398	7.63273	8.90655	10.1170	11.6509
20	7.43386	8.26040	9.59083	10.8508	12.4426
21	8.03366	8.89720	10.28293	11.5913	13.2396
22	8.64272	9.54249	10.9823	12.3380	14.0415
23	9.26042	10.19567	11.6885	13.0905	14.8479
24	9.88623	10.8564	12.4011	13.8484	15.6587
25	10.5197	11.5240	13.1197	14.6114	16.4734
26	11.1603	12.1981	13.8439	15.3791	17.2919
27	11.8076	12.8786	14.5733	16.1513	18.1138
28	12.4613	13.5648	15.3079	16.9279	18.9392
29	13.1211	14.2565	16.0471	17.7083	19.7677
30	13.7867	14.9535	16.7908	18.4926	20.5992
40	20.7065	22.1643	24.4331	26.5093	29.0505
50	27.9907	29.7067	32.3574	34.7642	37.6886
60	35.5346	37.4848	40.4817	43.1879	46.4589
70	43.2752	45.4418	48.7576	51.7393	55.3290
80	51.1720	53.5400	57.1532	60.3915	64.2778
90	59.1963	61.7541	65.6466	69.1260	73.2912
100	67.3276	70.0648	74.2219	77.9295	82.3581

(table continued)

TABLE A.15 A Chi-Square Table: Values of χ_α^2 (concluded)

df	$\chi_{.10}^2$	$\chi_{.05}^2$	$\chi_{.025}^2$	$\chi_{.01}^2$	$\chi_{.005}^2$
1	2.70554	3.84146	5.02389	6.63490	7.87944
2	4.60517	5.99147	7.37776	9.21034	10.5966
3	6.25139	7.81473	9.34840	11.3449	12.8381
4	7.77944	9.48773	11.1433	13.2767	14.8602
5	9.23635	11.0705	12.8325	15.0863	16.7496
6	10.6446	12.5916	14.4494	16.8119	18.5476
7	12.0170	14.0671	16.0128	18.4753	20.2777
8	13.3616	15.5073	17.5346	20.0902	21.9550
9	14.6837	16.9190	19.0228	21.6660	23.5893
10	15.9871	18.3070	20.4831	23.2093	25.1882
11	17.2750	19.6751	21.9200	24.7250	26.7569
12	18.5494	21.0261	23.3367	26.2170	28.2995
13	19.8119	22.3621	24.7356	27.6883	29.8194
14	21.0642	23.6848	26.1190	29.1413	31.3193
15	22.3072	24.9958	27.4884	30.5779	32.8013
16	23.5418	26.2962	28.8454	31.9999	34.2672
17	24.7690	27.5871	30.1910	33.4087	35.7185
18	25.9894	28.8693	31.5264	34.8053	37.1564
19	27.2036	30.1435	32.8523	36.1908	38.5822
20	28.4120	31.4104	34.1696	37.5662	39.9968
21	29.6151	32.6705	35.4789	38.9321	41.4010
22	30.8133	33.9244	36.7807	40.2894	42.7956
23	32.0069	35.1725	38.0757	41.6384	44.1813
24	33.1963	36.4151	39.3641	42.9798	45.5585
25	34.3816	37.6525	40.6465	44.3141	46.9278
26	35.5631	38.8852	41.9232	45.6417	48.2899
27	36.7412	40.1133	43.1944	46.9630	49.6449
28	37.9159	41.3372	44.4607	48.2782	50.9933
29	39.0875	42.5569	45.7222	49.5879	52.3356
30	40.2560	43.7729	46.9792	50.8922	53.6720
40	51.8050	55.7585	59.3417	63.6907	66.7659
50	63.1671	67.5048	71.4202	76.1539	79.4900
60	74.3970	79.0819	83.2976	88.3794	91.9517
70	85.5271	90.5312	95.0231	100.425	104.215
80	96.5782	101.879	106.629	112.329	116.321
90	107.565	113.145	118.136	124.116	128.299
100	118.498	124.342	129.561	135.807	140.169

Source: C. M. Thompson, "Tables of the Percentage Points of the χ^2 Distribution," *Biometrika* 32 (1941), pp. 188–89. Reproduced by permission of the Biometrika Trustees.

TABLE A.16 Critical Values for Spearman's Rank Correlation Coefficient

n	$\alpha = .05$	$\alpha = .025$	$\alpha = .01$	$\alpha = .005$	n	$\alpha = .05$	$\alpha = .025$	$\alpha = .01$	$\alpha = .005$
5	.900	—	—	—	18	.399	.476	.564	.625
6	.829	.886	.943	—	19	.388	.462	.549	.608
7	.714	.786	.893	—	20	.377	.450	.534	.591
8	.643	.738	.833	.881	21	.368	.438	.521	.576
9	.600	.683	.783	.833	22	.359	.428	.508	.562
10	.564	.648	.745	.794	23	.351	.418	.496	.549
11	.523	.623	.736	.818	24	.343	.409	.485	.537
12	.497	.591	.703	.780	25	.336	.400	.475	.526
13	.475	.566	.673	.745	26	.329	.392	.465	.515
14	.457	.545	.646	.716	27	.323	.385	.456	.505
15	.441	.525	.623	.689	28	.317	.377	.448	.496
16	.425	.507	.601	.666	29	.311	.370	.440	.487
17	.412	.490	.582	.645	30	.305	.364	.432	.478

Source: E. G. Olds, "Distribution of Sums of Squares of Rank Differences for Small Samples," *Annals of Mathematical Statistics*, 1938, 9. Reproduced with the permission of the editor, *Annals of Mathematical Statistics*.

TABLE A.17　Cumulative Areas under the Standard Normal Curve

z	.00	.01	.02	.03	.04	.05	.06	.07	.08	.09
−3.4	.0003	.0003	.0003	.0003	.0003	.0003	.0003	.0003	.0003	.0002
−3.3	.0005	.0005	.0005	.0004	.0004	.0004	.0004	.0004	.0004	.0003
−3.2	.0007	.0007	.0006	.0006	.0006	.0006	.0006	.0005	.0005	.0005
−3.1	.0010	.0009	.0009	.0009	.0008	.0008	.0008	.0008	.0007	.0007
−3.0	.0013	.0013	.0013	.0012	.0012	.0011	.0011	.0011	.0010	.0010
−2.9	.0019	.0018	.0018	.0017	.0016	.0016	.0015	.0015	.0014	.0014
−2.8	.0026	.0025	.0024	.0023	.0023	.0022	.0021	.0021	.0020	.0019
−2.7	.0035	.0034	.0033	.0032	.0031	.0030	.0029	.0028	.0027	.0026
−2.6	.0047	.0045	.0044	.0043	.0041	.0040	.0039	.0038	.0037	.0036
−2.5	.0062	.0060	.0059	.0057	.0055	.0054	.0052	.0051	.0049	.0048
−2.4	.0082	.0080	.0078	.0075	.0073	.0071	.0069	.0068	.0066	.0064
−2.3	.0107	.0104	.0102	.0099	.0096	.0094	.0091	.0089	.0087	.0084
−2.2	.0139	.0136	.0132	.0129	.0125	.0122	.0119	.0116	.0113	.0110
−2.1	.0179	.0174	.0170	.0166	.0162	.0158	.0154	.0150	.0146	.0143
−2.0	.0228	.0222	.0217	.0212	.0207	.0202	.0197	.0192	.0188	.0183
−1.9	.0287	.0281	.0274	.0268	.0262	.0256	.0250	.0244	.0239	.0233
−1.8	.0359	.0351	.0344	.0336	.0329	.0322	.0314	.0307	.0301	.0294
−1.7	.0446	.0436	.0427	.0418	.0409	.0401	.0392	.0384	.0375	.0367
−1.6	.0548	.0537	.0526	.0516	.0505	.0495	.0485	.0475	.0465	.0455
−1.5	.0668	.0655	.0643	.0630	.0618	.0606	.0594	.0582	.0571	.0559
−1.4	.0808	.0793	.0778	.0764	.0749	.0735	.0721	.0708	.0694	.0681
−1.3	.0968	.0951	.0934	.0918	.0901	.0885	.0869	.0853	.0838	.0823
−1.2	.1151	.1131	.1112	.1093	.1075	.1056	.1038	.1020	.1003	.0985
−1.1	.1357	.1335	.1314	.1292	.1271	.1251	.1230	.1210	.1190	.1170
−1.0	.1587	.1562	.1539	.1515	.1492	.1469	.1446	.1423	.1401	.1379
−0.9	.1841	.1814	.1788	.1762	.1736	.1711	.1685	.1660	.1635	.1611
−0.8	.2119	.2090	.2061	.2033	.2005	.1977	.1949	.1922	.1894	.1867
−0.7	.2420	.2389	.2358	.2327	.2296	.2266	.2236	.2206	.2177	.2148
−0.6	.2743	.2709	.2676	.2643	.2611	.2578	.2546	.2514	.2483	.2451
−0.5	.3085	.3050	.3015	.2981	.2946	.2912	.2877	.2843	.2810	.2776
−0.4	.3446	.3409	.3372	.3336	.3300	.3264	.3228	.3192	.3156	.3121
−0.3	.3821	.3783	.3745	.3707	.3669	.3632	.3594	.3557	.3520	.3483
−0.2	.4207	.4168	.4129	.4090	.4052	.4013	.3974	.3936	.3897	.3859
−0.1	.4602	.4562	.4522	.4483	.4443	.4404	.4364	.4325	.4286	.4247
−0.0	.5000	.4960	.4920	.4880	.4840	.4801	.4761	.4721	.4681	.4641
0.0	.5000	.5040	.5080	.5120	.5160	.5199	.5239	.5279	.5319	.5359
0.1	.5398	.5438	.5478	.5517	.5557	.5596	.5636	.5675	.5714	.5753
0.2	.5793	.5832	.5871	.5910	.5948	.5987	.6026	.6064	.6103	.6141
0.3	.6179	.6217	.6255	.6293	.6331	.6368	.6406	.6443	.6480	.6517
0.4	.6554	.6591	.6628	.6664	.6700	.6736	.6772	.6808	.6844	.6879
0.5	.6915	.6950	.6985	.7019	.7054	.7088	.7123	.7157	.7190	.7224
0.6	.7257	.7291	.7324	.7357	.7389	.7422	.7454	.7486	.7517	.7549
0.7	.7580	.7611	.7642	.7673	.7704	.7734	.7764	.7794	.7823	.7852
0.8	.7881	.7910	.7939	.7967	.7995	.8023	.8051	.8078	.8106	.8133
0.9	.8159	.8186	.8212	.8238	.8264	.8289	.8315	.8340	.8365	.8389
1.0	.8413	.8438	.8461	.8485	.8508	.8531	.8554	.8577	.8599	.8621
1.1	.8643	.8665	.8686	.8708	.8729	.8749	.8770	.8790	.8810	.8830
1.2	.8849	.8869	.8888	.8907	.8925	.8944	.8962	.8980	.8997	.9015
1.3	.9032	.9049	.9066	.9082	.9099	.9115	.9131	.9147	.9162	.9177
1.4	.9192	.9207	.9222	.9236	.9251	.9265	.9279	.9292	.9306	.9319
1.5	.9332	.9345	.9357	.9370	.9382	.9394	.9406	.9418	.9429	.9441
1.6	.9452	.9463	.9474	.9484	.9495	.9505	.9515	.9525	.9535	.9545
1.7	.9554	.9564	.9573	.9582	.9591	.9599	.9608	.9616	.9625	.9633
1.8	.9641	.9649	.9656	.9664	.9671	.9678	.9686	.9693	.9699	.9706
1.9	.9713	.9719	.9726	.9732	.9738	.9744	.9750	.9756	.9761	.9767
2.0	.9772	.9778	.9783	.9788	.9793	.9798	.9803	.9808	.9812	.9817
2.1	.9821	.9826	.9830	.9834	.9838	.9842	.9846	.9850	.9854	.9857
2.2	.9861	.9864	.9868	.9871	.9875	.9878	.9881	.9884	.9887	.9890
2.3	.9893	.9896	.9898	.9901	.9904	.9906	.9909	.9911	.9913	.9916
2.4	.9918	.9920	.9922	.9925	.9927	.9929	.9931	.9932	.9934	.9936
2.5	.9938	.9940	.9941	.9943	.9945	.9946	.9948	.9949	.9951	.9952
2.6	.9953	.9955	.9956	.9957	.9959	.9960	.9961	.9962	.9963	.9964
2.7	.9965	.9966	.9967	.9968	.9969	.9970	.9971	.9972	.9973	.9974
2.8	.9974	.9975	.9976	.9977	.9977	.9978	.9979	.9979	.9980	.9981
2.9	.9981	.9982	.9982	.9983	.9984	.9984	.9985	.9985	.9986	.9986
3.0	.9987	.9987	.9987	.9988	.9988	.9989	.9989	.9989	.9990	.9990
3.1	.9990	.9991	.9991	.9991	.9992	.9992	.9992	.9992	.9993	.9993
3.2	.9993	.9993	.9994	.9994	.9994	.9994	.9994	.9995	.9995	.9995
3.3	.9995	.9995	.9995	.9996	.9996	.9996	.9996	.9996	.9996	.9997
3.4	.9997	.9997	.9997	.9997	.9997	.9997	.9997	.9997	.9997	.9998

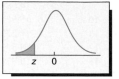

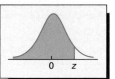

Chapter 1

1.3
a. Quantitative
b. Quantitative
c. Qualitative
d. Quantitative
e. Qualitative

1.7 Noranda Inc., Manufacturers Life Insurance, Royal Bank of Canada, BCE Inc., Imperial Oil

1.9 0.6

1.15
a. Not in control
b. The plot shows a sharp increase, revealing instability.

1.17
a. Yes, in control. There is constant variation at a horizontal level.
b. Most breaking strengths will be between 21.3 kg and 24.5 kg.

1.21 Ordinal, nominative, ordinal, nominative, ordinal, nominative

Chapter 2

2.3 Distribution has a positive skew (to the right).

2.5
a. Class length = 1.6
b. Positively skewed with a tail to the right

2.7 The 61 home runs hit by Maris would be considered an outlier.

2.9 No; plot missed throws over time; player is improving

2.13
a. Mean = 20, Median = 20, Mode = 20
b. Mean = 503, Median = 501, Mode = 501

2.15
a. Yes, because $\bar{x} < 6$
b. Median = 5.25; mean is slightly larger than the median; positively skewed (right)

2.17
a. Mean = 272.333; median = 68 (Canada's value)
b. U.S. numbers skew the distribution.
c. Histogram is probably best plot for the data.

2.19
a. Mean = 2201.0000; median = 1,478 (Mexico's value)
b. Mean > median (because of U.S. values)
c. Histogram is probably best plot for the data.

2.21
a. Mean = 467.5 = median
b. Only two values; mean is the median
c. Histogram is probably best plot for the data.

2.29 Count = 10; mean = 20,167.50; sample variance = 705,139,612.50; sample standard deviation = 26,554.47; minimum = 625; maximum = 79,000; range = 78,375

2.31 a. $\bar{x} = 134.5$; $s^2 = 276.7$; $s = 16.63$

b. [117.87, 151.13]; [101.24, 167.76]; [84.61, 184.39]
c. Yes; $190 is not within the 99.73% interval.
d. $z_{157} = 1.353$; $z_{132} = -0.150$; $z_{109} = -1.533$; $z_{145} = 0.631$; $z_{125} = -0.571$; $z_{139} = 0.271$

2.33
a. It is somewhat reasonable.
b. [2.985, 7.935]; [0.51, 10.41]; [−1.965, 12.885]
c. Yes, because the upper limit of the 68.26% interval is less than 8 minutes
d. 66% fall into [$\bar{x} \pm s$]; 96% fall into [$\bar{x} \pm 2s$]; 100% fall into [$\bar{x} \pm 3s$]. Yes, they are reasonably valid.

2.35
a. It is skewed with a tail to the right.
b. [32.085, 41.035]; 73% [27.61, 45.54]; 95.23% [23.135, 49.985]; 96.83%
c. Inconsistent with the empirical rule, but consistent with Chebyshev's theorem
d. Positively skewed (to the right)

2.37
a. 99.73% tolerance interval = [2.96, 3.046]
b. Yes
c. 99.73% tolerance interval = [2.976, 3.024]

2.41
a. Mean = 1.74; median = 1.75; mode = 1.90; standard deviation = 0.246; variance = 0.060; range = 0.8
c. Mean = 7.69; median = 8.00; mode = 8.00; standard deviation = 1.282; variance = 1.643; range = 3.8

2.47 Pie chart

2.49
a. Stock funds: $60,000; bond funds: $30,000; govt. securities: $10,000
b. Stock funds: $78,000 (63.36%); bond funds: $34,500 (28.03%); govt. securities: $10,600 (8.61%)
c. Stock funds: $73,860; bond funds: $36,930; govt. securities: $12,310

2.53
a. Yes; the relationship appears to be linear (y increases as x increases).
b. Low sales
c. Not necessarily

2.63 8.8157%

2.65 Mean = 112.83%; variance = 3,780.56; standard deviation = 61.49%

2.69
a. 7.36%
b. $6,187,500

2.71
b. 2002–03: −21.3%
2003–04: 21.9%
2004–05: 9.3%

c. −0.036
d. $832,501

2.77
a. Approximately 75%
b. Approximately 425

Chapter 3

3.3
b1. *AA*
b2. *AA, BB, CC*
b3. *AB, AC, BA, BC, CA, CB*
b4. *AA, AB, AC, BA, CA*
b5. *AA, AB, BA, BB*
c. 1/9, 1/3, 2/3, 5/9, 4/9

3.5
b1. *PPPN, PPNP, PNPP, NPPP*
b2. Outcomes with ≤2 *P*'s (11)
b3. Outcomes with ≥1 *P* (15)
b4. *PPPP, NNNN*
c. 1/4, 11/16, 15/16, 1/8

3.7 0.15

3.11
a1. 0.25
a2. 0.40
a3. 0.10
c1. 0.55
c2. 0.45
c3. 0.45

3.13
a. 5/8 b. 13/20
c. 7/20 d. 1/2
e. 7/8

3.15
a. 0.3215 b. 0.2519
c. 0.278 d. 0.1597

3.19
a. 0.2 b. 0.6
c. Dependent

3.21 0.55

3.23 0.1692

3.25 0.31

3.27
b. 0.40
c. Yes; $P(FRAUD|FIRE) = P(FRAUD)$

3.29
a. 0.874
b. 0.996
c. 0.004

3.31 a. 0.0295 b. 0.9705

3.35 $P(A_1|B) = 0.098$
$P(A_2|B) = 0.610$
$P(A_3|B) = 0.292$

3.37 a. 0.089 b. No

3.39 $P(\text{specialist 1}|\text{incorrect}) = 0.247$
$P(\text{specialist 2}|\text{incorrect}) = 0.616$
$P(\text{specialist 3}|\text{incorrect}) = 0.137$

3.41
b. $P(\text{in}|\text{reads "in"}) = 0.9863$
$P(\text{out}|\text{reads "in"}) = 0.0137$
c. $P(\text{in}|\text{reads "out"}) = 0.6667$
$P(\text{out}|\text{reads "out"}) = 0.3333$

3.45 Both stocks rise: 0.36
Both stocks decline: 0.09
Exactly one declines: 0.42

3.47 0.8942

3.49 0.9451

3.51 0.2567

3.53 0.454

3.55 0.813

3.57 0.797

3.59 a. 0.317
    b. Yes
3.61 a. $P(A \cap B) = 0$
    b. $P(A)P(B) > 0$
    c. No; $P(A|B) = 0$ but $P(A) > 0$.
3.63 0.5455
3.65 a. 0.186   c. 0.625   e. 0.833

Chapter 4
4.3 a. Discrete
    b. Discrete
    c. Continuous
    d. Discrete
    e. Discrete
    f. Continuous
    g. Continuous
4.5 $p(x) \geq 0$ for each x.

$\sum_{\text{all } x} p(x) = 1$

4.9 a. 0.8, 0.4
    b. 1.15, 0.90967
    c. 1.6, 2.1071
4.11 a. 0.667, 0.444, 0.667, [−0.667, 2.001], [−1.334, 2.668]
    b. 1.5, 0.75, 0.866, [−0.232, 3.232], [−1.098, 4.098]
    c. 2, 1, 1, [0, 4], [−1, 5]
4.13 $500
4.15 a.

x	$p(x)$
$400	0.995
−$49,600	0.005

    b. $150
    c. $1,250
4.17 −$5.60
4.23 a $p(x) = \dfrac{6!}{x!(6-x)!}(0.3)^x(0.7)^{6-x}$
    b1. $P(x = 5) = 0.0102$
    b2. $P(x \geq 3) = 1 - P(x \leq 2) = 1 - 0.7443 = 0.2557$
    b3. $P(x \leq 2) = 0.7443$
    b4. $P(x \geq 1) = 1 - P(x = 0) = 1 - 0.1176 = 0.8824$
4.25 a1. 0.0625
    a2. 0.3125
    b1. 0.4119
    b2. 0.2517
    b3. 0.0059
    c. No; $P(x < 5)$ is very small.
4.27 a. 0.9996, 0.0004
    b. 0.4845, 0.5155
    c. $p = 1/35$
    d. 0.000040019
4.31 a. $\mu_x = 2, \sigma_x^2 = 2,$
    $\sigma_x = 1.414$
    b. [−0.828, 4.828], 0.9473
    [−2.242, 6.242], 0.9955
4.33 a. 0.7851
    b. 0.2149
    c. 0.1912
    d. 0.0088
4.35 a. Approximately zero
    b. Rate of comas unusually high
4.37 a.

x	$p(x)$
0	4/9
1	4/9
2	1/9

    b. $p(x) = 0.16, 0.48, 0.36$
    c. $p(x) = 0.12, 0.56, 0.32$
4.39 a1. 2/3, 2/3
    a2. 1.2, 0.693
    a3. 1.2, 0.632

    b. 1.2
    c. 0.693
4.41 a. $12,000
    b. At least $6,000
4.43 a. Binomial
    b. 0.0104
    c. No; probability is very small.
4.45 a. 0.0498
    b. 0.9962
    c. 0.0038
    d. 0.9574
    e. 0.1157
4.47 0.9995
4.49 0.3232; not much evidence against it
4.51 0.0293; claim probably not true

Chapter 5
5.7 1/125
5.9 a. 3, 3, 1.73205
    b. 0.57733
5.11 a. $f(x) = 1/20$ for $120 \leq x \leq 140$.
    c. 0.5
    d. 0.25
5.13 1/6
5.15 a. 4.5 cm
    b. 1.0, 0.57733
5.23 a. −1; one σ below μ
    b. −3; three σ below μ
    c. 0; equals μ
    d. 2; two σ above μ
    e. 4; four σ above μ
5.25 a. 2.33   d. −2.33
    b. 1.645   e. −1.645
    c. 2.05   f. −1.28
5.27 a. 696   f. 335.5
    b. 664.5   g. 696
    c. 304   h. 700
    d. 283   i. 300
    e. 717
5.29 a1. 0.9830
    a2. 0.0033
    a3. 0.0456
    b. 947
5.31 a. 0.7257
    b. 0.7257
    c. 0.5478
    d. 0.2877
    e. 0.1379
    f. 0.0384
5.33 a. 10%, 90%, −13.968
    b. −1.402, 26.202
5.35 a. $[\mu \pm 2.33\sigma]$
    b. [21.2593, 24.7207]
5.37 $z = -0.44$, so $x = $2,780$.
5.39 a. A: 0.3085
    B: 0.4013
    B is investigated more often.
    b. A: 0.8413
    B: 0.6915
    A is investigated more often.
    c. B
    d. Investigate if cost variance exceeds $5,000.5987.
5.41 Both np and $n(1 - p) \geq 5$.
5.43 a. $np = 80$ and $n(1 - p) = 120$ both ≥ 5.
    b1. 0.0558
    b2. 0.9875

    b3. 0.0125
    b4. 0.0025
    b5. 0.0015
5.45 a1. $np = 200$ and $n(1 - p) = 800$ both ≥ 5.
    a2. 200; 12.6491
    a3. Less than 0.001
    b. No
5.47 $\mu = 400; \sigma = 17.8885;$
    $z = -2.33; x = 441.68 \cong 442$
5.53 a. $P(x) = 3e^{3x}$ for $x \geq 0$.
    c. 0.9502
    d. 0.4226
    e. 0.0025
    f. 1/3, 1/9, 1/3
    g. 0.9502
5.55 a. $P(x) = (2/3)e^{-(2/3)x}$ for $x \geq 0$.
    c1. 0.8647
    c2. 0.2498
    c3. 0.0695
    c4. 0.2835
5.57 a1. 0.1353
    a2. 0.2325
    a3. 0.2212
    b. Probably not; probability is 0.2212.
5.59 a. 0.8944
    b. 73.68
5.61 a. 0.8944
    b. 0.7967
    c. 0.6911
5.63 298
5.65 0.9306
5.67 c. The probability of a return greater than 50% is essentially zero.
    d. $P(x < 0) = 0.7881$ for "fixed income."
5.69 2/3
5.71 a. 0.0062
    b. 0.6915
    c. 3.3275
5.73 0.7745

Chapter 6
6.7 a. 10, 0.16, 0.4
    b. 500, 0.0025, 0.05
    c. 3, 0.0025, 0.05
    d. 100, 0.000625, 0.025
6.9 a. Normally distributed
    No; sample size is large (≥ 30).
    b. $\mu_{\bar{x}} = 20, \sigma_{\bar{x}} = 0.5$
    c. 0.0228
    d. 0.1093
6.11 a. Normal distribution because $n \geq 30$
    b. 6; 0.247
    c. 0.0143
    d. 1.43%; conclude $\mu < 6$
6.13 a1. 0.2206
    a2. 0.0027
    b. Yes; the probability of observing the sample is very small if the mean is actually 1.5.
6.19 a. 0.5, 0.001, 0.0316
    b. 0.1, 0.0009, 0.03
    c. 0.8, 0.0004, 0.02
    d. 0.98, 0.0000196, 0.004427
6.21 a. Approximately normal
    b. 0.9, 0.03
    c1. 0.0228
    c2. 0.8664
    c3. 0.6915

6.23   a. $P(\hat{p} \geq 0.39) =$

$$P\left(\frac{\hat{p} - p}{\sqrt{\dfrac{p(1-p)}{n}}} \geq \frac{0.39 - 1/3}{\sqrt{\dfrac{1/3 \cdot 2/3}{1{,}317}}}\right)$$

$$= P(Z \geq 4.36) \cong 0$$

    b. $\hat{p} = 0.39$, therefore unlikely.

6.25   a1.   0.7372

    a2.   0.9756

6.27   a.   Less than 0.001

    b.   Yes

6.29   a.   0.3085

    b.   0.0013

    c.   More difficult for average; yes

6.31   a. $P(\hat{p} \leq 0.61) =$

$$P\left(\frac{\hat{p} - p}{\sqrt{\dfrac{p(1-p)}{n}}} \leq \frac{0.61 - 2/3}{\sqrt{\dfrac{2/3 \cdot 1/3}{1{,}201}}}\right)$$

$$= P(Z \leq -4.17) \cong 0$$

    b.   It seems very unlikely that $p = 2/3$, given $\hat{p} = 0.61$.

6.33   a.   0.0206

    b.   0.1357

6.35   a.   Less than 0.001

    b.   Yes; conclude that $p < 0.5$.

6.37   a.   [22.274, 23.526]

    b.   [22.6786, 23.1214]

    c.   40 (a more accurate estimate the larger the sample size)

6.39   a.   0.0017

    b.   Unlikely

6.41   a.   Less than 0.001

    b.   Yes

Chapter 7

7.3   a.   Larger

    b.   Smaller

    c.   Smaller

    d.   Larger

7.5   a.   [49.608, 50.392]

    b.   [49.485, 50.515]

    c.   [49.566, 50.434]

    d.   [49.744, 50.256]

    e.   [49.4, 50.6]

7.7   a.   [4.976, 5.944], [4.824, 6.096]

    b.   Yes; 95% interval is below 6.

    c.   No; 99% interval extends above 6.

    d.   Fairly convinced

7.9   a.   [3.653, 7.707]

    b.   3.653

7.11   a.   [548,522.8, 614,263.2]

    b.   [538,208.94, 624,577.06]

    c.   Not confident

7.15   1.363, 2.201, 4.025

    1.440, 2.447, 5.208

7.17   a.   [4.311, 7.689], [3.442, 8.558]

    b.   Can be 95% confident; cannot be 99% confident

7.19   a.   [13.065, 14.535]

    b.   Yes; 95% interval is below 17.

7.21   a.   [786.609, 835.391]

    b.   Yes; 95% interval is above 750.

7.23   [4.969, 5.951]; yes

7.29   a.   37

    b. $580{,}000 \pm 25{,}005.09$

7.31   a.   47

    b.   328

7.33   44

7.35   a. $p = 0.5$

    b. $p = 0.3$

    c. $p = 0.8$

7.37   a.   [0.304, 0.496], [0.286, 0.514], [0.274, 0.526]

    b.   [0.066, 0.134], [0.060, 0.140], [0.055, 0.145]

    c.   [0.841, 0.959], [0.830, 0.970], [0.823, 0.977]

    d.   [0.464, 0.736], [0.439, 0.761], [0.422, 0.778]

7.39   a.   [0.473, 0.610]

    b.   No; the interval extends below 0.5.

7.41   a.   [0.3804, 0.4596]; no

    b.   [0.5701, 0.6299]; yes

    c.   95% margin of error is 0.03.

7.43   a.   [0.611, 0.729]

    b.   Yes; interval above 0.6

7.45   [0.264, 0.344]

    Yes; 95% interval exceeds 0.20.

7.47   a. $\hat{p} = 0.02$, [0.0077, 0.0323]

    b. $\hat{p} = 0.054$, [0.034, 0.074]

    c.   Yes

7.49   1,430

7.53   a.   [$514.399, $549.601]

    b. $5,559,932; [$5,375,983.95, $5,743,880.05]

    c.   Claim is very doubtful.

7.55   a.   2,954; [2,723, 3,185] Yes; interval above 2,500

    b.   No; interval extends below 3,000.

7.57   a.   204

    b.   371

7.61   68.26% tolerance interval: [22.2472, 23.7328]

    95.44% tolerance interval: [21.5044, 24.4756]

    99.73% tolerance interval: [20.7616, 25.2184]

    95% confidence interval: [22.7599, 23.2201]

7.63   68.26%: [40.3076, 45.5924]

    95.44%: [37.6652, 48.2348]

    99.73%: [35.0228, 50.8772]

    95% CI: [42.2952, 43.6048]

7.65   a. $\hat{p} = 0.3054$; [0.2635, 0.3473]

    b.   Yes; yes

    c.   968

7.67   2,301.28; [737.60, 3,864.96]

7.69   a. $19,316,814; [$16,541,476, $22,092,152]

    b. $22,092,152

7.71   a.   [25.1562, 27.2838]

    b.   Yes; not much more than 25

7.73   Fixed annuities: [7.685%, 7.975%]; differs from 8.31%

    Domestic large cap stocks: [9.108%, 17.732%]; does not differ from 11.71%

    Domestic midcap stocks: [9.788%, 20.272%]; does not differ from 13.64%

    Domestic small cap stocks: [16.327%, 28.693%]; differs from 14.93%

7.75   [0.61025, 0.66975]

7.77   a.   [0.796, 0.856]

    b.   Yes; interval is above 0.75.

Chapter 8

8.1 H_0 status quo

    H_a hoped-for or suspected condition exists

8.5   Type I

8.7   The probability of a Type II error becomes too large.

8.9   a. $H_0: \mu \geq 6$ versus $H_a: \mu < 6$

    b.   Type I: decide $\mu < 6$ when $\mu \geq 6$ Type II: decide $\mu \geq 6$ when $\mu < 6$

8.11   a. $H_0: \mu = 355$ versus $H_a: \mu \neq 355$

    b.   Type I: decide $\mu \neq 355$ (readjust filler) when $\mu = 355$ (no adjustment is needed) Type II: decide $\mu = 355$ (do not readjust) when $\mu \neq 355$ (readjustment may be needed)

8.13   A 0.05 probability that the network will advertise the ZX-900 achieves a shorter mean stopping distance than its competitor when it really does not

8.17   1.28; reject H_0

8.19   2.33; reject H_0

8.21 p value = 0.0062; reject at all α except 0.001

8.23 -2

8.25 -1.645; reject H_0

8.27 -3.09; do not reject H_0

8.29   Strong

8.31   a. $z = -2.19$; reject at $\alpha = 0.10, 0.05$

    b. p value = 0.0143; reject at an α of 0.10 or 0.05

    c.   Strong

8.33   a. $z = 2.41$; reject H_0; shut down and repair

    b. $z = 1.31$; do not reject H_0; do not shut down

    c. $z = 3.09$; reject H_0; shut down and repair

8.35   a.   For two-sided H_a, use rejection points $z_{\alpha/2}$. Reject H_0 if $|z| > z_{\alpha/2}$.

    b.   The p value is twice the area under the standard normal curve to the right of $|z|$. Reject H_0 if the p value is less than α.

8.37 -3

8.39 $\alpha = 0.05$

    $z_{0.05/2} = 1.96$

    Because $|-3| > 1.96$, reject H_0 with $\alpha = 0.05$.

8.41   Because $|-3|$ is not greater than 3.29, cannot reject H_0 with $\alpha = 0.001$

8.43   Because p value = 0.0026 is less than 0.01, there is very strong evidence that H_0 is false.

8.45   a. $p = 0.0026$; $z = 3$; reject H_0; readjust

    b. $p = 0.0164$; $z = -2.4$; cannot reject H_0; do not readjust

    c. $p = 0.2302$; $z = 1.2$; cannot reject H_0; do not readjust

8.47   a. $z = -27.8859$; reject H_0

    b. $z = 10.16$; reject H_0

8.51 $-t_{0.005} = -3.355, -t_{0.0005} = -5.041$

    Because $-5.041 < -4.30 < -3.355$, reject H_0 at $\alpha = 0.10, 0.05, 0.01$, but not at $\alpha = 0.001$.

8.53   a. p value = 0.006; reject H_0 at 0.10, 0.05, and 0.01, but not at 0.001.

    b.   Very strong evidence

8.55 b. Reject H_0 at $\alpha = 0.10$, $\alpha = 0.05$, and $\alpha = 0.01$; do not reject at $\alpha = 0.001$; very strong evidence that H_0 is false

8.57 a. p value $= 0.001$ so reject H_0 at $\alpha = 0.1$, 0.05, and 0.01, but do not reject at $\alpha = 0.001$.
b. Very strong evidence

8.59 $t = 2.899$; the p value of 0.0025 means we would reject at $\alpha = 0.1$, 0.05, and 0.01, but not at $\alpha = 0.001$.

8.65 a. Yes   e. Yes
b. No   f. No
c. Yes   g. Yes
d. Yes   h. Yes

8.67 a. $z = -2.18$; do not reject H_0
b. 0.0292
c. Reject at 0.10, 0.05; do not reject at 0.01, 0.001

8.69 a. $H_0: p \leq 0.50$ versus $H_a: p > 0.50$
b. $z = 1.19$; do not reject at any α; little evidence
c. $z = 2.53$; very strong
d. $\hat{p} = 0.54$ based on much larger sample; stronger evidence p greater than 0.50

8.71 a. $H_0: p \leq 0.18$ versus $H_a: p > 0.18$
b. 0.0329; reject H_0 at 0.10, 0.05, not at 0.01 or 0.001; strong evidence
c. Perhaps; subjective

8.73 a. $H_0: p = 0.95$ versus $H_a: p < 0.95$
b. $z = -14.68$; reject H_0 at each value of α; extremely strong evidence
c. Probably; $\hat{p} = 0.79$ far below claimed 0.95

8.75 a. $t = 2.5$; because $2.492 < 2.5 < 3.467$, reject H_0 at $\alpha = 0.10$, 0.05, 0.01, but not at $\alpha = 0.001$. There is very strong evidence that $\mu > 0.10$.
b. $t = 1.11$; because $1.11 < 1.318$, do not reject H_0 at any of the given values of α; little evidence

8.77 a. Because p value $= 0.0174$, reject H_0 for $\alpha = 0.1$ and 0.05, but not $\alpha = 0.01$ and 0.005.
b. Strong evidence

8.79 $p = 0.0322$; do not reject H_0

8.81 a. $H_0: p \leq 0.60$, $H_a: p > 0.60$
b. $z = 2.58$; because $2.33 < 2.58 < 3.09$, reject H_0 at $\alpha = 0.10$, 0.05, 0.01, but not at 0.001; very strong evidence.

8.83 $z = 5.81$; p value < 0.001, so there is extremely strong evidence.

Chapter 9

9.1 a. $\mu_1 < \mu_2$ d. $\mu_1 > \mu_2$
b. $\mu_1 = \mu_2$ e. $\mu_1 > \mu_2$
c. $\mu_1 < \mu_2$ f. $\mu_1 \neq \mu_2$

9.7 $[-11.784, -10.216]$; yes; between 10.216 and 11.784 higher

9.9 $[-1.15, -0.45]$; 95% confident that the average number of cups of coffee drunk by students at the University of Alberta is greater, on average, by anywhere from 0.45 cups to 1.15 cups

9.11 $[1.124, 1.276]$; yes

9.15 $[23.568, 36.432]$; yes; the entire interval is above 20.

9.17 $[0.509, 0.971]$; yes; 95% confident that the difference in mean expenses between stock funds and municipal bond funds is at least 0.509 percent (thus at least 0.50 percent)

9.19 $[\$1.10, \$100.90]$

9.25 a. $[100.141, 106.859]$; yes
$[98.723, 108.277]$; no

9.27 1.84 to 6.16

9.29 a. $[0.40, 0.92]$
b. Yes

9.33 $[-0.178, -0.122]$; yes; the entire interval is below zero.

9.35 $[0.021, 0.111]$; 95% confident that proportion is less in 2006 than in 1999

9.37 a. $[-0.2556, -0.1444]$
b. $[0.0285, 0.0915]$; proportions have changed

9.39 a. p value $= 0.0367$; reject H_0
b. p value $= 0.0367$; reject H_0
c. p value $= 0.9778$; cannot reject H_0
d. p value $= 0.015$; reject H_0
e. p value $= 0.1075$; cannot reject H_0
f. p value $= 0.1251$; cannot reject H_0

9.41 a. $z = 10$; reject H_0; conclude $\mu_1 > \mu_2$
b. p value $= 0.0228$; reject $H_0: \mu_1 - \mu_2 = 4$ at 0.10 and 0.05; do not reject at 0.01 or 0.001

9.43 a. The statement $H_0: \mu_1 - \mu_2 = 0$ suggests that the population mean times between the two service methods are equal. The statement $H_a: \mu_1 - \mu_2 < 0$ suggests that average service time for the express checkout is less than the average service time for the self-serve checkout.
b. $z = -2.72$; reject H_0 at $\alpha = 0.05$ and conclude that $\mu_1 < \mu_2$
c. The p value is $P(z < -2.72) = 0.0033$. We would reject H_0 at $\alpha = 0.10$, 0.05, 0.01, but not at 0.001.

9.45 a. $H_0: \mu_1 - \mu_2 \leq 0$ versus $H_a: \mu_1 - \mu_2 > 0$
b. $z = 1.41$; do not reject H_0; cannot conclude $\mu_1 > \mu_2$; cannot show to be harmful

9.47 a. $H_0: \mu_1 - \mu_2 = 0$ and $H_a: \mu_1 - \mu_2 > 0$, where μ_1 is the true average test score from the first test and μ_2 is the true average test score from the second test.
b. $z = 3.67$; reject H_0
c. Very strong evidence

9.49 a. $H_0: \mu_1 - \mu_2 \geq 0$ versus $H_a: \mu_1 - \mu_2 < 0$
b. $z = -4.02$; reject H_0 at each value of α; extremely strong evidence

9.53 $t(11) = 3.39$; reject at 0.10, 0.025, 0.01, but not 0.001

9.55 a. $H_0: \mu_A - \mu_B \leq 0$ versus $H_a: \mu_A - \mu_B > 0$
b. $t = 1.97$; reject H_0 with $\alpha = 0.10$ and 0.05, but not with $\alpha = 0.01$ or 0.001

9.57 a. $t = 2.32$; strong evidence
b. $t = -4.31$; very strong evidence

9.59 a. $H_0: \mu_A - \mu_B = 0$ versus $H_a: \mu_A - \mu_B < 0$
b. $t = -1.59$; reject H_0 at $\alpha = 0.10$ but not at 0.05, 0.01, or 0.001

9.63 $t = 3.39$, $df = 11$, so $t_{0.005} = 3.106$ and $t_{0.0005} = 4.437$
Reject at $\alpha = 0.1$, 0.05, and 0.01.
Fail to reject for $\alpha = 0.001$.

9.65 a. $H_0: \mu_A - \mu_O = 0$ versus $H_a: \mu_A - \mu_O \neq 0$
b. 9 df; $t_{0.025} = 2.262$ and $t_{0.005} = 3.25$
Because $2.262 < 2.31 < 3.25$, reject H_0 at $\alpha = 0.10$, 0.05, but not $\alpha = 0.01$, 0.001. There is strong evidence that H_0 is false.

9.67 a. $t = 5$; reject H_0 at each α
b. $t = 2$; reject H_0 at 0.10 and 0.05 but not 0.01 and 0.001

9.69 a. $t = 6.18$; reject $H_0: \mu_d = 0$
b. Min. 2.01; max. 4.49; endpoints of 95% interval

9.73 $z = -2.08$; reject H_0 at 0.10 and 0.05 but not at 0.01 and 0.001

9.75 a. $H_0: p_1 - p_2 = 0$ versus $H_a: p_1 - p_2 \neq 0$
b. $p = 0.0019$; $z = 2.89$; reject H_0 at $\alpha = 0.10$, 0.05, 0.01, but not 0.001

9.77 a. Since $5.467 > 1.645$, reject H_0.
b. $z = 1.54$; do not reject H_0

9.81 a. 2.96
b. 4.68
c. 3.16
d. 8.81

9.83 a. $F = 3.24$; do not reject
b. $F = 3.24$; do not reject

9.85 a. magnanimous: $z = 3.13$; reject at 0.01 but not at 0.001
pensions: $z = 3.35$; reject at all α
stock options: $z = 3.99$; reject at all α
managing the household: $z = 3.92$; reject at all α
corporate wife who travels: $z = 5.76$; reject at all α
lifestyle of corporate wife: $z = 4.11$; reject at all α
b. magnanimous: $[0.0303, 0.1297]$
pensions: $[0.0505, 0.1895]$
stock options: $[0.0773, 0.2227]$
managing the household: $[0.0810, 0.2390]$
corporate wife who travels: $[0.1540, 0.3060]$
lifestyle of corporate wife: $[0.0848, 0.2352]$

9.87 a. $H_0: \mu_T - \mu_B = 0$ versus $H_a: \mu_T - \mu_B \neq 0$; $t = 0.42$; cannot reject H_0
b. $[-0.30, 0.46]$
c. No influence

9.89 a. $z = 1.7$; do not reject H_0
  b. 0.03; [−0.005, 0.065]
  c. reject H_0 at $\alpha = 0.10$; [0.001, 0.059]

9.91 $F = 1.44$; do not reject H_0

Chapter 10 (Answers to some even-numbered exercises also given)

10.1 Response variable: the dependent variable (or variable of interest)
Factor: independent variables in a designed experiment
Treatments: values of a factor (or combination of factors)
Experimental units: entities to which treatments are assigned

10.3 Response: time to stabilize emergency condition
Factor: display panel
Treatments: panels A, B, C
Experimental units: air traffic controllers

10.5 Constant variance, normality, independence

10.7 To determine which treatment means differ and to estimate how large the differences are

10.9 a. $F = 184.57$; p value = 0.000; reject H_0; shelf heights differ
  b. bottom − middle: −21.4; [−25.12, −17.68]
  bottom − top: 4.3; [0.58, 8.02]
  middle − top: 25.7; [21.98, 29.42]
  Middle shelf maximizes mean sales.
  c. bottom − middle: [−24.45, −18.35]
  bottom − top: [1.25, 7.35]
  middle − top: [22.65, 28.75]
  d. bottom: [53.65, 57.96]
  middle: [75.04, 79.36]
  top: [49.34, 53.66]

10.11 a. $F = 43.36$, p value = 0.000; reject H_0; bottle designs differ
  b. $B − A$: [11.56, 20.84]
  $C − A$: [3.56, 12.84]
  $C − B$: [−12.64, −3.36]
  c. $B − A$: [12.41, 19.99]
  $C − A$: [4.41, 11.99]
  $C − B$: [−11.79, −4.21]
  d. μ_A: [13.92, 19.28]
  μ_B: [30.12, 35.48]
  μ_C: [22.12, 27.48]

10.12 $F = 16.42$; p value < 0.001; reject H_0; brands differ

10.13 Divot − Alpha: [38.41, 127.59]
Divot − Century: [50.21, 139.39]
Divot − Best: [−14.39, 74.79]
Century − Alpha: [−56.39, 32.79]
Century − Best: [−109.19, −20.01]
Best − Alpha: [8.21, 97.39]
Best and Divot appear to be most durable.
Divot: [313.26, 359.94]
Best: [283.06, 329.74]
Alpha: [230.26, 276.94]
Century: [218.46, 265.14]

10.15 When differences between experimental units may be concealing any true differences between the treatments

10.17 a. $F = 36.23$; p value = 0.000; reject H_0; sales methods differ
  b. $F = 12.87$; p value = 0.007; reject H_0; employee effects differ
  c. Method 1 − Method 2: [−2.30, 2.96]
  Method 1 − Method 3: [2.37, 7.63]
  Method 1 − Method 4: [3.70, 8.96]
  Method 2 − Method 3: [2.04, 7.30]
  Method 2 − Method 4: [3.37, 8.63]
  Method 3 − Method 4: [−1.30, 3.96]
  Methods 1 and 2

10.19 a. $F = 441.75$; p value = 0.000; reject H_0; keyboard brand effects differ
  b. $F = 107.69$; p value = 0.000; reject H_0; specialist effects differ
  c. $A − B$: [8.55, 11.45]
  $A − C$: [12.05, 14.95]
  $B − C$: [2.05, 4.95]
  Keyboard A

10.21 a. $F = 5.78$; p value =0.0115; reject H_0; soft drink sales effects differ
  b. Coca-Cola Classic − New Coke: [7.99, 68.01]
  Coca-Cola Classic − Pepsi: [−0.71, 59.31]
  New Coke − Pepsi: [−38.71, 21.31]
  c. Yes; mean sales of Coca-Cola Classic were significantly higher than those for New Coke.

10.25 a. Plot suggests little interaction. $F = 0.66$; p value = 0.681; do not reject H_0; conclude no interaction
  b. $F = 26.49$; p value = 0.000; reject H_0; display panel effects differ
  c. $F = 100.80$; p value = 0.000; reject H_0; emergency condition effects differ
  d. $A − B$: [0.49, 5.91]
  $A − C$: [−6.81, −1.39]
  $B − C$: [−10.01, −4.59]
  e. 1 − 2: [−10.43, −4.17]
  1 − 3: [−18.13, −11.87]
  1 − 4: [0.77, 7.03]
  2 − 3: [−10.83, −4.57]
  2 − 4: [8.07, 14.33]
  3 − 4: [15.77, 22.03]
  f. Panel B. No, there is no interaction.
  g. [6.37, 12.63]

10.27 a. Plot suggests interaction exists. $F = 24.73$; p value = 0.001; reject H_0; conclude interaction exists; cannot test separately
  b. House design C and supervisor 1; [17.72, 19.88]

10.29 $F = 40.79$; p value < 0.0001; reject H_0; drug effects differ; all pairwise differences significant with $\alpha = 0.05$
$Y − X$: [9.18, 21.82]
$Z − X$: [−17.52, −4.88]

$Z − Y$: [−33.02, −20.38]
μ_Y: [34.73, 43.67]
All intervals are 95%.

10.31 Loan officer effects differ (p value < 0.0001).
Evaluation method effects differ (p value < 0.0001).
$D − B$: [−4.25, −3.25]
$F − B$: [−3.25, −2.25]
$D − F$: [−1.50, −0.50]
4 − 1: [−4.58, −3.42]
3 − 1: [−3.58, −2.42]
2 − 1: [−1.91, −0.75]
4 − 2: [−3.25, −2.09]
3 − 2: [−2.25, −1.09]
4 − 3: [−1.58, −0.42]

10.33 F(int) = 0.09; do not reject H_0; conclude no interaction
$F(1) = 3.31$; reject H_0; degree of attendance effects significant
$F(2) = 0.23$; do not reject H_0; prior information effects not significant

10.35 F(int) = 0.19; p value = 0.9019; do not reject H_0; conclude no interaction
$F(1) = 48.63$; p value = 0.000; reject H_0; fertilizer type effects differ
$F(2) = 78.90$; p value = 0.000; reject H_0; wheat type effects differ
Using Tukey comparisons:
Fertilizer types A and B differ with $\alpha = 0.01$.
Wheat types M and N, M and O, M and P, O and P each differ with $\alpha = 0.01$.

Chapter 11 (Answers to some even-numbered exercises also given)

11.1 $s_{xy} = 0.4447$; $r_{xy} = 0.9678$; very strong positive relationship

11.3 When the plot suggests a linear relationship between y and x

11.5 β_1 = change in the mean value of y associated with a one-unit increase in x
β_0 = mean value of y when $x = 0$

11.6 When data are observed in time sequence, the data are called time series data. Cross-sectional data are observed at a single point in time.

11.7 Plot has a straight-line appearance (with a positive slope).

11.8 a. Mean service time when 4 copiers are serviced
  b. Mean service time when 6 copiers are serviced
  c. Change in mean service time associated with an additional copier serviced
  d. Mean service time when no copiers are serviced; no
  e. All factors other than number of copiers serviced; work environment, number of distractions

11.9 Plot looks reasonably linear.

11.10   a. Mean demand when price difference is 0.10
b. Mean demand when price difference is -0.05
c. Change in mean demand per dollar increase in the price difference
d. Mean demand when price difference equals 0; yes
e. All factors other than price difference; advertising budget, type of ads

11.11   b. The plot of y versus x appears linear (with a positive slope).

11.12   a. Mean labour cost when batch size is 60
b. Mean labour cost when batch size is 30
c. Change in mean labour cost per unit increase in batch size
d. Mean labour cost when batch size is zero; questionable
e. All factors other than batch size; wages, overtime

11.13   b. Plot looks reasonably linear with a positive slope.

11.14   a. Mean sales price for 2,000 $(x = 20)$ square foot homes
b. Mean sales price for 1,800 $(x = 18)$ square foot homes
c. Change in mean sales price per one unit (100 square foot) increase in home size
d. Mean sales price when home size $= 0$; no
e. All factors other than home size; upkeep, location

11.15   The quality or goodness of the fit of the least squares line to the observed data

11.17   Evaluate $\hat{y} = b_0 + b_1 x$ for the given value of x.

11.19   a. $b_0 = 11.4641$, $b_1 = 24.6022$
b_0: 0 copiers, 11.46 minutes of service
b_1: each additional copier adds 24.6022 minutes of service on average
No. The interpretation of b_0 does not make practical sense since it indicates that 11.46 minutes of service would be required for a customer with no copiers.
b. 100; $\hat{y} = 11.4641 + 24.6022(4) = 109.873$, or 109.9 minutes

11.21   a. $SS_{xy} = 100,982.33$; $SS_{xx} = 9,952.667$; $b_1 = 10.1463$; $b_0 = 18.4875$
b. b_1 is the estimated increase in mean labour cost (10.1463) for every one-unit increase in the batch size.
b_0 is the estimated mean labour cost (18.4875) when batch size $= 0$; no.
c. $\hat{y} = 18.4880 + 10.1463x$
d. 600; $\hat{y} = 18.4880 + 10.1463(60) = 627.266$

11.23   (1) Mean of error terms $= 0$
(2) Constant variance

(3) Normality
(4) Independence

11.25   21.3002; 4.61521
11.27   74.67624; 8.64154
11.29   27.853025; 5.2776
11.31   a. $\alpha = 0.05$: strong evidence
b. $\alpha = 0.01$: very strong evidence

11.33   a. $b_0 = 11.4641$; $b_1 = 24.6022$
b. $SSE = 191.7017$; $s = 4.615$
c. $s_{b_1} = 0.8045$; $t = 30.580$
d. $t > 2.262$; reject $H_0: \beta_1 = 0$; strong evidence that regression relationship is significant
e. $t > 3.250$; reject $H_0: \beta_1 = 0$; very strong evidence that regression relationship is significant
f. p value $= 0.000$; reject $H_0: \beta_1 = 0$ at all values of α; extremely strong evidence that regression relationship is significant
g. [22.782, 26.422]
h. [21.987, 27.217]
i. $s_{b_0} = 3.4390$; $t = 3.334$
j. p value $= 0.0087$; reject $H_0: \beta_0 = 0$ at all values of α except 0.001; very strong evidence that the intercept is significant
k. $SS_{xx} = 32.909$; $s_{b_0} = 3.439$; $s_{b_1} = 0.8045$

11.35   a. $b_0 = 18.4875$; $b_1 = 10.1463$
b. $SSE = 746.7624$; $s = 8.6415$
c. $s_{b_1} = 0.0866$; $t = 117.1344$
d. Reject $H_0: \beta_1 = 0$ with $\alpha = 0.05$; regression relationship is significant (strong evidence)
e. Reject $H_0: \beta_1 = 0$ with $\alpha = 0.01$; regression relationship is significant (very strong evidence)
f. p value $= 0.000$; reject $H_0: \beta_1 = 0$ at all values of α; regression relationship is significant (extremely strong evidence)
g. [9.9533, 10.3393]
h. [9.872, 10.421]
i. $s_{b_0} = 4.6766$; $t = 3.9532$
j. p value $= 0.0027$; reject $H_0: \beta_0 = 0$ at all values of α except $\alpha = 0.001$; intercept is significant (very strong evidence)
k. $SS_{xx} = 9,952.667$; $s_{b_0} = 4.6766$; $s_{b_1} = 0.0866$

11.37   [3.091, 5.770]
11.41   a. 109.873; [106.721, 113.025]
b. 109.873; [98.967, 120.779]
d. 113 minutes
11.43   a. 627.263; [621.054, 633.472]
b. 627.263; [607.032, 647.494]
c. [618.42, 636.10]; [598.48, 656.04]
11.45   114.945; [102.024, 127.867]
11.49 $r^2 = 0.792$; $r = 0.890$
11.51 $r^2 = 0.88$; $r = 0.938$
11.57   a. $F = 935.149$
b. Reject H_0 with $\alpha = 0.05$; significant
c. Reject H_0 with $\alpha = 0.01$; significant

d. p value less than 0.001; reject H_0 at all values of α; significant
e. $t_a^2 = 935.15 = F$
11.59   a. $F = 13,720.4877$
b. Reject H_0 with $\alpha = 0.05$; significant
c. Reject H_0 with $\alpha = 0.01$; significant
d. p value $= 0.000$; reject H_0 at all values of α; significant
11.65   No violations indicated
11.67   Cyclical plot; $d = 0.473 < 1.27$; conclude positive autocorrelation exists; $4 - 0.473 = 3.527 > 1.45$; conclude no negative autocorrelation exists
11.69   Constant variance assumption violated
11.71   a. Yes; plot appears linear
b. $b_0 = 306.619$; $b_1 = -27.714$
c. $\hat{y} = 306.619 - 27.714x$
d. p value $= 0.000$; significant
e. For \$2.10: 248.420; [244.511, 252.327]
For \$2.75: 230.405; [226.697, 234.112]
For \$3.10: 220.705; [216.415, 224.994]
11.73   a. $\hat{y} = b_0 + b_1(15.00) = 0.847 + 0.6105(15.00) = 10.0045$; 95% C.I.: [8.494, 11.514]
b. 10.0045; 95% P.I.: $[-0.310, 20.318]$
11.75   Aggressive stocks: [0.0075, 0.0251]
Defensive stocks: $[-0.0066, -0.0026]$
Neutral stocks: [0.0051, 0.0124]

Chapter 12 (Answers to some even-numbered exercises also given)

12.1 y: dependent variable; $x_1, \ldots, x_k$: independent (predictor) variables
12.2   Mean value of y when the values of the independent variables are $x_1, x_2, \ldots, x_k$
12.3   Unknown regression parameters relating mean value of y to $x_1, \ldots, x_k$
12.4   Describes the effects on y of all factors other than $x_1, x_2, \ldots, x_k$
12.5 β_0 is the mean value of y when all predictor variables equal zero.
β_1 is the change in mean y associated with a one-unit increase in x_1 when all other predictor variables stay the same.
β_2 is the change in mean y associated with a one-unit increase in x_2 when all other predictor variables stay the same.
12.7   a. Linear relationship
b. Mean demand for Fresh when $x_1 = \$3.70$, $x_2 = \$3.90$, $x_3 = \$650,000$
c. β_0: y intercept has no practical meaning
β_1: change in mean demand when x_1 increases by \$1 and x_2 and x_3 unchanged
β_2, β_3 similar to β_1
ε: effects on y of all factors other than x_1, x_2, x_3

12.9 SSE

12.11   a. $b_0 = 29.347$,
     $b_1 = 5.6128$,
     $b_2 = 3.8344$

     b. $\hat{y} = 29.347 +$
       $5.6128(20) +$
       $3.8344(8) = 172.28$;
       point estimate = point prediction

12.13   a. $b_0 = 1,946.8020$,
     $b_1 = 0.0386$,
     $b_2 = 1.0394$,
     $b_3 = -413.7578$

     b. $\hat{y} = 1946.8020 + 0.0386(56,194)$
       $+ 1.0394(14,077.88)$
       $- 413.7578(6.89)$
       $= 15,896.25$

     c. $17,207.31 - 15,896.25 =$
       $1,311.06$ greater than $\hat{y}$

12.14 σ^2, σ

12.15   a.   Proportion of total variation explained by the model
     b. $\bar{R}^2$ avoids overestimating the importance of the independent variables.

12.16   Tests to see if at least one independent variable is significant

12.17   a. $SSE = 73.6$;
     $s^2 = 10.5$;
     $s = 3.24164$
     b.   Total variation = 7,447.5; unexplained variation = 73.6; explained variation = 7374
     c. $R^2 = 0.99$; $\bar{R}^2 = 0.987$
     d. $F(\text{model}) = 350.87$
     e. $F(\text{model}) = 350.87 > F_{0.05} = 4.74$; reject H_0: $\beta_1 = \beta_2 = 0$ with $\alpha = 0.05$; model significant
     f. $F(\text{model}) = 350.87 > F_{0.01} = 9.55$; model significant with $\alpha = 0.01$
     g. p value = 0.000; model significant at each value of α

12.19   a. $SSE = 1,798,712.2$; $s^2 = 149,892.7$; $s = 387.1598$
     b.   Total variation = 464,126,601.6; unexplained variation = 1,798,712.2; explained variation = 462,327,889.4
     c. $R^2 = 0.9961$; $\bar{R}^2 = 0.9952$
     d. $F(\text{model}) = 1,028.1309$
     e. $F(\text{model}) = 1,028.1309 > F_{0.05} = 3.49$; reject H_0: $\beta_1 = \beta_2 = \beta_3 = 0$ with $\alpha = 0.05$; model significant
     f. $F(\text{model}) = 1,028.1309 > F_{0.01} = 5.95$; model significant with $\alpha = 0.01$
     g. p value < 0.001; model significant at each value of α

12.22   a. $b_0 = 29.347$; $s_{b_0} = 4.891$; $t = 6.00$;
     $b_1 = 5.6128$; $s_{b_1} = 0.2285$;
     $t = 24.56$;
     $b_2 = 3.8344$; $s_{b_2} = 0.4332$; $t = 8.85$
     b. β_0: $t = 6.00 > t_{0.025} = 2.365$; reject H_0: $\beta_0 = 0$ with $\alpha = 0.05$
     β_1: $t = 24.56 > 2.365$; reject H_0: $\beta_1 = 0$ with $\alpha = 0.05$
     β_2: $t = 8.85 > 2.365$; reject H_0: $\beta_2 = 0$ with $\alpha = 0.05$

β_0, x_1, x_2 all significant with $\alpha = 0.05$

     c. β_0: $t = 6.00 > t_{0.005} = 3.499$; reject H_0: $\beta_0 = 0$ with $\alpha = 0.01$
     β_1: $t = 24.56 > 3.499$; reject H_0: $\beta_1 = 0$ with $\alpha = 0.01$
     β_2: $t = 8.85 > 3.499$; reject H_0: $\beta_2 = 0$ with $\alpha = 0.01$
     β_0, x_1, x_2 all significant with $\alpha = 0.01$
     d.   For H_0: $\beta_0 = 0$, p value = 0.001 $< \alpha = 0.01$; reject H_0 at $\alpha = 0.10, 0.05, 0.01$; β_0 significant at $\alpha = 0.10, 0.05, 0.01$, not at $\alpha = 0.001$.
     For H_0: $\beta_1 = 0$, p value = 0.000 $<$ each value of α.
     Reject H_0: $\beta_1 = 0$ at each value of α.
     x_1 significant at each value of α
     For H_0: $\beta_2 = 0$, p value = 0.000 $<$ each value of α.
     Reject H_0: $\beta_2 = 0$ at each value of α.
     x_2 significant at each value of α.
     e. β_0: [17.780, 40.914]
     β_1: [5.072, 6.153]
     β_2: [2.810, 4.860]
     f. β_0: [12.233, 46.461]
     β_1: [4.813, 6.412]
     β_2: [2.319, 5.350]

12.23   a. $b_0 = 7.5891$; $s_{b_0} = 2.4450$; $t = 3.104$
     $b_1 = -2.3577$; $s_{b_1} = 0.6379$; $t = -3.696$
     $b_2 = 1.6122$; $s_{b_2} = 0.2954$; $t = 5.459$
     $b_3 = 0.5012$; $s_{b_3} = 0.1259$; $t = 3.981$
     b. β_0: $t = 3.104 > t_{0.025} = 2.056$; reject H_0: $\beta_0 = 0$ with $\alpha = 0.05$
     β_1: $|t| = 3.696 > 2.056$; reject H_0: $\beta_1 = 0$ with $\alpha = 0.05$
     β_2: $t = 5.459 > 2.056$; reject H_0: $\beta_2 = 0$ with $\alpha = 0.05$
     β_3: $t = 3.981 > 2.056$; reject H_0: $\beta_3 = 0$ with $\alpha = 0.05$
     β_0, x_1, x_2, x_3 all significant with $\alpha = 0.05$.
     c.   In each case, $|t| > t_{0.005} = 2.779$; reject appropriate H_0.
     β_0, x_1, x_2, x_3 all significant with $\alpha = 0.01$
     d.   For H_0: $\beta_0 = 0$, p value = 0.0046 $< \alpha = 0.01$; reject H_0 at each α except $\alpha = 0.001$.
     For H_0: $\beta_1 = 0$, p value = 0.0010 $< \alpha = 0.01$; reject H_0 at each α except $\alpha = 0.001$.
     For H_0: $\beta_2 = 0$, p value < 0.0001 $< \alpha = 0.001$; reject H_0 at each value of α.
     For H_0: $\beta_3 = 0$, p value = 0.0005 $< \alpha = 0.001$; reject H_0 at each value of α.
     β_0 and x_1 significant at $\alpha = 0.01$; x_2 and x_3 significant at $\alpha = 0.001$
     e. β_0: [2.5633, 12.6149]
     β_1: [−3.6690, −1.0464]

β_2: [1.0051, 2.2193]
β_3: [0.2424, 0.7599]
     f. β_1: [−4.1304, −0.5850]
     β_0: [0.7944, 14.3838]
     β_1: [−4.1304, −0.5850]
     β_2: [0.7913, 2.4331]
     β_3: [0.1513, 0.8511]

12.25   Distance of $x_1, x_2, \ldots, x_k$ from $\bar{x}_1, \bar{x}_2, \ldots, \bar{x}_k$

12.27   a.   172.28; [168.56, 175.99]
     b.   172.28; [163.76, 180.80]
     c.   [166.79, 177.77]; [159.68, 184.88]

12.29   [14,906.24, 16,886.26]; $y = 17,207.31$ is unusually high (above interval).

12.31 $\beta_0 + \beta_1 x + \beta_2 x^2$ expresses the mean value of y as a linear function of the parameters β_0, β_1, and β_2. β_0, β_1, and β_2 are regression parameters relating the mean value of y to x. ε is an error term that describes the effects on y of all factors other than x and x^2. y is the criterion variable.

12.33   First interval shorter; model that uses x_4

12.35   Multiply x_1 by x_2 to form $x_1 x_2$.

12.37   a.   2.0122, 1.6633, 1.3144, 0.9655, 0.6166
     b.   3.8342, 3.4853, 3.1364, 2.7875, 2.4386
     c.   Because the point estimates for part b are larger

12.39   a.   108.93328; 156.73012
     b.   129.75562; 183.74788
     c.   As x_1 increases, mean y increases at a faster rate when x_2 is higher.

12.43   a.   Linear plots with different y intercepts for mutual and stock companies
     b. β_2: difference between mean times for mutual and stock companies
     c. p value < 0.001; reject H_0: $\beta_2 = 0$ with $\alpha = 0.05$ and $\alpha = 0.01$; company type is significant; [4.9770, 11.1339]
     d.   No interaction

12.45   a.   The point estimate of the effect on the mean of campaign B compared to campaign A is $b_4 = 0.2695$. The 95% confidence interval is [0.1262, 0.4128]. The point estimate of the effect on the mean of campaign C compared to campaign A is $b_5 = 0.4396$. The 95% confidence interval is [0.2944, 0.5847]. Campaign C is probably most effective even though intervals overlap.
     b. $\hat{y} = 8.7154 - 2.768(3.7) + 1.6667(3.9) + 0.4927(6.5) + 0.4396 = 8.61621$; confidence interval = [8.5138, 8.71862]; prediction interval = [8.28958, 8.94285]
     c. β_5 = effect on mean of campaign C compared to campaign B
     d. β_5 is significant at $\alpha = 0.1$ and $\alpha = 0.05$ because p value = 0.0179.

Thus, there is strong evidence that β_5 is greater than 0. 95% confidence interval: [0.0320,0.3081]; since it does not overlap 0, we are at least 95% confident that β_5 is greater than 0.

12.47 Complete: $y = \beta_0 + \beta_1 x_1 + \beta_2 x_2 + \cdots + \beta_g x_g + \beta_{g+1} x_{g+1} + \cdots + \beta_k x_k + \varepsilon$
Reduced: $y = \beta_0 + \beta_1 x_1 + \beta_2 x_2 + \cdots + \beta_g x_g + \varepsilon$

12.49 F = 19.7003; reject H_0 at 0.05 and 0.01

12.51 $F = 0.1502$; do not reject H_0 at 0.05

12.55 Second $\bar{R}^2$, smallest C, smallest p value, second-smallest s; desirable to have a large store with a small percentage of the floor space for the prescription department

12.59 a. Curved appearance
b. $d = 1.62$; $d_{L,0.05} = 1.28$ and $d_{U,0.05} = 1.57$; since $d > d_{U,0.05}$, there is no first-order autocorrelation.

12.63 Original hospital 17: with hospital 14 included, Cook's D = 5.033; without hospital 14, Cook's D = 1.317
Original hospital 16: with hospital 14 included, Cook's D = 0.897; without hospital 14, Cook's D = 1.384

12.65 0 or 1; the two possible outcomes

12.67 1.63, which means that for an increase of 1 in the score on test 1, the odds of a potential employee being successful increase by 63%.

12.69 $\hat{y} = 30{,}626 + 3.893(28{,}000) - 29{,}607(1.56) + 86.52(1{,}821.7) \cong 251{,}056$

12.71 For emerging countries,
$\hat{y} = 56.9171 - 0.5574x_1 - 18.2934(0) + 0.3537x_1(0) = 56.9171 - 0.5574x_1.$
For developing countries,
$\hat{y} = 56.9171 - 0.5574x_1 - 18.2934(1) + 0.3537x_1(1) = 38.6237 - 0.2037x_1.$
The nature of the interaction is that the impact (slope) of credit rating is less severe in the case of developing countries.

12.73 a. β_5: $b_5 = 0.2137$ with p value = 0.0022; effect of B versus A significant at $\alpha = 0.01$, but not at $\alpha = 0.001$; [0.0851, 0.3423]
β_6: $b_6 = 0.3818$ with p value less than 0.001; effect of C versus A significant at $\alpha = 0.001$; [0.2551, 0.5085]
b. β_6: $b_6 = 0.1681$ with p value = 0.0147; effect of C versus B significant at $\alpha = 0.05$; but not at $\alpha = 0.01$; [0.0363, 0.2999]
d. Prediction interval for the third model is slightly shorter.

12.75 $|-4.96226| > 2$. Removing observation 17 will substantially change the point prediction of y_{17}.

Chapter 13

13.3 a. $S = 4$; p value = 0.375; do not reject H_0
b. $S = 5$; p value = 0.031; reject H_0

13.5 a. p value = 0.0059; reject H_0

13.7 a. $S_1 = 4, S_2 = 5, S = 5$
b. p value = 1.0; do not reject H_0 at any α; conclude no difference

13.11 $T_1 = 120.5$; do not reject H_0; no difference

13.13 Differences exist.

13.17 $T^- = 3$; reject H_0 at $\alpha = 0.02$

13.19 $T = 0$; reject H_0; conclude scores differ

13.23 Reject H_0; panels differ

13.25 $H = 14.36$; reject H_0; display heights differ; $H = 13.35$; reject H_0

13.27 At $\alpha = 0.05$, we would reject H_0; $H = 9.04$, $df = 2$, $p = 0.011$

13.29 a. $r_s = 1 - \dfrac{6 \sum d_i^2}{n(n^2 - 1)}$
b. For each tie, calculate an average rank and assign that value to the tied cases.

13.31 $r_s = 0.986$; reject H_0 if $r_s > r_a$; since $0.986 > 0.523, 0.623, 0.736$, and 0.818, reject H_0

13.33 The critical value for X^2 with 2 degrees of freedom and $\alpha = 0.05$ is 5.99147; reject H_0; the drugs are different

13.35 Wilcoxon signed ranks test for paired differences: reject H_0 if $T^+ \le T_0$ (for a one-sided test); reject H_0: $1 < 11$

13.37 $T_1 = 75 \ge T_4 = 49$; reject H_0; the loan rates do differ

Chapter 14

14.7 a. Each $E_i \ge 5$
b. $\chi^2 = 300.605$; reject H_0

14.9 a. $\chi^2 = 137.14$; reject H_0
b. Differences between brand preferences

14.11 a1. (0, 10.185)
a2. (10.185, 14.147)
a3. (14.147, 18.108)
a4. (18.108, 22.069)
a5. (22.069, 26.030)
a6. (26.030, ∞)
b1. 0.0228; 1.5
b2. 0.1359; 9
b3. 0.3413; 22
b4. 0.3413; 22
b5. 0.1359; 9
b6. 0.0228; 1.5
c. Can use χ^2 test
d. H_0: the probabilities that a randomly selected payment time will be in intervals 1, 2, 3, 4, 5, and 6 are $p_1 = 0.0228$, $p_2 = 0.1359$, $p_3 = 0.3413$, $p_4 = 0.3413$, $p_5 = 0.1359$, and $p_6 = 0.0228$ versus H_a: the above null hypothesis is not true
e. 1, 9, 30, 15, 8, 2
$\chi^2 = 5.581$
f. Fail to reject; normal

14.13 $\chi^2 = 9.473 + 1.399 + 1.347 + 0.450 + 0.757 = 13.426$

Since $13.426 > X^2_{0.05} = 9.48773$ (with 4 degrees of freedom), reject H_0.

14.17 $X^2(1) = 0.50$, is less than $X^2_{critical}$ of 3.84; fail to reject H_0

14.19 a. $X^2 = 8.929$; reject H_0
b. The test is valid because the number of cells exceeds 4, the average expected value is at least 5, and the smallest expected value, 4, is at least 1.
c. Yes
d. Dependent

14.21 a. $X^2(3) = 3.28$, which is less than the critical value of 7.8147; fail to reject H_0
b. The responses appear to be fairly equally distributed.

14.23 a. $X^2 = 10.023 > X^2_{0.05}$ (1 degree of freedom); we reject H_0: independence
b. $X^2 = 6.989 > X^2_{0.05} = 3.84146$ (1 degree of freedom); we reject H_0: independence
d. Yes

14.25 $X^2 = 0.04 > X^2_{0.05} = 3.84146$ (1 degree of freedom); we do not reject H_0: independence; conclude relationships not the same

14.27 $X^2 = 10.076 > X^2_{0.05} = 7.8147$ with 3 degrees of freedom; reject H_0; not a normal distribution

14.29 $X^2(2) = 11.45$; reject H_0

14.31 $X^2(8) = 38.37$; reject H_0

Chapter 15

15.5 Small facility

15.7 a. $10 million, $10.5 million, $3 million
b. Medium facility

15.9 a. $12.2 million
b. $1.7 million

15.11 a. Location C at $4 million
b. Location A

15.15 a. Expected payoff and probability of each sample outcome
b. Expected payoff of alternative chosen using the expected monetary value criterion with the prior probabilities
c. Expected payoff of sampling minus the expected payoff of no sampling
d. Difference between the EVIS and the cost of sampling

15.19 a. 0.485, 0.8247, 0.0928, 0.0825
b. 0.300, 0.1667, 0.700, 0.1333
c. 0.215, 0.2325, 0.2093, 0.5581

15.21 a. $822
b. $580
c. $242
d. $242

15.25 a. 0.73, 0.9863, 0.0137
b. 0.27, 0.6667, 0.3333

15.27 a. Do not send; $14,958.90
b. Send; $14,500

15.33 $0 to $500,000

15.35 Expected utility (investing) = 0.66; expected utility (not investing) = 0.70
Decision maker should not invest.

15.37
a. Research project should continue:
$(0.7)(23) + (0.3)(-2) = \$15.5$
b. Should be licensed; slightly
better return:
License: $23
Develop: $(0.25)(43) + (0.55)(21) + (0.2)(3) = \$22.9$

15.39 Build large; $62 million

15.41 0.5455

15.43
b. Using expected monetary value,
the expected value of option (1)
is $750,000 and the expected
value of option (2) is $500,000.

15.45
b. Renew lease; $2,775,000
c. Sign; EVPI = $1,575,000

Chapter 16

16.5
a. Straight-line growth
b. $\hat{y} = 290.089474 + 8.667669(21) = 472.1$

16.7 Square root ($y_t^{0.5}$); quartic root
($y_t^{0.25}$); logarithmic ($\ln y_t$)

16.9 439.703; [389.915, 495.848]

16.15 Positive linear trend

16.17 666.6, 881.6, 482.1, 299.9

16.19 a. 15.01, 40.54, 56.82, 22.02

b. [12.21, 17.81]; [37.69, 43.39];
[53.90, 59.74]; [19.04, 25.00]

16.25 35,592.7;
[31,325.5, 39,860]

16.27 810.04;
[774.95, 845.13]

16.31 Method B; method A

16.35
b. Prices of the precious metals
declined from the base year
of 1988.

16.37
a. $F(1, 16) = 36.71$; $p < 0.001$; yes
b. 2006: 30.1; 2007: 28.9; 2008:
27.8; 2009: 26.6; 2010: 25.5

REFERENCES

Abraham, B., and J. Ledolter. *Statistical Methods for Forecasting.* New York, NY: John Wiley & Sons, 1983.

Akaah, Ishmael P., and Edward A. Riordan. "Judgments of Marketing Professionals about Ethical Issues in Marketing Research: A Replication and Extension." *Journal of Marketing Research,* February 1989, pp. 112–20.

Ashton, Robert H., John J. Willingham, and Robert K. Elliott. "An Empirical Analysis of Audit Delay." *Journal of Accounting Research* 25, no. 2 (Autumn 1987), pp. 275–92.

Axcel, Amir. *Complete Business Statistics.* 3rd ed. Burr Ridge, IL: Irwin/McGraw-Hill, 1996.

Bayus, Barry L. "The Consumer and Durable Replacement Buyer." *Journal of Marketing* 55 (January 1991), pp. 42–51.

Beattie, Vivien, and Michael John Jones. "The Use and Abuse of Graphs in Annual Reports: Theoretical Framework and Empirical Study." *Accounting and Business Research* 22, no. 88 (Autumn 1992), pp. 291–303.

Blauw, Jan Nico, and Willem E. During. "Total Quality Control in Dutch Industry." *Quality Progress* (February 1990), pp. 50–51.

Blodgett, Jeffrey G., Donald H. Granbois, and Rockney G. Walters. "The Effects of Perceived Justice on Complainants' Negative Word-of-Mouth Behavior and Repatronage Intentions." *Journal of Retailing* 69, no. 4 (Winter 1993), pp. 399–428.

Bowerman, Bruce L., and Richard T. O'Connell. *Forecasting and Time Series: An Applied Approach.* 3rd ed. Belmont, CA: Duxbury Press, 1993.

Bowerman, Bruce L., and Richard T. O'Connell. *Linear Statistical Models: An Applied Approach.* 2nd ed. Boston, MA: PWS-KENT Publishing Company, 1990, pp. 457, 460–64, 729–974.

Box, G. E. P., and G. M. Jenkins. *Time Series Analysis: Forecasting and Control.* 2nd ed. San Francisco, CA: Holden-Day, 1976.

Boyd, Thomas C., and Timothy C. Krehbiel. "The Effect of Promotion Timing on Major League Baseball Attendance." *Sport Marketing Quarterly,* 1999, 8(4), pp. 23–34.

Brown, R. G. *Smoothing, Forecasting and Prediction of Discrete Time Series.* Englewood Cliffs, NJ: Prentice Hall, 1962.

Carey, John; Robert Neff; and Lois Therrien. "The Prize and the Passion." *Business Week* (Special 1991 bonus issue: The Quality Imperative), January 15, 1991, pp. 58–59.

Carslaw, Charles A. P. N., and Steven E. Kaplan. "An Examination of Audit Delay: Further Evidence from New Zealand." *Accounting and Business Research* 22, no. 85 (1991), pp. 21–32.

Cateora, Philip R. *International Marketing.* 9th ed. Homewood, IL: Irwin/McGraw-Hill, 1993, p. 262.

Clemen, Robert T. *Making Hard Decisions: An Introduction to Decision Analysis.* 2nd ed. Belmont, CA: Duxbury Press, 1996, p. 443.

Conlon, Edward J., and Thomas H. Stone. "Absence Schema and Managerial Judgment." *Journal of Management* 18, no. 3 (1992), pp. 435–54.

Cooper, Donald R., and C. William Emory. *Business Research Methods.* 5th ed. Homewood, IL: Richard D. Irwin, 1995, pp. 434–38, 450–51, 458–68.

Cuprisin, Tim. "Inside TV & Radio." *The Milwaukee Journal Sentinel,* April 26, 1995.

Dawson, Scott. "Consumer Responses to Electronic Article Surveillance Alarms." *Journal of Retailing* 69, no. 3 (Fall 1993), pp. 353–62.

Deming, W. Edwards. *Out of the Crisis.* Cambridge, MA: Massachusetts Institute of Technology Center for Advanced Engineering Study, 1986, pp. 18–96, 312–14.

Dielman, Terry. *Applied Regression Analysis for Business and Economics.* Belmont, CA: Duxbury Press, 1996.

Dillon, William R., Thomas J. Madden, and Neil H. Firtle. *Essentials of Marketing Research.* Homewood, IL: Richard D. Irwin Inc., 1993, pp. 382–84, 416–17, 419–20, 432–33, 445, 462–64, 524–27.

Dondero, Cort. "SPC Hits the Road." *Quality Progress,* January 1991, pp. 43–44.

Draper, N., and H. Smith. *Applied Regression Analysis.* 2nd ed. New York, NY: John Wiley & Sons, 1981.

Farnum, Nicholas R. *Modern Statistical Quality Control and Improvement.* Belmont, CA: Duxbury Press, 1994, p. 55.

Fitzgerald, Neil. "Relations Overcast by Cloudy Conditions." *CA Magazine,* April 1993, pp. 28–35.

Garvin, David A. *Managing Quality.* New York, NY: Free Press/ Macmillan, 1988.

Gibbons, J. D. *Nonparametric Statistical Inference.* 2nd ed. New York: McGraw-Hill, 1985.

Gitlow, Howard; Shelly Gitlow; Alan Oppenheim; and Rosa Oppenheim. *Tools and Methods for the Improvement of Quality.* Homewood, IL: Richard D. Irwin, 1989, pp. 14–25, 533–53.

Guthrie, James P., Curtis M. Grimm, and Ken G. Smith. "Environmental Change and Management Staffing: A Reply." *Journal of Management* 19, no. 4 (1993), pp. 889–96.

Kuhn, Susan E. "A Closer Look at Mutual Funds: Which Ones Really Deliver?" *Fortune,* October 7, 1991, pp. 29–30.

Kumar, V., Roger A. Kerin, and Arun Pereira. "An Empirical Assessment of Merger and Acquisition Activity in Retailing." *Journal of Retailing* 67, no. 3 (Fall 1991), pp. 321–38.

Magee, Robert P. *Advanced Managerial Accounting.* New York, NY: Harper & Row, 1986, p. 223.

Mahmood, Mo Adam, and Gary J. Mann. "Measuring the Organizational Impact of Information Technology Investment: An Exploratory Study." *Journal of Management Information Systems* 10, no. 1 (Summer 1993), pp. 97–122.

Martocchio, Joseph J. "The Financial Cost of Absence Decisions." *Journal of Management* 18, no. 1 (1992), pp. 133–52.

Mendenhall, W., and J. Reinmuth. *Statistics for Management Economics.* 4th ed. Boston, MA: PWS-KENT Publishing Company, 1982.

The Miami University Report. Miami University, Oxford, OH, vol. 8, no. 26, 1989.

Moore, David S. *The Basic Practice of Statistics.* 2nd ed. New York: W. H. Freeman and Company, 2000.

Moore, David S., and George P. McCabe. *Introduction to the Practice of Statistics.* 2nd ed. New York: W. H. Freeman, 1993.

Morris, Michael H., Ramon A. Avila, and Jeffrey Allen. "Individualism and the Modern Corporation: Implications for Innovation and Entrepreneurship." *Journal of Management* 19, no. 3 (1993), pp. 595–612.

Neter, J., M. Kutner, C. Nachtsheim, and W. Wasserman. *Applied Linear Statistical Models.* 4th ed. Homewood, IL: Irwin/McGraw-Hill, 1996.

Neter, J., W. Wasserman, and M. H. Kutner. *Applied Linear Statistical Models.* 2nd ed. Homewood, IL: Richard D. Irwin, 1985.

Nunnally, Bennie H., Jr., and D. Anthony Plath. *Cases in Finance.* Burr Ridge, IL: Richard D. Irwin, 1995, pp. 12–1–12–7.

Olmsted, Dan, and Gigi Anders. "Turned Off." *USA Weekend,* June 2–4, 1995.

Ott, Lyman. *An Introduction to Statistical Methods and Data Analysis.* 2nd ed. Boston, MA: PWS-Kent, 1987.

SAS User's Guide. 1982 Edition. Cary, NC: SAS Institute, 1982.

Schaeffer, R. L., William Mendenhall, and Lyman Ott. *Elementary Survey Sampling.* 3rd ed. Boston, MA: Duxbury Press, 1986.

Scherkenbach, William. *The Deming Route to Quality and Productivity: Road Maps and Roadblocks.* Washington, D.C.: Ceepress Books, 1986.

Seigel, James C. "Managing with Statistical Models." SAE Technical Paper 820520. Warrendale, PA: Society for Automotive Engineers, Inc., 1982.

Sichelman, Lew. "Random Checks Find Loan Application Fibs." *The Journal-News* (Hamilton, Ohio), Sept. 26, 1992 (originally published in *The Washington Post*).

Siegel, Andrew F. *Practical Business Statistics.* 2nd ed. Homewood, IL: Richard D. Irwin, 1990, p. 588.

Silk, Alvin J., and Ernst R. Berndt. "Scale and Scope Effects on Advertising Agency Costs." *Marketing Science* 12, no. 1 (Winter 1993), pp. 53–72.

Stevenson, William J. *Production/Operations Management.* 6th ed. Homewood, IL: Irwin/McGraw-Hill, 1999, p. 228.

Thomas, Anisya S., and Kannan Ramaswamy. "Environmental Change and Management Staffing: A Comment." *Journal of Management* 19, no. 4 (1993), pp. 877–87.

Von Neumann, J., and O. Morgenstern. *Theory of Games and Economic Behavior.* 2nd ed. Princeton, N.J.: Princeton University Press, 1947.

Walton, Mary. *The Deming Management Method.* New York, NY: Dodd, Mead & Company, 1986.

Weinberger, Marc G., and Harlan E. Spotts. "Humor in U.S. versus U.K. TV Commercials: A Comparison." *Journal of Advertising* 18, no. 2 (1989), pp. 39–44.

Wright, Thomas A., and Douglas G. Bonett. "Role of Employee Coping and Performance in Voluntary Employee Withdrawal: A Research Refinement and Elaboration." *Journal of Management* 19, no. 1 (1993) pp. 147–61.

PHOTO CREDITS

A Table of Areas under the Standard Normal Curve

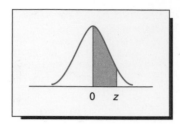

z	.00	.01	.02	.03	.04	.05	.06	.07	.08	.09
0.0	.0000	.0040	.0080	.0120	.0160	.0199	.0239	.0279	.0319	.0359
0.1	.0398	.0438	.0478	.0517	.0557	.0596	.0636	.0675	.0714	.0753
0.2	.0793	.0832	.0871	.0910	.0948	.0987	.1026	.1064	.1103	.1141
0.3	.1179	.1217	.1255	.1293	.1331	.1368	.1406	.1443	.1480	.1517
0.4	.1554	.1591	.1628	.1664	.1700	.1736	.1772	.1808	.1844	.1879
0.5	.1915	.1950	.1985	.2019	.2054	.2088	.2123	.2157	.2190	.2224
0.6	.2257	.2291	.2324	.2357	.2389	.2422	.2454	.2486	.2517	.2549
0.7	.2580	.2611	.2642	.2673	.2704	.2734	.2764	.2794	.2823	.2852
0.8	.2881	.2910	.2939	.2967	.2995	.3023	.3051	.3078	.3106	.3133
0.9	.3159	.3186	.3212	.3238	.3264	.3289	.3315	.3340	.3365	.3389
1.0	.3413	.3438	.3461	.3485	.3508	.3531	.3554	.3577	.3599	.3621
1.1	.3643	.3665	.3686	.3708	.3729	.3749	.3770	.3790	.3810	.3830
1.2	.3849	.3869	.3888	.3907	.3925	.3944	.3962	.3980	.3997	.4015
1.3	.4032	.4049	.4066	.4082	.4099	.4115	.4131	.4147	.4162	.4177
1.4	.4192	.4207	.4222	.4236	.4251	.4265	.4279	.4292	.4306	.4319
1.5	.4332	.4345	.4357	.4370	.4382	.4394	.4406	.4418	.4429	.4441
1.6	.4452	.4463	.4474	.4484	.4495	.4505	.4515	.4525	.4535	.4545
1.7	.4554	.4564	.4573	.4582	.4591	.4599	.4608	.4616	.4625	.4633
1.8	.4641	.4649	.4656	.4664	.4671	.4678	.4686	.4693	.4699	.4706
1.9	.4713	.4719	.4726	.4732	.4738	.4744	.4750	.4756	.4761	.4767
2.0	.4772	.4778	.4783	.4788	.4793	.4798	.4803	.4808	.4812	.4817
2.1	.4821	.4826	.4830	.4834	.4838	.4842	.4846	.4850	.4854	.4857
2.2	.4861	.4864	.4868	.4871	.4875	.4878	.4881	.4884	.4887	.4890
2.3	.4893	.4896	.4898	.4901	.4904	.4906	.4909	.4911	.4913	.4916
2.4	.4918	.4920	.4922	.4925	.4927	.4929	.4931	.4932	.4934	.4936
2.5	.4938	.4940	.4941	.4943	.4945	.4946	.4948	.4949	.4951	.4952
2.6	.4953	.4955	.4956	.4957	.4959	.4960	.4961	.4962	.4963	.4964
2.7	.4965	.4966	.4967	.4968	.4969	.4970	.4971	.4972	.4973	.4974
2.8	.4974	.4975	.4976	.4977	.4977	.4978	.4979	.4979	.4980	.4981
2.9	.4981	.4982	.4982	.4983	.4984	.4984	.4985	.4985	.4986	.4986
3.0	.4987	.4987	.4987	.4988	.4988	.4989	.4989	.4989	.4990	.4990